D1245140

The ARRL Antenna Book

FOR RADIO COMMUNICATIONS

Twenty-Second Edition

Published by:

ARRL

the national association for Amateur Radio™
Newington, CT 06111 USA

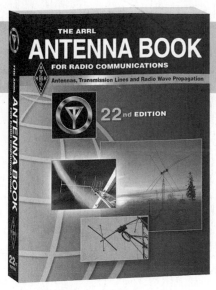

Front Cover

Bottom: A portion of the cage dipole antenna used at ARRL Headquarters station W1AW in Newington, Connecticut. Photo by Steve Ford, WB8IMY

Middle: An aurora display in the Norwegian city of Tromso highlights an Optibeam OB6-6 six element beam for 6 meters below a five-element LFA Yagi for 4 meters. Photo by Hans Christian Larssen, LA9AKA.

Top: A 20-meter quad antenna and an icy sunrise in Spokane, Washington. Photo by Gordon Grove, WA7LNC.

Back Cover
A multiband horizontal delta array.

Editor
H. Ward Silver, NØAX

Contributing Editors
Steven R. Ford, WB8IMY
Mark J. Wilson, K1RO

Editorial Assistant
Maty Weinberg, KB1EIB

Production
Michelle Bloom, WB1ENT
Sue Fagan, KB1OKW — Cover Art
Jodi Morin, KA1JPA
Nancy G. Hallas, W1NCY
David F. Pingree, N1NAS
Carol Michaud, KB1QAW

Contributors to the 22nd Edition
Alan Applegate, KØBG
Alan Bloom, N1AL
Gary Breed, K9AY
Kent Britain, WA5VJB
Paul Danzer, N1II
Frank Donovan, W3LPL
Doug Grant, K1DG
Dave Hallidy, K2DH
Ken Harker, WM5R
Dick Jansson, KD1K
Ed Karl, KØKL
Hal Kennedy, N4GG
Phil Koch, K3UA
Roy Lewallen, W7EL
Carl Luetzelschwab, K9LA
Domenic Mallozzi, N1DM
Dennis Miller, KM9O
Steve Morris, K7LXC
Greg Ordy, W8WWV
Ulrich Rohde, N1UL
Rudy Severns, N6LF
John Stanley, K4ERO
Dean Straw, N6BV
Joe Taylor, K1JT
Frank Witt, AI1H

Copyright © 2011 by

The American Radio Relay League, Inc.

Copyright secured under the Pan-American Convention

All rights reserved. No part of this work may be reproduced in any form except by written permission of the publisher. All rights of translation are reserved.

Printed in the USA

Quedan reservados todos los derechos

ISBN: 978-0-87259-694-8 Softcover
     978-0-87259-680-1 Hardcover

Twenty-second Edition

Foreword

As the Amateur Service grew during the pre-World War II era, technology began to outgrow the all-encompassing technical reference of the times, *The ARRL Handbook*. It is a telling observation that the first additional reference text was devoted to antennas and transmission lines and radio wave propagation. That first edition of *The ARRL Antenna Book*, published in 1939, addressed what today's amateurs know well — that antennas and their associated technical concepts and systems are key to success in Amateur Radio. That focus continues in this latest 22nd edition of the book.

Not only are antennas fundamental to Amateur Radio but amateurs are encouraged, even expected, to experiment with the development and construction of an ever-improving array of designs and configurations. Even in a time of electronic miniaturization and sophisticated software, the antenna system remains an element of the service accessible to every amateur. FCC Part 97.1, the Basis and Purpose for the Amateur Service, is clear when it refers to the "Continuation and extension of the amateur's proven ability to contribute to the advancement of the radio art." Antennas are at the forefront of fulfilling that purpose.

This edition continues the tradition established more than 70 years ago as it summarizes a broad swath of antenna technology of interest to the amateur community. The book is intended to serve as both a means of education and as a source of design instruction and information. In these pages you will find theoretical material and practical, hands-on advice from knowledgeable and experienced amateurs — there are 213 different listed or referenced authors in the text alone. We have rearranged the new contributions and material from previous editions to provide a more effective learning experience that couples directly to practical designs.

In particular, we are fortunate to include with the book *EZNEC ARRL 5.0* antenna modeling software, contributed by Roy Lewallen, W7EL, recipient of the 2011 Technical Excellence Award from the Dayton Hamvention. Antenna modeling has fundamentally changed antenna design and development and *EZNEC* software sets the amateur standard. An entire chapter is devoted to antenna modeling and an extensive *EZNEC* tutorial by Greg Ordy, W8WWV, is also included on the book's CD-ROM. Popular software written by this book's previous editor, Dean Straw, N6BV, is again included in this edition: *HFTA* (HF Terrain Analysis), *TLW* (Transmission Line for Windows), and *YW* (Yagi for Windows).

You'll also notice that we have made more use of material from our sibling organization, the Radio Society of Great Britain (RSGB). RSGB publications are renowned for their quality and provide alternative perspectives and treatment of antenna topics. Articles from the Wireless Institute of Australia (WIA) also make appearances. We are grateful for their support in this new edition.

Antenna system design takes a new emphasis in this edition. Material previously distributed throughout the book has been collected into a single chapter, **HF Antenna Systems Design** dealing with the effects of local terrain, antenna height, ground conductivity, desired coverage "footprint" and other similar topics. The goal is to help the amateur make better choices to achieve the desired communications objectives by considering "the big picture" as the antenna system components are selected.

New and completely rewritten material includes:

■ "Building Antenna Systems and Towers" by Steve Morris, K7LXC

■ "Effects of Ground" by Rudy Severns N6LF, including a major update on radial systems and elevated radials

■ "Mobile VHF and UHF Antennas" by Alan Applegate KØBG

■ The chapter "Mobile and Maritime HF Antennas" has been rewritten by Alan Applegate KØBG and Rudy Severns N6LF, as well.

■ The tables listing vendors of Antenna System Materials and Services have been updated and will be maintained as a downloadable spreadsheet on the book's new website, **www.arrl.org/antenna-book**.

Recognizing the new ways in which antennas are being used and installed, there are new chapters on **Portable Antennas** and **Stealth and Limited-Space Antennas**. These will surely expand in future editions. An area long unaddressed but of value to all amateurs now has its own chapter, **Antenna System Troubleshooting**.

Every edition of the *ARRL Antenna Book* features some exciting new antenna projects. This edition includes the C-pole ground-independent HF antenna by Brian Cake, KF2YN; Patch and Vivaldi Antennas for microwave applications; Kent Britain, WA5VJB's famous "Cheap Yagis" for VHF and UHF use; a 40 Meter Moxon beam by Dave Leeson, W6NL; a TV-to-ham Log-Periodic Conversion by John Stanley, K4ERO; a detailed treatment of his receiving loop antenna design by Gary Breed, K9AY; and a new set of Half-Element Designs for Yagis by Stan Stockton, K5GO.

There are dozens of new supporting PDF files on the CD-ROM. Every project includes the complete construction details. Numerous *QST* articles supplementing or supporting the book's contents are included. You'll find some familiar antenna projects from previous editions included, too. New CD-ROM-only material includes:

- Antenna tuner comparisons and analysis by Bob Neese, KØKR
- Spreadsheets for calculating ground effects by Rudy Severns, N6LF
- "Active Antennas" by Ulrich Rohde, N1UL

The indexes have all been redone to make it easier for the reader to find specific topics. Separate Author and Project Indexes are now included. The structure of the book follows the improved layout of the 2011 *ARRL Handbook* — there is a more detailed master Table of Contents and one at the beginning of each chapter, numbered to three levels, making the book far easier to navigate.

We hope you'll agree that this new edition of *The ARRL Antenna Book* does more than just keep pace with antennas in Amateur Radio. The new material and software, reorganization for better learning and application, expanded use of the CD-ROM and the ARRL website, all make for a more useful reference and learning tool. Wherever there is Amateur Radio, there will surely be an antenna and just as surely, *The ARRL Antenna Book* will be there, too.

David Sumner, K1ZZ
Chief Executive Officer
Newington, Connecticut
September 2011

Contents

A detailed Table of Contents is included at the beginning of each chapter.

ARRL Member Services

 **Get Involved**
www.arrl.org/get-involved

 **Join or Renew**
www.arrl.org/join

 **Donate**
www.arrl.org/donate

 **Shop**
www.arrl.org/shop

ARRL Membership Benefits

Your ARRL membership includes *QST* magazine, plus dozens of other services and resources to help you **Get Started**, **Get Involved** and **Get On the Air**. ARRL members enjoy Amateur Radio to the fullest!

Members-Only Web Services

Create an online ARRL Member Profile, and get access to ARRL members-only Web services. Visit **www.arrl.org/myARRL** to register.

- **QST Archive and Periodicals Search** – **www.arrl.org/qst**
  Browse ARRL's extensive online *QST* archive (1915-2007). A searchable index for *QEX* and *NCJ* is also available.

- **Free E-Newsletters**
  Subscribe to a variety of ARRL E-newsletters and e-mail announcements: ham radio news, radio clubs, public service, contesting and more!

- **Product Review Archive** – **www.arrl.org/qst**
  Search for, and download, *QST* Product Reviews published from 1980 to present.

- **E-Mail Forwarding Service**
  E-mail sent to your **arrl.net** address will be forwarded to any e-mail account you specify.

- **Customized ARRL.org home page**
  Customize your home page to see local ham radio events, clubs and news.

- **ARRL Member Directory**
  Connect with other ARRL members via a searchable online Member Directory. Share profiles, photos and more with members who have similar interests.

ARRL Technical Information Service — www.arrl.org/tis

Get answers on a variety of technical and operating topics through ARRL's Technical Information Service. ARRL Lab experts and technical volunteers can help you overcome hurdles and answer all your questions.

ARRL as an Advocate — www.arrl.org/regulatory-advocacy

ARRL supports legislation and regulatory measures that preserve and protect access to Amateur Radio Service frequencies. Members may contact the **ARRL Regulatory Information Branch** for information on FCC rules; problems with antenna, tower and zoning restrictions; and reciprocal licensing procedures for international travelers.

ARRL Group Benefit Programs* — www.arrl.org/benefits

- **ARRL "Special Risk" Ham Radio Equipment Insurance Plan**
  Insurance is available to protect you from loss or damage to your station, antennas and mobile equipment by lightning, theft, accident, fire, flood, tornado, and other natural disasters.

- **The ARRL Visa Signature® Card**
  Every purchase supports ARRL programs and services.

- **MetLife® Auto, Home, Renters, Boaters, Fire Insurance and Banking Products**
  ARRL members may qualify for up to a 10% discount on home or auto insurance.

  * ARRL Group Benefit Programs are offered by third parties through contractual arrangements with ARRL. The programs and coverage are available in the US only. Other restrictions may apply.

ARRL Programs

Public Service — **www.arrl.org/public-service**
Amateur Radio Emergency Service® – **www.arrl.org/ares**
Emergency Communications Training – **www.arrl.org/emcomm-training**

Radiosport
Awards – **www.arrl.org/awards**
Contests – **www.arrl.org/contests**
QSL Service – **www.arrl.org/qsl**
Logbook of the World – **www.arrl.org/lotw**

Community
Radio Clubs (ARRL-affiliated clubs) – **www.arrl.org/clubs**
Hamfests and Conventions – **www.arrl.org/hamfests**
ARRL Field Organization – **www.arrl.org/field-organization**

Licensing, Education and Training
Find a License Exam Session – **www.arrl.org/exam**
Find a Licensing Class – **www.arrl.org/class**
ARRL Continuing Education Program – **www.arrl.org/courses-training**
Books, Software and Operating Resources – **www.arrl.org/shop**

Quick Links and Resources
QST – ARRL members' journal – **www.arrl.org/qst**
QEX – *A Forum for Communications Experimenters* – **www.arrl.org/qex**
NCJ – *National Contest Journal* – **www.arrl.org/ncj**
Support for Instructors – **www.arrl.org/instructors**
Support for Teachers – **www.arrl.org/teachers**
ARRL Volunteer Examiner Coordinator (ARRL VEC) – **www.arrl.org/vec**
Public and Media Relations – **www.arrl.org/media**
Forms and Media Warehouse – **www.arrl.org/forms**
FCC License Renewal – **www.arrl.org/fcc**
Foundation, Grants and Scholarships – **www.arrl.org/arrl-foundation**
Advertising – **www.arrl.org/ads**

Interested in Becoming a New Ham?

www.arrl.org/newham
e-mail **newham@arrl.org**
Tel 1-800-326-3942 (US)

Contact Us

ARRL – The national association for Amateur Radio™
225 Main Street
Newington, CT 06111-1494 USA
Tel 1-860-594-0200, Mon-Fri 8 AM to 5 PM ET (except holidays)
FAX 1-860-594-0259
e-mail **hqinfo@arrl.org**
Web site – **www.arrl.org**

 Facebook
www.facebook.com/ARRL.org

 Twitter
twitter.com/arrl · **twitter.com/w1aw** · **twitter.com/arrl-youth**

The American Radio Relay League, Inc.

The American Radio Relay League, Inc. is a noncommercial association of radio amateurs, organized for the promotion of interest in Amateur Radio communication and experimentation, for the establishment of networks to provide communication in the event of disasters or other emergencies, for the advancement of the radio art and of the public welfare, for the representation of the radio amateur in legislative matters, and for the maintenance of fraternalism and a high standard of conduct.

ARRL is an incorporated association without capital stock chartered under the laws of the State of Connecticut, and is an exempt organization under Section 501(c)(3) of the Internal Revenue Code of 1986. Its affairs are governed by a Board of Directors, whose voting members are elected every three years by the general membership. The officers are elected or appointed by the directors. The League is noncommercial, and no one with a pervasive and continuing conflict of interest is eligible for membership on its Board.

"Of, by, and for the radio amateur," the ARRL numbers within its ranks the vast majority of active amateurs in the nation and has a proud history of achievement as the standard-bearer in amateur affairs.

A *bona fide* interest in Amateur Radio is the only essential qualification of membership; an Amateur Radio license is not a prerequisite, although full voting membership is granted only to licensed amateurs in the US.

Membership inquiries and general correspondence should be addressed to the administrative headquarters: ARRL, 225 Main Street, Newington, Connecticut 06111-1494.

The seed for Amateur Radio was planted in the 1890s, when Guglielmo Marconi began his experiments in wireless telegraphy. Soon he was joined by dozens, then hundreds, of others who were enthusiastic about sending and receiving messages through the air—some with a commercial interest, but others solely out of a love for this new communications medium. The United States government began licensing Amateur Radio operators in 1912.

By 1914, there were thousands of Amateur Radio operators—hams—in the United States. Hiram Percy Maxim, a leading Hartford, Connecticut inventor and industrialist, saw the need for an organization to band together this fledgling group of radio experimenters. In May 1914 he founded the American Radio Relay League (ARRL) to meet that need.

Today ARRL, with approximately 150,000 members, is the largest organization of radio amateurs in the United States. The ARRL is a not-for-profit organization that:
• promotes interest in Amateur Radio communications and experimentation
• represents US radio amateurs in legislative matters, and
• maintains fraternalism and a high standard of conduct among Amateur Radio operators.

At ARRL headquarters in the Hartford suburb of Newington, the staff helps serve the needs of members. ARRL is also International Secretariat for the International Amateur Radio Union, which is made up of similar societies in 150 countries around the world.

ARRL publishes the monthly journal *QST*, as well as newsletters and many publications covering all aspects of Amateur Radio. Its headquarters station, W1AW, transmits bulletins of interest to radio amateurs and Morse code practice sessions. The ARRL also coordinates an extensive field organization, which includes volunteers who provide technical information and other support services for radio amateurs as well as communications for public-service activities. In addition, ARRL represents US amateurs with the Federal Communications Commission and other government agencies in the US and abroad.

Membership in ARRL means much more than receiving *QST* each month. In addition to the services already described, ARRL offers membership services on a personal level, such as the ARRL Volunteer Examiner Coordinator Program and a QSL bureau.

Full ARRL membership (available only to licensed radio amateurs) gives you a voice in how the affairs of the organization are governed. ARRL policy is set by a Board of Directors (one from each of 15 Divisions). Each year, one-third of the ARRL Board of Directors stands for election by the full members they represent. The day-to-day operation of ARRL HQ is managed by a Chief Executive Officer.

No matter what aspect of Amateur Radio attracts you, ARRL membership is relevant and important. There would be no Amateur Radio as we know it today were it not for the ARRL. We would be happy to welcome you as a member! (An Amateur Radio license is not required for Associate Membership.) For more information about ARRL and answers to any questions you may have about Amateur Radio, write or call:

ARRL — The national association for Amateur Radio
225 Main Street
Newington CT 06111-1494
Voice: 860-594-0200
Fax: 860-594-0259
E-mail: **hq@arrl.org**
Internet: **www.arrl.org/**

Prospective new amateurs call (toll-free):
800-32-NEW HAM (800-326-3942)
You can also contact us via e-mail at **newham@arrl.org**
or check out *ARRLWeb* at **http://www.arrl.org/**

Common Schematic Symbols Used in Circuit Diagrams

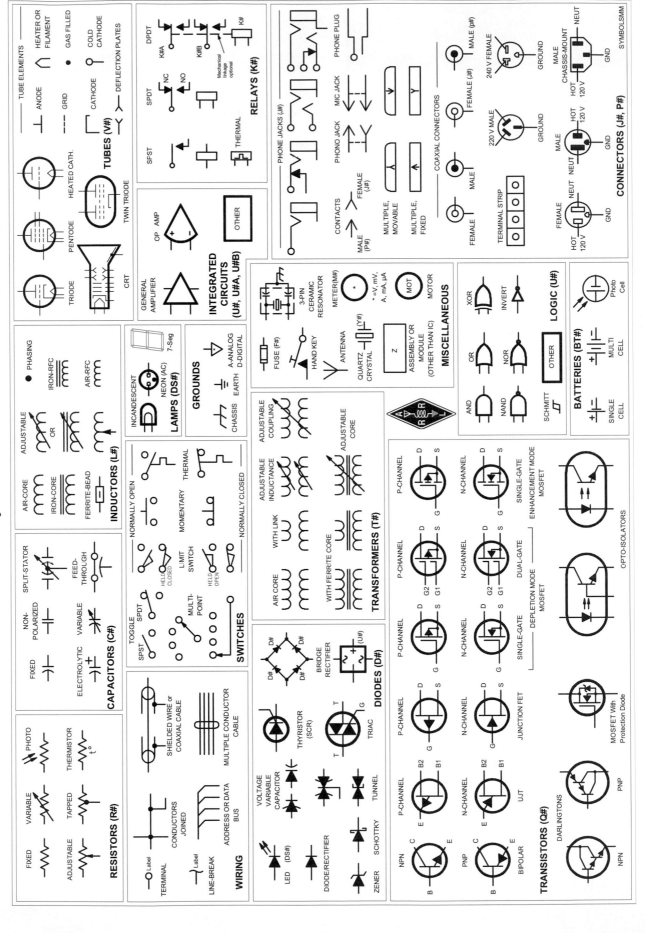

TABLE OF CONTENTS

Chapter 1

Antenna Fundamentals

While there are an enormous variety of antennas, they share basic characteristics and all are designed to radiate and receive electromagnetic waves. In this chapter, we begin by defining what an electromagnetic wave is and how it is described. We then define the most important characteristics of an antenna — impedance, directivity and polarization — and show how those characteristics are measured and displayed. Finally, a section reviews how exposure to those waves affects the human body and the measures necessary for all amateurs to use antennas and electromagnetic waves safely.

1.1 INTRODUCTION TO ELECTROMAGNETIC FIELDS AND WAVES

1.1.1 E AND H FIELDS

In 1820 Hans Oerstad discovered that a current flowing in a wire would deflect the needle of a nearby compass. We attribute this effect to a magnetic or H-field, which at any given location is denoted by the letter H. The magnetic field's amplitude is expressed in A/m (Amperes/meter) along with a direction. (Direction can also be expressed as some value of phase with respect to a reference.) Because a magnetic field has *both* amplitude and direction, it is a *vector*. Symbols representing a vector are printed in bold-face.

Figure 1.1 shows a typical experimental arrangement that demonstrates the presence of a magnetic field. The shape of the magnetic field is roughly shown by the distribution of the iron filings. This field distribution is very similar to that around a vertical antenna.

A compass needle (a small magnet itself) will try to align itself parallel to H. As the compass is moved around the conductor, the orientation of the needle changes accordingly. The orientation of the needle gives the direction of H. If you attempt to turn the needle away from alignment you will discover a torque trying to restore the needle to its original

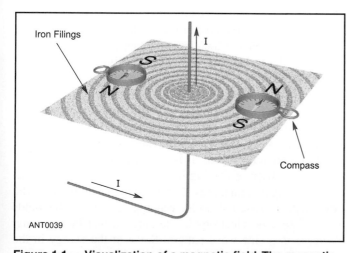

Figure 1.1 — Visualization of a magnetic field. The magnetic lines of force that surround a conductor with an electric current flowing in it are shown by iron filings and small compass needles. The needles point in the direction of the magnetic or H-field. The filings give a general view of the field distribution in the plane perpendicular to the conductor.

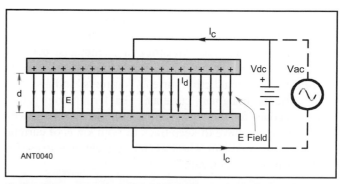

Figure 1.2 — Visualization of an electric field, $E = V_{dc}/d$. When the dc source is replaced with an ac source there will be a displacement current (I_d) flowing between the capacitor plates.

Math Tutorials

You will encounter a fair amount of intermediate-level mathematics in this book. If you would like to brush up on your math skills or learn about an unfamiliar topic, a list of free online math tutorials is included on the CD-ROM included with this book and on the ARRL website under "Math Tutorials" at **www.arrl.org tech-prep-resource-library**.

position. The torque is proportional to the strength of the magnetic field at that point. This strength is called the *field intensity* or amplitude of H at that point. If a larger current flows in the conductor the amplitude of H will increase in proportion. Currents flowing in an antenna also generate an H-field.

An antenna will also have an electric or E-field, which can be visualized using a parallel-plate capacitor, as shown in **Figure 1.2**. If we connect a battery with a dc potential across the capacitor plates there will be an electric field E established between the plates, as indicated by the lines and directional arrows between the plates. (Like H, the electric field also has an amplitude and direction and so is a vector as well.) The magnitude of vector E is expressed in V/m (volts per meter), so for a potential of V volts and a spacing of d meters, $E = V/d$ V/m. The amplitude of E will increase with voltage and/or a smaller separation distance (d). In an antenna, there will be ac potential differences between different parts of the antenna and from the antenna to ground. These ac potential differences establish the electric field associated with the antenna.

1.1.2 CONDUCTION AND DISPLACEMENT CURRENTS

If we replace the dc voltage source in Figure 1.2 with an ac source, an ac current will flow in the circuit. In the conductors between the ac source and the capacitor plates, current (I_c) flows, because of the movement of charge, usually electrons. But in the space between the capacitor plates (particularly in a vacuum) there are no charge carriers available to carry a conduction current. Nonetheless, current still flows in the complete circuit, and we attribute this to a *displacement current* (I_d) flowing between the capacitor plates to account for the continuity of current in the circuit. Displacement and conduction currents are two different phenomena but they both represent current, just two different kinds. Some observers prefer to call conduction currents "currents" and displacement currents "imaginary currents." That terminology is OK, but to account for the current flow in a closed circuit with capacitance you have to keep track of both kinds of current, whatever you call them. The accepted convention is to use the term "displacement current."

1.1.3 ELECTROMAGNETIC WAVES

An electromagnetic wave, as the name implies, is composed of both an electric field and a magnetic field that vary

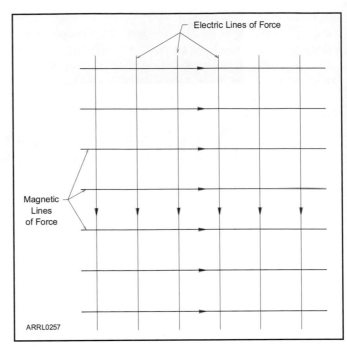

Figure 1.3 — Representation of electric and magnetic lines of force in an electromagnetic wavefront. Arrows indicate the instantaneous directions of the fields for a wavefront in a wave traveling toward you, out of the page. Reversing the direction of one of the fields would also reverse the direction of the wave.

with time. Electric and magnetic fields that do not change with time, such as those created by a dc current or voltage, are called *electrostatic fields*. The fields of a radio wave are created by an ac current in an antenna, usually having the form of a sine wave. As a result, the fields in a radio wave vary in the same sinusoidal pattern, increasing and decreasing in strength and reversing direction with the same frequency, f, as the ac current. It is the movement of electrons — specifically the acceleration and deceleration as the ac current moves back and forth — that creates the electromagnetic wave.

The two fields of the electromagnetic wave are oriented at right angles to each other as shown by **Figure 1.3**. The term "lines of force" in the figure means the direction in which a force would be felt by an electron (from the electric field) or by a magnet (from the magnetic field). The direction of the right angle from the electric and magnetic fields, clockwise or counterclockwise, determines the direction the wave travels, as illustrated in the figure. This is called a *propagating wave*.

To an observer staying in one place, such as a stationary receiving antenna, the electric and magnetic fields of the wave appear to oscillate as the wave passes. That is, the fields create forces on electrons in the antenna that increase and decrease in a sine wave pattern. Some of the energy in the propagating wave is transferred to the electrons as the forces from the changing fields cause them to move. This creates a sine wave current in the antenna with a frequency determined by the rate at which the field strength changes as the wave passes.

If the observer is moving in the same direction as the wave and at the same speed, however, the strength of the fields will not change. To that observer, the electric and magnetic field strengths are fixed, as in a photograph. This is a *wavefront* of the electromagnetic wave; a flat surface or plane moving through space on which the electric and magnetic fields have a constant value as illustrated in Figure 1.3.

Just as an ac voltage is made up of an infinite sequence of instantaneous voltages, each slightly larger or smaller than the next, an infinite number of wavefronts make up a propagating electromagnetic wave, one behind another like a deck of cards. The direction of the wave is the direction in which the wavefronts move. The fields on each successive wavefront have a slightly different strength so as they pass a fixed location, the detected field strength changes as well. The fixed observer "sees" fields with strengths that vary as a sine wave.

Figure 1.4 is a drawing of what would happen if we could suddenly freeze all of the wave-fronts in the wave and take measurements of the electric and magnetic field strengths in each. In this example, the electric field is oriented vertically and the magnetic field horizontally. (Each of the vertical lines in the electric field can be thought of as representing an individual wavefront.) All of the wavefronts are moving in the direction indicated — the whole set of them moves together at the same speed. As the wave — the set of wavefronts — moves past the receiving antenna, the varying field strengths of the different wavefronts is perceived as a continuously changing wave. What we call a "wave" is really this entire group of wavefronts moving through space.

One more important note about electromagnetic waves: The electric and magnetic fields are *coupled*, that is they are both aspects of the same entity, the electromagnetic wave. They are not perpendicular electric and magnetic fields that simply happen to be in the same place at the same time! The fields cannot be separated, although the energy in the wave can be detected as electric or magnetic force. The fields are created as a single entity — an electromagnetic wave — by the motion of electrons in the transmitting antenna.

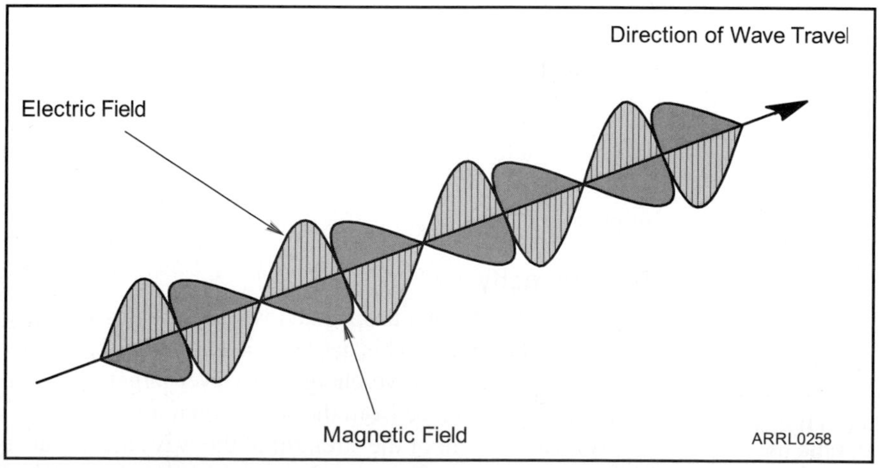

Speed of Propagation and Wavelength

Because the velocity of wave propagation is so great, we tend to ignore it. Only $\frac{1}{7}$ of a second is needed for a radio wave to travel around the world — but in working with antennas the time factor is extremely important. The wave concept evolved because an alternating current flowing in a wire (antenna) creates propagating electric and magnetic fields. We can hardly discuss antenna theory or performance at all without involving travel time, consciously or otherwise.

Electromagnetic waves propagate at the speed of light for the medium through which they travel. The speed of light is highest in the vacuum of free space, approximately 300 million or 3×10^8 meters per second. It is often more convenient to remember the speed as 300 m/µs. (A more exact value is 299.7925 m/µs). This is called the wave's *velocity of propagation* and is represented by the familiar "speed of light" symbol, c.

It is also useful to know a radio wave's *wavelength* — the distance traveled during one complete cycle of a wave. Since one complete cycle takes 1/f the velocity of a wave is the speed of light, c, the wavelength, λ, is thus:

$$\lambda = c / f \tag{1}$$

In free-space

$$\lambda = 299.7925 \times 10^8 / f$$

where λ is the free-space wavelength in meters.

More convenient approximate formulas for use at radio frequencies are:

$$\lambda \text{ in meters} = 300 / f \text{ in MHz, and} \tag{2}$$

$$\lambda \text{ in feet} = 983.6 / f \text{ in MHz} \tag{3}$$

The ratio between the wave's velocity in a specific medium and that of free space is called the medium's *velocity factor* (VF) and is a value between 0 and 1. If the medium is air, the reduction in velocity of propagation can be ignored in most discussions of propagation at frequencies below 30 MHz. In the VHF range and higher, temperature and moisture content of the medium have increasing effects on the communication range, as will be discussed later in the **Radio Wave Propagation** chapter. In materials such as glass or plastic the wave's velocity can be quite a bit lower than that of free space. For example, in polyethylene (commonly used as a center insulator in coaxial cable), the velocity of propagation is about ⅔ that in free space. In distilled water (a good insulator) the speed is about ⅑ that of free space.

Figure 1.4 — Representation of the magnetic and electric field strengths of an electromagnetic wave. In the diagram, the electric field is oriented vertically and the magnetic field horizontally.

Direction of Wave Travel

Electric Field

Magnetic Field

ARRL0258

Phase of Waves

There will be few pages in this book where phase, wavelength and frequency do not enter the discussion. It is essential to have a clear understanding of their meaning in order to understand the design, installation, adjustment or use of antennas, matching systems or transmission lines in detail. In essence, *phase* means *time*. When something goes through periodic variations as an alternating current does, corresponding instants in succeeding periods are *in phase*.

It is important to distinguish between phase and *polarity*. Polarity is simply a convention that assigns a positive and negative direction or convention. Reversing the leads on a feed line reverses a signal's polarity but does not change its phase.

Phase is a relative measure of time within and between waveforms. The points A, B and C in **Figure 1.5** are all in phase. They are corresponding instants in the current flow, at intervals of 1 λ. The distance between A and B or between B and C is one wavelength. This is a conventional view of a sine wave alternating current, with time progressing to the right. It also represents the *instantaneous* value of intensity of the traveling fields, if distance is substituted for time in the horizontal axis. The field-intensity distribution follows the sine curve, in both amplitude and polarity, corresponding exactly to the time variations in the current that produced the fields. Remember that this is an *instantaneous* picture of the many wavefronts similar to Figure 1.4.

Waves used in radio communication may have frequencies from about 10,000 to several billion Hz. Suppose the frequency is 30 MHz. One cycle, or period, is completed in 1/30,000,000 second. The wave is traveling at 300,000,000 meters per second through the air, so it will move only 10 meters during the time that the current is going through one complete period of alternation. The electromagnetic field 10 meters away from the antenna is caused by the current that was flowing one period earlier in time. The field 20 meters away is caused by the current that was flowing two periods earlier, and so on.

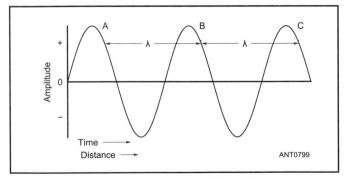

Figure 1.5 — The instantaneous amplitude of both fields (electric and magnetic) varies sinusoidally with time as shown in this graph. Since the fields travel at constant velocity, the graph also represents the instantaneous distribution of field intensity along the wave path. The distance between two points of equal phase such as A-B and B-C is the wave's wavelength.

If each period of the current is simply a repetition of the one before it, the currents at corresponding instants in each period will be identical. The fields caused by those currents will also be identical. As the fields move outward from the antenna they become more thinly spread over larger and larger spherical surfaces centered on the antenna. The field amplitudes decrease with distance from the antenna but they do not lose their identity with respect to the instant of the period at which they were generated. They are, and they remain, in phase. In the example above, on the spherical surfaces separated by intervals of 10 meters measured outward from the antenna, the phase of the waves at any given instant is identical.

These spherical surfaces are the wavefronts described earlier. When the sphere is so large that the surface is essentially flat, the wavefront is called a *plane wave*. On every part of this surface, the wavefront, the wave has the same phase. The wavelength is the distance between two wavefronts having the same phase at any given instant. This distance must be measured perpendicular to the wave fronts along the line that represents the direction of travel.

Wave Polarization

A wave like that in Figure 1.3 is said to be *polarized* in the direction of the electric lines of force. The polarization here is vertical, because the electric lines are perpendicular to the surface of the Earth. If the electric lines of force are horizontal, the wave is said to be horizontally polarized. Horizontally and vertically polarized waves may be classified generally under *linear polarization*. Linear polarization can be anything between horizontal and vertical. In free space, "horizontal" and "vertical" have no meaning, since the reference of the seemingly horizontal surface of the Earth has been lost.

In many cases the polarization of waves is not fixed, but rotates continually, sometimes at random. When this occurs the wave is said to be *elliptically polarized*. A gradual shift in polarization in a medium is known as *Faraday rotation*. For space communication, *circular polarization* is commonly used to overcome the effects of Faraday rotation. A circularly polarized wave rotates its polarization through 360° as it travels a distance of one wavelength in the propagation medium. The direction of rotation as viewed from the transmitting antenna defines the direction of circularity — right-hand (clockwise) or left-hand (counterclockwise). Linear and circular polarization may be considered as special cases of elliptical polarization.

Field Intensity

The energy from a propagated wave decreases with distance from the source. This decrease in strength is caused by the spreading of the wave energy over ever-larger spherical surfaces as the distance from the source increases.

A measurement of the strength of the wave at a distance from the transmitting antenna is its *field intensity*, which is synonymous with *field strength*. The strength of a wave is measured as the voltage between two points lying on an electric line of force in the plane of the wave front. The standard of measure for field intensity is the voltage developed in a wire that is 1 meter long, expressed as volts per meter. (If the wire were 2 meters long, the voltage developed would be divided by two to determine the field strength in volts per meter.)

The voltage in a wave is usually low so the measurement is made in millivolts or microvolts per meter. The voltage goes through time variations like those of the current that caused the wave. It is measured like any other ac voltage — in terms of the RMS value or, sometimes, the peak value. It is fortunate that in amateur work it is not necessary to measure actual field strength as the equipment required is elaborate. We need to know only if an adjustment has been beneficial, so relative measurements are satisfactory. These can be made easily with home-built equipment.

Wave Attenuation

In free space, the field intensity of the wave varies inversely with the distance from the source, once in the radiating far field of the antenna. If the field strength at 1 mile from the source is 100 millivolts per meter, it will be 50 millivolts per meter at 2 miles, and so on. The relationship between field intensity and power density is similar to that for voltage and power in ordinary circuits. They are related by the impedance of free space, which is approximately 377 Ω. A field intensity of 1 volt per meter is therefore equivalent to a power density of

$$P = \frac{E^2}{Z} = \frac{1\,(volt/m)^2}{377\ \Omega} = 2.65\,mW/m^2 \qquad (4)$$

Because of the relationship between voltage and power, the power density therefore varies with the square root of the field intensity, or inversely with the *square* of the distance. If the power density at 1 mile is 4 mW per square meter, then at a distance of 2 miles it will be 1 mW per square meter.

It is important to remember this so-called *spreading loss* when antenna performance is being considered. Gain can come only from narrowing the radiation pattern of an antenna, which concentrates the radiated energy in the desired direction. There is no "antenna magic" by which the total energy radiated can be increased.

In practice, attenuation of the wave energy may be much greater than the inverse-distance law would indicate. The wave does not travel in a vacuum and the receiving antenna seldom is situated so there is a clear line of sight. The Earth is spherical and the waves do not penetrate its surface appreciably, so communication beyond visual distances must be by some means that will bend the waves around the curvature of the Earth. These means involve additional energy losses that increase the path attenuation with distance, above that for the theoretical spreading loss in a vacuum.

1.2 ANTENNA IMPEDANCE

1.2.1 RADIATION RESISTANCE

The power supplied to an antenna is dissipated in two ways: radiation of electromagnetic waves and heat losses in the wire and nearby conductors and dielectrics material. The radiated power is what we want, the useful part, but it represents a form of "loss" just as much as the power used in heating the wire or nearby dielectrics is a loss. In either case, the dissipated power is equal to I^2R.

In the case of heat losses, R is a real resistance. In the case of radiation, however, R is a "virtual" resistance, which, if replaced with an actual resistor of the same value, would dissipate the power actually radiated from the antenna. This resistance is called the *radiation resistance*. Radiation resistance represents the work done by the electrons in the antenna in transferring the energy from the signal source to the radiated electromagnetic wave. The total power in the antenna is therefore equal to $I^2\,(R_R+R)$, where R_R is the radiation resistance and R represents the total of all the loss resistances.

In ordinary antennas operated at amateur frequencies, the power lost as heat in the conductor does not exceed a few percent of the total power supplied to the antenna. Expressed in decibels, the loss is less than 0.1 dB. The RF loss resistance of copper wire even as small as #14 AWG is very low compared with the radiation resistance of an antenna that is reasonably clear of surrounding objects and is not too close to the ground. You can therefore assume that the ohmic loss in a reasonably well-located antenna is negligible and that the total resistance shown by the antenna (the feed point resistance) is radiation resistance. As a radiator of electromagnetic waves, such an antenna is a highly efficient device. (This is not true for antennas close to the ground and for electrically-small antennas such as small loops and mobile antennas.)

1.2.2 CURRENT AND VOLTAGE DISTRIBUTION

When power is fed to an antenna, the current and voltage vary along its length. The current is minimum at the ends, regardless of the antenna's length. The current does not actually reach zero at the current minima, because of capacitance at the antenna ends. Insulators, loops at the antenna ends and support wires all contribute to this capacitance, which is also called the *end effect*. The opposite is true of the RF voltage. That is, there is a voltage maximum at the ends.

In the case of a half-wave antenna there is a current maximum at the center and a voltage minimum at the center as illustrated in **Figure 1.6**. The pattern of alternating current and voltage minimums ¼ wavelength apart repeats every ½ wavelength along a linear antenna as shown in Figure 1.6B. The phase of the current and voltage are inverted in each successive half-wavelength section.

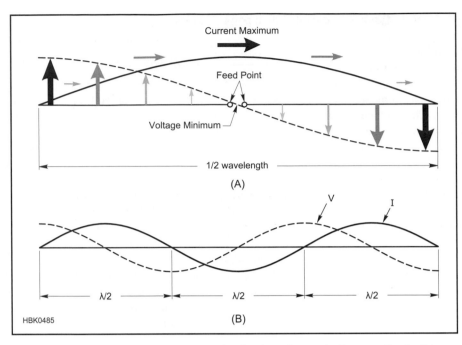

Figure 1.6 — The current and voltage distribution along a half-wave dipole (A) and for an antenna made from a series of half-wave dipoles.

The voltage is not zero at its minimum because of the resistance of the antenna, which consists of both the RF resistance of the wire (ohmic loss resistance) and the radiation resistance as noted previously.

1.2.3 FEED POINT IMPEDANCE

Since amateurs are free to choose our operating frequencies within assigned bands we need to consider how the feed point impedance of a particular antenna varies with frequency within a particular band or even in several different bands if we intend to use one antenna on multiple bands.

There are two forms of impedance associated with any antenna: *self impedance* and *mutual impedance*. As you might expect, self impedance is what is measured at the feed point terminals of an antenna located completely away from the influence of any other conductors.

Self Impedance

The current that flows into an antenna's feed point must be supplied at a finite voltage. The self impedance of the antenna is simply equal to the voltage applied to its feed point divided by the current flowing into the feed point according to Ohm's Law. Where the current and voltage are exactly in phase, the impedance is purely resistive with zero reactance and the antenna is *resonant*. (Amateurs often use the term "resonant" rather loosely, usually meaning "nearly resonant" or "close-to resonant." Resonance has nothing to do with the value of the impedance, only that it is purely resistive.)

Except at the one frequency where it is exactly resonant, the current in an antenna has a different phase compared to the applied voltage. In other words, the antenna exhibits a feed point impedance that is not just a pure resistance. The feed point impedance is composed of either capacitive or inductive reactance in series with a resistance.

Mutual Impedance

Mutual, or coupled, impedance is due to the parasitic effect of nearby conductors located within the antenna's reactive near field. This includes the effect of ground which is a lossy conductor, but a conductor nonetheless. Mutual impedance is defined using Ohm's Law, just like self impedance. However, mutual impedance is the ratio of voltage in one conductor, divided by the current in another (coupled) conductor. Mutually coupled conductors can distort the pattern of a highly directive antenna, as well as change the impedance seen at the feed point. Mutual impedance will be considered in detail in the chapter, **HF Yagi and Quad Antennas**, where it is essential for proper operation of these beam antennas.

Is Resonance Required?

Please recognize that an antenna need not be resonant in order to be an effective radiator. There is in fact nothing magic about having a resonant antenna, provided of course that you can devise some efficient means to feed the antenna. Many amateurs use nonresonant (even random-length) antennas fed with openwire transmission lines and antenna tuners. They radiate signals just as well as those using coaxial cable and resonant antennas and as a bonus can usually be used on multiple frequency bands. It is important to consider an antenna and its feed line as a system in which all losses should be kept to a minimum.

1.3 ANTENNA DIRECTIVITY AND GAIN

1.3.1 THE ISOTROPIC RADIATOR

Before we can fully describe practical antennas, we must first introduce a completely theoretical antenna, the *isotropic radiator*. Envision, if you will, an infinitely small antenna at a point located in outer space, completely removed from anything else around it. Then consider an infinitely small transmitter feeding this infinitely small, point antenna. You now have an isotropic radiator.

The uniquely useful property of this theoretical point-source antenna is that it radiates equally well in all directions. That is to say, an isotropic antenna favors no direction at the expense of any other. In other words, it has absolutely no *directivity*, which is the property of radiating or receiving more strongly in some directions than in others. The isotropic radiator is useful as a measuring stick for comparison with actual antenna systems.

You will find later that real, practical antennas all exhibit some degree of directivity. The radiation from a practical antenna never has the same intensity in all directions and may even have zero radiation in some directions. The fact that a practical antenna displays directivity (while an isotropic radiator does not) is usually desirable. The directivity of a real antenna is often carefully tailored to emphasize radiation in particular directions. For example, a receiving antenna that favors certain directions can discriminate against interference or noise coming from other directions, thereby increasing the signal-to-noise ratio for desired signals coming from the favored direction.

1.3.2 DIRECTIVITY AND THE RADIATION PATTERN

The directivity of an antenna is directly related to the pattern of its radiated field intensity in free space. A graph showing the actual or relative field intensity at a fixed distance as a function of the direction from the antenna system, is called a *radiation pattern*. Since we can't actually see electromagnetic waves making up the radiation pattern of an antenna, we can consider an analogous situation.

Figure 1.7 represents a flashlight shining in a totally darkened room. To quantify what our eyes are seeing we might use a sensitive light meter like those used by photographers, with a scale graduated in units from 0 to 10. We place the meter directly in front of the flashlight and adjust the distance so the meter reads 10, exactly full scale. We also carefully note the distance. Then, always keeping the meter the same distance from the flashlight and keeping it at the same height above the floor, we move the light meter around the flashlight, as indicated by the arrow, and take light readings at a number of different positions.

After all the readings have been taken and recorded, we plot those values on a sheet of polar graph paper, like that shown in **Figure 1.8**. The values read on the meter are plotted at an angular position corresponding to that at which each meter reading was taken. Following this, we connect the plotted points with a smooth curve, also shown in the figure.

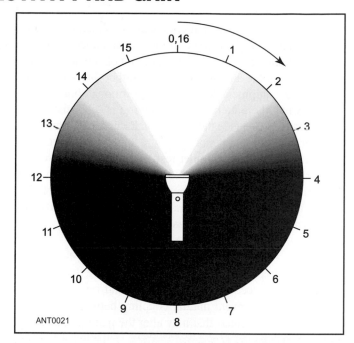

Figure 1.7 — The beam from a flashlight illuminates a totally darkened area a shown here. Readings taken with a photographic light meter at the 16 points around the circle may be used to plot the radiation pattern of the flashlight.

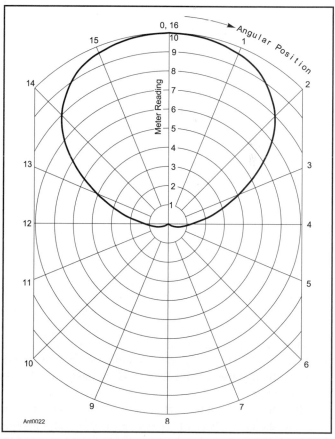

Figure 1.8 — The radiation pattern of the flashlight in Figure 1.7. The measured values are plotted and connected with a smooth curve.

When this is finished, we have completed a radiation pattern for the flashlight.

Antenna radiation patterns can be constructed in a similar manner. Power is fed to the antenna under test and a field-strength meter indicates the amount of signal. We might wish to rotate the antenna under test, rather than moving the measuring equipment to numerous positions about the antenna. Since the pattern while receiving is the same as that while transmitting (see the section on Reciprocity later in this chapter), a source antenna fed by a low-power transmitter illuminates the antenna under test and the signal intercepted by the antenna under test is fed to a receiver and measuring equipment. Additional information on the mechanics of measuring antenna patterns is contained in the chapter **Antennas and Transmission-Line Measurements**.

1.3.3 NEAR AND FAR FIELDS

Some precautions must be taken to assure that the measurements are accurate and repeatable and one of the most important is to prevent mutual coupling between the source and receiving antennas that may alter the pattern you are trying to measure.

This sort of mutual coupling can occur in the region very close to the antenna under test. This region is called the *reactive near-field* region. The term "reactive" refers to the fact that the mutual impedance between the transmitting and receiving antennas can be either capacitive or inductive in nature. The reactive near field is sometimes called the "induction field," meaning that the magnetic field usually is predominant over the electric field in this region. The antenna acts as though it were a rather large, lumped-constant inductor or capacitor, storing energy in the reactive near field rather than propagating it into space.

For simple wire antennas, the reactive near field is considered to be within about a half wavelength from an antenna's radiating center. Later on, in the chapters dealing with arrays of antennas, you will find that mutual coupling between elements can be put to good use to purposely shape the radiated pattern. For making pattern measurements, however, we do not want to be too close to the antenna being measured.

The strength of the reactive near field decreases in a complicated fashion as you increase the distance from the antenna. Beyond the reactive near field, the antenna's radiated field is divided into two other regions: the *radiating near field* and the *radiating far field*. Historically, the terms *Fresnel* and *Fraunhöfer* fields have been used for the radiating near and far fields, but these terms have been largely supplanted by the more descriptive terminology used here. Even inside the reactive near-field region, both radiating and reactive fields coexist although the reactive field predominates very close to the antenna.

Because the boundary between the fields is not a precise distance, experts debate where one field begins and another leaves off but the boundary between the radiating near and far fields is generally accepted as:

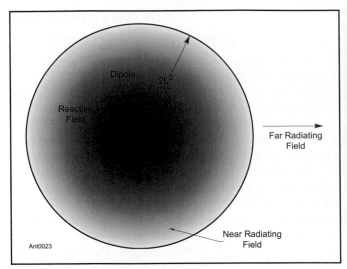

Figure 1.9 — The fields around a radiating antenna. Very close to the antenna, the reactive field dominates. Within this area mutual impedances are observed between the antenna and any other antennas or conductors. Outside the reactive near field, the near radiating field dominates up to the distance shown where L is the length of the largest dimension of the antenna. Beyond the near/far field boundary lies the far radiating field, where power density varies as the inverse square of radial distance.

$$D = \frac{2L^2}{\lambda} \qquad (5)$$

where L is the largest dimension of the physical antenna expressed in the same units of measurement as the wavelength λ. Remember, many specialized antennas do not follow the rule of thumb in Eq 5 exactly. **Figure 1.9** depicts the three fields in front of a simple wire antenna.

Throughout the rest of this book we will discuss mainly the radiating far fields, those forming the propagating electromagnetic waves and which will simply be referred to as the "far field." Far field radiation is distinguished by the fact that the intensity is inversely proportional to the distance, and that the electric and magnetic components, although perpendicular to each other in the wave front, are in phase as defined earlier. The total energy is equally divided between the electric and magnetic fields. Beyond several wavelengths from the antenna these are the only fields we need to consider. This is why for accurate measurement of radiation patterns, we must place our measuring instrumentation at least several wavelengths away from the antenna under test.

1.3.4 TYPES OF RADIATION PATTERNS

In the example of the flashlight, the plane of measurement was at one consistent height above the floor. In **Figure 1.10A** a similar radiation pattern is shown for a half-wavelength dipole (see the **Dipoles and Monopoles** chapter) in free-space, measured in a single plane containing the antenna wire. The antenna is located at the exact center of the plot with its orientation specified by the two-headed

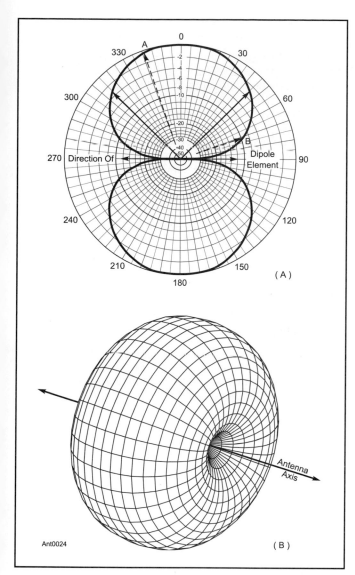

Figure 1.10 — Radiation patterns of a half-wavelength dipole in free space. At A, the pattern in the plane containing the wire axis. The length of each dashed-line arrow represents the relative field strength in that direction, referenced to the direction of maximum radiation at right angles to the wire's axis. The arrows at approximately 45° and 315° are the half-power or –3 dB points. At B, a wire grid representation of the solid pattern for the same antenna.

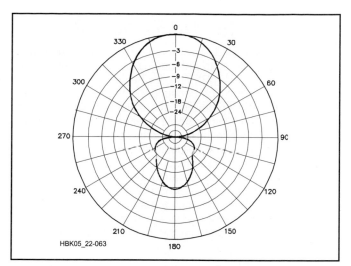

Figure 1.11 — Azimuthal pattern of a typical three-element Yagi beam antenna in free space. The Yagi's boom is aligned along the 0° to 180° axis and the beam's elements are in the plane of the pattern.

arrow. The antenna radiates best broadside to the wire axis and hardly at all off the ends of the wire.

Radiation patterns are graphic representations of an antenna's directivity. Shown in polar coordinates (see the math tutorial reference on the CD-ROM for information about polar coordinates), the angular scale shows direction and the scale from the center of the plot to the outer ring. The smooth line in the shape of a figure-8 shows the relative strength of the antenna's radiated signal at each angle.

The pattern in **Figure 1.11** shows both *nulls* (angles at which a pattern minimum occurs) and *lobes* (radiation at angles between nulls). The *main lobe* is the lobe with the highest amplitude unless noted otherwise and unless several plots are being compared, the peak amplitude of the main lobe is placed at the outer ring as a reference point. The peak of the main lobe can be located at any angle. All other lobes are *side lobes* which can be at any angle, including to the rear of the antenna. In addition to the labels showing the main lobe and nulls in the pattern, the so-called *half-power* points on the main lobe are shown. These are the angles at which the power is one-half of the peak value in the main lobe.

Actually, the pattern for any antenna is three-dimensional and therefore cannot be represented by a single-plane drawing. The total radiation pattern of an antenna in free space would be found by measuring the field strength at every point on the surface of an imaginary sphere having the antenna at its center. The information so obtained would then be used to construct a solid figure, where the distance from a fixed point (representing the antenna) to the surface of the figure is proportional to the field strength from the antenna in any given direction. Figure 1.10B shows a three-dimensional solid representation of the radiation pattern of a half-wave dipole. Figure 1.10A can be thought of as a cross-section of the solid pattern through the axis of the antenna. Two such diagrams, one in the plane containing the straight wire of a dipole and one in the plane perpendicular to the wire, can convey a great deal of information. After a little practice and with the exercise of some imagination, the complete solid pattern can be visualized with fair accuracy from inspection of the two planar diagrams, provided of course that the solid pattern of the antenna is smooth such as for simple antennas like the dipole of Figure 1.10.

Azimuth and Elevation Patterns

When a radiation pattern is shown for an antenna mounted over ground rather than in free space, we automatically gain two frames of reference: *an azimuth angle* and an *elevation angle*. The azimuth angle is usually referenced to 0° in

Introduction to the Decibel

The power gain and pattern measurements such as front-to-back ratio of an antenna system are usually expressed in decibels (dB). The decibel is a practical unit for measuring power ratios because it is more closely related to the actual effect produced at a distant receiver than the power ratio itself. One decibel represents a just-detectable change in signal strength, regardless of the actual value of the signal voltage. A 20-decibel (20 dB) increase in signal, for example, represents 20 observable steps in increased signal. The power ratio (100 to 1) corresponding to 20 dB gives an entirely exaggerated idea of the improvement in communication to be expected. The number of decibels corresponding to any power ratio is equal to 10 times the common logarithm of the power ratio, or

$$dB = 10 \log_{10} \frac{P_1}{P_2}$$

If the voltage ratio is given, the number of decibels is equal to 20 times the common logarithm of the ratio. That is,

$$dB = 20 \log_{10} \frac{V_1}{V_2}$$

When a voltage ratio is used, both voltages must be measured across the same value of impedance. Unless this is done the decibel figure is meaningless, because it is fundamentally a measure of a power ratio.

The main reason a decibel is used is that successive power gains expressed in decibels may simply be added together. Thus a gain of 3 dB followed by a gain of 6 dB gives a total gain of 9 dB. In ordinary power ratios, the ratios must be multiplied together to find the total gain.

A reduction in power is handled simply by subtracting the requisite number of decibels. Thus, reducing the power to ½ is the same as subtracting 3 decibels. For example, a power gain of 4 in one part of a system and a reduction to ½ in another part gives a total power gain of 4 × ½ = 2. In decibels, this is 6 − 3 = 3 dB. A power reduction or loss is simply indicated by including a negative sign in front of the appropriate number of decibels.

When P_2 or V_2 are some fixed reference value, a letter is added to "dB" to indicate "decibels with respect to" the reference value. This allows absolute values of power and voltage to be expressed in dB, as well. You will often encounter dBm (P_2 = 1 mW) and dBμV (V_2 = 1 μV) in Amateur Radio.

For more information about the decibel, read "Power and Decibels" on the ARRL website at **www.arrl.org/files/file/Get%20Licensed/PowerAndDec.pdf**.

---

the direction of maximum radiation from the antenna or it could be referenced to True North for an antenna oriented in a particular compass direction.

The elevation angle is referenced to the horizon at the Earth's surface, where the elevation angle is 0°. Of course, the Earth is round but because its radius is so large, it can in this context be considered to be flat in the area directly under the antenna. An elevation angle of 90° is directly above the antenna (the *zenith*) and the angles then reduce back to 0° toward the horizon directly behind the antenna. (Professional antenna engineers often describe an antenna's orientation with respect to the point directly overhead — using the zenith angle, rather than the elevation angle. The elevation angle is computed by subtracting the zenith angle from 90°.)

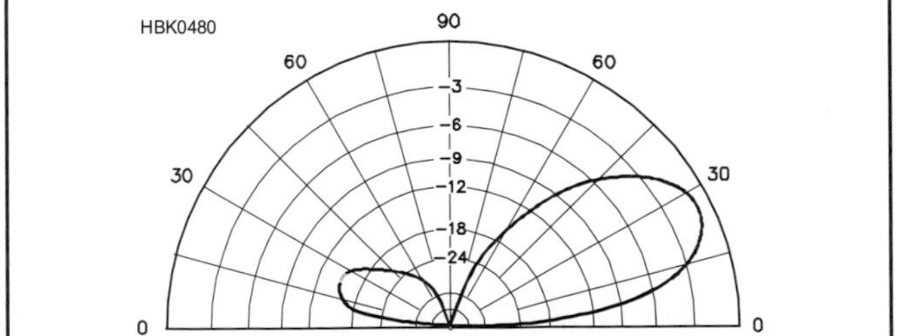

Figure 1.11 is an *azimuthal* or *azimuth pattern* that shows the antenna's gain in all horizontal directions (azimuths) around the antenna. As with a map, 0° is at the top and bearing angle increases clockwise. (This is different from polar plots generated for mathematical functions in which 0° is at the right and the angle increases counter-clockwise.)

Figure 1.12 is an *elevation pattern* that shows the same antenna's directivity but this time at all vertical angles. In this case, the horizon at 0° is located to both sides of the antenna and the zenith (directly overhead) at 90°. The plot shown in Figure 1.12 assumes the presence of ground (drawn from 0° to 0°). The ground reflects or blocks radiation at negative elevation angles, making below-surface radiation plots unnecessary. In free-space, the plot would include the missing semicircle with −90° at the bottom. Without the ground reference, the term "elevation" has little meaning, however.

For amateur work, relative values of field strength (rather than absolute values) are quite adequate in pattern plotting. In other words, it is not necessary to know how many microvolts per meter a particular antenna will produce at a distance of 1 mile when excited with a specified power level. (This is the kind of specification that AM broadcast stations must meet to certify their antenna systems to the FCC.)

Regardless of whether the data is collected by measurements, simulated by computer software, or calculated from theoretical equations, it is common to normalize the plotted values so the field strength in the direction of maximum radiation coincides with the outer edge of the chart. That way, on a given system of polar coordinate scales the shape of the pattern is not altered by proper normalization, only its size.

Figure 1.12 — Elevation pattern of a three-element Yagi beam antenna placed 1/2 wavelength above ground. The Yagi's boom lies on the 0°-0° axis and the elements are perpendicular to the page on the same axis.

(See the sidebar "Coordinate Scales for Radiation Patterns" later in this chapter for information about how radiation pattern scales are determined.)

E and H-Plane Patterns

You'll also encounter *E-plane* and *H-plane radiation patterns*. These show the antenna's radiation pattern in the plane parallel to the E-field or H-field of the antenna. For antennas with horizontal elements, the E-field is in the horizontal plane so the E-plane radiation pattern is the same as an azimuthal pattern in the plane of the antenna. The H-field is perpendicular to the E-field, so the H-plane pattern is in a plane perpendicular to the E-plane pattern. If the E-plane pattern is an azimuthal pattern, then the H-plane pattern will be an elevation pattern.

It's important to remember that the E-plane and H-plane do not have a fixed relationship to the Earth's surface. For example, the E-plane pattern from a horizontal dipole is an azimuthal pattern but if the same dipole is oriented vertically, the E-plane pattern becomes an elevation pattern. For this reason, most E- and H-plane radiation patterns are created with the antenna in free space.

1.3.5 DIRECTIVITY AND GAIN

Let us now examine directivity more closely. As mentioned previously, all practical antennas, even the simplest types such as dipoles, exhibit directivity. Here's another picture that may help explain the concept of directivity. **Figure 1.13A** shows a balloon blown into its usual spherical shape. This represents a "reference" isotropic source. Squeezing the balloon in the middle in Figure 1.13B produces a dipole-like figure-8 pattern with peak levels at top and bottom larger than the reference sphere. Compare this with Figure 1.13C. Next, squeezing the bottom end of the balloon produces a pattern that gives even more "gain" compared to the reference.

Free-space directivity can be expressed quantitatively by comparing the three-dimensional pattern of the antenna under consideration with the perfectly spherical three-dimensional pattern of an isotropic antenna. For an isotropic antenna, the field strength (and thus power per unit area, or *power density*) is the same everywhere on the surface of an imaginary sphere having a radius of many wavelengths and centered on the antenna. For a directive antenna radiating the same total power as an isotropic antenna and surrounded by the same sphere, the directivity results in greater power density at some points on the sphere and less at others. The ratio of the maximum power density to the average power density taken over the entire sphere (which is the same as from the isotropic antenna under the specified conditions) is the numerical measure of the directivity of the antenna.

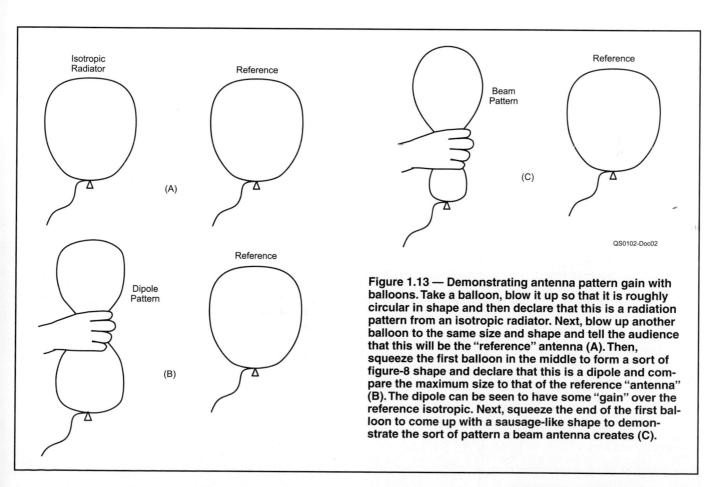

Figure 1.13 — Demonstrating antenna pattern gain with balloons. Take a balloon, blow it up so that it is roughly circular in shape and then declare that this is a radiation pattern from an isotropic radiator. Next, blow up another balloon to the same size and shape and tell the audience that this will be the "reference" antenna (A). Then, squeeze the first balloon in the middle to form a sort of figure-8 shape and declare that this is a dipole and compare the maximum size to that of the reference "antenna" (B). The dipole can be seen to have some "gain" over the reference isotropic. Next, squeeze the end of the first balloon to come up with a sausage-like shape to demonstrate the sort of pattern a beam antenna creates (C).

Coordinate Scales for Radiation Patterns

A number of different systems of coordinate scales or grids are in use for plotting antenna patterns. Antenna patterns published for amateur audiences are sometimes placed on rectangular grids, but more often they are shown using polar coordinate systems. Polar coordinate systems may be divided generally into three classes: linear, logarithmic and modified logarithmic.

A very important point to remember is that the shape of a pattern (its general appearance) is highly dependent on the grid system used for the plotting. This is exemplified in **Figure 1.A**, where the radiation pattern for a beam antenna is presented using three coordinate systems discussed in the paragraphs that follow.

Linear Coordinate Systems

The polar coordinate system in Figure 1.A (part A) uses linear coordinates. The concentric circles are equally spaced, and are graduated from 0 to 10. Such a grid may be used to prepare a linear plot of the power contained in the signal. For ease of comparison, the equally spaced concentric circles have been replaced with appropriately placed circles representing the decibel response, referenced to 0 dB at the outer edge of the plot. In these plots the minor lobes are suppressed. Lobes with peaks more than 15 dB or so below the main lobe disappear completely because of their small size. This is a good way to show the pattern of an array having high directivity and small minor lobes. Linear coordinate patterns are not common, however.

Logarithmic Coordinate System

Another coordinate system used by antenna manufacturers is the logarithmic grid, where the concentric grid lines are spaced according to the logarithm of the voltage in the signal. If the logarithmically spaced concentric circles are replaced with appropriately placed circles representing the decibel response, the decibel circles are graduated linearly. In that sense, the logarithmic grid might be termed a linear-log grid, one having linear divisions calibrated in decibels.

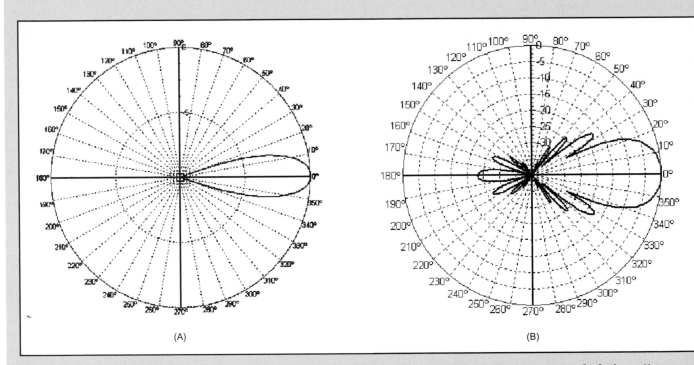

(A) (B)

Figure 1.A — Radiation pattern plots for a high-gain Yagi antenna on different grid coordinate systems. At A, the pattern on a linear-power dB grid. Notice how details of side lobe structure are lost with this grid. At B, the same pattern on a grid with constant 5 dB circles. The side lobe level is exaggerated when this scale is employed. At C, the same pattern on the modified log grid used by ARRL. The side and rearward lobes are clearly visible on this grid. The concentric circles in all three grids

This grid enhances the appearance of the minor lobes. If the intent is to show the radiation pattern of an array supposedly having an omnidirectional response, this grid enhances that appearance. An antenna having a difference of 8 or 10 dB in pattern response around the compass appears to be closer to omnidirectional on this grid than on any of the others. See Figure 1.A (part B).

ARRL Log Coordinate System

The modified logarithmic grid used by the ARRL has a system of concentric grid lines spaced according to the logarithm of 0.89 times the value of the signal voltage. In this grid, minor lobes that are 30 and 40 dB down from the main lobe are distinguishable. Such lobes are of concern in VHF and UHF work. The spacing between plotted points at 0 dB and –3 dB is significantly greater than the spacing between –20 and –23 dB, which in turn is significantly greater than the spacing between –50 and –53 dB.

For example, the scale distance covered by 0 to –3 dB is about ¹⁄₁₀ of the radius of the chart. The scale

distance for the next 3-dB increment (to –6 dB) is slightly less, 89% of the first, to be exact. The scale distance for the next 3-dB increment (to –9 dB) is again 89% of the second. The scale is constructed so that the progression ends with –100 dB at chart center.

The periodicity of spacing thus corresponds generally to the relative significance of such changes in antenna performance. Antenna pattern plots in this publication are made on the modified-log grid similar to that shown in Figure 1.A (part C).

Rectangular Grid

Antenna radiation patterns can also be plotted on rectangular coordinates with gain on the vertical axis in dB and angle on the horizontal axis as shown in Figure 1.A (part D). Multiple patterns in polar coordinates can be difficult to read, particularly close to the center of the plot. Using a rectangular grid makes it easier to evaluate low-level minor lobes and is especially useful when several antennas are being compared.

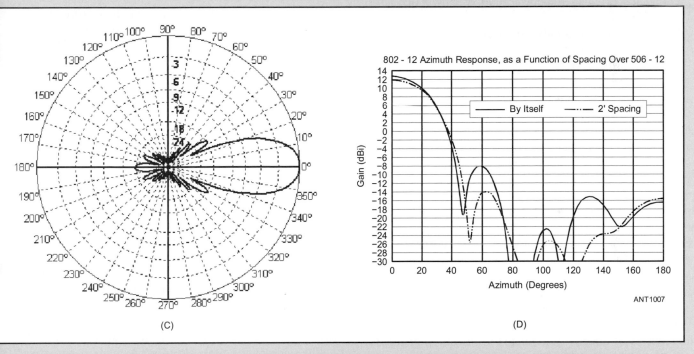

(C)   (D)

are graduated in decibels referenced to 0 dB at the outer edge of the chart. The patterns look quite different, yet they all represent the same antenna response! D shows the rectangular azimuthal patterns of two VHF Yagi antennas. This example shows how a rectangular plot allows easier comparison of antenna patterns away from the main lobe.

Directivity is computed as:

$$D = \frac{P}{P_{av}} \tag{6}$$

where

D = directivity
P = power density at its maximum point
    on the surface of the sphere
P_{av} = average power density

The *gain* of an antenna is closely related to its directivity. Because directivity is based solely on the shape of the directive pattern, it does not take into account any power losses that may occur in an actual antenna system. To determine gain, these losses must be subtracted from the power supplied to the antenna. The loss is normally a constant percentage of the power input, so the antenna gain is:

$$G = k\frac{P}{P_{av}} = kD \tag{7}$$

where

G = gain (expressed as a power ratio, usually in dB)
D = directivity
k = efficiency (power radiated divided by
    power input) of the antenna
P and P_{av} are as above

For many of the antenna systems used by amateurs, the efficiency is quite high (the loss amounts to only a few percent of the total). In such cases the gain is essentially equal to the directivity. The more the directive diagram is compressed — or, in common terminology, the sharper the lobe — the greater the power gain of the antenna. This is a natural consequence of the fact that as power is taken away from a larger and larger portion of the sphere surrounding the radiator, it is added to the volume represented by the narrow lobes. Power is therefore concentrated in some directions at the expense of others. In a general way, the smaller the volume of the solid radiation pattern, compared with the volume of a sphere having the same radius as the length of the largest lobe in the actual pattern, the greater the power gain.

As stated above, the gain of an antenna is related to its directivity, and directivity is related to the shape of the directive pattern. A commonly used index of directivity, and therefore the gain of an antenna, is a measure of the width of the major lobe (or lobes) of the plotted pattern. The width is expressed in degrees at the half-power or –3 dB points and is often called the *beamwidth*.

This information provides only a general idea of relative gain, rather than an exact measure. This is because an absolute measure involves knowing the power density at every point on the surface of a sphere, while a single diagram shows the pattern shape in only one plane of that sphere. It is customary to examine at least the E-plane and the H plane patterns before making any comparisons between antennas.

A simple approximation for gain over an isotropic radiator can be used, but only if the side lobes in the antenna's pattern are small compared to the main lobe and if the resistive losses in the antenna are small. When the radiation pattern is complex, numerical integration is employed to give the actual gain.

$$G \approx \frac{41253}{H_{3dB} \times E_{3dB}} \tag{8}$$

where H_{3dB} and E_{3dB} are the half-power points, in degrees, for the H and E-plane patterns.

1.3.6 RADIATION PATTERN MEASUREMENTS

Given the basic radiation pattern and scales, it becomes easy to define several useful measurements or metrics by which antennas are compared by using their azimuthal patterns. Next to gain, the most commonly-used metric for directional antennas is the *front-to-back ratio* (*F/B*) or just "front-to-back". This is the difference in dB between the antenna's gain in the specified "forward" direction and in the opposite direction. The front-to-back ratio of the antenna in Figure 1.11 is about 11 dB. *Front-to-side ratio* is also used and is the difference between the antenna's "forward" gain and gain at right angles to the forward direction. This assumes the radiation pattern is symmetric and is of most use to antennas such as Yagis and quads that have elements arranged in parallel planes. The front-to-side ratio of the antenna in Fig 1.11 is more than 30 dB. Because the antenna's rear-ward pattern can have large amplitude variations, the *front-to-rear ratio* is sometimes used. Front-to-rear uses the average of rear-ward gain over a specified angle, usually the 180° semicircle opposite the direction of the antenna's maximum gain, instead of a single gain figure at precisely 180° from the forward direction.

In Fig 1.11, the antenna's beamwidth is about 54°, since the pattern crosses the –3 dB gain scale approximately 27° to either side of the peak direction. Antenna patterns with comparatively small beamwidths are referred to as "sharp" or "narrow."

An antenna with an azimuthal pattern that shows equal gain in all directions is called *omnidirectional*. This is not the same as an isotropic antenna that has equal gain in all directions, both vertical both horizontal.

1.4 ANTENNA POLARIZATION

We've now examined the first two of the three major properties used to characterize antennas: the impedance and the radiation pattern. The third general property is polarization. An antenna's polarization is defined to be that of its electric or E-field, in the direction where the field strength is maximum.

For example, if a half-wavelength dipole is mounted horizontally over the Earth, the electric field is strongest perpendicular to its axis (that is, at right angle to the wire) and parallel to the Earth. Thus, since the maximum electric field is horizontal, the polarization in this case is also considered to be horizontal with respect to the Earth. If the dipole is mounted vertically, its polarization will be vertical. See **Figure 1.14**. Note that if an antenna is mounted in free space, there is no frame of reference and hence its polarization is indeterminate.

Antennas composed of a number of elements arranged so that their axes lie in the same or parallel directions have the same polarization as that of any one of the elements. For example, a system composed of a group of horizontal dipoles is horizontally polarized. If both horizontal and vertical elements are used in the same plane and radiate in phase, however, the polarization is the resultant of the contributions made by each set of elements to the total electromagnetic field at a given point some distance from the antenna. In such a case the resultant polarization is still linear, but is tilted between horizontal and vertical.

In directions other than those where the radiation is maximum, the resultant wave even for a simple dipole is a combination of horizontally and vertically polarized components. The radiation off the ends of a horizontal dipole is actually vertically polarized, albeit at a greatly reduced amplitude compared to the broadside horizontally polarized radiation — the sense of polarization changes with compass direction.

Thus it is often helpful to consider the radiation pattern from an antenna in terms of polar coordinates, rather than trying to think in purely linear horizontal or vertical coordinates. The reference axis in the polar system shown in **Figure 1.15** is vertical to the earth under the antenna. The zenith angle is usually referred to as θ (Greek letter theta) and the azimuth angle is referred to as φ (Greek letter phi). Instead of zenith angles, most amateurs are more familiar

with elevation angles, where a zenith angle of 0° is the same as an elevation angle of 90°, straight overhead. Native *NEC* or *MININEC* computer programs use zenith angles rather than elevation angles, although most commercial versions automatically reduce these to elevation angles.

If vertical and horizontal elements in the same plane are fed out of phase (where the beginning of the RF period applied to the feed point of the vertical element is not in time phase with that applied to the horizontal), the resultant polarization is elliptical. Circular polarization is a special case of elliptical polarization. The wave front of a circularly polarized signal appears (to a stationary observer) to rotate every 90° between vertical and horizontal, making a complete 360° rotation once every period. *Instantaneous polarization* is the polarization of the wave at the stationary observer at a specific instant in time. *Circular polarization* is frequently used for space communications, and is discussed further in the chapter **Antennas for Space Communications**.

Sky-wave transmission usually changes the polarization of traveling waves. (This is discussed in the chapter **Radio Wave Propagation**.) The polarization of receiving and transmitting antennas in the 3 to 30 MHz range, where almost all communication is by means of sky wave, need not be the same at both ends of a communication circuit (except for distances of a few miles). In this range the choice of polarization for the antenna is usually determined by factors such as the height of available antenna supports, polarization of man-made RF noise from nearby sources, probable energy losses in nearby objects, the likelihood of interfering with neighborhood electronics and general convenience.

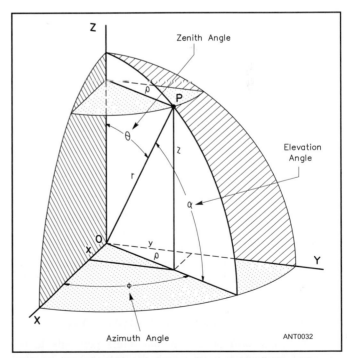

Figure 1.15 — Diagram showing polar representation of a point P lying on an imaginary sphere surrounding a point-source antenna. The various angles associated with the coordinate system are shown referenced to the x, y, and z-axes.

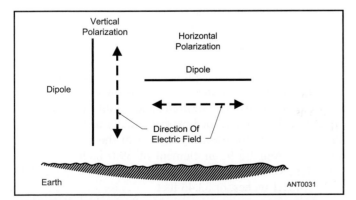

Figure 1.14 — Vertical and horizontal polarization of a dipole above ground. The direction of polarization is the orientation of the electric field in the direction of maximum field strength.

1.5 OTHER ANTENNA CHARACTERISTICS

Besides the three main characteristics of impedance, directivity and polarization, there are some other useful properties of antennas.

1.5.1 RECIPROCITY IN RECEIVING AND TRANSMITTING

Many of the properties of a resonant antenna used for reception are the same as its properties in transmission. It has the same directive pattern in both cases, and delivers maximum signal to the receiver when the signal comes from a direction in which the antenna has its best response. The impedance of the antenna is the same, at the same point of measurement, in receiving as in transmitting. This is the principle of *reciprocity*.

In the receiving case, the antenna is the source of power delivered to the receiver, rather than the load for a source of power (as in transmitting). Maximum possible output from the receiving antenna is obtained when the load to which the antenna is connected is the same as the feed point impedance of the antenna. We then say that the antenna is matched to its load.

The power gain in receiving is the same as the gain in transmitting, when certain conditions are met. One such condition is that both antennas must work into load impedances matched to their own impedances, so that maximum power is transferred in both cases. In addition, the comparison antenna should be oriented so it gives maximum response to the signal used in the test. That is, it should have the same polarization as the incoming signal and should be placed so its direction of maximum gain is toward the signal source.

In long-distance transmission and reception via the ionosphere, the relationship between receiving and transmitting, however, may not be exactly reciprocal. This is because the waves do not always follow exactly the same paths at all times and so may show considerable variation in the time between alternations between transmitting and receiving. Also, when more than one ionospheric layer is involved in the wave travel (see the chapter **Radio Wave Propagation**), it is sometimes possible for reception to be good in one direction and poor in the other over the same path.

Wave polarization usually shifts in the ionosphere. The tendency is for the arriving wave to be elliptically polarized, regardless of the polarization of the transmitting antenna. Vertically polarized antennas can be expected to show no more difference between transmission and reception than horizontally polarized antennas. On the average, however, an antenna that transmits well in a certain direction also gives favorable reception from the same direction, despite ionospheric variations.

1.5.2 ANTENNA BANDWIDTH

The *bandwidth* of an antenna refers generally to the range of frequencies over which the antenna can be used to obtain a specified level of performance. The bandwidth can be specified in units of frequency (MHz or kHz) or as a percentage of the antenna's design frequency.

Popular amateur usage of the term antenna bandwidth most often refers to the 2:1 SWR (standing wave ratio) bandwidth, such as, "The 2:1 *SWR bandwidth* is 3.5 to 3.8 MHz" or "The antenna has a 10% SWR bandwidth" or "On 20 meters, the antenna has an SWR bandwidth of 200 kHz." (Standing wave ratio is discussed in the **Transmission Lines** chapter.) Other specific bandwidth terms are also used, such as the *gain bandwidth* (the bandwidth over which gain is greater than a specified level) and the *front-to-back ratio bandwidth* (the bandwidth over which front-to-back ratio is greater than a specified level).

As operating frequency is lowered, an equivalent bandwidth in percentage becomes narrower in terms of frequency range in kHz or MHz. For example, a 5% bandwidth at 21 MHz is 1.05 MHz (more than wide enough to cover the whole band) but at 3.75 MHz only 187.5 kHz! Because of the wide percentage bandwidth of the lower frequency bands (160 meters is 10.5% wide, 80 meters is 13.4% wide) it is difficult to design an antenna with a bandwidth that covers the whole band.

It is important to recognize that SWR bandwidth does not always relate directly to gain bandwidth. Depending on the amount of feed line loss, an 80 meter dipole with a relatively narrow 2:1 SWR bandwidth can still radiate a good signal at each end of the band, provided that an antenna tuner is used to allow the transmitter to load properly. Broadbanding techniques, such as fanning the far ends of a dipole to simulate a conical type of dipole, can help broaden the SWR bandwidth.

1.5.3 FREQUENCY SCALING

Any antenna design can be scaled in size for use on another frequency or on another amateur band. The dimensions of the antenna may be scaled with Eq 9 below.

$$D = \frac{f1}{f2} \times d \qquad (9)$$

where

D = scaled dimension
d = original design dimension
f1 = original design frequency
f2 = scaled frequency (frequency of intended operation)

From this equation, a published antenna design for, say, 14 MHz can be scaled in size and constructed for operation on 18 MHz, or any other desired band. Similarly, an antenna design could be developed experimentally at VHF or UHF and then scaled for operation in one of the HF bands. For example, from Eq 9, an element of 39.0 inches length at 144 MHz would be scaled to 14 MHz as follows: D = 144/14 × 39 = 401.1 inches, or 33.43 feet.

To scale an antenna properly, all physical dimensions must be scaled, including element lengths, element spacings, boom diameters and element diameters. Lengths and spacings may be scaled in a straightforward manner as in the above example, but element diameters are often not as conveniently scaled. For example, assume a 14 MHz antenna is modeled at 144 MHz and perfected with ⅜-inch cylindrical elements. For proper scaling to 14 MHz, the elements should be cylindrical, of 144/14 × ⅜ or 3.86 inches diameter. From a realistic standpoint, a 4-inch diameter might be acceptable, but cylindrical elements of 4-inch diameter in lengths of 33 feet or so would be quite unwieldy (and quite expensive, not to mention heavy). Choosing another, more suitable diameter is the only practical answer.

Diameter Scaling

Simply changing the diameter of dipole type elements during the scaling process is not satisfactory without making a corresponding element-length correction. This is because changing the diameter results in a change in the length/diameter (l/d) ratio from the original design, and this alters the corresponding resonant frequency of the element. The element length must be corrected to compensate for the effect of the different diameter actually used.

To be more precise, however, the purpose of diameter scaling is not to maintain the same resonant frequency for the element, but to maintain the same ratio of self-resistance to self-reactance at the operating frequency — that is, the Q of the scaled element should be the same as that of the original element. This is not always possible to achieve exactly for elements that use several telescoping sections of tubing.

Tapered Elements

Rotatable beam antennas are usually constructed with elements made of metal tubing. The general practice at HF is to taper the elements with lengths of telescoping tubing. The center section has a large diameter, but the ends are relatively small. This reduces not only the weight, but also the cost of materials for the elements. Tapering of HF Yagi elements is discussed in detail in the chapter on **HF Yagi and Quad Antennas**.

Length Correction for Tapered Elements

The effect of tapering an element is to alter its electrical length. That is to say, two elements of the same length, one cylindrical and one tapered but with the same average diameter as the cylindrical element, will not be resonant at the same frequency. The tapered element must be made longer than the cylindrical element for the same resonant frequency.

A procedure for calculating the length for tapered elements has been worked out by Dave Leeson, W6NL, from work done by Schelkunoff at Bell Labs and is presented in Leeson's book, *Physical Design of Yagi Antennas*. On the *ARRL Antenna Book* website is a subroutine called *EFFLEN.FOR*. It is written in Fortran and is used in the *SCALE* program to compute the effective length of a tapered element. The algorithm uses the Leeson-Schelkunoff algorithm and is commented step-by-step to show what is happening. Calculations are made for only one half of an element, assuming the element is symmetrical about the point of boom attachment.

Also, read the documentation SCALE.PDF for the *SCALE* program, which will automatically do the complex mathematics to scale a Yagi design from one frequency to another, or from one taper schedule to another. (Both *SCALE* and EFFLEN.FOR are available for download from **www.arrl.org/antenna-book**.)

1.5.4 EFFECTIVE RADIATED POWER (ERP)

In many instances it is important to evaluate the effectiveness of the total antenna system from the transmitter to the radiated signal. This is done by computing the system's *effective radiated power* (*ERP*). ERP is calculated by beginning with the *transmitter power output* (*TPO*), subtracting attenuation in the transmission line and all losses from connectors or other devices between the transmitter and antenna, and then adding the antenna gain. All of the gain and loss values are stated in decibels so that the calculations are straightforward additions and subtractions. If antenna gain is specified in dBi (decibels with respect to an isotropic antenna), the result is EIRP — Effective Isotropic Radiated Power. ERP and EIRP calculations are most often used in Amateur Radio in association with frequency coordination as described in the **Repeater Antenna Systems** chapter.

Here is an example calculation of a typical repeater antenna system

TPO = 100 watts = 50 dBm

Transmission line attenuation = 2.4 dB

Losses in RF connectors and antenna coupling network = 1.7 dB

Antenna gain = 7.5 dBi

EIRP = 50 dBm − 2.4 dB − 1.7 dB + 7.5 dB = 53.4 dBm = 219 watts

1.6 RF RADIATION AND ELECTROMAGNETIC FIELD SAFETY

Amateur Radio is basically a safe activity. In recent years, however, there has been considerable discussion and concern about the possible hazards of electromagnetic radiation (EMR), including both RF energy and power-frequency (50-60 Hz) electromagnetic (EM) fields. FCC regulations set limits on the maximum permissible exposure (MPE) allowed from the operation of radio transmitters. These regulations do not take the place of RF-safety practices, however. This section deals with the topic of RF safety.

This section was prepared by members of the ARRL RF Safety Committee and coordinated by Dr Robert E. Gold, WB0KIZ. It summarizes what is now known and offers safety precautions based on the research to date.

All life on Earth has adapted to survive in an environment of weak, natural, low-frequency electromagnetic fields (in addition to the Earth's static geomagnetic field). Natural low-frequency EM fields come from two main sources: the sun and thunderstorm activity. But in the last 100 years, man-made fields at much higher intensities and with a very different spectral distribution have altered this natural EM background in ways that are not yet fully understood. Researchers continue to look at the effects of RF exposure over a wide range of frequencies and levels.

Both RF and 60-Hz fields are classified as *nonionizing radiation,* because the frequency is too low for there to be enough photon energy to ionize atoms. (*Ionizing radiation*, such as X-rays, gamma rays and even some ultraviolet radiation has enough energy to knock electrons loose from their atoms. When this happens, positive and negative ions are formed.) Still, at sufficiently high power densities, EMR poses certain health hazards. It has been known since the early days of radio that RF energy can cause injuries by heating body tissue. (Anyone who has ever touched an improperly grounded radio chassis or energized antenna and received an *RF burn* will agree that this type of injury can be quite painful.) In extreme cases, RF-induced heating in the eye can result in cataract formation, and can even cause blindness. Excessive RF heating of the reproductive organs can cause sterility. Other health problems also can result from RF heating. These heat-related health hazards are called *thermal effects.* A microwave oven is a positive application of this thermal effect.

There also have been observations of changes in physiological function in the presence of RF energy levels that are too low to cause heating. These functions return to normal when the field is removed. Although research is ongoing, no harmful health consequences have been linked to these changes.

In addition to the ongoing research, much else has been done to address this issue. For example, FCC regulations set limits on exposure from radio transmitters. The Institute of Electrical and Electronics Engineers, the American National Standards Institute and the National Council for Radiation Protection and Measurement, among others, have recommended voluntary guidelines to limit human exposure to RF energy. The ARRL has established the RF Safety Committee, consisting of concerned medical doctors and scientists, serving voluntarily to monitor scientific research in the fields and to recommend safe practices for radio amateurs.

1.6.1 THERMAL EFFECTS OF RF ENERGY

Body tissues that are subjected to *very high* levels of RF energy may suffer serious heat damage. These effects depend on the frequency of the energy, the power density of the RF field that strikes the body and factors such as the polarization of the wave.

At frequencies near the body's natural resonant frequency, RF energy is absorbed more efficiently, and an increase in heating occurs. In adults, this frequency usually is about 35 MHz if the person is grounded, and about 70 MHz if insulated from the ground. Individual body parts may be resonant at different frequencies. The adult head, for example, is resonant around 400 MHz, while a baby's smaller head resonates near 700 MHz. Body size thus determines the frequency at which most RF energy is absorbed. As the frequency is moved farther from resonance, less RF heating generally occurs. *Specific absorption rate (SAR)* is a term that describes the rate at which RF energy is absorbed in tissue.

Maximum permissible exposure (MPE) limits are based on whole-body SAR values, with additional safety factors included as part of the standards and regulations. This helps explain why these safe exposure limits vary with frequency. The MPE limits define the maximum electric and magnetic field strengths or the plane-wave equivalent power densities associated with these fields, that a person may be exposed to without harmful effect — and with an acceptable safety factor. The regulations assume that a person exposed to a specified (safe) MPE level also will experience a safe SAR.

Nevertheless, thermal effects of RF energy should not be a major concern for most radio amateurs, because of the power levels we normally use and the intermittent nature of most amateur transmissions. Amateurs spend more time listening than transmitting, and many amateur transmissions such as CW and SSB use low-duty-cycle modes. (With FM or RTTY, though, the RF is present continuously at its maximum level during each transmission.) In any event, it is rare for radio amateurs to be subjected to RF fields strong enough to produce thermal effects, unless they are close to an energized antenna or un-shielded power amplifier. Specific suggestions for avoiding excessive exposure are offered later in this chapter.

1.6.2 ATHERMAL EFFECTS OF EMR

Research about possible health effects resulting from exposure to the lower level energy fields, the athermal effects, has been of two basic types: epidemiological research and laboratory research.

Scientists conduct laboratory research into biological mechanisms by which EMR may affect animals including humans. Epidemiologists look at the health patterns of large groups of people using statistical methods. These epidemiological studies have been inconclusive. By their basic design, these studies do not demonstrate cause and effect, nor do they postulate mechanisms of disease. Instead, epidemiologists look for associations between an environmental factor and an observed pattern of illness. For example, in the earliest research on malaria, epidemiologists observed the association between populations with high prevalence of the disease and the proximity of mosquito infested swamplands. It was left to the biological and medical scientists to isolate the organism causing malaria in the blood of those with the disease, and identify the same organisms in the mosquito population.

In the case of athermal effects, some studies have identified a weak association between exposure to EMF at home or at work and various malignant conditions including leukemia and brain cancer. A larger number of equally well designed and performed studies, however, have found no association. A risk ratio of between 1.5 and 2.0 has been observed in positive studies (the number of observed cases of malignancy being 1.5 to 2.0 times the "expected" number in the population). Epidemiologists generally regard a risk ratio of 4.0 or greater to be indicative of a strong association between the cause and effect under study. For example, men who smoke one pack of cigarettes per day increase their risk for lung cancer tenfold compared to nonsmokers, and two packs per day increases the risk to more than 25 times the nonsmokers' risk.

Epidemiological research by itself is rarely conclusive, however. Epidemiology only identifies health patterns in groups — it does not ordinarily determine their cause. And there are often confounding factors: Most of us are exposed to many different environmental hazards that may affect our health in various ways. Moreover, not all studies of persons likely to be exposed to high levels of EMR have yielded the same results.

There also has been considerable laboratory research about the biological effects of EMR in recent years. For example, some separate studies have indicated that even fairly low levels of EMR might alter the human body's circadian rhythms, affect the manner in which T lymphocytes function in the immune system and alter the nature of the electrical and chemical signals communicated through the cell membrane and between cells, among other things. Although these studies are intriguing, they do not demonstrate any effect of these low-level fields on the overall organism.

Much of this research has focused on low-frequency magnetic fields, or on RF fields that are keyed, pulsed or modulated at a low audio frequency (often below 100 Hz). Several studies suggested that humans and animals can adapt to the presence of a steady RF carrier more readily than to an intermittent, keyed or modulated energy source.

The results of studies in this area, plus speculations concerning the effect of various types of modulation, were and have remained somewhat controversial. None of the research to date has demonstrated that low-level EMR causes adverse health effects.

Given the fact that there is a great deal of ongoing research to examine the health consequences of exposure to EMF, the American Physical Society (a national group of highly respected scientists) issued a statement in May 1995 based on its review of available data pertaining to the possible connections of cancer to 60-Hz EMF exposure. This report is exhaustive and should be reviewed by anyone with a serious interest in the field. Among its general conclusions were the following:

1. The scientific literature and the reports of reviews by other panels show no consistent, significant link between cancer and power line fields.

2. No plausible biophysical mechanisms for the systematic initiation or promotion of cancer by these extremely weak 60-Hz fields has been identified.

3. While it is impossible to prove that no deleterious health effects occur from exposure to any environmental factor, it is necessary to demonstrate a consistent, significant and causal relationship before one can conclude that such effects do occur.

In a report dated October 31, 1996, a committee of the National Research Council of the National Academy of Sciences has concluded that no clear, convincing evidence exists to show that residential exposures to electric and magnetic fields (EMFs) are a threat to human health.

A National Cancer Institute epidemiological study of residential exposure to magnetic fields and acute lymphoblastic leukemia in children was published in the *New England Journal of Medicine* in July 1997. The exhaustive, seven-year study concludes that if there is any link at all, it is far too weak to be concerned about.

Readers may want to follow this topic as further studies are reported. Amateurs should be aware that exposure to RF and ELF (60 Hz) electromagnetic fields at all power levels and frequencies has not been fully studied under all circumstances. "Prudent avoidance" of any avoidable EMR is always a good idea. Prudent avoidance doesn't mean that amateurs should be fearful of using their equipment. Most amateur operations are well within the MPE limits. If any risk does exist, it will almost surely fall well down on the list of causes that may be harmful to your health (on the other end of the list from your automobile). It does mean, however, that hams should be aware of the potential for exposure from their stations, and take whatever reasonable steps they can take to minimize their own exposure and the exposure of those around them.

Safe Exposure Levels

How much EM energy is safe? Scientists and regulators have devoted a great deal of effort to deciding upon safe RF-exposure limits. This is a very complex problem, involving difficult public health and economic considerations. The recommended safe levels have been revised downward several times over the years — and not all scientific bodies agree on this question even today. An Institute of Electrical and Electronics Engineers (IEEE) standard for recommended EM exposure limits was published in 1991 (see Bibliography). It replaced a 1982 American National Standards Institute (ANSI) standard. In the new standard, most of the permitted exposure levels were revised downward (made more

FCC RF-Exposure Regulations

FCC regulations control the amount of RF exposure that can result from your station's operation (§§97.13, 97.503, 1.1307 (b)(c)(d), 1.1310 and 2.1093). The regulations set limits on the maximum permissible exposure (MPE) allowed from operation of transmitters in all radio services. They also require that certain types of stations be evaluated to determine if they are in compliance with the MPEs specified in the rules. The FCC has also required that five questions on RF environmental safety practices be added to Novice, Technician and General license examinations.

These rules went into effect on January 1, 1998 for new stations or stations that file a Form 605 application with the FCC. Other existing stations had until September 1, 2000 to be in compliance with the rules.

THE RULES
Maximum Permissible Exposure (MPE)

All radio stations regulated by the FCC must comply with the requirements for MPEs, even QRP stations running only a few watts or less. The MPEs vary with frequency, as shown in **Table A**. MPE limits are specified in maximum electric and magnetic fields for frequencies below 30 MHz, in power density for frequencies above 300 MHz and all three ways for frequencies from 30 to 300 MHz. For compliance purposes, all of these limits must be considered separately. If any single limit is exceeded, the station is not in compliance.

The regulations control human exposure to RF fields, not the strength of RF fields. There is no limit to how strong a field can be as long as no one is being exposed to it, although FCC regulations require that amateurs use the minimum necessary power at all times (§97.311 [a]).

Environments

The FCC has defined two exposure environments — controlled and uncontrolled. A controlled environment is one in which the people who are being exposed are aware of that exposure and can take steps to minimize that exposure, if appropriate. In an uncontrolled environment, the people being exposed are not normally aware of the exposure. The uncontrolled environment limits are more stringent than the controlled environment limits.

Although the controlled environment is usually intended as an occupational environment, the FCC has determined that it generally applies to amateur operators and members of their immediate households. In most cases, controlled-environment limits can be applied to

---

Table A — (From §1.1310) Limits for Maximum Permissible Exposure (MPE)

(A) Limits for Occupational/Controlled Exposure

Frequency Range (MHz)	Electric Field Strength (V/m)	Magnetic Field Strength (A/m)	Power Density (mW/cm²)	Averaging Time (minutes)
0.3-3.0	614	1.63	(100)*	6
3.0-30	1842/f	4.89/f	(900/f²)*	6
30-300	61.4	0.163	1.0	6
300-1500	—	—	f/300	6
1500-100,000	—	—	5	6

f = frequency in MHz
* = Plane-wave equivalent power density (see Note 1).

(B) Limits for General Population/Uncontrolled Exposure

Frequency Range (MHz)	Electric Field Strength (V/m)	Magnetic Field Strength (A/m)	Power Density (mW/cm²)	Averaging Time (minutes)
0.3-1.34	614	1.63	(100)*	30
1.34-30	824/f	2.19/f	(180/f²)*	30
30-300	27.5	0.073	0.2	30
300-1500	—	—	f/1500	30
1500-100,000	—	—	1.0	30

f = frequency in MHz
* = Plane-wave equivalent power density (see Note 1).
Note 1: This means the equivalent far-field strength that would have the E or H-field component calculated or measured. It does not apply well in the near field of an antenna. The equivalent far-field power density can be found in the near or far field regions from the relationships: $P_d = |E_{total}|^2 / 3770$ mW/cm² or from $P_d = |H_{total}|^2 \times 37.7$ mW/cm².

your home and property to which you can control physical access. The uncontrolled environment is intended for areas that are accessible by the general public, such as your neighbors' properties.

The MPE levels are based on average exposure. An averaging time of 6 minutes is used for controlled exposure; an averaging period of 30 minutes is used for uncontrolled exposure.

Station Evaluations

The FCC requires that certain amateur stations be evaluated for compliance with the MPEs. Although an amateur can have someone else do the evaluation, it is not difficult for hams to evaluate their own stations. The ARRL book *RF Exposure and You* contains extensive information about the regulations and a large chapter of tables that show compliance distances for specific antennas and power levels. Generally, hams will use these tables to evaluate their stations. Some of these tables have been included in the FCC's information — OET Bulletin 65 and its Supplement B. If hams choose, however, they can do more extensive calculations, use a computer to model their antenna and exposure, or make actual measurements.

Categorical Exemptions

Some types of amateur stations do not need to be evaluated, but these stations must still comply with the MPE limits. The station licensee remains responsible for ensuring that the station meets these requirements.

The FCC has exempted these stations from the evaluation requirement because their output power, operating mode and frequency are such that they are presumed to be in compliance with the rules.

Stations using power equal to or less than the levels in **Table B** do not have to be evaluated. For the 100-W HF ham station, for example, an evaluation would be required only on 12 and 10 meters.

Hand-held radios and vehicle-mounted mobile radios that operate using a push-to-talk (PTT) button are also categorically exempt from performing the routine evaluation. Repeater stations that use less than 500 W ERP or those with antennas not mounted on buildings, if the antenna is at least 10 meters off the ground, also do not need to be evaluated.

Correcting Problems

Most hams are already in compliance with the MPE requirements. Some amateurs, especially those using indoor antennas or high-power, high-duty-cycle modes such as a RTTY bulletin station and specialized stations for moonbounce operations and the like may need to make adjustments to their station or operation to be in compliance.

The FCC permits amateurs considerable flexibility in complying with these regulations. As an example, hams can adjust their operating frequency, mode or power to comply with the MPE limits. They can also adjust their operating habits or control the direction their antenna is pointing.

More Information

This discussion offers only an overview of this topic; additional information can be found in *RF Exposure and You* and on the ARRL website at **www.arrl.org/rf-exposure-regulations-news**. The ARRL website also has links to the FCC website, as well as OET Bulletin 65 and Supplement B and links to software that hams can use to evaluate their stations.

Table B — Power Thresholds for Routine Evaluation of Amateur Radio Stations

Wavelength Band	Evaluation Required if Power* (watts) Exceeds:
MF	
160 m	500
HF	
80 m	500
75 m	500
40 m	500
30 m	425
20 m	225
17 m	125
15 m	100
12 m	75
10 m	50
VHF	
All bands	50
UHF	
70 cm	70
33 cm	150
23 cm	200
13 cm	250
SHF	
All bands	250
EHF	
All bands	250

Repeater stations (all bands)

Non-building-mounted antennas: Height above ground level to lowest point of antenna < 10 m and power > 500 W ERP
Building-mounted antennas: Power > 500 W ERP

*Transmitter power = Peak-envelope power input to antenna. For repeater stations *only,* power exclusion based on ERP (effective radiated power).

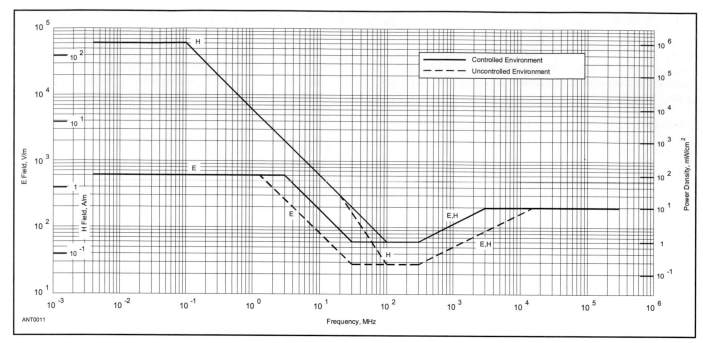

Figure 1.16 — 1991 RF protection guidelines for body exposure of humans. It is known officially as the "IEEE Standard for Safety Levels with Respect to Human Exposure to Radio Frequency Electromagnetic Fields, 3 kHz to 300 GHz."

stringent), to better reflect the current research. The new IEEE standard was adopted by ANSI in 1992.

The IEEE standard recommends frequency-dependent and time-dependent maximum permissible exposure levels. Unlike earlier versions of the standard, the 1991 standard recommends different RF exposure limits in controlled environments (that is, where energy levels can be accurately determined and everyone on the premises is aware of the presence of EM fields) and in uncontrolled environments (where energy levels are not known or where people may not be aware of the presence of EM fields). FCC regulations also include controlled/occupational and uncontrolled/general population exposure environments.

The graph in **Figure 1.16** depicts the 1991 IEEE standard. It is necessarily a complex graph, because the standards differ not only for controlled and uncontrolled environments but also for electric (E) fields and magnetic (H) fields. Basically, the lowest E-field exposure limits occur at frequencies between 30 and 300 MHz. The lowest H-field exposure levels occur at 100-300 MHz. The ANSI standard sets the maximum E-field limits between 30 and 300 MHz at a power density of 1 mW/cm² (61.4 V/m) in controlled environments — but at one-fifth that level (0.2 mW/cm² or 27.5 V/m) in uncontrolled environments. The H-field limit drops to 1 mW/cm² (0.163 A/m) at 100-300 MHz in controlled environments and 0.2 mW/cm² (0.0728 A/m) in uncontrolled environments. Higher power densities are permitted at frequencies below 30 MHz (below 100 MHz for H fields) and above 300 MHz, based on the concept that the body will not be resonant at those frequencies and will therefore absorb less energy.

In general, the 1991 IEEE standard requires averaging the power level over time periods ranging from 6 to

30 minutes for power-density calculations, depending on the frequency and other variables. The ANSI exposure limits for uncontrolled environments are lower than those for controlled environments, but to compensate for that the standard allows exposure levels in those environments to be averaged over much longer time periods (generally 30 minutes). This long averaging time means that an intermittently operating RF source (such as an Amateur Radio transmitter) will show a much lower power density than a continuous-duty station — for a given power level and antenna configuration.

Time averaging is based on the concept that the human body can withstand a greater rate of body heating (and thus, a higher level of RF energy) for a short time than for a longer period. Time averaging may not be appropriate, however, when considering nonthermal effects of RF energy.

The IEEE standard excludes any transmitter with an output below 7 W because such low-power transmitters would not be able to produce significant whole-body heating. (Recent studies show that hand-held transceivers often produce power densities in excess of the IEEE standard within the head.)

There is disagreement within the scientific community about these RF exposure guidelines. The IEEE standard is still intended primarily to deal with thermal effects, not exposure to energy at lower levels. A small but significant number of researchers now believe athermal effects also should be taken into consideration. Several European countries and localities in the United States have adopted stricter standards than the recently updated IEEE standard.

Another national body in the United States, the National Council for Radiation Protection and Measurement (NCRP), also has adopted recommended exposure guidelines. NCRP urges a limit of 0.2 mW/cm² for non-occupational exposure in the 30-300 MHz range. The NCRP guideline differs from IEEE in two notable ways: It takes into account the effects of modulation on an RF carrier and it does not exempt transmitters with outputs below 7 W.

The FCC MPE regulations are based on parts of the 1992 IEEE/ANSI standard and recommendations of the National Council for Radiation Protection and Measurement (NCRP). The MPE limits under the regulations are slightly different from the IEEE/ANSI limits. Note that the MPE levels apply to the FCC rules put into effect for radio amateurs on January 1, 1998. These MPE requirements do not reflect and include all the assumptions and exclusions of the IEEE/ANSI standard.

Cardiac Pacemakers and RF Safety

It is a widely held belief that cardiac pacemakers may be adversely affected in their function by exposure to electromagnetic fields. Amateurs with pacemakers may ask whether their operating might endanger themselves or visitors to their shacks who have a pacemaker. Because of this, and similar concerns regarding other sources of electromagnetic fields, pacemaker manufacturers apply design methods that for the most part shield the pacemaker circuitry from even relatively high EM field strengths.

It is recommended that any amateur who has a pacemaker, or is being considered for one, discuss this matter with his or her physician. The physician will probably put the amateur into contact with the technical representative of the pacemaker manufacturer. These representatives are generally excellent resources, and may have data from laboratory or "in the field" studies with specific model pacemakers.

One study examined the function of a modern (dual chamber) pacemaker in and around an Amateur Radio station. The pacemaker generator has circuits that receive and process electrical signals produced by the heart, and also generate electrical signals that stimulate (pace) the heart. In one series of experiments, the pacemaker was connected to a heart simulator. The system was placed on top of the cabinet of a 1-kW HF linear amplifier during SSB and CW operation. In another test, the system was placed in close proximity to several 1 to 5-W 2 meter hand-held transceivers. The test pacemaker was connected to the heart simulator in a third test, and then placed on the ground 9 meters below and 5 meters in front of a three-element Yagi HF antenna. No interference with pacemaker function was observed in these experiments.

Although the possibility of interference cannot be entirely ruled out by these few observations, these tests represent more severe exposure to EM fields than would ordinarily be encountered by an amateur — with an average amount of common sense. Of course, prudence dictates that amateurs with pacemakers, who use hand-held VHF transceivers, keep the antenna as far as possible from the site of the implanted pacemaker generator. They also should use the lowest transmitter output required for adequate communication. For high power HF transmission, the antenna should be as far as possible from the operating position, and all equipment should be properly grounded.

Low-Frequency Fields

Although the FCC doesn't regulate 60-Hz fields, some recent concern about EMR has focused on low-frequency energy rather than RF. Amateur Radio equipment can be a significant source of low-frequency magnetic fields, although there are many other sources of this kind of energy in the typical home. Magnetic fields can be measured relatively accurately with inexpensive 60-Hz meters that are made by several manufacturers.

Table 1-1 shows typical magnetic field intensities of Amateur Radio equipment and various household items. Because these fields dissipate rapidly with distance, "prudent avoidance" would mean staying perhaps 12 to 18 inches away from most Amateur Radio equipment (and 24 inches from power supplies with 1-kW RF amplifiers).

Determining RF Power Density

Unfortunately, determining the power density of the RF fields generated by an amateur station is not as simple as measuring low-frequency magnetic fields. Although sophisticated instruments can be used to measure RF power densities quite accurately, they are costly and require frequent recalibration. Most amateurs don't have access to such equipment, and the inexpensive field-strength meters that we do have are not suitable for measuring RF power density.

Table 1-2 shows a sampling of measurements made at Amateur Radio stations by the Federal Communications Commission and the Environmental Protection Agency in 1990. As this table indicates, a good antenna well removed from inhabited areas poses no hazard under any of the IEEE/ANSI guidelines. However, the FCC/EPA survey also indicates that amateurs must be careful about using indoor or attic-mounted antennas, mobile antennas, low directional arrays or any other antenna that is close to inhabited areas, especially when moderate to high power is used.

Ideally, before using any antenna that is in close

Table 1-1
Typical 60-Hz Magnetic Fields Near Amateur Radio Equipment and AC-Powered Household Appliances
Values are in milligauss.

Item	Field	Distance
Electric blanket	30-90	Surface
Microwave oven	10-100	Surface
	1-10	12"
Personal computer	5-10	Atop CRT monitor
	0-1	15" from screen
Electric drill	500-2000	At handle
Hair dryer	200-2000	At handle
HF transceiver	10-100	Atop cabinet
	1-5	15" from front
1-kW RF amplifier	80-1000	Atop cabinet
	1-25	15" from front

(Source: measurements made by members of the ARRL RF Safety Committee)

Table 1-2
Typical RF Field Strengths Near Amateur Radio Antennas

A sampling of values as measured by the Federal Communications Commission and Environmental Protection Agency, 1990

Antenna Type	Freq (MHz)	Power (W)	E Field (V/m)	Location
Dipole in attic	14.15	100	7-100	In home
Discone in attic	146.5	250	10-27	In home
Half sloper	21.5	1000	50	1 m from base
Dipole at 7-13 ft	7.14	120	8-150	1-2 m from Earth
Vertical	3.8	800	180	0.5 m from base
5-element Yagi	21.2	1000	10-20	In shack
			14	12 m from base at 60 ft
3-element Yagi	28.5	425	8-12	12 m from base at 25 ft
Inverted V	7.23	1400	5-27	Below antenna at 22-46 ft
Vertical on roof	14.11	140	6-9	In house
			35-100	At antenna tuner
Whip on auto roof	146.5	100	22-75	2 m antenna
			15-30	In vehicle
			90	Rear seat
5-element Yagi	50.1	500	37-50	10 m antenna at 20 ft

proximity to an inhabited area, you should measure the RF power density. If that is not feasible, the next best option is make the installation as safe as possible by observing the safety suggestions listed in **Table 1-3**.

It also is possible, of course, to calculate the probable power density near an antenna using simple equations. Such calculations have many pitfalls. For one, most of the situations where the power density would be high enough to be of concern are in the near field. In the near field, ground interactions and other variables produce power densities that cannot be determined by simple arithmetic. In the far field, conditions become easier to predict with simple calculations.

The boundary between the near field and the far field depends on the wavelength of the transmitted signal and the physical size and configuration of the antenna. The boundary between the near field and the far field of an antenna can be as much as several wavelengths from the antenna.

Computer antenna-modeling programs are another approach you can use. *MININEC* or other codes derived from *NEC* (Numerical Electromagnetics Code) are suitable for estimating RF magnetic and electric fields around amateur antenna systems.

These models have limitations. Ground interactions must be considered in estimating near-field power densities, and the "correct ground" must be modeled. Computer modeling is generally not sophisticated enough to predict "hot spots" in the near field — places where the field intensity may be

Table 1-3
RF Awareness Guidelines

These guidelines were developed by the ARRL RF Safety Committee, based on the FCC/EPA measurements of Table 1-2 and other data.

■ Although antennas on towers (well away from people) pose no exposure problem, make certain that the RF radiation is confined to the antennas' radiating elements themselves. Provide a single, good station ground (earth), and eliminate radiation from transmission lines. Use good coaxial cable or other feed line properly. Avoid serious imbalance in your antenna system and feed line. For high-powered installations, avoid end-fed antennas that come directly into the transmitter area near the operator.

■ No person should ever be near any transmitting antenna while it is in use. This is especially true for mobile or ground-mounted vertical antennas. Avoid transmitting with more than 25 W in a VHF mobile installation unless it is possible to first measure the RF fields inside the vehicle. At the 1-kW level, both HF and VHF directional antennas should be at least 35 ft above inhabited areas. Avoid using indoor and attic-mounted antennas if at all possible. If open-wire feeders are used, ensure that it is not possible for people (or animals) to come into accidental contact with the feed line.

■ Don't operate high-power amplifiers with the covers removed,

especially at VHF/UHF.

■ In the UHF/SHF region, never look into the open end of an activated length of waveguide or microwave feed-horn antenna or point it toward anyone. (If you do, you may be exposing your eyes to more than the maximum permissible exposure level of RF radiation.) Never point a high-gain, narrow-bandwidth antenna (a paraboloid, for instance) toward people. Use caution in aiming an EME (moonbounce) array toward the horizon; EME arrays may deliver an effective radiated power of 250,000 W or more.

■ With hand-held transceivers, keep the antenna away from your head and use the lowest power possible to maintain communications. Use a separate microphone and hold the rig as far away from you as possible. This will reduce your exposure to the RF energy.

■ Don't work on antennas that have RF power applied.

■ Don't stand or sit close to a power supply or linear amplifier when the ac power is turned on. Stay at least 24 inches away from power transformers, electrical fans and other sources of high-level 60-Hz magnetic fields.

far higher than would be expected, due to reflections from nearby objects. In addition, "nearby objects" often change or vary with weather or the season, so the model so laboriously crafted may not be representative of the actual situation, by the time it is running on the computer.

Intensely elevated but localized fields often can be detected by professional measuring instruments. These "hot spots" are often found near wiring in the shack, and metal objects such as antenna masts or equipment cabinets. But even with the best instrumentation, these measurements also may be misleading in the near field.

One need not make precise measurements or model the exact antenna system, however, to develop some idea of the relative fields around an antenna. Computer modeling using close approximations of the geometry and power input of the antenna will generally suffice. Those who are familiar with *MININEC* can estimate their power densities by computer modeling, and those who have access to professional power-density meters can make useful measurements.

While our primary concern is ordinarily the intensity of the signal radiated by an antenna, we also should remember that there are other potential energy sources to be considered. You also can be exposed to RF radiation directly from a power amplifier if it is operated without proper shielding. Transmission lines also may radiate a significant amount of energy under some conditions. Poor microwave waveguide joints or improperly assembled connectors are another source of incidental radiation.

Further RF Exposure Suggestions

Potential exposure situations should be taken seriously. Based on the FCC/EPA measurements and other data, the "RF awareness" guidelines of Table 1-3 were developed by the ARRL RF Safety Committee. A longer version of these guidelines, along with a complete list of references, appeared in a *QST* article by Ivan Shulman, MD, WC2S ("Is Amateur Radio Hazardous to Our Health?" *QST*, Oct 1989, pp 31-34). For more information or background, see the list of RF Safety References in the next section.

In addition, the ARRL has published a book, *RF Exposure and You*, that is helping hams comply with the FCC's RF-exposure regulations. The ARRL also maintains an RF-exposure news page on its website. See **www.arrl. org/rf-exposure**. This site contains reprints of selected *QST* articles on RF exposure and links to the FCC and other useful sites.

1.7 BIBLIOGRAPHY

TEXTBOOKS ON ANTENNAS

C. A. Balanis, *Antenna Theory, Analysis and Design* (New York: Harper & Row, 1982).

D. S. Bond, *Radio Direction Finders*, 1st ed. (New York: McGraw-Hill Book Co).

W. N. Caron, *Antenna Impedance Matching* (Newington: ARRL, 1989).

K. Davies, *Ionospheric Radio Propagation — National Bureau of Standards Monograph 80* (Washington, DC: U.S. Government Printing Office, Apr 1, 1965).

R. S. Elliott, *Antenna Theory and Design* (Englewood Cliffs, NJ: Prentice Hall, 1981).

A. E. Harper, *Rhombic Antenna Design* (New York: D. Van Nostrand Co, Inc, 1941).

K. Henney, *Principles of Radio* (New York: John Wiley and Sons, 1938), p 462.

H. Jasik, *Antenna Engineering Handbook*, 1st ed. (New York: McGraw-Hill, 1961).

W. C. Johnson, *Transmission Lines and Networks*, 1st ed. (New York: McGraw-Hill Book Co, 1950).

R. C. Johnson and H. Jasik, *Antenna Engineering Handbook*, 2nd ed. (New York: McGraw-Hill, 1984).

R. C. Johnson, *Antenna Engineering Handbook*, 3rd ed. (New York: McGraw-Hill, 1993).

E. C. Jordan and K. G. Balmain, *Electromagnetic Waves and Radiating Systems*, 2nd ed. (Englewood Cliffs, NJ: Prentice-Hall, Inc, 1968).

R. Keen, *Wireless Direction Finding*, 3rd ed. (London: Wireless World).

R. W. P. King, *Theory of Linear Antennas* (Cambridge, MA: Harvard Univ. Press, 1956).

R. W. P. King, H. R. Mimno and A. H. Wing, *Transmission Lines, Antennas and Waveguides* (New York: Dover Publications, Inc, 1965).

King, Mack and Sandler, *Arrays of Cylindrical Dipoles* (London: Cambridge Univ Press, 1968).

M. G. Knitter, Ed., *Loop Antennas — Design and Theory* (Cambridge, WI: National Radio Club, 1983).

M. G. Knitter, Ed., *Beverage and Long Wire Antennas — Design and Theory* (Cambridge, WI: National Radio Club, 1983).

J. D. Kraus, *Electromagnetics* (New York: McGraw-Hill Book Co).

J. D. Kraus, *Antennas*, 2nd ed. (New York: McGraw-Hill Book Co, 1988).

E. A. Laport, *Radio Antenna Engineering* (New York: McGraw-Hill Book Co, 1952).

J. L. Lawson, *Yagi-Antenna Design*, 1st ed. (Newington: ARRL, 1986).

D. B. Leeson, *Physical Design of Yagi Antennas* (Newington: ARRL, 1992).

P. H. Lee, *The Amateur Radio Vertical Antenna Handbook*, 2nd ed. (Port Washington, NY: Cowen Publishing Co., 1984).

A. W. Lowe, *Reflector Antennas* (New York: IEEE Press, 1978).

M. W. Maxwell, *Reflections III - Transmission Lines and Antennas*, 3rd edition (CQ Communications, 2010).

G. M. Miller, *Modern Electronic Communication* (Englewood Cliffs, NJ: Prentice Hall, 1983).

V. A. Misek, *The Beverage Antenna Handbook* (Hudson, NH: V. A. Misek, 1977).

T. Moreno, *Microwave Transmission Design Data* (New York: McGraw-Hill, 1948).

L. A. Moxon, HF *Antennas for All Locations* (Potters Bar, Herts: Radio Society of Great Britain, 1982), pp 109-111.

Ramo and Whinnery, *Fields and Waves in Modern Radio* (New York: John Wiley & Sons).

V. H. Rumsey, *Frequency Independent Antennas* (New York: Academic Press, 1966).

P. N. Saveskie, *Radio Propagation Handbook* (Blue Ridge Summit, PA: Tab Books, Inc, 1980).

S. A. Schelkunoff, *Advanced Antenna Theory* (New York: John Wiley & Sons, Inc, 1952).

S. A. Schelkunoff and H. T. Friis, *Antennas Theory and Practice* (New York: John Wiley & Sons, Inc, 1952).

J. Sevick, *Transmission Line Transformers* (Atlanta: Noble Publishing, 1996).

H. H. Skilling, *Electric Transmission Lines* (New York: McGraw-Hill Book Co, Inc, 1951).

M. Slurzburg and W. Osterheld, *Electrical Essentials of Radio* (New York: McGraw-Hill Book Co, Inc, 1944).

G. Southworth, *Principles and Applications of Waveguide Transmission* (New York: D. Van Nostrand Co, 1950).

F. E. Terman, *Radio Engineers' Handbook*, 1st ed. (New York, London: McGraw-Hill Book Co, 1943).

F. E. Terman, *Radio Engineering*, 3rd ed. (New York: McGraw-Hill, 1947).

G. B. Welch, *Wave Propagation and Antennas* (New York: D. Van Nostrand Co, 1958), pp 180-182.

The GIANT Book of Amateur Radio Antennas (Blue Ridge Summit, PA: Tab Books, 1979), pp 55-85.

Radio Broadcast Ground Systems, available from Smith Electronics, Inc, 8200 Snowville Rd, Cleveland, OH 44141.

Radio Communication Handbook, 5th ed. (London: RSGB, 1976).

Wiley Electrical and Electronics Engineering Dictionary (Wiley — IEEE Press: 2004)

TABLE OF CONTENTS

Chapter 2

Dipoles and Monopoles

Dipoles and monopoles are not only popular antennas, they are the basic elements from which most antennas used by amateurs are constructed, including beams. This chapter explores the basic characteristics of these antennas in support of the specific designs the reader will encounter later in the book. Material from previous editions is augmented by contributions from the dipole and vertical chapters of the 5th edition of *ON4UN's Low-Band DXing*.

2.1 DIPOLES

The *dipole* is a fundamental form of antenna — in its most common form it is approximately one-half wavelength (½ λ) long at the frequency of use. It is the unit from which many more complex forms of antennas are constructed. The name di- meaning *two*, and -pole meaning *part*, relates to the opposite voltages applied to each half of the antenna so that it has two electrical halves as in **Figure 2.1**. A dipole is resonant when its electrical length is some odd multiple of ½ λ so that the current and voltage in the antenna are exactly 90° out of phase as shown in **Figure 2.2**.

2.1.1 RADIATION PATTERNS

The radiation pattern of a dipole antenna in free space is strongest at right angles to the wire as shown in **Figure 2.3**, a free-space radiation pattern. In an actual installation, the figure-8 pattern is less directive due to reflections from ground and other conducting surfaces. As the dipole is raised to ½ λ or greater above ground, nulls off the ends of the dipole become more pronounced. Sloping the antenna above ground and coupling to the feed line tend to distort the pattern slightly.

As a horizontal dipole is brought closer to ground, reflections from the ground combine with the direct radiation to create lobes at different angles as shown in **Figure 2.4**. In addition, the directivity of the dipole also changes with height. For example, **Figure 2.5** shows the dipole's three-dimensional

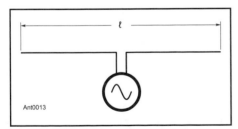

Figure 2.1 — **The center-fed dipole antenna. It is assumed that the source of power is directly at the antenna feed point, with no intervening transmission line. Although λ/2 is the most common length for amateur dipoles, the length of a dipole antenna can be any fraction of a wavelength.**

Figure 2.2 — **The current and voltage distribution along a half-wave dipole (A) and for an antenna made from a series of half-wave dipoles (B).**

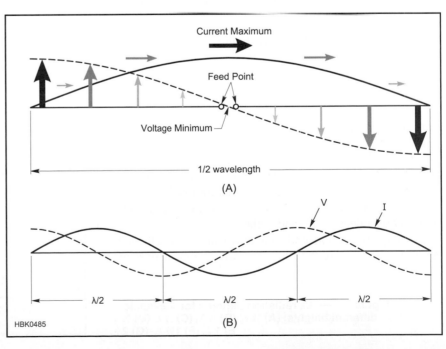

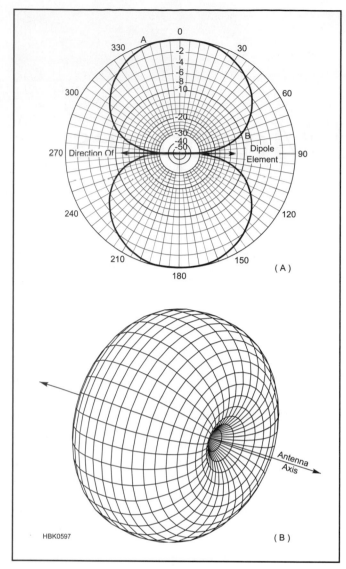

Figure 2.3 — Response of a dipole antenna in free space in the plane of the antenna with the antenna oriented along the 90° to 270° axis (A). The full three-dimensional pattern of the dipole is shown at (B). The pattern at A is a cross-section of the three-dimensional pattern taken directly through the axis of the antenna.

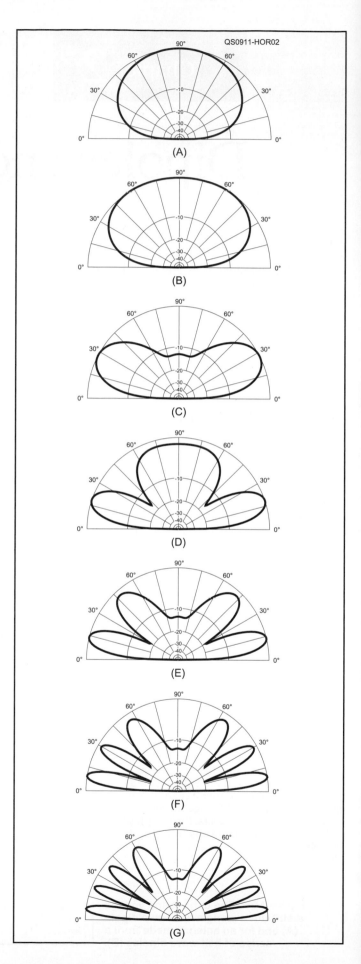

pattern at a height of ½ λ. The deep null along the axis of the wire in Figure 2.5 is filled in with a substantial amount of radiation.

Figure 2.6 shows the radiation pattern for dipoles at different heights above ground and at four different elevation angles from 15° to 60°. You can see that for low heights (the H = ¼ λ figure) the dipole becomes almost omnidirectional at elevation angles of 60° and higher.

The type of ground under the dipole also affects the radiation pattern. **Figure 2.7** illustrates what happens over two

Figure 2.4 — Six radiation patterns for the dipole at different heights: **(A)** ⅛ λ, **(B)** ¼ λ, **(C)** ½ λ, **(D)** ¾ λ, **E)** 1 λ, **(F)** 1½ λ, **(G)** 2 λ.

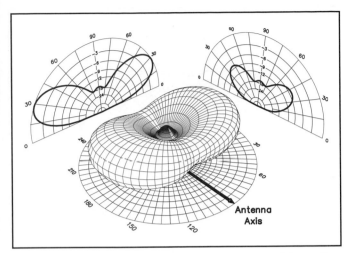

Figure 2.5 — Three-dimensional representation of the radiation patterns of a half-wave dipole, ½ λ above ground.

$$\text{Length (ft)} = \frac{492 \times 0.95}{f \text{ (MHz)}} = \frac{468}{f \text{ (MHz)}} \qquad \text{(Eq 1)}$$

Example: A half-wave antenna for 7150 kHz (7.15 MHz) is 468/7.15 = 65.5 feet or about 65 feet, 6 inches.

For antennas at higher frequencies and/or higher above ground, use a numerator value closer to the free-space value, such as 485 to 490. Include additional wire for attaching insulators and be prepared to adjust the length of the antenna once installed in its intended position.

Above 30 MHz use the following formulas, particularly for antennas constructed from rod or tubing. K is taken from Figure 2.8.

$$\text{Length (ft)} = \frac{492 \times K}{f \text{ (MHz)}} \qquad \text{(Eq 2)}$$

$$\text{Length (in)} = \frac{5904 \times K}{f \text{ (MHz)}} \qquad \text{(Eq 3)}$$

Example: Find the length of a half-wave antenna at 50.1 MHz, if the antenna is made of ½-inch-diameter tubing. At 50.1 MHz, a half wavelength in space is

$$\frac{492}{50.1} = 9.82 \text{ ft}$$

The ratio of half wavelength to conductor diameter (changing wavelength to inches) is

$$\frac{(9.82 \text{ ft} \times 12 \text{ in/ft})}{0.5 \text{ in}} = 235.7$$

From Figure 2.8, K = 0.945 for this ratio. The length of the antenna, from Equation 2 is

$$\frac{492 \times 0.945}{50.1} = 9.28 \text{ ft}$$

or 9 feet 3⅜ inches. The answer is obtained directly in inches by substitution in Equation 3

$$\frac{5904 \times 0.945}{50.1} = 111.4 \text{ in}$$

The impedance and resonant frequency of an antenna also depend on the diameter of the conductors that make up its elements in relation to the wavelength. As diameter of a

different types of ground; very poor soil (desert) and saltwater. These two types of ground represent the extremes of what amateurs are likely to encounter and most installations will be somewhere in between these two examples.

2.1.2 EFFECTS OF CONDUCTOR DIAMETER

The physical length of a resonant ½-λ antenna will not be exactly equal to the half wavelength of a radio wave of that frequency in free space, but depends on the thickness of the conductor in relation to the wavelength as shown in **Figure 2.8**. For antennas over ground, the height above ground also affects the antenna's physical length as in the example of **Table 2-1** showing the resonant, half-wavelength length for a 20 meter dipole at various electrical heights. Nearby conducting surfaces and materials will also affect resonant length.

An additional shortening effect occurs with wire antennas supported by insulators at the ends (and at the feed point) because of the capacitance added to the system by the loops of wire through the insulators. This shortening is called *end effect*.

The following formula is sufficiently accurate for dipoles below 10 MHz at heights of ⅛ to ¼ λ and made of common wire sizes. To calculate the length of a half-wave antenna in feet,

Table 2-1
Variation in Dipole Performance with Height

Height in Wavelengths at 14.175 MHz (feet)	Resonant Length in Feet (Lx/f)	Feed point Impedance in Ω (SWR)	Max Gain (dBi) at Angle (Degrees)
⅛ (8.8)	33.0 (467.8)	31.5 (1.59)	7.4 @ 90
¼ (17.4)	32.9 (466.4)	81.7 (1.63)	5.6 @ 62
½ (34.7)	34.1 (483.4)	69.6 (1.39)	7.4 @ 28
¾ (52.0)	33.4 (473.4)	73.4 (1.47)	7.3 @ 18
1 (69.4)	33.9 (480.5)	71.9 (1.44)	7.7 @ 14
1½ (104.1)	33.8 (479.1)	72.0 (1.44)	7.8 @ 9
2 (138.8)	33.8 (479.1)	72.3 (1.45)	7.9 @ 7

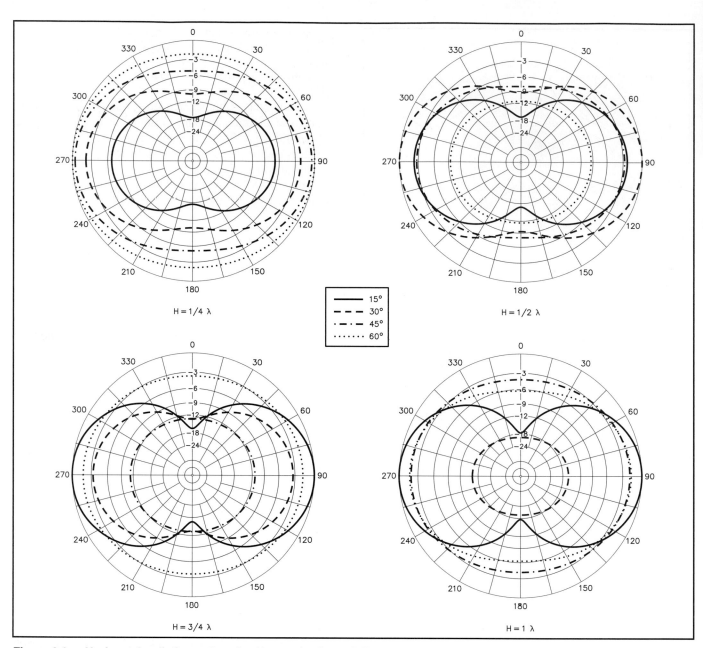

Figure 2.6 — Horizontal radiation pattern for ½-wave horizontal dipole at various heights above ground for wave angles of 15°, 30°, 45° and 60° (modeled over good ground).

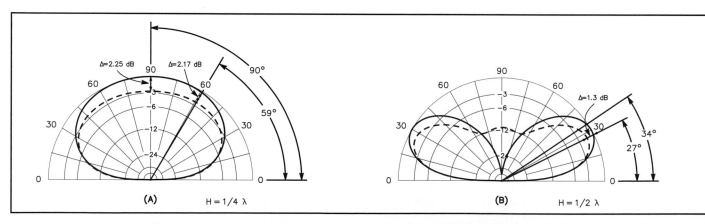

Figure 2.7 — Vertical radiation patterns over two types of ground: saltwater (solid line in each set of plots) and very poor ground (dashed line in each set of plots). The wave angles as well as the gain difference between saltwater and poor ground are given for four antenna heights.

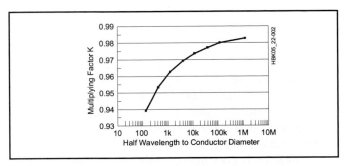

Figure 2.8 — Effect of antenna diameter on length for half-wavelength resonance in free-space, shown as a multiplying factor, K. The thicker the conductor relative to the wavelength, the shorter the physical length of the antenna at resonance. For antennas over ground, additional factors affect the antenna's electrical length.

conductor increases, its capacitance per unit length increases and inductance per unit length decreases. This has the effect of lowering the frequency at which the antenna element is resonant, as illustrated by the graph in Figure 2.8. The larger the conductor diameter in terms of wavelength, the smaller its *length-to-diameter ratio (l/d)* and the lower the frequency at which a specific length of that conductor is ½ λ long electrically.

$$l/d = \frac{\lambda/2}{d} = \frac{300}{2f \times d} \qquad \text{(Eq 4)}$$

where f is in MHz and d is in meters. For example, a ½-λ dipole for 7.2 MHz made from #12 AWG wire (0.081 inch dia) has an l/d ratio of

$$l/d = \frac{300}{2f \times d} = \frac{300}{2 \times 7.2 \times \dfrac{0.081 \text{ in}}{39.37 \text{ in/m}}} = 10,126$$

The effect of l/d is accounted for by the factor K which is based on l/d. From Figure 2.8 an l/d ratio of 10,126 corresponds to K ≈ 0.975, so the resonant length of that ½-wave dipole would be K × (300 / 2f) = 20.31 meters instead of the free-space 20.83 meters.

Most wire antennas at HF have l/d ratios in the range of 2500 to 25,000 with K = 0.97 to 0.98. The value of K is taken into account in the classic formula for ½-wave dipole length, 468/f (in MHz). If K = 1, the formula would be 492/f (in MHz).

For single-wire HF antennas, the effects of ground and antenna construction make a precise accounting for K unnecessary in practice. At and above VHF, the effects of l/d ratio can be of some importance, since the wavelength is small.

Since the radiation resistance is affected relatively little by l/d ratio, but the decreased L/C ratio causes the Q of the antenna to decrease. This means that the change in antenna impedance with frequency will be less, increasing the antenna's SWR bandwidth. This is often used to advantage on the lower HF bands by using multiple conductors in a cage or fan to decrease the l/d ratio.

2.1.3 FEED POINT IMPEDANCE

A feed line is attached directly to the dipole, generally at the center with an insulator separating the antenna's conductor into two sections. Such a dipole is referred to as being *center-fed*. One conductor of the feed line is attached to each section. The point at which the feed line is attached is the dipole's *feed point*.

The dipole's feed point impedance is the ratio of voltage to current at the feed point. Referring back to Figure 2.2A, the feed point impedance of a half-wave dipole will be low at the center (where voltage is minimum and current is maximum) and high on each end (where voltage is maximum and current is minimum).

If a dipole is fed at the center and excited (supplied with power) at the third harmonic, the situation changes to that of Figure 2.2B. The dipole's physical length has not changed but its electrical length at the third harmonic has tripled — it is now three half-wavelengths long. If fed in the center, the same low impedance (low voltage/high current) is presented to the feed line. This situation occurs for all odd harmonics of the dipole's fundamental frequency because the center of the dipole is at a low impedance point and will present a reasonably low SWR to coaxial feed lines.

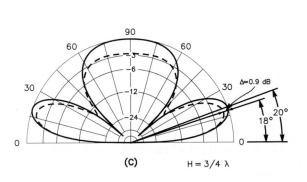

(C)   H = 3/4 λ

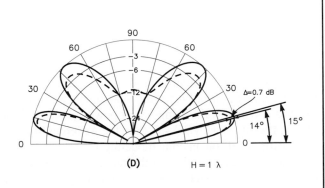

(D)   H = 1 λ

The situation is reversed if the dipole is excited at an even harmonic. Remove the right-most half-wavelength section in Figure 2.2B as the dipole is now electrically one full wavelength long. At the center of this antenna, voltage is high and current is low so the impedance is high and SWR will be high on any common feed line, coaxial or parallel-conductor. This is the situation at all even harmonics of the dipole's fundamental frequency and is sometimes referred to as *anti-resonance*.

At frequencies in between harmonics, the feed point impedance will take some intermediate value. When fed with parallel-conductor line and a wide-range impedance-matching unit, a dipole can be used on nearly any frequency, including non-resonant frequencies. (An example of such an antenna system is presented in the chapter **Single Band MF and HF Antennas**.)

A dipole can be fed anywhere along its length, although the impedance of the antenna will vary as the ratio of voltage and current change. One common variation is the *off-center-fed (OCF)* dipole where the feed point is offset from center by some amount and an impedance transformer used to match the resulting moderately high impedance that occurs on several bands to that of coaxial cable.

Feed Point Impedance in Free-Space

In free space the theoretical impedance of a half-wavelength antenna made of an infinitely thin conductor is 73 + j 42.5 Ω. This antenna exhibits both resistance and reactance. The positive sign in the + j 42.5 Ω reactive term indicates that the antenna exhibits an inductive reactance at its feed point. The antenna is slightly long electrically, compared to the length necessary for exact resonance, where the reactance is zero.

The feed point impedance of any antenna is affected by the wavelength-to-diameter ratio (λ/dia) of the conductors used. Theoreticians like to specify an "infinitely thin" antenna because it is easier to handle mathematically.

What happens if we keep the physical length of an antenna constant, but change the thickness of the wire used in its construction? Further, what happens if we vary the frequency from well below to well above the half-wave resonance and measure the feed point impedance? **Figure 2.9** graphs the impedance of a 100-foot long, center-fed dipole in free space, made with extremely thin wire — in this case, wire that is only 0.001 inch in diameter. There is nothing particularly significant about the choice here of 100 feet. This is simply a numerical example.

We could never actually build such a thin antenna (and neither could we install it in free space), but we can model how this antenna works using a very powerful piece of computer software called *NEC-4.1*. (See the **Antenna Modeling** chapter for details on antenna modeling.)

The frequency applied to the antenna in Figure 2.9 is varied from 1 to 30 MHz. The x-axis has a logarithmic scale because of the wide range of feed point resistance seen over the frequency range. The y-axis has a linear scale representing the reactive portion of the impedance. Inductive reactance

is positive and capacitive reactance is negative on the y-axis. The bold figures centered on the spiraling line show the frequency in MHz.

At 1 MHz, the antenna is very short electrically, with a resistive component of about 2 Ω and a series capacitive reactance about –5000 Ω. Close to 5 MHz, the line crosses the zero-reactance line, meaning that the antenna goes through half-wave resonance there. Between 9 and 10 MHz the antenna exhibits a peak inductive reactance of about 6000 Ω. It goes through full-wave resonance (again

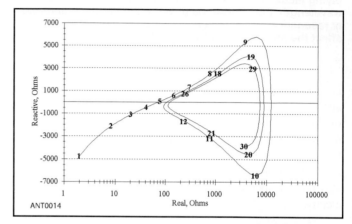

Figure 2.9 — Feed point impedance versus frequency for a theoretical 100-foot long dipole in free space, fed in the center and made of extremely thin 0.001-inch diameter wire. The y-axis is calibrated in positive (inductive) series reactance up from the zero line, and negative (capacitive) series reactance in the downward direction. The range of reactance goes from –6500 Ω to +6000 Ω. Note that the x-axis is logarithmic because of the wide range of the real, resistive component of the feed point impedance, from roughly 2 Ω to 10,000 Ω. The numbers placed along the curve show the frequency in MHz.

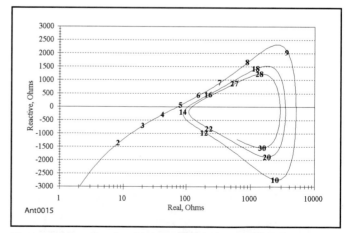

Figure 2.10 — Feed point impedance versus frequency for a theoretical 100-foot long dipole in free space, fed in the center and made of thin 0.1-inch (#10 AWG) diameter wire. Note that the range of change in reactance is less than that shown in Figure 2.9, ranging from –2700 Ω to +2300 Ω. At about 5000 Ω, the maximum resistance is also less than that in Figure 2.9 for the thinner wire, where it is about 10,000 Ω.

crossing the zero-reactance line) between 9.5 and 9.6 MHz. At about 10 MHz, the reactance peaks at about –6500 Ω. Around 14 MHz, the line again crosses the zero-reactance line, meaning that the antenna has now gone through ³⁄₄-wave resonance.

Between 19 and 20 MHz, the antenna goes through ⁴⁄₄-wave resonance, which is twice the full-wave resonance or four times the half-wave frequency. If you allow your mind's eye to trace out the curve for frequencies beyond 30 MHz, it eventually spirals down to a resistive component somewhere between 200 and 3000 Ω. Thus, we have another way of looking at an antenna—as a sort of transformer, one that transforms the free-space impedance into the impedance seen at its feed point.

Now look at **Figure 2.10**, which shows the same kind of spiral curve, but for a thicker-diameter wire, one that is 0.1 inch in diameter. This diameter is close to #10 AWG wire, a practical size we might actually use to build a real dipole. Note that the y-axis scale in Figure 2.10 is different from that in Figure 2.9. The range is from –3000 Ω in Figure 2.10, while it was –7000 Ω in Figure 2.9. The reactance for the thicker antenna ranges from +2300 to –2700 Ω over the whole frequency range from 1 to 30 MHz. Compare this with the range of +5800 to –6400 Ω for the very thin wire in Figure 2.9.

Figure 2.11 shows the impedance for a 100-foot long dipole using really thick, 1.0-inch diameter wire. The reactance varies from +1000 to –1500 Ω, indicating once again that a larger diameter antenna exhibits less of an excursion in the reactive component with frequency. Note that at the half-wave resonance just below 5 MHz, the resistive component of the impedance is still about 70 Ω, just about what it is for a much thinner antenna. Unlike the reactance, the half-wave radiation resistance of an antenna doesn't radically change with wire diameter, although the maximum level of resistance at full-wave resonance is lower for thicker antennas.

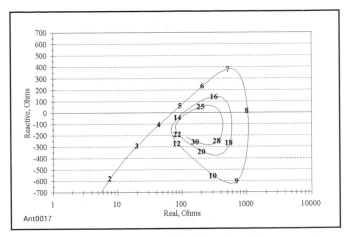

Figure 2.12 — Feed point impedance versus frequency for a theoretical 100-foot long dipole in free space, fed in the center and made of very thick 10.0-inch diameter wire. This ratio of length to diameter is about the same as a typical rod type of dipole element commonly used at 432 MHz. The maximum resistance is now about 1,000 Ω and the peak reactance range is from about –625 Ω to +380 Ω. This performance is also found in "cage" dipoles, where a number of paralleled wires are used to simulate a fat conductor.

Figure 2.12 shows the results for a very thick, 10-inch diameter wire. Here, the excursion in the reactive component is even less: about +400 to –600 Ω. Note that the full-wave resonant frequency is about 8 MHz for this extremely thick antenna, while thinner antennas have full-wave resonances closer to 9 MHz. Note also that the full-wave resistance for this extremely thick antenna is only about 1000 Ω, compared to the 10,000 Ω shown in Figure 2.9. All half-wave resonances shown in Figures 2.9 through 2.12 remain close to 5 MHz, regardless of the diameter of the antenna wire. Once again, the extremely thick, 10-inch diameter antenna has a resistive component at half-wave resonance close to 70 Ω. And once again, the change in reactance near this frequency is very much less for the extremely thick antenna than for thinner ones.

Now, we grant you that a 100-foot long antenna made with 10-inch diameter wire sounds a little odd! A length of 100 feet and a diameter of 10 inches represent a ratio of 120:1 in length to diameter. However, this is about the same length-to-diameter ratio as a 432 MHz half-wave dipole using 0.25-inch diameter elements, where the ratio is 109:1. In other words, the ratio of length-to-diameter for the 10-inch diameter, 100 foot long dipole is not that far removed from what might actually be used at UHF.

Another way of highlighting the changes in reactance and resistance is shown in **Figure 2.13**. This shows an expanded portion of the frequency range around the half-wave resonant frequency, from 4 to 6 MHz. In this region, the shape of each spiral curve is almost a straight line. The slope of the curve for the very thin antenna (0.001-inch diameter) is steeper than that for the thicker antennas (0.1 and 1.0-inch diameters). **Figure 2.14** illustrates another way of looking at the impedance data above and below the half-wave resonance. This is

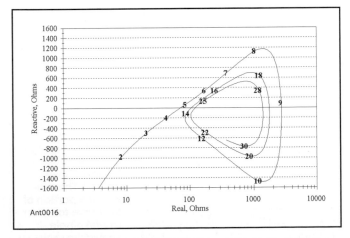

Figure 2.11 — Feed point impedance versus frequency for a theoretical 100-foot long dipole in free space, fed in the center and made of thick 1.0-inch diameter wire. Once again, the excursion in both reactance and resistance over the frequency range is less with this thick wire dipole than with thinner ones.

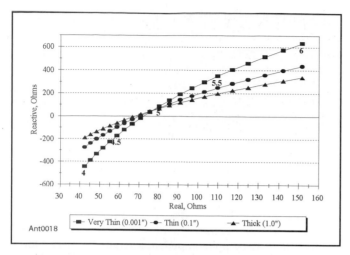

Figure 2.13 — Expansion of frequency range around half-wave resonant point of three center-fed dipoles of three different thicknesses. The frequency is shown along the curves in MHz. The slope of change in series reactance versus series resistance is steeper for the thinner antennas than for the thick 1.0-inch antenna, indicating that the Q of the thinner antennas is higher.

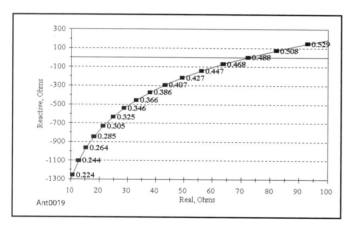

Figure 2.14 — Another way of looking at the data for a 100-foot, center-fed dipole made of #14 AWG wire in free space. The numbers along the curve represent the fractional wavelength, rather than frequency as shown in Figure 2.13. Note that this antenna goes through its half-wave resonance at about 0.488 λ, rather than exactly at a half-wave physical length.

for a 100-foot dipole made of #14 AWG wire. Instead of showing the frequency for each impedance point, the wavelength is shown, making the graph more universal in application.

Just to show that there are lots of ways of looking at the same data, recall that Figure 2.8 graphs the constant "K" used to multiply the free-space half-wavelength as a function of the ratio between the half-wavelength and the conductor diameter. The curve approaches the value of 1.00 for an infinitely thin conductor, in other words an infinitely large ratio of half-wavelength to diameter.

The behavior of antennas with different λ/diameter ratios corresponds to the behavior of ordinary series-resonant circuits having different values of Q. When the Q of a circuit is low, the reactance is small and changes rather slowly as the

applied frequency is varied on either side of resonance. If the Q is high, the converse is true. The response curve of the low-Q circuit is broad; that of the high-Q circuit sharp. So it is with antennas—the impedance of a thick antenna changes slowly over a comparatively wide band of frequencies, while a thin antenna has a faster change in impedance. Antenna Q is defined

$$Q = \frac{f_0 \Delta X}{2 R_0 \Delta f}$$

(Eq 5)

where f_0 is the center frequency, ΔX is the change in the reactance for a Δf change in frequency, and R_0 is the resistance at f_0. For the "Very Thin," 0.001-inch diameter dipole in Figure 2.9, a change of frequency from 5.0 to 5.5 MHz yields a reactance change from 86 to 351 Ω, with an R_0 of 95 Ω. The Q is thus 14.6. For the 1.0-inch-diameter "Thick" dipole in Figure 2.11, $\Delta X = 131$ Ω and R_0 is still 95 Ω, making Q = 7.2 for the thicker antenna, roughly half that of the thinner antenna.

Let's recap. The dipole can be described as a transducer or as a sort of transformer to a range of free-space impedances. Now, we just compared the antenna to a series-tuned circuit. Near its half-wave resonant frequency, a center-fed λ/2 dipole exhibits much the same characteristics as a conventional series-resonant circuit. Exactly at resonance, the current at the input terminals is in phase with the applied voltage and the feed point impedance is purely resistive. If the frequency is below resonance, the phase of the current leads the voltage; that is, the reactance of the antenna is capacitive. When the frequency is above resonance, the opposite occurs; the current lags the applied voltage and the antenna exhibits inductive reactance. Just like a conventional series-tuned circuit, the antenna's reactance and resistance determines its Q.

Effect of Height Above Ground on Feed Point Impedance

The feed point impedance of an antenna varies with height above ground because of the effects of energy reflected from and absorbed by the ground. For example, a ½-λ (or half-wave) center-fed dipole will have a feed point impedance of approximately 75 Ω in *free space* far from ground, but **Figure 2.15** shows that only at certain electrical heights

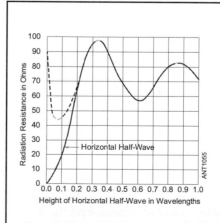

Figure 2.15 — Curves showing the radiation resistance of a horizontal half-wavelength dipole at various heights above ground. The broken-line portion of the curve for a horizontal dipole shows the resistance over *average* real earth, the solid line for perfectly conducting ground.

above ground will the feed point impedance be 75 Ω. The feed point impedance will vary from very low when the antenna is close to the ground to a maximum of nearly 100 Ω at 0.34 λ above ground, varying around 75 Ω as the antenna is raised farther. The 75-Ω feed point impedance is most likely to be realized in a practical installation when the horizontal dipole is approximately ½, ¾ or 1 λ above ground. This is why few amateur λ/2-dipoles exhibit a center-fed feed point impedance of 75 Ω, even though they may be resonant.

Figure 2.15 also compares the effects of perfect ground and typical soil at low antenna heights. The effect of height on the radiation resistance of a horizontal half-wave antenna is not drastic so long as the height of the antenna is greater than 0.2 λ. Below this height, while decreasing rapidly to zero over perfectly conducting ground, the resistance decreases less rapidly with height over actual lossy ground. At lower heights the resistance stops decreasing at around 0.15 λ, and thereafter increases as height decreases further. The reason for the increasing resistance is that more and more energy from the antenna is absorbed by the ground as the height drops below ¼ λ, seen as an increase in feed point impedance.

2.1.4 EFFECT OF FREQUENCY ON RADIATION PATTERN

Earlier, we saw how the feed point impedance of a fixed-length center-fed dipole in free space varies as the frequency is changed. What happens to the radiation pattern of such an antenna as the frequency is changed?

In general, the greater the length of a center-fed antenna, in terms of wavelength, the larger the number of lobes into which the pattern splits. A feature of all such patterns is the fact that the main lobe is always the one that makes the smallest angle with (is closest to) the antenna wire. Furthermore, this angle becomes smaller as the length of the antenna is increased.

Let's examine how the free-space radiation pattern changes for a 100-foot long wire made of #14 AWG wire as the frequency is varied. (Varying the frequency effectively changes the electrical length of a fixed-length wire.)

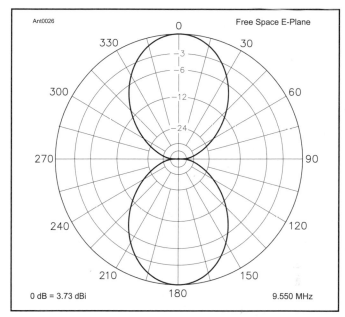

Figure 2.17 — Free-space E-Plane radiation pattern for a 100-foot dipole at its full-wave resonant frequency of 9.55 MHz. The gain has increased to 3.73 dBi, because the main lobes have been focused and sharpened compared to Figure 2.16.

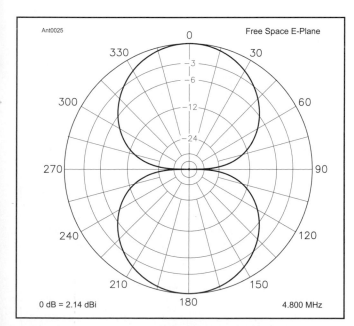

Figure 2.16 — Free-space E-Plane radiation pattern for a 100-foot dipole at its half-wave resonant frequency of 4.80 MHz. This antenna has 2.14 dBi of gain. The dipole is located on the line from 90° to 270°.

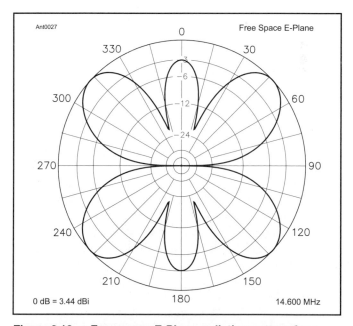

Figure 2.18 — Free-space E-Plane radiation pattern for a 100-foot dipole at its 3/2λ resonant frequency of 14.60 MHz. The pattern has broken up into six lobes, and thus the peak gain has dropped to 3.44 dBi.

Figure 2.16 shows the E-plane pattern at the λ/2 resonant frequency of 4.8 MHz. This is a classical dipole pattern, with a gain in free space of 2.14 dBi referenced to an isotropic radiator.

Figure 2.17 shows the free-space E-plane pattern for the same antenna, but now at the full-wave (2 λ/2) resonant frequency of 9.55 MHz. Note how the pattern has been pinched in at the top and bottom of the figure. In other words, the two main lobes have become sharper at this frequency, making the gain 3.73 dBi, higher than at the λ/2 frequency.

Figure 2.18 shows the pattern at the 3 λ/2 frequency of 14.6 MHz. More lobes have developed compared to Figure 2.16. This means that the power has split up into more lobes and consequently the gain decreases a small amount, down to 3.44 dBi. This is still higher than the dipole at its λ/2 frequency, but lower than at its full-wave frequency. Figure 2.19 shows the E-plane response at 19.45 MHz, the 4 λ/2, or 2 λ, resonant frequency. Now the pattern has reformed itself into only four lobes, and the gain has as a consequence risen to 3.96 dBi.

In Figure 2.20 the response has become quite complex at the 5 λ/2 resonance point of 24.45 MHz, with ten lobes showing. Despite the presence all these lobes, the main lobes now show a gain of 4.78 dBi. Finally, Figure 2.21 shows the pattern at the 3λ (6 λ/2) resonance at 29.45 MHz. Despite the fact that there are fewer lobes taking up power than at 24.45 MHz, the peak gain is slightly less at 29.45 MHz, at 4.70 dBi.

The pattern — and hence the gain — of a fixed-length antenna varies considerably as the frequency is changed. Of course, the pattern and gain change in the same fashion if the frequency is kept constant and the length of the wire is varied. In either case, the wavelength is changing. It is also evident that certain lengths reinforce the pattern to provide more peak gain. If an antenna is not rotated in azimuth when the frequency is changed, the peak gain may occur in a different direction than you might like. In other words, the main lobes change direction as the frequency is varied.

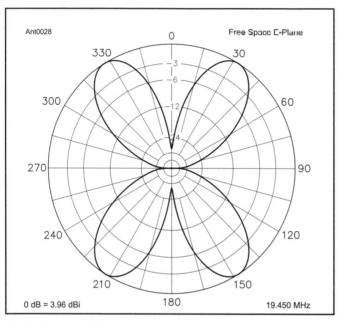

Figure 2.19 — Free-space E-Plane radiation pattern for a 100-foot dipole at twice its full-wave resonant frequency of 19.45 MHz. The pattern has been refocused into four lobes, with a peak gain of 3.96 dBi.

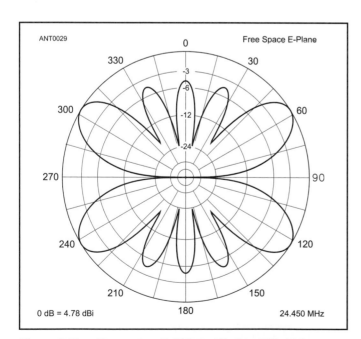

Figure 2.20 — Free-space E-Plane radiation pattern for a 100-foot dipole at its 5/2λ resonant frequency of 24.45 MHz. The pattern has broken down into ten lobes, with a peak gain of 4.78 dBi.

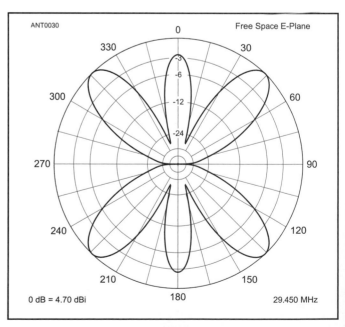

Figure 2.21 — Free-space E-Plane radiation pattern for a 100-foot dipole at three times its full-wave resonant frequency of 29.45 MHz. The pattern has returned to six lobes, with a peak gain of 4.70 dBi.

2.1.5 FOLDED DIPOLES

Figure 21.22 shows a *folded dipole* constructed from open-wire transmission line. The dipole is made from a ½-λ section of open-wire line with the two conductors connected together at each end of the antenna. The top conductor of the open-wire length is continuous from end to end. The lower conductor, however, is cut in the middle and the feed line attached at that point. Open-wire transmission line is then used to connect the transmitter.

A folded dipole has exactly the same gain and radiation pattern as a single-wire dipole. However, because mutual coupling divides the antenna current between the upper and lower conductors, the ratio of voltage to current at the feed point (the feed point impedance) is multiplied by the square of the number of conductors in the antenna. In this case, there are two conductors in the antenna, so the feed point impedance is $2^2 = 4$ times that of a single-wire dipole. A three-wire folded dipole would have a nine times higher feed point impedance and so forth. If the diameter of the conductors are different, the ratio will not be an exact square of the number of conductors.

A common use of the folded dipole is to raise the feed point impedance of the antenna to present a better impedance match to high impedance feed line. For example, if a very long feed line to a dipole is required, open-wire feed line would be preferable because of its lower loss. By raising the dipole's feed point impedance, the SWR on the open-wire line is reduced from that of a single-wire dipole fed with open-wire feed line.

2.1.6 VERTICAL DIPOLES

A half-wave dipole can also be oriented vertically over ground instead of horizontally, becoming a *vertical dipole*. The dipole's pattern becomes generally omnidirectional. The characteristics of ground under and near the vertical dipole have a large effect on its radiation pattern as shown in **Figure 2.23**.

In Figure 2.23A and B with the bottom of the vertical dipole very close (λ/80) to a saltwater ground plane the vertical dipole can have a gain of 6.1 dBi. Gain drops to about 0 dBi over good soil and lower over poorer soils. As with all vertical antennas, it is mainly the quality of the ground close to the antenna that determines how good a low-angle radiator the vertical dipole will be as discussed in the chapter **Effects of Ground**. Raising the half-wave vertical higher above the ground introduces multiple lobes as shown in Figure 2.23C and D with the antenna's bottom tip ⅛ λ above ground.

The radiation resistance of the vertical dipole also depends on the height of its lower tip above ground as shown in **Figure 2.24**. As with the horizontal dipole, the radiation resistance varies above and below the free-space value of 73.5 Ω but not as much as for the horizontal dipole since its feed point is farther above ground.

In practice, it is not possible to obtain symmetrical currents in the upper and lower halves of the vertical dipole at HF due to the asymmetrical relationship of the two sections to ground. Further, the presence of the feed line introduces a third conductor for common-mode current that can influence the antenna's performance unless decoupled. Thus, the radiation patterns are unlikely to be very close to the ideal patterns shown here.

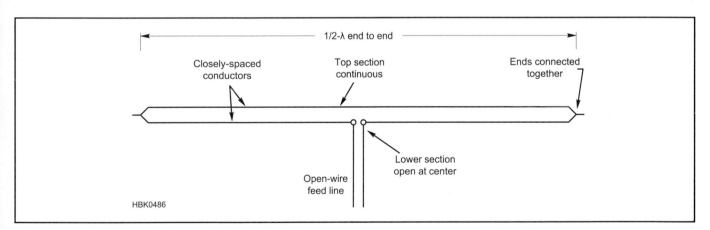

Figure 2.22 — The folded dipole is most often constructed from open-wire transmission line with the ends connected together. The close proximity of the two conductors and the resulting coupling act as an impedance transformer to raise the feed point impedance over that of a single-wire dipole by the square of the number of conductors used.

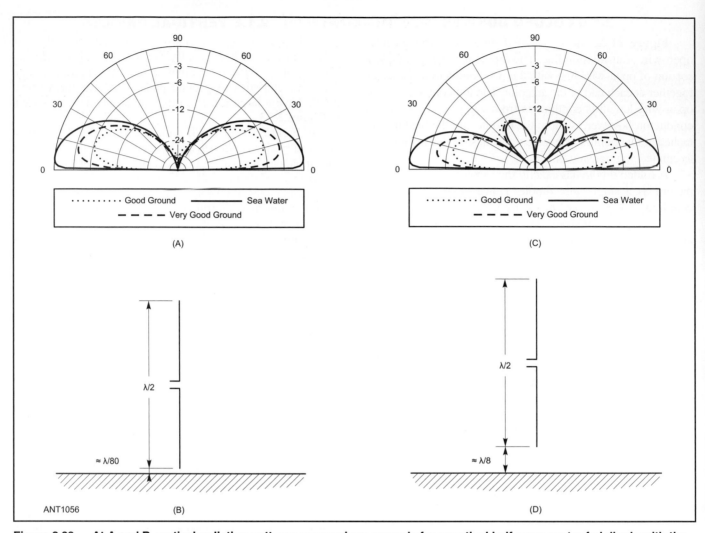

Figure 2.23 — At A and B, vertical radiation patterns over various grounds for a vertical half-wave center-fed dipole with the bottom tip just clearing the ground. The gain is as high as 6.1 dBi over ground and the feed point impedance is 100 Ω. At C and D, the vertical radiation patterns of the half-wave vertical dipole with the bottom tip ⅛ λ off the ground. Note the appearance of lobes in the radiation pattern at high elevation angles.

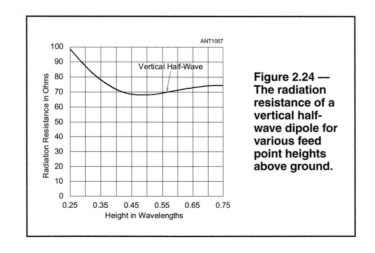

Figure 2.24 — The radiation resistance of a vertical half-wave dipole for various feed point heights above ground.

2.2 MONOPOLES

Another simple form of antenna derived from a dipole is called a *monopole*. The name suggests that this is one half of a dipole, and so it is. The monopole is always used in conjunction with a ground plane, which acts as a sort of electrical mirror. See **Figure 2.25**, where a λ/2 dipole and a λ/4 monopole are compared. The image antenna for the monopole is the dotted line beneath the ground plane. The image forms the missing second half of the antenna, transforming a monopole into the functional equivalent of a dipole.

Monopoles are usually mounted vertically with respect to the surface of the ground. As such, they are called *vertical monopoles*, or simply *verticals*. A practical vertical is supplied power by feeding the radiator against a ground system, usually made up of a series of paralleled wires radiating from and laid out in a circular pattern around the base of the antenna. These wires are called *radials* since they extend radially from the base of the antenna.

The term *ground plane* is also used to describe a vertical antenna employing a vertical radiating element (usually λ/4 long) and a *counterpoise* system, another name for the ground plane that supplies the missing half of the antenna. The counterpoise for a ground-plane antenna usually consists of four λ/4-long radials elevated well above the ground. See **Figure 2.26**.

The chapter **Effects of Ground** devotes much attention to the requirements for an efficient grounding system for vertical monopole antennas. The chapter **Single Band MF and HF Antennas** gives more information on practical ground-plane verticals at HF. Ground-plane antennas at higher frequencies are discussed in the chapter **VHF and UHF Antenna Systems** and **Mobile VHF and UHF Antennas**.

2.2.1 CHARACTERISTICS OF A λ/4 MONOPOLE

The free-space directional characteristics of a λ/4 monopole with its ground plane are very similar to that of a λ/2 antenna in free space. The gain for the λ/4 monopole is slightly less because the H-plane pattern for the λ/2 antenna is compressed compared to the monopole.

Like a λ/2 antenna, the λ/4 monopole has an omnidirectional radiation pattern in the plane perpendicular to the monopole.

The current in a λ/4 monopole varies practically sinusoidally (as is the case with a λ/2 dipole), and is highest at the ground-plane connection. The voltage is highest at the open (top) end and minimum at the ground plane. The feed point resistance close to λ/4 resonance of a vertical monopole over a perfect ground plane is one-half that for a λ/2 dipole at its λ/2 resonance. This is because half of the radiation resistance of a full-size λ/2 dipole has been replaced by an electrical image that does not actually exist and so cannot radiate power.

The word "height" applied to a vertical monopole antenna whose base is on or near the ground has the same meaning as length when applied to λ/2 dipole antennas. Some texts refer to heights in electrical degrees, referenced to a free-space wavelength of 360°, or height may be expressed in terms of the free-space wavelength.

Figure 2.27, which shows the feed point impedance of a vertical antenna made of #14 AWG wire, 50 feet long,

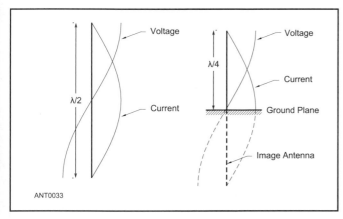

Figure 2.25 — The λ/2 dipole antenna and its λ/4 ground-plane counterpart. The "missing" quarter wavelength is supplied as an image in "perfect" (that is, high-conductivity) ground.

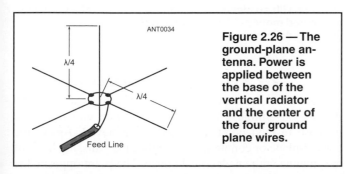

Figure 2.26 — The ground-plane antenna. Power is applied between the base of the vertical radiator and the center of the four ground plane wires.

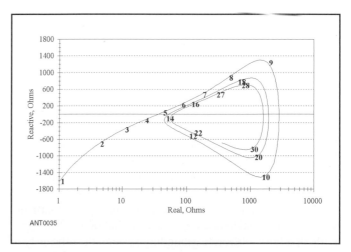

Figure 2.27 — Feed point impedance versus frequency for a theoretical 50-foot-high grounded vertical monopole made of #14 AWG wire. The numbers along the curve show the frequency in MHz. This was computed using "perfect" ground. Real ground losses will add to the feed point impedance shown in an actual antenna system.

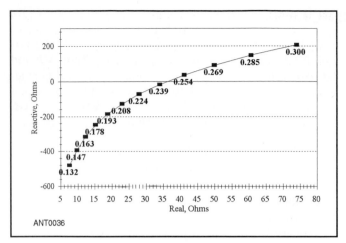

Figure 2.28 — Feed point impedance for the same antennas as in Figure 2.25, but calibrated in wavelength rather than frequency over the range from 0.132 to 0.300 λ, above and below the quarter-wave resonance.

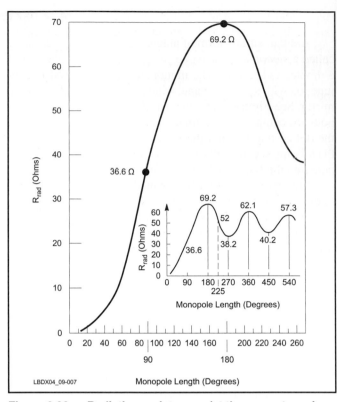

Figure 2.29 — Radiation resistances (at the current maximum) of monopoles with sinusoidal current distribution. The chart can also be used for dipoles, but all values must be doubled.

located over perfect ground. Impedance is shown over the whole HF range from 1 to 30 MHz. Again, there is nothing special about the choice of 50 feet for the length of the vertical radiator; it is simply a convenient length for evaluation.

Figure 2.28 shows an expanded portion of the frequency range above and below the λ/4 resonance, but now calibrated in terms of wavelength. Note that this particular antenna goes through λ/4 resonance at a length of 0.244 λ, not at exactly 0.25 λ. The exact length for resonance varies with the diameter of the wire used, just as it does for the λ/2 dipole at its λ/2 resonance. The range shown in Figure 2.28 is from 0.132 λ to 0.300 λ, corresponding to a frequency range of 2.0 to 5.9 MHz.

The variation of a monopole's radiation resistance with electrical length or height is shown in **Figure 2.29** from 0° to 270°. Note that for the λ/4 monopole (a length of 90°) the radiation resistance is 36.6 Ω, one-half the radiation resistance of a λ/2 dipole. The radiation resistance is measured at the current maximum, which for monopoles longer than λ/4 will be above the base of the antenna.

The reactive portion of the feed point impedance is highly dependent on the length/dia ratio of the conductor, as was discussed previously for a horizontal center-fed dipole. The impedance curve in Figures 2.25 and 2.26 is based on a #14 AWG conductor having a length/dia ratio of about 800 to 1. As usual, thicker antennas can be expected to show less reactance at a given height, and thinner antennas will show more.

The efficiency of a real vertical antenna over real earth often suffers dramatically compared with that of a λ/2 antenna. Without a fairly elaborate grounding system, the efficiency is not likely to exceed 50%, and it may be much less, particularly at monopole heights below λ/4. In addition, the gain of a monopole at angles close to the ground plane is highly dependent on the conductivity of the ground-plane. Both effects are discussed extensively in the chapter **Effects of Ground**.

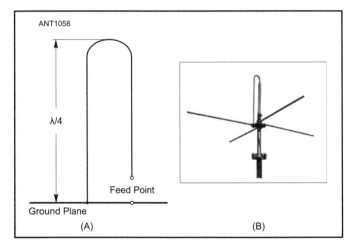

Figure 2.30 — The folded monopole antenna (A) can be nderstood similarly to the folded dipole with the ground-plane or counterpoise supplying the "missing half" of the antenna with an electrical image. An example of a commercial folded monopole is depicted in (B).

2.2.2 FOLDED MONOPOLES

A folded monopole, shown in **Figure 2.30**, can be understood similarly to the folded dipole and the same increase in feed point impedance is achieved. Again, the ground-plane or counterpoise supplies the "missing half" of the antenna with an electrical image. The point opposite the feed point is electrically neutral in the λ/4 folded monopole and so is connected to the ground plane as in Figure 2.30A. An example of a commercial folded monopole is depicted in Figure 2.30B.

The increased feed point impedance of the folded monopole is often misunderstood as reducing ground losses due to the lower current at the feed point. This analysis neglects the equal amount of current that also flows in the folded conductor at its attachment to the ground plane. The total amount of current flowing in the ground system is thus the same as in the non-folded monopole and no reduction in ground loss is obtained.

2.3 BIBLIOGRAPHY

The dipole and monopole are discussed extensively in the references listed in the Bibliography for the **Antenna Fundamentals** chapter.

J. Devoldere, *ON4UN's Low-Band DXing*, Fifth Edition (Newington: ARRL, 2010).

W. Silver, "Hands-On Radio: Experiment #84 — Antenna Height," *QST*, Nov 2009, pp 64-65.

W. Silver, "Hands-On Radio: Experiment #92 — The 468 Factor," *QST*, Sep 2010, pp 53-54.

TABLE OF CONTENTS

Chapter 3

The Effects of Ground

The **Antenna Fundamentals** chapter dealt mainly with ideal antennas in free space, completely removed from the influence of ground. Real antennas however, are placed over ground and in some cases right on or even under the ground surface. The presence of ground can have a profound effect on the behavior of an antenna, including the feed point impedance, the efficiency and the radiation pattern. This chapter is devoted to describing the interactions between antennas and ground and ways to reduce ground losses close to the antenna. For the purposes of this chapter the terms "soil" or "earth" are considered equivalent to "ground". In some cases "ground" may actually be fresh water or seawater.

We will begin by examining the characteristics of typical soils and then proceed to interactions between grounds and antennas. The interaction discussion is divided between two areas around the antenna: the *reactive near field* and the *radiating far field*. The reactive near field only exists very close to the antenna itself, essentially within one wavelength. In this region the antenna acts as though it were a large lumped-constant R-L-C tuned circuit where energy is stored in the fields close to the antenna. Only a portion of this energy is radiated. The RF current in the antenna will induce currents in the ground which in turn will affect the currents in the antenna. These interactions can modify the feed point impedance of an antenna and, due to the currents flowing in the ground, add power losses. This loss represents power supplied to the antenna from the transmitter but not radiated so there is a net reduction in signal for a given power input to the antenna. For vertical antennas located on or near ground, this can be very significant.

In the radiating far field, the presence of ground profoundly influences the radiation pattern of an antenna. The interaction differs depending on the antenna polarization with respect to the ground. For horizontally polarized antennas, the shape of the radiated pattern in elevation plane depends primarily on the antenna's height above ground. For vertically polarized antennas, both the shape and the strength of the radiated pattern in the elevation plane strongly depend on the nature of the ground itself, as well as the height of the antenna above ground.

The material in this chapter assumes a flat ground surface surrounding the antenna. An extensive discussion of how to account for non-flat ground is presented in the chapter **HF Antenna System Design**, including use of the *HFTA* terrain analysis software by Dean Straw, N6BV.

3.1 EFFECTS OF GROUND IN THE REACTIVE NEAR FIELD

Sections 3.1 and 3.2 of this chapter have been expanded and reworked by the original author, Rudy Severns, N6LF to accommodate the results of work done since the previous version.

3.1.1 ELECTRICAL CHARACTERISTICS OF GROUND

One way to investigate the characteristics of a given sample of soil would be to fabricate a simple parallel plate capacitor as shown in **Figure 3.1**. First we might measure the

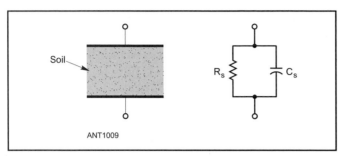

Figure 3.1 — Equivalent circuit for soil characteristics.

capacitance (C_s) and the shunt resistance (R_s) without any soil between the plates. We would expect to get a very high value for R_s and some modest capacitance proportional to the plate areas and inversely proportional to the plate spacing. If we then fill the space between the plates with the soil we're interested in and repeat the R_s and C_s measurements, the chances are we will see a marked change in both: much lower R_s and higher C_s. What this experiment tells us is that soil acts like a lossy capacitor. When an RF current flows in the soil there will be some loss associated with R_s. The trick is to keep the RF current out of the soil at least near the antenna.

R_s is inversely related to the soil conductivity (σ) and C_s is directly related to the relative permittivity (dielectric constant) (ε_r). We can infer values for σ and ε_r from measurements made on the capacitor with and without the soil between the plates. The unit for σ is Siemens per meter (S/m). ε_r is dimensionless. At HF both σ and ε_r are needed for the determination of ground losses or radiation patterns and are an important part of antenna modeling.

A century of measurements on different soils has shown that both σ and ε_r vary over a wide range depending on location, soil composition, stratification of the soil, soil moisture

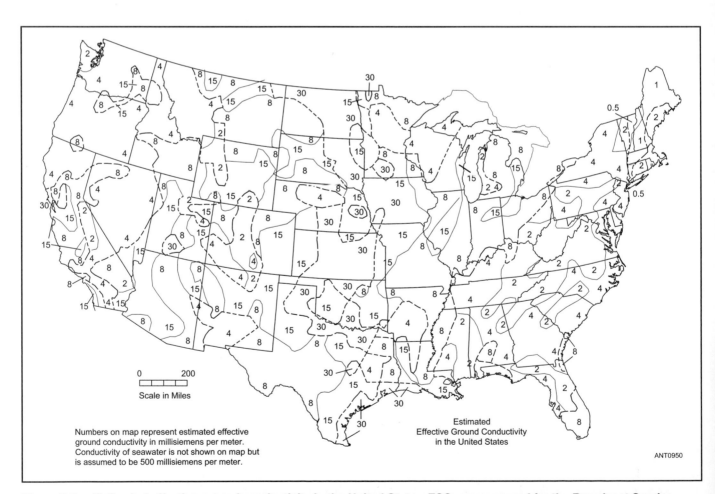

Numbers on map represent estimated effective ground conductivity in millisiemens per meter. Conductivity of seawater is not shown on map but is assumed to be 500 millisiemens per meter.

Estimated Effective Ground Conductivity in the United States

Figure 3.2 — Estimated effective ground conductivity in the United States. FCC map prepared for the Broadcast Service, showing typical conductivity for continental USA. Values are for the band 500 to 1500 kHz. Values are for flat, open spaces and often will not hold for other types of commonly found terrain, such as seashores, river beds, etc.

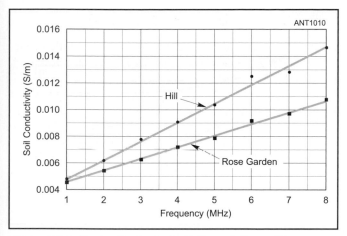

Figure 3.3 — Typical soil conductivity variation with frequency.

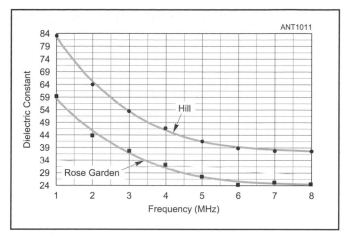

Figure 3.4 — Typical soil permittivity variation with frequency.

Table 3-1
Conductivities and Dielectric Constants for Common Types of Earth

Surface Type	Dielectric Constant	Conductivity (S/m)	Relative Quality
Fresh water	80	0.001	
Salt water	81	5.0	
Pastoral, low hills, rich soil, typ Dallas, TX, to Lincoln, NE areas	20	0.0303	Very good
Pastoral, low hills, rich soil typ OH and IL	14	0.01	
Flat country, marshy, densely wooded, typ LA near Mississippi River	12	0.0075	
Pastoral, medium hills and forestation, typ MD, PA, NY, (exclusive of mountains and coastline)	13	0.006	
Pastoral, medium hills and forestation, heavy clay soil, typ central VA	13	0.005	Average
Rocky soil, steep hills, typ mountainous	12-14	0.002	Poor
Sandy, dry, flat, coastal	10	0.002	
Cities, industrial areas	5	0.001	Very Poor
Cities, heavy industrial areas, high buildings	3	0.001	Extremely poor

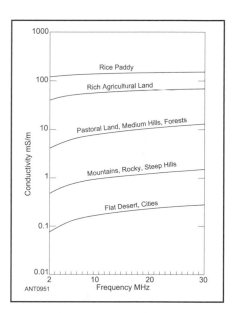

Figure 3.5 — Ground conductivity variation with frequency for different types of soils.

content and many other variables. **Table 3-1** lists typical characteristics for a variety of typical grounds.

Real soils seldom have these exact pairs of σ and ε_r. For a given value of σ, ε_r can vary widely. Both σ and ε_r tend to increase with soil moisture content so it is normal to have higher ε_r when you have higher σ. However, it is also possible to have moderate values of σ but quite high values for ε_r. Soils with clay particles often have high ε_r. For fresh water at 23° C, ε_r = 78, so you may wonder how soil can have an ε_r higher than water. The higher values are the result of polarization effects that can occur in clay soils. It is quite possible to have ε_r > 100, at least at lower HF frequencies. In general, conductivity will increase with frequency and permittivity will decrease initially at lower HF but level out at higher frequencies.

Much of the data on soil conductivity stems from work at broadcast band frequencies. **Figure 3.2** is a graphic of typical ground conductivity for the United States. While useful for BC (AM broadcast) station planning this graphic is of limited use to amateurs because it averages the conductivity over large areas and the primary concern is ground wave propagation at BC frequencies. Amateurs are usually more concerned with the soil close to their antennas where the conductivity can vary dramatically from the large area average.

Soil characteristics vary not only with location and time of year but also with frequency. **Figures 3.3** and **3.4** show the variation of σ and ε_r with frequency at two locations at a typical amateur QTH (N6LF). See this chapter's section "Ground Parameters for Antenna Analysis" for methods of measuring ground parameters for antenna modeling and design.

George Hagn and his associates at SRI have made a very large number of ground characteristic measurements at many different places in the world.[1] **Figure 3.5** shows the results of some of this work.

3.1.2 SKIN DEPTH IN SOIL

It is very probable that the soil at a given location will be stratified (vary with depth) so it will be necessary to take some average value. The question is then "how deep do I have to go to make the average?" This question is best answered by determining the depth to which the fields or the RF currents penetrate the soil. This penetration depth is often expressed in terms of the "skin depth" where the skin depth (δ) is the depth at which the current or the field has been attenuated to 1/e or 37% (e = 2.71828...) of its value at the ground surface. Skin depth is also used in the calculation of ground loss.

Knowing σ and ε_r, the skin depth in an arbitrary material can be determined from:

$$\delta = \left(\frac{\sqrt{2}}{\omega\sqrt{\mu\varepsilon}}\right)\left[\sqrt{1+\left(\frac{\sigma}{\omega\varepsilon}\right)^2}-1\right]^{-1/2} \tag{1}$$

where

δ = skin or penetration depth [meters]
$\omega = 2\pi f$, f = frequency [hertz]
σ = conductivity [siemens/meter, S/m]
$\mu = \mu_r\mu_o$ = permeability
μ_o = permeability of vacuum = $4\pi 10^{-7}$ [henry/meter]
μ_r = relative permeability [dimensionless]
$\varepsilon = \varepsilon_r\varepsilon_o$ = permittivity [farad/meter]
ε_o = permittivity of vacuum = 8.854×10^{-12} [farad/meter]
ε_r = relative permittivity [dimensionless]

A graph of Eq 1 for typical grounds is given in **Figure 3.6**.

Skin depth varies with frequency and soil characteristics. For example, at 1.8 MHz δ varies from about 16 cm in seawater to 15 m in poor soil. As we go up in frequency

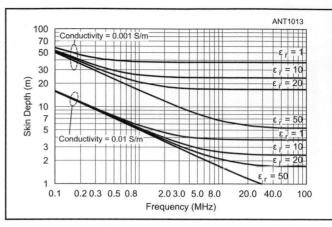

Figure 3.7 — Examples of skin depth as a function of ε_r for two different conductivities.

the skin depth decreases, roughly proportional to $1/\sqrt{f}$, until at some point it flattens out.

The soil types in Figure 3.6 represent the typical values used in antenna modeling. An example of the effect of differing ε_r for soils with σ = 0.001 and 0.01 S/m is shown in **Figure 3.7**. In Figure 3.7, we can see several interesting things. At low frequencies (in the BC band) the values for δ converge and ε_r makes little difference. This is one reason why soil characteristics from BC data seldom include the permittivity. At high frequencies the curves are flat with a value that depends on σ and ε_r.

3.1.3 WAVELENGTH IN SOIL

Because soil is a complex medium where both σ and ε_r are significantly different from their values in free space, the wavelength in soil (λ) may differ greatly from the wavelength in free space (λ_o). This is important for antennas and radial systems close to or buried in the ground. In general the wavelength in soil will be considerably shorter than the free space wavelength and this must be taken into account for wire segmentation during modeling.

The wavelength in free space (λ_o) is:

$$\lambda_o = \frac{299.79}{f(\text{MHz})} \text{ in meters} \tag{2}$$

The wavelength in soil (λ) is:

$$\lambda = \frac{\lambda_o}{\left[\varepsilon_r^2 + \left(\frac{\sigma}{\omega\varepsilon_o}\right)^2\right]^{1/4}} \tag{3}$$

Figure 3.8 gives examples of wavelength as a function of frequency for different soils, salt and fresh water and free space. It can be seen that the wavelength in soil is typically much smaller than in free space.

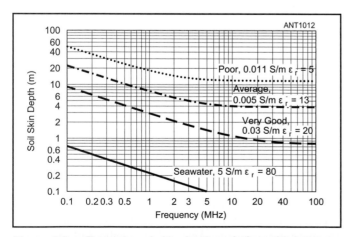

Figure 3.6 — Examples of skin depth variation with frequency for different grounds.

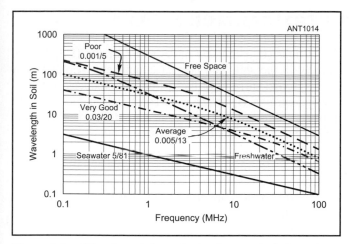

Figure 3.8 — Wavelength in typical soils as a function of frequency.

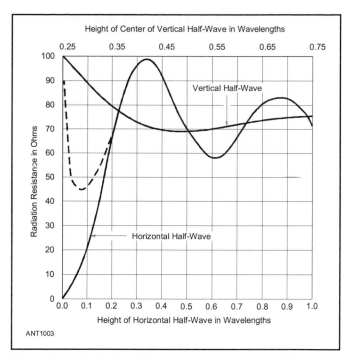

Figure 3.9 — Variation of feed point resistance with height for vertical and horizontal antennas.

3.1.4 FEED POINT IMPEDANCE VERSUS HEIGHT ABOVE GROUND

Radiation directly downward from the antenna will reflect vertically from the ground and, in passing the antenna on the upward journey, induce a current in it. The magnitude and phase of the current depends on the height of the antenna above the reflecting surface and the characteristics of the surface.[10] The total current in the antenna consists of two components: the amplitude of the first is determined by the excitation from the transmitter and the second component is induced in the antenna by the wave reflected from the ground. This second component of current, while considerably smaller than the first at most useful antenna heights, is by no means insignificant. At some heights, the two components will be in phase but at other heights the two components are out of phase. Changing the height of the antenna above ground will change the current amplitude at the feed point (we are assuming that the power input to the antenna is constant). A higher current at the same input power means that the effective resistance of the antenna is lower, and vice versa. In other words, the feed point resistance of the antenna is affected by the height of the antenna above ground because of mutual coupling between the antenna and the ground beneath it.

The electrical characteristics of the ground affect both the amplitude and the phase of reflected signals. For this reason, the electrical characteristics of the ground under the antenna will have some effect on the impedance of that antenna, the reflected wave having been influenced by the ground. Different impedance values may be encountered when an antenna is erected at identical heights but over soils with different characteristics.

Figure 3.9 gives an example of the way the feed point impedance of horizontal and vertical half-wave antennas can vary with height above ground. The height of the vertical half-wave is the distance from the bottom of the antenna to ground. For horizontally polarized half-wave antennas, the differences between the effects of perfect ground and real earth are negligible if the antenna height is greater than 0.2 λ. At lower heights, the feed point resistance over perfect ground decreases rapidly as the antenna is brought closer to a theoretically perfect ground. However, over real earth, the resistance actually begins increasing again at heights below about 0.08 λ as indicated by the dashed line. The reason for the increasing resistance at very low heights is that the field of the antenna interacts more strongly with the ground increasing ground losses. This increase in loss is reflected in an increased value for the feed point resistance.

3.2 GROUND SYSTEMS FOR VERTICAL MONOPOLES

In this section we look at vertical monopoles which are shorter than λ/2 and require some sort of ground system in order to make up for the "missing" part of the antenna and, just as importantly, reduce the power dissipated in the near field. (For the purposes of this chapter, the term "vertical" should be understood to represent a vertical monopole antenna mounted on or near the ground.)

Because the losses in the soil near a vertical are a function of the electric and magnetic field intensities close to the antenna we will begin by looking at these fields. The next step will be to show what the actual soil losses are and how that loss is distributed in the soil near the base of the vertical. Finally we'll describe ground systems which can greatly reduce this loss.

3.2.1 FIELDS NEAR THE BASE OF A VERTICAL

In this section we will be examining the E and H fields at ground level within λ/2 of the base of typical verticals. (See the **Antenna Fundamentals** chapter for a discussion of E and H fields.) This may seem like an abstract exercise but it's important because it allows us to visualize what's happening in the soil around the base of a vertical, giving us both the amplitude and location of the ground currents and their associated losses. This information will guide us in the design and optimization of ground systems.

A vertical antenna has two field components that induce currents in the ground around the antenna: E_z and H_Φ. **Figure 3.10** shows in a general way the electric-field component (E_z, in V/m) and magnetic-field component (H_Φ, in A/m) in the region near a vertical. Both of these field components will induce currents (I_V and I_H) in the soil. Because the soil near the antenna typically has relatively high resistance this results in power loss in the soil. Power dissipated in the ground is subtracted from the power supplied to the antenna weakening your signal.

As shown in Figure 3.10, the tangential component of the H-field (H_Φ) induces horizontal currents (I_H) flowing radially in the soil. The normal component (perpendicular to the ground surface) of the E-field (E_z) induces vertically flowing currents (I_v) in the soil. These field-induced ground currents will decrease as we go deeper into the soil with the rate of decrease a function of the skin depth in the particular soil.

We can determine E_z and H_Φ from either modeling (near-field calculations with *NEC*-based software, for example) or directly from equations. It turns out that the field intensities close to the base (<λ/2) of a vertical (within λ/2) over real

Figure Calculation Spreadsheet

Many of the graphs in this chapter were generated using equations for the fields in an *Excel* spreadsheet. This spreadsheet, "Chapter 3 – Figures.xls", is available on the CD-ROM accompanying this book. The variables in the spreadsheet are "live" — that is, you may change them in accordance with your own ground conditions or antenna. The initial worksheet in the file provides additional information.

Table 3-2
Base Excitation Currents as a Function of Vertical Height (h) in Wavelengths
The input power is 1500 W.

h (λ)	Io (A)	Rr (Ω)
0.050	39.7	0.95
0.125	15.1	6.57
0.250	6.45	36.1
0.375	2.53	234

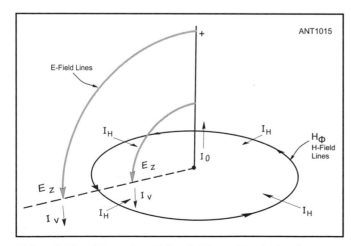

Figure 3.10 — Examples of the fields and currents close to a vertical.

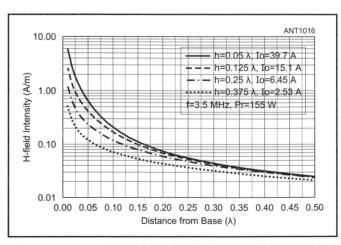

Figure 3.11 — H_Φ intensity as a function of distance from the base in wavelengths. Data is for a vertical at 3.5 MHz.

ground are very close to the values for perfect ground. This allows us to use much simpler modeling or equations. The following graphs for field intensities assume perfect ground.

The base currents and the resistive part of the feed point impedance at the base of verticals with different heights (h) are given in **Table 3-2**. These are the values of current which result from an input power of 1.5 kW for an ideal vertical over perfect ground.

Figure 3.11 shows the H-field intensity within λ/2 of the base of the vertical for four different vertical heights (h): 0.05 λ, 0.125 λ, 0.250 λ and 0.375 λ. **Figure 3.12** shows the E-field intensity for the same values of h. Both of these graphs make the same two points:

1) Field intensity increases rapidly as you approach the base, particularly within a radius <λ/8, and

2) The shorter the antenna, the higher the fields for the same power input.

In the case of the E-field, the minimum field occurs for h = 0.25 λ and then increases again as h is increased beyond 0.25 λ. Ground losses are proportional to the square of the field intensity. In other words, if you double the intensity the power loss increases by 4 times! *This tells us that we must pay special attention to the ground system within λ/8 of the base and that short verticals require additional attention to the ground system.*

Another point which can be inferred from Figure 3.12 is the very high voltages which can be present on the antenna. The shorter the antenna and the higher the power level, the higher these voltages will be. Verticals taller than λ/4 can also have very high voltages near the base. This is a very real safety hazard! Touching a vertical while transmitting can lead to severe RF burns.

Figures 3.13 and **3.14** show the field intensities for a λ/4 vertical at frequencies from 1.8 to 28 MHz. At a given distance in λ, both E and H fields increase with frequency but, as the dashed line in Figure 3.13 indicates, at a given fixed physical distance the H-field intensity is constant, independent of frequency. However, as the dashed line in Figure 3.14 shows, the E-field at a given physical distance is not constant but increases with frequency.

This behavior may seem a bit strange because it says that the field distributions do not scale linearly with frequency! Keep in mind that the base current at all frequencies was set to 6.45 A (P_r = 1500 W, h = 0.250 λ). As the frequency was changed the height of the vertical was reduced from 135 feet at 1.8 MHz to 8.8 feet at 28 MHz. The high current point on a vertical (h ≤ λ/4) is at the base but the high voltage point is at the top. As we change frequency and alter h, the H-field is primarily influenced by the base current which does not change amplitude or location. However, the E-field is primarily influenced by the high voltage at the top of the vertical which is moving closer to ground as we go up in frequency. Normally we scale the dimensions of the ground system as we go up in frequency. If we elect to use λ/4 radials they will be approximately 34 feet on 40 meters, 17 feet on 20 meters, etc. The problem is that the fields are not scaling with frequency. At a given distance in λ the fields are higher as we go up in frequency. These observations tell us that for a given size (in λ) ground system *as we go up in frequency the ground loss will increase!*

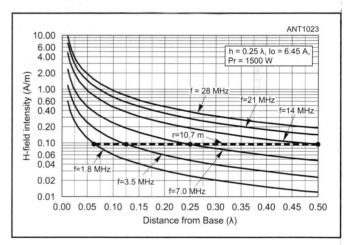

Figure 3.13 — H_Φ intensity as a function of distance from the base in wavelengths. Data is for a λ/4 vertical.

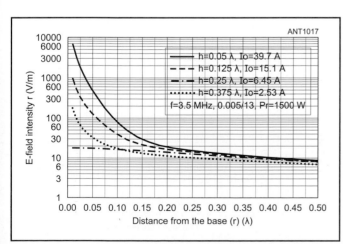

Figure 3.12 — E_z intensity as a function of distance from the base in wavelengths. Data is for a vertical at 3.5 MHz.

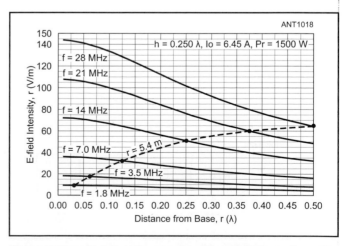

Figure 3.14 — E_z intensity as a function of distance from the base in wavelengths. Data is for a λ/4 vertical.

As shown earlier, soil conductivity typically improves as we go up in frequency but that varies over a wide range and may not help as much as we would like. Better to be conservative and not count on the increase in σ unless you have actually measured your particular soil characteristics.

3.2.2 RADIATION EFFICIENCY AND POWER LOSSES IN THE SOIL

We can discuss the efficiency of an antenna by using an equivalent circuit model like that shown in **Figure 3.15** for the resistive part of the feed point impedance. We account for the radiated power (P_r) by assuming there is a resistor we call the *radiation resistance* (R_r) through which the antenna base current (I_o) flows. The radiated power (P_r) is then:

$$P_r = R_r I_o^2 \qquad (4)$$

Similarly, we can account for the power dissipated in the ground (P_g) by adding a loss resistance (R_g) in series with R_r. The ground loss is:

$$P_g = R_g I_o^2 \qquad (5)$$

Additional losses due to conductors, loading coils, etc can also be simulated by adding more series loss resistances to the equivalent circuit but for this discussion we will ignore these additional losses although they can be significant in real antennas. The total input power (P_T) is simply the sum of P_r and P_g

The efficiency (η) of a vertical can be expressed as:

$$\eta = \frac{P_r}{P_r + P_g} = \frac{P_r}{P_T} \qquad (6)$$

This can be restated in terms of resistances as:

$$\eta = \frac{R_r}{R_r + R_g} = \frac{1}{1 + \dfrac{R_g}{R_r}} \qquad (7)$$

In essence, efficiency is the ratio of the radiated power to the total input power. Another way of saying this is that efficiency depends on the ratio of ground loss resistance to radiation resistance. The smaller we make R_g the more power will be radiated for a given input power. Reducing R_g is the purpose of the ground system.

We can determine P_g near the vertical from the E- and H-fields shown earlier. Given P_g and I_o we can calculate R_g and from that the radiation efficiency. For this discussion we will omit the mathematical details but these can be found in the spreadsheet referenced earlier.

In the following discussion the radiated power is kept constant at 1.5 kW but the total input power may be much greater because it will include the power dissipated in the soil which can become very large for short antennas with limited ground systems. The ground losses shown in **Figures 3.16** and **3.17** are what you would see if the ground system were simply a long stake driven into the soil beneath the antenna. The size of these losses makes it clear why we need to add a radial ground system around the base of a vertical.

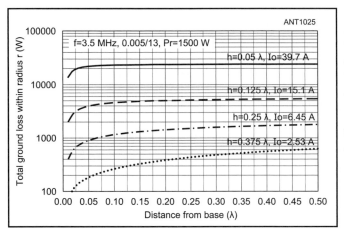

Figure 3.16 — Total ground loss within a fixed radius around verticals of different heights at 3.5 MHz.

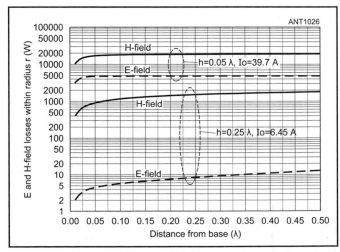

Figure 3.17 — Comparison between E- and H-field losses for two antenna heights.

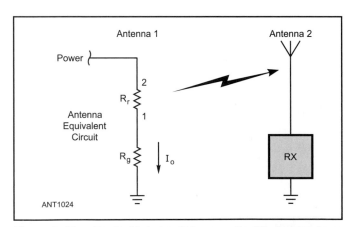

Figure 3.15 — Equivalent circuit for a vertical in terms of R_r and R_g.

Table 3-3
Efficiency for Verticals of Different Heights with Ground System Consisting of Only a Ground Stake in Average Soil

Height (h) (λ)	Efficiency (%)	Power Loss (dB)
0.050	4	−13.8
0.125	21	−6.7
0.250	46	−3.4
0.375	71	−1.5

Figure 3.16 shows the total ground loss (including both E- and H-field losses) within a radius r (in λ) around the base of verticals with different heights at 3.5 MHz, over average ground ($\sigma = 0.005$ S/m and $\varepsilon_r = 13$). For all heights the loss is significant but becomes almost astronomical for very short antennas. For example, the loss associated with the 0.050 λ vertical (about 13 feet for 3.5 MHz) amounts to a signal loss of almost 14 dB; in other words, over 20 kW of power is lost in the ground in order to produce 1.5 kW of radiated power. The efficiency of each antenna (using the values for R_r listed in Table 3-2) is listed in **Table 3-3**.

The efficiencies listed in Table 3-3 make it clear why some additional ground system beyond a simple ground stake is highly desirable in most installations. Keep in mind that these numbers are for one particular ground type (average). Poorer grounds will have even higher losses but better soils will have lower losses. Even a $\lambda/4$ vertical will have more than 3 dB of signal loss for a given input power because over half the input power is dissipated in the soil. This shows us that *the shorter the vertical, the more critical the ground system is!*

Figure 3.16 also shows that most of the loss is occurring within $\lambda/8$ of the base which correlates with the field intensities shown in Figures 3.13 and 3.14. When designing radial ground systems this ground loss distribution is reflected in the need to increase the number of radials close to the base.

Figure 3.16 shows the total loss in the soil due to both E- and H-fields. However, the relative contribution of each field component to the total varies greatly with the height of the vertical. Figure 3.17 shows a comparison between the E and H losses for h = $\lambda/4$ and h = 0.05 λ. For the $\lambda/4$ vertical the E-field losses are very small compared to the H-field losses but for the shorter vertical both the E- and H-field losses increase dramatically and the E-field loss is comparable to the H-field loss. In very short verticals the E-field losses can become larger than the H-field losses.

3.2.3 WIRE GROUND SYSTEMS

Figure 3.18 illustrates what we mean by a "radial" ground system. The ground system wires are connected together at the base of the antenna and arranged radially outward from the base. Why radial wires? Why not wires in circles or some other shape? As shown in Figure 3.10, the H-field lines have the form of circles around the base of the vertical. When the H-field passes over a conductor there will be a current

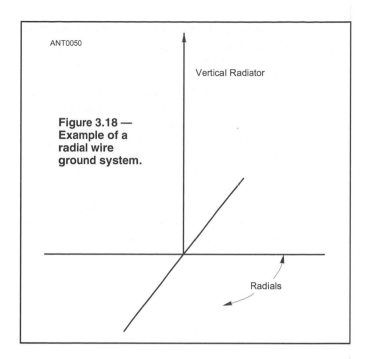

Figure 3.18 — Example of a radial wire ground system.

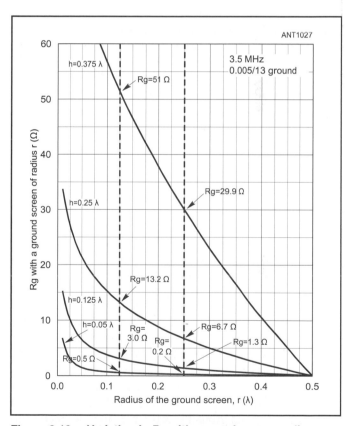

Figure 3.19 — Variation in R_g with ground screen radius. Normalized to include losses out to r = 0.5 λ.

induced in the conductor which flows at right angles to the H-field vector. In a wire ground system the optimum orientation for the wires is at right angles to the field (i.e. radially). If the wire were oriented parallel to the field (in a circle) there would be no current induced in the wire and the current would simply flow in the soil instead. In some cases where multiple verticals are present (i.e. in an array for example) it may not be practical to use only radial wires. Some form of coarse mesh may be needed.

Buried or Ground Surface Radial Systems

There are different ways to install wire ground systems: the wires may be buried in the soil a few inches or lying on the ground surface or elevated several feet above ground or even some combination of these. In addition, in elevated systems there may be interconnections between the radial wires to form what is called a "counterpoise". Another possibility is to use a coarse rectangular mesh, either on the ground surface or elevated. We will discuss all these options but for the moment we'll focus on radial systems either buried or lying on the ground surface.

If we know the values for E and H, I_o and the soil electrical characteristics we can determine P_g. We can then determine R_g directly from P_g:

$$R_g = \frac{P_g}{I_o^2} \tag{8}$$

R_g is *not* a resistance unique to a particular ground system that you can measure with some kind of ohmmeter. It is simply the relation between a given excitation current (I_o) and the power dissipated in the soil (P_g) for a given vertical. P_g in turn depends not only on the soil characteristics but on both I_o *and* the details of the vertical itself, i.e. height, loading, etc. For this reason R_g for a given ground system *will change* as we change the vertical even if the soil characteristics and the physical ground system itself are kept constant.

Ideal Ground Screens

Initially we'll assume that the ground system is ideal: i.e. a high conductivity ground screen that covers the soil from the base out to some radius "r". This ideal ground screen will give us the minimum possible R_g for ground system of a given radius. Later we'll look at R_g for more practical wire ground systems with a limited number of radials to see how they compare. From the ideal ground screen information we will know what the ultimate limits are and can determine when adding more wire might result in only a small improvement. Surprisingly, it does not take a large number of radials to give a good approximation of an ideal ground screen.

Figure 3.19 is an example of R_g as a function of ground screen radius for several antenna heights at 3.5 MHz, over average ground. As we saw in Figure 3.16, near the base of the vertical the total ground loss is large but as we move outward from the base the *additional* ground loss becomes much smaller. This means that the values for R_g fall quickly as r initially increases but as the radius of the screen gets larger, the rate of decrease in R_g slows down.

If we take the values for R_r from Table 3-2 and combine these with the values for R_g in Figure 3.19 and use Eq 8, we can calculate the efficiency as shown in **Figure 3.20**. The efficiency is stated in dB so that this graph tells us directly how much our signal will improve as we expand the radius of the ground screen. For example, for h = 0.25 λ, expanding

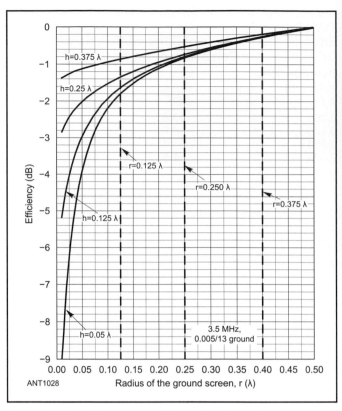

Figure 3.20 — Efficiency in dB as a function of ground screen radius.

the screen radius from 0.01 λ to 0.125 λ increases the signal by 1.5 dB. If we further increase the radius to 0.250 λ we pick up another 0.6 dB and if we go to a screen radius of 0.375 λ the gain is an additional 0.4 dB. Clearly there is a substantial advantage to having a screen with a radius of at least λ/8 but as we increase the size, the incremental improvement gets smaller. In general for amateur applications expanding the ground screen radius beyond λ/4 is seldom worth the additional cost and effort at least on the lower bands (160 and 80 meters). But as pointed out earlier, we can make a case for larger ground systems (in terms of λ) at higher frequencies.

Figure 3.19 shows R_g for one frequency and one ground characteristic. **Figures 3.21** and **3.22** show what happens to R_g as we change frequency or ground characteristics for a given height (λ/4 in this example).

Figure 3.21 is a graph of the changes in R_g with frequency for several different screen radii. This graph is for a λ/4 vertical over average ground. What the figure shows us is that for a given antenna, screen radius (in wavelengths) and ground characteristic, R_g can increase significantly as we go to higher frequencies. For example with r = λ/4, R_g = 7 Ω at 3.5 MHz but at 28 MHz a λ/4 screen has an R_g = 12 Ω. If we increased the screen radius at 28 MHz to 0.375 λ, R_g drops back down to 5 Ω. Expanding the screen radius from λ/4 to 3λ/8 at 28 MHz means extending the radial lengths from 2.7 meters (8.8 feet) to 4 meters (13.2 feet) which is very practical. The message is: *as we go higher in frequency we should consider using a ground screen with a larger radius (larger in λ)*

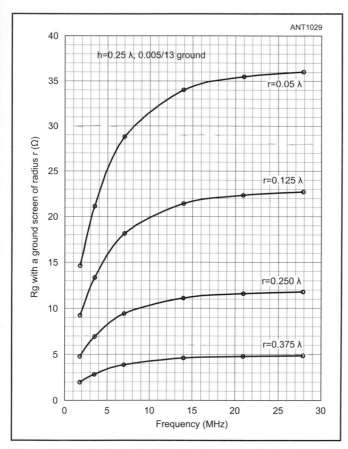

Figure 3.21 — Variation in R$_g$ with frequency for h = λ/4 for several ground screen radii (in wavelengths) over average ground.

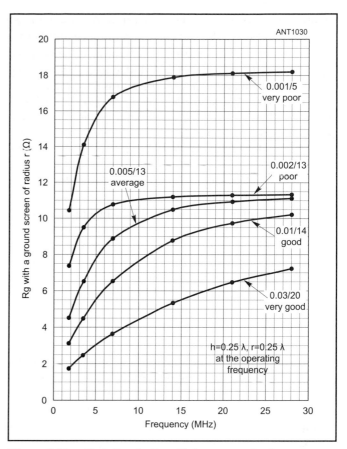

Figure 3.22 — Variation in R$_g$ with frequency for h = r = λ/4 at the operating frequency.

and/or more radials. Fortunately, as we go up in frequency the wavelength gets shorter so it's easier to add more and/or longer radials for a given total amount of wire.

From Figure 3.22 we see that with lower quality soils R$_g$ is significantly higher and it becomes increasingly important to use a more extensive ground system to maintain efficiency.

Real Wire Radial Systems

In practice, ground systems are usually made with wire in the form of a radial fan like that shown in Figure 3.18. How a particular ground system performs compared to an ideal ground screen can be determined using mathematical analysis or from *NEC* software modeling or from actual measurements on real antennas. All three routes give essentially the same answers but for this discussion we will use actual measurements on real antennas and also some *NEC* modeling results.

Figure 3.23 shows the measured signal improvement as λ/4 (33 feet) radials lying on the ground surface were added to different 40 meter antennas: a λ/4 vertical, a λ/8 vertical with sufficient top-loading to resonate it, a λ/8 vertical resonated with an inductor at the base and a 7.5 foot 40 meter mobile whip.

The measurements began with only a single ground stake, no radials. Figure 3.23 shows the increase in signal strength (for a constant input power) for each antenna as the

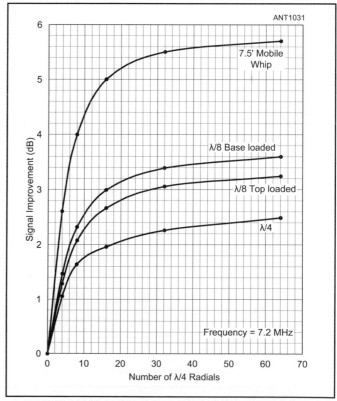

Figure 3.23 — Signal improvement for typical 40-meter verticals as the radial number is increased from 0 to 64.

number of λ/4 radials was increased from 0 to 64. Initially, as radials were added, the signal improved rapidly but by the time there were 16 radials, the rate of increase in signal improvement turned a corner and started to decrease. Going from 32 to 64 radials the improvement was only a fraction of a dB (0.2 dB). What this tells us is that a radial fan with 32 or more radials is a good approximation of an ideal ground screen, at least for λ/4 radials. For short, loaded antennas over poor soils, 64 radials might be justified and should be considered. However, the standard broadcast ground system of 120, 0.4 λ radials would probably be a waste of copper for most amateur installations.

Another important thing we see in Figure 3.23 is that short loaded antennas benefit more from the same ground system. This is because (as shown earlier) the E- and H-field intensities are much higher close to the base of shorter antennas. Note also that in short antennas, moving the loading up the vertical, top-loading for example or placing the loading coil above the base, improves the signal for a given ground system.

The soil over which this experiment was conducted would be rated as very good ($\sigma = 0.015$ S/m, $\varepsilon_r = 30$). Over that soil the improvement going from 0 to 64 radials ranged from 2.5 to 5.7 dB. Over poor or even average soils the improvement would be substantially greater. Figure 3.23 also shows how important is to have at least a simple radial system. Sixteen

radials is pretty much the practical minimum, especially over poor soils.

Measuring the signal strength for a given input power to the antenna, as radials are added to the ground system is a very direct way to gauge when adding more radials will give only a small improvement but for most amateurs that's not very practical. There is a simpler way to gauge when there are sufficient radials in the ground system. We can look at the feed point impedance which is a simple, direct measurement. An example of the variation of the resistive part (R_{in}) of the input impedance as radials are added to a ground system is given in **Figure 3.24**. The values are for the same antennas used in Figure 3.23. Note that for the 7.5 foot mobile whip, the series resistance of the loading coil has been subtracted from the measured feed point impedance.

If we assume that $R_{in} = R_r + R_g$ and that R_r is constant as we add radials (a reasonable approximation), then the leveling out of the curves for radial numbers above 16 can be interpreted as meaning that the minimum R_g for that radial length has been reached. Again, we see that 16 radials are pretty much the minimum but by the time we get to 32 radials the rate of change is quite small. Figures 3.23 and 3.24 tell the same tale.

Optimizing Radial Lengths

In the real world the amount of wire available for a ground system may be limited. How should we use the available wire: a few long radials or a bunch of short ones?[2,3,4] We can use *NEC* modeling to address this question. **Figures 3.25** and **3.26** show the signal improvement as both the number and the length of the radials are changed. Both figures assume f = 1.8 MHz and average ground ($\sigma = 0.005$ S/m, $\varepsilon_r = 13$). Figure 3.25 is for h = λ/8 and Figure 3.26 is for h = λ/4. These figures illustrate a number of important points and provide a guide to the optimal use of a given total length of radial wire. The 0 dB reference is four λ/8 radials. In both figures we see that when only a few radials are employed (<16) there is very little increase in signal when longer radials are used. In general, from both modeling and experiments, we can say that a few long radials make a poor ground system.[5] From the graphs we can see that longer radials become effective only as we increase the number of radials.

These graphs show how to optimize your signal for a given total length of radial wire. The dashed lines connect points which have the same total wire length in the ground system. For example, if we have a total of 2 λ of wire we could make four λ/2 radials or eight λ/4 radials or 16 λ/8 radials. From the graphs we can see that with a total of 2 λ of wire the best radial system would be 16 λ/8 radials. That would be an improvement of over 3 dB for the λ/8 vertical and 1 dB for the λ/4 vertical. Similarly, if 4 λ of wire is available then the optimum use would be 32 λ/8 radials. When we go to 8 λ of wire, things change a bit. For the h = λ/8 antenna either 64 λ/8 or 32 λ/4 radials will work about the same. However, for the h = λ/4 antenna the best use of the wire would be 32 λ/4 radials. The reason that a large number of short radials are

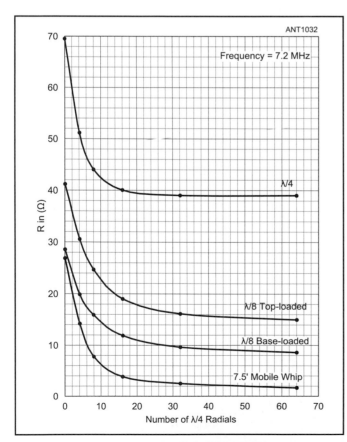

Figure 3.24 — Variation in R_g as a function of the number of λ/4 radials.

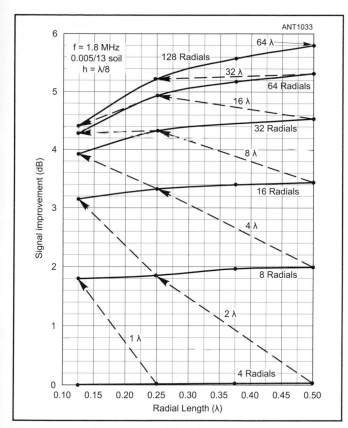

Figure 3.25 — Comparison of radial lengths and number versus signal improvement for a given total amount of radial wire (in λ). In this example h = λ/8.

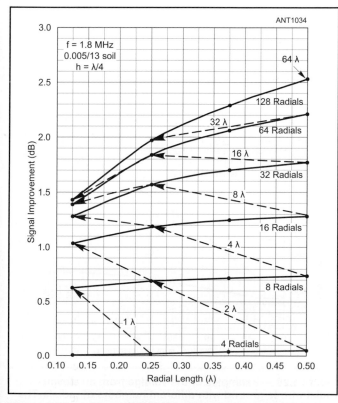

Figure 3.26 — Comparison of radial lengths and number versus signal improvement for a given total amount of radial wire (in λ). In this example h = λ/4.

effective stems directly from the high field intensities close to the base of a vertical. The first priority is to reduce the losses close to the base. As more wire becomes available and the losses close to the base have been reduced then reducing the losses further out becomes useful.

A bit of long held conventional wisdom among amateurs is that "the length of the radials should be similar to the height of the vertical." Figures 3.25 and 3.26 give partial support to that belief. When 8 λ of wire is available, λ/8 radials will work fine for a λ/8 vertical but a smaller number of λ/4 radials work better for the λ/4 vertical. This stems from the much higher field intensities associated with the λ/8 vertical. In short antennas it's very important to use numerous radials close to the base. But in both cases, when sufficient wire is available, there comes a point where fewer but longer radials are a better choice.

Radial Screens with Missing Sectors

In many installations a vertical may have to be located close to an obstacle such as a building or a driveway and it may not be possible to have a full 360° symmetrical radial field. The lack of radials in a subsector of the radial system will increase ground loss because there aren't any radials in that sector to keep the field out of the soil! In addition there will be pattern distortion. Depending on the size of the missing radial sector and the soil characteristics the signal reduction and pattern distortion can be several dB.[6] This is definitely undesirable but may be unavoidable in some situations. If the obstacle is a building, locating the antenna along one side will result in a 180° missing sector but if the antenna can be moved to a corner of the building the missing sector will only be 90° which will be a significant improvement over the 180° case. From the earlier discussion we know that the ground close to the base is the most critical. If possible, the antenna should be moved away from the structure and a fan of short radials inserted in the missing sector. Of course the building itself may have considerable effect on the antenna. It's generally a good idea to keep antennas as far as possible from structures. *If space is limited in all directions, it may be better to move the antenna away from the structure and accept short radials all the way around.*

3.2.4 ELEVATED GROUND SYSTEMS

Ground systems can elevated above ground and electrically isolated from ground. The most common system uses four or more λ/4 radial wires placed a few feet above ground. Another form of elevated system consists of a number of radial wires, which have lengths <λ/4, perhaps with a skirt wire connecting the outer ends of the radial wires as well as interconnecting wires between the radials closer to the base. It is also possible to use an elevated wire mesh. These last two options are often referred to as a "counterpoise" or "capacitive" ground system. A λ/4 vertical with several λ/4 radials (usually four radials) is called a "ground-plane" antenna. Ground plane antennas are discussed in the **Dipoles and Monopoles** chapter.

Elevated Systems with Simple Radial Wires

In this section we discuss radial systems made from straight wires of the same length for single band use. Multiband and counterpoise systems are discussed in following sections.

For a number of years there has been much discussion regarding the relative merits of buried or ground surface radials versus elevated radials. Modeling using *NEC* software has consistently indicated that a few elevated radials should perform as well as a large number of radials on the ground. Modeling has also predicted that the signal would improve very quickly with height even for small elevations. To verify these modeling predictions a carefully controlled series of experiments were performed at 7.2 MHz directly comparing the signal from a vertical using either an on-the-ground system with many radials or an elevated system with only a few radials.[7]

The experiment began with the base of the vertical at ground level with four λ/4 radials lying on the ground surface. The signal strength at a remote point was recorded. This was used as the reference level (0 dB). The next step was to elevate the base of the antenna and the four radials in increments from zero to 48 inches. At each point the change in signal from the reference level was recorded. The second part of the experiment left all the radials on the ground surface but starting with four radials incrementally increased the number of radials. **Figure 3.27** shows the results of that experiment. The *NEC* modeling predictions agree well with the observed behavior:

1) Even a small elevation makes a considerable difference in signal and

2) The elevated system is equivalent to the ground system with 32 or more radials.

One additional point should be emphasized regarding this experimental work. For the 4-radial elevated system to work as well as the multiple radial ground based system, during the experiment it was found that very great care had to be taken to assure that the radial geometry was highly symmetric, the radial lengths identical and that the currents in the radials were all equal and in phase with the base current as discussed below.

Safety Consideration with Elevated Radials

Before looking more closely at the assertion that four elevated radials are equivalent to many ground-based radials we need to consider a safety issue. Like a vertical located at ground level, elevated verticals will have high voltages on the vertical but in addition, elevated radial systems can have very high fields and voltages on and near the radial wires. **Figure 3.28** gives examples of the voltage from a radial wire to ground for 4, 12 and 32 λ/4 radial systems.

Note that the voltages vary from 250 V_{RMS} to nearly 2000 V_{RMS}! These voltages are proportional to $\sqrt{P_{in}}$ so that if you drop the power from 1500 W to 100 W, a factor of 15:1, the voltages only drop by a factor of less than four. Even at 100 W, they are still very high! For safety reasons, elevated radial systems are usually placed well above head-height,

8 feet or more. This is done so that people or animals cannot accidentally run into the wires but also because the high voltages which are present on the radials, particularly at the ends, can cause severe RF burns. This hazard is typical of elevated ground systems.

Given the high potentials at the ends of the radials, high quality insulators should be used at the radial ends. In addition to the high voltages, the E-field intensities are also very high near the radial ends. This means there is a danger of corona discharge which can erode the wire or even damage a plastic insulator. Where the radial wires are attached to the insulators, care should be taken that the wire ends do not form any sharp points which could be sites for corona discharge. Usually a ball of solder is used to cover the wire end. This

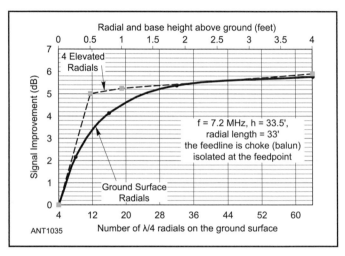

Figure 3.27 — Comparison between four elevated λ/4 radials and λ/4 radials on the ground surface. Note that this graph has two different horizontal axes. The arrows associate the plots with the appropriate horizontal axis.

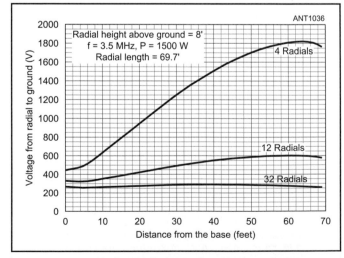

Figure 3.28 — Examples of the voltage from an elevated radial wire to ground with different numbers of radials. The input power to the vertical is 1500 W, the operating frequency is 3.5 MHz and the radial system is elevated 8 feet above ground.

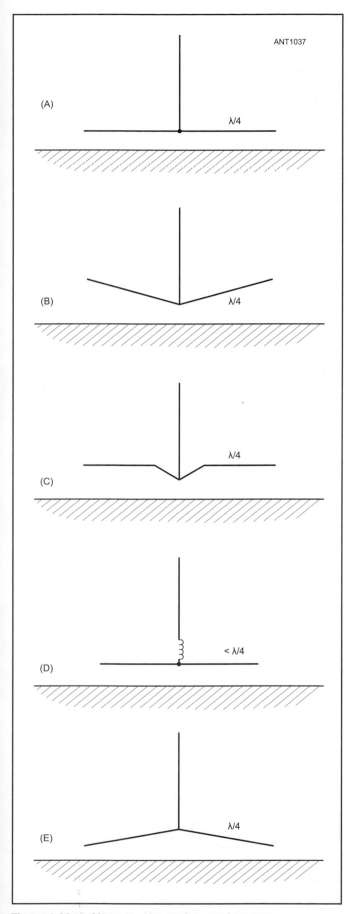

Figure 3.29 — Alternate elevated ground system configurations.

problem will become more acute as the altitude of the station increases.

Some Alternative Elevated Systems

It is not always practical to have the base of the antenna high above ground. For example, a 20 meter λ/4 vertical will only be about 17 feet long and made from small diameter aluminum tubing. Elevating this is not a great challenge. But a 160 meter λ/4 vertical will be about 130 feet high and probably made from tower sections or heavy tubing. It may not be possible to elevate the base of the larger antennas very high. As an alternative, the elevated radials can be arranged in several ways as shown in **Figure 3.29**. The simplest approach when the base is close to ground as shown in (B) is to just slope the radials out at an angle. While this approach can place the radial tips well above head height it still leaves a lot of the radial at low heights. Another approach (C) is to slope the initial portion of the radial upward at an angle of 45° until a height of 8 feet is reached and then to run the rest of the radial out at constant height. These are referred to as "gull wing" radials.[8]

Another problem that often arises (particularly on 80 and 160 meters) is that there may not be enough space for full λ/4 radials. That's OK because as shown in Figure 3.29D, shorter radials can be used and an inductor added at the base of the antenna to resonate it.[9] (Note, it is also possible to place individual inductors in each radial which may be helpful in balancing the current division between the radials.) Another alternative configuration is shown in Figure 3.29E. In this case the base is higher than the ends of the radials. This configuration is often used at 20 meters and above where the radials are self-supporting conductors. When the radials are anchored only at the base some droop to the outer end of the radials would be normal. In some cases the radials are deliberately sloped downward to increase the feed point impedance and provide a lower SWR. It should be pointed out that configurations (B) and (C), where the radials slope upward from the base, will have lower feed point impedances and somewhat reduced SWR bandwidths.[7]

This raises the question: how much is the antenna performance degraded by these alternate schemes? Again this can be addressed either with modeling or experimentally. The earlier experiment comparing elevated and ground surface radials on 40 meters was extended to compare the alternatives given in Figure 3.29. The results are listed in **Table 3-4**. All

Table 3-4
Signal Comparison Between Different Elevated Radial Systems.

Radial System Configuration	Relative Signal
(A) Base and four radials elevated 4 ft	0.00 dB
(B) Base at ground level, radial ends at 4 ft	−0.47 dB
(C) Base at ground level, gull-wing-radials, ends at 4 ft	−0.65 dB
(D) Base and radials at 4 ft, λ/8 radials with L = 2.2 µH	−0.36 dB
(E) Base at 4 ft and radial ends at 3 ft	+0.10 dB

the alternatives were tested with four radials at 7.2 MHz. The base tuning inductor in option (D) had a Q of 350. The conventional system with all of the radials and the base elevated to the same height is used as the 0 dB reference. Except for (E), there is a small penalty associated with the alternate elevated radial configurations (on the order of –0.5 dB) which may be acceptable in many situations.

Problems with Elevated Radials

The simplicity of elevated systems with only three or four radials is very attractive because, at least in principle, they can be just as effective as much more extensive ground based systems. However, as pointed out above with regard to the experimental work, elevated systems with small numbers of radials are very sensitive to the mechanical details of the radials: i.e. length, droop, asymmetry in the radial fan, nearby conductors and so forth. The input impedance, current division between radials, radiation pattern, resonant frequency and efficiency of the antenna are all sensitive to even small asymmetries. It has been demonstrated experimentally that radial geometry asymmetry[9] and irregularities in ground characteristics under the radial fan[10] will cause problems. The following discussion explores some of these problems.

Typically a vertical with an elevated ground system will be fabricated with the vertical and the radial lengths calculated from L = 234/f in MHz which is 5% shorter than a free-space λ/4. The common wisdom that 5% shortening should be used is derived from work done in the 1930s but is only an approximation. When the base impedance of an actual antenna is checked, the resonant frequency will often be substantially different from what was expected and dependent on the number of radials as well as their length.

NEC modeling can be used to explore what's happening. The modeling is done in two steps: first model the vertical radiator element over a perfect ground and adjust its length to resonate at the desired frequency (7.2 MHz in this example). This example uses a #12 AWG wire and to be resonant at

7.2 MHz, h = 32.22 feet which is about 5.5% shorter than free space. The next step in the modeling is to add various numbers of horizontal #12 AWG wire radials. Each of the radials has the same length as the vertical (L = 32.22 feet). **Figure 3.30** shows the resonant frequency as a function of the number of radials from 2 to 128.

The resonant frequency of the complete antenna with the radials approaches the desired 7.2 MHz but doesn't quite get there. Even when a large number of λ/4 radials are used, the radial fan is not the same as an infinite ideal ground. In general, elevated systems should start with radials and perhaps the vertical radiator, with a length corresponding to the free space value for λ/4 (L = 246/f in MHz) and then trim the radials to resonate the antenna at the desired frequency. There is another reason for starting with a vertical that is a bit taller. When the radials are trimmed to resonate the antenna, the length of the radials will be somewhat shorter than might be expected. This saves wire and reduces the footprint.

A very common problem in elevated systems is that the radials may not all be exactly the same length. Experimentally this has been shown to cause non-uniform current division between the radials which can have a serious effect on the performance of the antenna.[9] We can model an example to demonstrate how severe this effect can be. Start with a 40 meter λ/4 vertical with four radials as shown in **Figure 3.31**, where the base of the vertical and the radials are placed 8 feet above average ground (σ = 0.005 S/m, ε_r = 13). Radials 1 and 2 form a pair of opposing radials with a length = L. Radials 3 and 4 are a second opposing pair of radials with length = M. First we model the antenna with all the radials the same length (L = M) and then with radials that differ in length (L ≠ M). The initial length for the vertical and the radials was made 34.1 feet to resonate the antenna at 7.2 MHz.

The modeled feed point impedances (from 7.0 to 7.3 MHz) for three different radial length configurations are compared in **Figure 3.32** which is a graph of R_{in} versus X_{in} ($Z_{in} = R_{in} + jX_{in}$ = feed point impedance) as the frequency

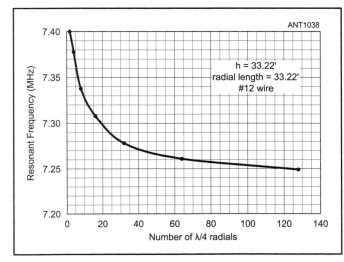

Figure 3.30 — Resonant frequency of a λ/4 vertical for different numbers of elevated radials.

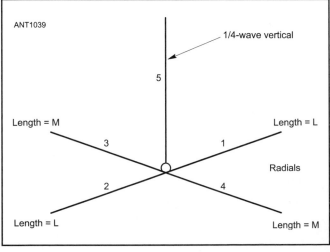

Figure 3.31 — 40-meter λ/4 vertical with four radials. Vertical height is 34.1 feet. The radial lengths are varied.

is varied from 7.0 to 7.3 MHz. The plot on the left is for the case where all the radials are identical (L = M = 34.1 feet). The looping plot on the right is for case where L = 35.6 feet and M = 33.1 feet, this represents a length error of ±2.9%. The middle plot is for L = 34.6 feet and M = 33.6 feet, which is a length error of ±1.4%. Clearly even small radial length asymmetry can have a dramatic effect on the feed point impedance and resonant frequency. The resonant frequency is the point at which $X_{in} = 0$.

But feed point impedance is not the only problem created by asymmetric radial lengths. **Figure 3.33** compares modeled radiation patterns between symmetric and asymmetric systems at 7.25 MHz. The amount of pattern distortion varies across the band from a fraction of a dB at 7.0 MHz to 3 dB at 7.25 MHz. Besides the distortion, the gain in all directions is smaller for the asymmetric case. Computing the average gains for the symmetric and asymmetric cases in Figure 3.33, there is about a 1.6 dB difference. What this tells us is that asymmetric radials can lead to significantly higher ground losses!

The pattern distortion and increased ground loss with asymmetric radials occurs because the radial currents with asymmetric radial lengths can be much different from the symmetric case. An example is given in **Figure 3.34**. The graph bars represent the current amplitudes at the base of the vertical and each of the radials immediately adjacent to the base of the vertical. The black bars are for symmetric radial lengths (L = M = 34.1 feet) and the red bars are for asymmetric radials (L = 35.1 feet and M = 33.1 feet). In the symmetric

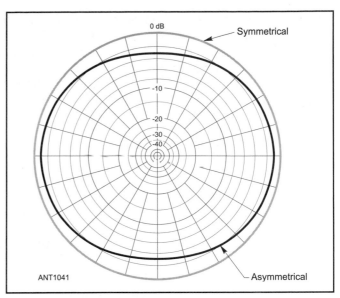

Figure 3.33 — Azimuthal radiation pattern at an elevation angle of 22 degrees, comparing symmetric (L = M = 34.1 feet) and asymmetric (L = 35.1 feet, M = 33.1 feet) radials at 7.25 MHz.

case each of the radials has a current of 0.25 A which sums to 1 A, the current at the base of the vertical. The radial currents are also in phase with the base current.

With asymmetric radials the picture is very different: the current amplitudes are different between radial pairs 1 and 2 and 3 and 4 and the sum of the current amplitudes is *not*

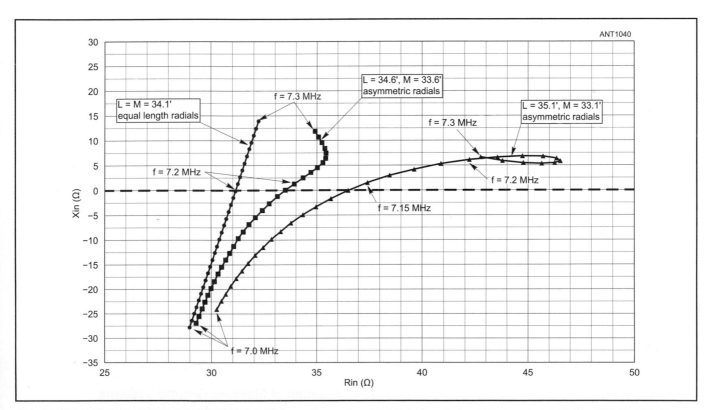

Figure 3.32 — A comparison of the input impedances ($Z_{in} = R_{in} + jX_{in}$) from 7.0 to 7.3 MHz at the feed point of the vertical for symmetric and asymmetric radial lengths.

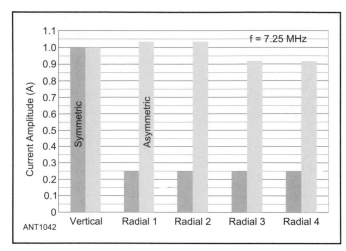

Figure 3.34 — Comparison of radial current at the bases of the vertical and the radials with symmetric (L = M = 34.1 feet) and asymmetric (L = 35.1 feet and M = 33.1 feet) radial lengths. The radials are numbered as shown in Figure 3.31. The current shown is the magnitude.

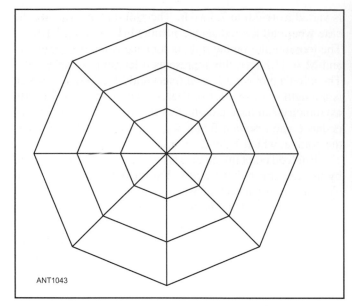

Figure 3.35 — Example of a wire counterpoise ground system.

1 A, it is much larger! This would seem to violate Kirchhoff's current law which requires the **vector** sum of the currents at a node to be zero. In this case the radial currents in the two pairs of radials are not in phase with each other or the vertical base current. The current in radials 1 and 2 is shifted by –62° from the base current and the current in radials 3 and 4 is shifted by +89°. The radial currents still sum *vectorially* to 1 A however. These large asymmetric currents go a long way towards explaining the increased loss and pattern distortion.

How can we tell if there is a problem in an existing radial fan? One way is to measure the current amplitudes in the individual radials close to the base of the vertical.[13] If the current amplitudes are significantly different between the radials *and/or* if the sum of the current amplitudes in the radials is greater than the base current then you have a problem. These measurements can be made with a RF ammeter. More accurate measurements which also show the phase can be made using current transformers and an oscilloscope (see the section "Practical Aspects of Phased Array Design" in the **Multielement Arrays** chapter) or a vector network analyzer (see the **Antenna and Transmission Line Measurements** chapter).[13]

The sensitivity to asymmetric radial lengths is reduced when a larger number of radials are employed. The primary effect of additional elevated radials (>4) is to reduce the sensitivity to radial asymmetry, nearby conductors, variations in ground conductivity or objects under the radial fan, and, as shown in Figure 3.28, more numerous radials reduce the potentials on the radials. More numerous radials also reduce the E-field intensity below the radial fan. *Whenever possible an elevated ground system should use 10 or more radials.* If you follow that rule you are very likely to get the performance you expect. With small numbers of elevated radials the results can be hit or miss.

Sometimes it's not possible to have a symmetric radial fan of λ/4 radials. This is often the case on 160 or 80 meters. Because each installation will be unique it is difficult to give general advice but certainly the first step should be to model the proposed antenna with different radial options to get a feeling for how well they might work. One option is to keep the radial fan symmetric with a radius smaller than λ/4. You can then resonate the vertical with an inductor as shown in Figure 3.29D, add some top-loading to the vertical, make the vertical taller, or some combination of all three. With short radials it may be helpful to add a skirt wire at the ends of the radials as shown in **Figure 3.35**. Adding a skirt wire to the radial system will reduce the size of the base loading inductance.

Counterpoise Systems

In the early days of radio, operating wavelengths were in the hundreds or thousands of meters. Very often a ground system with λ/4 radials was not possible. Early on it was recognized that an elevated system of wires called a "counterpoise" or "capacitive ground" with dimensions much smaller than λ/4 could be very effective. Figure 3.35 shows a typical example that looks very much like a spider web. Rectangular counterpoises made with a coarse rectangular mesh were also very common. Amateurs have done some experimental work on counterpoise systems.[10] On 80 or 160 meters the normal λ/4 radial system may well be too large for many amateur locations so a counterpoise can be a practical option. However, it is recommended that the proposed installation be carefully modeled and optimized *before* construction to avoid surprises.

Isolation of Elevated Ground Systems

In an elevated ground system it is good practice to isolate the feed line with a common mode choke (i.e. a current balun

— see the **Transmission Line Coupling and Impedance Matching** chapter). Simply attaching a coaxial feed line to the antenna and running it back down to ground can increase ground loss and in some cases have a strong effect on the resonant frequency and behavior of the impedance across the band. The effects of not isolating the feed line vary from slight to severe depending on the details of each installation. Elevated systems with small numbers of radials are particularly sensitive. An additional problem with asymmetric radials is that they can greatly increase the voltage across the balun, leading to larger losses in the balun core.

3.2.5 DIFFERENCES BETWEEN RADIAL SYSTEMS

Ground systems using elevated radials, radials lying on the ground surface, or buried radials can all provide good performance but there are some differences with practical consequences which need to be recognized. As shown in **Figure 3.36**, the current distribution on a λ/4 radial is different for each of those arrangements.

When a radial is placed very close to the ground, the velocity of propagation along the radial is slower so that the radial is effectively electrically longer and the current maximum moves out onto the radial as shown in Figure 3.36B. This has two consequences: First, it can increase the ground loss and, second, it can affect the feed point impedance and resonant frequency of the vertical.[14,15] Note from the current distribution, that the ground surface radial behaves more like an elevated radial than a buried one. Ground surface radials can affect the resonant frequency of the antenna.

An example of this is given in **Figure 3.37**. The experiment from which the data in Figure 3.37 was obtained began with no radials and only a single ground stake. As radials were added, the resonant frequency of the antenna was measured. Initially the change in resonant frequency was quite rapid but by 32 radials the rate of change slowed and the resonant frequency stabilized. The additional ground loss when <8 radials are used can be significant, providing another reason for not using a few long radials.[14]

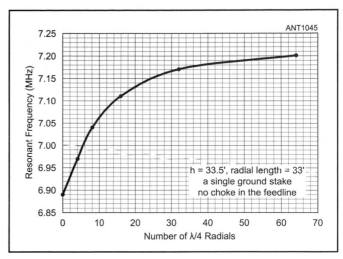

Figure 3.37 — A typical example of the effect on resonant frequency as the number of ground surface radials is varied.

For bare radials, well buried in the soil, the radial current distribution is exponential due to the damping effect of the soil conductivity (Figure 3.36C). In general, changing the radial number in buried systems does not greatly affect resonance except possibly in very low conductivity soils. The change in current distribution as a radial is taken from the surface into the soil is not abrupt. Radials just below the surface will behave much like radials right on the surface. The rate of change depends on the soil characteristics so don't be surprised if you see some shift in resonance as more radials are added with shallow burial.

Multiband Radial Systems

Multiband verticals are very popular which raises the question of what kind of ground system to use with them? In practice, the most common ground system, either on the ground or elevated, has four λ/4 radials *for each band*. For example if the vertical operates on 7, 14, 21 and 28 MHz there will be a total of 16 radials which is about 280 feet of radial wire. Multiband ground systems have been evaluated experimentally and shown to work very well.[15] Even though the most common system has only four radials on each band, coupling between the radials seems to minimize the elevated system problems discussed earlier. One alternative (for either

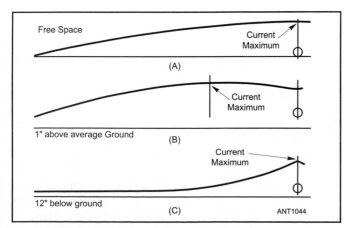

Figure 3.36 — Examples of current distribution on radials in elevated, ground surface and buried systems.

Advice on Ground Systems

With so many configurations and options available, some advice on ground systems is in order: Buried, ground surface or elevated radial systems can all be very efficient. However, no matter which configuration is chosen, a few long radials are not likely to provide a satisfactory ground system. If you want an efficient ground system don't skimp on the radials! Try to use at least 20 or more radials on the ground and 10 or more in elevated systems.

on-the-ground or elevated systems) for a 40-10 meter vertical would be to use 30 or more 40 meter λ/4 radials without any of the shorter higher band radials. This also works well yielding an improvement of about 1 dB over the standard system. However, 30 radials on 40 meters total about 2100 feet of wire which is almost eight times the total wire in the standard system!

Radial Wire Size and Material

If the recommended number of radials is used, the wire size used in a radial system usually has only a small effect on the electrical performance. For a given amount of copper it is much better to use many small diameter radials instead of a few large ones. The practical issues are more mechanical than electrical: i.e. is the wire sturdy enough for installation and will it survive burial in the soil or lying on the soil surface for extended periods? In the case of elevated radial systems, is the wire strong enough to be stretched between the supports and, in climates where icing is a problem, is it strong enough for the possible ice load? The wire can be either insulated or bare although in the case of buried radials insulated wire may resist corrosion longer. Wire sizes as small as #22 AWG may be acceptable if there are a large number of radials. Either copper or aluminum wire can be used. Steel wire is very strong and inexpensive but both copper and aluminum

wire have much better conductivity. Generally speaking galvanized fence wire should be viewed as an emergency measure. Although aluminum wire is attractive because it's much cheaper than copper, it has much lower corrosion resistance and may not be suitable for buried installations in most soils. Aluminum has the additional problem that it is difficult to solder and usually requires mechanical connections which may not be reliable when exposed to the weather for long periods. Either solid or stranded wire can be used in ground systems although in buried systems solid wire may be more corrosion resistant. For elevated systems where severe ice loading is expected Copperweld or Alumaweld wire can be used. These are steel wires with a thick copper or aluminum cladding. This construction gives both good conductivity and great strength. However, any damage to the cladding will expose bare steel to the elements, resulting in corrosion.

Insulated copper wire will frequently be less expensive than bare wire and in addition, insulated wire of many different kinds is often available inexpensively from surplus sources. It is not necessary to strip the insulation from the wire to use it for radials except to connect it at the base of the antenna or to other radials. In an elevated system loading by the insulation will make the radials electrically 2-3% longer but add little loss. For buried radials the insulation may provide some corrosion protection.

3.3 THE EFFECT OF GROUND IN THE FAR FIELD

The properties of the ground in the far field of an antenna are very important, especially for a vertically polarized antenna. Even if the ground-radial system for a vertical has been optimized to reduce ground-return losses in the reactive near field to an insignificant level, the electrical properties of the ground may still diminish far-field performance to lower levels than "perfect-ground" analyses might lead you to expect. The key is that *ground reflections* from horizontally and vertically polarized waves behave very differently.

This section, from earlier editions, uses an alternate convention in which k and ε_r refer to the same quantity and are interchangeable, as are σ and G. Both are in common use in the technical literature.

3.3.1 REFLECTIONS IN GENERAL

First, let us consider the case of flat ground. Over flat ground, either horizontally or vertically polarized downgoing waves launched from an antenna into the far field strike the surface and are reflected by a process very similar to that by which light waves are reflected from a mirror. As is the case with light waves, the angle of reflection is the same as the angle of incidence, so a wave striking the surface at an angle of, say, 15° is reflected upward from the surface at 15°.

The reflected waves combine with direct waves (those radiated at angles above the horizon) in various ways. Some of the factors that influence this combining process are the height of the antenna, its length, the electrical characteristics of the ground, and the polarization of the wave. At some

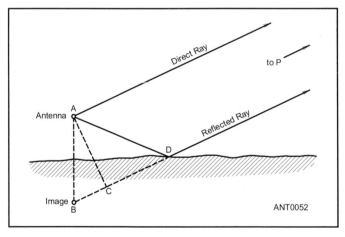

Figure 3.38 — At any distant point, P, the field strength will be the vector sum of the direct ray and the reflected ray. The reflected ray travels farther than the direct ray by the distance BC, where the reflected ray is considered to originate at the image antenna.

elevation angles above the horizon the direct and reflected waves are exactly in phase — that is, the maximum field strengths of both waves are reached at the same time at the same point in space, and the directions of the fields are the same. In such a case, the resultant field strength for that angle is simply the sum of the direct and reflected fields. (This represents a theoretical increase in field strength of 6 dB over the free-space pattern at these angles.)

At other elevation angles the two waves are completely out of phase — that is, the field intensities are equal at the same instant and the directions are opposite. At such angles, the fields cancel each other. At still other angles, the resultant field will have intermediate values. Thus, the effect of the ground is to increase radiation intensity at some elevation angles and to decrease it at others. When you plot the results as an elevation pattern, you will see *lobes* and *nulls*, as described in the **Antenna Fundamentals** chapter.

The concept of an *image antenna* is often useful to show the effect of reflection. As **Figure 3.38** shows, the reflected ray has the same path length (AD equals BD) that it would if it originated at a virtual second antenna with the same characteristics as the real antenna, but situated below the ground just as far as the actual antenna is above it.

Now, if we look at the antenna and its image over perfect ground from a remote point on the surface of the ground, we will see that the currents in a horizontally polarized antenna and its image are flowing in opposite directions, or in other words, are 180° out of phase. But the currents in a vertically polarized antenna and its image are flowing in the *same* direction — they are *in* phase. This 180° phase difference between the vertically and horizontally polarized reflections off ground is what makes the combinations with direct waves behave so very differently.

3.3.2 FAR-FIELD GROUND REFLECTIONS AND THE VERTICAL ANTENNA

A vertical's azimuthal directivity is omnidirectional. A λ/2 vertical over ideal, perfectly conducting earth has the elevation-plane radiation pattern shown by the solid line in **Figure 3.39**. Over real earth, however, the pattern looks more like the shaded one in the same diagram. In this case, the low-angle radiation that might be hoped for because of perfect-ground performance is not realized in the real world.

Now look at **Figure 3.40A**, which compares the computed elevation-angle response for two half-wave dipoles at 14 MHz. One is oriented horizontally over ground at a height of λ/2 and the other is oriented vertically, with its center just over λ/2 high (so that the bottom end of the wire doesn't actually touch the ground). The ground is "average" in dielectric constant (13) and conductivity (0.005 S/m). At a 15° elevation angle, the horizontally polarized dipole has almost 7 dB more gain than its vertical brother. Contrast Figure 3.40A to the comparison in Figure 3.40B, where the peak gain of a vertically polarized half-wave dipole over seawater, which is virtually perfect for RF reflections, is quite comparable with

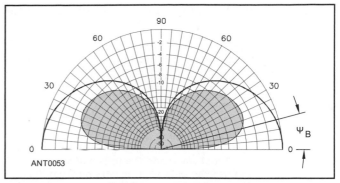

Figure 3.39 — Vertical-plane radiation pattern for a ground-mounted half-wave vertical. The solid line is the pattern for perfect earth. The shaded pattern shows how the response is modified over average earth (k = 13, G = 0.005 S/m) at 14 MHz. ψ is the pseudo-Brewster angle (PBA), in this case 14.8°.

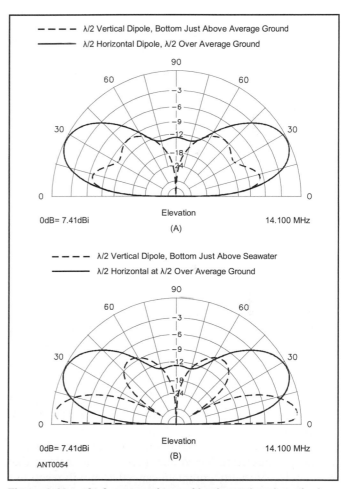

Figure 3.40 — At A, comparison of horizontal and vertical λ/2 dipoles over average ground. Average ground has conductivity of 5 mS/m and dielectric constant of 13. Horizontal dipole is λ/2 high; vertical dipole's bottom wire is just above ground. Horizontal antenna is much less affected by far-field ground losses compared with its vertical counterpart. At B, comparison of 20 meter λ/2 vertical dipole whose bottom wire is just above seawater with λ/2-high horizontal dipole over average ground. Seawater is great for verticals!

Real-World Ground Surfaces

The material in this chapter deals with the effects of ground assuming that the ground surface around the antenna is flat. This is obviously not the case in the majority of actual installations! Accounting for the effects of non-flat ground is included in the chapter **HF Antenna System Design**, including an extensive discussion on the use of *HFTA* terrain analysis software by Dean Straw, N6BV.

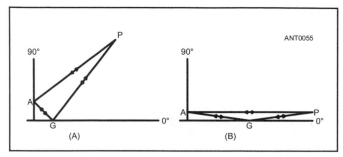

Figure 3.41 — The direct wave and the reflected wave combine at point P to form the pattern (P is very far from the antenna). At A the two paths AP and AGP differ appreciably in length, while at B these two path lengths are nearly equal.

the horizontal dipole's response at 15°, and exceeds the horizontally polarized antenna dramatically below 15° elevation.

To understand in a qualitative fashion why the desired low-angle radiation from a vertical is not delivered when the ground isn't "perfect," examine **Figure 3.41A**. Radiation from each antenna segment reaches a point P in space by two paths; one directly from the antenna, path AP, and the other by reflection from the earth, path AGP. (Note that P is so far away that the slight difference in angles is insignificant — for practical purposes the waves are parallel to each other at point P.)

If the earth were a perfectly conducting surface, there would be no phase shift of the vertically polarized wave upon reflection at point G. The two waves would add together with some phase difference because of the different path lengths. This difference in path lengths of the two waves is why the free-space radiation pattern differs from the pattern of the same antenna over ground.

Now consider a point P that is close to the horizon, as in Figure 3.41B. The path lengths AP and AGP are almost the same, so the magnitudes of the two waves add together, producing a maximum at zero angle of radiation. The arrows on the waves point both ways since the process works similarly for transmitting and receiving.

With real earth, however, the reflected wave from a vertically polarized antenna undergoes a change in both *amplitude* and *phase* in the reflection process. Indeed, at a low-enough elevation angle, the phase of the reflected wave will actually change by 180° and its magnitude will then subtract from that of the direct wave. At a zero takeoff angle, it will be almost equal in amplitude, but 180° out of phase with the direct wave.

Note that this is very similar to what happens with horizontally polarized reflected and direct waves at low elevation angles. Virtually complete cancellation will result in a deep null, inhibiting any radiation or reception at 0°. For real-world soils, the vertical loses the theoretical advantage it has at low elevation angles over a horizontal antenna, as Figure 3.40A so clearly shows.

The degree that a vertical works better than a horizontal antenna at low elevation angles is largely dependent on the characteristics of the ground around the vertical, as we'll next examine.

3.3.3 THE PSEUDO-BREWSTER ANGLE (PBA) AND THE VERTICAL ANTENNA

Much of the material presented here regarding pseudo-Brewster angle was prepared by Charles J. Michaels, W7XC (SK), and first appeared in July 1987 *QST*, with additional information in *The ARRL Antenna Compendium, Vol 3*.[12]

Most fishermen have noticed that when the sun is low, its light is reflected from the water's surface as glare, obscuring the underwater view. When the sun is high, however, the sunlight penetrates the water and it is possible to see objects below the surface of the water. The angle at which this transition takes place is known as the *Brewster angle*, named for the Scottish physicist, Sir David Brewster (1781-1868).

A similar situation exists in the case of vertically polarized antennas; the RF energy behaves as the sunlight in the optical system, and the earth under the antenna acts as the water. The *pseudo-Brewster angle* (PBA) is the angle at which the reflected wave is 90° out of phase with respect to the direct wave. "Pseudo" is used here because the RF effect is similar to the optical effect from which the term gets its name. Below this angle, the reflected wave is between 90° and 180° out of phase with the direct wave, so some degree of cancellation takes place. The largest amount of cancellation occurs near 0°, and steadily less cancellation occurs as the PBA is approached from below.

The factors that determine the PBA for a particular location *are not related to the antenna itself, but to the ground around it*. The first of these factors is earth conductivity, σ, which is a measure of the ability of the soil to conduct electricity. Conductivity, measured in siemens/meter is the inverse of resistivity. The second factor is the dielectric constant, ε_r, which is a unit-less quantity that corresponds to the capacitive effect of the earth. (See the section "Electrical Characteristics of Ground" earlier in this chapter for a discussion of both σ and ε.) For both of these quantities, the higher the number, the better the ground (for vertical antenna

Table 3-5
Pseudo-Brewster Angle Variation with Frequency, Dielectric Constant, and Conductivity

Frequency (MHz)	Dielectric Constant	Conductivity (S/m)	PBA (degrees)
7	20	0.0303	6.4
13	0.005	13.3	
13	0.002	15.0	
5	0.001	23.2	
3	0.001	27.8	
14	20	0.0303	8.6
13	0.005	14.8	
13	0.002	15.4	
5	0.001	23.8	
3	0.001	29.5	
21	20	0.0303	10.0
13	0.005	15.2	
13	0.002	15.4	
5	0.001	24.0	
3	0.001	29.8	

purposes). The third factor determining the PBA for a given location is the frequency of operation. The PBA increases with increasing frequency, all other conditions being equal.

As the frequency is increased, the role of the dielectric constant in determining the PBA becomes more significant. **Table 3-5** shows how the PBA varies with changes in ground conductivity, dielectric constant and frequency. The table shows trends in PBA dependency on ground constants and frequency.

At angles below the PBA, the reflected vertically polarized wave subtracts from the direct wave, causing the radiation intensity to fall off rapidly. Similarly, above the PBA, the reflected wave adds to the direct wave, and the radiated pattern approaches the perfect-earth pattern. **Figure 3.42** shows the PBA, usually labeled ψ_B.

When plotting vertical-antenna radiation patterns over real earth, the reflected wave from an antenna segment is multiplied by a factor called the *vertical reflection coefficient*, and the product is then added vectorially to the direct wave to get the resultant. The reflection coefficient consists of an attenuation factor, A, and a phase angle, ϕ, and is usually expressed as $A\angle\phi$. (ϕ is always a negative angle, because the earth acts as a lossy capacitor in this situation.) The following equation can be used to calculate the reflection coefficient for vertically polarized waves, for earth of given conductivity and dielectric constant at any frequency and elevation angle (also called the wave angle in many texts).

$$A_{Vert}\angle\phi = \frac{k'\sin\psi - \sqrt{k' - \cos^2\psi}}{k'\sin\psi + \sqrt{k' - \cos^2\psi}} \qquad (9)$$

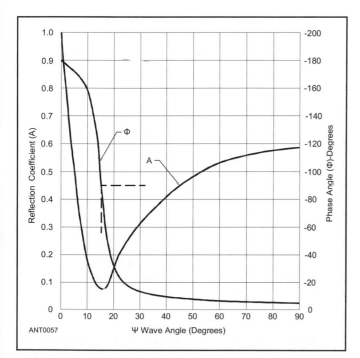

Figure 3.42 — Reflection coefficient for vertically polarized waves. A and ϕ are magnitude and angle for wave angles ψ. This case is for average earth, (k = 13, G = 0.005 S/m), at 21 MHz.

where

$A_{Vert}\angle\phi$ = vertical reflection coefficient
ψ = elevation angle

$$k' = k - j\left|\frac{1.8\times10^4 \times G}{f}\right|$$

k = dielectric constant of earth (k for air = 1)
G = conductivity of earth in S/m
f = frequency in MHz
j = complex operator ($\sqrt{-1}$)

(Reminder: k and ε_r refer to the same quantity and are interchangeable, as are σ and G. Both are in common use in the technical literature.)

Solving this equation for several points illustrates the effect of earth on vertically polarized signals at a particular location for a given frequency range. **Figure 3.42** shows the reflection coefficient as a function of elevation angle at 21 MHz over average earth (G = 0.005 S/m, and k = 13). Note that as the phase curve, ψ, passes through 90°, the attenuation curve (A) passes through a minimum at the same wave angle ψ. This is the PBA. At this angle, the reflected wave is not only at a phase angle of 90° with respect to the direct wave, but is so low in amplitude that it does not aid the direct wave by a significant amount. In the case illustrated in Figure 3.42 this elevation angle is about 15°.

Variations in PBA with Earth Quality

From Eq 9, it is quite a task to search for either the 90° phase point or the attenuation curve minimum for a wide variety of earth conditions. Instead, the PBA can be calculated directly from the following equation.

$$\psi_B = \arcsin\sqrt{\frac{k-1+\sqrt{\left(x^2+k^2\right)^2\left(k-1\right)^2 + x^2\left[\left(x^2+k^2\right)^2-1\right]}}{\left(x^2+k^2\right)^2-1}} \qquad (10)$$

where k, G and f are as defined for Eq 9, and

$$x = \frac{1.8\times10^4 \times G}{f}$$

Figure 3.43 shows curves calculated using Eq 10 for several different earth conditions, at frequencies between 1.8 and 30 MHz. As expected, poorer earths yield higher PBAs. Unfortunately, at the higher frequencies (where low-angle radiation is most important for DX work), the PBAs are highest. The PBA is the same for both transmitting and receiving.

Relating PBA to Location and Frequency

Table 3-2 presented earlier in this chapter lists the physical descriptions of various kinds of earth with their respective conductivities and dielectric constants, as mentioned earlier. Note that in general, the dielectric constants and conductivities are higher for better earths. This enables the labeling of the earth characteristics as extremely poor, very poor, poor,

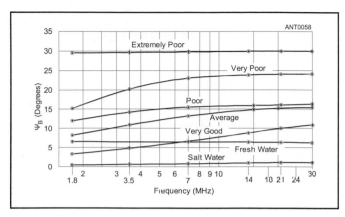

Figure 3.43 — Pseudo-Brewster angle (ψ) for various qualities of earth over the 1.8 to 30-MHz frequency range. Note that the frequency scale is logarithmic. The constants used for each curve are given in Table 3-5.

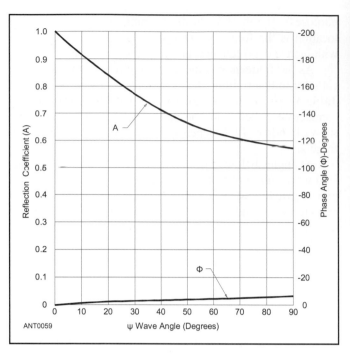

Figure 3.44 — Reflection coefficient for horizontally polarized waves (magnitude A at angle φ), at 21 MHz over average earth (k = 13, G = 0.005 S/m).

average, very good, and so on, without the complications that would result from treating the two parameters independently.

Fresh water and salt water are special cases; in spite of high resistivity, the fresh-water PBA is 6.4°, and is nearly independent of frequency below 30 MHz. Salt water, because of its extremely high conductivity, has a PBA that never exceeds 1° in this frequency range. The extremely low conductivity listed for cities (the last case) in Table 3-5 results more from the clutter of surrounding buildings and other obstructions than any actual earth characteristic. The PBA at any location can be found for a given frequency from the curves in Figure 3.43. (The map presented earlier as Figure 3.2 shows approximate conductivity values for different areas in the continental United States.)

3.3.4 FLAT-GROUND REFLECTIONS AND HORIZONTALLY POLARIZED WAVES

The situation for horizontal antennas is different from that of verticals. **Figure 3.44** shows the reflection coefficient for horizontally polarized waves over average earth at 21 MHz. Note that in this case, the phase-angle departure from 0° never gets very large, and the attenuation factor that causes the most loss for high-angle signals approaches unity for low angles. Attenuation increases with progressively poorer earth types.

In calculating the broadside radiation pattern of a horizontal λ/2 dipole, the perfect-earth image current, equal to the true antenna current but 180° out of phase with it) is multiplied by the horizontal reflection coefficient given by Eq 11 below. The product is then added vectorially to the direct wave to get the resultant at that elevation angle. The reflection coefficient for horizontally polarized waves can be calculated using the following equation.

$$A_{Horiz} \angle \phi = \frac{\sqrt{k' - \cos^2 \psi} - \sin \psi}{\sqrt{k' - \cos^2 \psi} + \sin \psi} \tag{11}$$

where

$A_{Horiz} \angle \phi$ = horizontal reflection coefficient
ψ = elevation angle

$$k' = k - j \left| \frac{1.8 \times 10^4 \times G}{f} \right|$$

k = dielectric constant of earth
G = conductivity of earth in S/m
f = frequency in MHz
j = complex operator ($\sqrt{-1}$)

For a horizontal antenna near the earth, the resultant pattern is a modification of the free-space pattern of the antenna. **Figure 3.45** shows how this modification takes place for a horizontal λ/2 antenna over a perfectly conducting flat surface. The patterns at the left show the relative radiation when one views the antenna from the side; those at the right show the radiation pattern looking at the end of the antenna. Changing the height above ground from λ/4 to λ/2 makes a significant difference in the high-angle radiation, moving the main lobe down lower.

Note that for an antenna height of λ/2 (Figure 3.45, bottom), the out-of-phase reflection from a perfectly conducting surface creates a null in the pattern at the zenith (90° elevation angle). Over real earth, however, a *filling in* of this null occurs because of ground losses that prevent perfect reflection of high-angle radiation.

At a 0° elevation angle, horizontally polarized antennas also demonstrate a null, because out-of-phase reflection cancels the direct wave. As the elevation angle departs from 0°, however, there is a slight filling-in effect so that over other-than-perfect earth, radiation at lower angles is enhanced compared to a vertical. A horizontal antenna will often outperform a vertical for low-angle DX work, particularly over

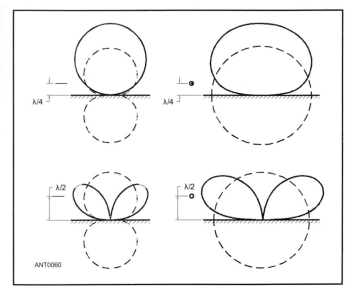

Figure 3.45 — Effect of the ground on the radiation from a horizontal half-wave dipole antenna, for heights of one-fourth and one-half wavelength. Broken lines show what the pattern would be if there were no reflection from the ground (free space).

lossy types of earth at the higher frequencies.

Reflection coefficients for vertically and horizontally polarized radiation differ considerably at most angles above ground, as can be seen by comparison of Figures 3.42 and 3.44. (Both sets of curves were plotted for the same ground constants and at the same frequency, so they may be compared directly.) This is because, as mentioned earlier, the image of a horizontally polarized antenna is out-of-phase with the antenna itself, and the image of a vertical antenna is in-phase with the actual radiator.

The result is that the phase shifts and reflection magnitudes vary greatly at different angles for horizontal and vertical polarization. The magnitude of the reflection coefficient for vertically polarized waves is greatest (near unity) at very low angles, and the phase angle is close to 180°. As mentioned earlier, this cancels nearly all radiation at very low angles. For the same range of angles, the magnitude of the reflection coefficient for horizontally polarized waves is also near unity, but the phase angle is near 0° for the specific conditions shown in Figures 3.42 and 3.44. This causes reinforcement of low-angle horizontally polarized waves. At some relatively high angle, the reflection coefficients for horizontally and vertically polarized waves are equal in magnitude and phase. At this angle (approximately 81° for the example case), the effect of ground reflection on vertically and horizontally polarized signals will be the same.

3.3.5 DIRECTIVE PATTERNS OVER REAL GROUND

As explained in the **Antenna Fundamentals** chapter, because antenna radiation patterns are three-dimensional, it is helpful in understanding their operation to use a form of representation showing the elevation-plane directional characteristic for different heights. It is possible to show selected elevation-plane patterns oriented in various directions with respect to the antenna axis. In the case of the horizontal half-wave dipole, a plane running in a direction along the axis and another broadside to the antenna will give a good deal of information.

The effect of reflection from the ground can be expressed as a separate *pattern factor*, given in decibels. For any given elevation angle, adding this factor algebraically to the value for that angle from the free-space pattern for that antenna gives the resultant radiation value at that angle. The limiting conditions are those represented by the direct ray and the reflected ray being exactly in-phase and exactly out-of-phase, when both (assuming there are no ground losses) have equal amplitudes. Thus, the resultant field strength at a distant point may be either 6 dB greater than the free-space pattern (twice the field strength), or zero, in the limiting cases.

Horizontally Polarized Antennas

The way in which pattern factors vary with height for horizontal antennas over flat earth is shown graphically in the plots of **Figure 3.46**. The solid-line plots are based on perfectly conducting ground, while the shaded plots are based on typical real-earth conditions. These patterns apply to horizontal antennas of any length. While these graphs are, in fact, radiation patterns of horizontal single-wire antennas (dipoles) as viewed from the axis of the wire, it must be remembered that the plots merely represent pattern factors.

Figure 3.47 shows vertical-plane radiation patterns in the directions off the ends of a horizontal half-wave dipole for various antenna heights. These patterns are scaled so they may be compared directly to those for the appropriate heights in Figure 3.46. Note that the perfect-earth patterns in Figures 3.46A and 3.46B are the same as those in the upper part of Figure 3.45. Note also that the perfect-earth patterns of Figures 3.47B and 3.46D are the same as those in the lower section of Figure 3.45. The reduction in field strength off the ends of the wire at the lower angles, as compared with the broadside field strength, is quite apparent. It is also clear from Figure 3.47 that, at some heights, the high-angle radiation off the ends is nearly as great as the broadside radiation, making the antenna essentially an omnidirectional radiator.

In vertical planes making some intermediate angle between 0° and 90° with the wire axis, the pattern will have a shape intermediate between the broadside and end-on patterns. By visualizing a smooth transition from the end-on pattern to the broadside pattern as the horizontal angle is varied from 0° to 90°, a fairly good mental picture of the actual solid pattern may be formed. An example is shown in **Figure 3.48**. At A, the elevation-plane pattern of a half-wave dipole at a height of λ/2 is shown through a plane 45° away from the favored direction of the antenna. At B and C, the pattern of the same antenna is shown at heights of 3λ/4 and 1λ (through the same 45° off-axis plane). These patterns are scaled so they may be compared directly with the broadside and end-on patterns for the same antenna

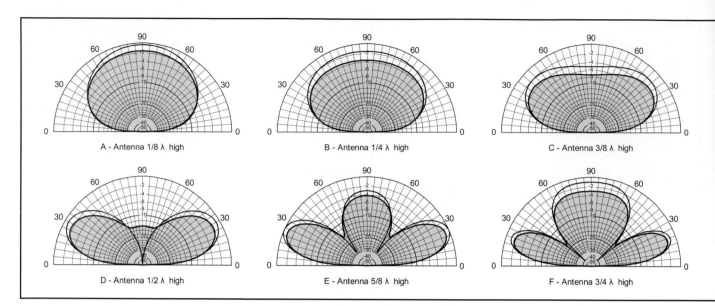

Figure 3.46 — Reflection factors for horizontal dipole antennas at various heights above flat ground. The solid-line curves are the perfect-earth patterns (broadside to the antenna wire); the shaded curves represent the effects of average earth (k = 13, G = 0.005 S/m) at 14 MHz. Add 7 dB to values shown for absolute gain in dBd referenced to dipole in free space, or 9.15 dB for gain in dBi. For example, peak gain over perfect earth at ⅝ λ height is 7 dBd (or 9.15 dBi) at 25° elevation.

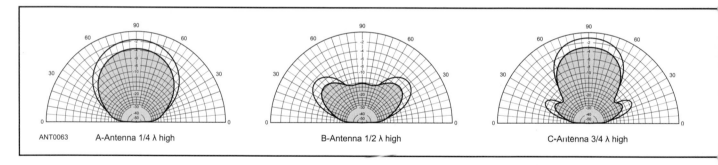

Figure 3.47 — Vertical-plane radiation patterns of horizontal half-wave dipole antennas off the ends of the antenna wire. The solid-line curves are the flat, perfect-earth patterns, and the shaded curves represent the effects of average flat earth (k = 13, G = 0.005 S/m) at 14 MHz. The 0-dB reference in each plot corresponds to the peak of the main lobe in the favored direction of the antenna (the maximum gain). Add 7 dB to values shown for absolute gain in dBd referenced to dipole in free space, or 9.15 dB for gain in dBi.

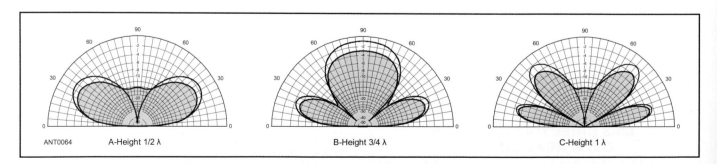

Figure 3.48 — Vertical-plane radiation patterns of half-wave horizontal dipole antennas at 45° from the antenna wire over flat ground. The solid-line and shaded curves represent the same conditions as in Figures 3.46 and 3.47. These patterns are scaled so they may be compared directly with those of Figures 3.46 and 3.47.

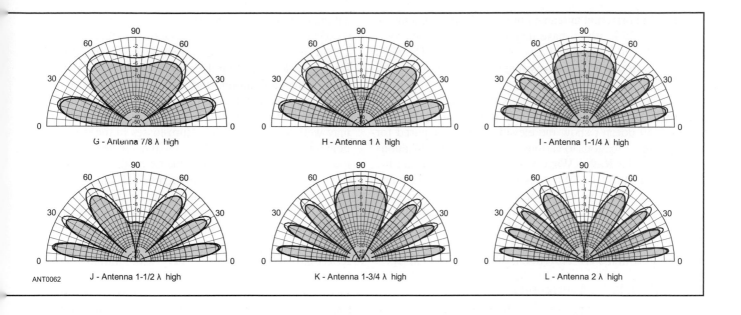

G - Antenna 7/8 λ high

H - Antenna 1 λ high

I - Antenna 1-1/4 λ high

J - Antenna 1-1/2 λ high

ANT0062

K - Antenna 1-3/4 λ high

L - Antenna 2 λ high

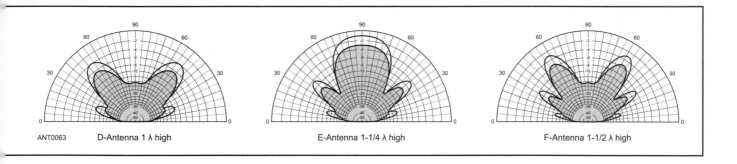

ANT0063

D-Antenna 1 λ high

E-Antenna 1-1/4 λ high

F-Antenna 1-1/2 λ high

(at the appropriate heights) in Figures 3.47 and 3.48.

The curves presented in **Figure 3.49** are useful for determining heights of horizontal antennas that give either maximum or minimum reinforcement at any desired wave angle. For instance, if you want to place an antenna at a height so that it will have a null at 30°, the antenna should be placed where a broken line crosses the 30° line on the horizontal scale. There are two heights (up to 2 λ) that will yield this null angle: 1 λ and 2 λ.

As a second example, you may want to have the ground reflection give maximum reinforcement of the direct ray from a horizontal antenna at a 20° elevation angle. The antenna height should be 0.75 λ. The same height will give a null at 42° and a second lobe at 90°.

Figure 3.49 is also useful for visualizing the vertical

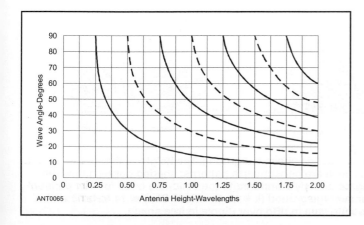

Figure 3.49 — Angles at which nulls and maxima (factor = 6 dB) in the ground-reflection factor appear for antenna heights up to two wavelengths over flat ground. The solid lines are maxima, dashed lines nulls, for all horizontal antennas. See text for examples. Values may also be determined from the trigonometric relationship $\theta = \arcsin(A/4h)$, where θ is the wave angle and h is the antenna height in wavelengths. For the first maximum, A has a value of 1; for the first null A has a value of 2, for the second maximum 3, for the second null 4, and so on.

pattern of a horizontal antenna. For example, if an antenna is erected at 1.25 λ, it will have major lobes (solid-line crossings) at 12° and 37°, as well as at 90° (the zenith). The nulls in this pattern (dashed-line crossings) will appear at 24° and 53°.

The Y-axis in Figure 3.49 plots the wave angle versus the height in wavelength above flat ground on the X-axis. Figure 3.49 doesn't show the elevation angles required for actual communications to various target geographic locations of interest. The **Radio Wave Propagation** chapter and the CD-ROM in the back of this book give details about the range of angles required for target locations around the world. It is very useful to overlay plots of these angles together with the elevation pattern for horizontally polarized antennas at various heights above flat ground. This will be demonstrated in detail later in the **HF Antenna System Design** chapter.

Vertically Polarized Antennas

In the case of a vertical λ/2 dipole or a ground-plane antenna, the horizontal directional pattern is simply a circle at any elevation angle (although the actual field strength will vary, at the different elevation angles, with the height above ground). Hence, one vertical pattern is sufficient to give complete information (for a given antenna height) about the antenna in any direction with respect to the wire. A series of such patterns for various heights is given in **Figure 3.50**. Rotating the plane pattern about the zenith axis of the graph forms the three-dimensional radiation pattern in each case.

The solid-line curves represent the radiation patterns of the λ/2 vertical dipole at different feed point heights over perfectly conducting ground. The shaded curves in Figure 3.50 show the patterns produced by the same

antennas at the same heights over average ground (G = 0.005 S/m, k = 13) at 14 MHz. The PBA in this case is 14.8°.

In short, far-field losses for vertically polarized antennas are highly dependent on the conductivity and dielectric constant of the earth around the antenna, extending far beyond the ends of any radials used to complete the ground return for the near field. Putting more radials out around the antenna may well decrease ground-return losses in the reactive near field for a vertical monopole, but will not increase radiation at low elevation launch angles in the far field, unless the radials can extend perhaps 100 wavelengths in all directions! Aside from moving to the fabled "salt water swamp on a high hill," there is very little that someone can do to change the character of the ground that affects the far-field pattern of a real vertical. Classical texts on verticals often show elevation patterns computed over an "infinitely wide, infinitely conducting ground plane." Real ground, with finite conductivity and less than perfect dielectric constant, can severely curtail the low-angle radiation at which verticals are supposed to excel.

While real verticals over real ground are not a sure-fire method to achieve low-angle radiation, cost versus performance and ease of installation are still attributes that can highly recommend verticals to knowledgeable builders. Practical installations for 160 and 80 meters rarely allow amateurs to put up horizontal antenna high enough to radiate effectively at low elevation angles. After all, a half-wave on 1.8 MHz is 273 feet high, and even at such a lofty height the peak radiation for a horizontal antenna would be at a 30° elevation angle, which is higher than desired for long-distance communication. A simple ground-mounted vertical with a reasonable radial field will almost always give much better results in this case.

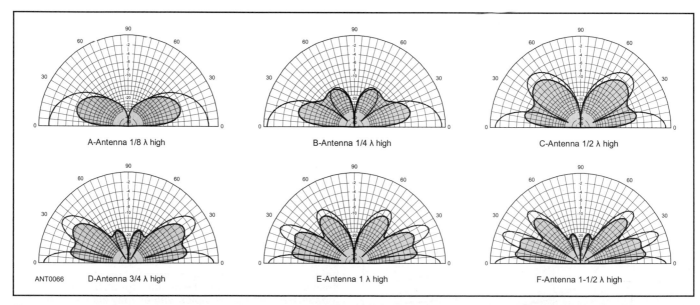

ANT0066

A-Antenna 1/8 λ high
B-Antenna 1/4 λ high
C-Antenna 1/2 λ high
D-Antenna 3/4 λ high
E-Antenna 1 λ high
F-Antenna 1-1/2 λ high

Figure 3.50 — Vertical-plane radiation patterns of a ground-plane antenna above flat ground. The height is that of the ground plane, which consists of four radials in a horizontal plane. Solid lines are perfect-earth patterns; shaded curves show the effects of real earth. The patterns are scaled — that is, they may be directly compared to the solid-line ones for comparison of losses at any wave angle. These patterns were calculated for average ground (k = 13, G = 0.005 S/m) at 14 MHz. The PBA for these conditions is 14.8°. Add 6 dB to values shown for absolute gain in dBd over dipole in free space.

3.4 GROUND PARAMETERS FOR ANTENNA ANALYSIS

This section is taken from an article in *The ARRL Antenna Compendium, Vol 5* by R. P. Haviland, W4MB. In the past, amateurs paid very little attention to the characteristics of the earth (ground) associated with their antennas. There are two reasons for this. First, these characteristics are not easy to measure — even with the best equipment, extreme care is needed. Second, almost all hams have to put up with what they have — there are very few who can afford to move because their location has poor ground conditions! Further, the ground is not a dominant factor in the most popular antennas — a tri-band Yagi at 40 feet or higher, or a 2 meter vertical at roof height, for example.

Even so, there has been a desire and even a need for ground data and for ways to use it. It is very important for vertically polarized antennas. Ground data is useful for antennas mounted at low heights generally, and for such specialized ones as Beverage receiving antennas. The performance of such antennas changes a lot as the ground changes.

3.4.1 IMPORTANCE OF GROUND CONDITIONS

To see why ground conditions can be important, let us look at some values. For a frequency of 10 MHz, *CCIR Recommendation 368* (see Bibliography), gives the distance at which the signal is calculated to drop 10 dB below its free-space level as:

Conductivity (mS/meter)	Distance for 10 dB Drop (km)
5000	100
30	15
3	0.3

The high-conductivity condition is for sea-water. Inter-island work in the Caribbean on 40 and 80 meters is easy, whereas 40 meter ground-wave contact is difficult for much of the USA, because of much lower ground conductivity. On the other hand, the Beverage works because of poor ground conductivity.

Figure 3.51 shows a typical set of expected propagation curves for a range of frequencies. This data is also from *CCIR Recommendation 368* for relatively poor ground, with a dielectric constant of 4 and a conductivity of 3 mS/m (one millisiemens/meter is 0.001 mho/meter). The same data is available in the *Radio Propagation Handbook*. There are equivalent FCC curves, found in the book *Reference Data for Radio Engineers*, but only the ones near 160 meters are useful. In Florida the author has difficulty hearing stations across town on ground wave, an indication of the poor soil conditions — reflected sky-wave signals are often stronger.

3.4.2 SECURING GROUND DATA

There are only two basic ways to approach this matter of ground data. One is to use generic ground data typical to the area. The second is to make measurements, which haven't really gotten easier. For most amateurs, the best approach seems to be a combination of these — use some simple measurements, and then use the generic data to make a better estimate. Because of equipment costs and measurement difficulties, none of these will be highly accurate for most hams. But they will be much better than simply taking some condition preset into an analysis program. Having a good set of values to plug into an analysis can help you evaluate the true worth of a new antenna project.

Generic Data

In connection with its licensing procedure for broadcast stations, the FCC has published generic data for the entire country. This map was presented earlier as Figure 3.2, showing the "estimated effective ground conductivity in the United States." A range of 30:1 is shown, from 1 to 30 mS/m. An equivalent chart for Canada has been prepared, originally by DOT, now DOC.

Of course, some judgment is needed when trying to use this data for your location. Broadcast stations are likely to be in open areas, so the data should not be assumed to apply to the center of a city. And a low site near the sea is likely to have better conductivity than the generic chart for, say, the coast of Oregon. Other than such factors, this chart gives a good first value and a useful cross-check if some other method is used.

Still another FCC-induced data source is the license application of your local broadcast station. This includes calculated and measured coverage data. This may include specific ground data, or comparison of the coverage curves with the CCIR or FCC data to give the estimated ground conductivity. Another set of curves for ground conditions are those prepared by SRI (see References). These give the conductivity and dielectric constant versus frequency for typical terrain conditions. These are reproduced as **Figures 3.52** and **3.53**. By inspecting your own site, you may select the curve most appropriate to your terrain. The curves are based on measurements at a number of sites across the USA, and are averages of the measured values.

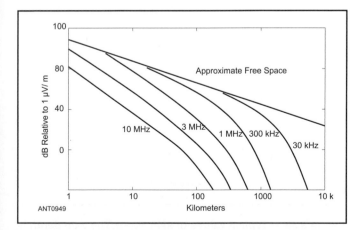

Figure 3.51 — Variation of field strength with distance. Typical field strengths for several frequencies are shown. This is from CCIR data for fairly poor soil, with dielectric constant of 4 and conductivity of 3 mS/m. The curves for good soil are closer to the free-space line, and those for sea water are much closer to the free-space line.

Figures **3.54** through **3.56** are data derived from these measurements. Figure 3.54 gives the ground-dissipation factor. Sea water has low loss (a high dissipation factor), while soil in the desert or in the city is very lossy, with a low dissipation factor. Figure 3.55 gives the skin depth, the distance for the signal to decease to 63% of its value at the surface.

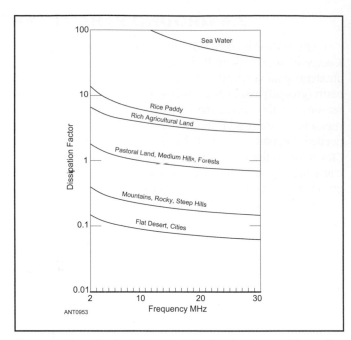

Figure 3.54 — Typical values of dissipation factor. The soil behaves as a leaky dielectric. These curves showing the dimensionless dissipation factor versus frequency for various types of soils and for sea water. The dissipation factor is inversely related to soil conductivity. Among other things, a high dissipation factor indicates that a signal penetrating the soil or water will decrease in strength rapidly with depth.

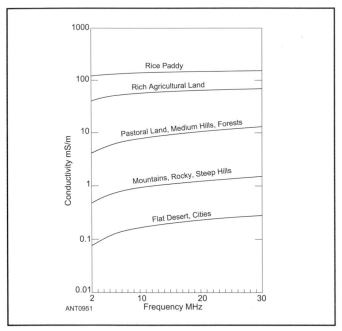

Figure 3.52 — Typical terrain conductivities versus frequency for 5 types of soils. This was measured by SRI. Units are mS/m. Conductivity of seawater is usually taken as 5000 mS/m. Conductivity of fresh water depends on the impurities present, and may be very low. To extrapolate conductivity values (for 500 to 1500 kHz) shown in Figure 3.2 for a particular geographic area to a different frequency, move from the conductivity at the left edge of this figure to the desired frequency. For example, in rocky New Hampshire, with a conductivity of 1 mS/m at BC frequencies, the effective conductivity at 14 MHz would be approximately 4 mS/m.

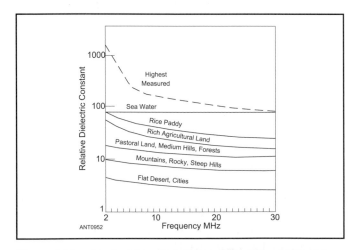

Figure 3.53 — Typical terrain relative dielectric constant for the 5 soil types of Figure 3.52, plus sea water. The dashed curve shows the highest measured values reported, and usually indicates mineralization.

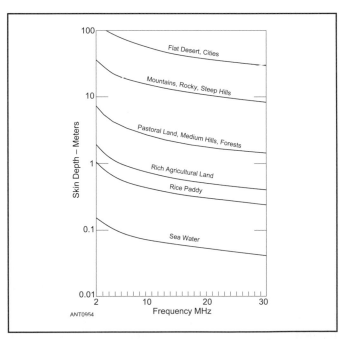

Figure 3.55 — Typical values of skin depth. The skin depth is the depth at which a signal will have decreased to 1/e of its value at the surface (to about 30%). The effective height above ground is essentially the same as the physical height for sea water, but may be much greater for the desert. For practical antennas, this may increase low-angle radiation, but at the same time will increase ground losses.

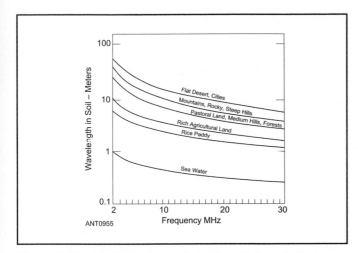

Figure 3.56 — Typical values of wavelength in soil. Because of its dielectric constant, the wavelength in soils and water will be shorter than that for a wave traveling in air. This can be important, since in a Method of Moment the accuracy is affected by the number of analysis segments per wavelength. Depending on the program being used, adjust the number of segments for antennas wholly or partly in the earth, for ground rods, and for antennas very close to earth.

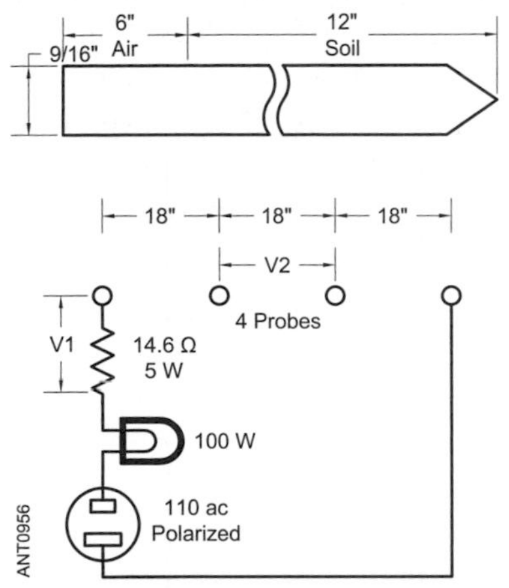

Figure 3.57 — Low-frequency conductivity measurement system. A 60-Hz measuring system devised by W2FNQ and used by W2FMI. The basic system is widely used in geophysics. Use care to be certain that the plug connection is correct. A better system would use a lower voltage and an isolation transformer. Measure the value of V_2 with no power applied — there may be stray ground currents present, especially if there is a power station or an electric railway close.

Penetration is low in high-conductivity areas and deep in low-conductivity soil. Finally, Figure 3.56 shows the wavelength in the earth. For example, at 10 meters (30 MHz), the wavelength in sea water is less than 0.3 meters. Even in the desert, the wavelength has been reduced to about 6 meters at this frequency. This is one reason why buried antennas have peculiar properties. Lacking other data, it is suggested that the values of Figure 3.52 and 3.53 be used in computer antenna modeling programs.

Measuring Ground Conditions

M.C. Waltz, W2FNQ (SK) developed a simple technique to measure low-frequency earth conductivity, which has been used by Jerry Sevick, W2FMI (SK). The test setup is drawn in **Figure 3.57**, and uses a very old technique of 4-terminal resistivity measurements. For probes of 9/16-inch diameter, spaced 18 inches and penetrating 12 inches into the earth, the conductivity is:

$$G = 21\, V_1/V_2 \text{ mS/m} \qquad (12)$$

The voltages are conveniently measured by a digital voltmeter, to an accuracy of about 2%. In soil suitable for farming, the probes can be copper or aluminum. The strength of iron or Copperweld may be needed in hard soils. A piece of 2×4 or 4×4 lumber with guide holes drilled through it will help maintain proper spacing and vertical alignment of the probes. Use care when measuring — there is a shock hazard. An isolating transformer with a 24 V secondary instead of 120 V will reduce the danger.

Ground conditions vary quite widely over even small areas. It is best to make a number of measurements around the area of the antenna, and average the measured values.

While this measurement gives only the low-frequency conductivity, it can be used to select curves in Figure 3.52 to give an estimate of the conductivity for the common ham bands. Assume that the 60 Hz value is valid at 2 MHz, and find the correct value on the left axis. Move parallel to the curves on the figure to develop the estimated curve for other soil conditions.

A small additional refinement is possible. If the dielectric constant from Figure 3.53 is plotted against the conductivity from Figure 3.52 for a given frequency, a scatter plot develops, showing a trend to higher dielectric constant as conductivity increases. At 14 MHz, the relation is:

$$k = \sqrt{1000/G} \qquad (13)$$

where k is the dielectric constant and G is the measured conductivity. Using these values in *MININEC* or *NEC* calculations should give better estimates than countrywide average values.

Direct Measurement of Ground Properties

For really good values, both the conductivity and dielectric constant should be measured at the operating frequency. One way of doing this is the two-probe technique described in George Hagn's article[1] and in reference 16. This was the technique used to secure the data for Figures 3.52 through 3.56. The principle is sketched in **Figure 3.58**. In essence, the two probes form a short, open-circuited, two-wire transmission line. As shown by the equations for such lines, the input impedance is a function of the conductivity and dielectric constant of the medium. A single measurement is difficult to calculate, since the end effect of the two probes must be determined, a complex task if they are pointed for easy driving. The calculation is greatly simplified if a set of measurements is made with several sets of probes that vary in length by a

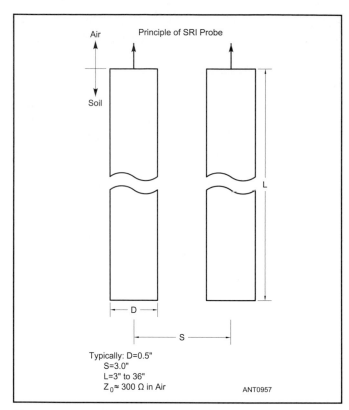

Figure 3.58 — High-frequency conductivity/dielectric constant measurement system. System for measuring ground conditions at frequencies up to about 100 MHz, devised by SRI and used to obtain the data in Figures 3.52 through 56. Basically, this is a section of transmission line with soil as the dielectric. Requires measurement of high impedances to good accuracy.

fixed ratio, since the measured difference is largely due to the increased two-wire length, with some change due to the change in soil moisture with depth.

The impedance to be measured is high because of the short line length, so impedance bridges are not really suitable. An RF vector impedance meter, such as the HP-4193A, is probably the best instrument to use, with an RF susceptance bridge, such as the GR-821A, next best. With care, a Q-meter can be substituted. Because of the rarity of these instruments among amateurs, this method of measurement is not explored further here.

Table 3-6
Calculated Values of Drive Resistance
Drive resistance in ohms, for a 40 meter dipole at 40-feet elevation versus conductivity and dielectric constant

Conductivity (mS/m)	Dielectric Constant		
	-------- 3 --------	------- 15 -------	------ 80 ------
10	$89.78 - j\,12.12$	$88.53 - j\,10.69$	$88.38 - j\,7.59$
1	$80.05 - j\,17.54$	$83.72 - j\,10.23$	$87.33 - j\,6.98$
0.1	$76.44 - j\,15.69$	$83.18 - j\,9.85$	$97.30 - j\,6.46$

The value measured by W2DU was $72.59 - j\,1.28\ \Omega$, and compares closest to the poor soil condition of dielectric constant of 3 and conductivity of 0.1 mS/m.

Indirect Measurement

Since the terminal impedance and resonant frequency of an antenna change as the antenna approaches earth, measurement of an antenna at one or more heights permits an analysis of the ground characteristics. The technique is to calculate the antenna drive impedance for an assumed ground condition, and compare this with measured values. If not the same, another set of ground conditions is assumed, and the process is repeated. It is best to have a plan to guide the assumptions.

In connection with his studies of transmission lines, Walt Maxwell, W2DU, made such measurements on 20, 40 and 80 meters. Some of the data was included in his book *Reflections*.[17] The following example is based on his 80 meter data. Data is from his Table 20-1, for a 66-foot, 2-inch dipole of #14 AWG wire at 40 feet above ground. His table gives an antenna impedance of $72.59 + j\,1.38\ \Omega$ at 7.15 MHz.

Table 3-6 shows calculated antenna impedances for ground conductivities of three different ground conductivities: 10, 1 and 0.1 mS/m, and for dielectric constants of 3, 15 and 80. The nearest value to the measured drive impedance is for a conductivity of 0.1 mS/m and a dielectric constant of 3. Figures 3.52 and 3.53 indicate that these are typical of flat desert and city land. The effect on antenna performance is shown in **Figure 3.59**. The maximum lobe gain for soil typical of a city is over 2 dB lower than that for the high-conductivity, high-dielectric constant value. Note that the maximum lobe occurs for a radiation angle that is directly overhead.

The ground at the W2DU QTH is a suburban Florida lot, covered with low, native vegetation. The ground is very sandy (a fossil sand dune), and is some 60-70 feet above sea-level. Measurements were made near the end of the Florida dry season. The water table is estimated to be 20 to 30 feet below the surface. Thus the calculated and measured values are reasonably consistent.

In principle, a further analysis, using values around 0.1 mS/m conductivity and 3 for dielectric constant, will give a better ground parameter estimate. However, the results should be taken with a grain of salt, because the opportunities for error in the computer modeling must be considered. The antenna should have no sag, and its length and height should be accurate. The measurement must be with accurate equipment, free from strays, such as current on the outer conductor of the coax. The feed point gap effect must be estimated. Further, the ground itself under the antenna must be flat and have constant characteristics for modeling to be completely accurate.

Finally, the feed line length and velocity constant of the transmission line must be accurately measured for transfer of the measured values at the feeding end of the transmission line to the antenna itself. Because of all the possibilities for error, most attempts at precision should be based on measured values at two or three frequencies, and

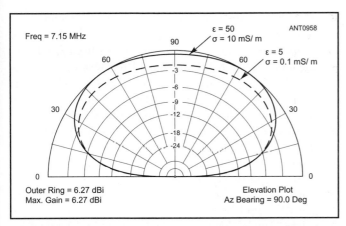

Figure 3.59 — Plot showing computed elevation patterns for 40-foot high, 40 meter dipole for two different ground conditions: poor ground, with dielectric constant of 3 and conductivity of 0.1 mS/m, and good ground, with dielectric constant of 50 and conductivity of 10 mS/m. Note that for a low horizontal antenna, high-angle radiation is most affected by poor ground, with low-angle radiation least affected by ground characteristics.

preferably at two or three heights. Orienting the antenna to right angles for another set of measurements may be useful. Obviously, this can involve a lot of detailed work.

The author was not been able to find any guidelines for the best height or frequency. The data in the article *Exact Image Method for Impedance Computation of Antennas above the Ground* suggests that a height of 0.3 λ will give good sensitivity to ground conditions.[18] Very low heights may give confusing results, since several combinations of ground parameters can give nearly the same drive impedance. Both this data and experience suggest that sensitivity to ground for heights above 0.75 λ is small or negligible.

If an overall conclusion about ground characteristics is needed, we can just restate from the first paragraph — it is not greatly important for the most common horizontally polarized antenna installations. But it's worth taking a look when you need to depart from typical situations, or when the performance of a vertically polarized antenna is contemplated. Then the techniques outlined here can be helpful.

3.5 REFERENCES AND BIBLIOGRAPHY

REFERENCES

1. George H. Hagn, SRI, "HF Ground Measurements at the Lawrence Livermore National Laboratory (LLNL) Field Site," *Applied Computational Electromagnetics Society Journal and Newsletter*, Vol 3, Number 2, Fall 1988.
2. Christman, Al, K3LC, "Ground System Configurations for Vertical Antennas," *QEX*, Jul/Aug 2005, pp 28-37
3. Christman, Al, K3LC, "Maximum-Gain Radial Ground Systems for Vertical Antennas," *National Contest Journal*, Mar/Apr 2004, pp 5-10.
4. Stanley, John, K4ERO, "Optimum Ground Systems for Vertical Antennas," *QST*, Dec 1976, pp 13-15.
5. Severns, Rudy, N6LF, "An Experimental Look at Ground Systems for HF Verticals," *QST*, Mar 2010, pp 30-33.
6. Severns, Rudy, N6LF, "Experimental Determination of Ground System Performance for HF Verticals, Part 7, Ground Systems with Missing Sectors," *QEX*, Jan/Feb 2010, pp 18-19.
7. Severns, Rudy, N6LF, "Experimental Determination of Ground System Performance for HF Verticals, Part 3, Comparisons Between Ground Surface and Elevated Radials," *QEX*, Mar/Apr 2009, pp 29-32.
8. Christman, Al, K3LC, "Gull-Wing Vertical Antennas," *National Contest Journal*, Nov/Dec 2000, pp 14-18.
9. Dick Weber, K5IU, "Optimum Elevated Radial Vertical Antennas," *Communications Quarterly*, Spring 1997, pp 9-27.

10. Doty, Frey and Mills, "Efficient Ground Systems for Vertical Antennas," *QST*, Feb 1983, pp 20-25.
11. Brown, Lewis and Epstein, "Ground Systems as a Factor in Antenna Efficiency," *Proc. IRE* , June 1937.
12. C. J. Michaels, "Horizontal Antennas and the Compound Reflection Coefficient," *The ARRL Antenna Compendium*, Vol 3 (Newington: ARRL, 1992).
13. Severns, Rudy, N6LF, "Experimental Determination of Ground System Performance for HF Verticals, Part 1, Test Setup and Instrumentation", *QEX*, Jan/Feb 2009, pp 21-25.
14. Severns, Rudy, N6LF, "Experimental Determination of Ground System Performance for HF Verticals, Part 2, Test Setup and Instrumentation," *QEX*, Jan/Feb 2009, pp 48-52.
15. Severns, Rudy, N6LF, "Experimental Determination of Ground System Performance for HF Verticals, Part 6, Ground Systems for Multi-band Verticals," *QEX*, Nov/Dec 2009, pg. 19-24
16. Severns, Rudy, N6LF, "Measurement of Soil Electrical Parameters at HF," *QEX*, Nov/Dec 2006, pp 3-8.
17. M. W. Maxwell, *Reflections III — Transmission Lines and Antennas*, 3rd edition (New York: CQ Communications, 2010).
18. I. Lindell, E. Alanen, K. Mannerslo, "Exact Image Method for Impedance Computation of Antennas Above the Ground," *IEEE Trans. On Antennas and Propagation*, AP-33, Sep 1985, pp 937-945.

BIBLIOGRAPHY

Source material and more extended discussion of the topics covered in this chapter can be found in the references listed below and in the textbooks listed at the end of the **Antenna Fundamentals** chapter.

B. Boothe, "The Minooka Special," *QST*, Dec 1974, pp 15-19, 28.

G. Brown, "The Phase And Magnitude Of Earth Currents Near Radio Transmitting Antennas," *Proc. IRE*, Feb 1935, pp 168-182.

CCIR Recommendation 368, Documents of the CCIR XII Plenary Assembly, ITU, Geneva, 1967.

R. Collin and F. Zucker, *Antenna Theory*, Chap 23 by J. Wait, Inter-University Electronics Series (New York: McGraw-Hill, 1969), Vol 7, pp 414-424.

T. Hulick, "A Two-Element Vertical Parasitic Array For 75 Meters," *QST*, Dec 1995, pp 38-41.

R. Jones, "A 7-MHz Vertical Parasitic Array," *QST*, Nov 1973, pp 39-43, 52.

T. Larsen, "The E-Field and H-Field Losses Around Antennas With a Radial Ground Wire System," *Journal of Research of the National Bureau of Standards*, D. Radio Propagation, Vol 66D, No. 2, Mar-Apr 1962, pp 189-204.

D. A. McNamara, C. W. I. Pistorius, J. A. G. Malherbe, *Introduction to the Geometrical Theory of Diffraction* (Norwood, MA: Artech House, 1994).

C. J. Michaels, "Some Reflections on Vertical Antennas," *QST*, Jul 1987, pp 15-19.

Radio Broadcast Ground Systems, available from Smith Electronics, Inc, 8200 Snowville Rd, Cleveland, OH 44141.

Reference Data for Radio Engineers, 5th edition (Indianapolis: Howard W. Sams, 1968), Chapter 28.

R. Severns, "Verticals, Ground Systems and Some History," *QST*, Jul 2000, pp 38-44.

J. Sevick, "The Ground-Image Vertical Antenna," *QST*, Jul 1971, pp 16-19, 22

J. Sevick, "The W2FMI 20-Meter Vertical Beam," *QST*, Jun 1972, pp 14-18.

J. Sevick, "The W2FMI Ground-Mounted Short Vertical," *QST*, Mar 1973, pp 13-18, 41.

J. Sevick, "A High Performance 20-, 40- and 80-Meter Vertical System," *QST*, Dec 1973, pp 30-33.

J. Sevick, "The Constant-Impedance Trap Vertical," *QST*, Mar 1974, pp 29-34.

J. Sevick, "Short Ground-Radial Systems for Short Verticals," *QST*, Apr 1978, pp 30-33.

J. Sevick, "Measuring Soil Conductivity," *QST*, Mar 1981, pp 38- 39.

J. Stanley, "Optimum Ground Systems for Vertical Antennas," *QST*, Dec 1976, pp 13-15.

F. E. Terman, *Radio Engineers' Handbook*, 1st ed. (New York, London: McGraw-Hill Book Co, 1943).

TABLE OF CONTENTS

Chapter 4

Radio Wave Propagation

Because radio communication is carried on by means of electromagnetic waves traveling through the Earth's atmosphere, it is important to understand the nature of these waves and their behavior in the propagation medium. Most antennas will radiate the power applied to them efficiently, but no antenna can do all things equally well, under all circumstances. Whether you design and build your own antennas, or buy them and have them put up by a professional, you'll need propagation know-how for best results, both during the planning stages and while operating your station.

The material in this chapter has been updated by Carl Luetzelschwab, K9LA, including the progress of sunspot Cycle 24 and new sources of solar information.

4.1 THE NATURE OF RADIO WAVES

The basic concepts and behavior of electromagnetic radio waves are presented in the chapter **Antenna Fundamentals**. This section discusses additional characteristics of radio waves that have particular importance to the study of how the waves propagate.

4.1.1 BENDING OF RADIO WAVES

Radio waves and light waves are both propagated as electromagnetic energy. Their major difference is in wavelength, since radio-reflecting surfaces are usually much smaller in terms of wavelength than those for light. In material of a given electrical conductivity, long waves penetrate deeper than short ones, and so require a thicker mass for good reflection. Thin metal however is a good reflector of even long-wavelength radio waves. With poorer conductors, such as the Earth's crust, long waves may penetrate quite a few feet below the surface.

The path of a *ray* traced from its source to any point on a spherical surface is considered to be a straight line — a radius of the sphere. An observer on the surface of the sphere would think of it as being flat, just as the Earth seems flat to us. A radio wave far enough from its source to appear flat is called a *plane wave*. From here on, we will be discussing primarily plane waves.

Reflection occurs at any boundary between materials of differing dielectric constant. Familiar examples with light are reflections from water surfaces and window panes. Both water and glass are transparent for light, but their dielectric constants are very different from that of air. Light waves, being very short, seem to bounce off both surfaces. Radio waves, being much longer, are practically unaffected by glass, but their behavior upon encountering water may vary, depending on the purity of that medium. Distilled water is a good insulator; salt water is a relatively good conductor.

Depending on their wavelength (and thus their frequency), radio waves may be reflected by buildings, trees, vehicles, the ground, water, ionized layers in the upper atmosphere, or at boundaries between air masses having different temperatures and moisture content. Ionospheric and atmospheric conditions are important in practically all communication beyond purely local ranges.

Refraction is the bending of a ray as it passes from one medium to another at an angle. The appearance of bending of a straight stick, where it enters water at an angle, is an example of light refraction known to us all. The degree of bending of radio waves at boundaries between air masses increases with the radio frequency. There is slight atmospheric bending in our HF bands. It becomes noticeable at 28 MHz, more so at 50 MHz, and it is much more of a factor in the higher VHF range and in UHF and microwave propagation.

Diffraction of light over a solid wall prevents total darkness on the far side from the light source. This is caused largely by the spreading of waves around the top of the wall, due to the interference of one part of the beam with another.

The dielectric constant of the surface of the obstruction may affect what happens to our radio waves when they encounter terrestrial obstructions — but the radio *shadow area* is never totally dark. See the chapter **Effects of Ground** for more information on diffraction.

The three terms, reflection, refraction and diffraction, were in use long before the radio age began. Radio propagation is nearly always a mix of these phenomena, and it may not be easy to identify or separate them while they are happening when we are on the air. This book tends to rely on the words *bending* and *scattering* in its discussions, with appropriate modifiers as needed. The important thing to remember is that any alteration of the path taken by energy as it is radiated from an antenna is almost certain to affect on-the-air results — which is why this chapter on propagation is included in a book on antennas.

4.1.2 GROUND WAVES

As we have already seen, radio waves are affected in many ways by the media through which they travel. This has led to some confusion of terms in earlier literature concerning wave propagation. Waves travel close to the ground in several ways, some of which involve relatively little contact with the ground itself. The term *ground wave* has had several meanings in antenna literature, but it has come to be applied to any wave that stays close to the Earth, reaching the receiving point without leaving the Earth's lower atmosphere. This distinguishes the ground wave from a *sky wave*, which utilizes the ionosphere for propagation between the transmitting and receiving antennas.

The wave could also travel directly between the transmitting and receiving antennas, when they are high enough so they can "see" each other — this is commonly called the *direct wave*. The ground wave also travels between the transmitting and receiving antennas by reflections or diffractions off intervening terrain between them. The ground-influenced wave may interact with the direct wave to create a vector-summed resultant at the receiver antenna.

In the generic term ground wave, we also will include ones that are made to follow the Earth's curvature by bending in the Earth's lower atmosphere, or *troposphere*, usually no more than a few miles above the ground. Often called *tropospheric bending*, this propagation mode is a major factor in amateur communications above 50 MHz.

4.1.3 THE SURFACE WAVE

A ground wave could be traveling in actual contact with the ground where it is called the *surface wave*. As the frequency is raised, the distance over which surface waves can travel without excessive energy loss becomes smaller and smaller. The surface wave can provide coverage up to about 100 miles in the standard AM broadcast band during the daytime, but attenuation is high. As can be seen from **Figure 4.1**, the attenuation increases with frequency. The surface wave is of little value in amateur communication, except possibly at 1.8 MHz. Vertically polarized antennas must be used, which tends to limit amateur surface-wave communication to the

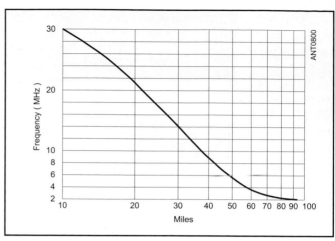

Figure 4.1 — Typical HF ground-wave range as a function of frequency.

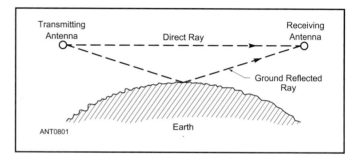

Figure 4.2 — The ray traveling directly from the transmitting antenna to the receiving antenna combines with a ray reflected from the ground to form the space wave. For a horizontally polarized signal a reflection as shown here reverses the phase of the ground-reflected ray.

bands and installations for which large vertical antennas can be erected.

4.1.4 THE SPACE WAVE

Propagation between two antennas situated within line of sight of each other is shown in **Figure 4.2**. Energy traveling directly between the antennas is attenuated to about the same degree as in free space. Unless the antennas are very high or quite close together, an appreciable portion of the energy is reflected from the ground. This reflected wave combines with direct radiation to affect the actual signal received.

In most communication between two stations on the ground, the angle at which the wave strikes the ground will be small. For a horizontally polarized signal, such a reflection reverses the phase of the wave. If the distances traveled by both parts of the wave were the same, the two parts would arrive out of phase, and would therefore cancel each other. The ground-reflected ray in Figure 4.2 must travel a little further, so the phase difference between the two depends on the lengths of the paths, measured in wavelengths. The wavelength in use is important in determining the useful signal strength in this type of communication.

If the difference in path length is 3 meters, the phase

difference with 160 meter waves would be only $360° \times 3/160 = 6.8°$. This is a negligible difference from the $180°$ shift caused by the reflection, so the effective signal strength over the path would still be very small because of cancellation of the two waves. But with 6 meter radio waves the phase length would be $360° \times \frac{3}{6} = 180°$. With the additional $180°$ shift on reflection, the two rays would add. Thus, the space wave is a negligible factor at low frequencies, but it can be increasingly useful as the frequency is raised. It is a dominant factor in local amateur communication at 50 MHz and higher.

Interaction between the direct and reflected waves is the principle cause of *mobile flutter* observed in local VHF communication between fixed and mobile stations. The flutter effect decreases once the stations are separated enough so that the reflected ray becomes inconsequential. The reflected energy can also confuse the results of field-strength measurements during tests on VHF antennas.

As with most propagation explanations, the space-wave picture presented here is simplified, and practical considerations dictate modifications. There is always some energy loss when the wave is reflected from the ground. Further, the phase of the ground-reflected wave is not shifted exactly $180°$, so the waves never cancel completely. At UHF, ground-reflection losses can be greatly reduced or eliminated by using highly directive antennas. By confining the antenna pattern to something approaching a flashlight beam, nearly all the energy is in the direct wave. The resulting energy loss is low enough that microwave relays, for example, can operate with moderate power levels over hundreds or even thousands of miles. Thus we see that, while the space wave is inconsequential below about 20 MHz, it can be a prime asset in the VHF realm and higher.

4.1.5 VHF/UHF PROPAGATION BEYOND LINE OF SIGHT

From Figure 4.2 it appears that use of the space wave depends on direct line of sight between the antennas of the communicating stations. This is not literally true, although that belief was common in the early days of amateur communication on frequencies above 30 MHz. When equipment became available that operated more efficiently and after antenna techniques were improved, it soon became clear that VHF waves were actually being bent or scattered in several ways, permitting reliable communication beyond visual distances between the two stations. This was found true even with low power and simple antennas. The average communication range can be approximated by assuming the waves travel in straight lines, but with the Earth's radius increased by one-third. The distance to the *radio horizon* is then given as

$$D_{miles} = 1.415\sqrt{H_{feet}} \qquad (1)$$

or

$$D_{km} = 4.124\sqrt{H_{meters}} \qquad (2)$$

where H is the height of the transmitting antenna, as shown in **Figure 4.3**. The formula assumes that the Earth is smooth

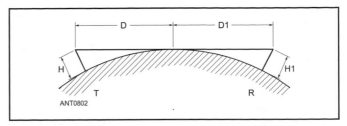

Figure 4.3 — The distance D to the horizon from an antenna of height H is given by equations in the text. The maximum line-of-sight distance between two elevated antennas is equal to the sum of their distances to the horizon as indicated here.

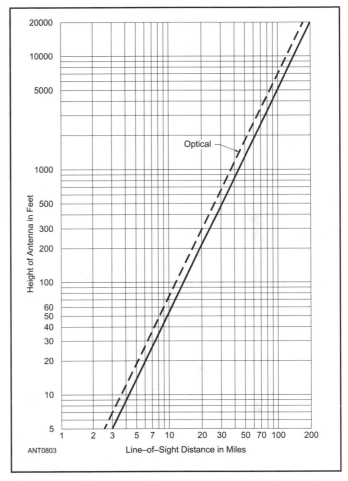

Figure 4.4 — Distance to the horizon from an antenna of given height. The solid curve includes the effect of atmospheric refraction. The optical line-of-sight distance is given by the broken curve.

out to the horizon, so any obstructions along the path must be taken into consideration. For an elevated receiving antenna the communication distance is equal to D + D1, that is, the sum of the distances to the horizon of both antennas. Radio horizon distances are given in graphic form in **Figure 4.4**. Two stations on a flat plain, one with its antenna 60 feet above ground and the other 40 feet, could be up to about 20 miles apart for strong-signal line-of-sight communication (11 + 9 mi). The terrain is almost never completely flat,

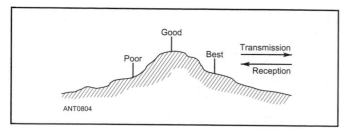

Figure 4.5 — Propagation conditions are generally best when the antenna is located slightly below the top of a hill on the side facing the distant station. Communication is poor when there is a sharp rise immediately in front of the antenna in the direction of communication.

however, and variations along the way may add to or subtract from the distance for reliable communication. Remember that energy is absorbed, reflected or scattered in many ways in nearly all communication situations. The formula or the chart will be a good guide for estimating the potential radius of coverage for a VHF FM repeater, assuming the users are mobile or portable with simple, omnidirectional antennas. Coverage with optimum home-station equipment, high-gain directional arrays, and SSB or CW is quite a different matter. A much more detailed method for estimating coverage on frequencies above 50 MHz is given later in this chapter.

For maximum use of the ordinary space wave it is important to have the antenna as high as possible above nearby buildings, trees, wires and surrounding terrain. A hill that rises above the rest of the countryside is a good location for an amateur station of any kind, and particularly so for extensive coverage on the frequencies above 50 MHz. The highest point on such an eminence is not necessarily the best location for the antenna. In the example shown in **Figure 4.5**, the hilltop would be a good site in all directions. But if maximum performance to the right is the objective, a point just below the crest might do better. This would involve a trade-off with reduced coverage in the opposite direction. Conversely, an antenna situated on the left side, lower down the hill, might do well to the left, but almost certainly would be inferior in performance to the right.

Selection of a home site for its radio potential is a complex business, at best. A VHF enthusiast dreams of the highest hill. The DX-minded HF ham may be more attracted by a dry spot near a salt marsh. A wide saltwater horizon, especially from a high cliff, just smells of DX. In shopping for ham radio real estate, a mobile or portable rig for the frequencies you're most interested in can provide useful clues. Two other helpful techniques to assess ham radio real estate are Google Earth (**www.google.com/earth/index.html**) and topographic maps (check with your local public library or go online for various sources of these maps).

4.1.6 ANTENNA POLARIZATION

If effective communication over long distances were the only consideration, we might be concerned mainly with radiation of energy at the lowest possible angle above the horizon. However, being engaged in a residential avocation

often imposes practical restrictions on our antenna projects. As an example, our 1.8 and 3.5-MHz bands are used primarily for short-distance communication because they serve that purpose with antennas that are not difficult or expensive to put up. Out to a few hundred miles, simple wire antennas for these bands do well, even though their radiation is mostly at high angles above the horizon. Vertical systems might be better for long-distance use, but they require extensive ground systems for good performance.

Horizontal antennas that radiate well at low angles are most easily erected for 7 MHz and higher frequencies — horizontal wires and arrays are almost standard practice for work on 7 through 29.7 MHz. Vertical antennas, such as a single omnidirectional antenna of multiband design, are also used in this frequency range. An antenna of this type may be a good solution to the space problem for a city dweller on a small lot, or even for the resident of an apartment building.

High-gain antennas are almost always used at 50 MHz and higher frequencies, and most of them are horizontal. The principal exception is mobile communication with FM through repeaters, discussed in the chapter **Repeater Antenna Systems**. The height question is answered easily for VHF enthusiasts — the higher the better.

The theoretical and practical effects of height above ground at HF are treated in detail in the chapter **Effects of Ground**. Note that it is the height in *wavelengths* that is important — a good reason to think in the metric system, rather than in feet and inches.

In working locally on any amateur frequency band, best results will be obtained with the same polarization at both stations, except on rare occasions when polarization shift is caused by terrain obstructions or reflections from buildings. Where such a shift is observed, mostly above 100 MHz or so, horizontal polarization tends to work better than vertical. This condition is found primarily on short paths, so it is not too important.

Although it has been stated by many that HF long distance communication by way of the ionosphere produces random polarization, the truth is there is more order to polarization than is generally acknowledged. The reason for this is the Earth's magnetic field.

The ionosphere, being immersed in this magnetic field, is a bi-refracting medium. That is, when an electromagnetic wave enters the ionosphere, it couples into two characteristic waves. These waves are the *ordinary wave* and the *extraordinary wave*.

On our HF bands (3.5 MHz and higher), both of these waves are circularly polarized and propagate with very similar ionospheric absorption. Thus the use of a horizontally-polarized or vertically-polarized antenna on HF is moot with respect to polarization, as one or the other or both characteristic waves will propagate. This also suggests that a station using a circularly-polarized antenna will have a 3 dB advantage over a station using a linearly-polarized antenna (horizontal or vertical). Additionally fading may be negated to a large extent through the use of a circularly-polarized antenna. Three good articles to read for practical experience with circularly-polarized antennas are "The Enhancement of HF Signals by Polarization Control" by B. Sykes, G2HCG, in the November 1990 issue of *Communications Quarterly*, "Polarization Diversity Aerials" by George Messenger, K6CT, (SK) in the December 1962 issue of the *RSGB Bulletin*, and "So We Bought A Spiralray" by Joe Marshall, WA4EPY, in the January 1965 issue of *73 Magazine*.

On 1.8 MHz two interesting effects occur because the operating frequency is close to the ionosphere's electron gyro-frequency. First, the extraordinary wave suffers significantly higher absorption than the ordinary wave, so for all intents and purposes only one characteristic wave propagates on 160 meters. Second, the ordinary wave is highly elliptical, approaching linear polarization. For stations at mid to high northern latitudes, vertical polarization couples the most energy into the ordinary wave — thus vertical polarization is generally the best way to go on Top Band. But other effects, like disturbances to propagation or high angle modes, sometimes dictate horizontal polarization. This is the origin of the oft-repeated statement on 160 meters that "you can't have enough antennas on Top Band."

Polarization Factors Above 50 MHz

In most VHF communication over short distances, the polarization of the space wave tends to remain constant. Polarization discrimination is high, usually in excess of 20 dB, so the same polarization should be used at both ends of the circuit. Horizontal, vertical and circular polarization all have certain advantages above 50 MHz, so there has never been complete standardization on any one of them.

Horizontal systems are popular, in part because they tend to reject man-made noise, much of which is vertically polarized. There is some evidence that vertical polarization shifts to horizontal in hilly terrain, more readily than horizontal shifts to vertical. With large arrays, horizontal systems may be easier to erect, and they tend to give higher signal strengths over irregular terrain, if any difference is observed.

Practically all work with VHF mobiles is now handled with vertical systems. For use in a VHF repeater system, the vertical antenna can be designed to have gain without losing the desired omnidirectional quality. In the mobile station a small vertical whip has obvious aesthetic advantages. Often a telescoping whip used for broadcast reception can be pressed into service for the 144-MHz FM rig. A car-top mount is preferable, but the broadcast whip is a practical compromise. Tests with at least one experimental repeater have shown that horizontal polarization can give a slightly larger service area, but mechanical advantages of vertical systems have made them the almost unanimous choice in VHF FM communication. Except for the repeater field, horizontal is the standard VHF system almost everywhere.

In communication over the Earth-Moon-Earth (EME) route the polarization picture is blurred, as might be expected with such a diverse medium. If the moon were a flat target, we could expect a 180° phase shift from the moon reflection process. But it is not flat. This plus the moon's *libration* (its slow oscillation, as viewed from the Earth), and the fact that waves must travel both ways through the Earth's entire atmosphere and magnetic field, provide other variables that confuse the phase and polarization issue. Building a huge array that will track the moon and give gains in excess of 20 dB is enough of a task that most EME enthusiasts tend to take their chances with phase and polarization problems. Where rotation of the element plane has been tried it has helped to stabilize signal levels, but it is not widely employed.

4.1.7 LONG-DISTANCE PROPAGATION OF VHF WAVES

The wave energy of VHF stations does not simply disappear once it reaches the radio horizon. It is scattered, but it can be heard to some degree for hundreds of miles, well beyond line-of-sight range. Everything on Earth, and in the regions of space up to at least 100 miles, is a potential forward-scattering agent.

Tropospheric scatter is always with us. Its effects are often hidden, masked by more effective propagation modes on the lower frequencies. But beginning in the VHF range, scatter from the lower atmosphere extends the reliable range markedly if we make use of it. Called *troposcatter*, this is what produces that nearly flat portion of the curves that will be described later (in the section where you can compute reliable VHF coverage range). With a decent station, you can consistently make troposcatter contacts out to 300 miles on the VHF and even UHF bands, especially if you don't mind weak signals and something less than 99% reliability. As long ago as the early 1950s, VHF enthusiasts found that VHF contests could be won with high power, big antennas and a good ear for signals deep in the noise. They still can.

Ionospheric scatter works much the same as the tropo version, except that the scattering medium is higher up, mainly the E region of the ionosphere but with some help from the D and F layers too. Ionospheric scatter is useful mainly above the MUF, so its useful frequency range depends on geography, time of day, season, and the state of the Sun. With near maximum legal power, good antennas and quiet locations, ionospheric scatter can fill in the skip zone with marginally readable signals scattered from ionized trails of meteors, small areas of random ionization, cosmic dust, satellites and whatever may come into the antenna patterns at 50 to 150 miles or so above the Earth. It's mostly an E-layer business, so it works all E-layer distances. Good antennas and keen ears help.

Transequatorial propagation (TE) was an amateur 50-MHz discovery in the years 1946-1947. (See Bibliography entry for *Beyond Line of Sight* by Pocock.) Amateurs of all continents observed it almost simultaneously on three separate north-south paths. These amateurs tried to communicate at 50 MHz, even though the predicted MUF was around 40 MHz for the favorable daylight hours. The first success came at night, when the MUF was thought to be even lower. A remarkable research program inaugurated by amateurs in Europe, Cyprus, Zimbabwe and South Africa eventually provided technically sound theories to explain the then-unknown mode.

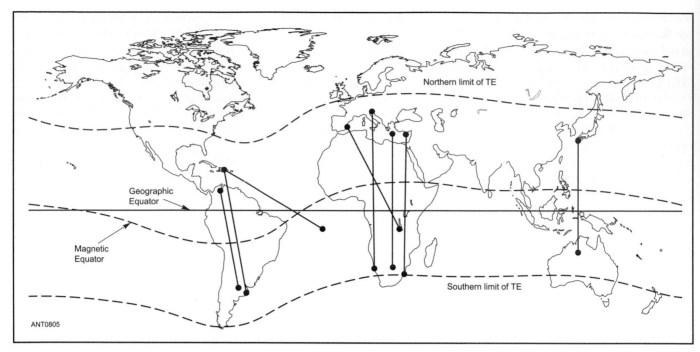

Figure 4.6 — Transequatorial spread-F propagation takes place between stations equidistant across the geomagnetic equator. Distances up to 8000 km (5000 miles) are possible on 28 through 432 MHz. Note that the geomagnetic equator is considerably south of the geographic equator in the Western Hemisphere.

It has been known for years that the MUF is higher and less seasonally variable on transequatorial circuits, but the full extent of the difference was not learned until amateur work brought it to light. As will be explained in a later section in more detail, the ionosphere over equatorial regions is higher, thicker and more dense than elsewhere. Because of its more constant exposure to solar radiation, the equatorial belt has high nighttime-MUF possibilities. TE can often work marginally at 144 MHz, and even at 432 MHz on occasion. The potential MUF varies with solar activity, but not to the extent that conventional F-layer propagation does. It is a late-in-the-day mode, taking over about when normal F-layer propagation goes out.

The TE range is usually within about 4000 km (2500 miles) either side of the geomagnetic equator. The Earth's magnetic axis is tilted with respect to the geographical axis, so the TE belt appears as a curving band on conventional flat maps of the world. See **Figure 4.6**. As a result, TE has a different latitude coverage in the Americas from that from Europe to Africa. The TE belt just reaches into the southern continental US. Stations in Puerto Rico, Mexico and even the northern parts of South America encounter the mode more often than those in favorable US areas. It is no accident that TE was discovered as a result of 50-MHz work in Mexico City and Buenos Aires.

Within its optimum regions of the world, the TE mode extends the usefulness of the 50-MHz band far beyond that of conventional F-layer propagation, since the practical TE MUF can be up to 1.5 times that of normal F2 based on analysis with ray tracing. Both its seasonal and diurnal characteristics are extensions of what is considered normal for 50-MHz propagation. In that part of the Americas south of about 20° North latitude, the existence of TE affects the whole character of band usage, especially in years of high solar activity.

Weather Effects on VHF/UHF Tropospheric Propagation

Changes in the dielectric constant of the medium can affect propagation. Varied weather patterns over most of the Earth's surface can give rise to boundaries between air masses of very different temperature and humidity characteristics. These boundaries can be anything from local anomalies to air-circulation patterns of continental proportions.

Under stable weather conditions, large air masses can retain their characteristics for hours or even days at a time. See **Figure 4.7**. Stratified warm dry air over cool moist air, flowing slowly across the Great Lakes region to the Atlantic Seaboard, can provide the medium for east-west communication on 144 MHz and higher amateur frequencies over as much as 1200 miles. More common, however, are communication distances of 400 to 600 miles under such conditions.

A similar inversion along the Atlantic Seaboard as a result of a tropical storm air-circulation pattern may bring VHF and UHF openings extending from the Maritime Provinces of Canada to the Carolinas. Propagation across the Gulf of Mexico, sometimes with very high signal levels, enlivens the VHF scene in coastal areas from Florida to Texas. The California coast, from below the San Francisco Bay Area to Mexico, is blessed with a similar propagation aid during the warmer months. Tropical storms moving west, across the Pacific below the Hawaiian Islands, may provide a transpacific long-distance VHF medium. Amateurs first exploited this on 144, 220 and 432 MHz, in 1957. It has been used fairly often in the summer months since, although not yearly.

The examples of long-haul work cited above may occur infrequently, but lesser extensions of the minimum operating range are available almost daily. Under minimum conditions there may be little more than increased signal strength over paths that are workable at any time.

There is a diurnal effect in temperate climates. At sunrise the air aloft is warmed more rapidly than that near the Earth's surface, and as the Sun goes lower late in the day the upper air is kept warm, while the ground cools. In fair, calm weather such sunrise and sunset *temperature inversions* can improve signal strength over paths beyond line of sight as much as 20 dB over levels prevailing during the hours of high sun. The diurnal inversion may also extend the operating range for a given strength by some 20 to 50%. If you would be happy with a new VHF antenna, try it first around sunrise!

There are other short-range effects of local atmospheric and topographical conditions. Known as *subsidence*, the flow of cool air down into the bottom of a valley, leaving warm air aloft, is a familiar summer-evening pleasure. The daily inshore-offshore wind shift along a seacoast in summer sets up daily inversions that make coastal areas highly favored as VHF sites. Ask any jealous 144-MHz operator who lives more than a few miles inland.

Tropospheric effects can show up at any time, in any season. Late spring and early fall are the most favored periods, although a winter warming trend can produce strong and stable inversions that work VHF magic almost equal to that of the more familiar spring and fall events.

Regions where the climate is influenced by large bodies of water enjoy the greatest degree of tropospheric bending. Hot, dry desert areas see little of it, at least in the forms described above.

Tropospheric Ducting

Tropospheric propagation of VHF and UHF waves can influence signal levels at all distances from purely local to something beyond 4000 km (2500 miles). The outer limits are not well known. At the risk of over simplification, we will divide the modes into two classes — extended local and long distance. This concept must be modified depending on the frequency under consideration, but in the VHF range the extended-local effect gives way to a form of propagation much like that of microwaves in a waveguide, called *ducting*. The transition distance is ordinarily somewhere around 200 miles. The difference lies in whether the atmospheric condition producing the bending is localized or continental in scope. Remember, we're concerned here with frequencies in the VHF range, and perhaps up to 500 MHz. At 10 GHz, for example, the scale is much smaller.

In VHF propagation beyond a few hundred miles, more than one weather front is probably involved, but the wave is propagated between the inversion layers and ground, in the main. On long paths over the ocean (two notable examples are California to Hawaii and Ascension Island to Brazil), propagation is likely to be between two atmospheric layers. On such circuits the communicating station antennas must be in the duct, or capable of propagating strongly into it. Here again, we see that the positions and radiation angles of the

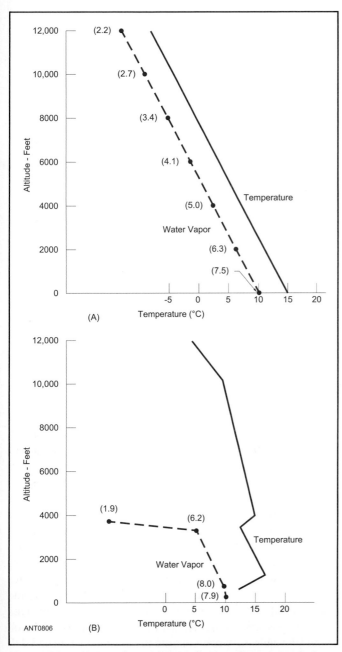

Figure 4.7 — Upper air conditions that produce extended-range communication on the VHF bands. At the top is shown the US Standard Atmosphere temperature curve. The humidity curve (dotted) is what would result if the relative humidity were 70%, from ground level to 12,000 feet elevation. There is only slight refraction under this standard condition. At the bottom is shown a sounding that is typical of marked refraction of VHF waves. Figures in parentheses are the "mixing ratio" — grams of water vapor per kilogram of dry air. Note the sharp break in both curves at about 3500 feet.

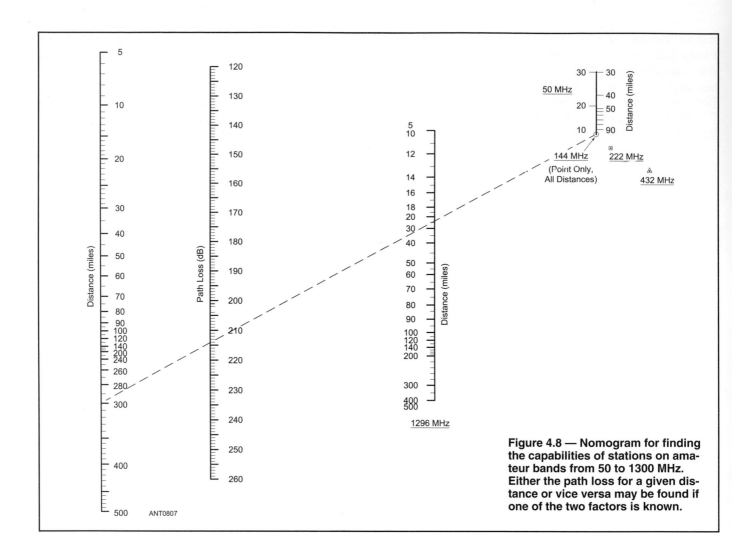

Figure 4.8 — Nomogram for finding the capabilities of stations on amateur bands from 50 to 1300 MHz. Either the path loss for a given distance or vice versa may be found if one of the two factors is known.

antennas are important. As with microwaves in a waveguide, the low-frequency limit for the duct is critical. In long-distance ducting it is also very variable. Airborne equipment has shown that duct capability exists well down into the HF region in the stable atmosphere west of Ascension Island. Some contacts between Hawaii and Southern California on 50 MHz are believed to have been by way of tropospheric ducts. Probably all contact over these paths on 144 MHz and higher bands is because of duct propagation.

Amateurs have played a major part in the discovery and eventual explanation of tropospheric propagation. In recent years they have shown that, contrary to beliefs widely held in earlier times, long-distance communication using tropospheric modes is possible to some degree on all amateur frequencies from 50 to at least 10,000 MHz.

4.1.8 RELIABLE VHF COVERAGE

In the preceding sections we discussed means by which amateur bands above 50 MHz may be used intermittently for communication far beyond the visual horizon. In emphasizing distance we should not neglect a prime asset of the VHF band: reliable communication over relatively short distances. The VHF region is far less subject to disruption of local

communication than are frequencies below 30 MHz. Since much amateur communication is essentially local in nature, our VHF assignments can carry a great load, and such use of the VHF bands helps solve interference problems on lower frequencies.

Because of age-old ideas, misconceptions about the coverage obtainable in our VHF bands persist. This reflects the thoughts that VHF waves travel only in straight lines, except when the DX modes described above happen to be present. However, let us survey the picture in the light of modern wave-propagation knowledge and see what the bands above 50 MHz are good for on a day-to-day basis, ignoring the anomalies that may result in extensions of normal coverage.

It is possible to predict with fair accuracy how far you should be able to work consistently on any VHF or UHF band, provided a few simple facts are known. The factors affecting operating range can be reduced to graph form, as described in this section. The information was originally published in November 1961 *QST* by D. W. Bray, K2LMG, (see the Bibliography at the end of this chapter).

To estimate your station's capabilities, two basic numbers must be determined: station gain and path loss. Station gain is made up of seven factors: receiver sensitivity, transmitted

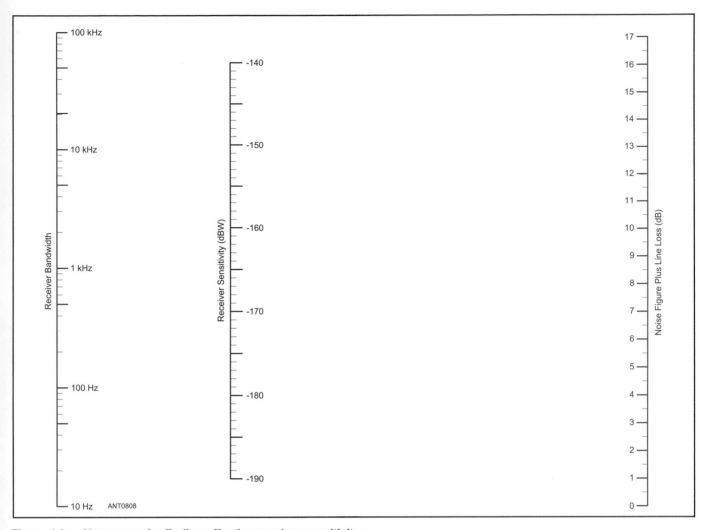

Figure 4.9 — Nomogram for finding effective receiver sensitivity.

power, receiving antenna gain, receiving antenna height gain, transmitting antenna gain, transmitting antenna height gain and required signal-to-noise ratio. This looks complicated but it really boils down to an easily made evaluation of receiver, transmitter, and antenna performance. The other number, path loss, is readily determined from the nomogram, **Figure 4.8**. This gives path loss over smooth Earth, for 99% reliability.

For 50 MHz, lay a straightedge from the distance between stations (left side) to the appropriate distance at the right side. For 1296 MHz, use the full scale, right center. For 144, 222 and 432, use the dot in the circle, square or triangle, respectively. Example: At 300 miles the path loss for 144 MHz is 214 dB.

To be meaningful, the losses determined from this nomogram are necessarily greater than simple free-space path losses. As described in an earlier section, communication beyond line-of-sight distances involves propagation modes that increase the path attenuation with distance.

VHF/UHF Station Gain

The largest of the eight factors involved in station design is receiver sensitivity. This is obtainable from **Figure 4.9**, if you know the approximate receiver noise figure

and transmission-line loss. If you can't measure noise figure, assume 3 dB for 50 MHz, 5 for 144 or 222, 8 for 432 and 10 for 1296 MHz, if you know your equipment is working moderately well. These noise figures are well on the conservative side for modern solid-state receivers.

Line loss can be taken from information in the **Transmission Lines** chapter for the line in use, if the antenna system is fed properly. Lay a straightedge between the appropriate points at either side of Figure 4.9, to find effective receiver sensitivity in decibels below 1 watt (dBW). Use the narrowest bandwidth that is practical for the emission intended, with the receiver you will be using. For CW, an average value for effective work is about 500 Hz. Phone bandwidth can be taken from the receiver instruction manual, but it usually falls between 2.1 to 2.7 kHz.

Antenna gain is next in importance. Gains of amateur antennas are often exaggerated. For well-designed Yagis the gain (over isotropic) run close to 10 times the boom length in wavelengths. (Example: A 24-foot Yagi on 144 MHz is 3.6 wavelengths long; $3.6 \times 10 = 36$, and $10 \log_{10} 36 = 15.5$ dBi in free space.) Add 3 dB for stacking, where used properly. Add 4 dB more for ground reflection gain. This varies in amateur work, but averages out near this figure.

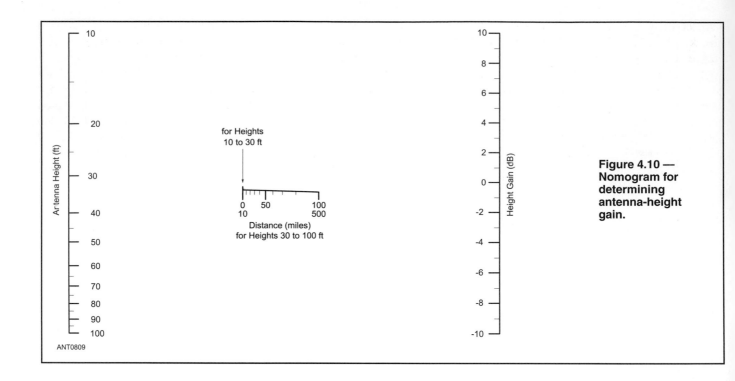

Figure 4.10 — Nomogram for determining antenna-height gain.

We have one more plus factor — antenna height gain, obtained from **Figure 4.10**. Note that this is greatest for short distances. The left edge of the horizontal center scale is for 0 to 10 miles, the right edge for 100 to 500 miles. Height gain for 10 to 30 feet is assumed to be zero. For 50 feet the height gain is 4 dB at 10 miles, 3 dB at 50 miles, and 2 dB at 100 miles. At 80 feet the height gains are roughly 8, 6 and 4 dB for these distances. Beyond 100 miles the height gain is nearly uniform for a given height, regardless of distance.

Transmitter power output must be stated in decibels above 1 watt. If you have 500 W output, add 10 log (500/1), or 27 dB, to your station gain. The transmission-line loss must be subtracted from the station gain. So must the required signal-to-noise ratio. The information is based on CW work, so the additional signal needed for other modes must be subtracted. Use a figure of 3 dB for SSB. Fading losses must be accounted for also. It has been shown that for distances beyond 100 miles, the signal will vary plus or minus about 7 dB from the average level, so 7 dB must be subtracted from the station gain for high reliability. For distances under 100 miles, fading diminishes almost linearly with distance. For 50 miles, use –3.5 dB for fading.

What It All Means

Add all the plus and minus factors to get the station gain. Use the final value to find the distance over which you can

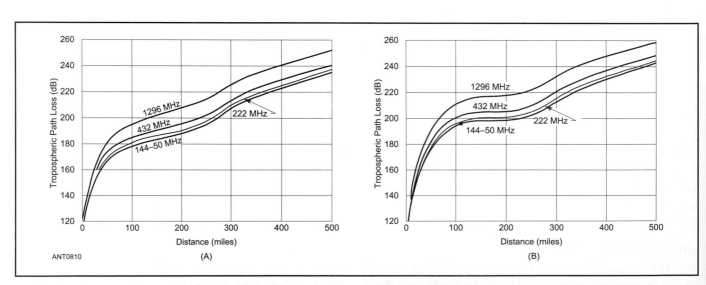

Figure 4.11 — Path loss versus distance for amateur frequencies above 50 MHz. At A are curves for 50% of the time; at B, for 99%. The curves at A are more representative of Amateur Radio requirements.

expect to work reliably from the nomogram, Figure 4.8. Or work it the other way around: Find the path loss for the distance you want to cover from the nomogram and then figure out what station changes will be needed to overcome it.

The significance of all this becomes more obvious when we see path loss plotted against frequency for the various bands, as in **Figure 4.11**. At the left this is done for 50% reliability. At the right is the same information for 99% reliability. For near-perfect reliability, a path loss of 195 dB (easily encountered at 50 or 144 MHz) is involved in 100-mile communication. But look at the 50% reliability curve: The same path loss takes us out to well over 250 miles. Few amateurs demand near-perfect reliability. By choosing our times, and by accepting the necessity for some repeats or occasional loss of signal, we can maintain communication out to distances far beyond those usually covered by VHF stations.

Working out a few typical amateur VHF station setups with these curves will show why an understanding of these factors is important to any user of the VHF spectrum. Note that path loss rises very steeply in the first 100 miles or so. This is no news to VHF operators; locals are very strong, but stations 50 or 75 miles away are much weaker. What happens beyond 100 miles is not so well known to many of us.

From the curves of Figure 4.11, we see that path loss levels off markedly at what is the approximate limit of working range for average VHF stations using wideband modulation modes. Work out the station gain for a 50-W station with an average receiver and antenna, and you'll find that it comes out around 180 dB. This means you'd have about a 100-mile working radius in average terrain, for good but not perfect reliability. Another 10 dB may extend the range to as much as 250 miles. Changing from wideband modes such as FM or AM phone to SSB and CW makes a major improvement in daily coverage on the VHF bands.

A bigger antenna, a higher one if your present beam is not at least 50 feet up, an increase in power to 500 W from 50 W, an improvement in receiver noise figure if it is presently poor — any of these things can make a big improvement in reliable coverage. Achieve all of them, and you will have very likely tripled your sphere of influence, thanks to that hump in the path-loss curves. This goes a long way toward explaining why using a 10-W packaged station with a small antenna, fun though it may be, does not begin to show what the VHF bands are really good for.

Terrain at VHF/UHF

The coverage figures derived from the above procedure are for average terrain. What of stations in mountainous country? Although an open horizon is generally desirable for the VHF station site, mountain country should not be considered hopeless. Help for the valley dweller often lies in the optical phenomenon known as *knife-edge diffraction*. A flashlight beam pointed at the edge of a partition does not cut off sharply at the partition edge, but is diffracted around it, partially illuminating the shadow area. A similar effect is observed with VHF waves passing over ridges; there is a shadow effect, but not a complete blackout. If the signal is strong where it strikes the mountain range, it will be heard well in the bottom of a valley on the far side. (See **The Effects of Ground** chapter for a more thorough discussion of the theory of diffraction.)

This is familiar to all users of VHF communications equipment who operate in hilly terrain. Where only one ridge lies in the way, signals on the far side may be almost as good as on the near side. Under ideal conditions (a very high and sharp-edged obstruction near the midpoint of a long-enough path so that signals would be weak over average terrain), knife-edge diffraction may yield signals even stronger than would be possible with an open path.

The obstruction must project into the radiation patterns of the antennas used. Often mountains that look formidable to the viewer are not high enough to have an appreciable effect, one way or the other. Since the normal radiation pattern from a VHF array is several degrees above the horizontal, mountains that are less than about three degrees above the horizon, as seen from the antenna, are missed by the radiation from the array. Moving the mountains out of the way would have substantially no effect on VHF signal strength in such cases.

Rolling terrain, where obstructions are not sharp enough to produce knife-edge diffraction, still does not exhibit a complete shadow effect. There is no complete barrier to VHF propagation — only attenuation, which varies widely as the result of many factors. Thus, even valley locations are usable for VHF communication. Good antenna systems, preferably as high as possible, the best available equipment, and above all, the willingness and ability to work with weak signals may make outstanding VHF work possible, even in sites that show little promise by casual inspection.

4.1.9 AURORAL PROPAGATION

The Earth has a *magnetosphere* or magnetic field surrounding it. NASA scientists have described the magnetosphere as a sort of protective "bubble" around the Earth that shields us from the solar wind. Under normal circumstances, there are lots of electrons and protons moving in our magnetosphere, traveling along magnetic lines of force that trap them and keep them in place, neither bombarding the earth nor escaping into outer space.

Sudden bursts of activity on the Sun are sometimes accompanied by the ejection of charged particles, often from so-called *Coronal Mass Ejections (CME)* because they originate from the Sun's outer coronal region. These charged particles can interact with the magnetosphere, compressing and distorting it. If the orientation of the magnetic field contained in a large blast of solar wind or in a CME is aligned opposite to that of the Earth's magnetic field, the magnetic bubble can partially collapse and the particles normally trapped there can be deposited into the Earth's atmosphere along magnetic lines near the North or South poles. This produces a visible or radio *aurora*. An aurora is visible if the time of entry is after dark.

The visible aurora is, in effect, fluorescence at E-layer height — a curtain of ions capable of refracting radio waves in the frequency range above about 20 MHz. D-region absorption increases on lower frequencies during auroras. The exact frequency ranges depend on many factors: time, season, position with relation to the Earth's auroral regions, and the level of solar activity at the time, to name a few.

The auroral effect on VHF waves is another amateur discovery, this one dating back to the 1930s. The discovery came coincidentally with improved transmitting and receiving techniques then. The returning signal is diffused in frequency by the diversity of the auroral curtain as a refracting (scattering) medium. The result is a modulation of a CW signal, from just a slight burbling sound to what is best described as a "keyed roar." Before SSB took over in VHF work, voice was all but useless for auroral paths. A sideband signal suffers, too, but its narrower bandwidth helps to retain some degree of understandability. Distortion induced by a given set of auroral conditions increases with the frequency in use. Fifty-MHz signals are much more intelligible than those on 144 MHz on the same path at the same time. On 144 MHz, CW is almost mandatory for effective auroral communication.

The number of auroras that can be expected per year varies with the geomagnetic latitude. Drawn with respect to the Earth's magnetic poles instead of the geographical ones, these latitude lines in the US tilt upward to the northwest. For example, Portland, Oregon, is 2° farther north (geographic latitude) than Portland, Maine. The Maine city's geomagnetic latitude line crosses the Canadian border before it gets as far west as its Oregon namesake. In terms of auroras intense enough to produce VHF propagation results, Portland, Maine, is likely to see about 10 times as many per year. Oregon's auroral prospects are more like those of southern New Jersey or central Pennsylvania.

The antenna requirements for auroral work are mixed. High gain helps, but the area of the aurora yielding the best returns sometimes varies rapidly, so sharp directivity can be a disadvantage. So could a very low radiation angle, or a beam pattern very sharp in the vertical plane. Experience indicates that few amateur antennas are sharp enough in either plane to present a real handicap. The beam heading for maximum signal can change, however, so a bit of scanning in azimuth may turn up some interesting results. A very large array, such as is commonly used for moonbounce (with azimuth-elevation control), should be worthwhile.

The incidence of auroras, their average intensity, and their geographical distribution as to visual sightings and VHF propagation effects all vary to some extent with solar activity. Auroral activity is generated by CMEs (most prevalent at the peak of a solar cycle) and coronal holes (most prevalent during the declining phase of a solar cycle), with the maximum auroral activity tending to occur from coronal holes. Like sporadic E, an unusual auroral opening can come at any season. There is a marked diurnal swing in the number of auroras. Favored times are late afternoon and early evening, late evening through early morning, and early afternoon, in about that order. Major auroras often start in early afternoon and carry through to early morning the next day.

4.2 HF SKY-WAVE PROPAGATION

As described earlier, the term *ground wave* is commonly applied to propagation that is confined to the Earth's lower atmosphere. Now we will use the term *sky wave* to describe modes of propagation that use the Earth's ionosphere. First, however, we must examine how the Earth's ionosphere is affected by the Sun.

4.2.1 THE ROLE OF THE SUN

Everything that happens in radio propagation, as with all life on Earth, is the result of radiation from the Sun. The variable nature of radio propagation here on Earth reflects the ever-changing intensity of ultraviolet and X-ray radiation, the primary ionizing agents in solar energy. Every day, solar nuclear reactions are turning hydrogen into helium, releasing an unimaginable blast of energy into space in the process. The total power radiated by the Sun is estimated at 4×10^{23} kW — that is, the number four followed by 23 zeroes. At its surface, the Sun emits about 60 *megawatts* per square meter. That is a very potent transmitter!

The Solar Wind

The Sun is constantly ejecting material from its surface in all directions into space, making up the so-called *solar wind*. Under relatively quiet solar conditions the solar wind blows around 200 miles per second — 675,000 miles per hour — taking away about two million tons of solar material each second from the Sun. You needn't worry — the Sun is not going to shrivel up anytime soon. It's big enough that it will take many billions of years before that happens.

A 675,000 mile/hour wind sounds like a pretty stiff breeze, doesn't it? Lucky for us, the density of the material in the solar wind is very small by the time it has been spread out into interplanetary space. Scientists calculate that the density of the particles in the solar wind is less than that of the best vacuum they've ever achieved on Earth. Despite the low density of the material in the solar wind, the effect on the Earth, especially its magnetic field, is very significant.

Before the advent of sophisticated satellite sensors, the Earth's magnetic field was considered to be fairly simple, modeled as if the Earth were a large bar magnet. The axis of this hypothetical bar magnet is oriented about 11° away from the geographic north-south pole. We now know that the solar wind alters the shape of the Earth's magnetic field significantly, compressing it on the side facing the Sun and elongating it on the other side — in the same manner as the tail of a comet is stretched out radially in its orientation from the Sun. In fact, the solar wind is also responsible for the shape of a comet's tail.

Partly because of the very nature of the nuclear reactions going on at the Sun itself, but also because of variations in the speed and direction of the solar wind, the interactions between the Sun and our Earth are incredibly complex. Even scientists who have studied the subject for years do not completely understand everything that happens on the Sun. Later in this chapter, we'll investigate the effects of the solar wind when conditions on the Sun are *not* "quiet." As far as amateur HF skywave propagation is concerned, the results of disturbed conditions on the Sun are not generally beneficial.

Sunspots

The most readily observed characteristic of the Sun, other than its blinding brilliance, is its tendency to have grayish black blemishes, seemingly at random times and at random places, on its fiery surface. (See **Figure 4.12**.) There are written records of naked-eye sightings of *sunspots* in the Orient back to more than 2000 years ago. As far as is known, the first indication that sunspots were recognized as part of the Sun was the result of observations by Galileo in the early 1600s, not long after he developed one of the first practical telescopes.

Galileo also developed the projection method for observing the Sun safely, but probably not before he had suffered

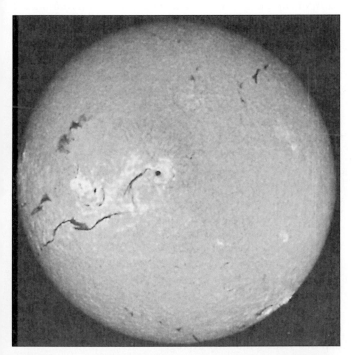

Figure 4.12 — Much more than sunspots can be seen when the sun is viewed through selective optical filters. This photo was taken through a hydrogen-alpha filter that passes a narrow light segment at 6562 angstroms. The bright patches are active areas around and often between sunspots. Dark irregular lines are filaments of activity having no central core. Faint magnetic field lines are visible around a large sunspot group near the disc center. (Photo courtesy of Sacramento Peak Observatory, Sunspot, New Mexico).

severe eye damage by trying to look at the Sun directly. (He was blind in his last years.) His drawings of sunspots, indicating their variable nature and position, are the earliest such record known to have been made. His reward for this brilliant work was immediate condemnation by church authorities of the time, which probably set back progress in learning more about the Sun for generations.

The systematic study of solar activity began about 1750, so a fairly reliable record of sunspot numbers goes back that far. (There are some gaps in the early data.) The record shows clearly that the Sun is always in a state of change. It never looks exactly the same from one day to the next. The most obvious daily change is the movement of visible activity centers (sunspots or groups thereof) across the solar disc, from east to west, at a constant rate. This movement was soon found to be the result of the rotation of the Sun, at a rate of approximately four weeks for a complete round. The average is about 27.5 days, the Sun's *synodic* rotation speed, viewed from the perspective of the Earth, which is also moving around the Sun in the same direction as the Sun's rotation.

Sunspot Numbers

Since the earliest days of systematic observation, our traditional measure of solar activity has been based on a count of sunspots. In these hundreds of years we have learned that the average number of spots goes up and down in cycles very roughly approximating a sine wave. In 1848, a method was introduced for the daily measurement of sunspot numbers. That method, which is still used today, was devised by the Swiss astronomer Johann Rudolph Wolf. The observer counts the total number of spots visible on the face of the Sun and the number of groups into which they are clustered, because neither quantity alone provides a satisfactory measure of sunspot activity. The observer's sunspot number for that day is computed by multiplying the number of groups he sees by 10, and then adding to this value the number of individual spots. Where possible, sunspot data collected prior to 1848 have been converted to this system.

As can readily be understood, results from one observer to another can vary greatly, since measurement depends on the capability of the equipment in use and on the stability of the Earth's atmosphere at the time of observation, as well as on the experience of the observer. A number of observatories around the world cooperate in measuring solar activity. A weighted average of the data is used to determine the *International Sunspot Number* or ISN for each day. (Amateur astronomers can approximate the determination of ISN values by multiplying their values by a correction factor determined empirically.)

A major step forward was made with the development of various methods for observing narrow portions of the Sun's spectrum. Narrowband light filters that can be used with any good telescope perform a visual function very similar to the aural function of a sharp filter added to a communications receiver. This enables the observer to see the actual area of the Sun doing the radiating of the ionizing energy, in addition to the sunspots, which are more a by-product than a cause. The photo of Figure 4.12 was made through such a filter. Studies of the ionosphere with instrumented probes, and later with satellites, manned and unmanned, have added greatly to our knowledge of the effects of the Sun on radio communication.

Daily sunspot counts are recorded, and monthly and yearly averages determined. The averages are used to see trends and observe patterns. Sunspot records were formerly kept in Zurich, Switzerland, and the values were known as *Zurich Sunspot Numbers*. They were also known as Wolf sunspot numbers. The official international sunspot numbers are now compiled at the Sunspot Index Data Center in Bruxelles, Belgium.

The yearly means (averages) of sunspot numbers from 1700 through 2002 are plotted in **Figure 4.13**. The cyclic nature of solar activity becomes readily apparent from this graph. The duration of the cycles varies from 9.0 to 12.7 years, but averages approximately 11.1 years, usually referred to as the 11-year solar cycle. The first complete cycle to be observed systematically began in 1755, and is numbered Cycle 1. Solar cycle numbers thereafter are consecutive. Cycle 23 began in October 1996 and peaked in April 2000. When this edition was prepared in 2011, we were in Cycle 24.

The "Quiet" Sun

For more than 60 years it has been well known that radio propagation phenomena vary with the number and size of sunspots, and also with the position of sunspots on the surface of the Sun. There are daily and seasonal variations in the Earth's ionized layers resulting from changes in the amount of ultraviolet light received from the Sun. The 11-year sunspot cycle affects propagation conditions because there is a direct correlation between sunspot activity and ionization.

Activity on the surface of the Sun is changing continually. In this section we want to describe the activity of the so-called quiet Sun, meaning those times when the Sun is not doing anything more spectacular than acting like a "normal" thermonuclear ball of flaming gases. The Sun and its effects on Earthly propagation can be described in statistical terms — that's what the 11-year solar cycle does. You may experience vastly different conditions on any particular day compared to what a long-term average would suggest.

An analogy may be in order here. Have you ever gazed into a relatively calm campfire and been surprised when suddenly a flaming ember or a large spark was ejected in your direction? The Sun can also do unexpected and sometimes very dramatic things. Disturbances of propagation conditions here on Earth are caused by disturbed conditions on the Sun. More on this later.

Individual sunspots may vary in size and appearance, or even disappear totally, within a single day. In general, larger active areas persist through several rotations of the Sun. Some active areas have been identified over periods up to about a year. Because of these continual changes in solar activity, there are continual changes in the state of the Earth's ionosphere and resulting changes in propagation conditions. A short-term burst of solar activity may trigger unusual propagation conditions here on Earth lasting for less than an hour.

Smoothed Sunspot Numbers (SSN)

Sunspot data are averaged or smoothed to remove the effects of short-term changes. The sunspot values used most often for correlating propagation conditions are *Smoothed Sunspot Numbers* (SSN), often called 12-month running average values. Data for 13 consecutive months are required to determine a smoothed sunspot number.

Long-time users have found that the upper HF bands are reliably open for propagation only when the average number of sunspots is above certain minimum levels. For example, between mid 1988 to mid 1992 during Cycle 22, the SSN stayed higher than 100. The 10 meter band was open then almost all day, every day, to some part of the world. However, by mid 1996, few if any sunspots showed up on the Sun and the 10 meter band consequently was rarely open. Even 15 meters, normally a workhorse DX band when solar activity is high, was closed most of the time during the low point in Cycle 22. So far as propagation on the upper HF bands is concerned, the higher the sunspot number, the better the conditions.

Each smoothed number is an average of 13 monthly means, centered on the month of concern. The 1st and 13th months are given a weight of 0.5. A monthly mean is simply the sum of the daily ISN values for a calendar month, divided by the number of days in that month. We would commonly call this value a monthly average.

This may all sound very complicated, but an example should clarify the procedure. Suppose we wished to calculate the smoothed sunspot number for June 1986. We would require monthly mean values for six months prior and six months after this month, or from December 1985 through December 1986. The monthly mean ISN values for these months are:

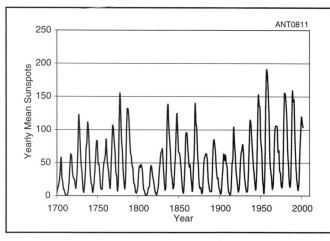

Figure 4.13 — Yearly means of smoothed sunspot numbers from data for 1700 through 2002. This plot clearly shows that sunspot activity takes place in cycles of approximately 11 years duration. There is also a longer-term periodicity in this plot, the Gleissberg 88-year cycle. Cycle 1, the first complete cycle to be examined by systematic observation, began in 1755.

Dec	85	17.3		Jul	86	18.1
Jan	86	2.5		Aug	86	7.4
Feb	86	23.2		Sep	86	3.8
Mar	86	15.1		Oct	86	35.4
Apr	86	18.5		Nov	86	15.2
May	86	13.7		Dec	86	6.8
Jun	86	1.1				

First we find the sum of the values, but using only one-half the amounts indicated for the first and 13th months in the listing. This value is 166.05. Then we determine the smoothed value by dividing the sum by 12: 166.05/12 = 13.8. (Values beyond the first decimal place are not warranted.) Thus, 13.8 is the smoothed sunspot number for June 1986. From this example, you can see that the smoothed sunspot number for a particular month cannot be determined until six months afterwards.

Generally the plots we see of sunspot numbers are averaged data. As already mentioned, smoothed numbers make it easier to observe trends and see patterns, but sometimes this data can be misleading. The plots tend to imply that solar activity varies smoothly, indicating, for example, that at the onset of a new cycle the activity just gradually increases. But this is definitely not so! On any one day, significant changes in solar activity can take place within hours, causing sudden band openings at frequencies well above the MUF values predicted from smoothed sunspot number curves. The durations of such openings may be brief, or they may recur for several days running, depending on the nature of the solar activity.

Solar Flux

Since the late 1940s an additional method of determining solar activity has been put to use — the measurement of *solar radio flux*. The quiet Sun emits radio energy across a broad frequency spectrum, with a slowly varying intensity. Solar flux is a measure of energy received per unit time, per unit area, per unit frequency interval. These radio fluxes, which originate from atmospheric layers high in the Sun's chromosphere and low in its corona, change gradually from day to day, in response to the activity causing sunspots. Thus, there is a degree of correlation between solar flux values and sunspot numbers.

One solar flux unit equals 10^{-22} joules per second per square meter per hertz. Solar flux values are measured daily at 2800 MHz (10.7 cm) at The Dominion Radio Astrophysical Observatory, Penticton, British Columbia, where daily data have been collected since 1991. (Prior to June 1991, the Algonquin Radio Observatory, Ontario, made the measurements.) Measurements are also made at other observatories around the world, at several frequencies. With some variation, the daily measured flux values increase with increasing frequency of measurement, to at least 15.4 GHz. The daily 2800 MHz Penticton value is sent to Boulder, Colorado, where it is incorporated into WWV propagation bulletins (see later section). Solar flux, just like a sunspot number, is a proxy (substitute) for the true ionizing radiation, as solar flux at 2800 MHz does not have enough energy to ionize any atmospheric constituent. Solar flux and sunspots numbers will be discussed later in the section on computer-prediction programs.

Correlating Sunspot Numbers and Solar Flux Values

Based on historical data, an exact mathematical relationship does not exist to correlate sunspot data and solar flux values. Comparing daily values yields almost no correlation. Comparing monthly mean values (often called monthly averages) produces a degree of correlation, but the spread in data is still significant. This is indicated in **Figure 4.14**, a scatter diagram plot of monthly mean sunspot numbers versus the monthly means of solar flux values adjusted to one astronomical unit. (This adjustment applies a correction for differences in distance between the Sun and the Earth at different times of the year.)

A closer correlation exists when smoothed (12-month running average) sunspot numbers are compared with

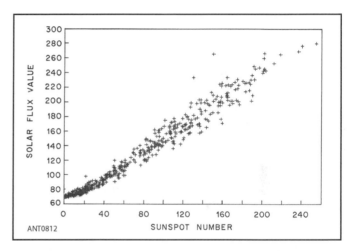

Figure 4.14 — Scatter diagram or X-Y plot of monthly mean sunspot numbers and monthly mean 2800-MHz solar flux values. Data values are from February 1947 through February 1987. Each "+" mark represents the intersection of data for a given month. If the correlation between sunspot number and flux values were consistent, all the marks would align to form a smooth curve.

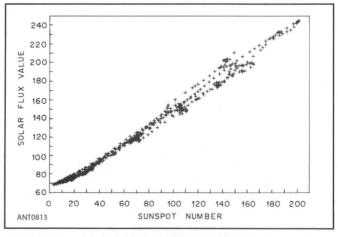

Figure 4.15 — Scatter diagram of smoothed, or 12-month running averages, sunspot numbers versus 2800-MHz solar flux values. The correlation of smoothed values is better than for monthly means, shown in Figure 4.14.

smoothed (12-month running average) solar flux values adjusted to one astronomical unit. A scatter diagram for smoothed data appears in **Figure 4.15**. Note how the plot points establish a better defined pattern in Figure 4.15. The correlation is still no better than a few percent, for records indicate a given smoothed sunspot number does not always correspond with the same smoothed solar flux value, and vice versa. **Table 4-1** illustrates some of the inconsistencies that exist in the historical data. Smoothed or 12-month running average values are shown.

Even though there is no precise mathematical relationship between sunspot numbers and solar flux values, it is helpful to have some way to convert from one to the other. The primary reason is that sunspot numbers are valuable as a long-term link with the past, but the great usefulness of solar flux values are their immediacy, and their direct bearing on our field of interest. (Remember, a smoothed sunspot number will not be calculated until six months after the fact.)

The following mathematical approximation has been derived to convert a smoothed sunspot number to a solar flux value.

$$F = 63.75 + 0.728\ S + 0.00089\ S^2 \qquad (3)$$

where

F = solar flux number
S = smoothed sunspot number

A graphic representation of this equation is given in **Figure 4.16**. Use this chart to make conversions graphically, rather than by calculations. With the graph, solar flux and sunspot number conversions can be made either way. The equation has been found to yield errors as great as 10% when historical data was examined. (Look at the August 1981 data in Table 4-1.) Therefore, conversions should be rounded to the nearest whole number, as additional decimal places are unwarranted. To make conversions from flux to sunspot number, the following approximation may be used.

$$S = 33.52\sqrt{85.12 + F} - 408.99 \qquad (4)$$

4.2.2 THE IONOSPHERE

There will be inevitable "gray areas" in our discussion of the Earth's atmosphere and the changes wrought in it by the Sun and by associated changes in the Earth's magnetic field. This is not a story that can be told in neat equations, or values carried out to a satisfying number of decimal places. The story must be told, and understood — with its well-known limitations — if we are to put up good antennas and make them serve us well.

Thus far in this chapter we have been concerned with what might be called our "above-ground living space" — that portion of the total atmosphere wherein we can survive without artificial breathing aids, or up to about 6 km (4 miles). The boundary area is a broad one, but life (and radio propagation) undergo basic changes beyond this zone. Somewhat farther out, but still technically within the Earth's atmosphere, the role of the Sun in the wave-propagation picture is a dominant one.

This is the *ionosphere* — a region where the air pressure is so low that free electrons and ions can move about for some time without getting close enough to recombine into neutral atoms. A radio wave entering this rarefied atmosphere, a region of relatively many free electrons, is affected in the same way as in entering a medium of different dielectric constant — its direction of travel is altered.

Ultraviolet (UV) radiation from the Sun is the primary cause of ionization in the outer regions of the atmosphere, the ones most important for HF propagation. However, there are other forms of solar radiation as well, including both hard and soft x-rays, gamma rays and extreme ultraviolet (EUV). The radiated energy breaks up or *photoionizes* atoms and molecules of atmospheric gases into electrons and positively

Table 4-1
Selected Historical Data Showing Inconsistent Correlation Between Sunspot Number and Solar Flux

Month	Smoothed Sunspot Number	Smoothed Solar Flux Value
May 1953	17.4	75.6
Sept 1965	17.4	78.5
Jul 1985	17.4	74.7
Jun 1969	106.1	151.4
Jul 1969	105.9	151.4
Dec 1982	94.6	151.4
Aug 1948	141.1	180.5
Oct 1959	141.1	192.3
Apr 1979	141.1	180.4
Aug 1981	141.1	203.3

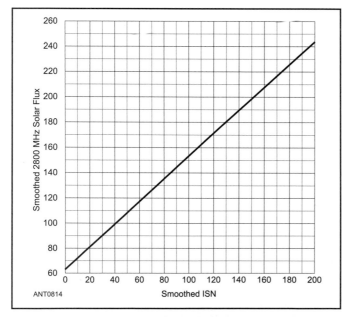

Figure 4.16 — Chart for conversions between smoothed International Sunspot Numbers and smoothed 2800-MHz solar flux. This curve is based on the mathematical approximation given in the text.

charged ions. The degree of ionization does not increase uniformly with distance from the Earth's surface. Instead there are relatively dense regions (layers) of ionization, each quite thick and more or less parallel to the Earth's surface, at fairly well-defined intervals outward from about 40 to 300 km (25 to 200 miles). These distinct layers are formed due to complex photochemical reactions of the various types of solar radiation with oxygen, ozone, nitrogen and nitrous oxide in the rarefied upper atmosphere.

Ionization is not constant within each layer, but tapers off gradually on either side of the maximum at the center of the layer. The total ionizing energy from the Sun reaching a given point, at a given time, is never constant, so the height and intensity of the ionization in the various regions will also vary. Thus, the practical effect on long-distance communication is an almost continuous variation in signal level, related to the time of day, the season of the year, the distance between the Earth and the Sun, and both short-term and long-term variations in solar activity. It would seem from all this that only the very wise or the very foolish would attempt to predict radio propagation conditions, but it is now possible to do so with a fair chance of success. It is possible to plan antenna designs, particularly the choosing of antenna heights, to exploit known propagation characteristics.

Ionospheric Layer Characteristics

The lowest known ionized region, called the *D layer* (or the *D region*), lies between 60 and 92 km (37 to 57 miles) above the Earth. In this relatively low and dense part of the atmosphere, atoms broken up into ions by sunlight recombine quickly, so the ionization level is directly related to sunlight. It begins at sunrise, peaks at local noon and disappears at sundown. When electrons in this dense medium are set in motion by a passing wave, collisions between particles are so frequent that a major portion of their energy may be used up as heat, as the electrons and disassociated ions recombine.

The probability of collisions depends on the distance an electron travels under the influence of the wave — in other words, on the wavelength. Thus, our 1.8- and 3.5-MHz bands, having the longest wavelengths, suffer the highest daytime absorption loss as they travel through the D layer, particularly for waves that enter the medium at the lowest angles. At times of high solar activity (peak years of the solar cycle) even waves entering the D layer vertically suffer almost total energy absorption around midday, making these bands almost useless for communication over appreciable distances during the hours of high sun. They "go dead" quickly in the morning, but come alive again the same way in late afternoon. The diurnal (daytime) D-layer effect is less at 7 MHz (though still marked), slight at 14 MHz and inconsequential on higher amateur frequencies.

The D region is ineffective in bending HF waves back to Earth, so its role in long-distance communication by amateurs is largely a negative one. It is the principal reason why our frequencies up through the 7-MHz band are useful mainly for short-distance communication during the high-sun hours.

The lowest portion of the ionosphere useful for long-distance communication by amateurs is the *E layer* (also known as the *E region*) about 100 to 115 km (62 to 71 miles) above the Earth. In the E layer, at intermediate atmospheric density, ionization varies with the Sun angle above the horizon, but solar ultraviolet radiation is not the sole ionizing agent. Solar X-rays and meteors entering this portion of the Earth's atmosphere also play a part. Ionization increases rapidly after sunrise, reaches maximum around noon local time, and drops off quickly after sundown. The minimum is after midnight, local time. As with the D layer, the E layer absorbs wave energy in the lower-frequency amateur bands when the Sun angle is high, around mid day. The other varied effects of E-region ionization will be discussed later.

Most of our long-distance communication capability stems from the tenuous outer reaches of the Earth's atmosphere known as the *F layer*. At heights above 100 miles, ions and electrons recombine more slowly, so the observable effects of the Sun develop more slowly. Also, the region holds its ability to reflect wave energy back to Earth well into the night. The *maximum usable frequency* (MUF) for F-layer propagation on east-west paths thus peaks just after noon at the midpoint, and the minimum occurs after midnight. We'll examine the subject of MUF in more detail later.

Judging what the F layer is doing is by no means that simple, however. The layer height may be from 160 to more than 500 km (100 to over 310 miles), depending on the season of the year, the latitudes, the time of day and, most capricious of all, what the Sun has been doing in the last few minutes and in perhaps the last three days before the attempt is made. The MUF between Eastern US and Europe, for example, has been anything from 7 to 70 MHz, depending on the conditions mentioned above, plus the point in the long-term solar-activity cycle at which the check is made.

During a summer day the F layer may split into two layers. The lower and weaker F_1 *layer*, about 160 km (100 miles) up, has only a minor role, acting more like the E than the F_2 *layer*. At night the F_1 region disappears and the F_2 region height drops somewhat.

Propagation information tailored to amateur needs is transmitted in all information bulletin periods by the ARRL Headquarters station, W1AW. Finally, solar and geomagnetic field data, transmitted hourly and updated eight times daily, are given in brief bulletins carried by the US Time Standard stations, WWV and WWVH, and also on Internet websites. But more on these services later.

Bending in the Ionosphere

The degree of bending of a wave path in an ionized layer depends on the density of the ionization and the length of the wave (inversely related to its frequency). The bending at any given frequency or wavelength will increase with increased ionization density and will bend away from the region of most-intense ionization. For a given ionization density, bending increases with wavelength (that is, it decreases with frequency).

Two extremes are thus possible. If the intensity of the ionization is sufficient and the frequency is low enough, even a wave entering the layer perpendicularly will be reflected back to Earth. Conversely, if the frequency is high enough or the ionization decreases to a low-enough density, a condition is reached where the wave angle is not affected enough by the ionosphere to cause a useful portion of the wave energy to return to the Earth. The frequency at which this occurs is called the *vertical-incidence critical frequency*. Each region in the ionosphere has a critical frequency associated with it, and this critical frequency will change depending on the date, time and state of the 11-year solar cycle.

Figure 4.17 shows a simplified graph of the electron density (in electrons per cubic meter) versus height in the ionosphere (in km) for a particular set of daytime and nighttime conditions. Free electrons are what return the signals you launch into the ionosphere back down to the Earth at some distance from your transmitter — the more free electrons in the ionosphere, the better propagation will be, particularly at higher frequencies.

Electron-density profiles are extremely complicated and vary greatly from one location to the next, depending on a bewildering variety of factors. Of course, this sheer variability makes it all the more interesting and challenging for hams to work each other on ionospheric HF paths!

The following discussion about sounding the ionosphere provides some background information about the scientific instruments used to decipher the highly intricate mechanisms behind ionospheric HF propagation.

4.2.3 SOUNDING THE IONOSPHERE

For many years scientists have *sounded* the ionosphere to determine its communication potential at various elevation angles and frequencies. The word "sound" stems from an old idea — one that has nothing to do with the audio waves that we can hear as "sounds." Long ago, sailors sounded the depths beneath their boats by dropping weighted ropes, calibrated in fathoms, into the water. In a similar fashion, the instrument used to probe the height of the ionosphere is called an *ionosonde*, or ionospheric sounder. It measures distances to various layers by launching a calibrated electronic signal directly up into the ionosphere.

Radar uses the same techniques as ionospheric sounding to detect targets such as airplanes. An ionosonde sends precisely timed pulses into the ionosphere over a range of MF and HF frequencies. The time of reception of an echo reflected from a region in the ionosphere is compared to the time of transmission. The time difference is multiplied by the speed of light to give the apparent distance that the wave has traveled from the transmitter to the ionosphere and back to the receiver. (It is an *apparent* or *virtual distance* because the speed of a wave slows very slightly in the ionosphere, just as the speed of propagation through any medium other than a vacuum slows down because of that medium.)

Another type of ionosonde sweeps the frequency of transmission, from low to high. This is called an "FM-CW," or more colorfully, a "chirpsounder." Since a received echo takes time to travel from the transmitter up to the reflection point and then back again to the receiver, the echo will be at a lower frequency than the still-moving frequency of the transmitter. The frequency difference is an indication of the height of the echo's reflection off the various ionospheric layers.

Vertical-Incidence Sounders

Most ionosondes are *vertical-incidence sounders*, bouncing their signals perpendicularly off the various ionized regions above it by launching signals straight up into the ionosphere. The ionosonde frequency is swept upwards until echos from the various ionospheric layers disappear, meaning that the critical frequencies for those layers have been exceeded, causing the waves to disappear into space.

Figure 4.18 shows a highly simplified ionogram for a

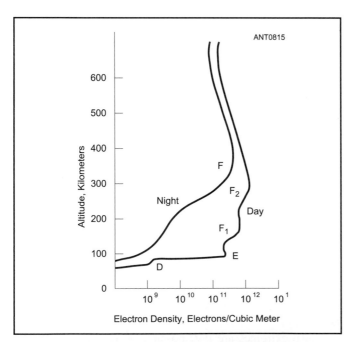

Figure 4.17 — Typical electron densities for nighttime and daytime conditions in the various ionospheric regions.

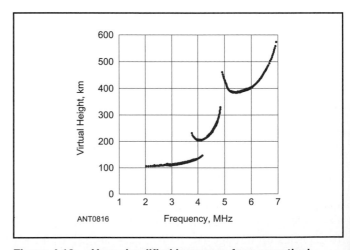

Figure 4.18 — Very simplified ionogram from a vertical-incidence sounder. The lowest trace is for the E region; the middle for the F₁ and the upper trace for the F₂ region.

typical vertical-incidence sounder. The echoes at the lowest height at the left-hand side of the plot show that the E region is about 100 km high. The F_1 region shown in the middle of the plot varies from about 200 to 330 km in this example, and the F_2 region ranges from just under 400 km to almost 600 km in height. [*In the amateur and professional literature, F_1 and F1 both refer to the same region — Ed.*] You can see that the F_1 and F_2 ionospheric regions take a "U" shape, indicating that the electron density varies throughout the layer. In this example, the peak in electron density is at a virtual height of the F_2 region of about 390 km, the lowest point in the F_2 curve.

Scientists can derive a lot of information from a vertical-incidence ionogram, including the critical frequencies for each region, where raising the frequency any higher causes the signals to disappear into space. In Figure 4.18, the E-region critical frequency (abbreviated f_oE) is about 4.1 MHz. The F_1-region critical frequency (abbreviated f_oF_1) is 4.8 MHz. The F2-region critical frequency (abbreviated f_oF_2) is this simplified diagram is 6.8 MHz.

The observant reader may well be wondering what the subscripted "o" in the abbreviations f_oE, f_oF_1 and f_oF_2 mean. The abbreviation "o" means "ordinary." When an electromagnetic wave is launched into the ionosphere, the Earth's magnetic field splits the wave into two independent waves — the "ordinary" (o) and the "extraordinary" (x) components. The ordinary wave reaches the same height in the ionosphere whether the Earth's magnetic field is present or not, and hence is called "ordinary." The extraordinary wave, however, is greatly affected by the presence of the Earth's magnetic field, in a very complex fashion.

Figure 4.19 shows an example of an actual ionogram

from the vertical Lowell Digisonde at Millstone Hill in Massachusetts, owned and operated by the Massachusetts Institute of Technology. This ionogram was made on June 18, 2000, and shows the conditions during a period of very high solar activity. The black-and-white rendition in Figure 4.19 of the actual color ionogram unfortunately loses some information. However, you can still see that a real ionogram is a lot more complicated looking than the simple simulated one in Figure 4.18.

The effects of noise and interference from other stations are shown by the many speckled dots appearing in the ionogram. The critical frequencies for various ionospheric layers are listed numerically at the left-hand side of the plot and the signal amplitudes are color-coded by the color bars at the right-hand side of the plot. The x-axis is the frequency, ranging from 1 to 11 MHz.

Compared to the simplified ionogram in Figure 4.18, Figure 4.19 shows another trace that appears on the plot from about 5.3 to 9.8 MHz, a trace shifted to the right of the darker ordinary trace. This second trace is the extraordinary (x) wave mentioned above. Since the x and o waves are created by the Earth's magnetic field, the difference in the ordinary and extraordinary traces is about ½ the *gyro frequency*, the frequency at which an electron will spiral down a particular magnetic field line. The electron gyro frequency is different at various places around the Earth, being related to the Earth's complicated and changing magnetic field. The extraordinary trace always has a higher critical frequency than the ordinary trace on a vertical-incidence ionogram, and it is considerably weaker than the ordinary trace, especially at frequencies below about 4 MHz because of heavy absorption.

The Big Picture Overhead

There are about 150 vertical-incidence ionosondes around the world. Ionosondes are located on land, even on a number of islands. There are gaps in sounder coverage, however, mainly over large expanses of open ocean. The compilation of all available vertical-incidence data from the worldwide network of ionospheric sounders results in global f_oF_2 maps, such as the map shown in **Figure 4.20**, a simulation from the highly sophisticated *PropLab Pro* computer program.

This simulation is for 1300 UTC, several hours after East Coast sunrise on Nov 25, 1998, with a high level of solar activity of 85 and a planetary A_p index of 5, indicating calm geomagnetic conditions. The contours of f_oF_2 peak over the ocean off the west coast of Africa at 38 MHz. Over the southern part of Africa, f_oF_2 peaks at 33 MHz.

These two "humps" in f_oF_2 form what is known as the "equatorial anomaly" and are caused by upwelling "fountains" of high electron concentration located in daylight areas about ±20° from the Earth's magnetic dip equator. The equatorial anomaly is important in transequatorial propagation. Those LU stations in Argentina that you can hear on 28 MHz from the US in the late afternoon, even during low portions of the solar cycle when other stations to the south are not

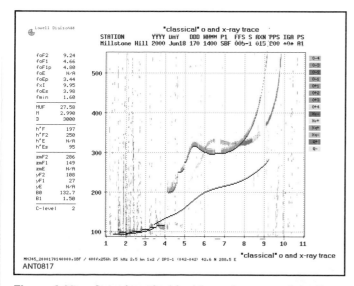

Figure 4.19 — Actual vertical-incidence ionogram from the Lowell Digisonde, owned and operated at Millstone Hill in Massachusetts by MIT. The ordinary (o) and extraordinary (x) traces are shown for heights greater than about 300 km. At the upper left are listed the computer-determined ionospheric parameters, such as f_oF_2 of 9.24 MHz and f_oF_1 at 4.66 MHz.

Table 4-2
Time and Frequency Stations Useful for Propagation Monitoring

Call	Frequency (MHz)	Location
WWV	2.5, 5, 10, 15, 20	Ft Collins, Colorado
WWVH	Same as WWV except 20	Kekaha, Kauai, Hawaii
CHU	3.330, 7.850, 14.670	Ottawa, Ontario, Canada
RID	5.004, 10.004, 15.004	Irkutsk, USSR*
RWM	4.996, 9.996, 14.996	Novosibirsk, USSR
VNG	2.5, 5, 8.634, 12.984, 16	Lyndhurst, Australia
BPM	2.5, 5, 10, 15	Xiang, China
BSF	5, 15	Taoyuan, Taiwan
LOL	5, 10, 15	Buenos Aires, Argentina

*The call, taken from an international table, may not be the one used during actual transmission. Locations and frequencies appear to be accurate as provided.

the Earth. Under usual conditions, the MUF will always be highest in the direction toward the Sun — to the east in the morning, to the south at noon (from northern latitudes), and to the west in the afternoon and evening.

For the strongest signals at the greatest distance, especially where the limited power levels of the Amateur Radio Service are concerned, it is important to work fairly near the MUF. It is at these frequencies where signals suffer the least loss. The MUFs can be estimated with sufficient accuracy by using the prediction charts that appear on the ARRL website (**www.arrl.org/propagation**) or by using a computer prediction program. The CD-ROM included with this book contains detailed and summary tables for more than 175 transmitting locations around the world. (See the section "When and Where HF Bands Are Open" later in this chapter.)

MUFs can also be observed with the use of a continuous coverage communications receiver. Frequencies up to the MUFs are in round-the-clock use today. When you "run out of signals" while tuning upward in frequency from your favorite ham band, you have a pretty good clue as to which band is going to work well, right then. Of course, it helps to know the direction to the transmitters whose signals you are hearing. Shortwave broadcasters know what frequencies to use, and you can hear them anywhere, if conditions are good. Time-and-frequency stations are also excellent indicators, since they operate around the clock. See **Table 4-2**. WWV is also a reliable source of propagation data, hourly, as discussed in more detail later in this chapter. And the NCDXF/IARU beacon system (**www.ncdxf.org/pages/beacons.html**) can give you a real-time picture of worldwide propagation on our 20, 17, 15, 12, and 10 meter bands

The value of operating near the MUF is two-fold. Under undisturbed conditions, the absorption loss decreases proportional to the square of a change in frequency. For example, the absorption loss is four times higher at 14 MHz than it is at 28 MHz. Perhaps more important, the hop distance is considerably greater as the MUF is approached. A transcontinental contact is thus much more likely to be made on a single hop on 28 MHz than on 14 MHz, so the higher frequency will give the stronger signal most of the time. The strong-signal reputation of the 28-MHz band is founded on this fact.

4.2.8 LOWEST USABLE FREQUENCY (LUF)

There is also a lower limit to the range of frequencies that provide useful communication between two given points by way of the ionosphere. *Lowest usable frequency* is abbreviated LUF. If it were possible to start near the MUF and work gradually lower in frequency, the signal would decrease in strength and eventually would disappear into the ever-present "background noise." This happens because signal absorption increases proportional to the square of the lowering of the frequency. The frequency nearest the point where reception became unusable would be the LUF. It is not likely that you would want to work at the LUF, although reception could be improved if the station could increase power by a considerable amount, or if larger antennas could be used at both ends of the path.

For example, when solar activity is very high at the peak of a solar cycle, the LUF often rises higher than 14 MHz on the morning Eastern US-to-Europe path on 20 meters. Just before sunrise in the US, the 20 meter band will be first to open to Europe, followed shortly by 15 meters, and then 10 meters as the Sun rises further. By mid-morning, however, when 10 and 15 meters are both wide open, 20 meters will become very marginal to Europe, even when both sides are running maximum legal power levels. By contrast, stations on 10 meters can be worked readily with a transmitter power of only 1 or 2 watts, indicating the wide range between the LUF and the MUF.

Frequently, the *window* between the LUF and the MUF for two fixed points is very narrow, and there may be no amateur frequencies available inside the window. On occasion the LUF may be higher than the MUF between two points. This

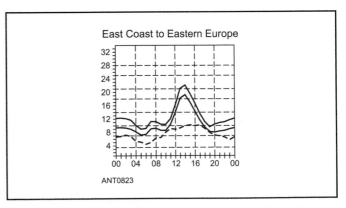

Figure 4.25 — Propagation prediction chart for East Coast of US to Europe. This appeared in December 1994 *QST*, where an average 2800-MHz (10.7-cm) solar flux of 83 was assumed for the mid-December to mid-January period. On 10% of these days, the highest frequency propagated was predicted at least as high as the uppermost curve (the Highest Possible Frequency, or HPF, approximately 21 MHz), and for 50% of the days as high as the middle curve, the MUF. The broken lines show the Lowest Usable Frequency (LUF) for a 1500-W CW transmitter.

means that, for the highest possible frequency that will propagate through the ionosphere for that path, the absorption is so great as to make even that frequency unusable. Under these conditions it is impossible to establish amateur sky-wave communication between those two points, no matter what frequency is used. (It would normally be possible, however, to communicate between either point and other points on some frequency under the existing conditions.) Conditions when amateur sky-wave communication is impossible between two fixed points occur commonly for long distances where the total path is in darkness, and for very great distances in the daytime during periods of low solar activity.

Figure 4.25 shows a typical propagation prediction from the ARRL web site (**www.arrl.org/propagation**). In this instance, the MUF and the LUF lines are blurred together at about 10 UTC, meaning that the statistical likelihood of any amateur frequency being open for that particular path at that particular time was not very good. Later on, after about 11 UTC, the gap between the MUF and LUF increased, indicating that the higher bands would be open on that path.

4.2.9 DISTURBED IONOSPHERIC CONDITIONS

So far, we have discussed the Earth's ionosphere when conditions at the Sun are undisturbed. There are three general types of major disturbances on the Sun that can affect radio propagation here on the Earth. On the air, you may hear people grousing about *Solar Flares*, *Coronal Holes* or *Sudden Disappearing Filaments*, especially when propagation conditions are not good. Each of these disturbances causes both electromagnetic radiation and ejection of material from the Sun.

Solar Flares

Solar flares are cataclysmic eruptions that suddenly release huge amounts of energy, including sustained, high-energy bursts of radiation from VLF to X-ray frequencies and vast amounts of solar material. Most solar flares occur around the peak of the 11-year solar cycle.

The first Earthly indication of a huge flare is often a visible brightness near a sunspot group, along with increases in UV, X-ray radiation and VHF radio noise. If the geometry between the Sun and Earth is right, intense X-ray radiation takes eight minutes, traveling the 93 million miles to Earth at the speed of light. The sudden increase in X-ray energy can immediately increase RF absorption in the Earth's lowest ionospheric layers, causing a phenomenon known as a *Sudden Ionospheric Disturbance* (SID).

An SID affects all HF communications on the sunlit side of the Earth. Signals in the 2 to 30-MHz range may disappear entirely, and even most background noise may cease in extreme cases. When you experience a big SID, your first inclination may be to look outside to see if your antenna fell down! SIDs may last up to an hour before ionospheric conditions temporarily return to normal.

Between 45 minutes and 2 hours after an SID begins, particles from the mass eruption on the Sun may begin to arrive. These high-energy particles are mainly protons and they can penetrate the ionosphere at the Earth's magnetic poles, where intense ionization can occur, with attendant absorption of HF signals propagating through the polar regions. This is called a *Polar Cap Absorption* (PCA) event and it may last for several days. A PCA results in spectacular auroral displays at high latitudes. The higher frequencies are the last to drop out and the first to return.

Coronal Holes

As described earlier in the section dealing with auroral propagation at VHF, a second major solar disturbance is a so-called "coronal hole" in the Sun's outer layer (the *corona*). Temperatures in the corona can be more than four million °C over an active sunspot region but more typically are about two million °C. A coronal hole is an area of somewhat lower temperature. Solar-terrestrial scientists have a number of competing theories about how coronal holes are formed.

Matter ejected through this "hole" takes the form of *plasma*, highly ionized gas made up of electrons, protons and neutral particles, traveling at speeds up to 1,000 km per second (2 million miles per hour). The plasma becomes part of the solar wind and can affect the Earth's magnetic field, but only if the Sun-Earth geometry is right. Plasma has a very interesting and somewhat bizarre ability. It can lock-in the orientation of the magnetic field where it originates and carry it outwards into space. However, unless the locked-in magnetic field orientation is aligned properly with the Earth's magnetic field, even a large plasma mass may not severely disrupt our magnetosphere, and thence our ionosphere.

Presently, we don't have the ability to predict very long in advance when the Sun might erupt in a disturbance that results in Earthly propagation problems. The SOHO and STEREO satellites can help determine whether a mass ejection is heading towards Earth, and the ACE satellite about 1 million miles away from Earth can give about an hour's warning whether the imbedded magnetic field in a mass ejection from the Sun might impact the Earth's magnetosphere, causing propagation problems for hams. The STEREO satellites also provide a 360° view of the Sun, allowing observation of the entire solar surface.

Statistically, coronal holes tend to occur most often during the declining phase of the 11-year solar cycle and they can last for a number of solar rotations. This means that a coronal hole can be a "recurring coronal hole," disrupting communications for several days about the same time each month for as long as a year, or even more.

Sudden Disappearing Filaments

A sudden disappearing filament (SDF) is the third major category of solar disturbance that can affect propagation. SDFs take their names from the manner in which they suddenly arch upward from the Sun's surface, spewing huge amounts of matter as plasma out into space in the solar wind. They tend to occur mostly during the rising phase of the 11-year solar cycle.

NOAA Scales

The Space Weather Prediction Center in Boulder, CO categorizes disturbances to propagation as G (Geomagnetic storms), S (Solar radiation storms), and R (Radio blackouts). Each category is reported on a scale of 1 to 5, with 1 being a minor disturbance and 5 being an extreme disturbance. Visit **www.swpc.noaa.gov/NOAAscales** for a discussion and explanation of these disturbances.

4.2.10 IONOSPHERIC (GEOMAGNETIC) STORMS

When the conditions are right, a flare, coronal hole or an SDF can launch a plasma cloud into the solar wind, resulting in an *ionospheric storm* here on Earth. Unlike a hurricane or a winter Nor'easter storm in New England, an ionospheric storm is not something we can see with our eyes or feel on our skins. We can't easily measure things occurring in the ionosphere some 200 miles overhead. However, we can see the indirect effects of an ionospheric storm on magnetic instruments located on the Earth's surface, because disturbances in the ionosphere are closely related to the Earth's magnetic field. The term *Geomagnetic Storm* ("Geo" means "Earth" in Greek) is used almost synonymously with ionospheric storm.

During a ionospheric storm, we may experience extraordinary radio noise and interference, especially at HF. You may hear solar radio emissions as increases of noise at VHF. A geomagnetic storm generally adds noise and weakens or disrupts ionospheric propagation for several days. Transpolar signals at 14 MHz or higher may be particularly weak, with a peculiar hollow sound or flutter — even more than normal for transpolar signals.

Depending on the severity of the disturbance to the Earth's geomagnetic field and the consequent disturbance of the ionosphere, propagation may be disrupted completely or it might be at least degraded for a period of time that ranges from a day to three or four days before returning to normal propagation conditions.

What can we do about the solar disturbances and related disturbed ionospheric propagation on Earth? The truth is that we are powerless faced with the truly awesome forces of solar disturbances like flares, coronal holes or sudden disappearing filaments. Perhaps there is some comfort, however, in understanding what has happened to cause our HF bands to be so poor. And as a definite consolation, conditions on the VHF bands are often exceptionally good just when HF propagation is remarkably poor due to solar disturbances. VHF operators enthusiastically look forward to conditions when they can engage in auroral communications — exactly the kind of conditions that have HF operators scratching their heads, wondering where the ionosphere went.

4.2.11 ONE-WAY PROPAGATION

On occasion a signal may be started on the way back toward the Earth by reflection from the F region, only to come down onto the top of the E region and be reflected back up again. This set of conditions is one possible explanation for the often-reported phenomenon called *one-way skip*. The reverse path may not necessarily have the same multilayer characteristic. The effect is more often a difference in the signal strengths, rather than a complete lack of signal in one direction, and many times there may be local noises that mask signals at one end of the path. It is important to remember these sorts of possibilities when a long-distance test with a new antenna system yields apparently conflicting results. Even many tests, on paths of different lengths and headings, may provide data that are difficult to understand. Communication by way of the ionosphere is not always a source of consistent answers to antenna questions.

Figure 4.25 shows the 80 meter path from New England to Europe with three different antennas. A really high dipole at a height of 200 feet above flat ground would certainly be an impressive antenna. But it would still be overshadowed dramatically by a four-square vertical array, at least at the low elevation angles needed often on this path. This is predicated on the four-square being located over salt water, which provides a virtually perfect RF ground. At an elevation angle of 7°, the four-square has 7 dB more gain than the 200-foot high dipole.

4.2.12 LONG AND SHORT PATH PROPAGATION

Propagation between any two points on the Earth's surface is usually by the shortest direct route — the *great-circle path* found by stretching a string tightly between the two points on a globe. If an elastic band going completely around the globe in a straight line is substituted for the string, it will show another great-circle path, going "the long way around." The long path may serve for communication over the desired circuit when conditions are favorable along the longer route. There may be times when communication is possible over the long path but not possible at all over the short path. Especially if there is knowledge of this potential at both ends of the circuit, long-path communication may work very well. Cooperation is almost essential, because both the aiming of directional antennas and the timing of the attempts must be right for any worthwhile result. The *IONCAP/VOACAP* computations in the preceding tables were made for short-path azimuths only.

Sunlight is a required element in long-haul communication via the F layer above about 10 MHz. This fact tends to define long-path timing and antenna aiming. Both are essentially the reverse of the "normal" for a given circuit. We know also that salt-water paths work better than overland ones. This can be significant in long-path work.

We can better understand several aspects of long-path propagation if you become accustomed to thinking of the Earth as a ball. This is easy if you use a globe frequently. A flat map of the world, of the azimuthal-equidistant projection type, is a useful substitute. The ARRL World Map is one, centered on Wichita, Kansas. A similar world map prepared by K5ZI and centered on Newington, Connecticut, is shown in **Figure 4.26**. These help to clarify paths involving those areas of the world.

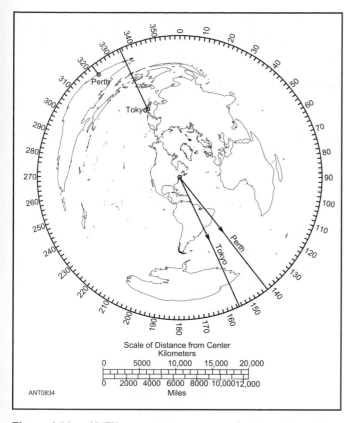

Figure 4.26 — K5ZI's computer-generated azimuthal-equi-distant projection centered on Newington, Connecticut. Land masses and information showing long paths to Perth and Tokyo have been added. Notice that the paths in both cases lie almost entirely over water, rather than over land masses.

Long-Path Examples

There are numerous long-path routes well known to DX-minded amateurs. Two long paths that work frequently and well when 28 MHz is open from the northeastern US are New England to Perth, Western Australia, and New England to Tokyo. Although they represent different beam headings and distances, they share some favorable conditions. By the long path, Perth is close to halfway around the world; Tokyo is about three-quarters of the way. On 28 MHz, both areas come through in the early daylight hours, Eastern Time, but not necessarily on the same days. Both paths are at their best around the equinoxes. (The sunlight is more uniformly distributed over transequatorial paths at these times.) Probably the factor that most favors both is the nature of the first part of the trip at the US end. To work Perth by way of long path, northeastern US antennas are aimed southeast, out over salt water for thousands of miles — the best low-loss start a signal could have. It is salt water essentially all the way, and the distance, about 13,000 miles, is not too much greater than the "short" path.

The long path to Japan is more toward the south, but still with no major land mass at the early reflection points. It is much longer, however, than that to Western Australia. Japanese signals are more limited in number on the long path than on the short, and signals on the average somewhat

weaker, probably because of the greater distance.

On the short path, an amateur in the Perth area is looking at the worst conditions — away from the ocean, and out across the huge land mass of North America, unlikely to provide strong ground reflections. The short paths to both Japan and Western Australia, from most of the eastern half of North America, are hardly favorable. The first hop comes down in various western areas likely to be desert or mountains, or both, and not favored as reflection points.

A word of caution: Don't count on the long-path signals always coming in on the same beam heading. There can be notable differences in the line of propagation via the ionosphere on even relatively short distances. There can be more variations on long path, especially on circuits close to halfway around the world. Remember, for a point exactly halfway around, all directions of the compass represent great-circle paths.

4.2.13 GRAY-LINE PROPAGATION

The *gray line*, sometimes called the *twilight zone*, is a band around the Earth between the sunlit portion and darkness. Astronomers call this the *terminator*. The terminator is a somewhat diffused region because the Earth's atmosphere tends to scatter the light into the darkness. **Figure 4.27** illustrates the gray line. Notice that on one side of the Earth, the gray line is coming into daylight (sunrise), and on the other side it is coming into darkness (sunset).

Propagation along the gray line is very efficient, particularly on the lower bands, especially on 80 or 160 meters, so greater distances can be covered than might be expected for the frequency in use. One major reason for this is that the D layer, which absorbs HF signals, disappears rapidly on the sunset side of the gray line, and has not yet built up on the sunrise side.

The gray line runs generally north and south, but varies as much as 23° either side of the north-south line. This variation is caused by the tilt of the Earth's axis relative to its orbital plane around the Sun. The gray line will be exactly north and south at the equinoxes (March 21 and September 21). On the first day of Northern Hemisphere summer, June 21, it is

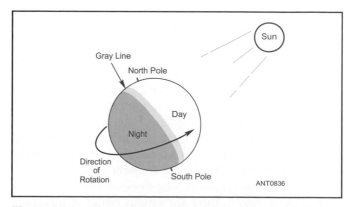

Figure 4.27 — The gray line or terminator is a transition region between daylight and darkness. One side of the Earth is coming into sunrise, and the other is just past sunset.

tilted to the maximum of 23° one way, and on December 21, the first day of winter, it is tilted 23° the other way.

To an observer on the Earth, the direction of the terminator is always at right angles to the direction of the Sun at sunrise or sunset. It is important to note that, except at the equinoxes, the gray-line direction will be different at sunrise from that at sunset. This means you can work different areas of the world in the evening than you worked in the morning.

It isn't necessary to be located inside the twilight zone in order to take advantage of gray-line propagation. The effects can be used to advantage before sunrise and after sunset. This is because the Sun "rises" earlier and "sets" later on the ionospheric layers than it does on the Earth below.

4.2.14 FADING

When all the variable factors in long-distance HF communication are taken in account, it is not surprising that signals vary in strength during almost every contact beyond the local range. In VHF communication we can also encounter some fading at distances greater than just to the visible horizon. These are mainly the result of changes in the temperature and moisture content of the air in the first few thousand feet above the ground.

On paths covered by HF ionospheric modes, the causes of fading are very complex — constantly changing layer height and density, random polarization shift, portions of the signal arriving out of phase, and so on. The energy arriving at the receiving antenna has components that have been acted upon differently by the ionosphere. Often the fading is very different for small changes in frequency. With a signal of a wideband nature, such as high-quality FM, or even double-sideband AM, the sidebands may have different fading rates from each other, or from the carrier. This causes severe distortion, resulting in what is termed *selective fading*. The effects are greatly reduced (but still present to some extent) when single-sideband (SSB) is used. Some immunity from fading during reception (but not to the distortion induced by selective fading) can be had by using two or more receivers on separate antennas, preferably with different polarizations, and combining the receiver outputs in what is known as a *diversity* receiving system.

4.2.15 SPORADIC E AND HF SCATTER MODES

In propagation literature there is a tendency to treat the various propagation modes as if they were separate and distinct phenomena. This they may be at times, but often there is a shifting from one to the other, or a mixture of two or more kinds of propagation affecting communication at one time. In the upper part of the usual frequency range for F-region work, for example, there may be enough tropospheric bending at one end (or both ends) to have an appreciable effect on the usable path length. There is the frequent combination of E and F-region propagation in long-distance work. And in the case of the E region, there are various causes of ionization that have very different effects on communication. Finally, there are weak-signal variations of both tropospheric and ionospheric modes, lumped under the term "scatter." We look at these phenomena separately here, but in practice we have to deal with them in combination, more often than not.

Sporadic E (E$_s$)

First, note that this is *E-subscript-s*, a usefully descriptive term, wrongly written "Es" so often that it is sometimes called "ease," which is certainly not descriptive. *Sporadic E* is ionization at E-layer height, but of different origin and communication potential from the E layer that affects mainly our lower amateur frequencies. *[The amateur and professional literature is not strict about the punctuation, with sporadic-E and Es used regularly — Ed.]*

The formative mechanism for sporadic E is believed to be wind shear. This explains ambient ionization being distributed and compressed into a ledge of high density, without the need for production of extra ionization. Neutral winds of high velocity, flowing in opposite directions at slightly different altitudes, produce shears. In the presence of the Earth's magnetic field, the ions are collected at a particular altitude, forming a thin, over-dense layer. Data from rockets entering E$_s$ regions confirm the electron density, wind velocities and height parameters.

The ionization is formed in clouds of high density, lasting only a few hours at a time and distributed randomly. They vary in density and, in the middle latitudes in the Northern Hemisphere, move rapidly from southeast to northwest. Although E$_s$ can develop at any time, it is most prevalent in the Northern Hemisphere between May and August, with a minor season about half as long beginning in December (the summer and winter solstices). The seasons and distribution in the Southern Hemisphere are not so well known. Australia and New Zealand seem to have conditions much like those in the US, but with the length of the seasons reversed, of course. Much of what is known about E$_s$ came as the result of amateur pioneering in the VHF range.

Correlation of E$_s$ openings with observed natural phenomena, including sunspot activity, is not readily apparent, although there is a meteorological tie-in with high-altitude winds. There is also a form of E$_s$, mainly in the northern part of the North Temperate Zone, that is associated with auroral phenomena.

At the peak of the long E$_s$ season, most commonly in late June and early July, ionization becomes extremely dense and widespread. This extends the usable range from the more common "single-hop" maximum of about 1400 miles to "double-hop" distances, mostly 1400 to 2500 miles. With 50-MHz techniques and interest improving in recent years, it has been shown that distances considerably beyond 2500 miles can be covered. There is also an E$_s$ "link-up" possibility with other modes, believed to be involved in some 50-MHz work between antipodal points, or even long-path communication beyond 12,500 miles.

When E$_s$ is particularly strong and widespread, even the HF bands can suddenly support *short skip* producing exceptionally strong signals from distances that would normally be in the no-signal "skip zone." Dean Straw, N6BV, distinctly remembers a spectacular 20 meter E_s opening in September 1994, during the "Hiram Percy Maxim/125" anniversary celebration, when he was living in New Hampshire. Signals on 20 meters were 30 to 40 dB over S9 from all along the Eastern Seaboard, from W2 to W4. One exasperated W3 complained that he had been calling in the huge pileup for 20 minutes. N6BV glanced at the S meter and saw that the W3 was 20 dB over S9, normally a very strong 20 meter SSB signal, but not when almost everybody else was 40 dB over S9! (See the Bibliography for N6BV's presentation on HF sporadic E.)

Such short-skip conditions caused by Sporadic E are more common on 10 meters than they are on 15 or 20 meters. They can result in excellent transatlantic 10 meter openings during the summer months — when 10 meters is not normally open for F_2 ionospheric propagation.

The MUF for E_s is not known precisely. It was long thought to be around 100 MHz, but in the last 25 years or so there have been thousands of 144-MHz contacts during the summer E_s season. Presumably, the possibility also exists at 222 MHz. The skip distance at 144 MHz does average much longer than at 50 MHz, and the openings are usually brief and extremely variable.

The terms "single" and "double" hop may not be accurate technically, since it is likely that cloud-to-cloud paths are involved. There may also be "no-hop" E_s. At times the very high ionization density produces critical frequencies up to the 50-MHz region, with no skip distance at all. It is often said that the E_s mode is a great equalizer. With the reflecting region practically overhead, even a simple dipole close to the ground may do as well over a few hundred miles as a large stacked antenna array designed for low-angle radiation. It's a great mode for low power and simple antennas on 28 and 50 MHz.

HF Scatter Modes

The term "skip zone" (where no signals are heard) should not be taken too literally. Two stations communicating over a single ionospheric hop can be heard to some degree by other stations at almost any point along the way, unless the two are running low power and using simple antennas. Some of the wave energy is *scattered* in all directions, including back to the starting point and farther.

Backscatter functions like a sort of HF ionospheric radar. **Figure 4.28** shows a schematic for a simple backscatter path. The signal launched from point A travels through the ionosphere back to earth at Point S, the scattering point. Here, the rough terrain of the land scatters signals in many directions, one of which propagates a weak signal back through the ionosphere to land at point B. Point B would normally be in the no-signal skip zone between A and S. Because backscatter signals arrive from multiple directions, through various paths through the ionosphere, they have a characteristic "hollow" sound, much like you get when you talk into a paper tube with its many internal reflections.

Because backscatter involves mainly scattering from the Earth at the point where the strong ionospherically propagated signal comes down, it is a part of HF over-the-horizon radar techniques. Amateurs using sounding techniques have shown that you can tell to what part of the world a band is usable (single-hop F) by probing the backscatter with a directive antenna and high transmitter power, even when the Earth contact point is open ocean. In fact, that's where the mode is at its best, because ocean waves can be efficient backscatter reflectors.

Backscatter is very useful on 28 MHz, particularly when that band seems dead simply because nobody is active in the right places. The mode keeps the 10 meter band lively in the low years of the solar cycle, thanks to the never-say-die attitude of some users. The mode is also an invaluable tool of 50-MHz DX aspirants, in the high years of the sunspot cycle, for the same reasons. On a high-MUF morning, hundreds of 6 meter beams may zero in on a hot spot somewhere in the Caribbean or South Atlantic, where there is no land, let alone other 6 meter stations — keeping in contact while they wait for the band to open to a place where there is somebody.

Sidescatter is similar to backscatter, except the ground scatter zone is off the direct line between participants. A typical example, often observed during the lowest years of the solar cycle, is communication on 28 MHz between the eastern US (and adjacent areas of Canada) and much of the European continent. Often, this may start as "backscatter chatter" between Europeans whose antennas are turned toward the Azores. Then suddenly the North Americans join the fun, perhaps for only a few minutes, but sometimes much longer, with beams also pointed toward the Azores. Duration of the game can be extended, at times, by careful reorientation of antennas at both ends, as with backscatter. The secret, of course, is to keep hitting the highest-MUF area of the ionosphere and the most favorable ground-reflection points.

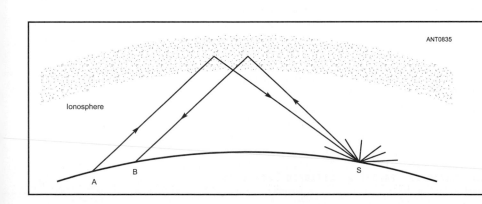

ANT0835

Figure 4.28 — Schematic of a simple backscatter path. Stations A and B are too close to make contact via normal F-layer ionospheric refraction. Signals scattered back from a distant point on the Earth's surface (S), often the ocean, may be accessible to both A and B to create a backscatter circuit.

The favorable route is usually, but not always, south of the great-circle heading (for stations in the Northern Hemisphere). There can also be sidescatter from the auroral regions. Sidescatter signals are stronger than backscatter signals using the same general area of ground scattering.

Sidescatter signals have been observed frequently on the l4-MHz band, and can take place on any band where there is a large window between the MUF and the LUF. For sidescatter communications to occur, the thing to look for is a common area to which the band is open from both ends of the path (the Azores, in the above example), when there is no direct-path opening. It helps if the common area is in the open ocean, where there is less scattering loss than over land.

4.3 WHEN AND WHERE HF BANDS ARE OPEN

4.3.1 THE PROPAGATION BIG PICTURE

A newcomer to the HF bands could easily be overwhelmed with the sheer amount of data available in the Summary (and particularly the Detailed) prediction tables described in the following sections and provided on the CD-ROM included with this book. So here's a long-term, "big-picture" view of HF propagation that might help answer some common questions. For example, what month really is the best for working DX around the clock? Or what level of solar activity is necessary to provide an opening between your QTH and somewhere in the South Pacific?

Table 4-3 is a table showing the number of hours in a

Table 4-3

The number of hours per day when a particular band is open to the target geographic areas in Table 4-4, as related to the level of solar activity (Very Low, Medium and Very High). This table is customized for Boston to the rest of the world. Some paths are open 24 hours a day, plus or minus QRM and local QRN, no matter what the level of solar activity is. See CD-ROM for other transmitting locations.

```
MA (Boston)
Hours Open to Each Region for Very-Low/Medium/Very-High SSNs


80 Meters:
Month  Europe     Far East   So. Amer.  Africa     So. Asia   Oceania    No. Amer.
Jan    17/17/16   5/ 4/ 3    17/17/16   16/16/15   8/ 7/ 5    11/10/ 9   24/24/24
Feb    17/16/15   3/ 3/ 2    17/16/16   15/15/14   6/ 4/ 4    10/ 9/ 9   24/24/24
Mar    15/15/14   3/ 2/ 1    16/16/15   15/13/13   4/ 4/ 3    9/ 8/ 7    24/24/24
Apr    13/13/12   1/ 0/ 0    16/16/14   13/13/13   3/ 3/ 1    9/ 8/ 7    24/24/24
May    12/11/10   0/ 0/ 0    16/15/14   12/11/10   2/ 1/ 1    7/ 6/ 6    24/24/24
Jun    10/ 9/ 8   0/ 0/ 0    14/14/14   11/10/10   1/ 1/ 0    6/ 5/ 5    24/24/24
Jul    11/11/ 9   0/ 0/ 0    15/14/14   11/11/11   2/ 1/ 1    7/ 6/ 5    24/24/24
Aug    13/11/11   0/ 0/ 0    16/16/14   13/12/11   3/ 2/ 1    7/ 7/ 6    24/24/24
Sep    14/13/11   2/ 1/ 0    17/16/14   13/13/12   4/ 4/ 2    9/ 8/ 8    24/24/24
Oct    15/15/13   3/ 2/ 1    17/17/16   14/14/13   5/ 4/ 4    9/ 9/ 7    24/24/24
Nov    17/17/15   4/ 4/ 2    17/17/16   16/15/14   8/ 7/ 4    11/10/ 9   24/24/24
Dec    19/18/17   7/ 6/ 4    18/18/17   16/16/16   11/ 9/ 7   12/11/11   24/24/24


40 Meters:
Month  Europe     Far East   So. Amer.  Africa     So. Asia   Oceania    No. Amer.
Jan    24/24/24   15/16/15   24/24/21   21/20/19   21/21/19   19/18/15   24/24/24
Feb    24/24/21   13/11/11   24/23/20   20/19/18   19/19/17   16/15/14   24/24/24
Mar    23/22/19   10/ 9/ 7   24/21/18   19/17/17   17/17/13   13/13/13   24/24/24
Apr    21/19/18   8/ 6/ 4    22/20/18   17/16/15   16/11/ 8   13/13/11   24/24/24
May    19/17/17   5/ 4/ 3    22/18/17   17/16/14   9/ 8/ 5    12/11/10   24/24/24
Jun    17/15/13   4/ 2/ 2    22/18/16   16/15/14   7/ 5/ 5    11/10/ 9   24/24/24
Jul    18/16/15   5/ 4/ 2    24/18/17   17/15/14   8/ 7/ 5    12/11/10   24/24/24
Aug    19/17/16   7/ 5/ 4    24/19/18   18/16/15   11/10/ 6   13/12/11   24/24/24
Sep    22/21/17   9/ 8/ 5    23/20/18   18/17/16   14/11/ 7   13/13/12   24/24/24
Oct    24/23/20   12/11/ 8   24/23/19   20/18/17   17/16/14   16/13/13   24/24/24
Nov    24/24/22   14/13/12   24/24/20   21/19/18   21/20/17   17/17/13   24/24/24
Dec    24/24/24   18/19/22   24/24/21   23/21/19   24/23/22   21/19/18   24/24/24
```

day during each month when each major HF band is open to the same receiving areas shown in Tables 4-4 and 4-5 shown in a later section of this chapter. The listing is for New England, for three levels of solar activity: Very Low, Medium and Very High. The number of hours are separated in Table 4-3 by slashes. (Versions of Table 4-3 for other areas around the US are on the CD-ROM that accompanies this book in **Table4-3.pdf**.)

Let's examine the conditions for New England to Europe on 15 meters for October. The entry shows "7/11/17," meaning that for a Very Low level of solar activity, 15 meters is open for 7 hours; for a Medium level, it is open for 11 hours and for a Very High level of solar activity it is open for 17 hours a day.

Even for a Very Low level of solar activity, the month with the most hours available per day from Boston to somewhere in Europe is October, with 7 hours, followed by the next largest month of March, with 6 hours. For a Very High level of solar activity, however, the 15 meter band is open to Europe for 18 hours in April, followed by 17 hours availability in September and October. Arguably, the CQ World Wide Contest Committee picked the very best month for higher-frequency propagation when they chose October for the Phone portion of that contest.

You can easily see that even at a Very High level of solar activity, the summer months are not very good to work DX, particularly on east-west paths. For example, the 10 meter band is very rarely open from New England to Europe after the month of April, even when solar activity is at the highest levels possible. Things pick up after September, even for a Medium level of solar activity. Again, October looks like the most fruitful month in terms of the number of hours 10 meters is open to Europe under all levels of solar conditions.

20 Meters:

Month	Europe	Far East	So. Amer.	Africa	So. Asia	Oceania	No. Amer.
Jan	13/16/22	15/22/22	24/24/24	20/21/21	18/20/22	18/23/22	24/24/24
Feb	12/18/23	13/21/24	24/24/24	22/22/24	15/21/24	18/23/24	24/24/24
Mar	15/18/24	17/20/24	24/24/24	22/24/24	18/21/24	16/24/24	24/24/24
Apr	15/20/24	19/22/24	24/24/24	21/24/24	19/22/24	18/24/24	24/24/24
May	19/23/24	22/24/24	24/24/24	23/24/24	23/24/24	21/24/24	24/24/24
Jun	22/24/24	24/24/24	24/24/24	24/24/24	24/24/24	24/24/24	24/24/24
Jul	19/24/24	24/24/24	24/24/24	21/24/24	24/24/24	23/24/24	24/24/24
Aug	15/20/24	20/24/24	24/24/24	20/24/24	20/24/24	19/24/24	24/24/24
Sep	16/19/24	17/21/24	24/24/24	21/24/24	18/21/24	17/24/24	24/24/24
Oct	15/21/24	16/20/24	24/24/24	22/24/24	19/22/24	17/24/24	24/24/24
Nov	14/20/23	14/22/24	24/24/24	20/24/24	17/21/24	19/23/24	24/24/24
Dec	11/17/24	13/22/24	24/24/24	17/23/24	12/22/24	16/24/24	24/24/24

15 Meters:

Month	Europe	Far East	So. Amer.	Africa	So. Asia	Oceania	No. Amer.
Jan	4/ 6/ 7	2/ 9/13	12/15/16	9/13/13	3/ 4/ 7	9/12/13	24/15/16
Feb	4/ 7/12	4/10/14	13/18/23	11/13/16	3/ 7/13	8/13/15	22/16/19
Mar	6/ 9/14	2/13/15	14/21/24	13/17/22	5/11/17	10/14/17	15/16/23
Apr	0/10/18	3/13/18	15/23/24	15/18/24	9/15/19	11/15/21	16/16/24
May	1/13/16	6/10/19	17/20/24	14/18/24	13/17/18	10/16/19	20/19/24
Jun	0/ 2/16	0/ 9/15	16/21/24	14/18/24	5/15/18	10/12/20	24/22/22
Jul	0/ 2/16	0/ 5/18	15/19/24	12/18/24	0/12/18	4/12/20	24/22/21
Aug	0/ 2/14	0/ 8/17	14/18/22	13/16/22	0/12/17	6/10/19	22/19/21
Sep	1/10/17	6/13/17	14/16/24	13/17/22	9/14/17	9/14/17	16/16/22
Oct	7/11/17	10/13/17	12/16/22	12/15/22	7/12/17	12/13/15	18/15/22
Nov	5/ 8/14	8/11/14	12/16/22	11/14/17	3/ 7/16	10/13/15	20/16/21
Dec	3/ 6/ 9	2/10/13	12/15/23	8/13/15	2/ 4/12	9/12/14	24/15/18

10 Meters:

Month	Europe	Far East	So. Amer.	Africa	So. Asia	Oceania	No. Amer.
Jan	0/ 1/ 4	0/ 1/ 8	6/11/13	0/ 7/10	0/ 1/ 3	0/ 3/11	23/24/24
Feb	0/ 2/ 7	0/ 2/10	8/12/14	0/ 9/13	0/ 3/ 5	0/ 7/13	24/24/24
Mar	0/ 0/ 8	0/ 1/10	10/14/20	1/11/14	0/ 0/ 8	0/ 7/13	23/24/24
Apr	0/ 0/ 8	0/ 0/ 8	7/14/21	0/12/17	0/ 0/13	0/ 5/11	18/24/24
May	0/ 0/ 0	0/ 0/ 1	7/12/20	1/10/17	0/ 1/12	0/ 2/11	17/20/22
Jun	0/ 0/ 0	0/ 0/ 0	7/11/18	0/ 3/17	0/ 0/ 0	0/ 0/ 2	21/19/23
Jul	0/ 0/ 0	0/ 0/ 0	2/ 9/19	0/ 2/18	0/ 0/ 7	0/ 0/ 6	16/16/24
Aug	0/ 0/ 0	0/ 0/ 0	2/10/17	0/ 1/16	0/ 0/10	0/ 0/ 8	17/17/24
Sep	0/ 0/ 8	0/ 1/10	7/13/18	0/11/16	0/ 0/10	0/ 2/ 9	19/24/24
Oct	0/ 5/ 9	0/ 2/11	10/12/16	7/12/14	0/ 5/ 9	0/ 8/12	24/24/24
Nov	0/ 4/ 8	0/ 3/11	9/12/15	5/10/13	0/ 3/ 6	4/10/12	24/24/24
Dec	0/ 3/ 6	0/ 1/ 8	8/11/13	1/ 8/12	0/ 1/ 4	2/ 7/12	23/23/24

Ten meters is open more regularly on north-south paths, such as from New England to South America or to southern Africa. It is open as much as 10 hours a day during March and October to far South America, and 7 hours a day in October to Africa — even during the lowest parts of the solar cycle. (Together with the sporadic-E propagation that 10 meters enjoys during the summer, this band can often be a lot of fun even during the sunspot doldrums. You just have to *be operating* on the band, rather than avoiding it because you know the sunspots are "spotty!")

Now, look at the 20 meter band in Table 4-3. From New England, twenty is open to somewhere in South America for 24 hours a day, no matter the level of solar activity. Note that Table 4-3 doesn't predict the level of signals available; it just shows that the band is open with a signal strength greater than 0 on the S meter.

Look ahead to Summary Table 4-4 for the predicted signal strengths in January at a Very Low level of solar activity. There, you can see that the signal strength from New England into deep South America is always S8 or greater for a big gun station. A lot of the time during the night the band sounds dead, simply because everyone is either asleep or operating on a lower frequency.

For the 40 meter band in Table 4-3, during the month of January the band is open to Europe for 24 hours a day, whatever the level of solar activity is. Look now at Table 4-4, and you'll see that the predicted level for Very Low solar activity varies from S4 to S9. Local QRM or QRN would probably disrupt communications on 40 meters in Europe for stateside signals weaker than perhaps S3 or S4. Even though you might well be able to hear Europeans from New England during the day, they probably won't hear you because of local conditions, including local S9+ European stations and atmospheric noise from nearby thunderstorms. New England stations with big antennas can often hear Europeans on 40 meters as early as noontime, but must wait until the late afternoon before the Europeans can hear them above their local noise and QRM.

Let's say that you want to boost your country total on 80 meters by concentrating on stations in the South Pacific. The best months would be from November to February in terms of the number of hours per day when the 80 meter band is open to Oceania. You can see by reading across the line for each month that the level of solar activity is not hugely important on 80 meters to any location. Common experience (backed by the statistical information in Table 4-6) is that the 80 meter band is open only marginally longer when sunspots are low.

This is true to a greater extent on 40 meters. Thus you may hear the generalization that the low bands tend to be better during periods of low solar activity, while the upper HF bands (above 10 MHz) tend to be better when the sun is more active.

Table 4-3 can give you a good handle on what months are the most productive for DXing and contesting. It should be no surprise to most veteran operators that the fall and winter months are the best times to work DX.

4.3.2 ELEVATION ANGLES FOR HF COMMUNICATION

It was shown in connection with Figure 4.23 that the distance at which a ray returns to Earth depends on the elevation angle at which it left the Earth (also known by other names: takeoff, launch or wave angle). The chapter **HF Antenna System Design** deals with the effects of local terrain, describing how the elevation angle of a horizontally polarized antenna is determined mainly by its height above the ground.

Although it is not shown specifically in Figure 4.23, propagation distance also depends on the layer height at the time, as well as the elevation angle. As you can probably imagine, the layer height is a very complex function of the state of the ionosphere and the Earth's geomagnetic field. There is a large difference in the distance covered in a single hop, depending on the height of the E or the F_2 layer. The maximum single-hop distance by the E layer is about 2000 km (1250 miles) or about half the maximum distance via the F_2 layer. Practical communicating distances for single-hop E or F layer work at various wave angles are shown in graphic form in **Figure 4.29**.

Actual communication experience usually does not fit the simple patterns shown in Figure 4.23. Propagation by means of the ionosphere is an enormously complicated business (which makes it all the more intriguing and challenging

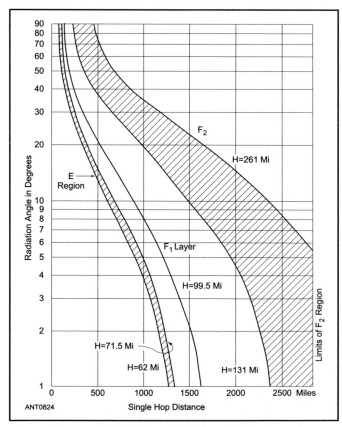

Figure 4.29 — Distance plotted against wave angle (one-hop transmission) for the nominal range of heights for the E and F_2 layers, and for the F_1 layer.

to radio amateurs, of course), even when the Sun is not in a disturbed state. Until the appearance of sophisticated computer models of the ionosphere, there was little definitive information available to guide the radio amateur in the design of antenna systems for optimal performance over all portions of the 11-year solar cycle.

The IONCAP Computer Propagation Model

Since the 1960s several agencies of the US government have been working on a detailed computer program that models the complex workings of the ionosphere. The program has been dubbed IONCAP, short for "Ionospheric Communications Analysis and Prediction Program." IONCAP was originally written for a mainframe computer, but later versions have been rewritten to allow them to be run by personal computers. IONCAP incorporates a detailed database covering almost three complete solar cycles. The program allows the operator to specify a wide range of parameters, including detailed antenna models for multiple frequency ranges, noise models tailored to specific local environments (from low-noise rural to noisy residential QTHs), minimum elevation angles suitable for a particular location and antenna system, different months and UTC times, maximum levels of multipath distortion, and finally solar activity levels, to name the most significant of a bewildering array of options.

While IONCAP has a well-justified reputation for being very *unfriendly* to use, due to its mainframe, non-interactive background, it is also the one ionospheric model most highly regarded for its accuracy and flexibility, both by amateurs and professionals alike. It is the program used for many years to produce the long-term MUF charts available on the ARRL web page on Propagation (**www.arrl.org/propagation**).

IONCAP is not well suited for short-term forecasts of propagation conditions based on the latest solar indices received from WWV. (The model of the ionosphere in IONCAP, as well as the models in all other propagation prediction programs, is a monthly median model.) It is an excellent tool, however, for long-range, detailed planning of antenna systems and shortwave transmitter installations, such as that for the Voice of America, or for radio amateurs. See the section later in this chapter describing other computer programs that can be used for short-term, interactive propagation predictions.

IONCAP/VOACAP Parameters

The elevation-angle statistical information contained in this section was compiled from thousands of VOACAP runs (an improved version of IONCAP developed by scientists from VOA, the Voice of America). These runs were done for a number of different transmitting locations throughout the world to important DX locations throughout the world. See the Bibliography entry for Straw on use of propagation prediction software.

Some assumptions were needed for setting VOACAP parameters. The transmitting and receiving sites were all assumed to be located on flat ground, with "average" ground conductivity and dielectric constant. Each site was assumed to have a clear shot to the horizon, with a minimum elevation angle less than or equal to 1°. Electrical noise at each receiving location was also assumed to be very low.

Transmitting and receiving antennas for the 3.5 to 30-MHz frequency range were specified to be isotropic-type antennas, but with +6 dBi gain, representing a good amateur antenna on each frequency band. These theoretical antennas radiate uniformly from the horizon, up to 90° directly overhead. With response patterns like this, these are obviously not real-world

Table 4-4

Boston, Massachusetts, to All of Europe

Elev	80 m	40 m	30 m	20 m	17 m	15 m	12 m	10 m
1	4.1	9.6	4.6	1.7	2.1	4.4	5.5	7.2
2	0.8	2.3	7.2	1.4	2.8	2.8	3.7	5.3
3	0.3	0.7	4.3	3.1	2.4	2.2	4.4	7.9
4	0.5	4.1	8.7	11.6	12.2	9.4	8.1	3.9
5	4.6	4.8	7.5	12.7	14.3	13.1	9.2	11.2
6	7.1	8.9	5.5	9.2	9.6	12.2	9.2	7.2
7	8.5	6.9	7.2	4.6	7.9	7.4	10.0	5.9
8	5.1	7.0	5.4	3.2	5.9	7.4	4.8	6.6
9	3.3	5.6	3.2	3.1	2.1	3.9	8.1	9.2
10	1.0	4.0	7.9	6.3	5.1	3.7	11.1	6.6
11	1.9	3.8	9.7	10.2	7.2	5.4	3.7	7.9
12	5.6	3.4	4.8	8.5	6.9	7.4	4.8	6.6
13	11.0	3.0	2.4	4.1	5.9	4.6	3.3	2.6
14	7.6	4.8	2.0	2.7	3.8	3.9	6.3	5.9
15	5.3	7.9	2.0	1.5	2.4	1.7	1.5	2.0
16	2.8	6.4	3.8	2.9	1.5	1.3	2.6	2.6
17	5.0	3.4	4.5	3.1	1.0	1.5	0.0	0.0
18	4.2	2.0	3.1	3.1	2.0	2.2	1.8	1.3
19	5.7	1.4	1.4	2.3	1.3	0.7	0.0	0.0
20	6.6	1.4	1.2	1.8	1.1	1.3	0.7	0.0
21	4.4	1.4	0.5	0.8	0.7	0.7	0.4	0.0
22	2.3	2.4	1.0	1.1	0.6	1.3	0.7	0.0
23	1.3	1.8	0.1	0.3	0.1	0.0	0.0	0.0
24	0.6	1.0	0.5	0.5	0.4	0.7	0.0	0.0
25	0.3	0.8	0.3	0.1	0.4	0.0	0.0	0.0
26	0.0	0.5	0.7	0.2	0.1	0.4	0.0	0.0
27	0.1	0.1	0.1	0.2	0.1	0.2	0.0	0.0
28	0.0	0.3	0.1	0.2	0.0	0.2	0.0	0.0
29	0.1	0.0	0.2	0.0	0.0	0.0	0.0	0.0
30	0.0	0.1	0.0	0.0	0.0	0.0	0.0	0.0
31	0.0	0.0	0.0	0.0	0.0	0.0	0.0	0.0
32	0.0	0.0	0.1	0.0	0.0	0.0	0.0	0.0
33	0.1	0.0	0.0	0.0	0.0	0.0	0.0	0.0
34	0.0	0.0	0.0	0.0	0.0	0.0	0.0	0.0
35	0.0	0.0	0.0	0.0	0.0	0.0	0.0	0.0

Percentage of time a particular frequency band is open on this specific propagation path.

antennas. They do, however, allow the computer program to explore all possible modes and elevation angles.

Looking at the Elevation-Angle Statistical Data

Table 4-4 shows detailed statistical elevation information for the path from Boston, Massachusetts, near ARRL HQ in Newington, Connecticut, to all of Europe. The data incorporated into Table 4-4 shows the percentage of time versus elevation angle for all HF bands from 80 meters to 10 meters, over all portions of the 11-year solar cycle. The CD-ROM accompanying this book contains more tables such as this for more than 150 transmitting sites around the world. These tables are used by the *HFTA* program (and earlier *YT* program) described in the **HF Antenna System Design** chapter and can also be imported into many programs, such as word processors or spreadsheets. Six important areas throughout the world are covered, one per table: all of Europe (from London, England, to Kiev, Ukraine), the Far East (centered on Japan), South America (Paraguay), Oceania (Melbourne, Australia), Southern Africa (Zambia) and South Asia (New Delhi, India).

You may be surprised to see in Table 4-4 that angles lower than 10° dominate the possible range of incoming angles for this moderate-distance path from New England to Europe. In fact, 1.7% of all the times when the 20 meter band is open to Europe, the takeoff angle is as low as 1°. You should recognize that very few real-world 20 meter antennas achieve much gain at such an extremely low angle — unless they just happen to be mounted about 400 feet high over flat ground or else are located on the top of a tall, steep mountain.

The situation is even more dramatic on 40 and 80 meters. **Figure 4.30** shows the "cumulative distribution function" of the total percentage of time (derived from Table 4-4) when 40 meters is open from Boston to the rest of the world, plotted against the elevation angle. For example, into Europe from Boston, 50% of the time when the band is open, it is at 10° or less. Into Japan from Boston, the statistics are even more revealing: 50% of the time when the band is open, the angle is 6° or less, and 90% of the time the angle is 13° or less!

Figure 4.31 shows the same sort of information for 80 meters from Boston to the world. For 50% of the time from Boston to Europe the elevation angle is 13° or less; at the 90% level the angle is 20° or less. For the path to Japan on 80 meters from Boston, 50% of the time the angle is 8° or less; at the 90% level, the angle is 13° or less. Now, to achieve peak gain on 80 meters at an elevation angle of 8° over flat land, a horizontally polarized antenna must be 500 feet high. You can begin to see why verticals can do very well on long-distance contacts on 80 meters, even when they are mounted over poorly conducting, rocky ground. Clearly, low angles are very important for successful DXing.

The Ionosphere Controls Propagation

You should always remember that it is the *ionosphere* that controls the elevation angles, *not* the transmitting antenna. The elevation response of a particular antenna only determines how strong or weak a signal is, at whatever angle (or angles) the ionosphere is supporting at that particular

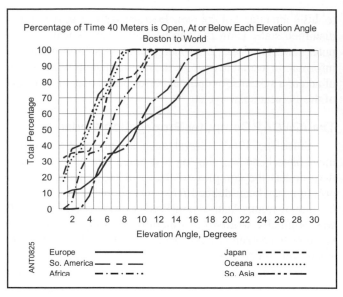

Figure 4.30 — The cumulative distribution function showing the total percentage of time that 40 meters is open, at or below each elevation angle, from Boston to the world. For example, 50% of the time the band is open to Europe from Boston, it is at 10° or less. The angles for DX work are indeed low.

instant, for that propagation path and for that frequency.

If only one propagation mode is possible at a particular time, and if the elevation angle for that one mode happens to be 5°, then your antenna will have to work satisfactorily at that very low angle or else you won't be able to communicate. For example, if your low dipole has a gain of −10 dBi at 5°, compared to your friend's Yagi on a mountain top with +10 dBi gain at 5°, then you will be down 20 dB compared

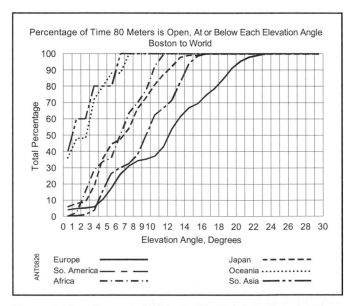

Figure 4.31 — The cumulative distribution function showing the total percentage of time that 80 meters is open, at or below each elevation angle, from Boston to the world. For example, 50% of the time the band is open to Europe from Boston, it is at 13° or less.

to his signal. It's not that the elevation angle is somehow *too low* — the real problem here is that you don't have *enough gain* at that particular angle where the ionosphere is supporting propagation. Many "flatlanders" can vividly recall the times when their mountain-top friends could easily work DX stations, while they couldn't even hear a whisper.

Looking at the Data — Further Cautions

A single propagation mode is quite common at the opening and the closing of daytime bands like 20, 15 or 10 meters, when the elevation angle is often lower (but not always) than when the band is wide open. The lower-frequency bands tend to support multiple propagation modes simultaneously. For example, **Figure 4.32** plots the signal strength (in dBµV) and the elevation angle for the dominant mode (with the strongest signal) over a 24-hour period from Newington to London in October, for a medium-level SSN = 70. The morning opening at 10 UTC starts out with a two-hop $2F_2$ mode (labeled 2F) at an elevation angle of 6°. By 11 UTC the mode has changed to a three-hop $3F_2$ (labeled 3F) at a 12° elevation angle. The band starts to close down with weaker signals after about 23 UTC. Note that this path actually supports both $2F_2$ and $3F_2$ modes most of the time. Either mode may be stronger than the other, depending on the particular time of day.

It is tempting to think that two-hop signals always occur at lower elevation launch angles, while three-hop signals require higher elevation angles. In reality, the detailed wor 22 UTC to 03 UTC, the elevation angles are higher than 11° for $2F_2$ hops. During much of the morning and early afternoon in Newington (from 11 to 13 UTC, and from 15 to 19 UTC), the angles are also higher than 11°. However, $3F_2$ hops are involved during these periods of time. The number

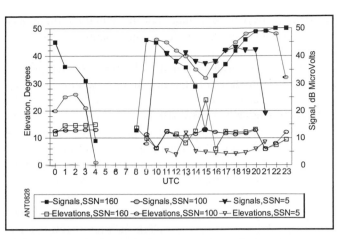

Figure 4.33 — October 20 meter signals and elevation angles for the full range of solar activity, from W1 to England. The elevation angle does not closely follow the level of solar activity. What is important in designing a station capable of covering all levels of solar activity is to have flexibility in antenna elevation pattern response — to cover a wide range of possible angles.

of hops is not directly related to the elevation angles needed — changing layer heights account for this.

Note that starting around 15 UTC, the mid-morning 20 meter "slump" (down some 10 dB from peak signal level) is caused by higher levels of mainly D-layer absorption when the Sun is high overhead. This condition favors higher elevation angles, since signals launched at lower angles must travel for a longer time through the lossy lower layer.

How does the situation change with different levels of solar activity? **Figure 4.33** overlays predicted signals and elevation angles for three levels of solar activity in October, again for the Newington-London path. Figure 4.34 shows the mid-morning slump dramatically when the solar activity is at a very high level, represented by SSN = 160. At 15 UTC, the signal level drops 35 dB from peak level, and the elevation angle rises all the way to 24°. By the way, as a percentage of all possible openings, the 24° angle occurs only rarely, 0.5% of the time. It barely shows up as a blip in Table 4-4. Elevation angles are *not* closely related to the level of solar activity.

IONCAP/VOACAP demonstrates that elevation angles do not follow neat, easily identified patterns, even over a 24-hour period — much less over all portions of the solar cycle. Merely looking at the percentage of all openings versus elevation angle, as shown in Table 4-4, does not tell the whole story, although it is probably the most statistically valid approach to station design, and possibly the most emotionally satisfying approach too. Neither is the whole story revealed by looking only at a snapshot of elevation angles versus time for one particular month, or for one solar activity level.

What is important to recognize is that the most effective antenna system will be one that can cover the *full range* of elevation angles, over the whole spectrum of solar activity, even if the actual angle in use at any one moment in time

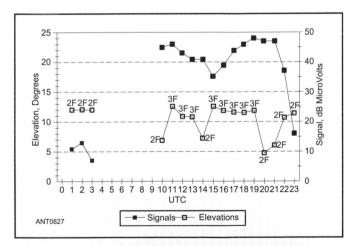

Figure 4.32 — Overlay of 20 meter signals and elevation angles, together with hop-mode information. This is for one month, October, at one level of solar activity, SSN=70, for the path from Newington, CT, to London, England. The mode of propagation does not closely follow the elevation angle. From 15 to 19 UTC the mode is $3F_2$ hops, and the elevation angle is approximately 12°. The same elevation angle is required from 23 to 03 UTC, but here the mode is $2F_2$ hops.

may not be easy to determine. For this particular path, from New England to all of Europe, an ideal antenna would have equal response over the full range of angles from 1° to 28°. Unfortunately, real-world antennas have a tough time covering such a wide range of elevation angles equally well.

Antenna Elevation Patterns

Figures 4.34 through **4.38** show overlays of the same sort of elevation angle information listed in Table 4-4, together with the elevation response patterns for typical antennas for the HF amateur bands 80, 40, 20, 15 and 10 meters. For example, Figure 4.36 shows an overlay for 20 meters, with three different types of 20 meter antennas. These are a 4-element Yagi at 90 feet, a 4-element Yagi at 120 feet and a large stack of four 4-element Yagis located at 120, 90, 60 and 30 feet. Each antenna is assumed to be mounted over flat ground. Placement on a hill with a long slope in the direction of interest would lower the required elevation angle by the amount of the hill's slope. For example, if a 10° launch angle is desired, and the antenna is placed on a hill with a slope of –5°, the antenna itself should be designed for a height that would optimize the response at 15° over flat ground — one wavelength high.

In Figure 4.36, the large stack of four 20 meter Yagis over flat ground comes closest to being ideal, but even this large array will not work well for that very small percentage of time when the angle needed is higher than about 20°. Some hams might conclude that the tiny percentage of time when the angles are very high doesn't justify an antenna tailored for that response. However, when that new DX country pops up on a band, or when a rare multiplier shows up in a contest, doesn't it always seem that the desired signal only comes in at some angle your antenna doesn't cover well? What do you do then, if your only antenna happens to be a large stack?

The answer to this, perhaps unique, high-angle problem lies in switching to using only the top antenna in the stack. In this example, the second elevation lobe of the 120-foot high antenna would cover the angles from 20° to 30° well, much better than the stack does. Note that the top antenna by itself would not be ideal for all conditions. It is simply too high much of the time when the elevation angles are higher than about 12°. The experience of many amateurs on the US East Coast with high 20 meter antennas bears this out — they find that 60 to 90-foot high antennas are far more consistent performers into Europe.

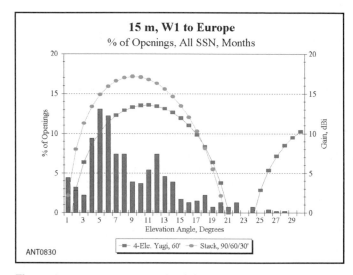

Figure 4.35 — 15 meter graph of the percentage of all openings versus elevation angles, together with overlay of elevation patterns over flat ground for two 15 meter antenna systems. Like 10 meters, 15 meter stacked antennas have wider footprints in elevation angle coverage for this example from New England to Europe.

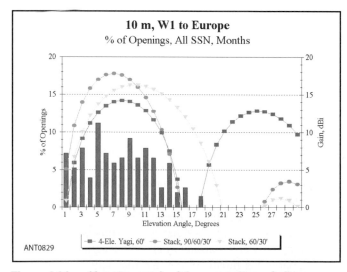

Figure 4.34 — 10 meter graph of the percentage of all openings versus elevation angles, together with overlay of elevation patterns over flat ground for three 10 meter antenna systems. Stacked antennas have wider "footprints" in elevation angle coverage for this example from New England to Europe.

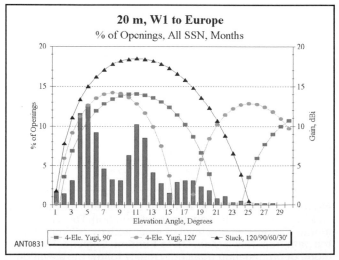

Figure 4.36 — 20 meter graph of the percentage of all openings from New England to Europe versus elevation angles, together with overlay of elevation patterns over flat ground for three 20 meter antenna systems.

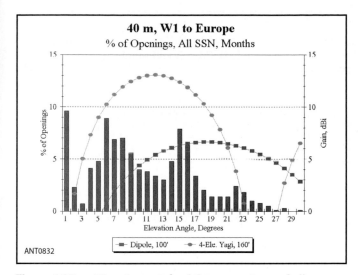

Figure 4.37 — 40 meter graph of the percentage of all openings from New England to Europe versus elevation angles, together with overlays of elevation patterns over flat ground for a 100-foot high dipole and a large 4-element Yagi at 160 feet. Achieving gain at very low elevation angles requires very high heights above ground.

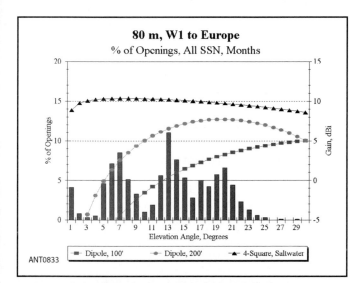

Figure 4.38 — 80 meter graph of the percentage of all openings from New England to Europe versus elevation angles, together with overlay of elevation patterns over flat ground for dipoles at two different heights. The 200-foot-high dipole clearly covers the necessary elevation angles better than does the 100-foot-high dipole, although a four-square vertical array located over saltwater is even better for all angles needed.

4.3.3 PROPAGATION PREDICTION TABLES

The CD-ROM included at the back of this book includes summary and detailed propagation predictions for more than 150 transmitting locations around the world. This propagation data was calculated using *CapMAN*, an upgraded variety of the mainframe propagation program *IONCAP*. An expanded set of tables by N6BV is available from Radioware, **www. radio-ware.com**. The predictions were done for default antennas and powers that are representative of a "big-gun"

station. Of course, not everyone has a big-gun station in his/her backyard, but this represents what the ultimate possibilities are, statistically speaking. After all, if the bands aren't open for the big guns, they are unlikely to be open for the "little pistols" too. (*CapMAN* was offered by Jim Tabor, KU5S, of Kangaroo Tabor Software — KU5S became a Silent Key in mid-2009, and his software is no longer supported.)

Let's see how propagation is affected if the smoothed sunspot number is 0 (corresponding to a smoothed solar flux of about 65), which is classified as a "Very Low" level of solar activity (in terms of SSN, the smoothed sunspot number). And we'll examine the situation for a sunspot number of 100 (a smoothed solar flux of 150), which is typical of a "Very High" portion of the solar cycle.

Five-Band Summary Predictions

Tables 4-5 and **4-6** are Summary tables showing the predicted signal levels (in S units) from Boston, Massachusetts, to the rest of the world for the month of January. The Boston transmitting site is representative of the entire New England area of the USA. The target geographic receiving regions for the major HF bands from 80 through 10 meters are tabulated versus UTC (Universal Coordinated Time) in hours. Table 4-5 represents a Very Low level of solar activity, while Table 4-6 is for a Very High level of solar activity.

Each transmitting location is organized by six levels of solar activity over the whole 11-year solar cycle:

- VL (Very Low: SSN between 0 to 20)
- LO (Low: SSN between 20 to 40)
- ME (Medium: SSN between 40 to 60)
- HI (High: SSN between 60 to 100)
- VH (Very High: SSN between 100 to 150)
- UH (Ultra High: SSN greater than 150)

The receiving geographic regions for each frequency band are abbreviated:

- EU All of Europe
- FE The Far East, centered on Japan
- SA South America, centered on Paraguay
- AF All of Africa, centered on Zambia
- AS South Asia, centered on India
- OC Oceania, centered on Sydney, Australia
- NA North America, all across the USA

These propagation files show the highest predicted signal strength (in S-units) throughout the generalized receiving area, for a 1500-W transmitter and rather good antennas on both sides of the circuit. The standard antennas are:

- 100-foot high inverted-V dipoles for 80 and 40 meters
- 3-element Yagi at 100 feet for 20 meters
- 4-element Yagi at 60 feet for 15 and 10 meters

For example, Summary Table 4-5 shows that in January during a period of Very Low solar activity, 15 meters is open to somewhere in Europe from Boston for only 4 hours, from 13 to 16 UTC, with a peak signal level between S4 and S7. Now look at Table 4-6, where 15 meters is predicted to be

Table 4-5

Printout of summary propagation table for Boston to the rest of the world, for a Very Low level of solar activity in the month of January. The abbreviations for the target geographic areas are: EU = Europe, FE = Far East, SA = South America, AF = Africa, AS = south Asia, OC = Oceania, and NA = North America.

Jan., MA (Boston), for SSN = Very Low, Sigs in S-Units. By N6BV, ARRL.

UTC	80 Meters EU FE SA AF AS OC NA	40 Meters EU FE SA AF AS OC NA	20 Meters EU FE SA AF AS OC NA	15 Meters EU FE SA AF AS OC NA	10 Meters EU FE SA AF AS OC NA	UTC
0	9 - 9+ 9 9 - 9+	9 8 9+ 9+ 9 2 9+	- 8 9+ 7 4 8 9+	- - - - - - 1	- - - - - - 2	0
1	9 - 9+ 9 9 - 9+	9 6 9+ 9+ 9+ 6 9+	- 4 9 4 2 6 9+	- - - - - - 1	- - - - - - 2	1
2	9 - 9+ 9+ 8 1 9+	9 6 9+ 9+ 9 8 9+	- 1 8 1 2 3 9+	- - - - - - 1	- - - - - - 2	2
3	9 - 9+ 9+ 8 6 9+	9 6 9+ 9+ 9 8 9+	- - 8 2 2 - 9+	- - - - - - 1	- - - - - - 2	3
4	9 - 9+ 9+ 1 8 9+	9 8 9+ 9+ 9 9 9+	- 1 8 7 2 - 9+	- - - - - - 1	- - - - - - 2	4
5	9 - 9+ 9+ - 9 9+	9 8 9+ 9+ 8 9 9+	- 1 9 8 2 - 9	- - - - - - 1	- - - - - - 2	5
6	9+ - 9+ 9+ - 9 9+	7 8 9+ 9+ 8 9 9+	- 1 9+ 8 - - 9	- - - - - - 1	- - - - - - 2	6
7	9 7 9+ 9 - 9 9+	7 8 9+ 9 8 9 9+	- 1 9+ 1 - 1 8	- - - - - - 1	- - - - - - 2	7
8	9 8 9+ 9 - 9 9+	8 9 9+ 9 8 9+ 9+	- 1 9+ - - 5 9	- - - - - - 1	- - - - - - 2	8
9	8 8 9+ 7 6 9 9+	8 9 9+ 9 9 9+ 9+	- - 9 1 - 7 9	- - - - - - 1	- - - - - - 2	9
10	5 8 9+ 4 6 9 9+	9 9 9+ 9 9 9+ 9+	- 3 9 5 - 6 9	- - - - - - 1	- - - - - - 2	10
11	3 8 9+ - 5 9 9+	8 9 9+ 7 9 9+ 9+	5 - 9+ 9 5 1* 8	- - - - - - 1	- - - - - - 2	11
12	1 8 9 - 4 9 9+	7 9 9+ 4 8 9 9+	9 5 9+ 9+ 9 2* 8	4 - 5 6 - - 1	- - - - - - 2	12
13	- 6 1 - - 7 9+	6 8 9+ 1 8 9 9+	9+ 9 9+ 9 9 7 8	9+ 9 9+ 9 7 - 1	- - - - - - 1	13
14	- - - - - 1 9+	5 7 8 - 8 8 9+	9+ 9 9+ 9 9 9 9+	7 2* 9+ 9 9 - 8	- - 5 - - - 1	14
15	- - - - - - 9+	4 6 5 - 6 7 9+	9+ 9 9+ 9 9 9 9+	7 5 9+ 9 2 2 5	- - 5 - - - -	15
16	- - - - - - 9+	5 6 4 2 5 4 9+	9+ 8 9+ 9+ 9 9 9+	5 1 9+ 8 2* 2 9	- - 5 - - - 1	16
17	- - - - - - 9+	6 5 5 5 6 1 9+	9+ 5 9+ 9+ 3 9 9+	- - 9+ 9 - 3 9+	- - 5 - - - 1	17
18	1 - - - - - 9+	8 6 6 7 6 - 9+	9+ 6 9+ 9+ 4 9 9+	- - 9+ 9 - 7 9+	- - 5 - - - 1	18
19	3 - - 2 - - 9+	9 7 8 8 8 - 9+	6 6 9+ 9+ 6 9 9+	- - 9+ 9 - 9 9+	- - 2 - - - 1	19
20	5 - 7 5 - - 9+	9 8 9+ 9 8 4 9+	1 7 9+ 9+ 8 9 9+	- - 9+ 4 - 9 9	- - - - - - 1	20
21	8 3 9 8 6 - 9+	9 8 9+ 9+ 9 7 9+	- 8 9+ 9 8 9 9+	- - 9+ - - 9 6	- - - - - - 1	21
22	9 3 9+ 9 8 - 9+	9 8 9+ 9+ 9 5 9+	- 9+ 9+ 9 8 9 9+	- - 9 - - 7 1	- - - - - - 1	22
23	9 2 9+ 9 9 - 9+	9 8 9+ 9+ 9 4 9+	- 9+ 9+ 9 5 9 9+	- 1 6 - - 2 3	- - - - - - 2	23
	EU FE SA AF AS OC NA	EU FE SA AF AS OC NA	EU FE SA AF AS OC NA	EU FE SA AF AS OC NA	EU FE SA AF AS OC NA	

Table 4-6

Printout of summary propagation table for Boston to the rest of the world, for a Very High level of solar activity in the month of January.

Jan., MA (Boston), for SSN = Very High, Sigs in S-Units. By N6BV, ARRL.

UTC	80 Meters EU FE SA AF AS OC NA	40 Meters EU FE SA AF AS OC NA	20 Meters EU FE SA AF AS OC NA	15 Meters EU FE SA AF AS OC NA	10 Meters EU FE SA AF AS OC NA	UTC
0	9+ - 9+ 9+ 8 - 9+	9+ 5 9+ 9+ 9 - 9+	1 9+ 9+ 9+ 9+ 9 9+	- 9 9+ 2 2 9+ 9+	- 1 8 - - 8 9+	0
1	9+ - 9+ 9+ 8 - 9+	9+ 4 9+ 9+ 9 2 9+	1 9 9+ 8 9+ 9+ 9+	- 3 9 - 7 9+ 9	- - - - - 4 2	1
2	9+ - 9+ 9+ 7 - 9+	9+ 4 9+ 9+ 9 7 9+	1 9 9+ 8 9 9+ 9+	- - 3 - - 7 9	- - - - - - 2	2
3	9+ - 9+ 9+ 1 2 9+	9+ 4 9+ 9+ 9 9 9+	- 7 9+ 7 8 9+ 9	- - - - - - -	- - - - - - 2	3
4	9+ - 9+ 9+ - 7 9+	9+ 5 9+ 9+ 8 9 9+	- 5 9+ 9 9 9 9+	- - 1 - - - -	- - - - - - 2	4
5	9+ - 9+ 9+ - 8 9+	9+ 6 9+ 9+ 7 9 9+	- 5 9+ 9 9 5 9+	- - - - - - -	- - - - - - 2	5
6	9+ - 9+ 9+ - 8 9+	9+ 7 9+ 9+ 7 9 9+	- 8 9+ 8 9 5 9+	- - 1 - - - -	- - - - - - 2	6
7	9+ - 9+ 9+ - 8 9+	9 8 9+ 9+ 7 9+ 9+	- 9 9+ - 7 9 9+	- - 1 - - - -	- - - - - - 2	7
8	9 7 9+ 9 - 8 9+	9 8 9+ 9+ 8 9+ 9+	- 9 9+ - 4 9+ 9+	- - 1 - - - 2	- - - - - - 2	8
9	8 7 9+ 7 - 8 9+	9 9 9+ 9 8 9+ 9+	- 6 9+ - 1 9+ 9+	- - - - - - 1	- - - - - - 2	9
10	5 8 9+ 2 3 8 9+	9 9 9+ 8 8 9 9+	4 - 9+ 9+ 1 5 9	- - - - - - -	- - - - - - 2	10
11	1 8 9+ - 4 9 9+	8 9 9+ 5 8 9 9+	9+ 4* 9+ 9+ 7 - 8	- - 9 9 - - -	- - - - - - 2	11
12	- 7 8 - 1 9 9+	6 9 9+ 1 8 9 9+	9+ 9 9+ 9 9 1* 9+	9 8* 9+ 9+ 9 5* -	- 2* 9 9 1 1* 2	12
13	- - - - - 2 9+	4 8 8 - 7 9 9+	9+ 9 9+ 9 9 9 9+	9+ 7 9+ 9+ 9+ 3* 9	9 5* 9+ 9+ 9 6* 2	13
14	- - - - - - 9+	2 7 4 - 5 8 9+	9+ 9 9+ 8 9 9 9+	9+ 9 9+ 9+ 9+ 9 9+	9 6* 9+ 9+ 9 1* 1	14
15	- - - - - - 9	1 5 - - 4 5 9+	9+ 9 9+ 9 9 9 9+	9+ 9+ 9+ 9+ 9+ 9 9+	9 5 9+ 9+ 6 6 8	15
16	- - - - - - 8	3 4 - - 3 1 9+	9+ 8 9 9 9 9 9+	9+ 9+ 9+ 9+ 9 9+ 9+	9 8 9+ 9+ - 8 9	16
17	- - - - - - 8	5 3 - 2 4 - 9+	9+ 8 9+ 9+ 9 9 9+	9+ 9 9+ 9+ 1* 9+ 9+	- 8 9+ 9+ - 8 9+	17
18	- - - - - - 9	7 4 2 5 5 - 9+	9+ 9 9+ 9+ 9 9 9+	9+ 9 9+ 9+ 1 9+ 9+	- 7 9+ 9+ - 9+ 9+	18
19	1 - - 1 - - 9+	8 5 6 8 7 - 9+	9+ 9 9+ 9+ 9 9 9+	- 9+ 9+ 9+ 2 9 9+	- 6 9+ 9+ - 9+ 9+	19
20	4 - 2 5 - - 9+	9 6 9 9 8 - 9+	9+ 9 9+ 9+ 9 9 9+	- 8 9+ 9+ 3 9 9+	- 1 9+ 9 - 9 9+	20
21	7 - 8 7 1 - 9+	9+ 7 9+ 9+ 8 1 9+	8 9 9+ 9+ 9 9 9+	- 6 9+ 9+ 3 9 9+	- - 9+ 5* - 9+ 9+	21
22	9 2 9+ 9 8 - 9+	9+ 7 9+ 9+ 9 - 9+	2 9+ 9+ 9+ 9 9 9+	- 9+ 9+ 9 1 9+ 9+	5 9 9+ 4* - 9 6	22
23	9 - 9+ 9 8 - 9+	9+ 7 9+ 9+ 9 - 9+	1 9+ 9+ 9+ 9 9 9+	- 9+ 9+ 6 - 9 9+	- 7 9+ 2* - 9 2	23
	EU FE SA AF AS OC NA	EU FE SA AF AS OC NA	EU FE SA AF AS OC NA	EU FE SA AF AS OC NA	EU FE SA AF AS OC NA	

open to Europe during a period of Very High solar activity for 7 hours, from 12 to 18 UTC, with peak signals ranging from S9 to S9+.

Both Tables 4-5 and 4-6 represent *snapshots* of predicted signal levels to generalized receiving locations — that is, they are computed for a particular month, from a particular transmitting location, and for a particular level of solar activity. These tables provide summary information that is particularly valuable for someone planning for an operating event such as a DXpedition or a contest.

What happens if you don't have a big-gun station with high antennas or the 1500-W power assumed in the analyses above? You can discount the S-Meter readings to reflect a smaller station:

- Subtract 2 S units for a dipole instead of a Yagi at same height on 20/15/10 meters
- Subtract 3 S units for a dipole at 50 feet instead of a Yagi at 100 feet on 20 meters
- Subtract 1 S unit for a dipole at 50 feet rather than a dipole at 100 feet on 40/80 meters
- Subtract 3 S units for 100 W rather than 1500 W
- Subtract 6 S units for 5 W (QRP) rather than 1500 W

For example, Table 4-5 predicts an S7 signal into Boston from Europe on 15 meters at 14 UTC. If a European station is using a dipole at 50 feet, with 100 W of power, what would this do to the predicted signal level in Boston? You would compute: S7 – 2 S units (for a dipole instead of Yagi) – 3 S units (100 W rather than 1500 W) = an S2 signal in Boston. A QRP station with a 4-element 15 meter Yagi at 60 feet would yield: S7 – 6 S units = an S1 signal in Boston.

More Detailed Predictions

Let's now look at table in **Figure 4.39**, which is the Detailed 20 meter page for the same conditions in Table 4-6: January at a Very High level of solar activity from Boston to the world. There are six such pages per month/SSN level, covering 160, 80, 40, 20, 15 and 10 meters.

In a Detailed prediction table, the world is divided into the 40 CQ Zones, with a particular sample location in each zone. For example, Zone 14 in Western Europe is represented by a location in London, England (call sign G), while Zone 25 is represented by a location in Tokyo, Japan (call sign JA1). Note that Zones with large ham populations are highlighted with dark shadowing for easy identification. For

Zone	00	01	02	03	04	05	06	07	08	09	10	11	12	13	14	15	16	17	18	19	20
01	9+	9+	9+	7	-	-	-	-	-	-	-	-	-	-	-	3	9+	9+	9+	9+	9+
02	9+	9	9	9	9	9	8	7	5	3	2	1	5	9+	9+	9+	9+	9+	9+	9+	9+
03	9+	9+	9+	7	7	1	1	5	8	8	3	-	-	1	9	9+	9+	9+	9+	9	9
04	9+	9+	9+	8	5	5	5	5	3	2	1	-	-	9+	9+	9+	9+	9+	9+	9+	9+
05	4	2	2	2	2	2	3	3	3	3	2	1	1	8	9+	9+	9+	9+	9+	9+	9+
06	9+	9+	7	9	9+	9+	9+	9+	9+	9+	9	8	9+	9+	9+	9+	9	9	9	9	9+
07	9+	9+	8	9	9	9	9	9	9	9+	9	9+	9+	9+	9+	9+	9	8	9	9	9+
08	9+	9+	9+	9+	9+	9+	9+	9+	9+	8	9	9+	9+	9+	9+	9+	9	9+	9+	9+	9+
09	9+	9+	9+	9+	9+	9+	9+	9+	9+	9+	9+	9+	9+	9+	9+	9	9	9	9	9+	9+
10	9+	8	9+	9	9	9	9	9	7	3	1	7	9+	9+	9	5	5	5	7	8	9+
11	9+	9+	9+	9	9	9+	9+	9	8	6	9	9+	8	2	1	-	-	1	4	8	9
12	9+	9+	9+	9+	9+	9+	9+	9	8	8	8	9+	9	8	2	1	1	-	1	3	7
13	9+	9+	9+	9+	9+	9+	9+	9+	8	8	8	9+	8	4	2	1	-	1	4	8	
14	-	-	-	-	-	-	-	-	-	-	-	9+	9+	9+	9+	9+	9+	9+	9+	9+	9+
15	-	-	-	-	-	-	-	-	-	-	4	9	9	9	9	9	9	9+	9+	9	8
16	1	1	1	-	-	-	-	-	-	-	-	8	9	9+	9+	9+	9	8	5	-	-
17	1	-	-	8	7	7	7	1	-	-	-	2	9	9	9	6	-	-	2	4	8
18	6	7	6	6	9	9	9	7	4	1	-	-	8	8	6	6	5	6	7	8	9
19	9+	9	9	6	5	5	8	8	8	4	-	-	2	6	8	8	7	4	4	7	
20	8	6	3	1	-	3	4	-	-	-	1	8	8	8	8	9	9	9	9+	9	9
21	9+	9	4	3	8	8	2	-	-	-	1	7	8	9	8	9	9	9	9	9	
22	7	5	8	7	6	7	5	-	-	-	-	6	9	9	9	9	3	2	2	2	8
23	9	9+	9	5	7	8	8	6	3	-	-	2*	8	8	5	6	8	8	8	8	9
24	9	9	9	5	4	5	7	8	6	1	-	1*	5	7	1	1	1	1	4	2	-
25	9	9	8	7	5	5	8	9	9	6	-	1	1	2	7	7	6	2	-	-	7
26	9	9	6	4	2	-	-	2	1	-	-	2*	9	9	9	9	8	7	5	4	5
27	9	8	7	-	-	-	5	7	7	1	-	-	1*	9	9	7	6	4	5	3	1*
28	9	8	1	-	-	-	-	-	-	-	-	4*	8	9	9	9	8	8	9	9	9
29	3*	4*	-	-	-	-	-	-	5	3	-	-	-	5	9	9	9	8	9	9	9
30	1*	-	-	-	-	1	3	9	9	4	-	-	-	9+	9	8	2	1	-	-	1
31	9	9+	9+	9+	8	2	2	6	4	-	-	-	-	-	-	9	9	8	7	6	
32	-	2	9	9	9	5	5	9	9+	9+	5	-	-	9+	9	9	8	5	3	1	-
33	-	-	-	-	-	-	-	-	-	-	9	9+	9	9	8	9	9	9+	9+	9+	9+
34	9	8	3	3	-	1	4	-	-	-	2	7	8	8	8	8	9	9	9	9+	9+
35	9+	8	-	-	2	7	5	-	-	-	9+	9+	8	5	4	3	7	9	9+	9+	9+
36	9+	9+	5	3	9	9	8	-	-	-	3	-	-	-	-	4	4	7	8	9	9+
37	9+	9	2	4	8	8	1	-	-	-	2	-	-	3	5	5	7	8	9	9	9+
38	9+	9+	8	7	8	9	6	-	-	-	-	-	-	1*	1	2	6	8	9	9+	

Figure 4.39 — The 20 meter page from Detailed propagation-prediction for the month of January, during Very High solar conditions, from Boston to 40 CQ Zones throughout the world. There are similar pages for each month/SSN level for 160, 80, 40, 20, 15 and 10 meters. These Detailed tables are very useful for planning DX operation.

example, Zones 3, 4 and 5 cover the USA, while Zones 14, 15 and 16 cover the majority of Europe. Zone 25 covers the big ham population in Japan.

Let's revisit the example above for computing the signal strength for a station in London, but this time on 20 meters. Again, we'll assume that the G station has a dipole at 50 feet and 100 W of transmitter power. At 14 UTC in Zone 14, the table in Figure 4.39 predicts a very healthy signal for the reference big-gun station, at S9+. This is a signal at least S9 + 10 dB. Here, we're going to round off the plus 10 dB to 2 S units, giving a fictional 11 S units to start. We discount this for the smaller station: S11 − 3 S units (for a dipole at 50 feet instead of a 3-element Yagi at 100 feet) − 3 S units (100 W rather than 1500 W) = S5 signal in Boston. This is a respectable signal and will probably get through, in the absence of stronger signals calling the Boston station at the same time, of course.

Here's another example of how to use the detailed propagation-prediction tables. Let's say that at 1230 UTC in January you work a VU2 station in New Delhi on 15 meters from Boston, where the local time is 7:30 AM. You need a 20 meter contact also for the 5-Band DXCC award, so you quickly check the table in Figure 4.39 for Zone 22 (VU) and

find that the predicted signal strength is S9. Your new VU2 friend is willing to jump to 20 meters and so you QSY to make the contact.

But perhaps you are late leaving for work and so you ask your new VU2 friend to make a schedule with you later that evening. Again, you consult the Detailed prediction table for 20 meters and find that signals are predicted to be S8 or stronger from 20 to 23 UTC, dropping to S7 at 00 UTC. You quickly ask your new friend whether he minds waking up at 4:30 AM his time to make a schedule with you at 2300 UTC, because New Delhi is 5½ hours ahead of UTC. You determined this using the program *GeoClock*, which runs in the background on *Windows*. *GeoClock* is a shareware program from **www.mygeoclock.com/geoclock**. Luckily, he's a very gracious fellow and agrees to meet you on a specific frequency at that time.

The detailed propagation-prediction tables give you all the information needed to plan your operations to maximize your enjoyment chasing DX. You can use these tables to plan a 48-hour contest next month, or next year — or you can use them to plan a schedule with your ham cousin on the West Coast on Saturday afternoon.

4.4 PROPAGATION PREDICTION SOFTWARE

Very reliable methods of determining the MUF for any given radio path have been developed over the last 50 years. As discussed previously, these methods are all based on the smoothed sunspot number (SSN) as the measure of solar activity. It is for this reason that smoothed sunspot numbers hold so much meaning for radio amateurs and others concerned with radio-wave propagation — they are the link to past (and future) propagation conditions.

Early on, the prediction of propagation conditions required tedious work with numerous graphs, along with charts of frequency contours overlaid, or overprinted, on world maps. The basic materials were available from an agency of the US government. Monthly publications provided the frequency-contour data a few months in advance. Only rarely did amateurs try their hand at predicting propagation conditions using these hard-to-use methods.

Today's powerful PCs have given the amateur wonderful tools to make quick-and-easy HF propagation predictions, whether for a contest or a DXpedition. The summary and detailed prediction tables described earlier in this chapter were generated using *CAPMan*, a modernized version of the mainframe *IONCAP* program, on a PC. (*Capman* is no longer available.)

While tremendously useful to setting up schedules and for planning strategy for contests, both the Summary and Detailed prediction tables located on the CD-ROM accompanying this book show signal strength. They do not show other information that is also in the underlying databases used to generate them. They don't, for example, show the dominant

elevation angles and neither do they show reliability statistics. You may want to run propagation-prediction software yourself to get into the really "nitty-gritty" details.

Modern programs are designed for quick-and-easy predictions of propagation parameters. See **Table 4-7** for a listing of a number of popular programs. (A collection of propagation prediction software is also available at **astrosurf. com/luxorion/qsl-review-propagation-software.htm**.) The basic input information required is the smoothed sunspot number (SSN) or smoothed solar flux, the date (month and day), and the latitudes and longitudes at the two ends of the radio path. The latitude and longitude, of course, are used to determine the great-circle radio path. Most commercial programs tailored for ham use allow you to specify locations by the call sign. The date is used to determine the latitude of the Sun, and this, with the sunspot number, is used to determine the properties of the ionosphere at critical points on the path.

Of course, just because a computer program predicts that a band will be open on a particular path, it doesn't follow that the Sun and the ionosphere will always cooperate! A sudden solar flare can result in a major geomagnetic storm, taking out HF communication anywhere from hours to days. There is still art, as well as a lot of science, in predicting propagation. In times of quiet geomagnetic activity, however, the prediction programs are good at forecasting band openings and closings.

4.4.1 SOLAR ACTIVITY DATA

Our propagation prediction programs were developed based on the very high correlation between a smoothed solar

Table 4-7
Features and Attributes of Propagation Prediction Programs

	ASAPS V. 6	VOACAP Windows	ACE-HF	W6ELProp V. 2.70	PropLab Pro V. 3
User Friendliness	Good	Good	Excellent	Good	Poor**
Operating System	Windows	Windows	Windows	Windows	Windows
Uses k or A index	No*	No	No	Yes	Yes
User library of QTHs	Yes	Yes	Yes-RX	Yes	No
Bearings, distances	Yes	Yes	Yes	Yes	Yes
MUF calculation	Yes	Yes	Yes	Yes	Yes
LUF calculation	Yes	Yes	Yes	No	Yes
Wave angle calculation	Yes	Yes	Yes	Yes	Yes
Vary minimum wave angle	Yes	Yes	Yes	Yes	Yes
Path regions and hops	Yes	Yes	Yes	Yes	Yes
Multipath effects	Yes	Yes	Yes	No	Yes
Path probability	Yes	Yes	Yes	Yes	Yes
Signal strengths	Yes	Yes	Yes	Yes	Yes
S/N ratios	Yes	Yes	Yes	No	Yes
Long-path calculation	Yes	Yes	Yes	Yes	Yes
Antenna selection	Yes	Yes	Yes	Indirectly	Yes
Vary antenna height	Yes	Yes	Yes	Indirectly	Yes
Vary ground characteristics	Yes	Yes	Yes	No	No
Vary transmit power	Yes	Yes	Yes	Indirectly	Yes
Graphic displays	Yes	Yes	Yes	Yes	2D/3D
UT-day graphs	Yes	Yes	Yes	Yes	Yes
Area Mapping	Yes	Yes	Yes	Yes	Yes
Documentation	Yes	On-line	Yes	Yes	Yes
Price class	AUD $375	$89	free	free	$240

Price classes are for mid-2011 and subject to change.
ASAPS - **www.ips.gov.au/Products_and_Services**
VOACAP - **www.voacap.com**
ACE-HF - **elbert.its.bldrdoc.gov/hf.html**
W6ELProp - **www.qsl.net/w6elprop**
PropLab Pro - **www.spacew.com/www/proplab.html**

*Uses T-inssdex available from IPS.
**Proplab Pro is more of a propagation analysis program, and a good understanding of the ionosphere is needed to use it properly.

index (originally the smoothed sunspot number, but equally good is the smoothed solar flux) and monthly median ionospheric parameters. Thus to use our prediction programs properly, you must use a smoothed solar index and understand that the outputs (usually signals strength and MUF) are statistical in nature over a month's time frame.

Future smoothed solar indices are available at **www.swpc.noaa.gov/ftpdir/weekly/Predict.txt**. The "Predicted" values at this web site for both indices are most likely what you should use. The "High" and "Low" values give the upper and lower boundary of the predicted parameter. If the solar activity is greater than expected, use the "High" value. If the solar activity is lower than expected, use the "Low" value.

Using the daily 10.7 cm solar flux or the daily sunspot number doesn't provide a more accurate picture of propagation. This comment is true even when including the K or A index. The reason for this is the significant day-to-day variation of the ionosphere, especially the F2 region. The F2 region varies on a day-to-day basis not only due to solar ionizing radiation, but due to events in the lower atmosphere coupling up to the ionosphere and due to a more complicated response

to the K and A indices than a single value.

Using values of 10.7 cm solar flux averaged over 7 days or even longer (3 months, for example) will drive the prediction results more towards how they were intended to be used — with a smoothed solar index. These results will be better than using a daily solar index, but there will still be a discrepancy between the index used and what the ionosphere is doing.

Historical smoothed sunspot numbers are available at **ftp://ftp.ngdc.noaa.gov/STP/SOLAR_DATA/SUNSPOT_NUMBERS/INTERNATIONAL/smoothed/SMOOTHED**, and are plotted in **Figure 4.40** starting with Cycle 19 and including the current prediction for Cycle 24 at the time of writing (April 2011).

For the most current data on what the Sun is doing, National Institute of Standards and Technology stations WWV and WWVH broadcast information on solar activity at 18 and 45 minutes past each hour, respectively. These propagation bulletins give the solar flux, geomagnetic A-Index, Boulder K-Index, and a brief statement of solar and geomagnetic activity in the past and coming 24-hour periods, in that

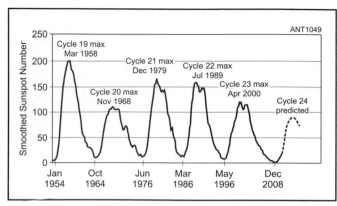

Figure 4.40 — Historical and predicted smoothed sunspot numbers for Cycles 19 through 24.

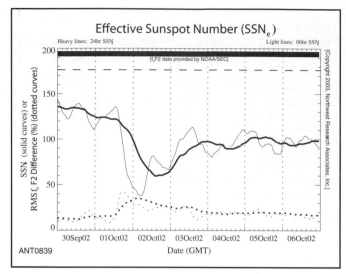

Figure 4.41 — Effective Sunspot Number (SSNₑ) produced by NWRA. Note the large drop in effective SSN due to a geomagnetic storm commencing Oct 1, 2002.

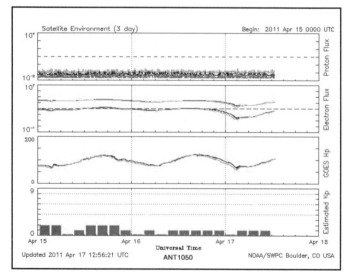

Figure 4.42 — Typical plot of planetary K index, Kp. Also included are plots of proton flux (from big solar flares), electron flux (a flat line means minimal geomagnetic field activity), and GOES Hp (another indicator of geomagnetic field activity). (Courtesy NOAA/SWPC)

order. The solar flux and A-Index are changed daily with the 2118 UT bulletin, the rest every three hours — 0018, 0318, 0618 UT and so on. On the web, up-to-date WWV information can be found at: **ftp://ftp.swpc.noaa.gov/pub/latest/ wwv.txt** or on the NOAA web page **www.swpc.noaa.gov**.

Some other useful web sites are: **dx.qsl.net/propagation**, **www.dxlc.com/solar**, and **hfradio.org/propagation. html**. The Solar Terrestrial Dispatch page contains a wealth of propagation-related information: **www.spacew.com**. You may also access propagation information on your local PacketCluster. Use the command SH/WWV/*n*, where *n* is the number of spots you wish to see (five is the default).

Another excellent method for obtaining an "equivalent sunspot number" (SSNₑ) is to go to the Space Weather site of Northwest Research Services: **www.nwra-az.com/spawx/ ssne24.html**. NWRA compares real-time ionospheric sounder data around the world with predictions using various levels of SSN looking for the best match. They thus "back into" the actual effective sunspot number. Note that this is necessarily a best fit of ionospheric sounder data to an equivalent sunspot number — it's not a perfect fit for all the data due to the dynamic hour-to-hour variability of the worldwide F2 region. **Figure 4.41** is a typical NWRA graph, which covers the week ending 6 October 2002. Note the sudden decrease in SSNe after a geomagnetic storm depressed SSNe by more than 50%.

The A-Index

The WWV/WWVH A-Index is a daily figure for the state of activity of the Earth's magnetic field. It is updated with the 2118/2145 UT bulletin. The A-Index tells you mainly how yesterday was, but it is very revealing when charted regularly, because geomagnetic disturbances nearly always recur at four-week intervals.

The K-Index

The K-Index (new every three hours) reflects Boulder readings of the Earth's geomagnetic field in the hours just preceding the bulletin data changes. It is the nearest thing to current data on radio propagation available. With new data every three hours, K-Index trend is important. Rising is bad news; falling is good, especially related to propagation on paths involving latitudes above 30° north. Because this is a Boulder, Colorado, reading of geomagnetic activity, it may not correlate closely with conditions in other areas.

The K-Index is also a timely clue to aurora possibilities. Values of 4, and rising, warn that conditions associated with auroras and degraded HF propagation are present in the Boulder area at the time of the bulletin's preparation. A NOAA web site that carries up-to-date planetary Kp data is **www.swpc.noaa.gov/today.html#satenv**. **Figure 4.42** is a plot of Kp along with three other parameters from satellite observatories.

4.5 BIBLIOGRAPHY

Source material and more extended discussion of topics covered in this chapter can be found in the references given below.

E. V. Appleton and W.R. Piggott, "Ionospheric Absorption Measurements during a Sunspot Cycle," *J. Atmos. Terr. Phys.*, Vol 3, p 141, 1954.

D. Bilitiza, *International Reference Ionosphere (IRI 90)*, National Space Science Data Center, Greenbelt, MD, 1990.

D. Bray, "Method of Determining VHF/HF Station Capabilities," *QST*, Nov 1961.

A. Brekke, "Physics of the Upper Polar Atmosphere," (New York, 1997: John Wiley and Sons).

R. R. Brown, "Demography, DXpeditions and Magneto-Ionic Theory," *The DX Magazine*, Vol. X, No. 2, p 44, Mar/Apr 1998.

R. R. Brown, *The Little Pistol's Guide to HF Communication* (Sacramento: WorldRadio Books, 1996). [Out of print]

R. R. Brown, "Signal Ducting on the 160 Meter Band," *Communications Quarterly*, p 65, Spring 1998.

R. R. Brown, "Unusual Low-Frequency Signal Propagation at Sunrise," *Communications Quarterly*, p 67, Fall 1998.

R. R. Brown,, "Atmospheric Ozone, a Meteorological Factor in Low-Frequency and 160 Meter Propagation," *Communications Quarterly*, Spring 1999.

K. Davies, *Ionospheric Radio* (London: Peter Peregrinus Ltd, 1990). Excellent technical reference.

R. Garcia, S. Solomon, S. Avery, G. C. Reid, "Transport of Nitric Oxide and the D-Region Winter Anomaly," *J. Geophys. Res.*, Vol 92, p 977, 1987.

J. Hall, "Propagation Predictions and Personal Computers," Technical Correspondence, *QST*, Dec 1990, pp 58-59 (description of *IONCAP* as used for ARRL publications).

E . Harper, *Rhombic Antenna Design* (New York: D. Van Nostrand Co, Inc, 1941).

H. Hertz, *Electric Waves*, translated by D. E. Jones (London: MacMillan, 1893).

R. D. Hunsucker, *Radio Techniques for Probing the Terrestrial Ionosphere* (New York: Springer-Verlag).

R. D. Hunsucker, J. K. Hargreaves, *The High Latitude Ionosphere and Its Effects on Radio Propagation* (Cambridge: Cambridge University Press, 2003).

W. D. Johnston, Computer-calculated and computer-drawn great-circle maps are offered. An 11×14-inch map is custom made for your location. Write to K5ZI, PO Box 640, Organ, NM 88052, tele 505-382-7804.

T.L. Killeen, R.M. Johnsson, "Upper Atmospheric Waves, Turbulence, and Winds: Importance for Mesospheric and Thermospheric Studies," **earth.agu.org/revgeo-phys/killee00/killee00.html**.

R. C. Luetzelschwab, K9LA's Amateur Radio Propagation website, **mysite.ncnetwork.net/k9la**.

J. L. Lynch, "The Maunder Minimum," *QST*, Jul 1976, p 24-26.

J. C. Maxwell, *A Treatise on Electricity and Magnetism*, Vols I and II (Oxford: Oxford University Press, 1873).

M. W. Maxwell, *Reflections — Transmission Lines and Antennas* (Newington, CT: ARRL, 1990) [out of print].

M. W. Maxwell, *Reflections II — Transmission Lines and Antennas* (Sacramento, CA: 2001).

L. F. McNamara, *The Ionosphere: Communications, Surveillance, and Direction Finding* (Malabar, FL: Krieger Publishing Company, 1991). Another excellent technical reference on propagation.

L. F. McNamara, *Radio Amateur's Guide to the Ionosphere* (Malabar, FL: Krieger Publishing Company, 1994). Excellent, quite-readable text on HF propagation.

A. K. Paul, "Medium Scale Structure of the F Region," *Radio Science*, Volume 24, No. 3, p. 301, 1989.

W. R. Piggott, K. Rawer, "URSI Handbook of Ionogram Interpretation and Reduction," Report UAG-50. World Data Center A for Solar-Terrestrial Physics, Boulder, CO, 1975.

E. Pocock, Ed., *Beyond Line of Sight: A History of VHF Propagation from the Pages of QST* (ARRL: 1992). [Out of print]

E. Pocock, "Sporadic-E Propagation at VHF: A Review of Progress and Prospects," *QST*, Apr 1988, pp 33-39.

E. Pocock, "Auroral-E Propagation at 144 MHz," *QST*, Dec 1989, pp 28-32.

E. Pocock, "Propagation Forecasting During Solar Cycle 22," *QST*, Jun 1989, pp 18-20.

G. C. Reid, "Ion Chemistry of the D-region," *Advances in Atomic and Molecular Physics*, Vol 12, Academic Press, 1976.

R. B. Rose, "MINIMUF: A Simplified MUF-Prediction Program for Microcomputers," *QST*, Dec 1982, pp 36-38

M. L. Salby, "Fundamentals of Atmospheric Physics," (Academic Press: Boulder, CO, 1996).

S. C. Shallon, W6EL: *W6ELProp*, a commercially prepared program written for Amateur Radio users; 11058 Queensland St, Los Angeles, CA 90034-3029.

R. D. Straw, *All the Right Angles* (New Bedford, PA: LTA, 1993). Out of print.

R. D. Straw, "*ASAPS* and *CAPMAN*: HF Propagation-Prediction Software for the IBM PC," *QST*, Dec 1994, pp 79-81.

R. D. Straw, "Heavy-Duty HF Propagation-Prediction/Analysis Software," Part 1: *QST*, Sep 1996, pp 28-32; Part 2: *QST*, Oct 1996, pp 28-30.

R. D. Straw, "HF Propagation and Sporadic-E — a Case Study: WRTC 2010," **tinyurl.com/2upmbaa**.

R. D. Straw, "Using Propagation Predictions for DXing," **www.voacap.com/documents/N6BV_Visalia_2010. pdf**.

TABLE OF CONTENTS

Chapter 5

Loop Antennas

A loop antenna is a closed-circuit antenna — that is, one in which a conductor is formed into one or more turns so its two ends are close together. Loops can be divided into two general classes — large loops in which both the conductor length and the loop dimensions are comparable with the wavelength and small loops in which both the total conductor length and the maximum linear dimension of a turn are very small compared with the wavelength.

Material on quad and delta loops is adapted from Chapter 10 of *Low-Band DXing,* 5th edition by John Devoldere, ON4UN. Material on small loops was written by Domenic Mallozzi, N1DM. Additional discussion of loop antennas can be found in these chapters: **Low-Band Antennas, Multiband Antennas** and **Receiving and Direction Finding Antennas**.

5.1 LARGE LOOPS

Resonant loop antennas have a circumference of 1 λ. The exact shape of the loop is not particularly important. In free space, the loop with the highest gain, however, is the loop with the shape that encloses the largest area for a given circumference. This is a circular loop, which is difficult to construct. Second best is the square loop (quad), and in third place comes the equilateral triangle (delta) loop (see the reference for Dietrich).

The maximum gain of a 1-λ loop over a λ/2 dipole in free space is approximately 1.35 dB. Delta loops are used extensively on the low bands at apex heights of λ4 to 3λ/8 above ground. At such heights the vertically polarized loops far outperform dipoles or inverted-V dipoles for low-angle DXing, assuming good ground conductivity.

Loops are generally erected with the plane of the loop perpendicular to the ground. Whether or not the loop produces a vertically or a horizontally polarized signal (or a combination of both) depends only on how (or on which side) the loop is being fed.

Another type of large loop antennas comprises the horizontally mounted loops, which have the plane of the loop parallel to the ground. These antennas produce horizontal radiation with takeoff angles determined, as usual, by the height of the horizontal loop over ground.

5.1.1 THE SQUARE OR QUAD LOOP

Belcher, WA4JVE; Casper, K4HKX; and Dietrich, WAØRDX, have published studies comparing the horizon-

tally polarized vertical quad loop with a dipole. (See the References and Bibliography section.) A horizontally polarized quad loop antenna (**Figure 5.1A**) can be seen as two short, end-loaded dipoles stacked λ/4 apart, with the top antenna at λ/4 and the bottom one just above ground level. The total length for a resonant loop is approximately 5 to 6% longer than the free-space wavelength.

There is no broadside radiation from the vertical wires of the quad because of the current opposition in the vertical members. In a similar manner, the vertically polarized quad loop consists of two top-loaded, λ/4 vertical dipoles, spaced λ/4 apart. Figure 5.1 shows how the current distribution along the elements produces cancellation of radiation from certain parts of the antenna, while radiation from other parts (the horizontally or vertically stacked short dipoles) is reinforced.

The square quad can be fed for either horizontal or vertical polarization merely by placing the feed point at the center of a horizontal arm or at the center of a vertical arm. At the higher frequencies in the HF range, where the quads are typically half to several wavelengths high, quad loops are usually fed to produce horizontal polarization, although there is no specific reason for this except maybe from a mechanical standpoint. Polarization by itself is of little importance at HF because of random rotation in the ionosphere.

Quad Loop Impedance

The radiation resistance of an equilateral quad loop in free space is approximately 120 Ω. The radiation resistance

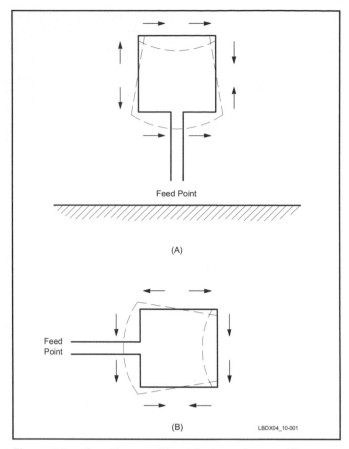

Figure 5.1 — Quad loops with a 1-λ circumference. The current distribution is shown for (A) horizontal and (B) vertical polarization. Note how the opposing currents in the two legs result in cancellation of the radiation in the plane of those legs, while the currents in the other legs are in-phase and reinforce each other in the broadside direction (perpendicular to the plane of the antenna).

for a quad loop as a function of its height above ground is given in **Figure 5.2**. The impedance data were obtained by modeling an equilateral quad loop over three types of ground (very good, average and very poor ground) using *NEC*.

The reactance data can assist you in evaluating the influence of the antenna height on the resonant frequency. The loop antenna was first modeled in free space to be resonant at 3.75 MHz and the reactance data was obtained with those free-space resonant-loop dimensions.

For the vertically polarized quad loop, the resistive part of the impedance changes very little with the type of ground under the antenna. The feed point reactance is influenced by the ground quality, especially at lower heights. For the horizontally polarized loop, the radiation resistance is noticeably influenced by the ground quality, especially at low heights. The same is true for the reactance.

Quad Loop Patterns — Vertical Polarization

The vertically polarized quad loop in Figure 5.1B can be considered as two shortened top-loaded vertical dipoles, spaced λ/4 apart. Broadside radiation from the horizontal elements of the quad is canceled, because of the opposition of currents in the vertical legs. The wave angle in the broadside direction will be essentially the same as for either of the vertical members. The resulting radiation angle will depend on the quality of the ground up to several wavelengths away from the antenna, as is the case with all vertically polarized antennas.

The quality of the reflecting ground will also influence the gain of the vertically polarized loop to a great extent. The quality of the ground is as important as it is for any other vertical antenna, meaning that vertically polarized loops close to the ground will not work well over poor soil.

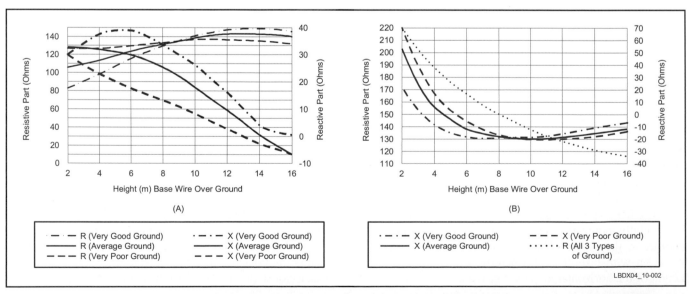

Figure 5.2 — Radiation resistance and feed point resistance for square loops at different heights above real ground. The loop was first dimensioned to be resonant in free space (reactance equal to zero), and those dimensions were used for calculating the impedance over ground. At A, for horizontal polarization, and at B, for vertical polarization. Analysis was with *NEC* at 3.75 MHz.

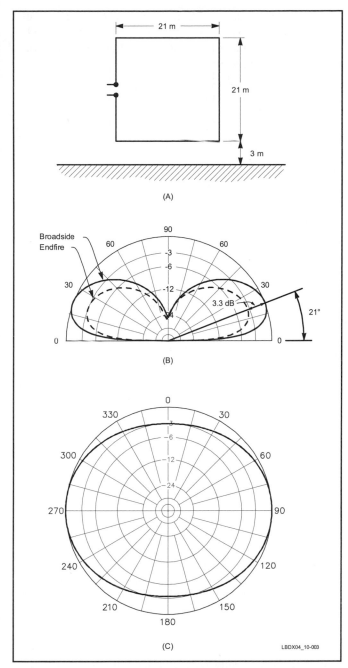

Figure 5.3 — Shown at A is a square loop, with its elevation-plane pattern at B and azimuth pattern at C. The patterns are generated for good ground. The bottom wire is 0.0375 λ above ground (3 meters or 10 feet on 80 meters). At C, the pattern is for a wave angle of 21°.

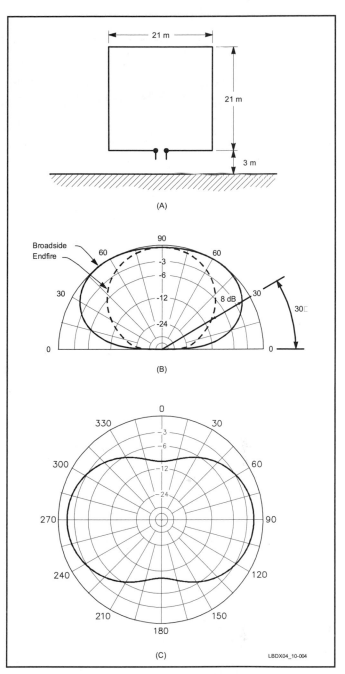

Figure 5.4 — Azimuth and elevation patterns of the horizontally polarized quad loop at low height (bottom wire 0.0375 λ above ground). At an elevation angle of 30°, the loop has a front-to-side ratio of approximately 8 dB.

Figure 5.3 shows both the azimuth and elevation radiation patterns of a vertically polarized quad loop with a top height of 0.3 λ (bottom wire at approximately 0.04 λ). This is a very realistic situation, especially on 80 meters. The loop radiates an excellent low-angle wave (lobe peak at approximately 21°) when operated over average ground. Over poorer ground, the wave angle would be closer to 30°. The horizontal directivity, Figure 5.3C, is rather poor, and amounts to approximately 3.3 dB of side rejection at any wave angle.

Quad Loop Patterns — Horizontal Polarization

A horizontally polarized quad-loop antenna (two stacked short dipoles) produces a wave angle that is dependent on the height of the loop. The low horizontally polarized quad (top at 0.3 λ) radiates most of its energy right at or near zenith angle (straight up).

Figure 5.4 shows directivity patterns for a horizontally polarized loop. The horizontal pattern, Figure 5.4C, is plotted for a takeoff angle of 30°. At low wave angles (20° to 45°),

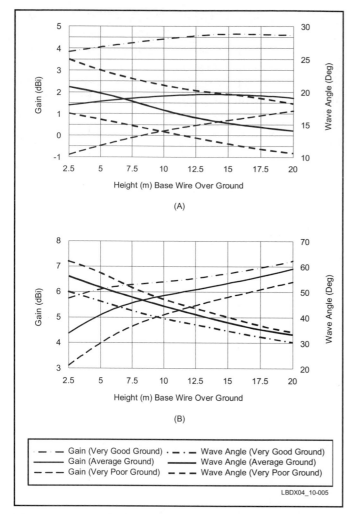

(A)

(B)

--- · — Gain (Very Good Ground)   — · — Wave Angle (Very Good Ground)
——— Gain (Average Ground)   ——— Wave Angle (Average Ground)
- - - Gain (Very Poor Ground)   — — Wave Angle (Very Poor Ground)

LBDX04_10-005

Figure 5.5 — Radiation angle and gain of the horizontally and the vertically polarized square loops at different heights over good ground. At A, for vertical polarization, and at B, for horizontal polarization. Note that the gain of the vertically polarized loop never exceeds 4.6 dBi, but its wave angle is low for any height (14 to 20°). The horizontally polarized loop can exhibit a much higher gain provided the loop is very high. Modeling was done over average ground for a frequency of 3.75 MHz, using *NEC*.

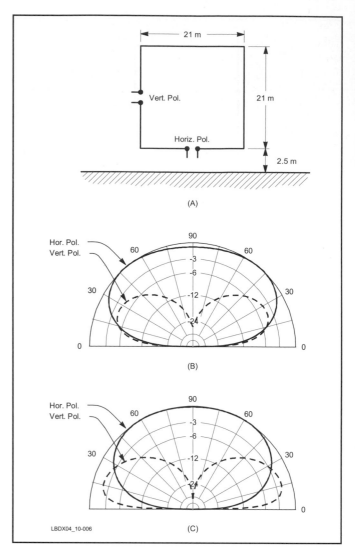

Figure 5.6 — Superimposed patterns for horizontally and vertically polarized square quad loops (shown at A) over very poor ground (B) and very good ground (C). In the vertical polarization mode the ground quality is of utmost importance, as it is with all verticals.

the horizontally polarized loop shows more front-to-side ratio (5 to 10 dB) than the vertically polarized rectangular loop.

Vertical versus Horizontal Polarization — Quad Loops

Vertically polarized loops should be used only where very good ground conductivity is available. From **Figure 5.5A** we see that the gain of the vertically polarized quad loop, as well as the wave angle, does not change very much as a function of the antenna height. This makes sense, since the vertically polarized loop is in the first place two phased verticals, each with its own radial.

However, the gain is drastically influenced by the quality of the ground. At low heights, the gain difference between very poor ground and very good ground is a solid 5 dB! The wave

angle for the vertically polarized quad loop at a low height (bottom wire at 0.03 λ) varies from 25° over very poor ground to 17° over very good ground. Vertically polarized delta loops at low height always require a good ground screen underneath the antenna (unless they are over excellent or perfect ground), exactly in the same way that a vertical with only one or two radials requires a good ground underneath the radials.

With a horizontally polarized quad loop the wave angle is very dependent on the antenna height, but not so much on the quality of the ground. At very low heights, the main wave angle varies between 50° and 60° (but is rather constant all the way up to 90°). As far as gain is concerned, there is a 2.5-dB gain difference between very good and very poor ground, which is only half the difference we found with the vertically polarized loop. Comparing the gain to the gain of the vertically polarized loop, we see that at very low antenna heights the gain is about 3-dB better than for the vertically polarized loop. But this gain exists at a high wave angle (50° to 90°), while the vertically polarized loop at very low heights radiates at 17° to 25°.

Figure 5.6 shows the vertical-plane radiation patterns for both types of quad loops over very poor ground and over very good ground on the same dB scale.

Rectangular Quad Loops

A rectangular quad loop with unequal side dimensions can be used with very good results on the low bands. The vertical and the horizontal radiation patterns for this quad loop

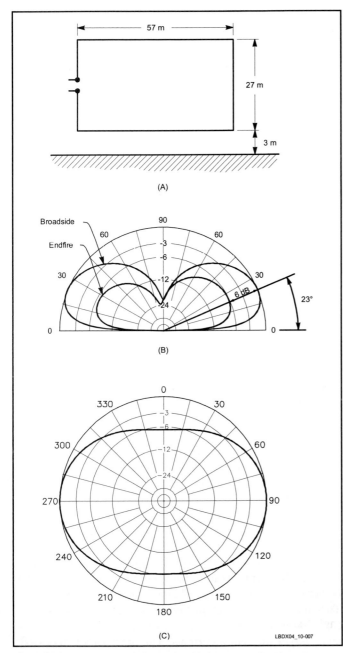

Figure 5.7 — At A, a rectangular loop with its baseline approximately twice as long as the vertical height. At B and C, the vertical and horizontal radiation patterns, generated over good ground. The loop was dimensioned to be resonant at 1.83 MHz. The azimuth pattern at C is taken at a 23° elevation angle.

over good ground are shown in **Figure 5.7**. The horizontal directivity is approximately 6 dB (front-to-side ratio).

Even in free space, the feed point impedance of the two configurations of this rectangular loop is not the same. When fed in the center of a short side, the radiation resistance of the antenna in Figure 5.7 at resonance is 44 Ω. When fed in the center of one of the long sides, the resistance is 215 Ω. Over real ground the feed point impedance is different in both configurations as well; depending on the quality of the ground, the impedance can vary by 40 to 90 Ω.

Feeding the Quad Loop

The quad loop feed point should be in the middle of the vertical or the horizontal wire. A balun should be used as described in the **Transmission Line Coupling and Impedance Matching** chapter. Alternatively, you could use open-wire feeders (for example, 450-Ω line). The open-wire-feeder alternative has the advantage of being a lightweight solution. With a tuner you will be able to cover a wide frequency range with no compromises.

5.1.2. TRIANGULAR OR DELTA LOOPS

Because of its shape, the delta loop with the apex on top is a very popular antenna as it needs only one support. As for the quad configuration, the length of the resonant delta loop is approximately 1.05 to 1.06 λ.

In free space the equilateral triangle produces the highest gain and the highest radiation resistance for a three-sided loop configuration. As we deviate from an equilateral triangle toward a triangle with a long baseline, the effective gain and the radiation resistance of the loop will decrease for a bottom corner-fed delta loop. In the extreme case (where the height of the triangle is reduced to zero), the loop has become a half-wavelength-long transmission line that is shorted at the end, which shows a zero-Ω input impedance (radiation resistance), and thus zero radiation.

Just as with the quad loop, we can switch from horizontal to vertical polarization by changing the position of the feed point on the loop. For horizontal polarization the loop is fed either at the center of the baseline or at the top of the loop. For vertical polarization the loop should be fed on one of the sloping sides, at λ/4 from the apex of the delta. **Figure 5.8** shows the current distribution in both cases.

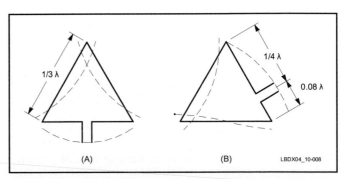

Figure 5.8 — Current distribution for equilateral delta loops fed for (A) horizontal and (B) vertical polarization.

Delta Loop Patterns — Vertical Polarization

As shown in **Figure 5.9**, in the vertical-polarization mode the delta loop can be seen as two sloping quarter-wave verticals (their apexes touch at the top of the support), while the baseline (and the part of the sloping section under the feed point) takes care of feeding the "other" sloping section with the correct phase. The top connection of the sloping verticals can be left open without changing anything about the operation of the delta loop. The same is true for the baseline, where the middle of the baseline could be opened without changing anything. These two points are the high-impedance points of the antenna. Either the apex or the center of the baseline must be shorted, however, in order to provide feed voltage to the other half of the antenna. Normally, of course, we use a fully closed loop in the standard delta loop, although for single-band operation this is not strictly necessary.

Assume we construct the antenna with the center of the horizontal bottom wire open. Now we can see the two half baselines as two λ/4 radials, one of which provides the necessary low-impedance point for connecting the shield of the coax. The other radial is connected to the bottom of the second sloping vertical, which is the other sloping wire of the delta loop. This is similar to a λ/4 vertical using a single elevated radial. The current distribution in the two quarter-wave radials is such that all radiation from these radials is effectively canceled.

The vertically polarized delta loop is really an array of two λ/4 verticals, with the high-current points spaced 0.25 λ to 0.3 λ, and operating in phase. The fact that the tops of the verticals are close together does not influence the performance to a large degree. The reason is that the current near the apex of the delta is at a minimum (it is current that creates radiation!). You can open the apex and move the vertical wires apart if you have a very tall support, in which case you will increase the gain of the antenna somewhat.

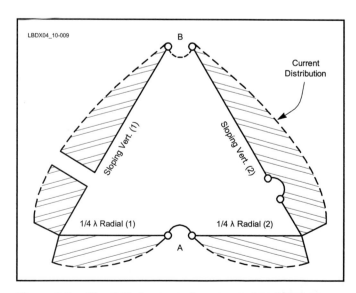

Figure 5.9 — The delta loop can be seen as two λ/4 sloping verticals, each using one radial. Because of the current distribution in the radials, the radiation from the radials is effectively canceled.

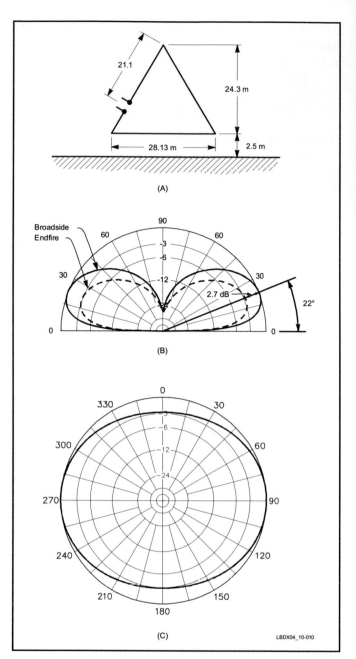

Figure 5.10 — Configuration and radiation patterns for a vertically polarized equilateral delta loop antenna. The model was calculated over good ground, for a frequency of 3.8 MHz. The elevation angle for the azimuth pattern at C is 22°.

Considering a pair of phased verticals, we know from the chapter **Effects of Ground** that the quality of the ground will be very important as to the efficient operation of the antenna. This does not mean that the delta loop requires radials. It has two elevated radials that are an integral part of the loop and take care of the return currents. The presence of the (lossy) ground under the antenna is responsible for near-field losses, unless we can shield it from the antenna by using a ground screen or a radial system, which should not be connected to the antenna.

As with all vertically polarized antennas, the quality of

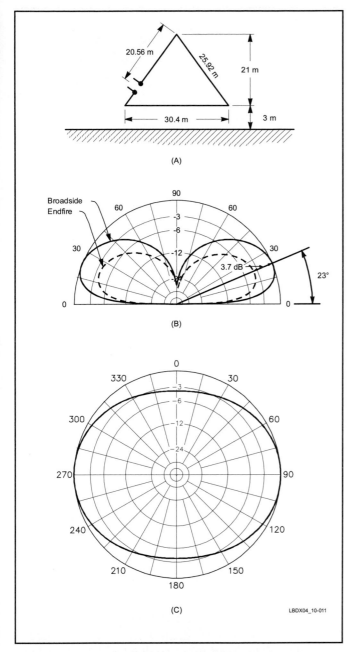

Figure 5.11 — Configuration and radiation patterns for the "compressed" delta loop, which has a baseline slightly longer than the sloping wires. The model was dimensioned for 3.8 MHz to have an apex height of 24 meters and a bottom wire height of 3 meters. Calculations are done over good ground at a frequency of 3.8 MHz. The azimuth pattern at C is for an elevation angle of 23°. Note that the correct feed point remains at λ/4 from the apex of the loop.

the ground within a radius of several wavelengths will determine the low-angle radiation of the loop antenna.

The Equilateral Triangle

Figure 5.10 shows the configuration as well as both the broadside and the end-fire vertical radiation patterns of the vertically polarized equilateral-triangle delta loop antenna. The model was constructed for a frequency of 3.75 MHz.

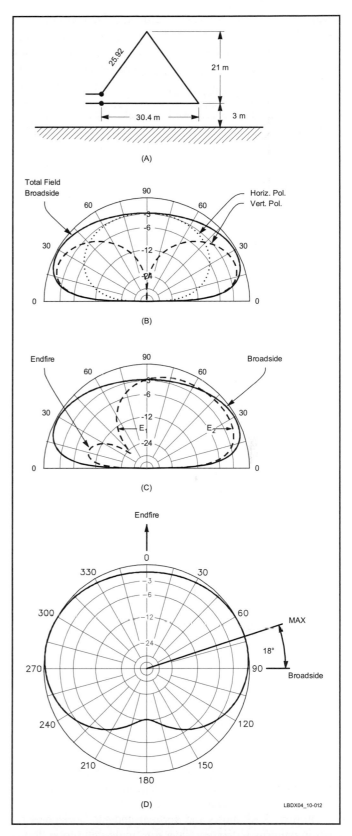

Figure 5.12 — Configuration and radiation patterns for the compressed delta loop of Figure 5.11 when fed in one of the bottom corners at a frequency of 3.75 MHz. Improper cancellation of radiation from the horizontal wire produces a strong high-angle horizontally polarized component. The delta loop now also shows a strange horizontal directivity pattern (at D), the shape of which is very sensitive to slight frequency deviations. This pattern is for an elevation angle of 29°.

The baseline is 2.5 meters above ground, which puts the apex at 26.83 meters. The model was made over good ground. The delta loop shows nearly 3 dB front-to-side ratio at the main wave angle of 22°. With average ground the gain is 1.3 dBi.

The Compressed Delta Loop

Figure 5.11 shows an 80 meter delta loop with the apex at 24 meters and the baseline at 3 meters. This delta loop has a long baseline of 30.4 meters. The feed point is again located λ/4 from the apex.

The front-to-side ratio is 3.8 dB. The gain with average ground is 1.6 dBi. In free space the equilateral triangle gives a higher gain than the "flat" delta. Over real ground and in the vertically polarized mode, the gain of the flat delta loop is 0.3 dB better than the equilateral delta, however. This must be explained by the fact that the longer baseline yields a wider separation of the two "sloping" verticals, yielding a slightly higher gain.

For a 100-kHz bandwidth (on 80 meters) the SWR rises to 1.4:1 at the edges. The 2:1 SWR bandwidth is approximately 175 kHz.

The Bottom-Corner-Fed Delta Loop

Figure 5.12 shows the layout of the delta loop being fed at one of the two bottom corners. The antenna has the same apex and baseline height as the compressed delta loop. Because of the "incorrect" location of the feed point, cancellation of radiation from the base wire (the two "radials") is not 100% effective, resulting in a significant horizontally polarized radiation component. The total field has a very uniform gain coverage (within 1 dB) from 25° to 90°. This may be a disadvantage for the rejection of high-angle signals when working DX at low wave angles.

Due to the "incorrect" feed point location, the end-fire radiation (radiation in line with the loop) has become asymmetrical. The horizontal radiation 2pattern shown in Figure 5.12D is for a wave angle of 29°. Note the deep side null (nearly 12 dB) at that wave angle. The loop actually radiates its maximum signal about 18° off the broadside direction. This feed point configuration (in the corner of the compressed loop) is to be avoided, as it really degrades the performance of the antenna.

Delta Loop Patterns — Horizontal Polarization

In the horizontal polarization mode, the delta loop can be seen as an inverted-V dipole on top of a very low dipole with its ends bent upward to connect to the tips of the inverted V. The loop will act as any horizontally polarized antenna over real ground; its wave angle will depend on the height of the antenna over the ground.

Figure 5.13 shows the vertical and the horizontal radiation patterns for an equilateral-triangle delta loop, fed at the center of the bottom wire. As anticipated, the radiation is maximum at the zenith. The front-to-side ratio is around 3 dB for a 15 to 45° wave angle. Over average ground the gain is 2.5 dBi. So far we have only spoken about relative patterns. What about real gain figures from the vertically and the horizontally polarized delta loops?

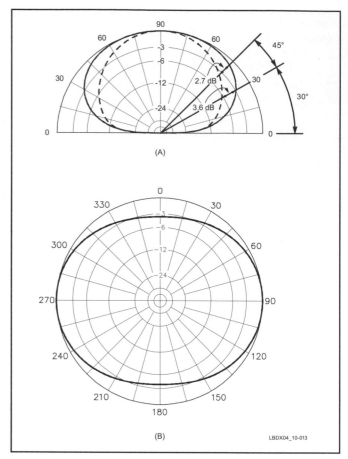

Figure 5.13 — Vertical and horizontal radiation patterns for an 80 meter equilateral delta loop fed for horizontal polarization, with the bottom wire at 3 meters. The radiation is essentially at very high angles, comparable to what can be obtained from a dipole or inverted-V dipole at the same (apex) height.

Vertical versus Horizontal Polarization — Delta Loops

Figure 5.14 shows the superimposed elevation patterns for vertically and horizontally polarized low-height equilateral triangle delta loops over two different types of ground (same dB scale).

Over very poor ground, the horizontally polarized delta loop is better than the vertically polarized loop for all wave angles above 35°. Below 35° the vertically polarized loop takes over, but quite marginally. The maximum gain of the vertically and the horizontally polarized loops differs by only 2 dB, but the big difference is that for the horizontally polarized loop, the gain occurs at almost 90°, while for the vertically polarized loop it occurs at 25°.

One might argue that for a 30° elevation angle, the horizontally polarized loop is as good as the vertically polarized loop. It is clear, however, that the vertically polarized antenna gives good high-angle rejection (rejection against local signals), while the horizontally polarized loop will not.

Over very good ground, the same thing that happens with any vertical happens with a vertically polarized delta: The performance at low angles is greatly improved with good ground. The vertically polarized loop is still better at any wave angle under 30° than when horizontally polarized. At a 10° radiation angle, the difference is as high as 10 dB.

In conclusion, over very poor ground, vertically polarized loops do not provide much better low-angle radiation when compared to the horizontally polarized loops. They

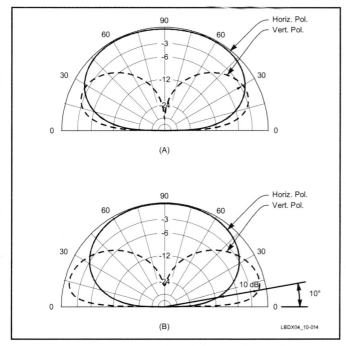

Figure 5.14 — Radiation patterns of vertically and horizontally polarized delta loops on the same dB scale. At A, over very poor ground, and at B, over very good ground. These patterns illustrate the tremendous importance of ground conductivity with vertically polarized antennas. Over better ground, the vertically polarized loop performs much better at low radiation angles, while over both good and poor ground the vertically polarized loop gives good discrimination against high-angle radiation. This is not the case for the horizontally polarized loop.

have the advantage of giving substantial rejection at high angles, however. Over good ground, Figure 5.14 shows that the vertically polarized loop will give up to 10 dB and more gain at low radiation angles as compared to the horizontally polarized loop, in addition to its high-angle rejection.

Feeding the Delta Loop

The feed point of the delta loop in free space is symmetrical. At high heights above ground the loop feed point is to be considered as symmetrical, especially when we feed the loop in the center of the bottom line (or at the apex), because of its full symmetry with respect to the ground.

Figure 5.15 shows the radiation resistance and reactance for both the horizontally and the vertically polarized equilateral delta loops as a function of height above ground. At low heights, when fed for vertical polarization, the feed point is to be considered as asymmetric, whereby the "cold" point is the point to which the "radials" are connected. The center conductor of a coax feed line goes to the sloping vertical section. Many users have, however, used (symmetric) open-wire line to feed the vertically polarized loop (e.g., 450-Ω line).

Most practical delta loops show a feed point impedance between 50 and 100 Ω, depending on the exact geometry and coupling to other antennas. In most cases the feed point can be reached, so it is quite easy to measure the feed point impedance using, for example, a good-quality noise bridge connected directly to the antenna terminals. If the impedance is much higher than 100 Ω (equilateral triangle), feeding via a 450-Ω open-wire feeder may be warranted. Alternatively, you could use an unun (unbalanced-to-unbalanced) transformer, which can be made to cover a very wide range of impedance ratios (see the **Transmission Lines** chapter). With somewhat compressed delta loops, the feed point impedance is usually between 50 and 100 Ω. Feeding can be done directly with a 50 or 70-Ω coaxial cable, or with a 50-Ω cable via a 70-Ω quarter-wave transformer since $Z_{ant} \approx 100$ Ω).

To keep any RF current from flowing on the outside of

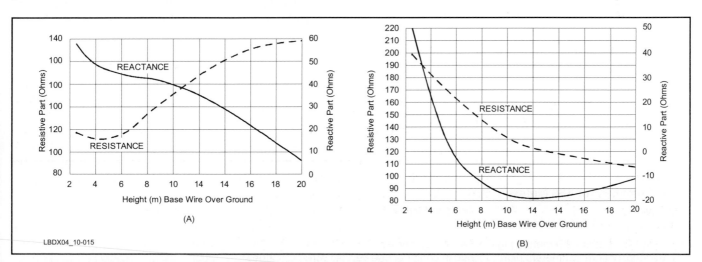

Figure 5.15 — Radiation resistance of (A) horizontally and (B) vertically polarized equilateral delta loops as a function of height above average ground. The delta loop was first dimensioned to be resonant in free space (reactance equals zero). Those dimensions were then used for calculating the impedance over real ground. Modeling was done at 3.75 MHz over good ground, using *NEC*.

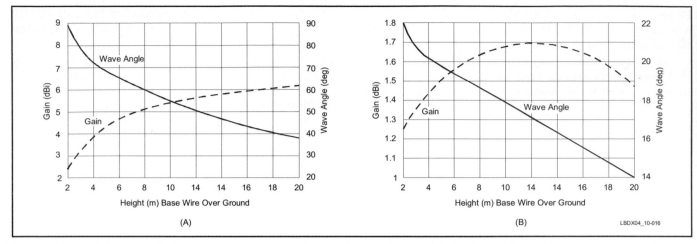

Figure 5.16 — Gain and radiation angle of (A) horizontally and (B) vertically polarized equilateral delta loops as a function of the height above ground. Modeling was done at 3.75 MHz over average ground, using *NEC*.

the coaxial feed line, use a balun or current choke although the feed point of the vertically polarized delta loop is not strictly symmetrical. These parasitic currents could upset the radiation pattern of the delta loop. For details on those baluns/common mode chokes see the **Transmission Line Coupling and Impedance Matching** chapter.

Delta Loop Gain and Radiation Angle

Figure 5.16 shows the gain and the main-lobe radiation angle for the equilateral delta loop at different heights. The values were obtained by modeling a 3.8-MHz loop over average ground using *NEC*.

Cunningham, K6SE (SK), investigated different configurations of single element loops for 160 meters, and came up with the results listed in **Table 5-1** (modeling done with *EZNEC* over good ground). These data correspond surprisingly well with those shown in Fig 10-16 (where the ground was average), which explains the slight difference in gain.

5.1.3 HORIZONTAL LOOPS

A large loop, installed horizontally over ground and in **Figure 5.17** is an excellent multiband antenna. A 1-λ circumference loop installed at a height of λ/2 or lower has a radiation pattern similar to a λ/2 dipole at the same height — omnidirectional, high-angle radiation. As the frequency

of operation increases the current distribution around the loop and the radiation pattern become more complex. The radiation lobes peak at lower elevation angles, generally approximating the angle of peak radiation for a dipole at the same electrical height.

The exact performance of the loop depends on shape, height, and frequency of use. DeMaw, W1FB (SK), analyzed a square, horizontal loop cut for resonance at 1.9 MHz. Peak gain varied from 0.28 dBd at 1.9 MHz (at an elevation angle of 90°) to a maximum of 7.00 dBd at 21.0 MHz (at an elevation angle of 14°). **Figure 5.18** shows the azimuth and elevation patterns for DeMaw's loop at 14 MHz, typical of this type of loop when operated above the loop's lowest resonant frequency. Cebik, W4RNL (SK), also analyzed large, horizontal loops at different frequencies and obtained similar results. (See the References for articles by both DeMaw and Cebik.)

Feed point impedance on the 1-λ resonant frequency is approximately 100 Ω and rises to a few hundred ohms or higher at higher frequencies. Because of the varying feed point impedance, it is recommended that the antenna be fed with parallel conductor transmission line to reduce feed line loss.

5.1.4 HALF-WAVE LOOPS

The smallest size of "large" loop generally used is one having a conductor length of ½ λ. The conductor is usually

Table 5-1
Loop Antennas for 160 Meters

Description	Feeding Method	Gain (dBi)	Elevation Angle (degrees)
Diamond loop, bottom 2.5 meters high	Fed in side corner	2.15	18.0
Square loop, bottom 2.5 meters high	Fed in center of one vertical wire	2.06	20.5
Inverted equilateral delta loop (flat wire on top)	Fed λ/4 from bottom	1.91	20.9
Regular equilateral delta loop	Fed λ/4 from top	1.90	18.1

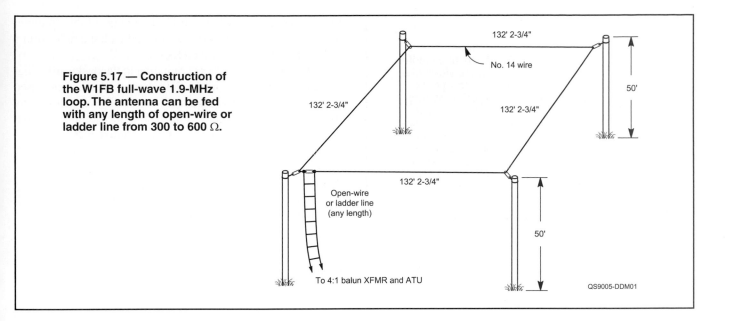

Figure 5.17 — Construction of the W1FB full-wave 1.9-MHz loop. The antenna can be fed with any length of open-wire or ladder line from 300 to 600 Ω.

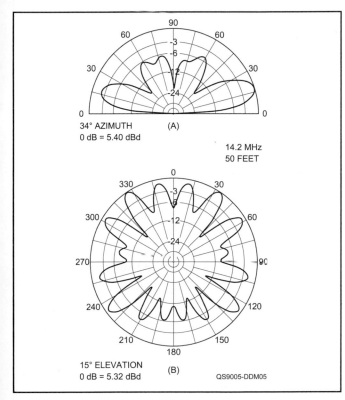

Figure 5.18 — Elevation (A) and azimuth (B) patterns for operation of the W1FB loop at 14.2 MHz.

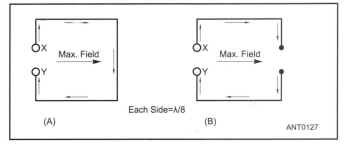

Figure 5.19 — Half-wave loops, consisting of a single turn having a total length of ½ λ.

formed into a square, as shown in **Figure 5.19**, making each side ⅛ λ long. When fed at the center of one side, the current flows in a closed loop as shown in Figure 5.19A. The current distribution is approximately the same as on a ½ λ wire, and so is a maximum at the center of the side opposite the terminals X-Y, and a minimum at the feed point. This current distribution causes the field strength to be a maximum in the plane of the loop and in the direction looking

from the low-current side to the high-current side. (See the referenced article by Cebik for additional discussion of this configuration.)

If the side opposite the feed point is opened at the center as shown in Figure 5.19B (strictly speaking, it is then no longer a loop because it is no longer a closed circuit), the direction of current flow remains unchanged but the maximum current flow and lowest impedance occurs at the feed point. This reverses the direction of maximum radiation.

The radiation resistance at a current maximum (which is also the resistance at X-Y in Figure 5.19B) is on the order of 50 Ω. The impedance at the feed point in Figure 5.19A is a few thousand ohms. This can be reduced by using two identical loops side by side with a few inches spacing between them and applying power between terminal X on one loop and terminal Y on the other.

Unlike a ½ λ dipole or a small loop, there is no direction in which the radiation from a loop of the type shown in Figure 5.19 is zero. There is appreciable radiation in the direction perpendicular to the plane of the loop, as well as to the "rear" — the opposite direction to the arrows shown. The front-to-back (F/B) ratio is approximately 4 to 6 dB. The small size and the shape of the directive pattern result in a

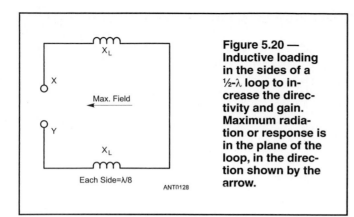

Figure 5.20 — Inductive loading in the sides of a ½-λ loop to increase the directivity and gain. Maximum radiation or response is in the plane of the loop, in the direction shown by the arrow.

loss of about 1 dB when the field strength in the optimum direction from such a loop is compared with the field from a ½ λ dipole in its optimum direction.

The ratio of the forward radiation to the backward radiation can be increased, and the field strength likewise increased at the same time to give a gain of about 1 dB over a dipole, by using inductive reactances to "load" the sides joining the front and back of the loop. This is shown in **Figure 5.20**. The reactances, which should have a value of approximately 360 Ω, decrease the current in the sides in which they are inserted and increase it in the side with the feed point. This increases the directivity and thus increases the efficiency of the loop as a radiator. Lossy coils can reduce this advantage greatly.

5.2 SMALL LOOP ANTENNAS

A "small" loop can be considered to be simply a rather large coil, and the current distribution in such a loop is the same as in a coil. That is, the current has the same phase and the same amplitude in every part of the loop. To meet this condition, the total length of conductor in the loop must not exceed about 0.1 λ.

The electrically small loop antenna has existed in various forms for many years. Probably the most familiar form of this antenna is the ferrite *loopstick* found in portable AM broadcast-band receivers. Amateur applications of the small loop include direction finding, low-noise directional receiving antennas for 1.8 and 3.5 MHz, and small transmitting antennas. Because the design of transmitting and receiving loops requires some different considerations, the two situations are examined separately in this section. Applications of small loops are presented in the **Receiving and Direction-Finding Antennas** and the **Stealth and Limited-Space Antennas** chapters.

5.2.1 THE BASIC SMALL LOOP

What is and what is not a small loop antenna? By definition, the loop is considered electrically small when its total conductor length is less than 0.1 λ — 0.085 is the number used in this section. This size is based on the fact that the current around the perimeter of the loop must be in phase. When the winding conductor is more than about 0.085 λ long, this is no longer true. This constraint results in a very predictable figure-eight radiation pattern, shown in **Figure 5.21**.

The simplest loop is a 1-turn untuned loop with a load connected to a pair of terminals located in the center of one of the sides, as shown in **Figure 5.22**. How its pattern is developed is easily pictured if we look at some "snapshots" of the antenna relative to a signal source. **Figure 5.23** represents a loop from above, and shows the instantaneous radiated voltage wave. Note that points A and B of the loop are receiving the same instantaneous voltage. This means that no current will flow through the loop, because there is no current flow between points of equal potential. A similar analysis of **Figure 5.24**, with the loop turned 90° from the position represented in Figure 5.23, shows that this position of the loop

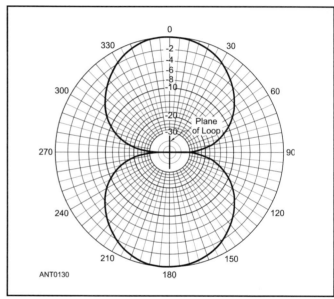

Figure 5.21 — Calculated small loop antenna radiation pattern.

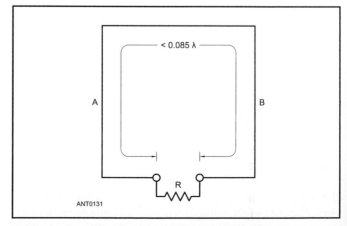

Figure 5.22 — Simple untuned small loop antenna.

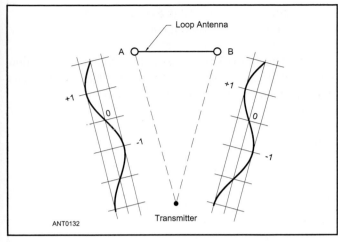

Figure 5.23 — Example of orientation of loop antenna that does not respond to a signal source (null in pattern).

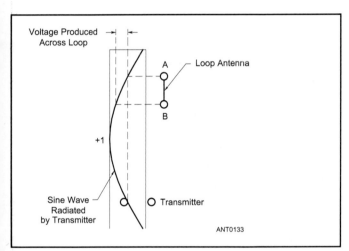

Figure 5.24 — Example of orientation of loop antenna for maximum response.

provides maximum response. Of course, the voltage derived from the passing wave is small because of the small physical size of the loop. Figure 5.21 shows the ideal radiation pattern for a small loop.

The voltage across the loop terminals is given by

$$V = \frac{2 \pi A N E \cos\theta}{\lambda} \qquad \text{(Eq 1)}$$

where

V = voltage across the loop terminals
A = area of loop in square meters
N = number of turns in the loop
E = RF field strength in volts per meter
θ = angle between the plane of the loop and the
    signal source (transmitting station)
λ = wavelength of operation in meters

This equation comes from a term called *effective height*. The effective height refers to the height (length) of a vertical piece of wire above ground that would deliver the same

voltage to the receiver. The equation for effective height is

$$h = \frac{2 \pi N A}{\lambda} \qquad \text{(Eq 2)}$$

where h is in meters and the other terms are as for Eq 1.

A few minutes with a calculator will show that, with the constraints previously stated, the loop antenna will have a very small effective height. This means it will deliver a relatively small voltage to the receiver, even with a large transmitted signal.

5.2.2 TUNED LOOPS

We can tune the loop by placing a capacitor across the antenna terminals. This causes a larger voltage to appear across the loop terminals because of the Q of the parallel resonant circuit that is formed.

The voltage across the loop terminals is now given by

$$V = \frac{2 \pi A N E Q \cos\theta}{\lambda} \qquad \text{(Eq 3)}$$

where Q is the loaded Q of the tuned circuit, and the other terms are as defined above.

Most amateur loops are of the tuned variety. For this reason, all comments that follow are based on tuned-loop antennas, consisting of one or more turns. The tuned-loop antenna has some particular advantages. For example, it puts high selectivity up at the "front" of a receiving system, where it can significantly help factors such as dynamic range. Loaded Q values of 100 or greater are easy to obtain with careful loop construction.

Consider a situation where the inherent selectivity of the loop is helpful. Assume we have a loop with a loaded Q of 100 at 1.805 MHz. We are working a DX station on 1.805 MHz and are suffering strong interference from a local station 10 kHz away. Switching from a dipole to a small loop will reduce the strength of the off-frequency signal by 6 dB (approximately one S unit). This, in effect, increases the dynamic range of the receiver. In fact, if the off-frequency station were further off frequency, the attenuation would be greater.

Another way the loop can help is by using the nulls in its pattern to null out on-frequency (or slightly off-frequency) interference. For example, say we are working a DX station to the north, and just 1 kHz away is another local station engaged in a contact. The local station is to our west. We can simply rotate our loop to put its null to the west, and now the DX station should be readable while the local will be knocked down by 60 or more dB. This obviously is quite a noticeable difference. Loop nulls are very sharp and are generally noticeable only on ground-wave signals (more on this later).

Of course, this method of nulling will be effective only if the interfering station and the station being worked are not in the same direction (or in exact opposite directions) from our location. If the two stations were on the same line from our location, both the station being worked and the undesired station would be nulled out. Luckily the nulls are very sharp, so as long as the stations are at least 10° off axis from each other, the loop null will be usable.

A similar use of the nulling capability is to eliminate local noise interference, such as that from a light dimmer in a neighbor's house. Just point the null at the offending light dimmer, and the noise should disappear.

Now that we have seen some possible uses of the small loop, let us look at the details of its design. First, the loop forms an inductor having a very small ratio of winding length to diameter. The equations for calculating inductance given in most radio handbooks assume that the inductor coil is longer than its diameter. However, F. W. Grover of the US National Bureau of Standards has provided equations for inductors of common cross-sectional shapes and small length-to-diameter ratios. (See the Bibliography at the end of this chapter.) Grover's equations are shown in **Table 5-2**. Their use will yield relatively accurate numbers; results are easily worked out with a scientific calculator or home computer.

The value of a tuning capacitor for a loop is easy to calculate from the standard resonance equations. The only matter to consider before calculating this is the value of distributed capacitance of the loop winding. This capacitance shows up between adjacent turns of the coil because of their slight difference in potential. This causes each turn to appear as a charge plate. As with all other capacitances, the value of the distributed capacitance is based on the physical dimensions of the coil. An exact mathematical analysis of its value is a complex problem. A simple approximation is given by Medhurst (see Bibliography) as:

$$C = HD \hspace{4cm} \text{(Eq 4)}$$

where

  C = distributed capacitance in pF
  H = a constant related to the length-to-diameter ratio of the coil (**Table 5-3** gives H values for length-to-

diameter ratios used in loop antenna work.)
  D = diameter of the winding in cm

Medhurst's work was with coils of round cross section. For loops of square cross section the distributed capacitance is given by Bramslev (see Bibliography) as

$$C = 60S \hspace{4cm} \text{(Eq 5)}$$

where

  C = the distributed capacitance in pF
  S = the length of the side in meters

If you convert the length in this equation to centimeters, you will find Bramslev's equation gives results in the same order of magnitude as Medhurst's equation.

This distributed capacitance appears as if it were a capacitor across the loop terminals. Therefore, when determining the value of the tuning capacitor, the distributed capacitance must be subtracted from the total capacitance required to resonate the loop. The distributed capacitance also determines the highest frequency at which a particular loop can be used, because it is the minimum capacitance obtainable.

Table 5-3
Values of the Constant H for Distributed Capacitance

Length to Diameter Ratio	H
0.10	0.96
0.15	0.79
0.20	0.78
0.25	0.64
0.30	0.60
0.35	0.57
0.40	0.54
0.50	0.50
1.00	0.46

5.2.3 ELECTROSTATICALLY SHIELDED LOOPS

Over the years, many loop antennas have incorporated an electrostatic shield. This shield generally takes the form of a tube around the winding, made of a conductive but nonmagnetic material (such as copper or aluminum). Its purpose is to maintain loop balance with respect to ground, by forcing the capacitance between all portions of the loop and ground to be identical. This is illustrated in **Figure 5.25**. It is necessary to maintain electrical loop balance to eliminate what is referred to as the *antenna effect*. When the antenna becomes unbalanced it appears to act partially as a small vertical antenna. This vertical pattern gets superimposed on the ideal figure-eight pattern, distorting the pattern and filling in the nulls. The type of pattern that results is shown in **Figure 5.26**.

Adding the shield has the effect of somewhat reducing the pickup of the loop, but this loss is generally offset by the increase in null depth of the loops. Proper balance of the loop antenna requires that the load on the loop also be balanced. This is usually accomplished by use of a balun transformer or a balanced input preamplifier. One important point regarding the shield is that it cannot form a continuous

Table 5-2
Inductance Equations for Short Coils (Loop Antennas)

Triangle:
$$L\,(\mu H) = 0.006\,N^2\,s\left[\ln\left(\frac{1.1547\,s\,N}{(N+1)\,\ell}\right) + 0.65533 + \frac{0.1348\,(N+1)\,\ell}{s\,N}\right]$$

Square:
$$L\,(\mu H) = 0.008\,N^2\,s\left[\ln\left(\frac{1.4142\,s\,N}{(N+1)\,\ell}\right) + 0.37942 + \frac{0.3333\,(N+1)\,\ell}{s\,N}\right]$$

Hexagon:
$$L\,(\mu H) = 0.012\,N^2\,s\left[\ln\left(\frac{2\,s\,N}{(N+1)\,\ell}\right) + 0.65533 + \frac{0.1348\,(N+1)\,\ell}{s\,N}\right]$$

Octagon
$$L\,(\mu H) = 0.016\,N^2\,s\left[\ln\left(\frac{2.613\,s\,N}{(N+1)\,\ell}\right) + 0.75143 + \frac{0.07153\,(N+1)\,\ell}{s\,N}\right]$$

where
  N = number of turns
  s = side length in cm
  ℓ = coil length in cm

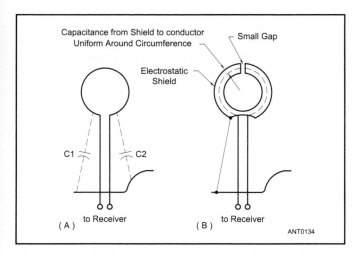

Figure 5.25 — At A, the loop is unbalanced by capacitance to its surroundings. At B, the use of an electrostatic shield overcomes this effect.

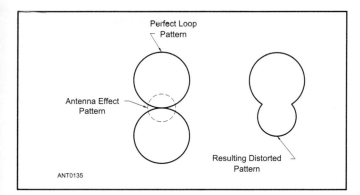

Figure 5.26 — Distortion in loop pattern resulting from antenna effect.

electrical path around the loop perimeter, or it will appear as a shorted coil turn. Usually the insulated break is located opposite the feed point to maintain symmetry. Another point to be considered is that the shield should be of a much larger diameter than the loop winding, or it will lower the Q of the loop.

Various construction techniques have been used in making shielded loops. Genaille located his loop winding inside aluminum conduit, while True constructed an aluminum shield can around his winding. Others have used pieces of hardline to form a loop, using the outer conductor as a shield. DeMaw used flexible coax with the shield broken at the center of the loop conductor in a multi-turn loop for 1.8 MHz. Goldman uses another shielding method for broadcast receiver loops. His shield is in the form of a barrel made of hardware cloth, with the loop in its center. (See Bibliography for above references.) All these methods provide sufficient shielding to maintain the balance. It is important to consider the effect of the shield configuration on antenna Q. A short letter by N1DM in *QEX* (July/Aug 1998, see References) discusses the Q of a loop antenna with a U-type shield versus a full box shield. His data shows between 54% and 89% degradation of Q for the full box case on an otherwise identical antenna configuration.

Use of coax cable to construct the shield may add some additional capacitive components which will limit the loop's higher frequency tuning range. Those designing a loop of this type should consider this fact when selecting the loop inductance the need to take this parasitic capacitance (in addition to the distributed capacitance) to obtain the desired higher frequency tuning point.

It is possible, as Nelson shows, to construct an unshielded loop with good nulls (60 dB or better) by paying great care to symmetry.

5.2.4 LOOP Q

As previously mentioned, Q is an important consideration in loop performance because it determines both the loop bandwidth and its terminal voltage for a given field strength. The loaded Q of a loop is based on four major factors. These are (1) the intrinsic Q of the loop winding, (2) the effect of the load, (3) the effect of the electrostatic shield, and (4) the Q of the tuning capacitor.

The major factor is the Q of the winding of the loop itself. The ac resistance of the conductor caused by skin effect is the major consideration. The ac resistance for copper conductors may be determined from

$$R = \frac{0.996 \times 10^{-6} \sqrt{f}}{d} \qquad \text{(Eq 6)}$$

where

R = resistance in ohms per foot
f = frequency in Hz
d = conductor diameter in inches

The Q of the inductor is then easily determined by taking the reactance of the inductor and dividing it by the ac resistance. If you are using a multi-turn loop and are a perfectionist, you might also want to include the loss from conductor proximity effect. This effect is described in detail later in this chapter, in the section on transmitting loops.

Improvement in Q can be obtained in some cases by the use of Litz wire (short for *Litzendraht*). Litz wire consists of strands of individual insulated wires that are woven into bundles in such a manner that each conductor occupies each location in the bundle with equal frequency. The Litz wire has a reduced ac resistance when compared to an equivalent cross section solid or stranded wire by taking into account the skin depth of conductors as frequency increases. Litz wire's improvement in ac resistance is due to the fact that the insulated individual strands result in more area of the total cross section of the conductor being in the skin depth region than for an equivalent diameter solid or stranded wire. (Stranded wire at ac acts the same as a solid wire of the same outside diameter.) Over 60% of the ac current is in this skin depth region. Therefore skin depth is more important to the calculation of ac resistance than the total conductor diameter.

Figure 5.27 shows an example of the skin depth of a solid conductor with radius R and a piece of Litz wire with an equivalent radius R. By examining the figure you can see that the cross sectional area of the current carrying skin effect

Table 5-4

Optimum Sizes of Individual Wires Used in Litz Wire

Frequency Range	Optimum AWG
60 Hz to 1 kHz	28
1 KHz to 10 KHz	30
10 KHz to 20 KHz	33
20 KHz to 50 KHz	36
50 KHz to 100 KHz	38
100 KHz to 200 KHz	40
200 KHz to 350 KHz	42
350 KHz to 850 KHz	44
850 KHz to 1.4 MHz	46
1.4 MHz to 2.8 MHz	48

(After Table 2 from New England Wire Technologies "Litz Wire Technical Information")

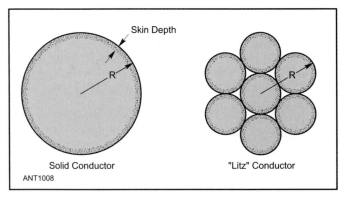

Figure 5.27 — Comparison of skin depth between conventional (A) and Litz wire (B).

region is double that of the solid wire. Litz wire is available in many configurations and the determining factor for the selection of a particular Litz wire starts with determining the optimum diameter of the individual insulated wire strands used in the construction of the particular cable. **Table 5-4** gives the values of optimum wire size based on frequency of use. When properly selected, Litz wire results in improved Q over solid or stranded wire of equivalent size, up to about 2.8 MHz. Above 2.8 MHz other effects quickly reduce the advantage of Litz wire. When using Litz wire it is important to realize that the ends of the Litz wire must be properly prepared so that all the strands of the wire are soldered to the connections of the capacitor and output connector. For those interested in the use of Litz wire the most common modern application is in high efficiency transformers and inductors in the kHz and low MHz range. Technical journals on transformer and magnetic design still present articles on the use of Litz wire with some regularity.

The Q of the tuned circuit of the loop antenna is also determined by the Q of the capacitors used to resonate it. In the case of air variables or dipped micas typically used this is not usually a problem. But if variable-capacitance diodes are used to remotely tune the loop, pay particular attention to the manufacturer's specification for Q of the diode at the frequency of operation. The tuning diodes can have a significant effect on circuit Q.

Now we consider the effect of load impedance on loop Q. In the case of a directly coupled loop (as in Figure 5.22), the load is connected directly across the loop terminals, causing it to be treated as a parallel resistance in a parallel-tuned RLC circuit. Obviously, if the load is of a low value, the Q of the loop will be low. A simple way to correct this is to use a transformer to step up the load impedance that appears across the loop terminals. In fact, if we make this transformer a balun, it also allows us to use our unbalanced receivers with the loop and maintain loop symmetry. Another solution is to use what is referred to as an inductively coupled loop, such as DeMaw's four-turn electrostatically shielded loop. A one-turn link is connected to the receiver. This turn is wound with the four-turn loop. In effect, this builds the transformer into the antenna.

Another solution to the problem of load impedance on loop Q is to use an active preamplifier with balanced input and unbalanced output. This method also has the advantage of amplifying the low-level output voltage of the loop to where it can be used with a receiver of even mediocre sensitivity.

There has been a significant amount of technical interest in this area over the last 20 years driven by low band DXers and AM band DXers. They have discovered that one of the critical issues to maximize performance of a loop/preamp combination is the dynamic range of the preamp. A poorly designed preamp may overload from local broadcast stations or have a poor noise figure itself which limits the ultimate performance observed with the loop antenna. Chris Trask, N7ZWY, has covered this in some detail with regards to the shortwave bands. Trask's excellent two-part article in the July/Aug and Sep/Oct 2003 issues of *QEX* (see References) includes a discussion of preamp requirements in Part 2. His design resulted in a noise figure of less than 2 dB from 6 to 14 MHz while obtaining a third order intercept of +5 dBm. The interested experimenter should consult that article.

In fact, the Q of the loop when used with a balanced preamplifier having high input impedance may be so high as to be unusable in certain applications. An example of this situation would occur where a loop is being used to receive a 5 kHz wide AM signal at a frequency where the bandwidth of the loop is only 1.5 kHz. In this case the detected audio might be very distorted. The solution to this is to put a Q-degrading resistor across the loop terminals to match the antennas bandwidth to the signal. The chapter **Receiving and Direction-Finding Antennas** also contains information about preamplifiers for use with loop antennas.

5.3 FERRITE-CORE LOOP ANTENNAS

The ferrite-core loop antenna is a special case of the air-core receiving loops considered up to now. Because of its use in every AM broadcast-band portable radio, the ferrite-core loop is, by quantity, the most popular form of the loop antenna. Broadcast-band reception is far from its only use; it is commonly found in radio-direction-finding equipment and low-frequency-receiving systems (below 500 kHz) for time and frequency standard systems. In recent years, design information on these types of antennas has been a bit sparse in the amateur literature, so the next few paragraphs are devoted to providing some details.

Ferrite-loop antennas are characteristically very small compared to the frequency of use. For example, a 3.5-MHz version may be in the range of 15 to 30 cm long and about 1.25 cm in diameter. Earlier in this chapter, effective height was introduced as a measure of loop sensitivity. The effective height of an air-core loop antenna was given by Eq 2.

If an air-core loop is placed in a field, in essence it cuts the lines of flux without disturbing them (**Figure 5.28A**). On the other hand, when a ferrite (magnetic) core is placed in the field, the nearby field lines are redirected into the loop (Figure 5.28B). This is because the reluctance of the ferrite material is less than that of the surrounding air, so the nearby flux lines tend to flow through the loop rather than through the air. (*Reluctance* is the magnetic analogy of resistance, while *flux* is analogous to current.) The reluctance is inversely proportional to the permeability of the rod core, μ_{rod}. (In some texts the rod permeability is referred to as effective permeability, μ_{eff}). This effect modifies the equation for effective height of a ferrite-core loop to

$$h = \frac{2 \pi N A \mu_{rod}}{\lambda} \qquad \text{(Eq 7)}$$

where

- h = effective height (length) in meters
- N = number of turns in the loop
- A = area of loop in square meters
- μ_{rod} = permeability of the ferrite rod
- λ = wavelength of operation in meters

This obviously is a large increase in "collected" signal. If the rod permeability were 90, this would be the same as making the loop area 90 times larger with the same number of turns. For example, a 1.25-cm diameter ferrite-core loop would have an effective height equal to an air-core loop 22.5 cm in diameter (with the same number of turns).

By now you might have noticed we have been very careful to refer to rod permeability. There is a very important reason for this. The permeability that a rod of ferrite exhibits is a combination of the material permeability or μ, the shape of the rod, and the dimensions of the rod. In ferrite rods, μ is sometimes referred to as initial permeability, μ_i, or toroidal permeability, μ_{tor}. Because most amateur ferrite loops are in the form of rods, we will discuss only this shape.

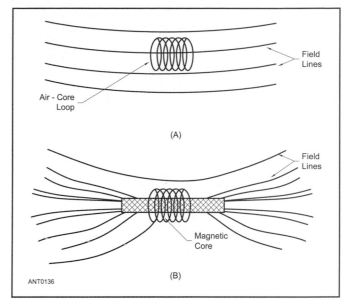

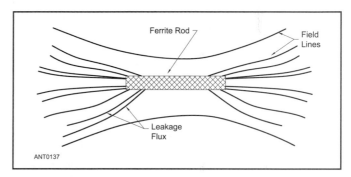

Figure 5.28 — At A, an air-core loop has no effect on nearby field lines. B illustrates the effect of a ferrite core on nearby field lines. The field is altered by the reluctance of the ferrite material.

Figure 5.29 — Example of magnetic field lines near a practical ferrite rod, showing leakage flux.

The reason that μ_{rod} is different from μ is a very complex physics problem that is well beyond the scope of this book. For those interested in the details, books by Polydoroff and by Snelling cover this subject in considerable detail. (See Bibliography.) For our purposes a simple explanation will suffice. The rod is in fact not a perfect director of flux, as is illustrated in **Figure 5.29**. Note that some lines impinge on the sides of the core and also exit from the sides. These lines therefore would not pass through all the turns of the coil if it were wound from one end of the core to the other. These flux lines are referred to as *leakage flux*, or sometimes as flux leakage.

Leakage flux causes the flux density in the core to be non-uniform along its length. From Figure 5.29 it can be seen that the flux has a maximum at the geometric center of the

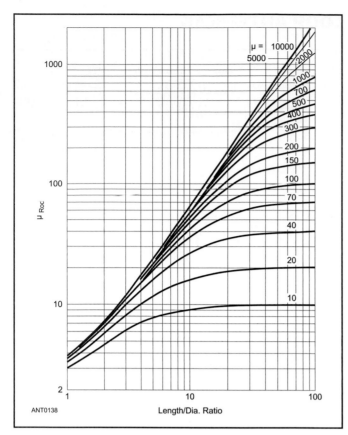

Figure 5.30 — Rod permeability, μ_{rod}, versus material permeability, μ, for different rod length-to-diameter ratios.

length of the core, and decreases as the ends of the core are approached. This causes some noticeable effects. As a short coil is placed at different locations along a long core, its inductance will change. The maximum inductance exists when the coil is centered on the rod. The Q of a short coil on a long rod is greatest at the center. On the other hand, if you require a higher Q than this, it is recommended that you spread the coil turns along the whole length of the core, even though this will result in a lower value of inductance. (The inductance can be increased to the original value by adding turns.) **Figure 5.30** gives the relationship of rod permeability to material permeability for a variety of values.

The change in μ over the length of the rod results in an adjustment in the term μ_{rod} for its so called "free ends" (those not covered by the winding). This adjustment factor is given by

$$\mu' = \mu_{rod} \sqrt[3]{a/b} \qquad \text{(Eq 8)}$$

where

    μ' = the corrected permeability
    a = the length of the core
    b = the length of the coil

This value of μ' should be used in place of μ_{rod} in Eq 7 to obtain the most accurate value of effective height.

All these variables make the calculation of ferrite loop

antenna inductance somewhat less accurate than for the air-core version. The inductance of a ferrite loop is given by

$$L = \frac{4 \pi N^2 A \mu_{rod} \times 10^{-4}}{\ell} \qquad \text{(Eq 9)}$$

where

    L = inductance in μH
    N = number of turns
    A = cross-sectional area of the core in square mm
    ℓ = magnetic length of core in mm

Experiments indicate that the winding diameter should be as close to that of the rod diameter as practical in order to maximize both inductance value and Q. By using all this information, we may determine the voltage at the loop terminals and its signal-to-noise ratio (SNR). The voltage may be determined from

$$V = \frac{2 \pi A N \mu' Q E}{\lambda} \qquad \text{(Eq 10)}$$

where

    V = output voltage across the loop terminals
    A = loop area in square meters
    N = number of turns in the loop winding
    μ' = corrected rod permeability
    Q = loaded Q of the loop
    E = RF field strength in volts per meter
    λ = wavelength of operation in meters

Lankford's equation for the sensitivity of the loop for a 10 dB SNR is

$$E = \frac{1.09 \times 10^{-10} \lambda \sqrt{f L b}}{A N \mu' \sqrt{Q}} \qquad \text{(Eq 11)}$$

where

    f = operating frequency in Hz
    L = loop inductance in henrys
    b = receiver bandwidth in Hz

Similarly, Belrose gives the SNR of a tuned loop antenna as

$$SNR = \frac{66.3 N A \mu_{rod} E}{\sqrt{b}} \sqrt{\frac{Qf}{L}} \qquad \text{(Eq 12)}$$

From this, if the field strength E, μ_{rod}, b, and A are fixed, then Q or N must increase (or L decrease) to yield a better SNR. Higher sensitivity can also be obtained (especially at frequencies below 2000 kHz) by bunching ferrite cores together to increase the loop area over that which would be possible with a single rod. Bowers and Bryant have built both 4 and 8-foot long ferrite loops for broadcast band DX'ing by using multiple ferrites cores bunched together and stacked lengthwise. Their 8-foot loop used over 100 pounds of ferrite cores. Marris, G2BZQ, also adopted the multiple core approach on 160 and 80 meters, constructing a 18 inch long multiple core ferrite loop using twelve ferrite rods each 6 inches long and ½ inch in diameter. He reported that there was no need for a preamp even when used for transatlantic reception. Marris noted that it is important to prepare the ends of the rods or cores before bonding them together. From a magnetic design point of view this is important to reduce the physical length of the air gaps between the individual lengthwise rods. This will maintain the best magnetic path (and maintain apparent permeability) for the antenna rods.

High sensitivity is important because loop antennas are not the most efficient collectors of signals, but they do offer improvement over other receiving antennas in terms of SNR. For this reason, you should attempt to maximize the SNR when using a small loop receiving antenna. In some cases there may be physical constraints that limit how large you can make a ferrite-core loop.

After working through Eq 11 or 12, in many cases you might find you still require some increase in antenna system gain to effectively use your loop. In these cases the addition of a low noise, high dynamic range preamplifier may be quite valuable even on the lower frequency bands where they are not commonly used.

The electrostatic shield discussed earlier with reference to air-core loops can be used effectively with ferrite-core loops. The question of how big this shield should be is hard to answer without some experimentation. A good starting point is found in Langford-Smith's book in which he recommends the shield diameter be at least twice the outside diameter of the coil. As in the air-core loop, a shield will reduce electrical noise and improve loop balance.

5.4 LOOP ANTENNA ARRAYS

Arrays of loop antennas, both in combinations with each other and with other antenna types, have been used for many years. The arrays are generally used to cure some "deficiency" in the basic loop for a particular application, such as a 180° ambiguity in the null direction, low sensitivity, and so forth.

5.4.1 A SENSING ELEMENT

For direction-finding applications the single loop suffers the problem of having two nulls that are 180° apart. This leads to an ambiguity of 180° when trying to find the direction to a transmitting station from a given location. A sensing element (often called a *sense antenna*) may be added to the loop, causing the overall antenna to have a cardioid pattern and only one null. The sensing element is a small vertical antenna whose height is equal to or greater than the loop effective height. This vertical is physically close to the loop, and when its omnidirectional pattern is adjusted so that its amplitude and phase are equal to one of the loop lobes, the patterns combine to form a cardioid. This antenna can be made quite compact by use of a ferrite loop to form a portable DF antenna for HF direction finding. The chapter **Receiving and Direction-Finding Antennas** contains additional information and construction projects using sensing elements.

5.4.2 PHASED ARRAYS OF LOOPS

A more advanced array that can develop more diverse patterns consists of two or more loops. Their outputs are combined through appropriate phasing lines and combiners to form a phased array.

5.4.3 CROSSED LOOPS

Two loops mounted perpendicular to each other can also be formed into an array that can be rotated without physically turning the loops themselves. This method was developed by Bellini and Tosi in 1907 and performs this apparently contradictory feat by use of a special transformer called a *goniometer*. The goniometer is basically has three coils, two fixed coils at right angles to each other which are connected to the appropriate loop antennas and a rotating coil centered on the other two. The two fixed coils can basically be thought of as transferring the signals from the antenna to the rotating coil The rotating coil then couples to these and based on the signal strength on each coil can determine the actual direction of the incoming signal. The goniometer is described in more detail in the chapter **Receiving and Direction Finding Antennas**. For those with an experimental bent Anderson published a construction article for a 160 meter crossed loop system including goniometer in Volume 1 of the *ARRL Antenna Compendium*. He used a completely balanced system using shielded twisted pair transmission line to a receiver with balanced inputs and also noted the better performance of these loops when electrostatically shielded.

5.4.4 SPACED LOOP ARRAYS

The use of multiple tuned loops in arrays is practical. In most cases these arrays use phasing lines to create a pattern with a deep notch in a desired direction. AM band DXers use this technique to null out nearby stations to allow reception of DX. Tuned arrays use techniques similar to those used in phasing vertical antennas with delay lines. Of course the fact that a loop antenna is not radiating equally in all azimuths as a vertical antenna must be accounted for in designing these arrays and calculating the resulting antenna patterns.

5.4.5 APERIODIC LOOP ARRAYS

The aperiodic loop array is a wide-band antenna. This type of array is useful over at least a decade of frequency, such as 2 to 20 MHz. Unlike most of the loops discussed up to now, the loop elements in an aperiodic array are un-tuned. Such arrays have been used commercially for many years. One loop used in such an array is shown in **Figure 5.31**. This loop is quite different from all the loops discussed so far in

The approximate radiation resistance of a loop in ohms is given by

$$R_R = 3.12 \times 10^4 \left(\frac{N\ A}{\lambda^2} \right)^2 \qquad \text{(Eq 13)}$$

where

N = number of turns
A = area of loop in square meters
λ = wavelength of operation in meters

The radiation resistance of a small transmitting loop is usually very small. For example, a 1-meter diameter, single-turn circular loop has a radius of 0.5 meters and an enclosed area of $\pi \times 0.5^2 = 0.785$ m^2. Operated at 14.0 MHz, the free-space wavelength is 21.4 meters and this leads to a computed radiation resistance of only $3.12 \times 10^{-4}\ (0.785/21.4^2)^2 = 0.092\ \Omega$.

Unfortunately the loop also has losses, both ohmic and from skin effect. By using this information, the radiation efficiency of a loop can be calculated from

$$\eta = \frac{R_R}{R_R + R_L} \qquad \text{(Eq 14)}$$

where

η = antenna efficiency in %
R_R = radiation resistance in Ω
R_L = loss resistance in Ω, which includes the loop's conductor loss plus the loss in the series-tuning capacitor.

A simple ratio of R_R versus R_L shows the effects on the efficiency, as can be seen from **Figure 5.34**. The loss resistance is primarily the ac resistance of the conductor. This can be calculated from Eq 6. A transmitting loop generally requires the use of copper conductors of at least ¾ inch in diameter in order to obtain reasonable efficiency. Tubing is as useful as a solid conductor because high-frequency currents flow only along a very small depth of the surface of the conductor; the center of the conductor has almost no effect on current flow.

Note that the R_L term above also includes the effect of the tuning capacitor's loss. Normally, the unloaded Q of a capacitor can be considered to be so high that any loss in the tuning capacitor can be neglected. For example, a very high-quality tuning capacitor with no mechanical wiping contacts, such as a vacuum-variable or a transmitting butterfly capacitor, might have an unloaded Q of about 5000. This implies a series loss resistance of less than about 0.02 Ω for a capacitive reactance of 100 Ω. This relatively tiny loss resistance can become significant, however, when the radiation resistance of the loop is only on the order of 0.1 Ω! Practical details for curbing capacitor losses are covered later in this chapter.

At this point you may ask the question, what radiation efficiency can reasonably be expected from a small loop. Luckily, Boswell, Tyler and White published an article in a professional journal which considers the efficiency of a simple 1 meter diameter loop made from (22 mm diameter copper tube) over 80 through 30 meters. Their results were 0.25 percent on 80 meters and 18 percent on 30 meters. The low numbers should not preclude considering the loop as in many cases this is the only reasonable solution to transmitting for the amateurs in a restricted space antenna situation. It is important to note that small transmitting loops (like their receiving cousins) have narrow 2:1 SWR bandwidth, meaning if you wish to change frequency across a wide range of frequencies, expect to have to do some tuning. In commercial loops this is usually done remotely using a small stepper or gear motor to rotate an appropriate capacitor.

In the case of multi-turn loops there is an additional loss related to a term called *proximity effect*. The proximity effect occurs in cases where the turns are closely spaced (such as being spaced one wire diameter apart). As these current-carrying conductors are brought close to each other, the current density around the circumference of each conductor gets redistributed. The result is that more current per square meter is flowing at the surfaces adjacent to other conductors. This means that the loss is higher than a simple skin-effect analysis would indicate, because the current is bunched so it flows through a smaller cross section of the conductor than if the other turns were not present.

As the efficiency of a loop approaches 90%, the proximity effect is less serious. But unfortunately, the less efficient the loop, the worse the effect. For example, an 8-turn transmitting loop with an efficiency of 10% (calculated by the skin-effect method) actually only has an efficiency of 3% because of the additional losses introduced by the proximity effect. If you are contemplating construction of a multi-turn transmitting loop, you might want to consider spreading the conductors apart to reduce this effect. G. S. Smith includes graphs that detail this effect in his 1972 IEEE paper and Trask, N7ZWY, examined the details of this loss for receiving antennas and recommends spacing turns at least five wire diameters to reduce this effect. His recommendation also applies to the transmitting variety of the loop antenna.

The components in a resonated transmitting loop are subject to both high currents and voltages as a result of the large circulating currents found in the high-Q tuned circuit formed by the antenna. This makes it important that any fixed capacitors have a high RF current rating, such as transmitting

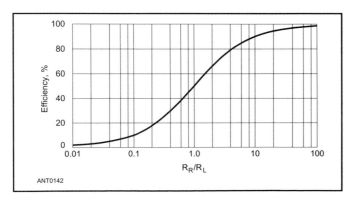

Figure 5.34 — Effect of ratio of R_R/R_L on loop efficiency.

ANT0142

micas or the Centralab 850 series. Be aware that even a 100-W transmitter can develop currents in the tens of amperes, and voltages across the tuning capacitor in excess of 10,000 V. This consideration also applies to any conductors used to connect the loop to the capacitors. A piece of #14 AWG may have more resistance than the rest of the loop conductor!

It is therefore best to use copper strips or the braid from a piece of large coax cable to make any connections. Make the best electrical connection possible, using soldered or welded joints. Using nuts and bolts should be avoided, because at RF these joints generally have high resistance, especially after being subjected to weathering. Trask has also noted that some flexible copper tubing is made from a lead/copper alloy. This should be avoided due to increased resistivity. Trask recommended rigid copper tubing, refrigeration tubing or large copper wire bc used.

An unfortunate consequence of having a small but high-efficiency transmitting loop is high loaded Q, and therefore limited bandwidth. This type of antenna may require retuning for frequency changes as little as 5 kHz. If you are using any wide-band mode such as AM or FM, this might cause fidelity problems and you might wish to sacrifice a little efficiency to obtain the required bandwidth.

A special case of the transmitting loop is that of the ferrite-loaded loop. This is a logical extension of the transmitting loop if we consider the improvement that a ferrite core makes in receiving loops. Unfortunately the transition to a transmitting antenna for the ferrite loaded loop is not a minor issue. Among the concerns is the saturation of the magnetic core. This often leads to defining the need for a rather large core that is larger than typical commercial ferrites available.). Recently Simpson and collaborators have been working on transmitting loops using egg-shaped ferrite cores with volumes of 2.2 cubic feet for use in a 2 MHz transmitting application. They have reported some success but the efficiency of these antennas is not high (<3%) and the cores are very heavy (622 pounds) for a power rating of 5 W. Along with the problem of having a very limited bandwidth this may limit the practical application of this type of antenna for amateurs in the foreseeable future.

5.6 BIBLIOGRAPHY

Source material and more extended discussion of topics covered in this chapter can be found in the references given below and in the textbooks listed in the References section of the **Antenna Fundamentals** chapter.

Aperiodic Loop Antenna Arrays (Hermes Electronics Ltd, Nov 1973).

C. F. W. Anderson, "A Crossed-Loop/Goniometer DF Antenna for 160 Meters," *The ARRL Antenna Compendium, Vol 1* (Newington: ARRL, 1985), pp 127-132.

D. Belcher, "Loops vs Dipole Analysis and Discussion," *QST*, Aug 1976, pp 34-37.

E. Bellini & A. Tosi, "A Directive System of Wireless Telegraph," *Proceedings of the Physical Society of London (UK)*, Vol 21: 1907: pp 305-328.

J. S. Belrose, "Ferromagnetic Loop Aerials," *Wireless Engineer*, Feb 1955, pp 41-46.

J. S. Belrose, "An Update on Compact Transmitting Loops," *QST*, Nov 1993, pp 37-40.

A. Boswell, A.J. Tyler, A. White, "Performance of a Small Loop Antenna in the 3-10 MHz Band," *IEEE Antennas and Propagation Magazine*, Vol. 47, No. 2, Apr 2005, pp 51-57.

B. Bowers and J. Bryant, "Very Large Ferrite Loops," *Fine Tuning Proceeding 1994-1995* (John H. Bryant, 1994), pp 18-1 to 18-6.

R. Capon, "You Can Build: A Compact Loop Antenna for 30 Through 12 Meters," *QST*, May 1994, pp 33-36.

LB Cebik, "Horizontally Oriented, Horizontally Polarized Large Wire Loop Antennas," 29 Mar, 1999, **www.cebik.com**

LB Cebik, "A Comparison of Closed and Interrupted Loop Antennas for 40 Meters", 15 Jan 2006, **www.cebik.com**

B. S. Collins, "A New High Performance HF Receiving Antenna," *Proceedings of the International Conference on Antennas and Propagation*, 28-30 Nov 1978, (London, UK: Institution of Electrical Engineers), pp 80-81

J. Dietrich, "Loops and Dipoles: A Comparative Analysis," *QST*, Sep 1985, pp 24-26.

D. DeMaw, "Beat the Noise with a Scoop Loop," *QST*, Jul 1977, pp 30-34.

D. DeMaw, "A Closer Look at Horizontal Loop Antennas," *QST*, pp 28-29, 35.

D. DeMaw and L. Aurick, "The Full-Wave Delta Loop at Low Height," *QST*, Oct 1984, pp 24-26.

M. F. DeMaw, *Ferromagnetic-Core Design and Application Handbook* (Englewood Cliffs, NJ: Prentice-Hall Inc, 1981).

R. G. Fenwick, "A Loop Array for 160 Meters," *CQ*, Apr 1986, pp 25-29.

D. Fischer, "The Loop Skywire," *QST*, Nov 1985, pp 20-22. Also "Feedback," *QST*, Dec 1985, p 53.

R. A. Genaille, "V.L.F. Loop Antenna," *Electronics World*, Jan 1963, pp 49-52.

R. S. Glasgow, *Principles of Radio Engineering* (New York: McGraw-Hill Book Co, Inc, 1936).

S. Goldman, "A Shielded Loop for Low Noise Broadcast Reception," *Electronics*, Oct 1938, pp 20-22.

F. W. Grover, *Inductance Calculation-Working Formulas and Tables* (New York: D. VanNostrand Co, Inc, 1946).

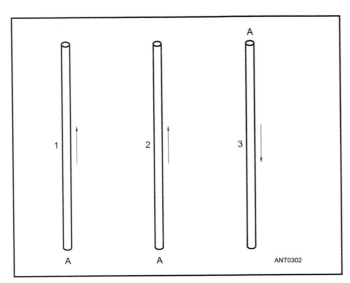

Figure 6.7 — This drawing illustrates the phase of currents in antenna elements, represented by the arrows. The currents in elements 1 and 2 are in phase, while that in element 3 is 180° out of phase with 1 and 2.

The phasing of driven elements depends on the direction of the element, the phase of the applied voltage, and the point at which the voltage is applied. In many systems used by amateurs, the voltages applied to the elements are exactly in or exactly out-of-phase with each other. Also, the axes of the elements are nearly always in the same direction, since parallel or collinear elements are invariably used. The currents in driven elements in such systems therefore are usually either exactly in or exactly out-of-phase with the currents in other elements. Reiterating from the **Antenna Fundamentals** chapter, it is important to distinguish between phase and *polarity*. Polarity is simply a convention that assigns a positive and negative direction or convention. Reversing the leads on a feed line reverses a signal's polarity.

It is possible to use phase differences of less than 180° in driven arrays. One important case is where the current in one set of elements differs by 90° from the current in another set. However, making provision for proper phasing in such systems is considerably more complex than in the case of simple 0° or 180° phasing, as described in a later section of this chapter.

In parasitic arrays the phase of the currents in the parasitic elements depends on the spacing and tuning, as described later.

Ground Effects

The effect of the ground is the same with a directive antenna as it is with a simple dipole antenna. The reflection factors discussed in the chapter **Effects of Ground** may therefore be applied to the vertical pattern of an array, subject to the same modifications mentioned in that chapter. In cases where the array elements are not all at the same height, the reflection factor for the mean height of the array may be used

for a close approximation. The mean height is the average of the heights measured from the ground to the centers of the lowest and highest elements.

6.1.2 MUTUAL IMPEDANCE

Consider two λ/2 elements that are fairly close to each other. Assume that power is applied to only one element, causing current to flow. This creates an electromagnetic field, which induces a voltage in the second element and causes current to flow in it as well. The current flowing in element 2 will in turn induce a voltage in element 1, causing additional current to flow there. The total current in 1 is then the sum (taking phase into account) of the original current and the induced current.

With element 2 present, the amplitude and phase of the resulting current in element 1 will be different than if element 2 were not there. This indicates that the presence of the second element has changed the impedance of the first. This effect is called *mutual coupling*. Mutual coupling results in a mutual impedance between the two elements. The mutual impedance has both resistive and reactive components. The actual impedance of an antenna element is the sum of its self-impedance (the impedance with no other antennas present) and its mutual impedances with all other antennas in the vicinity.

The magnitude and nature of the feed point impedance of the first antenna depends on the amplitude of the current induced in it by the second, and on the phase relationship between the original and induced currents. The amplitude and phase of the induced current depend on the spacing between the antennas and whether or not the second antenna is tuned to resonance.

In the discussion of the several preceding paragraphs, power is applied to only one of the two elements. Do not interpret this to mean that mutual coupling exists only in parasitic arrays! It is important to remember that mutual coupling exists between any two conductors that are located near one another.

Amplitude of Induced Current

The induced current will be largest when the two antennas are close together and are parallel. Under these conditions the voltage induced in the second antenna by the first, and in the first by the second, has its greatest value and causes the largest current flow. The coupling decreases as the parallel antennas are moved farther apart.

The coupling between collinear antennas is comparatively small, and so the mutual impedance between such antennas is likewise small. It is not negligible, however.

Phase Relationships

When the separation between two antennas is an appreciable fraction of a wavelength a measurable period of time elapses before the field from antenna 1 reaches antenna 2. There is a similar time lapse before the field set up by the current in number 2 gets back to induce a current in number 1. Hence the current induced in antenna 1 by antenna 2 will have a phase relationship with the original current in antenna 1 that depends on the spacing between the two antennas.

The induced current can range all the way from being completely in-phase with the original current to being completely out-of-phase with it. If the currents are in-phase, the total current is larger than the original current and the antenna feed point impedance is reduced. If the currents are out-of-phase, the total current is smaller and the impedance is increased. At intermediate phase relationships the impedance will be lowered or raised depending on whether the induced current is mostly in or mostly out-of-phase with the original current.

Except in the special cases when the induced current is exactly in or out-of-phase with the original current, the induced current causes the phase of the total current to shift with respect to the applied voltage. Consequently, the presence of a second antenna nearby may cause the impedance of an antenna to be reactive — that is, the antenna will be detuned from resonance — even though its self-impedance is entirely resistive. The amount of detuning depends on the magnitude and phase of the induced current.

Tuning Conditions

A third factor that affects the impedance of antenna 1 when antenna 2 is present is the tuning of number 2. If antenna 2 is not exactly resonant, the current that flows in it as a result of the induced voltage will either lead or lag the phase it would have if the antenna were resonant. This causes an additional phase advance or delay that affects the phase of the current induced back in antenna 1. Such a phase lag has an effect similar to a change in the spacing between self-resonant antennas. However, a change in tuning is not exactly equivalent to a change in spacing because the two methods do not have the same effect on the amplitude of the induced current.

6.1.3 MUTUAL IMPEDANCE AND GAIN

The mutual coupling between antennas is important because it can have a significant effect on the amount of current that will flow for a given amount of power supplied. And it is the amount of *current* flowing that determines the field strength from the antenna. Other things being equal, if the mutual coupling between two antennas is such that the currents are greater for the same total power than would be the case if the two antennas were not coupled, the power gain will be greater than that shown in Table 6-1.

On the other hand, if the mutual coupling is such as to reduce the current, the gain will be less than if the antennas were not coupled. The term *mutual coupling*, as used in this paragraph, assumes that the mutual impedance between elements is taken into account, along with the added effects of propagation delay because of element spacing and element tuning or phasing.

The calculation of mutual impedance between antennas is a complex problem. Data for two simple but important cases are graphed in Figures 6.8 and 9. These graphs do not show the mutual impedance, but instead show a more useful

quantity — the feed point resistance measured at the center of an antenna as it is affected by the spacing between two antennas.

As shown by the solid curve in **Figure 6.8**, the feed point resistance at the center of either antenna, when the two are *self-resonant*, parallel, and operated in-phase, decreases as the spacing between them is increased until the spacing is about 0.7 λ. This is a broadside array. The maximum gain is achieved from a pair of such elements when the spacing is in this region, because the current is larger for the same power and the fields from the two elements arrive in-phase at a distant point placed on a line perpendicular to the line joining the two antennas. (Self-resonance means the antenna is resonant in the absence of mutual coupling with any other antenna.)

The dashed line in Figure 6.8, representing two antennas operated 180° out-of-phase (end-fire), cannot be interpreted quite so simply. The feed point resistance decreases with spacing decreasing less than about 0.6 λ in this case. However, for the range of spacings considered, only when the spacing is 0.5 λ do the fields from the two antennas add up exactly in phase at a distant point in the favored direction. At smaller spacings the fields become increasingly out-of-phase, so the total field is less than the simple sum of the two. Smaller spacings thus decrease the gain at the same time that the reduction in feed point resistance is increasing it. For a lossless antenna, the gain goes through a maximum when the spacing is in the region of ⅛ λ.

The feed point resistance curve for two collinear elements in-phase, **Figure 6.9**, shows that the feed point resistance decreases and goes through a broad minimum in the region of 0.4 to 0.6 λ spacing between the adjacent ends of the antennas. As the minimum is not significantly less than the feed point resistance of an isolated antenna, the gain will not exceed the gain calculated on the basis of uncoupled

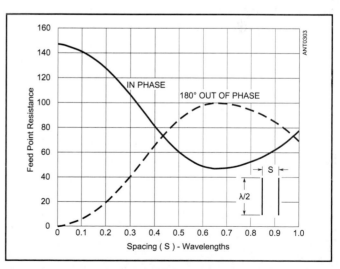

Figure 6.8 — Feed point resistance measured at the center of one element as a function of the spacing between two parallel ½-λ self-resonant antenna elements. For ground-mounted ¼-λ vertical elements, divide these resistances by two.

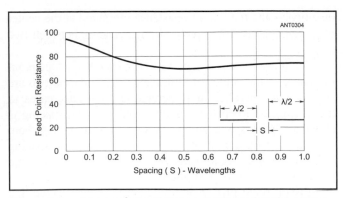

Figure 6.9 — Feed point resistance measured at the center of one element as a function of the spacing between the ends of two collinear self-resonant ½-λ antenna elements operated in phase.

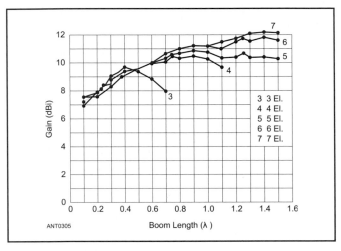

Figure 6.10 — Yagi gain for 3, 4, 5, 6 and 7-element beams as a function of boom length. (From *Yagi Antenna Design*, J. Lawson, W2PV.)

antennas. That is, the best that two collinear elements will give, even with optimum spacing, is a power gain of about 2 (3 dB). When the separation between the ends is very small — the usual method of operation — the gain is reduced.

6.1.4 GAIN AND ARRAY DIMENSIONS

The gain of an array is principally determined by the dimensions of the array, so long as there are a minimum number of elements. A good example of this is the relationship between boom length, gain and number of elements for an array such as a Yagi. **Figure 6.10** compares the gain versus boom length for Yagis with different numbers of elements. For given number of elements, notice that the gain increases as the boom length increases, up to a maximum. Beyond this point, longer boom lengths result in less gain for a given number of elements. This observation does not mean that it is always desirable to use only the minimum number of elements. Other considerations of array performance, such as front-to-back ratio, minor lobe amplitudes or operating bandwidth, may make it advantageous to use more than the minimum number of elements for a given array length. A specific example of this is presented in a later section in a comparison between a half-square, a bobtail curtain and a Bruce array.

In a broadside array the gain is a function of both the length and width of the array. The gain can be increased by adding more elements (with additional spacing) or by using longer elements (>λ/2), although the use of longer elements requires proper attention to current phase in the elements. In general, in a broadside array the element spacing that gives maximum gain for a minimum number of elements, is in the range of 0.5 to 0.7 λ. Broadside arrays with elements spaced for maximum gain will frequently have significant side lobes and associated narrowing of the main lobe beamwidth. Side lobes can be reduced by using more than the minimum number of elements, spaced closer than the maximum gain distance.

Additional gain can be obtained by expanding the array into a third dimension. An example of this is the stacking of end-fire arrays in a broadside configuration. In the case of stacked short end-fire arrays, maximum gain occurs with spacings in the region of 0.5 to 0.7 λ. However, for longer higher-gain end-fire arrays, larger spacing is required to achieve maximum gain. This is important in VHF and UHF arrays, which often use long-boom Yagis.

6.2 DRIVEN ARRAYS

Definitions in the preceding section apply to multi-element arrays of both types, driven and parasitic. However, there are special considerations for driven arrays that do not necessarily apply to parasitic arrays, and vice versa. Such considerations for Yagi and quad parasitic arrays are presented in the **HF Yagi and Quad Antennas** chapter. The remainder of this chapter is devoted to driven arrays.

Driven arrays in general are either broadside or end-fire, and may consist of collinear elements, parallel elements, or a combination of both. From a practical standpoint, the maximum number of usable elements depends on the frequency and the space available for the antenna. Fairly elaborate arrays, using as many as 16 or even 32 elements, can be installed in a rather small space when the operating frequency is in the VHF range and more at UHF. At lower frequencies the construction of antennas with a large number of elements is impractical for most amateurs.

Of course the simplest of driven arrays is one with just two elements. If the elements are collinear, they are always fed in-phase. The effects of mutual coupling are not great, as illustrated in Figure 6.9. Therefore, feeding power to each element in the presence of the other presents no significant problems. This may not be the case when the elements are parallel to each other. However, because the combination of spacing and phasing arrangements for parallel elements is infinite, the number of possible radiation patterns is endless.

This is illustrated in **Figure 6.11**. When the elements are fed in-phase, a broadside pattern always results. At spacings of less than ⅝ λ with the elements fed 180° out-of-phase, an end-fire pattern always results. With intermediate amounts of phase difference, the results cannot be so simply stated. Patterns evolve that are not symmetrical in all four quadrants.

Because of the effects of mutual coupling between the two driven elements, for a given power input greater or lesser currents will flow in each element with changes in spacing and phasing, as described earlier. This, in turn, affects the gain of the array in a way that cannot be shown merely by plotting the *shapes* of the patterns, as has been done in Figure 6.11. Therefore, supplemental gain information is also shown in Figure 6.11, adjacent to the pattern plot for each combination of spacing and phasing. The gain figures shown are referenced to a single element. For example, a pair of elements fed 90° out of phase with a spacing of λ/4 will have a gain in the direction of maximum radiation of 3.1 dB over a single element.

6.2.1 CURRENT DISTRIBUTION IN PHASED ARRAYS

In the plots of Figure 6.11, the two elements are assumed to be identical and self-resonant. In addition, currents of equal amplitude are assumed to be flowing at the feed point of each element, a condition that most often will not exist in practice without devoting special consideration to the feeder system. Such considerations are discussed in the next section of this chapter.

Most literature for radio amateurs concerning phased arrays is based on the assumption that if all elements in the array are identical, the *current distribution* in all the elements will be identical. This distribution is presumed to be that of a single, isolated element, or nearly sinusoidal. However, information published in the professional literature as early as the 1940s indicates the existence of dissimilar current distributions among the elements of phased arrays. (See Harrison and King references in the Bibliography.) Lewallen, in July 1990 *QST*, pointed out the causes and effects of dissimilar current distributions.

In essence, even though the two elements in a phased array may be identical and have exactly equal currents of the desired phase flowing at *the feed point*, the amplitude and phase relationships degenerate with departure from the feed point. This happens any time the phase relationship is not 0° or 180°. Thus, the field strengths produced at a distant point by the individual elements may differ. This is because the field from each element is determined by the *distribution* of the current, as well as its magnitude and phase.

The effects are minimal with shortened elements — verticals less than λ/4 or dipoles less than λ/2 long. The effects on radiation patterns begin to show at the above resonant lengths, and become profound with longer elements — λ/2 or longer verticals and 1 λ or longer center-fed elements. These effects are less pronounced with thin elements. The amplitude and phase degeneration takes place because the currents in the array elements are not sinusoidal. Even in two-element arrays with phasing of 0° or 180°, the currents are not sinusoidal, but in these two special cases they do remain identical.

The pattern plots of Figure 6.11 take element current distributions into account. The visible results of dissimilar distributions are incomplete nulls in some patterns and the development of very small minor lobes in others. For example, the pattern for a phased array with 90° spacing and 90° phasing has traditionally been published in amateur literature as a cardioid with a perfect null in the rear direction. Figure 6.11, calculated for 7.15-MHz self-resonant dipoles of #12 AWG wire in free space, shows a minor lobe at the rear and only a 33-dB front-to-back ratio.

It is characteristic of broadside arrays that the power gain is proportional to the length of the array but is substantially independent of the number of elements used, provided the optimum element spacing is not exceeded. This means, for example, that a five-element array and a six-element array will have the same gain, provided the elements in both are spaced so the overall array length is the same. Although this principle is seldom used for the purpose of reducing the number of elements because of complications introduced in feeding power to each element in the proper phase, it does illustrate the fact that there is nothing to be gained, in terms of more gain, by increasing the number of elements if the space occupied by the antenna is not increased proportionally.

Generally speaking, the maximum gain in the smallest linear dimensions will result when the antenna combines both broadside and end-fire directivity and uses both parallel and collinear elements. In this way the antenna is spread over a greater volume of space, which has the same effect as extending its length to a much greater extent in one linear direction.

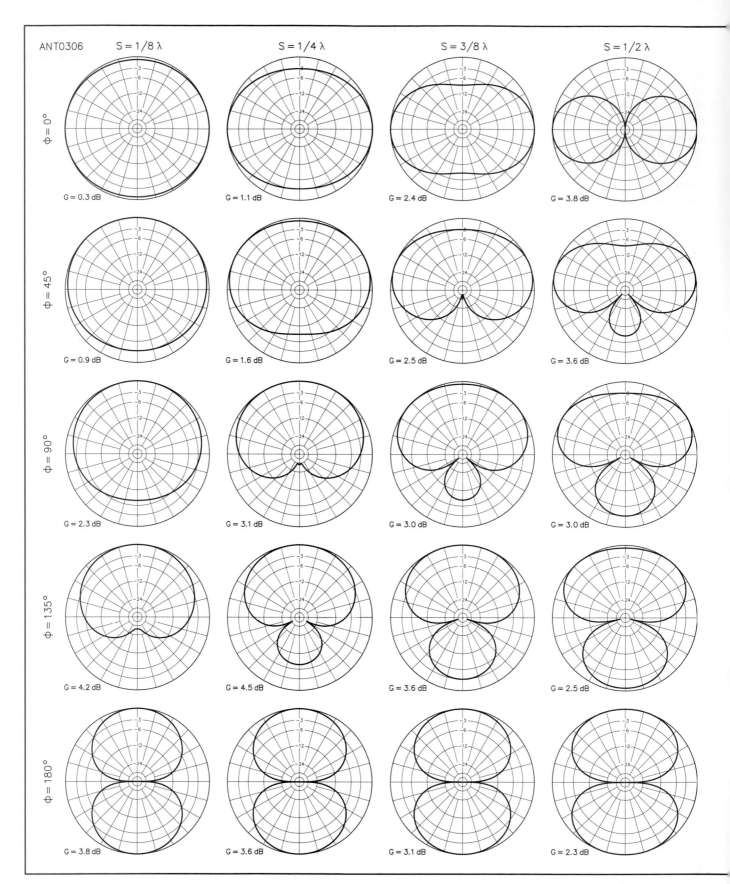

S = 1/8 λ   S = 1/4 λ   S = 3/8 λ   S = 1/2 λ

φ = 0°

G = 0.3 dB   G = 1.1 dB   G = 2.4 dB   G = 3.8 dB

φ = 45°

G = 0.9 dB   G = 1.6 dB   G = 2.5 dB   G = 3.6 dB

φ = 90°

G = 2.3 dB   G = 3.1 dB   G = 3.0 dB   G = 3.0 dB

φ = 135°

G = 4.2 dB   G = 4.5 dB   G = 3.6 dB   G = 2.5 dB

φ = 180°

G = 3.8 dB   G = 3.6 dB   G = 3.1 dB   G = 2.3 dB

Figure 6.11 — H-plane patterns of two identical parallel driven elements, spaced and phased as indicated (S = spacing, φ = phasing). The elements are aligned with the vertical (0°-180°) axis, and the element nearer the 0° direction (top of page) is of lagging phase at angles other than 0°. The two elements are assumed to be thin and self-resonant, with equal-amplitude currents flowing at the feed point. See text regarding current distributions. The gain figure associated with each pattern

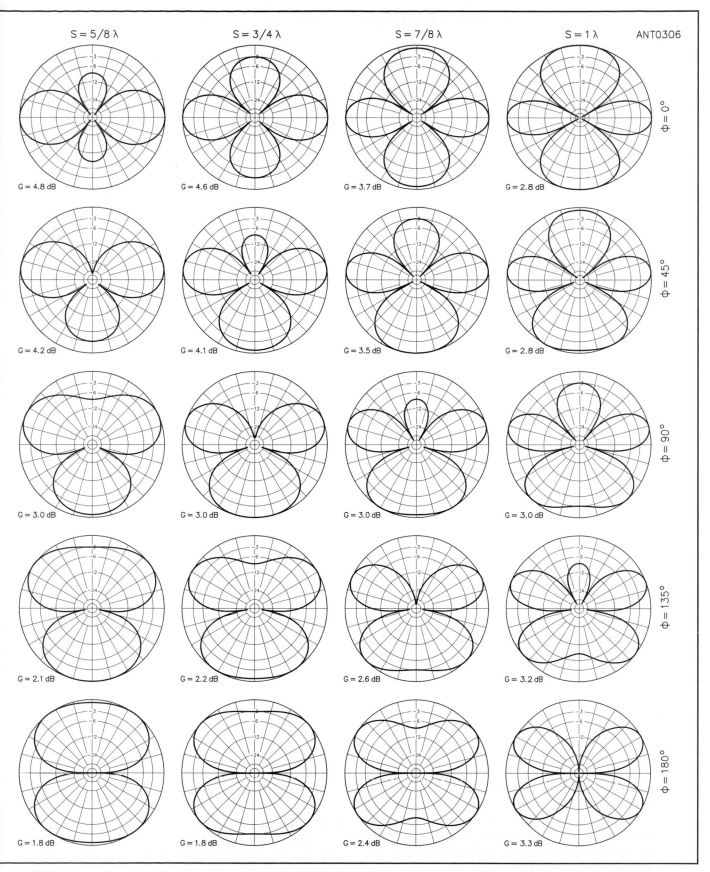

S = 5/8 λ S = 3/4 λ S = 7/8 λ S = 1 λ

φ = 0°
G = 4.8 dB   G = 4.6 dB   G = 3.7 dB   G = 2.8 dB

φ = 45°
G = 4.2 dB   G = 4.1 dB   G = 3.5 dB   G = 2.8 dB

φ = 90°
G = 3.0 dB   G = 3.0 dB   G = 3.0 dB   G = 3.0 dB

φ = 135°
G = 2.1 dB   G = 2.2 dB   G = 2.6 dB   G = 3.2 dB

φ = 180°
G = 1.8 dB   G = 1.8 dB   G = 2.4 dB   G = 3.3 dB

indicates that of the array over a single element. The plots represent the horizontal or azimuth pattern at a 0° elevation angle of two ¼-λ vertical elements over a perfect conductor, or the free-space vertical or elevation pattern of two horizontal ½-λ elements when viewed on end, with one element above the other. (Patterns computed with *ELNEC* — the predeccessor to *EZNEC*.)

6.3 PHASED ARRAY TECHNIQUES

Phased antenna arrays have become increasingly popular for amateur use, particularly on the lower frequency bands, where they provide one of the few practical methods to obtain substantial gain and directivity. This section on phased-array techniques was written by Roy Lewallen, W7EL, and updated for this edition.

The operation and limitations of phased arrays, how to design feed systems to make them work properly and how to make necessary tests and adjustments are discussed in the pages that follow. The examples deal primarily with vertical HF arrays, but the principles apply to VHF/UHF arrays and arrays made from other element types as well.

6.3.1 OVERVIEW

Much of this chapter is devoted to techniques for feeding phased arrays. Many people who have a limited acquaintance with phased array techniques believe this is a simple problem, consisting only of connecting array elements through "phasing lines" consisting of transmission lines of the desired electrical lengths. Unfortunately, except for a very few special cases, this approach won't achieve the desired array pattern.

Other proposed universal solutions, such as hybrid couplers or Wilkinson or other power dividers, also usually fail to achieve the necessary phasing. These approaches sometimes produce — often more by accident than design — results good enough to mislead the user into believing that the simple approach is working as planned. Confusion can result when an approach fails to work in different circumstances. This section will explain why the simple solutions don't work as often thought, and how to design feed systems that do consistently produce the desired results.

Very briefly, the reason why the simple phasing line approach fails is that the delay of current or voltage in a transmission line equals the line's electrical length only if the line is terminated in its characteristic impedance. And in phased arrays, element feed point impedances are profoundly affected by mutual coupling.

Consequently, even if each element has the correct impedance when isolated, it won't when all elements are excited. Furthermore, transmission lines that are not terminated in their characteristic impedance will transform both the voltage and current magnitude. The net result is that the array elements will have neither the correct magnitudes nor phases of current necessary for proper operation except in a few special cases. This isn't a minor effect of concern only to perfectionists, but often a major one that causes significant pattern distortion and poor or mis-located nulls. The problem is examined in greater depth later.

Power dividers and hybrid couplers also fail to achieve the desired result for different reasons which will be discussed below although in one common application hybrid couplers fortuitously provide results that are acceptable to many users. This chapter will show how to design array feed systems that will produce predicted element currents and array patterns.

Various *EZNEC* models are provided to illustrate concepts presented in this chapter. They can all be viewed with the *EZNEC-ARRL* software furnished on the CD included with this book. Step-by-step instructions for the examples are given in **Appendix A**.

6.3.2 FUNDAMENTALS OF PHASED ARRAYS

The performance of a phased array is determined by several factors. Most significant among these are the characteristics of a single element, reinforcement or cancellation of the fields from the elements and the effects of mutual coupling. To understand the operation of phased arrays, it is first necessary to understand the operation of a single antenna element.

Of primary importance is the strength of the field produced by the element. The field radiated from a linear (straight) element, such as a dipole or vertical monopole, is proportional to the sum of the elementary currents flowing in each part of the antenna element. For this discussion it is important to understand what determines the current in a single element.

The amount of current flowing at the base of a ground mounted vertical or ground-plane antenna is given by the familiar formula

$$I = \sqrt{\frac{P}{R}} \tag{2}$$

where

P is the power supplied to the antenna

R is the feed point resistance.

R consists of two parts, the loss resistance and the radiation resistance. The loss resistance, R_L, includes losses in the conductor, in the matching and loading components and dominantly (in the case of ground-mounted verticals) in ground losses. The power "dissipated" in the radiation resistance, R_R, is actually the power that is radiated, so maximizing the power dissipated by the radiation resistance is desirable. However, the power "dissipated" in the loss resistance truly is lost as heat, so resistive losses should be made as small as possible.

The radiation resistance of an element can be derived from electromagnetic field theory, being a function of antenna length, diameter and geometry. Graphs of radiation resistance versus antenna length are given in the **Dipoles and Monopoles** chapter. The radiation resistance of a thin resonant $\lambda/4$ ground-mounted vertical is about 36 Ω. A resonant $\lambda/2$ dipole in free space has a radiation resistance of twice this amount, about 73 Ω. Reducing the antenna lengths by one-half drops the radiation resistances to approximately 7 and 14 Ω, respectively.

The radiation resistance of a large variety of antennas can easily be determined by using *EZNEC-ARRL*, which is included on the CD in the back of this book. The radiation resistance is simply the feed point resistance (the resistive part of the feed point impedance) when all losses have been set to zero.

Radiation Efficiency

To generate a stronger field from a given radiator, it is necessary to increase the power P (the brute-force solution), decrease the loss resistance R_L (by putting in a more elaborate ground system for a vertical, for instance) or to somehow decrease the radiation resistance R_R so more current will flow with a given power input. This can be seen by expanding the formula for base current as

$$I = \sqrt{\frac{P}{R_R + R_L}} \qquad (3)$$

Splitting the feed point resistance into components R_R and R_L easily leads to an understanding of element efficiency. The efficiency of an element is the proportion of the total power that is actually radiated. The roles of R_R and R_L in determining efficiency can be seen by analyzing a simple equivalent circuit, shown in **Figure 6.12**.

The power dissipated in R_R (the radiated power) equals $I^2 R_R$. The total power supplied to the antenna system is

$$P = I^2 (R_R + R_L) \qquad (4)$$

so the efficiency (the fraction of supplied power that is actually radiated) is

$$Eff = \frac{I^2 R_R}{I^2 (R_R + R_L)} = \frac{R_R}{R_R + R_L} \qquad (5)$$

Efficiency is frequently expressed in percent, but expressing it in decibels relative to a 100%-efficient radiator gives a better idea of what to expect in the way of signal strength. The field strength of an element relative to a lossless but otherwise identical element, in dB, is

$$FSG = 10 \log \frac{R_R}{R_R + R_L} \qquad (6)$$

where FSG = field strength gain in dB.

For example, information presented by Sevick in March 1973 *QST* shows that a λ/4 ground-mounted vertical antenna with four 0.2-λ radials has a feed point resistance of about 65 Ω (see the Bibliography at the end of this chapter). The efficiency of such a system is 36/65 = 55.4%. It is rather disheartening to think that, of 100 W fed to the antenna, only 55 W is being radiated, with the remainder literally warming up the ground. Yet the signal will be only 10 log (36/65) = −2.57 dB relative to the same vertical with a perfect ground system. In view of this information, trading a small reduction in signal strength for lower cost and greater simplicity may become an attractive consideration.

So far, only the current at the base of a resonant antenna has been discussed, but the field is proportional to the sum of currents in each tiny part of the antenna. The field is a function of not only the magnitude of current flowing at the feed point, but also the distribution of current along the radiator and the length of the radiator. Nothing can be done at the feed point to change the current distribution, so for a given element the field strength is proportional to the feed point current. However, changing the radiator length or loading it at some point other than the feed point will change the current distribution.

More information on shortened or loaded radiators may be found in the **Antenna Fundamentals** and **Single-Band MF and HF Antennas** and in the Bibliography references of this chapter. The current distribution is also changed by mutual coupling to other array elements, although for most arrays this has only a minor effect on the pattern. This is discussed later in more detail. A few other important facts follow.

1) If there is no loss, the field from even an infinitesimally short radiator is less than ½ dB weaker than the field from a half-wave dipole or quarter-wave vertical. Without loss, all the supplied power is radiated regardless of the antenna length, so the only factor influencing gain is the slight difference in the patterns of very short and λ/2 antennas. The small pattern difference arises from different current distributions. A short antenna has a very low radiation resistance, resulting in a heavy current flow over its short length. In the absence of loss, this generates a field strength comparable to that of a longer antenna. Where loss is present — that is, in practical antennas — shorter radiators usually don't do so well, since the low radiation resistance leads to lower efficiency for a given loss resistance. Nevertheless, reasonably short antennas can achieve good efficiency if care is taken.

2) Caution must be used in calculating the efficiency of folded antennas. Folding transforms both the radiation resistance and loss resistance by the same factor, so their ratio and therefore the efficiency remains the same. It's easy to show that in a ground-mounted vertical array, folding reduces the current flowing from the feed line to the ground system by a factor of two due to the impedance transformation. However, the folded antenna has an additional connection to ground, which also carries half the original ground current. The result is that the same amount of current flows into the ground system, whether unfolded or folded, resulting in the same ground system loss. Analyses purporting to show otherwise invariably transform the radiation resistance but neglect to also transform the loss resistance and reach an incorrect conclusion.

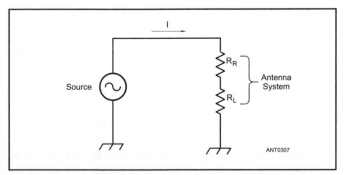

Figure 6.12 — Simplified equivalent circuit for a single-element resonant antenna. R_R represents the radiation resistance, and R_L the ohmic losses in the total antenna system.

3) The current flowing in an element with a given power input can be increased or decreased by mutual coupling to other elements. The effect is equivalent to changing the element radiation resistance. Mutual coupling is sometimes thought of as a minor effect, but often it is not minor!

Field Reinforcement and Cancellation

The mechanism by which phased arrays produce gain, and the role of mutual coupling in determining gain, were covered earlier in this chapter. One important point that can't be emphasized enough is that all antennas must abide by the law of *conservation of energy*. No antenna can radiate more power than supplied to it. The total amount of power it radiates is the amount it's supplied, less the amount lost as heat. This is true of all antennas, from the smallest "rubber ducky" to the most gigantic array.

Gain

Gain is strictly a relative measure, so the term is completely meaningless unless accompanied by a statement of just what it is relative to. One useful measure for phased array gain is *gain relative to a single similar element*. This is the increase in signal strength that would be obtained by replacing a single element by an array made from elements just like it. In some instances, such as investigating what happens to array performance when all elements become more lossy, it's useful to state gain relative to a more absolute, although unattainable standard: a lossless element.

And the most universal reference for gain is another unattainable standard, the *isotropic radiator*. This fictional antenna radiates absolutely equally in all directions. It's very useful because the field strength resulting from any power input is readily calculated, so if the gain relative to this standard is known, the field strength is also known for any radiated power. Gain relative to this reference is referred to as dBi, and it's the standard used by most modeling programs including *EZNEC-ARRL*. To find the gain of an array relative to a single element or other reference antenna such as a dipole, model both the array and the single element or other reference antenna in the same environment and subtract their dBi gains. Don't rely on some assumption about the gain of a single element — many people assume values that can be very wrong.

Nulls

Pattern nulls are very often more important to users of phased arrays than gain because of their importance in reducing both man-made and natural interference when receiving. Consequently, a good deal of emphasis is, and should be, placed on achieving good pattern nulls. Unfortunately, good nulls are much more difficult to achieve than gain and they are much more sensitive to array and feed-system imperfections.

As an illustration, consider two elements that each produce a field strength of, say, exactly 1 millivolt per meter (mV/m) at some distance many wavelengths from the array. In the direction in which the fields from the elements are in-phase, a total field of 2 mV/m results. In the direction in which they're out-of-phase, zero field results. The ratio of

maximum to minimum field strength of this array is 2/0, or infinity.

Now suppose, instead, that one field is 10% high and the other 10% low — 1.1 and 0.9 mV/m, respectively. In the forward direction, the field strength is still 2 mV/m, but in the canceling direction, the field will be 0.2 mV/m. The front-to-back ratio has dropped from infinity to 2/0.2, or 20 dB. (Actually, slightly more power is required to redistribute the field strengths this way, so the forward gain is reduced — but by only a small amount, less than 0.1 dB.) For most arrays, unequal fields from the elements have a minor effect on forward gain, but a major effect on pattern nulls. This is illustrated by *EZNEC* **Example: Nulls** in Appendix A.

Even with perfect current balance, deep nulls aren't assured. **Figure 6.13** shows the minimum spacing required for total field reinforcement or cancellation. If the element spacing isn't adequate, there may be no direction in which the fields are completely out-of-phase (see curve B of Figure 6.13). Slight physical and environmental differences between elements will invariably affect null depths, and null depths will also vary with elevation angle.

However, a properly designed and fed array can produce very impressive nulls. The key to producing good nulls, like producing gain, is controlling the strengths and phases of the fields from the elements. Just how to accomplish that is the subject of most of the remainder of this section. But be sure to keep in mind that producing good nulls is generally a much more difficult task than producing approximately the predicted gain.

Mutual Coupling

Mutual coupling was discussed briefly earlier in this chapter. Because it has an important and profound effect on both the performance and feed system design of phased arrays, it will be covered in greater depth here.

Mutual coupling refers to the effects which the elements in an array have on each other. Mutual coupling can occur intentionally or entirely unintentionally. People with multiple

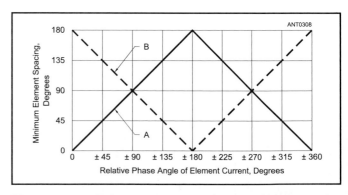

Figure 6.13 — Minimum element spacing required for total field reinforcement, curve A, or total field cancellation, curve B. Total cancellation results in pattern nulls in one or more directions. Total reinforcement does not necessarily mean there is gain over a single element, as the effects of loss and mutual coupling must also be considered.

antennas on a small lot (or car top) often discover that a better description of their system is a single antenna with multiple feed points. Current is induced in conductors in various antennas by mutual coupling, causing them to act like parasitic elements, which re-radiate and distort the antenna's pattern. The effects of mutual coupling are present whether or not the elements are driven.

Suppose that two driven elements are many wavelengths from each other. Each has some voltage and current at its feed point. For each element, the ratio of this voltage to current is the element self-impedance. If the elements are brought close to each other, the current in each element will change in magnitude and phase because of coupling with the field from the other element. The field from the first element changes the current in the second. This changes the field from the second, which alters the current in the first, and so forth until an equilibrium condition is reached in which the currents in all elements (hence, their fields) are totally interdependent.

The feed point impedances of all elements also are changed from their values when far apart, and all are dependent on each other. In a driven array, the changes in feed point impedances can cause additional changes in element currents, because the operation of many feed systems depends on the element feed point impedances. Significant mutual coupling occurs at spacings as great as a wavelength or more.

Connecting the elements to a feed system to form a driven array does not eliminate the effects of mutual coupling. In fact, in many driven arrays the mutual coupling has a greater effect on antenna operation than the feed system does. All feed-system designs must account for the impedance changes caused by mutual coupling if the desired current balance and phasing are to be achieved.

Several general statements can be made regarding the effects of mutual coupling on phased-array systems (unless loss is high enough to swamp mutual coupling effects as discussed in the next section).

1) The resistances and reactances of all elements of an array generally will be substantially different from the values when the elements are isolated (that is, very distant from other elements).

2) If the elements of a two-element array are identical and have equal currents that are in-phase or 180° out-of-phase, the feed point impedances of the two elements will be equal. But they will be different than for an isolated element. If the two elements are part of a larger array, their impedances can be very different from each other.

3) If the elements of a two-element array have currents that are neither in-phase (0°) nor out-of-phase (180°), their feed point impedances will not be equal. The difference will be considerable in typical amateur arrays.

4) The feed point resistances of the elements in a closely spaced, 180° out-of-phase array will be very low, resulting in poor efficiency due to ohmic losses unless care is taken to minimize loss. This is also true for any other closely spaced array with significant predicted gain.

It's essential to realize that this is not a minor effect and one that can be overlooked or ignored. See *EZNEC* **Example — Mutual Coupling** in Appendix A for an illustration of these phenomena.

Loss Resistance, Mutual Coupling and Antenna Gain

Loss reduces the effects of mutual coupling because the feed point impedance change resulting from mutual coupling is effectively in series with loss resistance. If the loss is great enough, two important results occur. First, the feed point impedance becomes independent of the presence of nearby current-carrying elements. This greatly simplifies feed system design — the simple "phasing-line" or hybrid-coupler feed system described below is adequate *provided that all elements are physically identical and the feed point of each element is matched to the Z_0 of the feed line and, if used, the hybrid coupler.*

The impedance matching restrictions are necessary to insure that the phasing line or hybrid coupler performs as expected. Identical elements are needed so that equal element currents will result in equal fields from the elements.

In the absence of mutual coupling effects, the maximum gain of an array of identical elements relative to a single (similarly lossy) element is simply 10 log(N), where N is the number of elements — providing that spacing is adequate for the fields to fully reinforce in some direction. If spacing is less, maximum gain will also be less. Of course, the array gain relative to a single lossless element will be very low, most likely a sizeable negative number when expressed in dB. So intentionally introducing loss isn't a wise idea for a transmitting array. It is sometimes an advantageous thing to do for a receiving array, however, as explained in the following section.

High-gain close-spaced arrays, such as the W8JK phased array (see *EZNEC-ARRL* example file **ARRL_W8JK.EZ** and accompanying Antenna Notes file), and most parasitic arrays depend heavily on mutual coupling to achieve their gain. Introduction of any loss to these arrays, which reduces the mutual coupling effects, has a profound effect on the gain. Consequently, parasitic or close-spaced driven arrays often produce disappointing results when made from grounded vertical elements unless each has a fairly elaborate (and therefore very low-loss) ground system.

If you place two low-loss elements very close together and feed them in-phase, mutual coupling reduces the array gain to essentially that of a single element, so there's no advantage to this configuration over a single element. However, if you have a single lossy element, for example a short vertical having a relatively poor ground system, you can improve the gain by up to 3 dB by adding a second, close spaced, element and ground system and feeding the two in-phase. Another way to look at this technique is that you're putting two equal ground system resistances in parallel, which effectively cuts the loss in half. The gain you can realize in practice depends on such things as the ground system overlap, but it might be a practical way to improve transmitting array performance in some situations.

6.3.3 FEEDING PHASED ARRAYS

The previous section explains why the fields from the elements must be very close to the ratios required by the array design. Since the field strengths are proportional to the currents in the elements, controlling the fields requires controlling the element currents. Since the desired current ratio is 1:1 for virtually all two-element and for most (but not all) larger amateur arrays, special attention is paid to methods of assuring equal element currents. But we will examine other current ratios also.

The Role of Element Currents

The field from a conductor is proportional to the current flowing on it. So if we're to control the relative strengths and phases of the fields from the elements, we have to control their currents. We usually do this by controlling the currents at the element feed points. But because the field from an element depends on the current everywhere along the element, elements having identical feed point currents will produce different fields if they have different current distributions — that is, if the way the current varies along the lengths of the elements is different.

A previous section explained that mutual coupling alters the current distribution, so in many arrays the current distributions will be different on the elements and consequently the relationship between the overall fields won't be the same as that between the feed point currents. Fortunately, this effect is relatively minor in thin, $\lambda/4$ monopole or $\lambda/2$ dipole elements. The most common arrays are made from elements in this category, so we can generally get very nearly the desired ratio of fields by creating the same ratio of feed point currents. Exceptions are detailed in the following section.

Feed Point vs Element Current

For most antennas, environmental factors are likely to cause greater performance anomalies than current distribution differences, and both can be corrected with minor feed system adjustments. The difference between field and feed point current ratios can become very significant, however, if the elements are very fat and/or close to $\lambda/2$ (monopole) or 1λ (dipole) long. In those cases, most of the feed systems described here won't produce the desired field ratios without major adjustment or modification, except in the special cases of 2-element arrays with identical elements having feed point currents in-phase or 180° out-of-phase. In those special cases, the element current distributions are the same for the same reason the feed point impedances are equal. This is explained later in the feed system sections.

To get an idea of just how large an element must be to disturb the pattern of an array with correct feed point currents, a two-element cardioid array of quarter wave vertical elements was modeled at 10 MHz. With thin, 0.1-inch diameter elements the front-to-back ratio was 35 dB, the very small reverse lobe caused by slightly unequal element current distributions. Increasing the element diameter to 20 inches decreased the front-to-back ratio to 20 dB. Returning the front-to-back ratio of the array of 20-inch elements to >35 dB required changing the feed point current ratio from the nominal value of 1.0 at an angle of 90° to 0.88 at 83°.

The same array was first modeled with 0.1-inch diameter elements, where it has a front-to-back ratio of 35 dB, then the elements were lengthened. The front-to-back ratio dropped to 20 dB at an element length of 36 feet, or about 0.37 λ. In that case, adjustment of the feed point current ratio to about 0.9 at about 83° restored a good front-to-back ratio.

In the discussion and development which follow, the assumption is made that the fields will be very nearly proportional to the feed point currents. If the elements are fat or long enough to make this assumption untrue, some adjustment of feed point current ratio will be necessary to achieve the desired pattern, particularly nulls. Most feed systems can be designed for any current ratio. Modeling will reveal the ratio required for the desired pattern, and then the feed system can be designed accordingly.

6.3.4 COMMON PHASED ARRAY FEED SYSTEMS

This section will first describe several popular approaches to feeding phased arrays that often don't produce the desired results. It will describe why they don't work as well as hoped. It also briefly discusses systems that could be used, but that often aren't appropriate or optimum for amateur arrays.

This will be followed in the next section by detailed descriptions of array feed systems that do produce the predicted element current ratios and array patterns.

The "Phasing-Line" Approach

For an array to produce the desired pattern, the element currents must have the required magnitude and the required phase relationship. As explained above, this can generally be achieved well enough by causing the feed point currents to have that same relationship.

On the surface, this sounds easy — just make sure that the difference in electrical lengths of the feed lines to the elements equals the desired phase angle. Unfortunately, this approach doesn't necessarily achieve the desired result. The first problem is that the phase shift through the line is not equal to its electrical length. The current (or, for that matter, voltage) delay in a transmission line is equal to its electrical length in only a few special cases — cases which don't exist in most amateur arrays! The impedance of an element in an array is frequently very different from the impedance of an isolated element and the impedances of all the elements in an array can be different from each other.

See the *EZNEC* **Example — Mutual Coupling** in Appendix A for a graphic illustration of the effect of mutual coupling on feed point impedance. Also look at the Four-Square array example in the **Phased Array Design Examples** section. The array in that example has one element with a *negative* feed point resistance, if ground loss is low. Without mutual coupling, the resistance of that same element would be about 36 Ω plus ground loss.

Because of mutual coupling, the elements seldom provide a matched load for the element feed lines. The effect of mismatch on phase shift can be seen in **Figure 6.14**. Observe

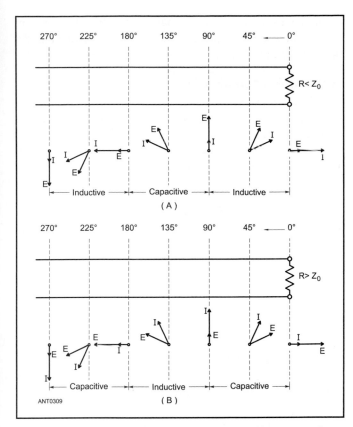

Figure 6.14 — Resultant voltages and currents along a mismatched line. At A, R less than Z_0, and at B, R greater than Z_0.

what happens to the phase of the current and voltage on a line terminated by a purely resistive impedance that is lower than the characteristic impedance of the line (Figure 6.14A). At a point 45° from the load the current has advanced less than 45°, and the voltage more than 45°. At 90° from the load both are advanced 90°. At 135° the current has advanced more and the voltage less than 135°. This apparent slowing down and speeding up of the current and voltage waves is caused by interference between the forward and reflected waves. It occurs on any line that is not terminated with a pure resistance equal to its characteristic impedance. If the load resistance is greater than the characteristic impedance of the line, as shown in Figure 6.14B, the voltage and current exchange angles. Adding reactance to the load causes additional phase shift. *The only cases in which the current (or voltage) delay is equal to the electrical length of the line are*

1) When the line is flat; that is, terminated in a purely resistive load equal to its characteristic impedance;

2) When the line length is an integral number of half wavelengths;

3) When the line length is an odd number of quarter wavelengths and the load is purely resistive; and

4) When other specific lengths are used for specific load impedances.

Just how much phase error can be expected if two feed lines are simply hooked up to form an array? There is no simple answer. Some casually designed feed systems might

deliver satisfactory results, but most will not. See the *EZNEC* **Example — "Phasing-Line" Feed** in Appendix A for the typical consequences of using this sort of feed system.

A second problem with simply connecting feed lines of different lengths to the elements is that the lines will change the *magnitudes* of the currents. The magnitude of the current (or voltage) out of a line does not equal the magnitude into that line, except in cases 1, 2 and 4 above. The feed systems presented later in this chapter assure currents that are correct in both magnitude and phase.

The elementary phasing-line approach *will* work in three very special but common situations. If the array consists of only two identical elements and those elements are fed in-phase, mutual coupling will modify the element impedances, but both will be modified exactly the same amount. Consequently, if the two elements are fed through equal-length transmission lines, the lines will transform and delay the currents by the same amount and result in equal, in-phase currents at the element feed points.

Similarly, an array of two identical elements fed 180° out of phase will have the same feed point impedances and can be fed with two lines of any length so long as one line is an electrical half wavelength longer than the other. But this can't be extended to any two elements in a larger array, since mutual coupling to the other elements can result in different feed point impedances. Methods will be described later which do assure a correct current ratio in this situation.

The third application in which the phasing-line approach works is in receiving arrays where the elements are very short in terms of wavelength and/or very lossy. In either of these cases, mutual coupling between elements is much less than an element's self-impedance. This allows the elements to be individually matched to the feed lines, with no significant change taking place when the elements are formed into an array. Under those conditions, the transmission lines can be matched and the lines used as simple delay lines with easily predictable phase shift and with no transformation of current or voltage magnitude other than cable loss. This is discussed in the later section on receiving antennas.

ON4UN's *Low-Band DXing* (see Bibliography) describes a modified phasing-line feed system method which works in some special cases where the feed point resistances are favorable to the approach. First, a quarter wave transmission line is connected to each element. Then a shunt inductor or capacitor is added at the input of the line to the lagging element in order to make the impedance at that point purely resistive. If the resulting resistance is close to the characteristic impedance of an available transmission line (e.g., 50 or 75 Ω), a simple delay line can be used to feed that element. See *EZNEC-ARRL* example **ARRL_Cardioid_Modified_Phasing_Line_Feed.EZ** and its accompanying Antenna Notes file for an example. When impedance values allow this feed method, it saves only one component compared to the L network feed method and isn't fully adjustable. And it has one component more than the "simplest" method to be described. The bandwidth of arrays fed using this method isn't significantly different from the other feed systems, so there's no clear advantage to using it. However, it might be a viable approach under some circumstances. More design information is available in *Low-Band DXing*.

The interested reader is encouraged to consult *Low-Band DXing* as it contains examples of additional feed system design approaches that produce a desired element magnitude and phase ratio.

Many arrays *can* be correctly fed with a feed system consisting of only transmission lines, but the technique requires knowledge of the element feed point impedances in a correctly fed array. Line lengths can then be computed that provide the correct ratio of currents into those particular load impedances. The line lengths generally differ by amount that's considerably different from the element phase angle difference, and appropriate line lengths can't always be found for all arrays. This technique is described more fully in the "The Simplest Phased Array Feed System — That Works" section later in this chapter and illustrated in the examples in "Phased Array Design Examples."

The Wilkinson Divider

The *Wilkinson divider*, sometimes called the *Wilkinson power divider*, was once heavily promoted as a means to distribute power among the elements of a phased array. While it's a very useful device for other purposes, it won't produce the desired current ratios in antenna elements. In most phased arrays, element feed point resistances are different and therefore require different amounts of power to achieve the desired equal magnitude currents. (See the section on mutual coupling above.) A Wilkinson divider is intended to deliver equal powers, not currents, to multiple loads. And it won't even do that when the load impedances are different. It might be useful in combining element outputs in receiving arrays in which element losses are high enough to swamp mutual coupling effects and effect impedance matches.

The Hybrid Coupler

Hybrid couplers are promoted as solving the problem of achieving equal magnitude currents with a 90° phase difference between elements. Unfortunately, standard 90° hybrids provide equal magnitude, quadrature (90° phased) currents only when the load impedances are equal and correct. And this simply isn't true of arrays with quadrature-fed elements, except for arrays consisting of short and/or lossy elements, usually suitable only for receiving. In those arrays, the hybrid coupler can be useful for the same reasons as the phasing-line approach, discussed in an earlier section.

Hybrid couplers can, however, be useful for feeding transmitting or low-loss phased arrays if suitably modified to function when terminated with the particular impedances presented by an array's elements. In *Low-Band DXing* (see the Bibliography), methods are described to modify the standard 90° hybrid design to provide approximate hybrid functionality when terminated in typical phased array impedance values. Methods are quite involved, as evidenced by more than 20 pages devoted to the topic. It is important to realize that no passive network, including the hybrid coupler, is

capable of providing equal magnitude 90° phased currents in loads with arbitrary impedances. See "The "Magic Bullet"" below for more information.

"Crossfire" Feed Method

Tom Rauch, W8JI, has described a "crossfire" feed system which is capable of producing a deep null in one direction over an exceptionally wide bandwidth. This method, generally suitable only for lossy receiving arrays, is described in more detail in this chapter's section "Receiving Arrays and Broadbanding."

Large Array Feed Systems

The author once worked on a radar system where the transmit array consisted of over 5000 separate dipole elements and the receive array over 4000 pairs of crossed dipoles, all over a metal reflecting plane, which was the sloping side of a 140 foot high building. In such large arrays, each element is in essentially the same environment as every other element except near the array edges, so almost all elements have very nearly the same feed point impedance. While producing the phase shifts and magnitude tapers is a considerable mathematical challenge, the problem of unequal element feed point impedances can largely be ignored. Consequently, feed methods for these large arrays are generally not suitable for typical amateur arrays of a few elements.

The Broadcast Approach

Networks can be designed to transform the element base impedances from their values in an excited array to, say, 50 Ω resistive. Then another network can be inserted at the junction of the feed lines to properly divide the power among the elements (not necessarily equally!). And finally, additional networks must be added to correct for the phase shifts and magnitude transformations of the other networks. This general approach is used by the broadcast industry, in installations that are typically adjusted only once for a particular frequency and pattern.

Although this technique can be used to correctly feed any type of array, design is difficult and adjustment is tedious since all adjustments interact. When the relative currents and phasing are adjusted, the feed point impedances change, which in turn affect the element currents and phasing, and so on. A further disadvantage of using this method is that switching the array direction is generally impossible. Information on applying this technique to amateur arrays can be found in Paul Lee's book, listed in the Bibliography.

The "Magic Bullet"

More than 15 years ago, the *Antenna Book* published specifications for a circuit that would provide equal-magnitude, 90° phased currents into two loads without respect to the load impedances. This would be a circuit that would guarantee exactly the correct currents in any two elements. In 1996, Kevin Schmidt, W9CF, formulated a mathematical proof that such a circuit — in fact, one resulting in any relative phase other than 0° or 180° — cannot exist if restricted to reciprocal elements. (That is, it can't exist unless directional components such as ferrite circulators are used.) Thus, in order to design a network to feed elements with currents of any other phase angle other than 0 or 180°, we must know the impedance of at least one element and correct feed system operation depends on that impedance. There's no way around this requirement. At the time of this writing, Schmidt's proof can be found at **fermi.la.asu.edu/w9cf/articles/magic/index.html**.

6.3.5 RECOMMENDED FEED METHODS FOR AMATEUR ARRAYS

The following feed methods are able to produce element feed point currents having a desired magnitude and phase relationship, resulting in desirable and predictable patterns. Most methods require knowing the feed point impedance of one or more array elements *when the array element currents are the correct values*. This isn't possible to measure directly, because if the element currents were correct, the feed system would already be working properly and no further design would be necessary.

By far the easiest way to get this information, if possible, is by computer modeling. Modeling programs such as *EZNEC-ARRL* (included with this book) allow you to construct an ideal array with perfect element currents then look at the resulting feed point impedances. Because of its simplicity and versatility, this approach is highly recommended and it's the one used for the array design examples in this chapter.

Some feed systems allow adjustment, so even an approximate result provides an adequate starting point on which to base the feed-system design. There are several other alternatives to computer modeling. One is to first eliminate the effects of coupling of the element to be measured from all other elements, usually by open circuiting the feed points of the other elements. Then the feed point impedance of the element is measured. Next, the impedance change due to mutual coupling from all other elements has to be calculated, based on the intended currents in the other elements, their lengths and their distances from the element being measured. Mutual impedance (which is not the same as the impedance change due to mutual coupling) between each pair of elements must be known for this calculation and it can be determined by measurement, calculation or from a graph.

The latter two methods are possible only for the simplest element types and measurement is very difficult to do accurately because it involves resolving very small differences between two relatively large values. Accuracy of a calculated result will be reduced if any elements are relatively fat (that is, they have a large diameter, because this impacts the current distribution) or they aren't perfectly straight and parallel.

So the only situations where you're likely to get good results from approaches other than modeling are the very easiest ones to model! Modeling also allows determination of the feed point impedances of many antennas that are impossible to calculate by manual or graphical methods. Therefore, the manual approach isn't discussed or used here. Appendix B, on the CD, contains equations and manual techniques from previous editions of *The ARRL Antenna Book*, for those who are interested. You can also find a great deal of additional information in many of the texts listed in the Bibliography, particularly Jasik and Johnson.

Current Forcing with λ/4 Lines — Elements In-Phase or 180° Out-of-Phase

The feed method introduced here has been used in its simplest form to feed television receiving antennas and other arrays, as presented by Jasik, pages 2-12 and 24-10 or Johnson, on his page 2-14. However, until first presented in the *ARRL Antenna Book*, this feed method was not widely applied to amateur arrays.

The method takes advantage of an interesting property of λ/4 transmission lines. (All references to lengths of lines are electrical length and lines are assumed to have negligible loss.) See **Figure 6.15**. The magnitude of the *current out* of a λ/4 transmission line is equal to the *input voltage* divided by the characteristic impedance of the line. This is independent of the load impedance. In addition, the phase of the output current lags the phase of the input voltage by 90°, also independent of the load impedance. These properties can be used to advantage in feeding arrays with certain phase angles between elements.

If any number of loads are connected to a common driving point through λ/4 lines of equal impedance, the currents in the loads will be *forced* to be equal and in-phase, regardless of the load impedances. So any number of in-phase elements can be correctly fed using this method, regardless of how their impedances might have been changed by mutual coupling. Arrays that require unequal currents can be fed through λ/4 lines of unequal impedances to achieve other current ratios.

The properties of λ/2 lines also are useful. Since the current out of a λ/2 line equals the input current shifted 180°, regardless of the load impedance, any number of half wavelengths of line may be added to the basic λ/4, and the current and phase forcing property will be preserved. For example, if one element is fed through a λ/4 line and another element is fed from the same point through a 3λ/4 line of the same characteristic impedance, the currents in the two elements will be forced to be equal in magnitude and 180° out-of-phase, regardless of the feed point impedances of the elements.

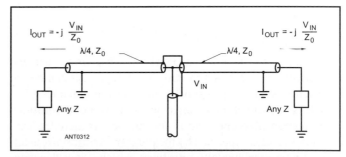

Figure 6.15 — A useful property of λ/4 transmission lines; see text. This property is utilized in the "current-forcing" method of feeding an array of coupled elements.

If an array of two, and only two, identical elements is fed in-phase or 180° out-of-phase with equal magnitude currents, both elements have the same feed point impedance. The reason is that each element sees exactly the same thing when looking at the other. In an in-phase array, each sees another element with an identical current; in an out-of-phase array, each sees another element with an equal magnitude current that's 180° out-of-phase, the same distance away in both cases. This isn't true in something like a 90° fed array, where one element sees another with a current leading its current by 90°, while the other sees another element with a lagging current.

With arrays fed in-phase or 180° out-of-phase, feeding the elements through equal lengths of feed line (in-phase) or lengths differing by 180° (out-of-phase) will lead to the correct current magnitude ratio and phase difference, regardless of the line length and regardless of how much the element feed point impedances depart from the lines' Z_0.

Unless the feed point impedances equal the line Z_0 or the lines are an integral number of half wavelengths long, the magnitudes of the currents out of the lines will not be equal to the input magnitudes, and the phase will not be shifted an amount equal to the electrical lengths of the lines. But both lines will produce the same transformation and phase shift because their load impedances are equal, resulting in a properly fed array. In practice, however, feed point impedances of elements frequently are different even in these arrays, because of such things as different ground systems (for ground mounted vertical elements), proximity to buildings or other antennas, or different heights above ground (for horizontal or elevated vertical elements).

In many larger arrays, two or more elements must be fed either in-phase or out-of-phase with equal currents, but coupling to other elements can cause their impedances to change unequally — sometimes extremely so. Using the current-forcing method allows the feed system designer to ignore all these effects, while guaranteeing equal and correctly phased currents in any combination and number of 0° and 180° fed elements.

This method is used to develop feed systems for the Four-Square and 4-element rectangular arrays in the "Practical Array Design" section. The front and rear elements of a Four-Square antenna provide a good example of elements having very different feed point impedances that are forced to have equal out-of-phase currents.

"The Simplest Phased Array Feed System — That Works"

This is the title of an article in *The ARRL Antenna Compendium, Vol 2*, which describes how arrays can be fed with a feed system consisting of only transmission lines. (The article is available for viewing at **www.eznec.com/Amateur/Articles/Simpfeed.pdf** and is also on the CD included with this book, and is supported by the program *Arrayfeed1*, available at **www.arrl.org/antenna-book**, which solves the equations presented in the article.)

As explained earlier in the "Phasing Line" section, this

method requires knowing what the element feed point impedances will be in a correctly fed array. Feed line lengths can then be computed, for most but not all arrays. These lengths will produce the desired current ratio in array elements that do present those feed point impedances. If you know the load impedances connected to transmission lines whose inputs are connected to a common source, it's simple to calculate the resulting load currents for any transmission line lengths. However, the reverse problem is much more difficult; that is, given the load impedances and desired currents to calculate the required cable lengths.

One way to solve the problem is to choose some feed line lengths, solve for the currents, examine the answer, adjust the feed line lengths, and try again until the desired currents are obtained. The author used this iterative approach, using first a programmable calculator and later a computer, for some time before developing a direct way of solving for the transmission-line lengths. The direct solution method is described briefly in the *Compendium* article.

Figure 6.16 shows the basic so-called "simplest" system applied to a two-element array. Although it resembles an elementary phasing-line system as described earlier, the critical difference is that the lengths of Lines 1 and 2 are calculated to provide the correct current relative magnitude transformation and phase shift when terminated with the actual feed point impedances.

The advantage to using this "simplest" feed system is indeed its simplicity. It's no more complicated than the

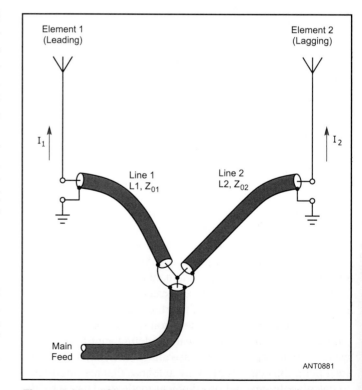

Figure 6.16 — "Simplest" feed system for 2-element array. No matching or phasing network is used here, only transmission lines.

elementary phasing-line approach but actually works as planned. The disadvantage over some other methods is that there's no convenient adjustment to compensate for environment factors, array imperfections or inaccurately known feed point impedances.

Also, while unusual, it's possible that no suitable feed line lengths can be found for some arrays, or at least none with practical feed line characteristic impedances. The difference in electrical feed line lengths almost never equals the difference in phase angles between element currents. This is because of the different line delays resulting from different feed point impedances.

Arrayfeed1 can do the calculations for any two elements (alone or in a larger array), a Four-Square array or a rectangular array in which two in-phase elements are driven at any current magnitude and phase relative to the other two in-phase elements. These possibilities cover a large number of common arrays.

Arrayfeed1 can also be applied to other types of arrays using the method described in the "Feeding Larger Arrays" section in Appendix B (on the CD). The required knowledge of element feed point impedances in a correctly fed array can be obtained using *EZNEC-ARRL*, also included on the CD. Examples of the design of a "simplest" feed system for several different arrays using *EZNEC-ARRL* and *Arrayfeed1* can be found in the "Phased Array Design Examples" section.

When a solution is possible for a given choice of line characteristic impedances, a second solution with different lengths is always available. See the comments in the introductory part of the "Phased Array Design Examples" section about choosing the solution to use.

An Adjustable L-Network Feed System

Adjustment of the current ratio of any two elements requires varying two independent quantities; for example, the magnitude and phase of the current ratio. Two degrees of freedom — adjustments that are at least partially independent — are required. The "simplest" all-transmission line feed system described earlier adjusts the lengths of the two transmission lines to achieve the correct ratio.

But if the antenna characteristics aren't well known — for example, if the ground resistance isn't known even approximately — then the initial "simplest" design won't be optimum and adjustment can be difficult and tedious. The current-forcing method produces correct currents independently of the element characteristics, so it doesn't require adjustment as long as the elements are identical. But it's suitable only for feeding elements in-phase or 180° out-of-phase and a few fixed current-magnitude ratios.

The addition of a simple network as shown in **Figure 6.17** allows you to easily adjust feeding of element pairs at other relative phase angles and/or magnitude ratios. Any desired current ratio (magnitude and phase) can be obtained with two elements fed with any lengths of wire, equal or unequal, by adding a network.

However, calculations for the general case are complex. The problem becomes much simpler if the transmission lines

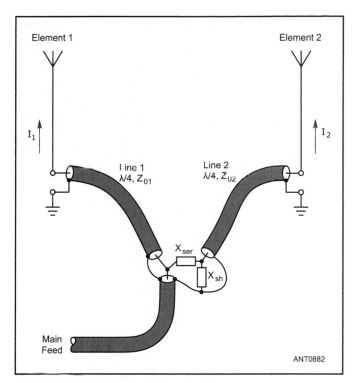

Figure 6.17 — The addition of a simple L network to Figure 6.16 allows you to easily adjust feeding of element pairs at other relative phase angles and/or magnitude ratios.

are restricted to lengths of odd multiples of $\lambda/4$, forming a modified "forcing" system that includes an added network. There are at least three additional advantages of this scheme. One is that a $\lambda/4$ line is easy to measure, even if the velocity factor isn't known. This is described in the "Practical Aspects of Phased Array Design" section.

Second is that the feed system becomes completely insensitive to the feed point impedance of one of the two elements. And the third is that the transmission lines of "forcing" systems feeding groups of elements in larger arrays can be used in place of the normal $\lambda/4$ lines. This greatly simplifies both the design of feed systems for larger arrays and the feed systems themselves. Note that both lines can be changed to $3\lambda/4$ if necessary to span the physical distance between elements, but both lines must be the same $3\lambda/4$ length.

This basic feed method can be used for any pair of elements, or for two groups of elements having forced equal currents. (See "Feeding Four Element and Larger Arrays" below) Many networks can accomplish the desired function, but a simple L network is adequate for most feed systems. The network can be designed to produce a phase lead or phase lag. The basic two-element L network feed system is shown in Figure 6.17. Many variations of this general method can be used, but the equations, program, and method to be discussed here apply only to the feed system shown.

If the phase angle of I_2/I_1 is negative (element 2 is lagging element 1), the L network will usually resemble a low-pass network (X_{ser} is an inductor and X_{sh} is a capacitor). But if the phase angle is positive (element 2 lagging element 1), the L network will resemble a high-pass network (X_{ser} is a capacitor and X_{sh} is an inductor). However, some current ratios and feed point impedances could result in both components being inductors or both being capacitors.

If it's desired to maintain symmetry in the feed system, X_{ser} can be divided into two components, each being inserted in series with a transmission line conductor. If X_{ser} is an inductor, the new components will each have half the value of the original X_{ser}, as shown in **Figure 6.18**. If X_{ser} is a capacitor, each of the new components will be twice the original value of X_{ser}.

Because of the current-forcing properties of λ/4 lines, we need to make the ratio of voltages at the inputs of the lines equal to the desired ratio of currents at the output ends of the lines; that is, at the element feed points. The job of the L network is to provide the desired voltage transformation. If the output-to-input voltage ratio of the network is, say, 2.0 at an angle of –60°, then the ratio of element currents (I_2/I_1) will be 2.0 at an angle of –60°. The voltage transformation of the network is affected by the impedance of element 2, but not by the impedance of element 1. So only the impedance of element 2 must be known to design the feed system.

Equations for designing the L network are given in Appendix B, but the program *Arrayfeed1* makes it unnecessary to solve them. The feed point impedance of the lagging element or group of elements must be known in order to design the network. This can best be determined by modeling the array with *EZNEC-ARRL*. The impedance can be manually calculated for some simple element and array types by using the equations in Appendix B, but those same types of element and array are simple to model.

Examples of the design of L network feed systems for several different arrays using *EZNEC-ARRL* and *Arrayfeed1* can be found in the "Phased Array Design Examples" section. A similar application of this feed system and a spreadsheet program for calculation was developed by Robye Lahlum, W1MK, and described in *Low-Band DXing* (see the Bibliography). *Arrayfeed1* can be used for the applications of the feed system described in that book if desired.

Additional Considerations

Feeding 4-Element and Larger Arrays

Both the simplest and L network feed systems described above can be extended to feeding larger arrays having two groups of elements in which all the elements in a group are in-phase or 180° out-of-phase with each other — basically, any group that can be fed with the current-forcing method. The elements in each group are connected to a common point with λ/4 or 3λ/4 lines to force the currents to be in the correct ratio within the group. Then the "simplest" or L network feed system can be used to produce the correct phasing between the two groups, just as it does between two individual elements.

Two common arrays that fit this description are the Four-Square and the 4-element rectangular array. But more elaborate arrays could be constructed and fed using this method, such as a pair of binomial arrays. (A single binomial array is described in the "Phased Array Design Example" section below.) The *Arrayfeed1* program incorporates additional calculations necessary for designing Four-Square and 4-element rectangular arrays. The general procedure for adapting the feed methods to other larger arrays can be found in Appendix B.

What If the Elements Aren't Identical?

Getting the desired pattern requires getting the correct relative magnitude and phase of the fields from the elements. If the elements are identical, which we've generally assumed up to this point, then producing currents of the desired magnitude and phase will create the desired *fields* (neglecting mutual coupling current distribution effects, discussed elsewhere).

But what if the elements aren't identical? Fortunately, the feed systems described here can still be used for any 2-element array and some more complex arrays, provided that the system can be accurately modeled. But a slightly different approach is required than for identical elements.

The first step is to model the array with a current source at the feed point of each element. Next, the magnitudes and phases of the model source currents are varied until the desired pattern is achieved. Then the ratio of feed point (source) currents is calculated. This value and the feed point impedances reported by the model are used for the feed system design. The feed system will produce the same ratio of currents as the model, resulting in the same pattern.

In general, this approach won't work with shunt fed towers or gamma-fed elements because of the difficulty of accurately modeling those structures as described in the following section.

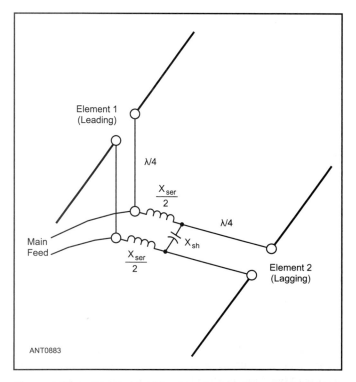

ANT0883

Figure 6.18 — Symmetrical feed system similar to Figure 6.17, in which the feed network is split into two symmetrical parts.

Shunt- and Gamma-Fed Towers and Elements

In a shunt-, gamma-, or similarly fed tower or element, the feed point current isn't the same as the main current flowing in the element. The ratio between the feed point current and element current isn't a constant, but depends on a number of factors. The ratio of currents in shunt- or gamma-fed elements is typically different — often vastly different — from the currents at the feed points. This complicates the design of feed systems for arrays of these elements.

An even more limiting problem is that the feed point impedances are difficult to determine. The feed point impedances of one or more elements in a properly fed array must be known in order to design a feed system for anything but 2-element in-phase or 180° out-of-phase arrays.

The only practical way to get this information for a shunt or gamma fed array is by modeling an array having the desired element currents. But Cebik has pointed out ("Two Limitations of NEC-4" — see the Bibliography) that many common antenna analysis programs, including *EZNEC-ARRL*, have difficulty accurately modeling folded dipoles with unequal diameter wires. The same problem applies to shunt and gamma-fed elements when the element diameter is significantly different from the diameter of the shunt or gamma feed wire. Without accurate feed point impedances, feed systems can't be designed to work without adjustment. It might be possible to get reasonably accurate results from a *MININEC*-based modeling program, but there are a number of issues which must be given great care when using one. (See Lewallen, "*MININEC* — The Other Edge of the Sword," listed in the Bibliography.)

If such a *MININEC* program is available, you would have to model the complete array including feed system, with sources at the normal feed points in the shunt or gamma wires. Next, you would have to adjust the magnitudes and phases of the sources to produce the desired pattern. The reported source impedances and currents would be the ones you would use to design the feed system. It's likely that some adjustment would be necessary, so an adjustable system such as the L network feed system described later would be best.

Loading, Matching and Other Networks

Adding a component such as a loading inductor in series with an element or element feed point won't change the ratio of element current to feed point current. As a result, a feed system designed to produce a particular ratio of element currents will still function properly if the elements contain series components. The extra feed point impedance introduced by the loading component(s) must be considered when designing the feed system, however. Similarly, end or top loading won't alter the relationship between feed point and element current, provided that the current distribution in the elements is essentially the same. (See "Feed point vs Element Current" previously.)

However, insertion of any *shunt* component, or a network containing a shunt component, *will* alter the relationship between feed point and element current because it will divert part of the feed line current that would otherwise flow into

the antenna. As a result, a feed system designed to deliver correct currents at the feed points will produce incorrect element currents and therefore an incorrect pattern. Therefore, any components or networks other than a series loading component should be avoided at any place in the feed system on the antenna side of the point at which the feed system splits to go to the various elements.

There are a few exceptions to this rule. If the feed point impedances of the elements when in the excited array are equal, then identical networks with or without shunt components can be put at the feed points of the elements and the proper element current ratio maintained — so long as the feed system is designed to deliver the proper feed point current ratio with the networks in place. Equal element impedances occur in arrays having only two identical elements fed in-phase or 180° out-of-phase, or arrays of any number of elements where the elements are electrically short and/or very lossy.

Baluns in Phased Arrays

For purposes of achieving the correct array pattern, baluns aren't usually required when feeding grounded vertical elements with coaxial cable feed lines. However, a balun might be desirable if current induced onto the outside of the feed line by mutual coupling to the elements is causing RF in the shack. And with arrays of dipole or other elevated elements, baluns can be important to achieve the proper element current ratio, as explained below.

First, however, the general rules for using baluns in phased arrays will be stated. Here, "main feed line" means the feed line going from the transmitter or receiver to the common point where the system splits to feed the various elements. "Phasing-system lines" means any transmission lines between that common point and any element. The rules are:

Rule 1: A balun or baluns (more specifically, a current, sometimes called a choke balun) should be used as necessary to suppress unbalanced current on the main feed line. This usually isn't required when feeding grounded elements with coaxial feed line from an unbalanced rig or tuner. Unbalanced current can occur on either coax or parallel-conductor line.

"Baluns: What They Do and How They Do It", listed in the Bibliography, describes conducted-imbalance (common-mode) currents. Imbalance can also be caused by mutual coupling to the array elements. Common-mode currents have at least two undesirable effects on array performance. First, the imbalance current can flow from the main feed line to the phasing system lines, not necessarily splitting in the right proportion to maintain the correct element current ratio. This can affect the array pattern. In practice, however, this effect is likely to be small unless the common-mode current is unusually large. Even a small common-mode current, however, results in main feed line radiation, and even a small amount of radiation can significantly degrade array pattern nulls. Any type of current balun can be used on the main feed line, at any place along the line, without any effect on the array pattern except to the extent that it reduces common mode current.

Rule 2: No balun or any other component or network

should be inserted in any phasing system line that will alter the line length or characteristic impedance. This means that baluns in phasing system lines must be of a type made from the phasing line itself. Options are the W2DU or "bead" balun, consisting of ferrite beads placed along the outside of the feed line; an air-core or "choke" balun made by winding part of the line into an approximately self-resonant or otherwise high-impedance coil; or winding part of the line onto a ferrite core or rod to make a several-turn winding. When coaxial cable is used, the feed system characteristics are dictated by the conditions *inside* the cable. Any cores placed on or winding of the *outside* prevents common-mode current on the outside but otherwise have no effect on the phasing performance. This rule applies equally to parallel-wire line, where the balun affects only common-mode current (equivalent to current on the outside of coax) while the phasing performance depends on differential mode current (equivalent to the current on the inside of coax).

Baluns are important when feeding dipole or other elevated arrays, unless a fully balanced tuner is used. This is because common-mode current represents a diversion of some of the current that should be going to the array elements. The presence of common-mode current means that the element currents are being altered from the desired ratio and therefore the pattern won't be as intended. A balun should be placed wherever a path for current exists other than along a parallel-line conductor or on the inside of a coaxial line. Such a path exists, for example, where a coaxial cable connects to a dipole, as shown in Figure 1 of the balun article referenced above. Or a path can exist where a parallel-conductor transmission line connects to an unbalanced tuner or to a coaxial line, as shown in Figure 2 of that article. In both those cases, a path exists for a common-mode current to flow on the outside of the coax cable. A balun presents a high impedance to this current, thereby reducing its magnitude, but remember that all baluns must conform to the rules above. **Figure 6.19** shows recommended balun locations for a coax-fed dipole array using an L network feed system.

Receiving Arrays and Broadbanding

While it might not be entirely intuitive, an array designed for a particular gain and pattern for transmitting that considers mutual coupling, element currents, field reinforcement and cancellation, and so forth, will perform exactly the same when receiving. So a receiving array can be designed by approaching the problem as though the array were to be used for transmitting.

However, at HF and below, the system requirements for transmitting and receiving antennas are different, so receiving-only arrays can be designed that aren't suitable for transmitting but are perfectly adequate for receiving in that frequency range. The reason, described in more detail in the **Long Wire and Traveling-Wave Antennas** chapter, is that at HF and below atmospheric noise is typically much greater than a receiver's internally generated noise. Lowering a receiving antenna's gain and efficiency reduces the signal and atmospheric noise both by the same factor. Because the

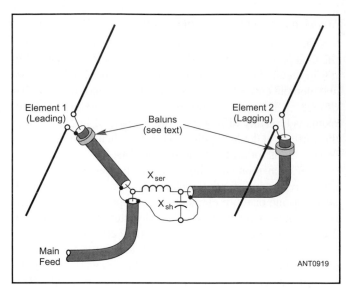

Figure 6.19 — Adding choke baluns to a two-dipole feed system to get rid of common-mode currents induced onto the coax shields.

overall noise is for practical purposes all atmospheric noise, the signal/noise ratio isn't affected by antenna efficiency.

Of course, a point can be reached where the atmospheric noise is so reduced by inefficiency that the receiver itself becomes the dominant source of noise, but this typically doesn't happen until the antenna is extremely inefficient. When transmitting, reduced efficiency lowers the transmitted signal, but it has no effect on the receiving station's noise. So reduced efficiency of a transmitting antenna results in a reduced signal/noise ratio at the receiving end, and consequently should be avoided.

Mutual coupling effects can be minimized by increasing the loss (and therefore reducing the efficiency) of the elements, or by reducing the element sizes to a small fraction of a wavelength. Doing the second without the first isn't usually a good idea because the feed point impedance tends to change rapidly with frequency for very small elements, making an antenna that works well over only a narrow bandwidth. But increasing loss broadens the bandwidth, even for small elements, as well as reducing mutual coupling effects. So this approach is often taken for designing a receiving-only array. With mutual coupling effects minimized because of loss, feed-system design becomes relatively simple, provided a few simple rules are followed. (See "Loss Resistance, Mutual Coupling, and Antenna Gain" above.)

The "crossfire" feed method described by Tom Rauch, W8JI (**www.w8ji.com**), delivers an array with very wide pattern bandwidth. That is, the pattern shape, particularly null direction and depth, stay nearly constant over a very large range of frequencies. The method requires elements whose feed point impedances stay nearly constant over the frequency range, which for a wide range requires high loss and low efficiency. As explained earlier, however, this is acceptable for receiving arrays and receiving arrays are usually the case for which deep and predictable pattern nulls are the most important. The basic idea for two elements is to use a delay line between the two whose delay in electrical degrees equals the element spacing in degrees then add a frequency-independent phase inversion to the line. A distant signal arriving at the first element creates a wave in the delay line connected to its feed point. That same signal arrives at the second element at the same time the wave from the first element reaches the end of the delay line. The signal from the second element is added to the inverted wave from the first element and, if the two are the same amplitude, complete cancellation occurs. This is independent of the frequency, and also of the element spacing provided that the delay line's electrical length is the same as the element spacing. See the design examples for additional information.

For ungrounded elements like dipoles, the inversion can easily be effected simply by reversing the feed line connections to one element by giving the phasing line a half twist. Or a broadband inverting transformer can be used for either grounded or ungrounded elements.

6.4 PHASED ARRAY DESIGN EXAMPLES

This section, also written by Roy Lewallen, W7EL, presents examples of feed-system design for several kinds of array using the design principles given in previous sections. All but the dipole example array are assumed to be made of λ/4 vertical elements. The dipole example illustrates that exactly the same method can be used for arrays of any shape of elements, including dipole, square (quad) and triangular. Likewise, the methods shown here apply equally well to VHF and UHF arrays. The first example includes more detail than the remaining ones, so you should read it before the others. Following the array design examples using the "simplest" and L network feed systems is an example of a receiving array using two different configurations of "crossfire" feed.

The *EZNEC-ARRL* program furnished with this *Antenna Book* edition is v. 5.0 which for the first time has the capability of incorporating L networks in the model. So the L network fed array can also be analyzed for accuracy and the effects of component and ground loss variation. **ARRL_Cardioid_L_Network_Example.EZ** models the cardioid array with L network feed system.

EZNEC-ARRL v. 5.0 also has provision for including transmission line loss. It can be instructive to add various amounts of loss to see the effect on pattern and bandwidth. The effect of loss will generally be most apparent on lines running with a high SWR, i.e., when terminated in an impedance very different from the characteristic impedance.

In the following sections, text in SMALL CAPS denotes menu or function button label or an input to the *EZNEC-ARRL* software used in the creation and modeling of these examples.

6.4.1 GENERAL ARRAY DESIGN CONSIDERATIONS

If either the "simplest" feed system (Figure 6.16) or L network feed system (Figure 6.17) is used, the feed point impedance of one or more elements — *when the array elements all have the correct currents* — must be known. By far the best way to determine this is by modeling. If accurate modeling isn't practical for some reason, an estimate should be made from an approximate model, and you should expect to have to adjust the feed system after building and installing it.

Manual calculation methods for some simple configurations are given in Appendix B (on the CD), but calculation is tedious and, as stated earlier, the configurations for which this method works are the very ones which are easiest to model. *EZNEC-ARRL* is used in the following examples to determine feed point impedance. Space doesn't permit detailed instructions here on creating the models, so they are included in complete form. They should provide a convenient starting point for any variations you might like to try. See the *EZNEC-ARRL* manual (accessed by clicking HELP/CONTENTS in the main *EZNEC-ARRL* window) for help in using this program.

In the following examples, vertical elements are close to λ/4 high and dipole elements close to λ/2, and their lengths have been adjusted for resonance when all other elements are absent or open circuited. There's actually no need in practice to make the elements self-resonant — it's simply used as a convenient reference point for these examples. You'll also find it interesting to see how much reactance is present at the feed points of the elements when in the arrays, knowing that it's very nearly zero when only one element is present.

In any real grounded vertical array, there is ground loss associated with each element. The amount of loss depends on the length and number of ground radials, and on the type and wetness of the ground under and around the antenna. This resistance becomes part of the feed point resistance, so it must be included in the model used to determine feed point impedance. The 90° Fed, 90° Spaced Array example below discusses how this is done. **Figure 6.20** gives resistance values for typical ground systems, based on measurements by Sevick (July 1971 and March 1973 *QST*). The values of feed system components based on Figure 6.20 will be reasonably close to correct, even if the ground characteristics are somewhat different than Sevick's.

Feed systems for the design example arrays to follow are based on the resistance values given below.

Number of Radials	Loss Resistance, Ω
4	29
8	18
16	9
Infinite	0

Elevated radial systems also have some ground loss, although it can be considerably less than a system with

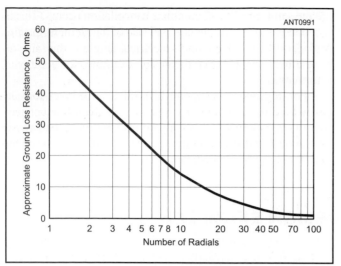

Figure 6.20 — Approximate ground system loss resistance of a resonant λ/4 ground-mounted vertical element versus the number of radials, based on measurements by Jerry Sevick, W2FMI. Moderate length radials (0.2 to 0.4 λ) were used for the measurements. The exact resistance, especially for only a few radials, will depend on the nature of the soil under the antenna. Add 36 Ω for the approximate feed point resistance of a thin resonant λ/4 vertical.

the same number of buried radials. This loss will be automatically included in the feed point impedance of a model which includes the elevated radials, so no further estimation is required. Be sure to use Perfect, High-Accuracy ground type when modeling an elevated radial system with *EZNEC-ARRL*. In other *NEC-2* based programs, this might be referred to as Sommerfeld type ground. More information can be found in the *EZNEC-ARRL* manual.

The matter of matching the array for the best SWR on the feed line to the station is not dealt with here, since it's a separate problem from that of the main topic, which is designing feed systems to produce a desired pattern. Some of the simpler arrays provide a match that is close to 50 or 75 Ω, so no further matching is required. However, as shown by program *Arrayfeed1*, many larger arrays present a less favorable impedance for direct connection and will require matching if a low SWR on the main feed line is required. If matching is necessary, the appropriate network should be placed in the single feed line running to the station. Attempts to improve the match by adjustment of the phasing L network, individual element lengths, matching at the element feed points or individual element feeder lengths will usually ruin the current balance of the array. Program *TLW*, included on the CD, can be used for designing an appropriate matching network. Additional information on impedance matching may be found in the **Transmission Line Coupling and Impedance Matching** chapter.

Choosing *Arrayfeed1* Solutions

When designing a feed system for a two-element array, *Arrayfeed1* program allows you to choose the characteristic impedances of the two transmission lines going to the

elements, which don't have to be equal, so you have your choice of more than one solution. However, directional array switching is much more difficult if the lines have different impedances, so in general you should use the same characteristic impedances.

For larger arrays, *Arrayfeed1* requires the feed lines to all elements to have the same impedance. In choosing the transmission line impedance values, usually you can simply use convenient impedances. But in general, you should avoid solutions where component reactance (X) values are vastly different (say, more than three times or less than one third as large) as the line characteristic impedances. Such networks will become more critical to adjust, and both the impedance and pattern will change more rapidly with changes in frequency. You can usually avoid this situation by choosing feed line impedances that are in the same ballpark as the element feed point impedances. The last example in the "Practical Array Design" section illustrates this problem and its solution.

When designing a "simplest" feed system, the most broadbanded and least critical system is usually one where the difference in electrical feed line lengths is closest to the relative element phase angle. Here, "broadbanded" means that the pattern changes less with frequency, not necessarily that the SWR changes less. However, an array that's broadbanded in the pattern sense is usually also relatively broadbanded with respect to SWR.

Arrayfeed1 reports the impedance seen at the main array feed point. While it might be tempting to choose the solution producing the lowest SWR on the main feed line, you'll end up with a less critical and more broadbanded system if you base your choice on the criteria given above, and provide separate impedance matching at the array's main feed point when necessary.

6.4.2 90° FED, 90° SPACED VERTICAL ARRAY

This example illustrates the design of both "simplest" and L network feed systems for a 2-element, 90° spaced and fed vertical array. The first task when using either feed system is to determine the feed point impedances of the elements when placed in an array having the desired element currents. The "simplest" feed system method requires knowledge of both element impedances, while the L network system requires you to know only one. Actually, it's equally easy to determine both as it is to find just one, using *EZNEC-ARRL*. (Appendix B contains equations for those interested in manual methods or for more insight as to how the impedances come about.) The first step is to specify the antenna we want. For this example, we'll specify:

- Frequency: 7.15 MHz.
- Two identical, one inch (2.54 cm) diameter, 33 feet (10.06 meter) long elements spaced 90 electrical degrees, with element currents equal in magnitude and 90° apart in-phase.
- 8 buried radial wires, 0.3 λ long, under each element.

A model of this antenna has been created and furnished with *EZNEC-ARRL*. So the next step is to start *EZNEC-ARRL*, click the OPEN button, enter ARRL_CARDIOID_EXAMPLE in the text box (or double-click it in the file list) to open example file **ARRL_Cardioid_Example.EZ**.

This *EZNEC* example model uses a *MININEC*-type ground, which is the same as perfect ground when calculating antenna currents and impedances. A real antenna would have some additional resistive loss due to the finite conductivity of the ground system. The only way to model a buried radial ground system with an *NEC-2* based program like *EZNEC* is to create radial wires just above the ground (using the Real, High-Accuracy ground type), because *NEC-2* can't handle buried conductors.

This provides only a moderate approximation of a buried system. Another way to estimate ground-system resistance is to measure the feed point impedance of a single element, then subtract from that the resistance reported for a model of that element over perfect (or *MININEC*-type) ground. For most uses, however, an adequate approximation can be made by simply referring to the graph of Figure 6.20. As stated previously, the feed system design depends on the feed point impedances of the elements, which in turn depend on the ground system resistance. So the ground system resistance must be known, approximately anyway, before designing the feed system. At the end of this example we'll investigate the effect of changes in the ground system or errors in estimating the resistance on the pattern.

For 8 radials, Figure 6.20 shows the ground system resistance to be about 18 Ω. This is included in the example model as a simple resistive load at the feed point of each element. Click the SRC DAT button to see the feed point impedances of the two elements. In this model, Source 1 is at the base of Wire 1 (element 1), and Source 2 is at the base of Wire 2 (element 2). Notice in the SOURCE DATA display that the Source 1 current has been specified at 1 amp at 0°, and Source 2 is 1 amp at −90°. So the Source 2-element is the lagging element. You should see impedances of $37.53 − j19.1$ Ω for element 1 and $68.97 + j18.5$ Ω for element 2. These are the feed point impedances resulting when the array is ideally fed, with equal magnitude and 90° phased currents. Record these values for use in *Arrayfeed1*.

Click the FF PLOT button to generate a plot of the azimuth pattern at an elevation angle of 10°. In the 2D Plot Window, open the FILE menu and select SAVE TRACE AS. Enter CARDIOID_IDEAL FEED in the FILE NAME box, then click SAVE. This saves the cardioid pattern plot so you can compare it later to the pattern you get with the transmission line feed system.

Now it's time to design the feed system. Refer to the appropriate subheading below for the design of each of the two kinds of feed systems. Both systems use program *Arrayfeed1* program.

"Simplest" (Transmission Line Only) Feed System

Start *Arrayfeed1*. In the ARRAY TYPE frame, select TWO ELEMENT. In FEED SYSTEM TYPE, select SIMPLEST. In the INPUTS frame, enter the following values:

Frequency MHz = 7.15; Feed point impedances – Leading

Element: R ohms = 37.53, X ohms = −19.1; Lagging Element: R ohms = 68.97, X ohms = 18.5 (these are the element R and X values from *EZNEC-ARRL*). We'll be discussing the array input impedance, so check the CALC ZIN box near the lower left corner of the main window if it's not already checked.

We're free to choose any transmission-line characteristic impedances we want, so long as we can get cables with those impedances. And the two cables don't have to have the same characteristic impedances. Each choice will lead to a different set of solutions. But sometimes a solution isn't possible, which then requires choosing different line impedances. Let's try 50 Ω for both lines. Enter 50 in both Z0 boxes.

Finally, enter 1 for the LAGGING:LEADING I MAG, and −90 for the PHASE. Click FIND SOLUTIONS. The result is no solution! So enter 75 into both the line impedance boxes and click FIND SOLUTIONS again. You should now see two sets of results in the Solutions frame, electrical lengths of 68.80° and 156.03° for the first solution and 131.69° and 185.00° for the second. (Notice that the difference in length between the two lines isn't 90° for either solution, although the first solution is quite close. It's normal for the feed line length difference to be different than the phase difference, due to the unequal element feed point impedances caused by mutual coupling.)

The solution with a line length difference closest to the element phase difference is usually preferable. Also, all else being equal, the solution with shortest lines is better providing that the lines will physically reach the elements. This is because the current magnitude and phase will change less with frequency than for a longer-length solution. However, there might be some cases where the change with frequency luckily compensates for the changing electrical distance between elements, so it's not a bad idea to model both solutions unless you plan on using the antenna over only a narrow frequency range.

In this case, the first solution looks best in all respects. The sum of the two lines in the first solution is about 225 electrical degrees. Assuming the lines have a velocity factor of 0.66, the total length of the lines will be more than 148 physical degrees. Since our two elements are spaced 90 physical degrees apart, the lines will comfortably reach. If they didn't, we could either use the second solution's lengths, use cable with a higher velocity factor or add a half wavelength to both the line lengths in the first solution.

The impedance ZIN shown by *Arrayfeed1* is the impedance at the input to the feed system, so it's the impedance that will be seen by the main feed line. The second solution provides nearly a perfect match for a 50-Ω transmission line. But the first solution is good for nearly all applications. Also a 50-Ω line connected to the first solution's feed system would have an SWR of only 1.65:1, which wouldn't require any matching under most circumstances. Normal line loss would reduce the SWR even more at the transmitter end of the feed coax.

To find the required physical line lengths, enter the cable velocity factor and make your choice of units in the PHYSICAL LENGTHS frame. The design is now complete; all you have to do is cut two lines to the specified lengths and connect one from a common feed point to each element as shown in Figure 6.16, or the screen capture from *Arrayfeed1* shown in **Figure 6.21**.

Next, we'll design an L network feed system for the same array.

L Network Feed System

In *Arrayfeed1*, select L NETWORK in the FEED SYSTEM TYPE frame. The program doesn't need to know the leading element impedance to calculate the L network values, but it does need it to calculate the array input impedance. If you want to know the impedance, check the ZIN box at the lower left corner of the main window, otherwise you can uncheck it and the input box for the leading element Z will disappear. The values from the "Simplest" analysis should still be present in the appropriate boxes; if not, refer to the "Simplest" feed system design above and re-enter the values. Again, we'll use 75 Ω for the line impedances, since that gave us a solution for the "Simplest" feed system. This feed system is more versatile, though, so we could use 50-Ω lines with this feed system if desired.

Click FIND SOLUTION and see the results in the SOLUTION frame. See screen capture in **Figure 6.22**. With 75-Ω lines, the L network consists of a series inductor of 1.815 µH and a shunt capacitor of 199.7 pF, connected as shown in the diagram in the left part of the program window. To find the physical length of the λ/4 lines, enter the velocity factor and choice of units in the PHYSICAL LENGTHS frame.

The main feed point impedance of $31.37 + j\ 25.94\ \Omega$ would result in about a 2.2:1 SWR on a 50-Ω feed line, which would be acceptable for many applications. It could easily be reduced to 1.6:1 by the simple addition of a series capacitor of 25.94 Ω reactance (858 pF) at the main feed point or, of course, reduced to 1:1 with a simple L network or other matching system designed with the *TLW* program.

Pattern Verification and Effect of Loss Resistance

L network *EZNEC* model **ARRL_Cardioid_TL_Example.EZ** has been created to model the "simplest" feed system just designed. Open it with *EZNEC-ARRL*. In the VIEW ANTENNA DISPLAY, you can see the boxes representing the transmission lines placed at the element bases. The other ends of the transmission lines are shown going to "virtual segment" (connection point) V1. The source is also connected to V1. In *EZNEC*, the physical locations of the ends of transmission line models don't have to be the same as the physical locations, so the view isn't a precise representation of what the actual setup would look like. (You can find more about this in **ARRL_Cardioid_TL_Example. txt**, the Antenna Notes file that accompanies example file **ARRL_Cardioid_TL_Example.EZ**.)

Click FF PLOT to generate a 2D pattern of the antenna. In the 2D Plot Window, open the FILE menu and select ADD TRACE. Select CARDIOID — IDEAL FEED (which you saved earlier) and click OPEN. The added plot overlays perfectly, indicating that the pattern using this feed system is identical to the pattern we got with perfect current sources at each feed point.

To check the feed point currents, click the CURRENTS button. In the resulting table, you can see that WIRE 1 SEGMENT 1 current is 0.56467 A at a phase of –56.73° and WIRE 2 SEGMENT 1 current is 0.56467 A at –146.7°. (If you get the correct phase angles but wrong magnitudes, open the main window OPTIONS menu, select POWER LEVEL, and make sure the ABSOLUTE V, I SOURCES box is checked.) The ratio is 1.0000 at an angle of –89.97°, which is within normal error bounds for the desired 1 at –90°.

As a check on *Arrayfeed1*, click the SRC DAT button to find the impedance seen by the source. This would be the impedance at the main feed line connection in the real array.

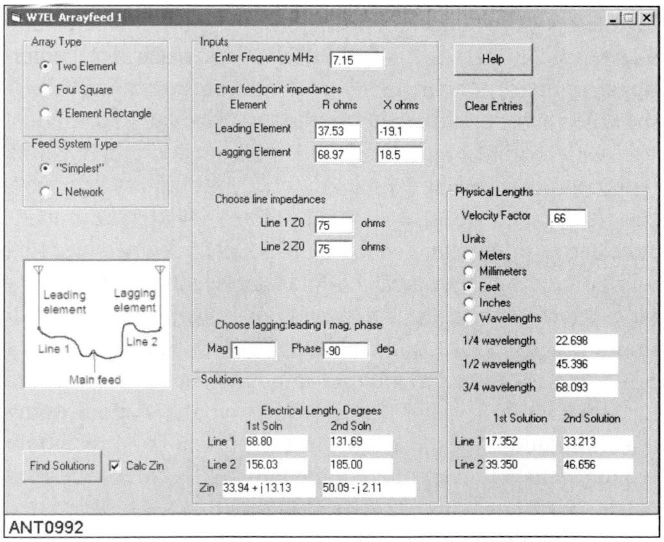

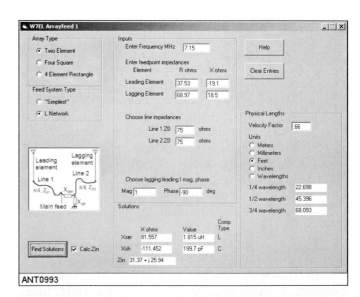

Figure 6.21 — Screen capture from *Arrayfeed1* program for "Simplest" 2-element phased array shown in Figure 6.16 and whose feed point impedances are modeled by *EZNEC-ARRL*.

Figure 6.22 — Screen capture from *Arrayfeed1* program for L network feed system using "current-forcing" properties of λ/4 feed lines.

EZNEC-ARRL reports 33.96 + j13.11 Ω, very close to the 33.94 + j13.13 Ω given by *Arrayfeed1* in Figure 6.21. Small differences of this order are normal and to be expected. This provides a further check that the *EZNEC-ARRL* model is correctly analyzing the *Arrayfeed1* feed system.

This *EZNEC-ARRL* model uses lossless transmission lines of a fixed physical length rather than a fixed electrical length (number of degrees), so they'll behave like real lines as the frequency is changed. By changing the *EZNEC* frequency and re-running the 2D plot, you can see that the front-to-back ratio degrades at 7.0 and 7.3 MHz. A slight adjustment of one or more line lengths, or a new *Arrayfeed1* solution at a slightly different frequency might produce a better compromise for some uses.

Other things you can try are to evaluate the second *Arrayfeed1* solution, or to try using different line impedances. (Keep the two line impedances equal if you anticipate doing array direction switching.) The effect of varying ground system resistance can also be evaluated by clicking the LOADS line in the main window and changing the load resistance values. For example, if the ground system resistance were 9 Ω instead of the 18 Ω we have assumed, the front-to-back ratio would drop from about 32 to about 20 dB. Note that changing the *EZNEC* ground conductivity in this model has no effect on the feed point current ratio. With a *MININEC* type ground, it's used only for pattern calculation — the ground is assumed perfect during impedance and current calculations, and the only ground system loss resistance in the model is what we've specifically put in as loads.

Not surprisingly, the forward gain is affected very little by changes in frequency or ground system loss. To find the gain relative to a single element, compare the reported dBi gain of **ARRL_Cardioid_Example** with the same model with one of the elements deleted. You'll find it's very close to 3.0 dB. The 90° fed, 90° spaced array is a special case of array where the effects of mutual coupling on the two elements are opposite and cancel, resulting in the same gain as if mutual coupling didn't exist. But mutual coupling most certainly does exist!

The second solution presented a more favorable main feed point impedance, so it would be tempting to use that one instead of the first solution. Replacing the feed line lengths with the second solution lengths to model the second solution shows that the front-to-back ratio deteriorates more at the band edges when the second solution is used. This might be tolerable if restricted frequency use is anticipated. But it does illustrate that the solution with shorter lines is generally more broadbanded and that the choice of solution shouldn't in general be based on the one giving the most favorable impedance.

6.4.3 A THREE-ELEMENT BINOMIAL BROADSIDE ARRAY

An array of three in-line elements spaced λ/2 apart and fed in-phase gives a pattern that is generally bidirectional. If the element currents are equal, the resulting pattern has a forward gain of 5.7 dB (for lossless elements) compared to a

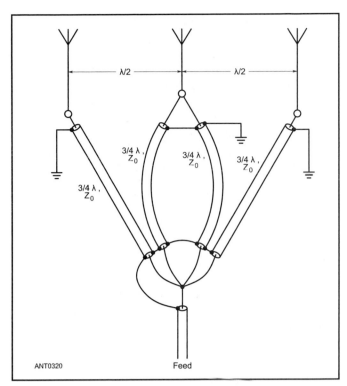

Figure 6.23 — Feed system for the three element 1:2:1 binomial array. All feed lines are ¾ electrical wavelength long and have the same characteristic impedance.

single element, but it has substantial side lobes. If the currents are tapered in a binomial coefficient 1:2:1 ratio (twice the current in the center element as in the two end elements), the gain drops slightly to just under 5.3 dB, the main lobes widen and the side lobes disappear.

The array is shown in **Figure 6.23**, and an *EZNEC-ARRL* model of the antenna over perfect ground to show the ideal pattern is provided as **ARRL_Binomial_Example.EZ**. To obtain a 1:2:1 current ratio in the elements, each end element is fed through a 3λ/4 line of impedance Z_0. Line lengths of 3λ/4 are chosen because λ/4 lines will not physically reach. The center element is fed from the same point through two parallel 3λ/4 lines of the same characteristic impedance. This is equivalent to feeding it through a line of impedance $Z_0/2$. The currents are thus forced to be in-phase and to have the correct ratio. **ARRL_Binomial_TL_Example.EZ** is an *EZNEC-ARRL* model that shows this feed system with lossless transmission lines. The reader is encouraged to experiment with this model to see the effect of changes in frequency, the addition of loss resistance (as resistive loads at the element feed points), transmission line loss, and other alterations on the array pattern and gain. You should also replace the perfect ground with *MININEC* type of ground to show how radiation patterns over real ground differ from the theoretical perfect-ground pattern.

6.4.4 A FOUR-SQUARE ARRAY

Several types of feed system are used for feeding this popular array, and most share a common problem — they

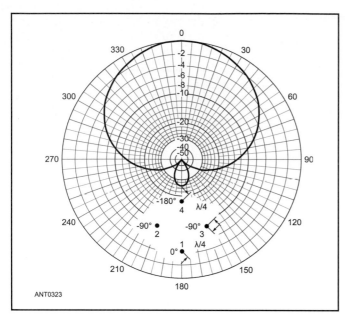

Figure 6.24 — Pattern and layout of the four-element Four-Square array. Gain is referenced to a single similar element; add 5.5 dB to the scale values shown.

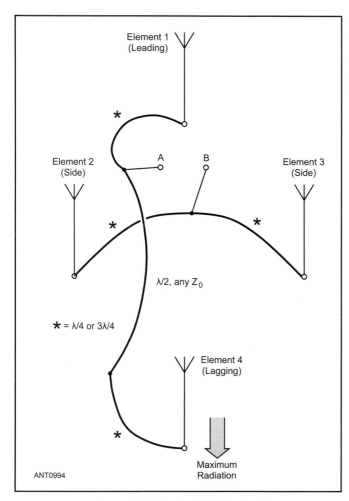

Figure 6.25 — "Simplest" feed system for the Four-Square array in Figure 6.24. Grounds and cable shields have been omitted for clarity.

don't provide the correct element current ratio — although a number of them produce a workable approximation. The feed systems described here are capable of producing exactly the correct current ratio. The only significant variable is the element feed point impedances, so the quality of the result depends on your ability to model the feed point impedances of a correctly fed array. As in the examples above, *EZNEC-ARRL* will be used for that purpose and *Arrayfeed1* for the design of the feed system itself.

In this array (see **Figure 6.24**), four elements are placed in a square with λ/4 sides. (A variation of the Four-Square uses wider spacing.) The rear and front elements (1 and 4) are 180° out-of-phase with each other. The side elements (2 and 3) are in phase with each other and 90° delayed from the front element. The magnitudes of the currents in all four elements are equal. The front and rear elements can be forced to be 180° out-of-phase and to have equal currents by using the current-forcing method described earlier. One element is connected to a line that is either λ/4 or 3λ/4 long, the other to a line that is λ/2 longer, and the two lines to a common point.

Likewise, the two side element currents are forced to be equal by connecting them to a common point via λ/4 or 3λ/4 lines. **Figure 6.25** shows the basic current-forcing system.

If the pattern is to be electrically rotated, it is necessary to bring lines from all four elements to a common location. If solid-polyethylene dielectric coaxial cable, which has a dielectric constant of 0.66, is used, λ/4 lines won't reach the center of the array. So 3λ/4 lines must be used. Alternatively, you can use λ/4 lines with foam or other dielectric having a velocity factor of more than about 0.71 (plus a little extra margin). These will reach to the center. Whatever your choice, three of the lines must be the same length and the fourth must be λ/2 longer.

In this array, the side elements (2 and 3) have equal impedances, but the rear and front (1 and 4) are different from each other, and both are different from the side elements. We have to know the feed point impedances of the front, rear and side elements in order to design the "simplest" feed system, but only the side element impedances are needed to design the L network system. Knowledge of all feed point impedances is necessary if the array main feed point impedance ZIN is to be calculated. *EZNEC-ARRL* model **4Square_Example. EZ** shows a 40-meter Four-Square array with 18 Ω of loss resistance at each element, to approximate an 8-radial per element ground system. (See the cardioid array example above for more information about modeling ground system loss.) Opening the file in *EZNEC-ARRL* and clicking the SRC DAT button gives the following impedances:

Source 1: $16.4 - j15.85 \; \Omega$
Sources 2 and 3: $57.47 - j19.44 \; \Omega$
Source 4: $77.81 + j54.8 \; \Omega$

It's interesting to note that the resistive part of source 1 is less than the 18 Ω of loss resistance we intentionally added to simulate ground system loss. That means that the element 1 feed point resistance would be negative if the ground resistance were less than about an ohm and a half. This isn't uncommon in phased arrays and simply means that the element is feeding power into the feed system. This power is coming via mutual coupling from the other elements.

"Simplest" (Transmission Line Only) Feed System

To design a "simplest" feed system, start *Arrayfeed1*. In the ARRAY TYPE frame, select 4 SQUARE, and select SIMPLEST in the FEED SYSTEM TYPE frame. In the INPUTS frame, enter the frequency and the impedances from *EZNEC-ARRL*:

Frequency = 7.15 MHz
Leading Element: R = 16.4, X = −15.85
Side elements: R = 57.47, X = −19.44
Lagging Element: R = 77.81, X = 54.8

We'll try using 50 Ω for all lines, so enter 50 into the next three boxes.

Enter 1 for the lagging:leading I magnitude and −90 for the phase.

Click FIND SOLUTIONS.

The result is shown in the SOLUTIONS frame, shown in **Figure 6.26**. As always when any solution exists, there are two to choose from. The one with the shortest lines is generally preferable, so we'll choose it. For this example, we'll use λ/4 lines with velocity factor of 0.82. So enter 0.82 in the VELOCITY FACTOR box in the PHYSICAL LENGTHS frame, and read the physical lengths from the bottom of that frame. The λ/4 lines (marked in the *Arrayfeed1* diagram with an asterisk) are 28.2 feet, line 1 is 7.483 feet and line 2 is 51.668 feet. The "simplest" feed system is shown in Figure 6.26, and the complete feed system consists of this connected to the array of Figure 6.25.

EZNEC-ARRL model **ARRL_4Square_TL_Example. EZ** simulates the array fed with this system. Comparison of the pattern plot to one from ideal-current model **ARRL_4Square_Example.EZ** and examination of the element currents verify that the feed system is producing the desired pattern and element currents. You can use **ARRL_4Square_Example.EZ** to investigate the effect of

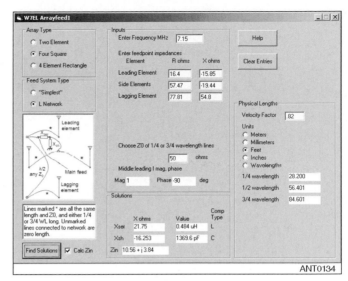

Figure 6.27 — L network setup for Four-Square array in Figure 6.25, fed with λ/4 (or 3λ/4) current-forcing feed system.

frequency change, ground loss and other changes on the array gain and pattern.

L Network Feed System

To design the L network feed system, simply change the FEED SYSTEM TYPE to L NETWORK and click FIND SOLUTIONS. The results you should see are a 0.484 µH inductor for the series component X_{ser}, and a 1369.6 pF capacitor for the shunt component X_{sh}. The L network feed system is shown in **Figure 6.27**, and the complete feed system consists of this L network connected to the array of Figure 6.25.

EZNEC-ARRL model **ARRL_4Square_L_Network_ Example.EZ** simulates the array fed with this system. You can compare it with the idealized feed system array and use it to see the effects of various parameter changes as you did with the "simplest" feed system model. Arrays have also been built using this feed system and the element currents measured, with exactly the expected results.

This array is more sensitive to adjustment than the 2-element 90° fed, 90° spaced array. Adjustment procedures and a method of remotely switching the pattern direction are described in the "Practical Aspects of Phased Array Design" section below.

6.4.5 A 4-ELEMENT RECTANGULAR ARRAY

The 4-element rectangular array shown with its pattern in **Figure 6.28** has appeared numerous times in amateur publications. However, many of the accompanying feed systems fail to deliver currents in the proper amounts and phases to the various elements. The array can be correctly fed using the principles discussed in this chapter and the design methods that follow.

Elements 1 and 2 can be forced to be in-phase and to have equal currents by feeding them through 3λ/4 lines. (As in the binomial and Four-Square array examples, 3λ/4

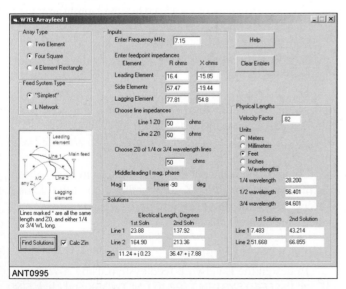

Figure 6.26 — Screen capture from *Arrayfeed1* for "Simplest" feed system for Four-Square feed system shown in Figure 6.25.

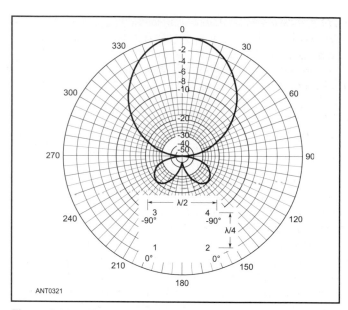

Figure 6.28 — Pattern and layout of the four-element rectangular array. Gain is referenced to a single similar element; add 6.8 dB to the scale values shown.

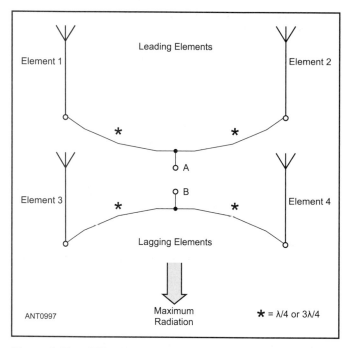

Figure 6.29 — "Simplest" feed system for four-element rectangular array, using four equal-length λ/4 (or 3λ/4) cables.

lines are chosen because λ/4 lines won't physically reach.) The currents in elements 3 and 4 can similarly be forced to be equal and in-phase. **Figure 6.29** shows the "current-forcing" feed system. Elements 3 and 4 are made to have currents of equal magnitude but of 90° phase difference from elements 1 and 2 by use of either a "simplest" all-transmission line feed system or an L network feed system. Both will be designed in this example.

For this array, we have to know the feed point impedances

of two elements (one of each pair) in order to design either type of feed system. *EZNEC-ARRL* model **Rectangular_Example.EZ** shows a 20-meter rectangular array with 18 Ω of loss resistance at each element, again to approximate an 8-radial per element ground system. (See the cardioid array example above for more information about modeling ground system loss.) Open the file in *EZNEC-ARRL* and click the SRC DAT button to find the following feed point impedances:

Sources 1 and 2: 21.44 – j 21.29 Ω
Sources 3 and 4: 70.81 – j 5.232 Ω

"Simplest" (Transmission-Line Only) Feed System

To design a "simplest" feed system, start program *Arrayfeed1*. In the ARRAY TYPE frame, select 4 ELEMENT RECTANGLE, and select SIMPLEST in the FEED SYSTEM TYPE frame. In the INPUTS frame, enter the frequency and the impedances from *EZNEC-ARRL*:

Frequency = 14.15 MHz
Leading Elements R = 21.44, X = –21.29
Lagging Elements R = 70.81, X = –5.232

We'll use 50 Ω for all lines, so enter 50 into the next three boxes.

Enter 1 for the LAGGING:LEADING I MAGNITUDE and –90 for the phase.

Click FIND SOLUTIONS.

The result will be "No Solution" — indicating this combination of line impedances can't be used. Several other combinations also produce this result, but making lines 1 and 2 each 75 Ω and the 3λ/4 lines 50 Ω does produce a solution. Enter 75 into the LINE 1 Z0 and LINE 2 Z0 boxes, and leave 50 in the CHOOSE Z0 OF 1/4 OR 3/4 WAVELENGTH LINES box, then click the FIND SOLUTIONS button. There won't be any problem making lines 1 and 2 reach, so we'll choose the first solution because the lines are shorter. The physical lengths of all the lines are shown in the PHYSICAL LENGTHS frame when the velocity factor is entered in the appropriate box. Assuming that we use coax with a velocity factor of 0.66 (and the example frequency of 14.15 MHz), the lengths are:

Line 1: 4.982 feet
Line 2: 20.153 feet
3λ/4 lines (marked with an asterisk in the *Arrayfeed1* diagram): 34.408 feet

The lines are connected following the diagram in the upper left part of the *Arrayfeed1* window. This completes the "simplest" feed system design. *EZNEC-ARRL* model **Rectangular_TL_Example.EZ** simulates an array fed with this system.

Comparison of the pattern plot to one from ideal-current **Rectangular_Example.EZ**, and examination of the element currents verify that the feed system is producing the desired pattern and element currents.

L-Network Feed System

To design the L network feed system using *Arrayfeed1*, change the FEED SYSTEM TYPE to L NETWORK and click FIND SOLUTIONS. The resulting L network values are a 0.199 μH inductor for the series component X_{ser} and a 684.2 pF capacitor for the shunt component X_{sh}. *EZNEC-ARRL* model **ARRL_Rectangular_L_Network_Example.EZ** simulates an array fed with this system.

6.4.6 120° FED, 60° SPACED DIPOLE ARRAY

This example shows the design of "simplest" and L network feed systems for a 2-element 20 meter dipole array, rather than a vertical array. No special accommodation is required for the array made from dipoles rather than vertical elements — the same methods can be used regardless of element shape. This example also shows that both the "simplest" and L network feed systems can readily be applied to elements that use phase angles other than 90°.

Any 2-element array made with identical elements spaced $\lambda/2$ or closer and having equal magnitude currents with a relative phase angle of 180° minus the spacing will produce a unidirectional pattern with a good null to the rear. In practice, very close spacings lead to very low feed point resistances, with consequent losses and very narrowband characteristics. But this 60° spaced array is well within the range of practical realization. File **ARRL_Dipole_Array_Example.EZ** is a model created for this array, with ideal element currents. Open this file in *EZNEC-ARRL* and click FF PLOT to show the pattern at an elevation angle of 10°. You can save this pattern for later comparison to the pattern with a "simplest" feed system by opening the FILE menu in the 2D PLOT window, selecting SAVE TRACE AS, entering a name for the trace file and clicking SAVE.

Following the same procedure as in the previous examples, we begin the array design by finding the element feed point impedances in the ideally fed array using *EZNEC-ARRL* numbers. Having already opened **ARRL_Dipole_Array_Example.EZ**, all that's needed is to click SRC DAT. The results are:

Leading element (source 1): $36.16 - j\ 46.05\ \Omega$
Lagging element (source 2): $49.56 + j\ 51.47\ \Omega$

"Simplest" (Transmission Line Only) Feed System

Select TWO ELEMENT for the ARRAY TYPE in *Arrayfeed1* and "SIMPLEST" for the FEED SYSTEM TYPE. Enter the frequency of 14.15 MHz and enter the element feed point impedances from *EZNEC-ARRL* into the appropriate boxes in the INPUTS frame. For line impedances, the section describing the "simplest" feed system recommends against choosing one which is very different from the element feed point impedances, but for fun let's try 300 Ω for the two lines and see what happens. Enter 300 in the LINE 1 Z0 and LINE 2 Z0 boxes. Finally, enter the LAGGING:LEADING I MAG, PHASE of 1 for MAG and –120 for PHASE.

Click FIND SOLUTIONS. For this example we'll assume that TV-type twinlead with a velocity factor of 0.8 is being used. So enter 0.8 for the VELOCITY FACTOR and read the physical line lengths in the PHYSICAL LENGTHS frame. A model of the array using the first solution has been created as **ARRL_Dipole_Array_TL_Example.EZ**. Open this file in *EZNEC-ARRL* and click FF Tab. You should see that the plot is virtually identical to the one saved earlier from the

ideal-current model. Note the gain and front-to-back ratio or 8.79 dBi and 31.01 dB respectively reported in the data box below the 2D plot.

Don't subtract 2.15 dB to find the gain relative to a single element! This isn't a free-space model, and the gain of a single dipole over ground is much greater than 2.15 dBi. Instead, delete one of the elements in **ARRL_Dipole_Array_Example.EZ** to find the gain of a single element and subtract that value from the array gain. You can use the undo feature or re-open the file to restore the array.

Now, go back to the model with the "simplest" feed system in *EZNEC-ARRL* and change the Frequency to 14.0 MHz. Click FF TAB again. The gain has decreased a little, to 8.54 dBi and the front-to-back ratio has also decreased, to 21.8 dB. At 14.3 MHz, the gain is slightly higher, 9.04 dBi, but the front-to-back is again worse, down to 18.64 dB. But this isn't bad overall.

Let's take a look at the second solution. Click the TRANS LINES line in the main *EZNEC-ARRL* window to open the TRANSMISSION LINES window. Change the length of the first line to 26.856 feet, the second to 28.356 feet, and press the Enter key to complete the change. Change the FREQUENCY back to 14.15 MHz and click FF TAB. You should see exactly the same pattern as for both the first solution and for the ideal current model. But now change the FREQUENCY to 14.0 MHz, click FF TAB, and look at the pattern.

What happened? The gain has dropped to 5.95 dBi and the front-to-back to only 3.1 dB. The array is now nearly bi-directional! It's almost as bad at 14.3 MHz. So we've created a terribly touchy system. The chance of its working correctly even at the design frequency is slim, because there are inevitably some differences between the model and real antenna.

We did have a clue this might happen. As stated in the section describing the "simplest" feed system, the best choices for line Z_0 and for the resulting solution give a difference in electrical line lengths about equal to the desired phase delay of the current. The difference in electrical line lengths for the first solution was about 152° — not as close to the 120° current phase difference as we'd like, but much better than the mere 9.7° difference of the lines for the second solution. While the 300-Ω line Z_0 is quite different from the element feed point impedances, the first solution result is quite good. If desired, you can try other line impedance values into *Arrayfeed1* and evaluate the results with *EZNEC-ARRL*.

Please see the information about baluns in the "Baluns in Phased Arrays" section. Baluns are placed the same as in Figure 6.19, which shows the L network feed system.

L-Network Feed System

To design an L network feed system, change the *Arrayfeed1* FEED SYSTEM TYPE to L NETWORK and click FIND SOLUTIONS. The results aren't good ones to use. The component reactance magnitudes of about 1573 and 2619 Ω are more than five times the 300-Ω Z_0 of the feed lines. As explained in the section describing the L network feed system, it's undesirable to have such a large ratio of component reactance to line Z_0. Among other problems, the inductor and capacitor values are quite extreme and capacitor stray inductance and inductor capacitance would have a significant impact on performance.

The problem occurs because the feed line impedance we chose is much larger than the element feed point impedances, so the λ/4 lines transform the feed point impedances to much higher values at the L network and main feed point. This feed system would be extremely critical, narrowbanded and difficult to adjust. We can do better by choosing feed line impedances that aren't too drastically different than the element feed point impedances. In this case, 50 or 75 Ω would be a much better choice than 300. Let's try 75.

In *Arrayfeed1*, change the LINE 1 Z0 and LINE 2 Z0 impedances from 300 to 75 and click FIND SOLUTIONS. L network component reactance magnitudes are now about 98 and 164 Ω, much better than before. This will be a relatively uncritical and broadbanded feed system.

Again, be sure to read the information about baluns in the "Baluns in Phased Arrays" section. Figure 6.19 shows the completed feed system including baluns. *EZNEC-ARRL* example file **ARRL_Dipole_Array_L_Network_Example. EZ** is a model of the array with L network feed. It does not include baluns, since the transmission line models support only differential mode currents and therefore have the implicit effect of including ideal baluns.

6.4.7 CROSSFIRE RECEIVING ARRAY

While any transmitting array can be used for receiving with the same gain and directivity, inefficient (lossy) arrays do well for HF and MF receiving but not for transmitting. High loss brings the potential for exceptionally wide bandwidth, simplified feed systems and compact size, so receive-only arrays are worth considering for many installations. The following example is for a simple 2-element array using the "crossfire" phasing principle discussed earlier. The same methods can be used for more complex arrays.

The general principle of "crossfire" phasing is to connect the elements together with a delay line with an electrical length equal to the distance between the elements. A frequency-independent phase inversion (such as a wide-band transformer or physical connection reversal of one of the transmission lines) is added somewhere in the feed system path to one but not both of the elements, causing frequency-independent cancellation of the signals from the two elements when the signal is coming from one end-fire direction. The result is a potentially deep pattern null in one direction over a wide range of frequencies. The pattern can be reversed using methods described later and more elaborate arrays such as the Four-Square can be designed to allow additional null directions by directional switching. Since transmission lines invariably have velocity factors less than one, a single delay line of the proper electrical length is too short in practice to reach between the elements. The method works equally well, however, using a line to each element from a common point, the only requirement being that the difference in their electrical lengths equals the correct delay length. That is how these example designs were created.

There are a number of ways to create a time delay but about the only practical way of achieving a constant time delay over a wide frequency range is to use a transmission line terminated in its characteristic impedance. The termination must, of course, maintain its impedance over the wide frequency range. The straightforward method of designing a receiving antenna therefore requires that the transmission lines from the elements to somehow be added together but with each properly terminated. This could be done with active circuits, for example, by terminating each line with a terminating resistor connected to the high impedance input of an amplifier or buffer circuit whose outputs can then be added (or subtracted, since an inversion is required somewhere) without affecting the transmission line termination. Passive methods include terminating each transmission line with a matched attenuator, then resistively combining the attenuator outputs. This effectively isolates the terminating impedance from the summing circuitry. Another passive method is to use a hybrid combiner (see **Figure 6.30**) The potential advantage of this method is its relative efficiency, resulting in higher signal (and noise) level output than the attenuator method. This is important only if the received signal level is otherwise small enough that receiver noise becomes apparent.

Another approach to the "crossfire" system is to design the array as though it were to be used for transmitting, even though its low efficiency would make it impractical for that purpose. The difference in this approach is that the transmission line termination is done at the element feed points rather than at the summing point (see **Figure 6.31**) Reciprocity assures that the same directional properties will exist when using the array for receiving, even though the transmission lines are properly terminated at their source rather than load ends. The following examples show this approach and the hybrid-terminated receiving array approach for comparison

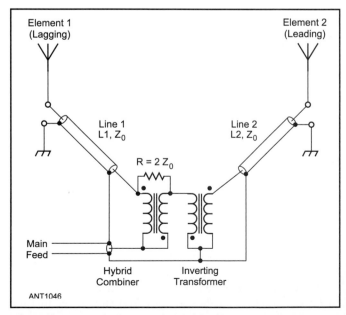

Figure 6.30 — "Crossfire" array with hybrid termination.

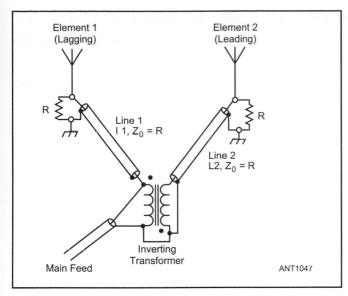

Figure 6.31 — "Crossfire" array with transmitting-type design.

and to illustrate that the reciprocal principle applies. Both arrays have the same pattern when receiving as they do for the modeled transmitting case.

Transmitting Array Type Design

A two-element "crossfire" array with transmitting-type design is included as *EZNEC-ARRL* example file **ARRL_Crossfire1_Example.EZ**. The array consists of two 30-foot-high vertical elements spaced 60 feet apart. These correspond to approximately $\frac{1}{16}$ wavelength and $\frac{1}{8}$ wavelength respectively at 1.85 MHz. Two transmission lines are used. This is being called a "transmitting array type design" because the transmission lines are terminated at the load end when driven by a transmitter, but are terminated at the load end in some other impedance when receiving.

Because the elements are electrically short, they have high feed point impedances, so parallel 50-Ω resistors at each feed point provide stable, near-50-Ω terminations for the transmission lines regardless of mutual coupling effects. The difference between the electrical lengths of the lines is 60 feet, the same as the line spacing. An ideal transformer is used in the model to effect the required phase inversion to one of the elements.

The model could be simplified by deleting the transformer and specifying a reverse connection of one of

the transmission lines, and the result would be the same. However, the included model more closely represents how the antenna would actually be implemented. The model shows a front-to-back ratio of better than 30 dB at 1 and 1.85 MHz, dropping to just over 20 dB at 4 MHz. Degradation at the higher frequency is due to the lower feed point impedance as the element becomes electrically longer. This dilutes the effectiveness of the 50-Ω feed point swamping resistors. Modeling with a program having plane-wave excitation capability confirms that the front-to-back ratio is the same when receiving as when transmitting.

An 18-Ω resistor is included at each element base to simulate the resistance of a moderately good ground system. However, because its value is small compared to the large impedance of a short element, it has no significant effect on the array performance. This indicates that the array will work well (for receiving) without an elaborate ground system.

Receiving Array Type Design — Hybrid Termination

EZNEC-ARRL example **ARRL_Crossfire_Hybrid_Feed_Example.EZ** uses the opposite design approach from the previous example. Instead of being terminated at the elements, the transmission lines are terminated at the ends where a receiver would be connected. Termination and signal addition are done with a hybrid combiner circuit consisting of a transformer and resistor. The inverting transformer is replaced in this model with a connection reversal of one of the transmission lines, for simplicity, as explained in the previous example. This model shows an improved front-to-back ratio of about 29 dB at 4 MHz compared to about 22 dB for the transmitting-type design, due to reduced sensitivity to mutual coupling and element impedance effects. Front-to-back ratio of the two examples is about the same at 1 and 1.85 MHz. This system is more efficient than the transmitting-type design, with signal (and noise) levels of about 5 dB greater at 4 MHz increasing to 14 dB greater at 1 MHz. This won't improve system signal-to-noise ratio unless the level of atmospheric noise is so low that receiver noise is audible.

Note: Modeling of the hybrid circuit and similar structures is difficult, requiring some experimenting and compromising to satisfy the requirements of the *NEC* calculating engine which isn't designed for analysis of loaded electrically small structures. Often, a suitable compromise isn't possible. This design is included for illustration only, not as encouragement to attempt to construct similar models.

6.5 PRACTICAL ASPECTS OF PHASED ARRAY DESIGN

With almost any type of antenna system, there is much that can be learned from experimenting with, testing and using various array configurations. In this section, Roy Lewallen, W7EL, extends his contribution to this book, sharing the benefit of years of his experience from actually building, adjusting and using phased arrays. There is much more work to be done in most of the areas covered here, and Roy encourages the reader to build on this work.

6.5.1 ADJUSTING PHASED ARRAY FEED SYSTEMS

If a phased array is constructed only to achieve forward gain, adjusting it is seldom worthwhile. This is because the forward gain of most arrays is quite insensitive to either the magnitude or phase of the relative currents flowing in the elements. If, however, good rejection of unwanted signals is desired, adjustment may be required. And achieving very deep nulls will almost surely require some adjustment.

The in-phase and 180° out-of-phase current-forcing method supplies very well-balanced and well-phased currents to elements without adjustment. If the pattern of an array fed using this method is unsatisfactory, it's generally the result of environmental differences — where the elements, even though furnished with correct currents, aren't generating the correct fields. Such an array can be optimized in a single direction, but a more general approach than the current-forcing method must be taken. Some possibilities are described by Paul Lee and Forrest Gehrke (see Bibliography).

Unlike the current-forcing method, the "simplest" and L network feed systems described earlier in this chapter are dependent on the self and mutual impedance of one or more elements. The required transmission-line lengths or L network component values can be computed to a high level of precision, but the results are only as good as the knowledge of the relevant feed point impedances.

While the simplest feed system doesn't readily lend itself to adjustment, the components of an L network can easily be made adjustable or can be experimentally changed in increments. A practical approach is to model the array as accurately as possible, design and build the feed system based on the model results and then adjust the network for the best performance.

Simple arrays such as the two-element 90° fed and spaced array can be adjusted as follows. Place a low-power signal source at a distance from the array (preferably several wavelengths), in the direction a null should be. While listening to the signal on a receiver connected to the array, alternately adjust the two L network components for the best rejection of the signal.

This has proved to be a very good way to adjust 2-element arrays. However, variable results were obtained when a Four-Square array was adjusted using this technique. The probable reason is that more than one combination of current balance and phasing can produce a null in a given direction but each produces a different overall pattern. So a different method must be used for adjusting more complex arrays.

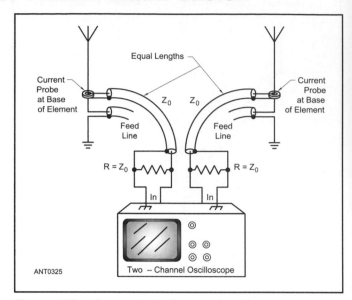

Figure 6.32 — One method of measuring element currents in a phased array. Details of the current probe are given in Figure 6.33. Caution: Do not run high power to the antenna system for this measurement, or damage to the test equipment may result.

This involves actually measuring the element currents in some way, and adjusting the network until the currents are correct. After adjusting the currents, small adjustments can be made to deepen the null(s) if desired.

Measuring Element Currents

You can measure the element currents two ways. One way is to measure them directly at the element feed points, as shown in **Figure 6.32**. A dual-channel oscilloscope is required to monitor the currents. This method is the most accurate and it provides a direct indication of the actual relative

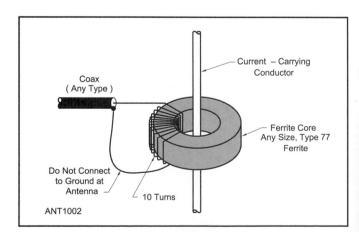

Figure 6.33 — The current probe for use in the test setup of Figure 6.32. The ferrite core is of type 77 ferrite or type 2 powdered iron and may be any size. The coax line must be terminated at the opposite end with a resistor equal to its characteristic impedance. You should build this probe in a plastic or metal box to provide mechanical ruggedness.

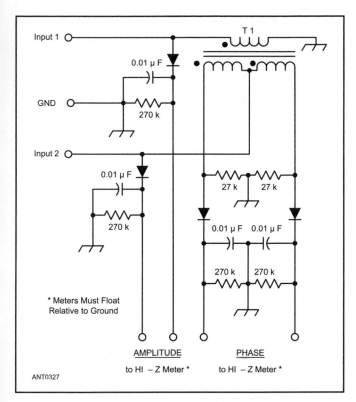

Figure 6.34 — Quadrature test circuit. All diodes are germanium, such as 1N34A, 1N270, or equiv. Hot carrier or silicon diodes can be used at higher power levels. All resistors are ¼ or ½ W, 5% tolerance. Capacitors are ceramic. Alligator clips are convenient for making the input and ground connections to the array.
T1 — 7 trifilar turns on an Amidon FT-37-43, -75, -77, or equivalent ferrite toroid core.

magnitudes and phases of the element currents. The current probe is shown in **Figure 6.33**. (Another current probe design by W8JI is presented at **www.w8ji.com/building_a_current_meter.htm**.)

Instead of measuring the element currents directly, you could measure them indirectly by measuring the voltages on the feed lines an electrical $\lambda/4$ or $3\lambda/4$ distance from the array. The voltages at these points are directly proportional to the element currents. This introduces additional variables that can reduce the accuracy of the result, but the method generally produces adequate performance. The 2-element arrays fed with the L network system and all the four-element arrays presented earlier have $\lambda/4$ or $3\lambda/4$ lines from all elements to a common location, making this second measurement method convenient. The voltages can be observed with a dual-channel oscilloscope, or, to adjust for equal-magnitude currents and 90° phasing, you can use the test circuit shown in **Figure 6.34**.

The test circuit is connected to the feed lines of two elements that are to be adjusted for 90° phasing (such as elements 1 and 2, or 2 and 4 of the Four-Square array of Figures 6.24 and 25). Adjust the L network components alternately until both meters read zero. Proper operation of the test circuit can be verified by disconnecting one of the inputs. The

phase output should remain close to zero. If not, there is an undesirable imbalance in the circuit, which must be corrected. Another means of verification is to first adjust the L network so the tester indicates correct phasing (zero volts at the phase output). Then reverse the tester input connections to the elements. The phase output should remain close to zero.

6.5.2 DIRECTIONAL SWITCHING OF ARRAYS

One ideal directional-switching method would take the entire feed system, including the lines to the elements and physically rotate it. The smallest possible increment of rotation would depend on the symmetry of the array — the feed system would need to rotate until the array again looks the same to it. For example, any 2-element array can be rotated 180° (although that wouldn't accomplish anything if the array is bidirectional to begin with). The 4-element rectangular array of Figures 6.28 and 29 can also be reversed, and the Four-Square array of Figures 6.24 and 25 can be switched in 90° increments.

Smaller switching increments can be accomplished only by reconfiguring the feed system, including any network if used, effectively creating a different kind of array. Switching in smaller increments than dictated by symmetry will create a different pattern in some directions than in others, and must be thoughtfully done to maintain equal and properly phased element currents. The methods illustrated here will deal only with switching in increments related to the array symmetry, except for one: a 2-element broadside/end-fire array.

In all arrays, the success of directional switching depends on the elements and ground systems being identical so that equal element currents result in equal fields. It's even more important in arrays fed with any method other than current forcing, because the effectiveness of those methods depends on the element feed point impedances. Few of us can afford the luxury of having an array many wavelengths away from all other conductors, so an array will nearly always perform somewhat differently in each direction. The array should be adjusted when steered in the direction requiring the most signal rejection in the nulls. Forward gain will, for all practical purposes, be equal in all the switched directions, since gain is much more tolerant of error than are nulls.

Basic Switching Methods

Following is a discussion of basic switching methods, how to power relays through the main feed line and other practical considerations. In diagrams, grounds are frequently omitted to aid clarity, but connections of the ground conductors must be carefully made. In fact, it is recommended that the ground conductors be switched just as the center conductors are, as explained in more detail in "Improving Array Switching Systems" below. In all cases, interconnecting lines must be very short.

A pair of elements spaced $\lambda/2$ apart can readily be switched between broadside and end-fire bidirectional patterns, using the current-forcing properties of $\lambda/4$ lines. The

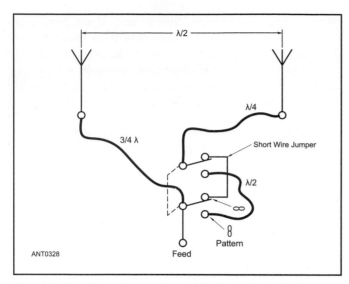

Figure 6.35 — Two-element broadside/end-fire switching. All lines must have the same characteristic impedance. Grounds and cable shields have been omitted for clarity.

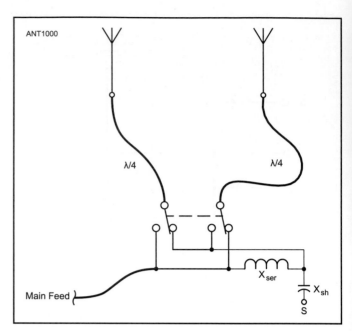

Figure 6.37 — Directional switching for 90°, 90° spaced 2-element array fed with an L network, current-forcing feed system.

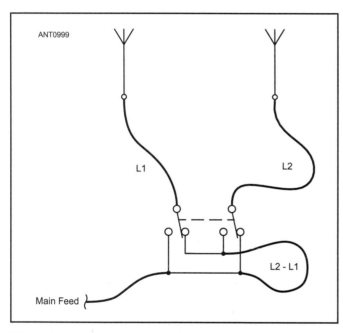

Figure 6.36 — Directional switching for 90°, 90° spaced 2-element array fed with a "simplest" feed system.

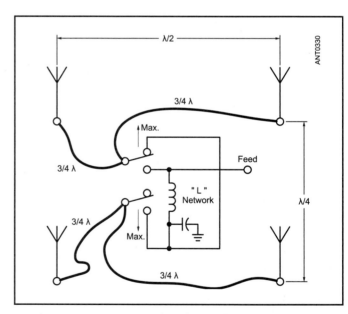

Figure 6.38 — Directional switching of a four-element rectangular array. All interconnections must be very short. As usual, grounds and cable shields have been omitted for clarity.

method is shown in **Figure 6.35**. The switching device can be a relay powered via a separate cable or by dc sent along the main feed line.

Figure 6.36 shows directional switching of a 90° fed, 90° spaced array fed with a "simplest" feed system, where L1 and L2 are the required lengths of the two feed lines. **Figure 6.37** shows how to switch the same array when fed with an L network, current-forcing system.

The rectangular array of Figure 6.28 can be switched in a similar manner, as shown in **Figure 6.38**. To switch a "simplest" fed rectangular array, use the switching circuit of Figure 6.36, but connect the two equal length lines to points

A and B of Figure 6.29 in place of the two elements shown in Figure 6.36.

Switching the direction of an array in increments of 90°, when permitted by symmetry, requires at least two relays. A method of 90° switching of the Four-Square array with L network feed is shown in **Figure 6.39**.

Powering Relays Through Feed Lines

All of the above switching methods can be implemented without additional wires to the switch box. A single-relay

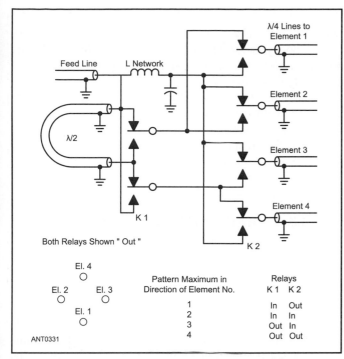

Figure 6.39 — Directional switching of the Four-Square array. All interconnections must be very short.

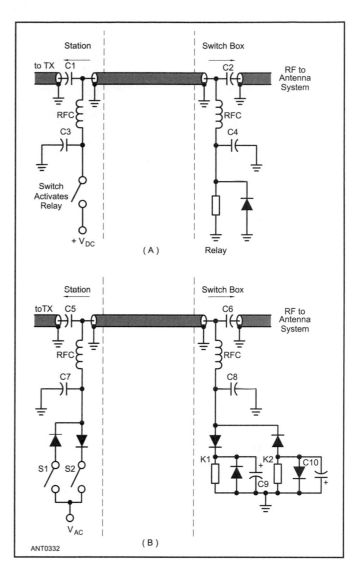

Figure 6.40 — Remote switching of relays. See text for component information. A one-relay system is shown at A, and a two-relay system at B. In B, S1 activates K1, and S2 activates K2. In addition, it is recommended to bypass each diode with a 0.001 - 0.01 µF disc ceramic capacitor to avoid generating harmonics and mixing products when transmitting.

system is shown in **Figure 6.40A**, and a two-relay system in Figure 6.40B. Small 12 or 24-V dc power relays can be used in either system at power levels up to at least a few hundred watts. Do not attempt to change directions while transmitting, however. Blocking capacitors C1 and C2 should be good quality ceramic or transmitting mica units of 0.01 to 0.1 µF. No problems have been encountered using 0.1 µF, 300-V monolithic ceramic units at RF output levels up to 300 W. C2 may be omitted if the antenna system is an open circuit at dc. C3 and C4 should be ceramic, 0.001 µF or larger.

In Figure 6.40B, capacitors C5 through C8 should be selected with the ratings of their counterparts in Figure 6.40A, as given above. Electrolytic capacitors across the relay coils, C9 and C10 in Figure 6.40B, should be large enough to prevent the relays from buzzing, but not so large as to make relay operation too slow. Final values for most relays will be in the range from 10 to 100 µF. They should have a voltage rating of at least double the relay coil voltage. Some relays do not require this capacitor. All diodes are 1N4001 or similar. A rotary switch may be used in place of the two toggle switches in the two-relay system to switch the relays in the desired sequence.

Improving Array-Switching Systems

The extra circuitry involved in switching arrays can degrade array performance by altering the relative currents fed to each element. One common cause is current sharing in common ground conductors, even when connections are kept very short. The author has seen a 30° phase shift in voltage along a 4-inch piece of #12 AWG wire in a 40 meter array feed system.

When the two conductors of a feed line are physically separated from each other the characteristic impedance increases. This is especially true when the main lines are coaxial cables. If currents from two elements share the ground conductor of a split line a relatively large voltage drop results. Voltage changes λ/4 from the elements translate to current changes at the elements. Although keeping all leads extremely short is sometimes adequate, the best way to reduce current sharing problems is to keep the two conductors of each transmission line as close together as possible, and switch both conductors of each line rather than just a single or "hot" conductor.

An example of a carefully designed switching system is shown in **Figure 6.41**. It avoids the problem of shared ground conductor currents, as well as another common problem, namely that effective line lengths are often different along different switching paths. Notice how the path from the main

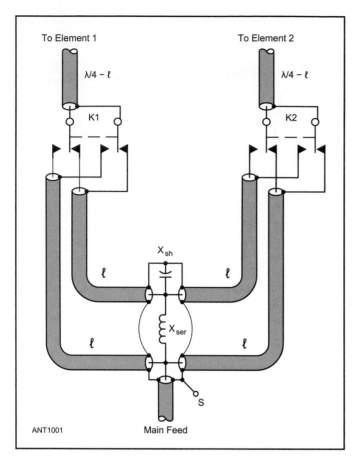

Figure 6.41 — A carefully designed L network, current-forcing switching system that switches both hot and shield conductors in feed coaxes.

feed point travels through a single line to each element with no common ground connections to other lines except at the main feed point. Notice also that the distance doesn't change as the direction is switched. The λ/4 lines going to the two elements must be shortened by the length ℓ of the lines on the feed side of the relays so that the total line length from the main feed point to each element is λ/4 (or 3λ/4).

You can see that in either relay position, there's an open ended stub of length ℓ connected at the main feed point and another at the output end of the L network. These will add capacitance at those points. Extra capacitance at the main feed point will alter the overall impedance seen by a transmitter, but won't otherwise have any effect on the array or its performance. The one at the output of the L network will, however, change the transformation and phase shift properties of the network. But it's easy to compensate — the value of the shunt capacitor element is simply reduced by the amount of capacitance added by the stub. The amount of capacitance for any kind of transmission line can be calculated from:

$$C\,(pF/ft) = \frac{1017}{Z_0\,VF}$$

or

$$C\,(pF/m) = \frac{3336}{Z_0\,VF}$$

where Z_0 = the characteristic impedance of the line and VF = the velocity factor. This works out to 31 pF/foot or 101 pF/meter for 50-Ω solid polyethylene insulated coax which has a velocity factor of 0.66.

The general principles illustrated in Figure 6.41 can be extended to other switching systems. If switching the ground conductors as described above isn't practical, use of a metal box for the switching circuitry is recommended, so that the relatively large surface area of the box can be used for the common ground conductors, minimizing their inductance. Always keep leads extremely short.

6.5.3 MEASURING THE ELECTRICAL LENGTH OF FEED LINES

When using the feed methods described earlier the feed lines must be very close to the correct length. For best results, they should be correct within 1% or so. This means that a line that is intended to be, say, λ/4 at 7 MHz, should actually be λ/4 at some frequency within 70 kHz of 7 MHz. A simple but accurate method to determine at what frequency a line is λ/4 or λ/2 is shown in **Figure 6.42A**. The far end of the line is short circuited with a very short connection. A signal

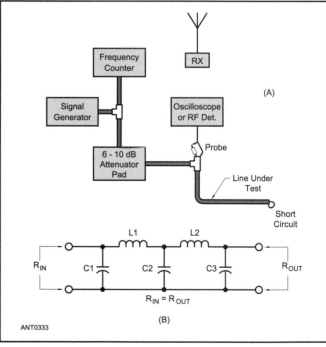

Figure 6.42 — At A, the setup for measurement of the electrical length of a transmission line. The receiver may be used in place of the frequency counter to determine the frequency of the signal generator. The signal generator output must be free of harmonics; the half-wave harmonic filter at B may be used outboard if there is any doubt. It must be constructed for the frequency band of operation. Connect the filter between the signal generator and the attenuator pad.
C1, C3 — Value to have a capacitive reactance = R_{IN}.
C2 — Value to have a capacitive reactance = ½ R_{IN}.
L1, L2 — Value to have an inductive reactance = R_{IN}.

is applied to the input and the frequency is swept until the impedance at the input is a minimum. This is the frequency at which the line is λ/2. Either the frequency counter or the receiver may be used to determine this frequency. The line is, of course, λ/4 at one half the measured frequency.

The detector can be a simple diode detector or an oscilloscope may be used if available. A 6 to 10 dB attenuator pad is included to prevent the signal generator from looking into a short circuit at the measurement frequency. The signal generator output must be free of harmonics. If there is any doubt, an outboard low-pass filter, such as a half-wave harmonic filter, should be used. The half-wave filter circuit is shown in Figure 6.42B, and must be constructed for the frequency band of operation.

Another satisfactory method is to use a noise or resistance bridge or antenna analyzer at the input of the line, again looking for a low impedance at the input while the output is short circuited. Simple resistance bridges are described in the **Antenna and Transmission Line Measurements** chapter.

Dip oscillators have been found to be unsatisfactory. The required coupling loop has too great an effect on measurements.

6.5.4 MEASURING ELEMENT SELF AND MUTUAL IMPEDANCES

The need for measuring element self and mutual impedances has been made largely unnecessary with the ready availability of modeling software. Few amateurs appreciate the considerable difficulty of making accurate impedance measurements and accurate mutual impedance measurements are very difficult even with professional test equipment and skills. Despite the limitations of computer modeling, results very often are better than measured values because of the multiple factors affecting measurement accuracy.

Those who are interested in measuring self and mutual impedances can find more detailed information about doing so in Appendix B on this book's CD. The information there is from earlier editions of *Antenna Book*.

6.6 BIBLIOGRAPHY

Source material and more extended discussion of topics covered in this chapter can be found in the references given below and in the textbooks listed at the end of the **Antenna Fundamentals** chapter.

D. W. Atchley, H. E. Stinehelfer, and J. F. White, "360°-Steerable Vertical Phased Arrays," *QST*, Apr 1976, pp 27-30.

G. H. Brown, "Directional Antennas," *Proc. IRE*, Vol 25, No. 1, Jan 1937, pp 78-145.

G. H. Brown, R. F. Lewis and J. Epstein, "Ground Systems as a Factor in Antenna Efficiency," *Proc. IRE*, Jun 1937, pp 753-787.

G. H. Brown and O. M. Woodward, Jr., "Experimentally Determined Impedance Characteristics of Cylindrical Antennas," *Proc. IRE*, Apr 1945.

L. B. Cebik, "Two Limitations of NEC-4", **www.cebik. com/model/fd.html**.

A. Christman, "Feeding Phased Arrays: An Alternate Method," *Ham Radio*, May 1985, pp 58-59, 61-64.

J. Devoldere, *ON4UN's Low-Band DXing*, 5th ed. (Newington, CT: ARRL, 2010).

EZNEC is an antenna-modeling computer program for Microsoft *Windows*. See **www.eznec.com** for full information.

F. Gehrke, "Vertical Phased Arrays," in six parts, *Ham Radio*, May-Jul, Oct and Dec 1983, and May 1984.

C. Harrison, Jr, and R. King, "Theory of Coupled Folded Antennas," *IRE Trans on Antennas and Propagation*, Mar 1960, pp131-135.

W. Hayward and D. DeMaw, *Solid State Design for the Radio Amateur* (Newington, CT: ARRL, 1977).

W. Hayward, *Radio Frequency Design* (Newington, CT: ARRL, 1994).

H. Jasik, *Antenna Engineering Handbook*, 1st ed. (New York: McGraw-Hill, 1961). Later editions are edited by Richard C. Johnson.

R. King and C. Harrison, Jr, "Mutual and Self-Impedance for Coupled Antennas," *Journal of Applied Physics*, Vol 15, Jun 1944, pp 481-495.

R. King, "Self- and Mutual Impedances of Parallel Identical Antennas," *Proc. IRE*, Aug 1952, pp 981-988.

R. W. P. King, *Theory of Linear Antennas* (Cambridge, MA: Harvard Univ Press, 1956), p 275ff.

H. W. Kohler, "Antenna Design for Field-Strength Gain," *Proc. IRE*, Oct 1944, pp 611-616.

J. D. Kraus, "Antenna Arrays with Closely Spaced Elements," *Proc. IRE*, Feb, 1940, pp 76-84.

J. D. Kraus, *Antennas*, 2nd ed. (New York: McGraw-Hill Book Co, 1988).

Johnson, Richard C., *Antenna Engineering Handbook*, 3rd ed. (New York: McGraw-Hill Inc, 1993). This is a later edition of the volume by the same name edited by H. Jasik.

E. A. Laport, *Radio Antenna Engineering* (New York: McGraw-Hill Book Co, 1952).

J. L. Lawson, "Simple Arrays of Vertical Antenna Elements," *QST*, May 1971, pp 22-27.

P. H. Lee, *The Amateur Radio Vertical Antenna Handbook*, 2nd ed. (Hicksville, NY: CQ Publishing, Inc., 1984).

R. W. Lewallen, "Baluns: What They Do and How They Do It," *The ARRL Antenna Compendium, Vol 1* (Newington: ARRL, 1985). Also available for viewing at **www.eznec. com/Amateur/Articles/Baluns.pdf**.

R. Lewallen, "The Impact of Current Distribution on Array Patterns," Technical Correspondence, *QST*, Jul 1990, pp 39-40. Also available for viewing at **www.eznec.com/Amateur/Articles/Current_Dist.pdf**.

R. Lewallen, "*MININEC* — The Other Edge of the Sword," *QST*, Feb 1991, pp 18-22. *ELNEC*, referenced in the article, is no longer available.

M. W. Maxwell, "Some Aspects of the Balun Problem," *QST*, Mar 1983, pp 38-40.

J. Sevick, "The Ground-Image Vertical Antenna," *QST*, Jul 1971, pp 16-19, 22.

J. Sevick, "The W2FMI Ground-Mounted Short Vertical," *QST*, Mar 1973, pp 13-28,41.

E. J. Wilkinson, "An N-Way Hybrid Power Divider," *IRE Transactions on Microwave Theory and Techniques*, Jan, 1960.

Radio Broadcast Ground Systems, available from Smith Electronics, Inc, 8200 Snowville Rd, Cleveland, OH 44141.

APPENDIX A — *EZNEC-ARRL* EXAMPLES

This appendix contains step-by-step procedures using *EZNEC-ARRL* (included on the *Antenna Book* CD) to illustrate various topics discussed in the main chapter. A standard *EZNEC* program type of v. 4.0 or later may also be used. Different versions, program types and calculating engines may give results that are slightly different from those shown in the examples. However, any differences should be insignificantly small.

EZNEC Example — Mutual Coupling

This example illustrates the effect of mutual coupling on feed point impedance. Open the **ARRL_Cardioid.EZ** file, which is mounted over "perfect" ground. Click the VIEW ANT button to see a diagram of the antenna, a 2-element array of vertical elements. Click on the WIRES line in the main window to open the Wires Window. Click the button at the left of the Wire 2 line, and then press the DELETE key on your keyboard to delete wire #2. After clicking OK, note that one of the verticals has disappeared from the View Antenna display, leaving a single element. Click SRC DAT and note that the feed point impedance of this single vertical is about $37 + j\,1\,\Omega$ — it's very nearly resonant.

Next, in the Wires Window, open the EDIT menu at the top and click UNDO DELETE WIRE(S) to restore the second element. Click SRC DAT again and notice that the feed point impedance of wire #1 is now about $21 - j\,19\,\Omega$. The feed point impedance of the second element, which is identical to the first, is about $52 + j\,21\,\Omega$. This difference, and the change from the self-impedance of $37 + j\,1\,\Omega$, is due to mutual coupling. As you see, it's not at all a minor effect.

As an additional exercise, change the magnitude or phase angle of the source at the base of wire #2 (click SOURCES in the main window), and see how this changes the feed point impedances of both elements. You should be able to confirm each of the four points enumerated in the "Mutual Coupling" section.

EZNEC Example — Nulls

This example illustrates the effect of current magnitude on nulls and gain. Again, open the **ARRL_Cardioid.EZ** file. Click the FF PLOT button to generate the azimuth pattern of an ideal array. Save the plot for future reference as follows: In the plot window, open the FILE menu and select SAVE TRACE AS. Enter the name CARDIOID and click SAVE. Now, in the main window click on the SOURCES line to open the Sources Window. Change the magnitude of source 1 from 1 to 1.1, and of source 2 from 1 to 0.9 and press ENTER on your keyboard so that *EZNEC-ARRL* will accept the last change.

Click FF PLOT to generate a pattern with the new currents. In the plot window, open the File menu and select ADD TRACE. Enter the name CARDIOID and click Open. You should now see the original plot and new plot overlaid. Notice that the null is much less deep with the altered currents, but the forward patterns are nearly identical. By clicking on the names of the traces, PRIMARY and CARDIOID, you can see in turn the gain and front-to-back ratio of each of the traces. The original, CARDIOID, has a front-to-back ratio of about 32 dB, while Primary, the new plot, has a ratio of about 22.5 dB. The forward gain, however, differs by only 0.02 dB, a completely insignificant amount.

EZNEC Example — "Phasing-Line" Feed

This example illustrates the effect of using a "phasing-line" feed. Open the **ARRL_CardTL.EZ** file. This is a model of an array fed with transmission lines whose lengths were designed using the *Arrayfeed1* program to take into account the actual load impedances of elements in a phased array. This model is mounted over "perfect" ground.

Click the VIEW ANT button to show the array. Note that the lengths of the lines from the source (circle) to the elements don't represent the actual physical lengths of the lines. In the main window, click on the TRANS LINES line to open the Transmission Lines window. In it you can see that the lengths of the feed lines, both of which are connected to the same source, are about 81° and 155°, a difference of 74° rather than 90°.

In the main window, click the CURRENTS button and take a look at the current shown for segment 1 of wires 1 and 2. These are the currents at the element feed points. The ratio of the magnitude of currents is 4.577/4.561 = 1.003, and the phase difference is −56.3°−(−147.5°) = 91.2°. (A more accurate determination of feed line lengths with program *Arrayfeed1* gives lengths of 80.61° and 153.70°, resulting in a current ratio of 1.000 at a phase of 90.02°. But the resulting pattern is very nearly the same.) But let's see what happens when we make the lines exactly 90° different in length.

First, click the FF PLOT button to generate the azimuth pattern of the original model. Save the plot for future reference as follows: In the plot window, open the FILE menu and select SAVE TRACE AS. Enter the name CARDTL and click SAVE. Now in the Transmission Lines Window, change the length of line number 1 from 80.56° to 90°. *Important:* In the line 1 Length box, enter 90D to make the line 90° long. If you omit the "d," it will become 90 meters long! Similarly, change the length of line 2 to 180° by entering 180D in the line 2 Length box, then press ENTER on your keyboard so that *EZNEC* will accept the last change.

Click FF PLOT to generate a pattern with the new line lengths. In the plot window, open the FILE menu and select ADD TRACE. Enter the name CARDTL and click OPEN. You should now see the original plot and new plot overlaid together. Notice that the gain of the modified model is about 1 dB greater than the original but the front-to-back ratio has deteriorated to about 10 dB.

Experiment with different combinations of line lengths that differ by 90°—for example, 45° and 135° (don't forget the 'd'!), or change the impedance of one or both lines and you'll see that you can get a wide variety of patterns. None, however, are likely to be as close to the ideal cardioid pattern as the original.

TABLE OF CONTENTS

Chapter 7

Log-Periodic Dipole Arrays

Log Periodic Dipole Array (*LPDA*) is one of a family of frequency-independent antennas. The LPDA forms a directional antenna with relatively constant characteristics across a wide frequency range. It may also be used with parasitic elements to achieve specific characteristics within a narrow frequency range. Common names for such hybrid arrays are the *log-cell Yagi* or the *Log-Yagi*. (Information on the log-cell Yagi is available on this book's CD-ROM.) Designs for log-periodic antennas at HF and VHF-UHF are presented in the **Multiband HF Antennas** and **VHF and UHF Antenna Systems** chapters. This chapter was contributed originally by L. B. Cebik, W4RNL (SK), with additional contributions from John Stanley, K4ERO.

7.1 BASIC LPDA DESIGN

The LPDA is the most popular form of log-periodic systems which also include zigzag, planar, trapezoidal, slot, and V forms. The appeal of the LPDA version of the log periodic antenna owes much to its structural similarity to the Yagi-Uda parasitic array. This permits the construction of directional LPDAs that can be rotated — at least within the upper HF and higher frequency ranges. Nevertheless, the LPDA has special structural as well as design considerations that distinguish it from the Yagi. Different construction techniques for both wire and tubular elements are illustrated later in this chapter.

The LPDA in its present form derives from the pioneering work of D. E. Isbell at the University of Illinois in the late 1950s. Although you may design LPDAs for large frequency ranges — for example, from 3 to 30 MHz or a little over 3 octaves — the most common LPDA designs that radio amateurs use are limited to a one-octave range, usually from 14 to 30 MHz. Amateur designs for this range tend to consist of linear elements. However, experimental designs for lower frequencies have used elements shaped like inverted Vs and some versions use vertically oriented ¼-λ elements over a ground system.

Figure 7.1 shows the parts of a typical LPDA. The structure consists of a number of linear elements, the longest of which is approximately ½ λ long at the lowest design frequency. The shortest element is usually about ½ λ long at a frequency well above the highest operating frequency. The antenna feeder, also informally called the *phase-line*, connects the center points of each element in the series, with a

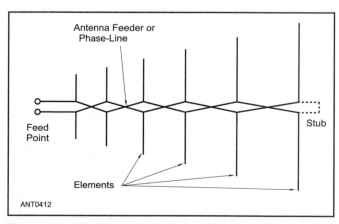

Figure 7.1 — The basic components of a log periodic dipole array (LPDA). The forward direction is to the left in this sketch. Many variations of the basic design are possible.

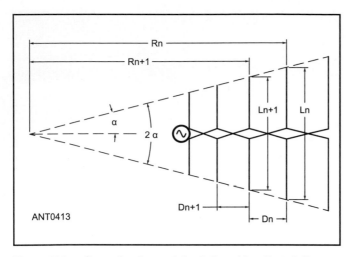

Figure 7.2 — Some fundamental relationships that define an array as an LPDA. See the text for the defining equations.

phase reversal or *crossover* between each element. A stub consisting of a shorted length of parallel-wire feed line is often added at the back of an LPDA.

The arrangement of elements and the method of feed yield an array with relatively constant gain and front-to-back ratio across the designed operating range. In addition, the LPDA exhibits a relatively constant feed point impedance, simplifying matching to a transmission line.

For the amateur designer, the most fundamental facets of the LPDA revolve around three interrelated design variables: α (alpha), τ (tau), and σ (sigma). Any one of the three variables may be defined by reference to the other two.

Figure 7.2 shows the basic components of an LPDA. The angle α defines the outline of an LPDA and permits every dimension to be treated as a radius or the consequence of a radius (R) of a circle. The most basic structural dimensions are the element lengths (L), the distance (R) of each

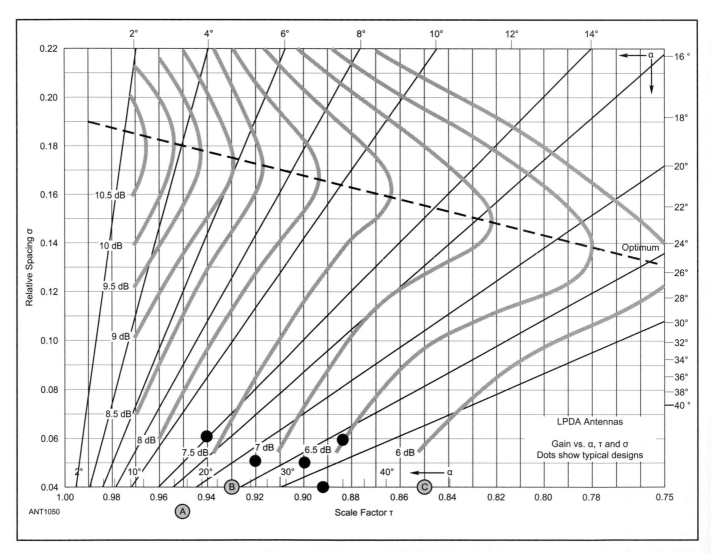

Figure 7.3 — The optimum value for σ lies on the straight line that intersects the constant-gain curves at different values of τ. Using the optimum value of σ to design an LPDA usually results in antenna that is impractically large at HF (see text). Points labeled "A", "B", and "C" represent values of σ and τ are given for the three design examples in this chapter; "9302", "8904", and "8504", respectively. (Graphic after Carrel, et al; see Bibliography.)

element from the apex of angle α, and the distance between elements (D). A single design constant, τ, defines all of these relationships in the following manner:

$$\tau = \frac{R_{n+1}}{R_n} = \frac{D_{n+1}}{D_n} = \frac{L_{n+1}}{L_n} \qquad (1)$$

where element n and n+1 are successive elements in the array working toward the apex of angle α. The value of τ is always less than 1.0 although effective LPDA design requires values as close to 1.0 as may be feasible.

The variable τ defines the relationship between successive element spacings but it does not itself determine the initial spacing between the longest and next longest elements upon which to apply τ successively. The initial spacing also defines the angle α for the array. Hence, we have two ways to determine the value of σ, the relative spacing constant:

$$\sigma = \frac{1-\tau}{4\tan\alpha} = \frac{D_n}{2L_n} \qquad (2)$$

where D_n is the distance between any two elements of the array and L_n is the length of the longer of the two elements. From the first of the two methods of determining the value of σ, we may also find a means of determining α when we know both τ and σ.

For any value of τ, we may determine the optimal value of σ:

$$\sigma_{opt} = 0.243\tau - 0.051 \qquad (3)$$

The combination of a value for τ and its corresponding optimal value of σ yields the highest performance of which an LPDA is capable. For values of τ from 0.80 through 0.98, the value of optimal σ varies from 0.143 to 0.187, in increments of 0.00243 for each 0.01 change in τ. This is illustrated by the graph in **Figure 7.3**, originally published by Carrel and updated by Butson and Thompson (see the Bibliography).

Practically however, using the optimal value of σ usually yields a total array length that is beyond amateur construction or tower/mast support capabilities. A design procedure more likely to result in a useful design at HF is to reduce σ until maximum gain begins to fall significantly. Consequently, amateur LPDAs usually employ compromise values of τ and σ that yield lesser but acceptable performance. The sidebar "Determining LPDA Design Parameters Quickly" shows how to arrive at acceptable values of τ and σ for use in *LPCAD* and similar software.

For a given frequency range, increasing the value of τ increases both the gain and the number of required elements. Increasing the value of σ increases both the gain and the overall boom length. A τ of 0.96 — which approaches the upper maximum recommended value for τ — yields an optimal σ of about 0.18, and the resulting array grows to over 100 feet long for the 14 to 30 MHz range. The maximum free space gain is about 11 dBi, with a front-to-back ratio that approaches 40 dB. Normal amateur practice, however, uses values of τ from about 0.88 to 0.95 and values of σ from about 0.03 to 0.06.

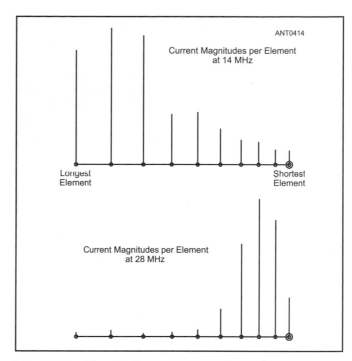

Figure 7.4 — The relative current magnitude on the elements of an LPDA at the lowest and highest operating frequencies for a given design. Compare the number of "active" elements, that is, those with current levels at least ¹⁄₁₀ of the highest level.

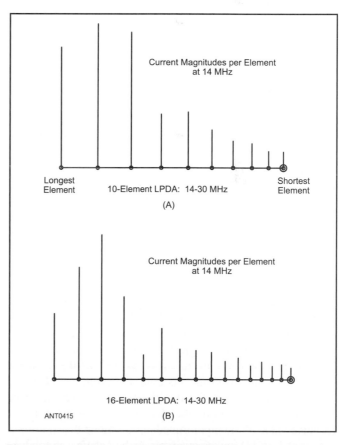

Figure 7.5 — Patterns of current magnitude at the lowest operating frequency of two different LPDA designs: a 10-element low-τ design and a 16-element higher-τ design.

Standard design procedures usually assign to the rear element a resonant frequency about 7% lower than the lowest design frequency with a physical length 5% lower than a free-space half wavelength. The upper frequency limit of the design is ordinarily set at about 1.3 times the highest design frequency. Since τ and σ set the increment between successive element lengths, the number of elements becomes a function of when the shortest element reaches the dipole length for the adjusted upper frequency.

The adjusted upper frequency limit results from the behavior of LPDAs with respect to the number of active elements. See **Figure 7.4**, which shows an edge view of a 10-element LPDA for 20 through 10 meters. The vertical lines represent the peak relative current magnitude for each element at the specified frequency. At 14 MHz, virtually every element of the array shows a significant current magnitude. However, at 28 MHz, only the forward 5 elements carry significant current. Without the extended design range to nearly 40 MHz, the number of elements with significant current levels would be severely reduced, along with upper frequency performance.

The need to extend the design equations below the lowest proposed operating frequency varies with the value of τ. In **Figure 7.5**, we can compare the current on the rear elements of two LPDAs, both with a σ value of 0.04. The upper design uses a τ of 0.89, while the lower design uses a value of 0.93. The most significant current-bearing element moves forward with increases in τ, reducing (but not wholly eliminating) the need for elements whose lengths are longer than a dipole for the lowest operating frequency.

7.1.1 LPDA DESIGN AND COMPUTERS

Originally, LPDA design proceeded through a series of design equations intended to yield the complete specifications for an array. More recent techniques available to radio amateurs include basic LPDA design software and antenna modeling software. One good example of LPDA design software is *LPCAD* by Roger Cox, WBØDGF, available for downloading from **wb0dgf.com/LPCAD.htm**. The user begins by specifying the lowest and highest frequencies in the design. The user then selects values for τ and σ or choices for the number of elements and the total length of the array. With this and other input data, the program provides a table of element lengths and spacings, using the adjusted upper and lower frequency limits described earlier. (A spreadsheet to assist with performing the calculations in this chapter was contributed by Dennis Miller, KM9O, and is available for downloading from **www.arrl.org/antenna-book**.)

The program also requests the diameters of the longest and shortest elements in the array, as well as the diameter of average element. From this data, the program calculates a recommended value for the characteristic impedance of the phase-line connecting the elements and the approximate resistive value of the input impedance. Among the additional data that *LPCAD* makes available is the spacing of conductors to achieve the desired characteristic impedance of the phase-line. These conductors may be round — as we would

Determining LPDA Design Parameters Quickly

LPCAD provides a very efficient method of arriving at a preliminary design for an LPDA. When using the program, it is much faster to use the boom length and number of elements input method rather than the τ and σ data entry method. Those parameters will be calculated along with all dimensions. For those wishing to better understand the trade-offs or who wish to use the formulas in this chapter to calculate all dimensions, the following procedure will help you to arrive at starting values of τ and σ that will make your progress towards a final design much more rapid.

The first consideration is the frequency range to be covered. Many ham LPDA designs cover about a 2:1 frequency range, for example, 14 to 29 MHz. Extending the high end of the frequency range adds little to the size and cost and can smooth out operation at the higher frequencies of interest. An LPDA with an 8:1 range will be only 1.8 times longer than an antenna with a 2:1 range, while the frequency range is 4 times more. However, use of a very wideband LPDA only at its high frequency end means most of the size and weight of the antenna is wasted since the largest parts of the antenna are inactive. Covering only the desired frequencies reduces boom length. **Figure 7.A** illustrates the different sizes of arrays having the same gain but different frequency coverage.

The lowest frequency determines the longest element length, which will be somewhat more than ½ wavelength at that frequency. An approximate length in feet can be gotten by dividing 500 by the frequency in MHz. This dimension is pretty much fixed, although in some large designs it is reduced somewhat by inductive or capacitive loading of the lowest frequency elements.

The boom length is the next logical parameter to be determined and will be based on what you can afford to build, raise, support and rotate versus the performance to be expected for various boom options. For a given frequency ratio — the longer the boom, the higher the gain. **Figure 7.B** will give

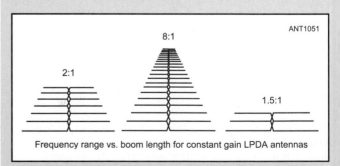

Frequency range vs. boom length for constant gain LPDA antennas

Figure 7.A — Comparison of boom length for several LPDA designs with the same gain but different ratios of maximum to minimum frequency coverage.

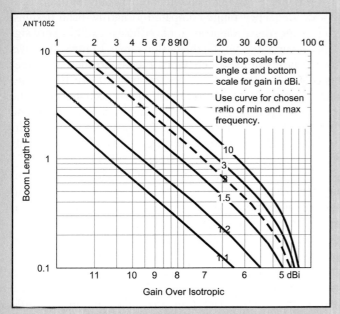

Figure 7.B — A chart relating gain, boom length factor, and α.

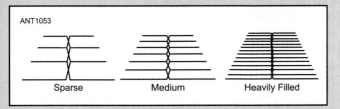

Figure 7.C — Illustration of sparse to heavily filled arrays.

some guidance as to the gain to be expected for a given boom length. The boom length factor (BLF) represents the boom length compared to the length of the longest element. As a rough rule of thumb, each doubling of the boom length will add about 1 dB of gain. Beyond a certain point, doubling the boom length to add 1 dB will be uneconomical. Keeping the boom to a reasonable length means accepting either a reduced frequency range or a lower gain.

Once a boom length is chosen, based on a trade-off between mechanical limits and the desired gain value and frequency range ratio, we can also read off the angle using this same graph, since gain is closely associated with α.

Once α is determined along with the frequency coverage, the shape and size of the antenna is defined. We must now decide how to fill up this outlined shape with elements. In other words, determine the number, length and spacing of the elements. The chart of Figure 7.3 is useful in this. This chart plots gain as a function of τ, σ and α. The α values are represented by the slanted lines between the marked degree values on the chart. Since we have determined the desired value of α, we can use that value to choose values of τ and σ.

For a given α value (dashed slanted lines), follow the corresponding line diagonally along and you will see the lower part of the line lies more or less parallel to a constant gain curve. The portion of a constant-α line on the bottom left represents a heavily filled array (more elements, closely spaced) while upper right portion of the constant, a line represents a sparsely filled array (fewer elements). (**see Figure 7.C**)

Notice that as the number of elements decreases (moving right and upwards on the constant-α gain may fluctuate a bit but will reach a point where it quickly falls off as you cross the "optimum σ" line. Values above this line represents a design that has too few elements to realize good performance. The interpretation of this "optimum σ" value is not obvious and perhaps its name was poorly chosen. It may be intended to give the value of σ for maximum gain for a given value of τ. However, this approach disregards the boom length factor. Designs that first choose τ and then use the optimum σ will be outrageously long — of course they will have high gain!

For a given antenna outline (length vs. width or constant-α) "optimum σ" is optimum only in that it indicates the point where further reduction in the number of elements will cause the gain to drop off. Thus, it gives a design with the least number of elements for a given gain. However, this design will not have the smoothest gain and SWR vs. frequency and the F/B ratio may be inadequate. For this reason, very few practical designs fall near the "optimum σ" line. All of the designs in this chapter fall well below the "optimum σ" as shown by the dots on the chart.

For designs with a higher α value, the gain should increase a bit with the more heavily filled arrays. Very narrow (long boom) arrays may have less gain if too heavily filled. It is not wise to approach the "optimum σ" line too closely in an attempt to reduce the element number. On the other hand, designs too far down the sloping a curve will be more expensive to build and will have greater wind load due to having more elements than necessary.

Having selected from the chart some τ and σ combinations that give us the design we want, we can now use software such as *LPCAD* to generate a detailed design using those values of τ and σ. This should result in a boom length fairly close to that desired. A second pass through the program may use the exact boom length desired and the number of elements calculated in the first pass, plus or minus one element. The program will then give us all of the mechanical dimensions, and also generate files for *NEC* analysis. Alternatively, we can proceed with the manual method given elsewhere in this chapter. If using that method we should come out close to the desired design on the first try and avoid multiple guesses as to where to start.

Several different designs that are close to that desired should be prepared as *NEC* files and an analysis done using *NEC*. This may show that a sparsely filled array may have excessive variation of gain and SWR vs. frequency or an inadequate F/B ratio or have other problems such as a weakness on an important frequency.
— *John Stanley, K4ERO*

use for a wire phase-line — or square — as we might use for double-boom construction.

An additional vital output from *LPCAD* is the conversion of the design into antenna modeling input files of several formats, including versions for *AO* and *NEC4WIN* (both *MININEC*-based programs), and a version in the standard **.NEC* format usable by many implementations of *NEC-2* and *NEC-4*, including *NECWin Plus*, *GNEC*, and *EZNEC Pro*. Every proposed LPDA design should be verified and optimized by means of antenna modeling, since basic design calculations rarely provide arrays that require no further work before construction. Moreover, some of the design equations are based upon approximations and do not completely predict LPDA behavior. Despite these limitations, most of the sample LPDA designs shown later in this chapter are based directly upon the fundamental calculations.

Modeling LPDA designs is most easily done on a version of *NEC*. The transmission line (TL) facility built into *NEC-2* and *NEC-4* alleviates the problem of modeling the phase-line as a set of physical wires, each section of which has a set of constraints in *MININEC* at the right-angle junctions with the elements. Although the *NEC* TL facility does not account for losses in the lines, the losses are ordinarily low enough to neglect.

NEC models do require some careful construction to obtain the most accurate results. Foremost among the cautions is the need for careful segmentation, since each element has a different length. The shortest element should have about 9 or 11 segments, so that it has sufficient segments at the highest modeling frequency for the design. Each element behind the shortest one should have a greater number of segments than the preceding element by the inverse of the value of τ. However, there is a further limitation. Since the transmission line is at the center of each element, *NEC* elements should have an odd number of segments to hold the phase-line centered. Hence, each segmentation value calculated from the inverse of τ must be rounded up to the nearest odd integer.

Initial modeling of LPDAs in *NEC-2* should be done with uniform-diameter elements, with any provision for stepped-diameter element correction turned off. Since these correction factors apply only to elements within about 15% of dipole resonance at the test frequency, models with stepped-diameter elements will correct for only a few elements at any test frequency. The resulting combination of corrected and uncorrected elements will not yield a model with assured reliability.

Once one has achieved a satisfactory model with uniform-diameter elements, the modeling program can be used to calculate stepped-diameter substitutes. Each uniform-diameter element, when extracted from the larger array, will have a resonant frequency. Once this frequency is determined, the stepped-diameter element to be used in final construction can be resonated to the same frequency. Although *NEC-4* handles stepped diameter elements with much greater accuracy than *NEC-2*, the process just described is also applicable to *NEC-4* models for the greatest precision.

7.1.2 LPDA BEHAVIOR

Although LPDA behavior is remarkably uniform over a wide frequency range compared to narrow-band designs, such as the Yagi-Uda array, it nevertheless exhibits very significant variations within the design range. **Figure 7.6** shows several facets of these behaviors. Figure 7.6 shows the free-space gain for three LPDA designs using 0.5-inch diameter aluminum elements. The designations for each model list the values of τ (0.93, 0.89, and 0.85) and of σ (0.02, 0.04, and 0.06) used to design each array. The resultant array lengths are listed with each designator. The total number of elements varies from 16 for "9302" to 10 for "8904" to 7 for "8504."

First, the gain is never uniform across the entire frequency span. The gain tapers off at both the low and high ends of the design spectrum. Moreover, the amount of gain undulates across the spectrum, with the number of peaks dependent upon the selected value of τ and the resultant number of elements. The front-to-back ratio tends to follow the gain level. In general, it ranges from less than 10 dB when the free-space gain is below 5 dBi to over 20 dB as the gain approaches 7 dBi. The front-to-back ratio may reach the high 30 dBs when the free-space array gain exceeds 8.5 dBi. Well-designed arrays, especially those with high values of τ and σ, tended to have well-controlled rear patterns that result in only small differences between the 180° front-to-back ratio and the averaged front-to-rear ratio.

Since array gain is a mutual function of both τ and σ, average gain becomes a function of array length for any given frequency range. Although the gain curves in Figure 7.6 interweave, there is little to choose among them in terms of average gain for the 14 to 18-foot range of array lengths. Well-designed 20 to 10 meter arrays in the 30-foot array length region are capable of about 7 dBi free-space gain, while 40-foot arrays for the same frequency range can achieve about 8 dBi free-space gain.

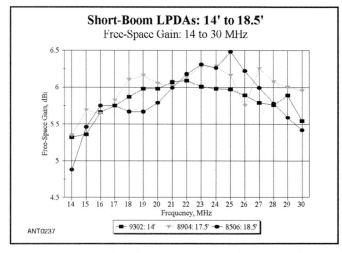

Figure 7.6 — The modeled free-space gain of three relatively small LPDAs of different design. Note the relationship of the values of τ and of σ for these arrays with quite similar performance across the 14-30 MHz span.

Exceeding an average gain of 8.5 dBi requires at least a 50-foot array length for this frequency range. Long arrays with high values of τ and σ also tend to show smaller excursions of gain and of front-to-back ratio in the overall curves. In addition, high-τ designs tend to show higher gain at the low frequency end of the design spectrum.

The frequency sweeps shown in Figure 7.6 are widely spaced at 1 MHz intervals. The evaluation of a specific design for the 14 to 30-MHz range should decrease the interval between check points to no greater than 0.25 MHz in order to detect frequencies at which the array may show a *performance weakness*. Weaknesses are frequency regions in the overall design spectrum at which the array shows unexpectedly lower values of gain and front-to-back ratio. In Figure 7.6 note the unexpected decrease in gain of model "8904" at 26 MHz. The other designs also have weak points, but they fall between the frequencies sampled.

In large arrays, these regions may be quite small and may occur in more than one frequency region. The weakness results from the harmonic operation of longer elements to the rear of those expected to have high current levels. Consider a 7-element LPDA with a boom about 12.25-feet long for 14 to 30 MHz using 0.5-inch aluminum elements. At 28 MHz, the rear elements operate in a harmonic mode as shown by the high relative current magnitude curves in **Figure 7.7**. The result is a radical decrease in gain, as shown in the "No Stub" curve of **Figure 7.8**. The front-to-back ratio also drops as a result of strong radiation from the long elements to the rear of the array.

Early designs of LPDAs called for terminating transmission-line stubs as standard practice to help eliminate such weak spots in frequency coverage. In contemporary designs, their use tends to be more specific for eliminating or moving frequencies that show gain and front-to-back weakness. (Stubs have the added function of keeping both sides of each element at the same dc level of static charge or discharge.) The model dubbed "8504" was fitted (by trial and error) with an 18-inch shorted stub of 600-Ω transmission line. As Figure 7.7B shows, the harmonic operation of the rear elements is attenuated. The "stub" curve of Figure 7.8 shows the smoothing of the gain curve for the array throughout the upper half of its design spectrum. In some arrays showing multiple weaknesses, a single stub may not eliminate all of them. However, it may move the weaknesses to unused frequency regions. Where full-spectrum operation of an LPDA is necessary, additional stubs located at specific elements may be needed.

Most LPDA designs benefit (with respect to gain and front-to-back ratio) from the use of larger-diameter elements. Elements with an average diameter of at least 0.5-inch are desirable in the 14 to 30 MHz range. However, standard designs usually presume a constant element length-to-diameter ratio. In the case of *LPCAD*, this ratio is about 125:1, which

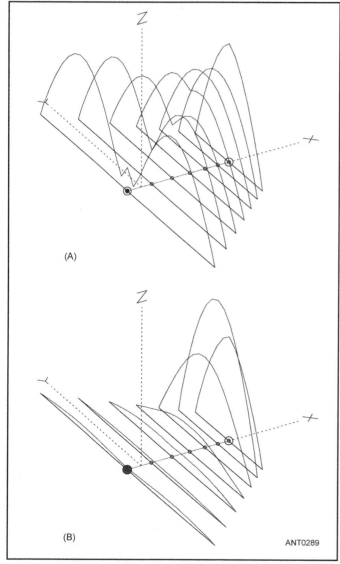

(A)

(B)

ANT0289

Figure 7.7 —The relative current magnitude on the elements of model "8504" at 28 MHz without and with a stub. Note the harmonic operation of the rear elements before a stub is added to suppress such operation.

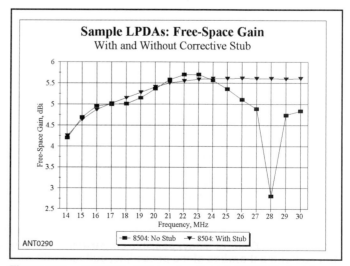

Figure 7.8 — A graph of the gain of model "8504" showing the frequency region in which a "weakness" occurs and its absence once a suitable stub is added to the array.

where ℓ_1 and ℓ_2 are the lengths of the rearmost elements, and d_{1-2} is the distance between the elements with the lengths ℓ_1 and ℓ_2. Determine the remaining element-to-element spacings from

$$d_{(n-1)-n} = \tau \, d_{(n-2)-(n-1)} \tag{18}$$

10) Choose R_0, the desired feed point resistance, to give the lowest SWR for the intended balun ratio and feed line impedance. R_0, the mean radiation resistance level of the LPDA input impedance, is approximated by:

$$R_0 = \frac{Z_0}{\sqrt{1 + \dfrac{Z_0}{4\sigma' Z_{AV}}}} \tag{19}$$

where the component terms are defined and/or calculated in the following way.

From the following equations, determine the necessary antenna feeder (phase-line) impedance, Z_0:

$$Z_0 = \frac{R_0{}^2}{8\,\sigma' Z_{AV}} + R_0 \sqrt{\left(\frac{R_0}{8\,\sigma' Z_{AV}}\right)^2 + 1} \tag{20}$$

σ' is the mean spacing factor and is given by

$$\sigma' = \frac{\sigma}{\sqrt{\tau}} \tag{21}$$

Z_{AV} is the average characteristic impedance of a dipole and is given by

$$Z_{AV} = 120\left[\ln\left(\frac{\ell_n}{\text{diam}_n}\right) - 2.25\right] \tag{22}$$

The ratio, ℓ_n/diam_n is the length-to-diameter ratio of the element n.

11) Once Z_0 has been determined, select a combination of conductor size and spacing to achieve that impedance, using the appropriate equation for the shape of the conductors. If an impractical spacing results for the antenna feeder, select a different conductor diameter and repeat step 11. In severe cases it may be necessary to select a different R_0 and repeat steps 10 and 11. Once a satisfactory feeder arrangement is found, the LPDA design is complete.

The resultant design should be subjected to extensive modeling tests to determine whether there are performance deficiencies or weaknesses that require modification of the design before actual construction.

7.3 BIBLIOGRAPHY

Source material and more extended discussion of the topics covered in this chapter can be found in the references listed below and in the textbooks listed at the end of the **Antenna Fundamentals**.

D. Allen, "The Log Periodic Loop Array (LPLA) Antenna," *The ARRL Antenna Compendium, Vol 3*, pp 115-117.

C. A. Balanis, *Antenna Theory, Analysis and Design*, 2nd Ed. (New York: John Wiley & Sons, 1997) Chapter 9.

P. C. Butson and G. T. Thompson, "A Note on the Calculation of the Gain of Log-Periodic Dipole Antennas," *IEEE Trans on Antennas and Propagation*, Vol AP-24, No. 1, Jan 1976, pp 105-106.

R. L. Carrel, "The Design of Log-Periodic Dipole Antennas," *1961 IRE International Convention Record*.

L. B. Cebik, "Notes on Standard Design LPDAs for 3-30 MHz," *QEX*, Part 1, May/Jun 2000, pp 23-38; Part 2, Jul/Aug 2000, pp 17-31.

R. H. DuHamel and D. E. Isbell, "Broadband Logarithmically Periodic Antenna Structures," *1957 IRE National Convention Record*, Part 1.

J. Fisher, "Development of the W8JF Waveram: A Planar Log-Periodic Quad Array," *The ARRL Antenna Compendium, Vol 1*, pp 50-54.

K. Heitner, "A Wide-Band, Low-Z Antenna — New Thoughts on Small Antennas," *The ARRL Antenna Compendium, Vol 1*, pp 48-49.

D. E. Isbell, "Log-Periodic Dipole Arrays," *IRE Transactions on Antennas and Propagation*, Vol. AP-8, No. 3, May 1960.

J. D. Kraus, *Antennas*, 2nd Ed. (New York: McGraw-Hill, 1988), Chapter 15.

R. A. Johnson, ed., *Antenna Engineering Handbook*, 3rd Ed. (New York: McGraw-Hill, 1993), Chapters 14 and 26.

C. Luetzelschwab, "Log Periodic Dipole Array Improvements," *The ARRL Antenna Compendium, Vol 6*, pp 74-76.

C. Luetzelschwab, "More Improvements to an LPDA," *The ARRL Antenna Compendium, Vol 7*, pp 121-122.

P. E. Mayes and R. L. Carrel, "Log Periodic Resonant-V Arrays," *IRE Wescon Convention Record*, Part 1, 1961.

P. E. Mayes, G. A. Deschamps, and W. T. Patton, "Backward Wave Radiation from Periodic Structures and Application to the Design of Frequency Independent Antennas," *Proc. IRE*.

C. T. Milner, "Log Periodic Antennas," *QST*, Nov 1959, pp 11-14.

W. I. Orr and S. D. Cowan, *Beam Antenna Handbook*, pp 251-253.

V. H. Rumsey, *Frequency Independent Antennas* (New York: Academic Press, 1966).

W. L. Stutzman and G. A. Thiele, *Antenna Theory and Design*, 2nd Ed. (New York: John Wiley & Sons, 1998), Chapter 6.

R. F. Zimmer, "Three Experimental Antennas for 15 Meters," *CQ*, Jan 1983, pp 44-45.

R. F. Zimmer, "Development and Construction of 'V' Beam Antennas," *CQ*, Aug 1983, pp 28-32.

Commercial Implementations of *MININEC* and *NEC-2* Programs

Ever since the source code for *NEC-2* and *MININEC* came into in the public domain, enterprising programmers have been upgrading, extending and improving these programs. There are a number of "freeware" versions available nowadays, and there are also a variety of commercial implementations.

This sidebar deals only with the most popular commercial versions, programs that many hams use. You should keep in mind that whatever program you choose will require an investment in learning time, if not in dollars. Your time is valuable, of course, and so is the ability to swap modeling files you create with other modelers. Studying model files, particularly when you are just starting out, is a great way to learn how the "experts" do their modeling. For example, there are archives of *EZNEC/ELNEC* files available on the Internet, since this popular modeling program has been around for a number of years. (*ELNEC* is the DOS-only, *MININEC*-core predecessor of *EZNEC*.)

The following table summarizes the main features and the pricing as of early 2011 for some popular commercial antenna modeling programs. The programs that use the *NEC-4* core require separate licenses from Lawrence Livermore National Laboratories.

Commercial Implementations of *MININEC* and *NEC-2* programs

Name	EZNEC 5.0 (5.0+ version)	EZNEC-Pro/2 (Pro4 version)	NEC-Win Plus	NEC-Win Pro	GNEC	Antenna Model
Manufacturer	Roy Lewallen	Roy Lewallen	Nittany Scientific	Nittany Scientific	Nittany Scientific	Teri Software
Core	NEC-2	NEC-2 (NEC-4)	NEC-2	NEC-2	NEC-2/NEC-4	MININEC
Operating System	Windows 32/64 bit	Windows 32/64 bit	Windows 32 bit	Windows 32 bit	Windows 32 bit	Windows 32 bit
Number Segments	500 (1500, + ver.)	20,000	10,000	10,000	80,000	Limited by memory
NEC-Card Inputs	No	Yes	Yes	Yes	Yes	No
Other Input	ASCII (NEC, + ver.)	ASCII,NEC	CAD *.DXF	CAD *.DXF	CAD *.DXF	No
Wires by Equation	No	No	Yes	Yes	Yes	Yes
Source Setting	By %	By %	By %	By %	By %	By %
Source Type	Current/ Voltage/Split	Current/ Voltage/Split	Current/ Voltage/Split	All types	All types	Current/Voltage
R + j X Loads	Yes	Yes	Yes	Yes	Yes	Yes
RLC Loads	Series, Parallel, Trap	Series, Parallel, Trap	Series, Parallel	Series, Parallel	Series, Parallel	Series, Parallel
True Trap Loads	Yes	Yes	No	No	No	No
Laplace Loads	Yes	Yes	Yes	Yes	Yes	No
Transmission Lines	Yes	Yes	Yes	Yes	Yes	No
Conductivity Table	Yes*	Yes*	Yes	Yes	Yes	Yes
Average Gain Test	Yes	Yes	Yes	Yes	Yes	Yes
Transmission Lines	Yes	Yes	Yes	Yes	Yes	No
View Geometry	Excellent	Excellent	Good	Good	Good	Very Good
Geometry Checking**	Yes	Yes	Yes	Yes	Yes	Yes
Easy Height Change	Yes	Yes	No	No	No	No
Polar Plots	ARRL, linear-dB	ARRL, linear-dB	ARRL, linear-dB	ARRL, linear-dB	ARRL, linear-dB	ARRL, linear-dB
	Az/El, Circ. (+ ver.)	Az/El, Circ.	Az/El Patterns	Az/El Patterns	Az/El Patterns	Az/El Patterns
Rectangular Plots	SWR	SWR	SWR, Zin	SWR, Zin, Az/El, Currents	SWR, Zin, Az/El, Currents	Gain, SWR, F/B, F/R, Rin, Xin
Operating Speed	Fast	Fast	Very Fast	Very Fast	Very Fast	Slow
Smith Chart	Yes (Freq sweep, + ver.)	Yes Freq sweep	No	Yes Freq sweep	Yes	Yes
Near/Far Field Tables	Both	Both	Far	Both	Both	Both
Ground Wave Analysis	No	Yes	No	Yes	Yes	No
Pricing	$89 Web; $99 CD-ROM, $139 (+ ver.)	$500 ($650) (must have NEC-4 license)	$150	$425	$795	$90

*Wire conductivity is the same for all wires.
**Excellent, Very Good, Good ratings from previous edition

produced some very capable commercial versions for the amateur market, many incorporating exciting graphics showing antenna patterns in 2D or 3D. These programs also simplify the creation of models for popular antenna types, and several come with libraries of sample antennas.

By the end of the 1980s, the speed and capabilities of personal computers had advanced to the point where PC versions of *NEC* became practical, and several versions are now available to amateurs. The most recent public-domain version is *NEC-2* and this is the computational core that we'll use as an example throughout this chapter.

Like *MININEC*, *NEC-2* is a general-purpose modeling package and it can be difficult to use and relatively slow in operation for certain specialized antenna forms. Thus, custom commercial software has been created for more user-friendly and speedier analysis of specific antenna varieties, mainly Yagi arrays described in the chapter on **HF Yagi and Quad Antennas**. Also see the sidebar, "Commercial Implementations of *MININEC* and *NEC-2* Programs."

For this edition of *The ARRL Antenna Book*, Roy Lewallen, W7EL, has graciously provided a special version of his *EZNEC 5.0* program, called *EZNEC-ARRL*. This version works with the specific antenna models also bundled on the CD-ROM. Please note that this ARRL-specific version of *EZNEC* is limited to a maximum of 20 segments (we'll

explain segments later) for all models except for the special ones included on this CD-ROM. You can find information on how to purchase the full-fledged version of *EZNEC* in the HELP section of the *EZNEC-ARRL* program.

The following material on antenna modeling is by necessity a summary since entire books have been written on this subject. Serious modelers may want to consider purchasing the modeling tutorials "Basic Antenna Modeling: A Hands on Tutorial" and "Intermediate Antenna Modeling: A Hands on Tutorial" by L. B. Cebik, W4RNL (SK) from **www.antennex. com**. The books contain a great deal of information, tips and techniques concerning antenna modeling by computer. We also strongly recommend that you read the HELP files in *EZNEC-ARRL*. There is a wealth of practical information on the finer points of antenna modeling there.

In addition to the material here, an additional tutorial on antenna modeling using *EZNEC* has been contributed by Greg Ordy, W8WWV and is included on the CD-ROM distributed with this book. It features alternate perspectives on topics in this chapter and covers additional material in depth. The tutorial was originally presented in support of a presentation at Contest University in 2011.

8.2 THE BASICS OF ANTENNA MODELING

This chapter will discuss the following antenna-modeling topics for *NEC-2*-based modeling software, using *EZNEC-ARRL* as an example:

- Program outputs
- Wire geometry
- Segmentation, warnings and limitations
- Source (feed point) placement
- Environment, including ground types and frequency
- Loads and transmission lines
- Testing the adequacy of a model

8.2.1 PROGRAM OUTPUTS

Instruction manuals for software programs traditionally start out describing in detail the input data needed by the program. They then demonstrate the output data the program can generate. We feel it is instructive, however, to turn things around and start out with a brief overview of the output from a typical antenna-modeling program.

We'll look at the output from public-domain *NEC-2*. Next, we'll look at the output information available from commercial adaptations of *NEC-2*, using *EZNEC-ARRL* provided by W7EL. After this brief overview of the output data, we'll look in detail at the input data needed to make a modeling program work. In the following discussions it will be very instructive if you to bring up *EZNEC-ARRL* on your computer and open the specific modeling files used in each example. [From now on in this chapter we'll refer merely to *EZNEC* rather than *EZNEC 5.0*, the official name or *EZNEC-ARRL*, a specialized subset of *EZNEC 5.0*. Where there are

specific differences between *EZNEC 5.0* and the limited-edition *EZNEC-ARRL* we'll identify them.]

Native *NEC-2*

Native *NEC-2* was written in the Fortran language, which stands for *Formula Translation*. The original program used Hollerith punch-cards to enter the program and input data. The output of the program was raw numeric data printed on many sheets of paper. Commercial software that uses the *NEC-2* computational core algorithms shields provides much easier methods of entering antenna design information and generates graphic output that is much easier to understand. Numerical tables are provided where they are useful, such as for source impedance and SWR at a single frequency, or the characteristics of a load or a transmission line. *EZNEC* produces the following types of graphs:

- Polar (linear-dB or ARRL-style) graphs of the far-field elevation and azimuth responses.
- 3-D wire-frame graph of the total far-field response.
- Graph of the SWR across a frequency band.
- Graphical display of the RF currents on various conductors in a model.
- Rotatable, zoom-able 3-D views of the wires used to make a model.
- Output to programs capable of generating Smith charts and performing other analysis

Figure 8.1 shows the computed far-field 2-D elevation and azimuth patterns for a 135-foot long horizontal dipole, mounted in a flattop configuration 50 feet above flat ground.

These figures were generated using *EZNEC* at 3.75 MHz. Figure 8.1C shows a 3-D wire-frame picture of the far-field response, but this time at 14.2 MHz.

Figure 8.2 shows the computed SWR curve over the frequency range 3.0 to 4.0 MHz for this dipole, fed with lossless 50-Ω transmission line. *EZNEC* generated this plot using the "SWR" button. Figures 8.1 and 8.2 are typical of the kind of graphical outputs that commercial implementations of the *NEC-2* computing core can produce — a vast improvement over tables of numbers from a mainframe computer's line printer! Now, let's get into the details of what kind of input data is required to run a typical method-of-moments antenna-modeling program.

8.2.2 PROGRAM INPUTS: WIRE GEOMETRY

Coordinates in an X, Y and Z World

The most difficult part of using a *NEC*-type of modeling program is setting up the antenna's geometry — you must condition yourself to think in three-dimensional, Cartesian coordinates. Each end point of a wire is represented by three numbers: an x, y and z coordinate. These coordinates represent the distance from the origin (x-axis), the width of an antenna (y-axis), and the height (z-axis).

An example should help sort things out. **Figure 8.3** shows a simple model of a 135-foot center-fed dipole, made of #14 copper wire placed 50 feet above flat ground. The common term for this antenna is "flattop dipole." For convenience, the ground is located at the origin of the coordinate system, at (0, 0, 0) feet, directly under the center of the dipole. **Figure 8.4** shows the *EZNEC* spreadsheet-like input data for this antenna. (Use model file: **Ch8-Flattop Dipole.EZ**.) *EZNEC* allows you to specify the type of conductor material from its main window, using the WIRE LOSS button to open a new window. We will click on the COPPER button for this dipole.

Above the origin, at a height of 50 feet on the z-axis, is the dipole's *feed point*, called a *source* in *NEC* terminology. The width of the dipole goes toward the left (that is, in the "negative-y" direction) one-half the overall length of 135 feet, or –67.5 feet. Toward the right, our dipole's other end is at +67.5 feet. The x-axis dimension of our dipole is zero, meaning that the dipole wire is parallel to and directly

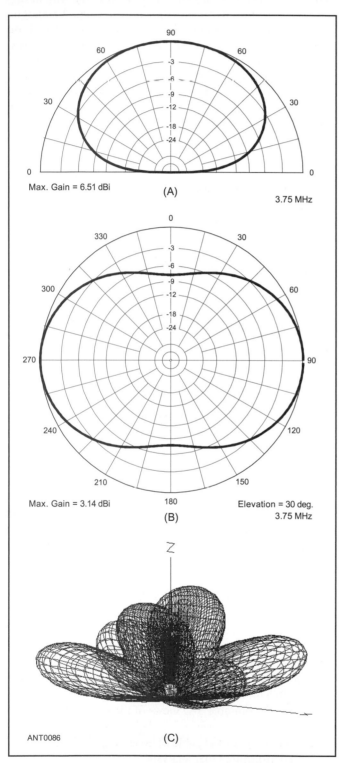

Figure 8.1 — At A, far-field elevation-plane pattern for a 135- foot-long horizontal dipole, 50 feet above flat ground, at 3.5 MHz. At B, the far-field azimuth-plane pattern at an elevation angle of 30°.

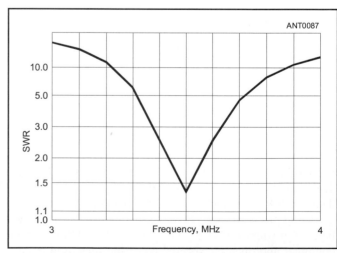

Figure 8.2 — SWR curve for 135-foot flattop dipole over the frequency range 3.0 to 4.0 MHz for a 50-Ω feed line. This antenna is an example and is not optimized for the amateur band.

above the x-axis. The dipole's ends are thus represented by two points, whose coordinates are (0, –67.5, 50) and (0, 67.5, 50) feet. The use of parentheses with a sequential listing of (x, y, z) coordinates is a common practice among antenna modelers to describe a wire end point.

Figure 8.3B includes some other useful information about this antenna beyond the wire geometry. Figure 8.3B

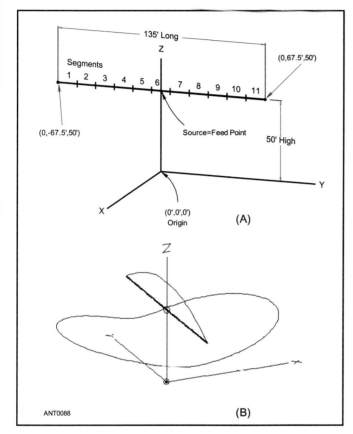

Figure 8.3 — At A, simple model for a 135-foot long horizontal dipole, 50 feet above the ground. The dipole is over the y-axis. The wire has been segmented into 11 segments, with the center of segment number 6 as the feed point. The left-hand end of the antenna is –67.5 feet from the center feed point and that the right-hand end is at 67.5 feet from the center. At B, *EZNEC* "View Antenna" screen, showing geometry of wire and the x, y and z axes. Overlaid on the wire geometry drawing are the current distribution along the wire and the far-field azimuthal response at an elevation angle of 30°.

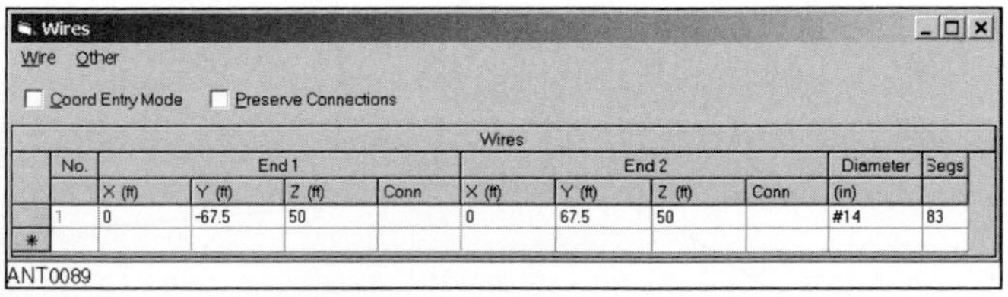

No.	End 1				End 2				Diameter	Segs
	X (ft)	Y (ft)	Z (ft)	Conn	X (ft)	Y (ft)	Z (ft)	Conn	(in)	
1	0	-67.5	50		0	67.5	50		#14	83

Figure 8.4 — *EZNEC* "View Wires" data entry screen for simple flattop dipole in Figure 8.3. The numbers shown are in feet, except for the wire diameter, which *EZNEC* allows you to specify as an AWG gauge, in this case #14. Note that 83 segments have been specified for this antenna for analysis over the range from 3.5 to 29.7 MHz.

overlays the wire geometry, the current distribution along the wire and the far-field azimuth response, in this case at an elevation angle of 30°.

Although not shown specifically in Figure 8.3, the thickness of the antenna is the diameter of the wire, #14 AWG. Note that native *NEC* programs specify the *radius* of the wire, rather than the diameter, but programs like *EZNEC* use the more intuitive diameter of a wire rather than the radius. *EZNEC* (and other commercial programs) also allows the user to specify the wire as an AWG gauge, such as #14 or #22, for example.

We've represented our simple dipole in Figure 8.3 using a single, straight wire. In fact, all antenna models created for method-of-moments programs are made of combinations of straight wires. This includes even complex antennas, such as helical antennas or round loops. (The mathematical basis for modeling complex antennas is that they can be simulated using straight-wire polygons. A circular loop, for example, can be modeled using an octagon.)

Segmentation and Specifying a Source Segment

We've specified the physical geometry of this simple one-wire dipole. Now several more modeling details surface — you must specify the number of *segments* into which the dipole is divided for the method-of-moments analysis and you must somehow feed the antenna. The *NEC-2* guideline for setting the number of segments is to use at least 10 segments per half-wavelength. This is a general rule of thumb, however, and in many models more dense segmentation is mandatory for good accuracy.

In Figure 8.3, we've specified that the dipole be divided into 11 segments for operation on the 80 meter band. This follows the rule of thumb above, since the 135-foot dipole is about one half-wavelength long at 3.5 MHz.

Setting the Source Segment

The use of 11 segments, an odd rather than an even number such as 10, places the dipole's feed point (a feed point is referred to as a *source* in *NEC*-speak, a word choice that can befuddle beginners) right at the antenna's center, at the center of segment number six. In concert with the "EZ" in its name, *EZNEC* makes choosing the source segment easy by allowing the user to specify a percentage along the wire, in this case 50% centers the source in the middle of the segment.

At this point you may very well be wondering why no center insulator is shown in the middle of our center-fed dipole. After all, a real dipole would have a center insulator. However, method-of-moments programs assume that a source generator is placed across an infinitely small gap in the antenna wire. While this is convenient from a mathematical point of view, the unstated use of such an infinitely small gap often confuses newcomers to the world of antenna modeling. We'll get into more details, caveats and limitations in source placement later in this chapter. For now, just trust that the model we've just described with 11 segments, fed at segment 6, will work well over the entire amateur band from 3.5 to 4.0 MHz.

Now, let's consider what would happen if we want to use our 135-foot long dipole on all HF amateur bands from 3.5 to 29.7 MHz, rather than just from 3.5 to 4.0 MHz. Instead of feeding such an antenna with coax cable, we would feed it with open-wire line and use an antenna tuner in the shack to create a 50-Ω load for the transmitter. To comply with the segmentation rule above, the number of segments used in the model should vary with frequency — or at least be segmented at or above the minimum recommended level at the highest frequency used. This is because a half-wavelength at 29.7 MHz is 16.6 feet, while a half-wavelength at 3.5 MHz is 140.6 feet. So the number of segments for proper operation on 29.7 MHz should be 10 × 135/16.6 = 81. We'll be a little more conservative than the minimum requirement and specify 83 segments. Figure 8.4 shows the *EZNEC* input spreadsheet for this model. (Use model file: **Ch8-Multiband Dipole.EZ**.)

The penalty for using more segments in a program like *NEC* is that the program slows down roughly as the square of the segments — double the number of segments and the speed drops by a factor of four (two squared). Using too few segments will result in inaccuracies, particularly in computing the feed point impedance. We'll delve into the area of segmentation density in more detail later when we discuss testing the adequacy of a model.

Segment Length-to-Wire-Diameter Ratio

Even if you're willing to live with the slowdown in computing speed for situations involving a large number of wire segments, you should make sure the ratio between the segment length and the diameter of any wire is greater than 1:1. This is to say that the length of each segment should be longer than the diameter of the wire to avoid internal limitations in the *NEC* program.

For the #14 wire specified in this simple 135-foot long dipole, it's pretty unlikely that you'll bump up against this limitation for any reasonable level of segmentation. After all, #14 wire has a diameter of 0.064 inch and 135 feet is 1620 inches. To stay above a segment length of 0.064 inch, the maximum number of segments is 1620/0.064 = 25,312. This is a very large number of segments and it would take a very long time to compute, assuming that your program can handle that many segments.

Staying above a 1:1 ratio in segment length to wire diameter can be more challenging at VHF/UHF frequencies, however. This is particularly true for fairly large "wires" made of aluminum tubing. Incidentally, this is another point where newcomers to antenna modeling can be led astray by the terminology. In a *NEC*-type program, all conductors in a model are considered to be wires, even if they consist of hollow aluminum or copper tubes. The skin effect keeps the RF current in any conductor confined to the outer surface of that conductor, and thus it doesn't matter whether the conductor is hollow or solid, or even a number of wire strands twisted together.

Let's look at a half-wave dipole at 420 MHz. This would be about 14.1 inches long. If you use ¼-inch diameter tubing

for this dipole, the maximum segment length meeting the 1:1 diameter-to-length ratio requirement is also ¼ inch long. The maximum number of segments then would be 14.1/0.25 = 56.4, rounded down to 56. From this discussion you should now understand why method-of-moments programs are known for using a "thin-wire approximation." Really fat conductors can get you into trouble, particularly at VHF/UHF.

Some Caveats and Limitations Concerning Geometry

Example: Inverted-V Dipole

Now, let's get a little more complicated and specify another 135-foot-long dipole, but this time configured as an inverted V. As shown in **Figure 8.5**, you must now specify two wires. The two wires join at the top, at (0, 0, 50) feet. (Again, the program doesn't use a center insulator in the model.)

If you are using a native version of *NEC*, you may have to go back to your high-school trigonometry book to figure out how to specify the end points of our "droopy" dipole, with its 120° included angle. Figure 8.5 shows the details, along with the trigonometric equations needed. *EZNEC* is indeed more "easy" here since it allows you to tilt the ends of each wire downward an appropriate number of degrees (in this case –30° at each end of the dipole) to automatically create an inverted-V configuration. **Figure 8.6A** shows the *EZNEC* spreadsheet describing this inverted-V dipole with a 120° included angle between the two wires.

See the *EZNEC* HELP section under "Wire Coordinate Shortcuts" for specific instructions on how to use the "elevation rotate end" shortcut "RE-30" to create the sloping wires easily by rotating the end of the wire down 30°. Now the specification of the source becomes a bit more complicated. The easiest way is to specify two sources, one on each end segment at the junction of the two wires. *EZNEC* does this automatically if you specify a so-called *split-source* feed. Figure 8.6B shows the two sources as two open circles at the top ends of the two wires making up the inverted-V dipole.

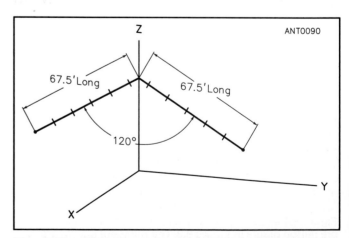

Figure 8.5 — Model for an inverted-V dipole with an included angle between the two legs of 120° apex at 50' high. Sine and cosine functions are used to describe the heights of the end points for the sloping arms of the antenna.

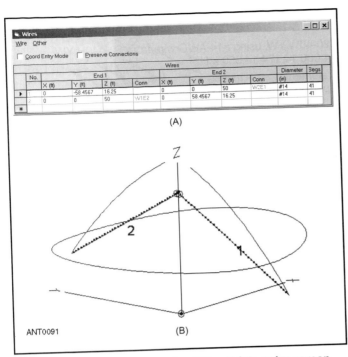

(A)

(B)

ANT0091

Figure 8.6 — At A, *EZNEC* "View Wires" data entry screen for inverted-V dipole in Figure 8.5. Now the ends of the inverted-V dipole are 16.25 feet above ground, instead of 50 feet for the flattop dipole. At B, *EZNEC* "View Antenna" screen, with overlay of geometry, current distribution and azimuth plot.

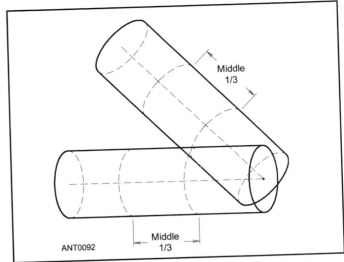

ANT0092

Figure 8.7 — A junction of two short, fat wire segments at an acute angle. This results in inter-penetration of the two wire volumes beyond the middle-⅓ recommended limit.

What *EZNEC* is doing is creating two sources, one in each of the segments immediately on either side of the junction of the two wires. *EZNEC* sums up the two source impedances to provide a single result.

Navigating in the View Antenna Window

At this point it's worthwhile to explore some of the ways you can look at the antenna you've designed using the *EZNEC* VIEW ANT button on the main window. Bring up the file **Ch8-Inverted V Dipole.EZ** in *EZNEC*, and click on the VIEW ANT button. You will see a small inverted-V dipole raised over the (0, 0, 0) origin on the ground directly under the feed point of the inverted-V dipole. First, "rotate" the dipole by holding down the left-mouse button and moving the mouse. You can orient the picture any way you wish.

Let's take a closer look at the junction of the two wires at the feed point. Click the CENTER ANT IMAGE checkbox toward the bottom of the window to anchor the center of the image at the center of the window, then move the *Zoom* slider upward to zoom in on the image. At some point the junction of the two slanted wires will move up beyond the edge of the window, so you will need to click on the left-hand side of the Z MOVE IMAGE slider to bring the junction back into view. You should be able to see a zoomed view of the junction along with the two open circles that represent the location of the split sources in the middle of the segments adjacent to the wire junction.

Place the mouse cursor over one of the slanted wires and

double click the left-mouse button. *EZNEC* will now identify that wire and show its length, as well as the length of each segment on that wire. Pretty slick, isn't it?

Short, Fat Wires and the Acute-Angle Junction

Another possible complication can arise for wires with short, fat segments, particularly ones that have only a small included angle between them. These wire segments can end up inter-penetrating within each other's volumes, leading to problems in a model. Once you think of each wire segment as a thick cylinder, you can appreciate the difficulty in connecting two wires together at their ends. The two wires always inter-penetrate each other's volume to some extent. **Figure 8.7** depicts this problem graphically for two short, fat wires joined at their ends at an acute angle. A rule of thumb is to avoid creating junctions where more than ⅓ of the wire volumes inter-penetrate. You can achieve this by using longer segment lengths or thinner wire diameters.

Some Other Practical Antenna Geometries

A Vertical Half-Wave Dipole

If you turn the 135-foot-long horizontal dipole in Figure 8.1 on its end you will create a vertical half-wave dipole that is above the origin of the x, y and z axes. See **Figure 8.8**, where the bottom end of the dipole is placed 8 feet off the ground to keep it away from humans and animals at (0, 0, 8) feet. The top end is thus at 8 + 135 = 143 feet off the ground at (0, 0, 143). Figure 8.8 also shows the current distribution and the elevation pattern for this antenna. (Use *EZNEC* model file: **Ch8-Vertical Dipole.EZ**.)

A Ground-Plane Antenna

The ground-plane model is more complicated than previous ones because a total of five wires are now needed: one for

9.1 HORIZONTAL ANTENNAS

9.1.1 DIPOLE ANTENNAS

Half-wave dipoles and variations of these can be a very good choice for an HF antenna. Where only single-band operation is desired, the $\lambda/2$ antenna fed with 50- or 75-Ω coaxial cable is a popular and inexpensive antenna. It can also be used on the third harmonic with some adjustment as explained in the project at the end of this section. The basic and most common construction is shown in **Figure 9.1**.

The length of the $\lambda/2$ dipole in feet is often stated as $\ell = 468/f$ (MHz) although this rarely results in an antenna resonant at the desired frequency as discussed in the chapter **Dipoles and Monopoles**. It is more practical to begin with a length of 485/f or 490/f (**Table 9-1** gives lengths for each of the ham bands from 1.8 through 50 MHz) and then adjust the antenna according to the following procedure:

1) Assemble the antenna with length ℓ_1 for a desired frequency of f_1 but do not make the attachments to the end insulators permanent. Twisting the antenna wire at the insulators will suffice during adjustment.

2) Raise the antenna to its desired position and determine the frequency of lowest SWR, f_2.

3) Assuming that f_2 is too low (the antenna is too long), calculate the desired length $\ell_2 = \ell_1 \times f_2 / f_1$. Trim the antenna to the desired length by removing equal amounts of wire on each end to maintain electrical balance at the feed point.

Example: A dipole intended to be used at 14.250 MHz is initially built with a physical length of 490 / 14.250 = 34.4 feet (34 feet 5 in). Once in place, f_2 is determined to be 13.795 MHz. Using step 3, the desired length should be 34.4 × 13.795 / 14.250 = 33.3 feet and the antenna is 34.4 – 33.3 = 1.1 feet (1 foot 1 inch) too long. Remove 6.5 inches from each end of the antenna.

Coaxial lines present support problems as a concentrated weight at the center of the antenna, tending to pull the center of the antenna down, so care must be taken to make the feed point connections strong and provide support for the cable. If a center support or conveniently located tree is available, insulators with a rope attachment point can be used to support the weight.

The feed line should come away from the antenna at right angles for the longest practical distance so as to preserve electrical balance and minimize the effect of the feed line shield's outer surface on the antenna. Adding a choke or current balun at the feed point helps to electrically isolate the shield surface and prevent common-mode current from flowing on the feed line. (See the **Transmission Line Coupling and Impedance Matching** chapter for a discussion of the use of baluns.)

Exact electrical balance is generally not critical for a dipole antenna to perform well. Common-mode current induced on the dipole's feed line shield will radiate a signal that generally serves to partially fill in some of the dipole's pattern nulls. Unless the common-mode current creates RF-related problems in the station, a balun is not required.

Shortening the Dipole

The simplest way to shorten a dipole is shown in **Figure 9.2**. If you do not have sufficient length between the supports, simply hang as much of the center of the antenna as possible between the supports and let the ends hang down. The ends can be straight down or may be at an angle as

Table 9-1
Starting Lengths for Amateur Band Dipoles

Freq (MHz)	Length in feet		
	468/f	485/f	490/f
1.85	253.0	262.2	264.9
3.6	130.0	134.7	136.1
3.9	120.0	124.4	125.6
5.3	88.3	91.5	92.5
7.1	65.9	68.3	69.0
10.1	46.3	48.0	48.5
14.15	33.1	34.3	34.6
18.1	25.9	26.8	27.1
21.2	22.1	22.9	23.1
24.9	18.8	19.5	19.7
28.2	16.6	17.2	17.4
29	16.1	16.7	16.9
50.1	9.3	9.7	9.8

Dipole or Doublet?

When does a dipole become a doublet and vice versa? There is no formal difference — these are just two different names for the same antenna. The term "doublet" is often applied to symmetrical center-fed antennas that are not resonant or that are used on multiple bands to distinguish them from the resonant center-fed dipole. This is a matter of convention only.

"Dipole" means "two poles" with the poles being the out-of-phase voltages on either side of the dipole. From the Wikipedia entry (**en.wikipedia.org/wiki/Dipole**) "An electric dipole is a separation of positive and negative

charges. The simplest example of this is a pair of electric charges of equal magnitude but opposite sign, separated by some (usually small) distance."

The antenna feed line supplies voltages with opposite polarity on either side of the feed point, creating the pair of electric poles. The poles cause current to flow in the antenna, creating the radiation. As the length increases beyond a half-wavelength, the situation is much less clear because multiple poles eventually appear. For example, a 3/2-wavelength wire is really a tri-pole!

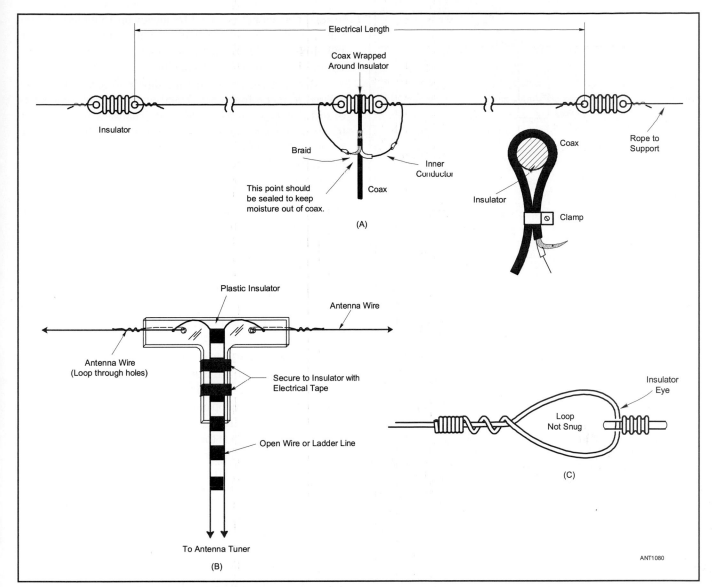

Figure 9.1 — Details of coax-fed dipole construction at A. The center-fed dipole is a balanced antenna and if coaxial cable feed line is used, a balun may be added at the feed point as described in the text. The dipole can also be fed with open-wire or ladder-line as shown at B. Detail of attaching an end insulator is shown at C. Note that the electrical length of the dipole extends to the tips of the loops of wire attached to the insulator.

indicated but in either case should be secured so that they do not move in the wind. As long as the center portion between the supports is at least λ/4, the radiation pattern will be very nearly the same as a full-length dipole.

The resonant length of the wire will be somewhat shorter than a full-length dipole and can best be determined by experimentally adjusting the length of ends, which may be conveniently near ground. Keep in mind that there can be very high voltages at the ends of the wires and for safety the ends should be kept out of reach.

Letting the ends hang down as shown is a form of capacitive end loading. Folding the ends back on the antenna is a type of *linear loading*. Both types of loading are discussed later in this chapter. While both techniques are efficient, it will also reduce the matching bandwidth — as does any form of loading.

A 40 - 15 Meter Dual-Band Dipole

As mentioned earlier, dipoles have harmonic resonances near odd multiples of their fundamental resonances. Because 21 MHz is the third harmonic of 7 MHz, 7-MHz dipoles are harmonically resonant in the popular ham band at 21 MHz. This is attractive because it allows you to install a 40 meter dipole, feed it with coax, and use it without an antenna tuner on both 40 and 15 meters.

But there's a catch: The third harmonic resonance is actually higher than three times the fundamental resonant frequency. This is because there is no end effect in the center portion of the antenna where there are no insulators.

An easy fix for this, as shown in **Figure 9.3**, is to add capacitive loading to the antenna about ¼-λ wavelength (at 21.2 MHz) away from the feed point in both halves of the dipole. Known as *capacitance hats*, the simple loading wires

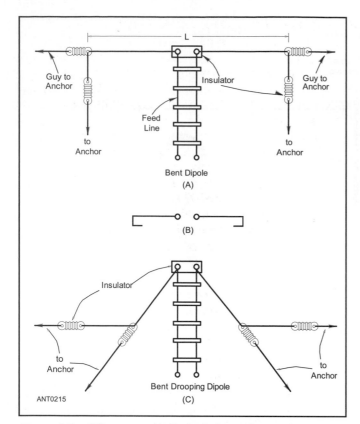

Figure 9.2 — When space is limited, the ends may be bent downward as shown at A, or back on the radiator as shown at B. The bent dipole ends may come straight down or be led off at an angle away from the center of the antenna. An inverted-V as C can be erected with the ends bent parallel to the ground when the support structure is not high enough.

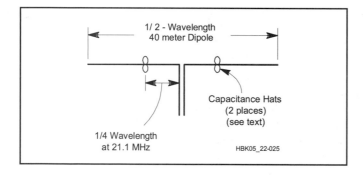

lower the antenna's resonant frequency on 15 meters without substantially affecting resonance on 40 meters. This scheme can also be used to build a dipole that can be used on 80 and 30 meters and on 75 and 10 meters.

Measure, cut and adjust the dipole to resonance at the desired 40 meter frequency. Then, cut two 2-foot-long pieces of stiff wire (such as #12 or #14 AWG house wire) and solder the ends of each one together to form two loops. Twist the loops in the middle to form figure-8s, and strip and solder the wires where they cross. Install these capacitance hats on the dipole by stripping the antenna wire (if necessary) and soldering the hats to the dipole about a third of the way out from the feed point (placement isn't critical) on each wire. To resonate the antenna on 15 meters, adjust the loop shapes until the SWR is acceptable in the desired segment of the 15 meter band. Conversely, you can move the hats back and forth along the antenna until the desired SWR is achieved and then solder the hats to the antenna.

9.1.2 FOLDED DIPOLES

Figure 9.4 shows a *folded dipole* constructed from a ½-λ section of two wires spaced 4 to 6 inches apart and connected together at each end of the antenna. Plastic spacers are generally used to separate the conductors and 600-Ω open-wire line can also be used. The top conductor is continuous from end to end. The lower conductor, however, is cut in the middle and the feed line attached at that point. Parallel-wire transmission line is then used to connect the transmitter.

A folded dipole has exactly the same gain and radiation pattern as a single-wire dipole. However, because of the mutual coupling between the upper and lower conductors, the feed point impedance of a single-wire dipole is multiplied by the square of the number of conductors in the antenna. In this case, there are two conductors in the antenna, so the feed point impedance is $2^2 = 4$ times that of a single-wire dipole. Using three wires increases feed point impedance by $3^2 = 9$ and so forth. The squared ratio requires both wires to have the same diameter.

Figure 9.3 — Figure-8-shaped capacitance hats made and placed as described in the text, can make a 40 meter dipole resonate anywhere in the 15 meter band.

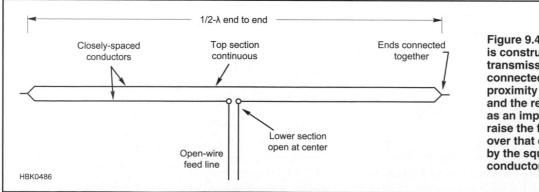

Figure 9.4 — The folded dipole is constructed from open-wire transmission line with the ends connected together. The close proximity of the two conductors and the resulting coupling act as an impedance transformer to raise the feed point impedance over that of a single-wire dipole by the square of the number of conductors used.

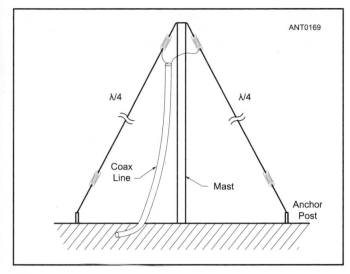

Figure 9.5 — The inverted-V dipole. The length and apex angle should be adjusted as described in the text.

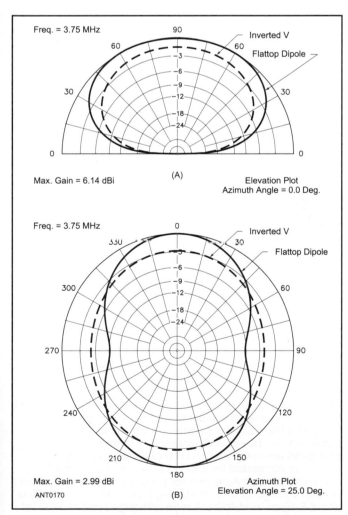

Figure 9.6 — At A, elevation and at B, azimuthal radiation patterns comparing a normal 80 meter dipole and an inverted-V dipole. The center of both dipoles is at 65 feet and the ends of the inverted-V are at 20 feet. The frequency is 3.750 MHz.

A common reason to use the folded dipole is to raise the feed point impedance of the antenna. This allows a low-loss parallel-wire line to be used with low SWR instead of coaxial cable when a very long feed line is required and using coax would result in too much loss. For example, a three-wire folded dipole would present a feed point impedance close to that of 450-Ω ladder line.

Another advantage of the two- and three-wire folded dipoles over the single-wire dipole is that they offer a better match over a wider band. This is particularly important if full coverage of the 3.5-MHz band is contemplated.

9.1.3 INVERTED-V DIPOLE

If only a single support is available, the halves of a dipole may be sloped to form an inverted-V dipole, as shown in **Figure 9.5**. This also reduces the horizontal space required for the antenna.

There will be some difference in performance between a horizontal dipole and the inverted-V as shown by the radiation patterns in **Figure 9.6**. There is small loss in peak gain and the pattern is less directional.

Bringing a dipole's wires toward each other results in a decrease of the resonant frequency and a decrease in feed point impedance and bandwidth. (This is true whether the dipole is constructed as an inverted-V or not.) Thus, to maintain the same resonant frequency, the length of the dipole must be decreased somewhat over that of the horizontal configuration.

The amount of shortening required varies with the circumstances of the installation but a reasonable rule of thumb would be 5% for every 45 degrees that the legs of the dipole are lowered from horizontal. It might be wise to start with an initial length for a horizontal dipole and then trim it in the inverted-V configuration according to the procedure given for horizontal dipoles.

The angle at the apex is not critical, although angles smaller than 90° begin to compromise performance significantly. Because of the lower feed point impedance, a 50-Ω feed line should be used.

If a close match to the feed line impedance is desired, the usual procedure is to adjust the angle for lowest SWR while keeping the dipole resonant by adjustment of length. Bandwidth may be increased by using multiconductor elements, such as a cage or fan configuration as discussed below.

9.1.4 END-FED ZEPP

Other than to obtain a convenient feed point impedance and to be somewhat balanced, there is no reason why a dipole has to be fed exactly at the center. In the early days, the λ/2 dipole (then called a "Hertz" or "Hertzian" antenna) was often fed at one end where it was called an "End-fed Zepp" after the Zeppelin airships from which it was first deployed.

Figure 9.7 shows a typical end-fed Zepp with a parallel-wire feed line. Since the feed line is connected at a low-current/high-voltage point on the antenna, the feed point impedance is quite high and often in the neighborhood of 3000-5000 Ω. This is too high to present a match to even the widest-spaced parallel-wire lines and so *tuned feeders* are often employed in

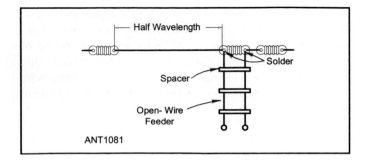

Figure 9.7 — An end-fed Zepp with a parallel-wire feed line connected at one end. Tuned feeders can be used to lower the high feed point impedance as described in the text.

which the feed line is an odd number of quarter-wavelengths long. Such a feed line transforms a high impedance into a low impedance as described in the **Transmission Lines** chapter, allowing low-impedance feed lines such as coax to be connected with a more manageable SWR.

To lower the high end impedance, the feed point can be moved away from the end toward the middle of the antenna. At some point a close match to the 300 to 450-Ω impedance of parallel-wire feed lines can be obtained. This feed point will not be electrically balanced and it is likely that some common-mode current will flow on the line. An impedance transformer and balun can be employed to isolate the feed line and this configuration is commonly known as the "off-center-fed dipole" described in the **Multiband HF Antennas** chapter.

9.1.5 SLOPING DIPOLES

Another variation of the single-support configuration is the λ/2 *sloping dipole* shown in **Figure 9.8A**. This antenna is also known as a *sloper* or *half-wave sloper* to distinguish it from the *half sloper* described in the section on vertically-polarized antennas. The feed point impedance depends on the height of the antenna above ground, the characteristics of the ground, and the angle the antenna makes with the ground. In most cases, an acceptable SWR for coaxial cable can be achieved by altering the direction and height.

The amount of slope from horizontal can vary from 0°, where the dipole is in a flattop configuration, all the way to 90°, where the dipole becomes fully vertical. The latter configuration is sometimes called a *Halfwave Vertical Dipole* (*HVD*) and is discussed in the section on vertically polarized antennas.

This antenna slightly favors the *forward direction* as shown in Figure 9.8B. With a non-conducting support and average to poor ground, signals off the back are weaker than those off the front. With a non-conducting mast and good

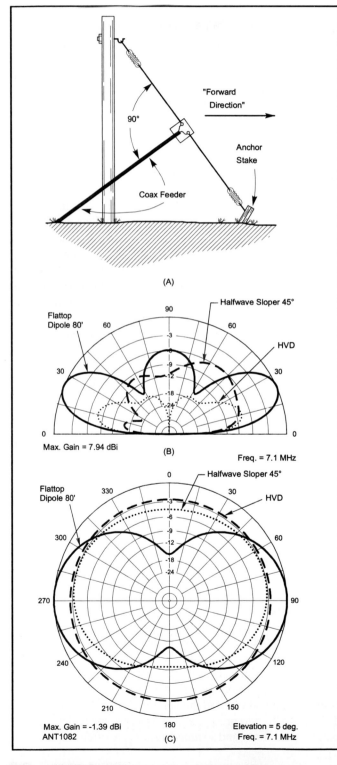

Figure 9.8 — Example of a sloping λ/2 dipole, or *full sloper*. On the lower HF bands, maximum radiation over poor to average ground is off the sides and in the *forward direction* indicated if a non-conductive support is used. A metal support will alter this pattern by acting as a parasitic element. How it alters the pattern is a complex issue depending on the electrical height of the support, what other antennas are located on it, and on the configuration of any guy wires. B compares the 40 meter azimuthal patterns at a DX takeoff angle of 5° for three configurations: a flattop dipole, a dipole tilted down 45° and an HVD (half wave vertical dipole). These are computed for ground with average conductivity and dielectric constant, and for a maximum height of 80 feet in each configuration. The sloping half wave dipole exhibits about 5 dB of front-to-back ratio, although even at its most favored direction it doesn't quite have the same maximum gain as the HVD or the flattop dipole. C shows the elevation patterns for the same antennas. Note that the sloping half wave dipole has more energy at higher elevation angles than either the flattop dipole or HVD.

ground, the response is omnidirectional with no gain in any direction.

A conductive support such as a tower acts as a parasitic element. (So does the coax shield, unless it is routed at 90° from the antenna.) The parasitic effects vary with ground quality, support height and other conductors on the support (such as a beam at the top or other wire antennas). With such variables, performance is very difficult to predict but that is no reason not to put up the antenna and experiment with it. Many hams report good results with a sloper.

Losses increase as the antenna ends approach the support or the ground, so the same cautions about the height of the antenna ends apply as for the inverted-V antenna.

The question arises about how to treat the feed line to make sure it doesn't accidentally become part of the radiating system. The ideal situation would be to bring the feed line out perpendicular to the sloping wire for an infinite distance. To prevent feed line radiation, route the coax away from the feed point at 90° from the antenna as far as possible.

An intensive modeling study on feeding the closely-related HVD was done for the book *Simple and Fun Antennas for Hams* (see Bibliography). This study indicated that directing the feed line at an angle down to the ground of as little as 30° from the antenna can work with only minor interaction, provided that common-mode decoupling chokes were employed at the feed point and a quarter-wavelength down the line from the feed point. (See the **Transmission Line Coupling and Impedance Matching** chapter.)

Two systems of multiple sloping dipoles are presented on this book's CD-ROM. A system designed for 7 MHz by K1WA and another for 1.8 MHz by K3LR give the builder some directivity while only requiring a single support. These systems can also be adapted to other bands.

9.1.6 BROADBAND DIPOLES

Producing a dipole with an SWR bandwidth covering an entire amateur band is difficult for the 160 meter and 80 meter bands due to their relative spans: approximately 10.5% for the 160 meter band and 13.4% for the 80 meter band from the lowest to the highest frequency of the allocation. Most single-wire dipoles have an SWR bandwidth of a few percent in comparison, making it difficult to cover these widest of our bands with just one antenna. The higher HF bands are much narrower in comparison and generally can be covered by a single-wire dipole.

The simplest way to increase the SWR bandwidth of a single-wire dipole is to increase the thickness of the wire (the length-to-diameter ratio) as discussed in the **Antenna Fundamentals** and **Dipoles and Ground-Planes** chapters. Since the range of available wire sizes is quite limited in the potential effect on bandwidth at MF and HF, the technique of employing multiple wires is used to create a larger-diameter conductor. (Additional methods of making broadband dipoles are discussed in the supplement "Broadband Antenna Matching" which is included on this book's CD-ROM in the folder associated with the **Transmission Line Coupling and Impedance Matching** chapter.)

There are three common methods of using multiple wires in this way: the cage, the fan and the open-sleeve. The cage shown in **Figure 9.9** is a very old design, having been employed during the early days of "wireless" to increase bandwidth of antennas used for spark signals with their very wide bandwidths. The cage consists of several wires (three or more) held apart by spreaders (insulating or non-insulating) and connected together at the ends and at the feed point. A project describing the cage dipole in use at W1AW on 80 meters is included at the end of this section.

A simplified variation on the cage is to create a "bow-tie" with just two wires in each leg of the dipole. The wires are tied together at the feed point and spread apart up to 10 feet at the ends of the dipole where they may be connected together or left separate. The bow-tie or "skeleton biconical dipole" was discussed by Hallas in May 2005 *QST*. (See the Bibliography.)

In both cases, extra tethers are usually required at the ends of the cage or fan to keep the antenna from twisting in the wind. Such antennas provide excellent electrical performance at the cost of some mechanical complexity and extra weight. They may not be suitable in areas where heavy icing or high wind speed is common.

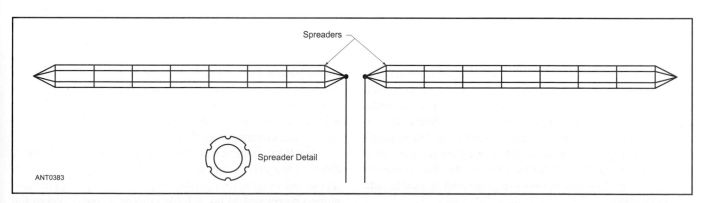

Figure 9.9 — Construction of a cage dipole. The spreaders need not be of conductive material and should be lightweight. Between adjacent conductors, the spacing should be 0.02 ℓ or less. The number of spreaders and their spacing along the dipole should be sufficient to maintain a relatively constant separation of the radiator wires. The spreaders can be round as shown in the detail or any suitable cross arrangement.

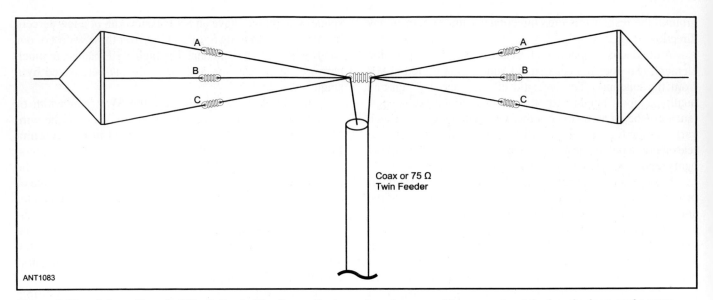

Figure 9.10 — A broad-banded "fan" dipole. The three dipoles a, b and c are cut to resonate at the band edges and center band frequency. This creates a single antenna that can be used over the entire 3.5 MHz band. On 80 meters, the dipole cut for 3.5 MHz will be approximately 7 feet longer than the one cut for 4 MHz. (Figure 9.10 from *Practical Wire Antennas*, courtesy RSGB — see Bibliography.)

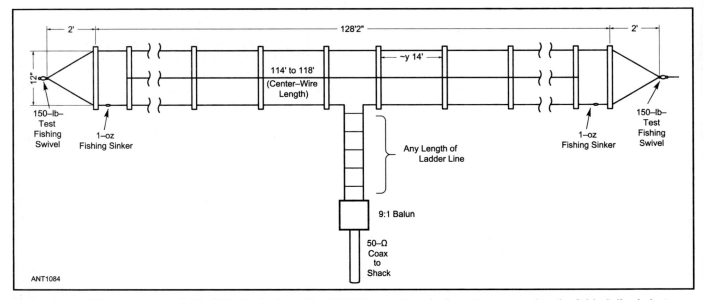

Figure 9.11 — The open-sleeve folded dipole designed by N6LF. The center wire is not connected to the folded dipole but couples to it and acts as the radiator at the upper end of the band.

A second method of broad-banding a dipole is to create a fan of two or more dipoles with close but not identical resonant frequencies. This is illustrated in **Figure 9.10** in which three dipoles are cut for the bottom, middle and top frequencies in the 80 meter band (3.5, 3.75, and 4 MHz) and fed in parallel at the feed point. This is similar to the bow-tie mentioned in the previous paragraph but the ends of the dipoles are not connected together. A nonconducting spreader is used to hold the wires apart.

The dipole impedances interact to some degree depending on how different the frequencies are at which they are resonant. Modeling is recommended at the expected height

above ground but may not give completely accurate results due to the very shallow angle at which the wires join at the feed point. Expect some adjustments as the three dipoles are adjusted to give the desired SWR curve across the band. Two dipoles can cover approximately two-thirds of the band.

The third method is to place a parasitic dipole extremely close to the driven dipole so that it couples to the driven dipole and essentially operates in parallel with it. This technique was refined to use a folded dipole as described in the July 1995 *QST* article, "A Wideband 80-meter Dipole" by Rudy Severns, N6LF which is included on this book's CD-ROM. **Figure 9.11** shows the basic idea in which an isolated

Figure 9.12 — The center insulator is constructed from a PVC pipe tee with end caps covering each end. Stainless steel eyebolts are used to hold the ends of the cage and solder lugs with jumpers connect to the cage wires. Inside the tee, jumpers connect the eyebolts to the SO-239 on the third pipe cap. A piece of PVC pipe is U-bolted to the inner crosspieces of both cage sections. The entire assembly is supported by a sidearm from one of the W1AW towers. The antenna was constructed by W1AW Chief Operator Joe Carcia, NJ1Q.

wire is placed in the center of a folded dipole cut for the low end of the band. The center wire has a higher resonant frequency than that of outer, longer folded dipole and so acts as the radiator at the higher frequency. This antenna was able to provide a 2:1 SWR bandwidth of 3.3 to 4.25 MHz. The referenced article also includes references to designs using the parasitic element without folding the driven dipole.

W1AW 80 Meter Cage Dipole

The 80 meter cage antenna used at W1AW is based loosely on a design that appeared in a December 1980 *QST* article by Allen Harbach, WA4DRU (SK). (See the Bibliography and the CD-ROM included with this book.) The antenna is used primarily for W1AW's scheduled transmissions. It is also used for regular visitor operations as well. The resonant frequency of the antenna is 3627 kHz but the overall SWR is less than 2:1 from 3580 to 3995 kHz.

The W1AW cage antenna differs from the original article in that it's meant to be in place for a long period of time. So, most parts of the antenna are designed more ruggedly than in the Harbach design.

Each leg of the dipole is a cage made of four 80 meter dipole antennas of #14 AWG stranded copper wire tied together both at the ends and at the feed point as shown in **Figure 9.12**. Although Copperweld or an equivalent heftier wire could have been used, this size wire was easy to work with. The four wires forming each leg of the dipole are separated using a crosspiece made of PVC pipe as shown in **Figure 9.13**. There is a crosspiece near the feed point and the ends. The spacing between the wires is three feet.

Each cage wire passes through one leg of each crosspiece. A keeper wire is soldered across around the end of the

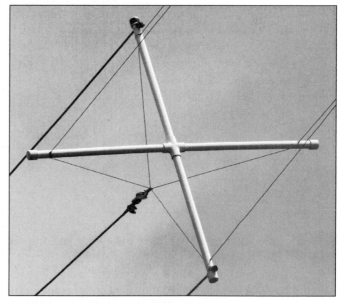

Figure 9.13 — The cage wires are kept separated by crosspieces of PVC pipe. The cage wires pass through a hole in the PVC pipe and a keeper wire is soldered to the cage wire on each side of the pipe to keep the crosspiece from moving along the wires.

PVC tube to the antenna wire on either side. This keeps the crosspiece from moving up and down the antenna. Exterior silicone caulk is applied to the hole in the tubing to seal it from moisture. Inside the crosspieces are oak dowels and the ends of the crosspieces are also capped. This adds rigidity to the crosspiece.

The feed point assembly is a homebrew PVC center

insulator consisting of a pair of 2-inch end caps attached to both ends of a 6-inch long, 2-inch PVC pipe tee. A stainless steel eyebolt with two solder lugs is mounted in the middle of each cap. One solder lug is on the outside of the cap for a connection to the antenna and the other is inside for connection to the SO-239 coax connector. The SO-239 is mounted on a third cap attached to the middle tee section.

An 8-turn coaxial choke is connected to the antenna at the center insulator. The choke is made from RG-213 coax using designs included in the **Transmission Line Coupling and Impedance Matching** chapter.

The center insulator assembly is bolted to a 4-foot length piece of 1-inch PVC pipe. The inner crosspieces are also bolted to this section of pipe as shown in the figure. This provides added support to the antenna. The center insulator and length of PVC are secured to the tower using a side-arm.

At the feed point, the four wires of each leg are brought together and looped through the eye-bolt. They are then twisted and soldered together and a short jumper of wire connects the twisted wires to a solder lug on the eyebolt. Inside each end cap, a jumper wire connects a second solder lug on the eyebolt to the SO-239 on the remaining cap.

At the outside ends of the cage, all four wires are brought to a common point, twisted together, and then attached to a strain insulator. The strain insulator and two of the crosspiece arms are tied off to the supports. This keeps the antenna legs from twisting in the breeze.

Tuning the antenna can be a bit tricky since each leg (wire) must be trimmed the same amount. It is best to start off with wire lengths calculated using the lowest operating frequency (for example, 3500 kHz). After trimming, the overall length of the antenna will be slightly smaller than that of a single-wire 80 meter dipole. This is because the radiating element is three feet in diameter — much thicker than a single-wire dipole.

While construction of this antenna is a bit more involved than that of a regular dipole, the result is a broadbanded antenna that doesn't require a tuner. The design specifications can also be recalculated to fit other amateur bands.

9.2 VERTICAL ANTENNAS

9.2.1 THE HALF-WAVE VERTICAL DIPOLE (HVD)

The simplest form of vertical is that of a half-wave vertical dipole, an HVD. This is a horizontal dipole turned 90° so that it is perpendicular to the ground under it. Of course, the top end of such an antenna must be at least a half wave above the ground or else it would be touching the ground. This poses quite a construction challenge if the builder wants a free-standing low-frequency antenna. Hams fortunate enough to have tall trees on their property can suspend wire HVDs from these trees. Similarly, hams with two tall towers can run rope catenaries between them to hold up an HVD.

A vertical half-wave dipole has some operational advantages compared to a more-commonly used vertical configuration — the quarter-wave vertical used with some sort of above-ground counterpoise or an on-ground radial system. See **Figure 9.14**, which shows the two configurations discussed here. In each case, the lowest part of each antenna is 8 feet above ground, to prevent passersby from being able to touch any live wire. Each antenna is assumed to be made of #14 AWG wire resonant on 80 meters.

Feeding a Half-Wave Vertical Dipole

Figure 9.15 compares elevation patterns for the two antennas for "average ground." You can see that the half-wave vertical dipole has about 1.5 dB higher peak gain, since it compresses the vertical elevation pattern down somewhat closer to the horizon than does the quarter-wave ground plane. Another advantage to using a half-wave radiator besides higher gain is that less horizontal "real estate" is needed compared to a quarter-wave vertical with its horizontal radials.

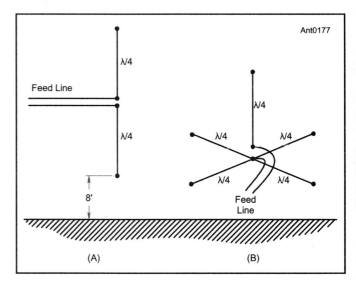

Figure 9.14 — At A, an 80 meter half-wave vertical dipole elevated 8 feet above the ground. The feed line is run perpendicularly away from the dipole. At B, a "ground plane" type of quarter-wave vertical, with four elevated resonant radials. Both antennas are mounted 8 feet above the ground to keep them away from passersby.

The obvious disadvantage to an HVD is that it is taller than a quarter-wave ground plane. This requires a higher support (such as a taller tree) if you make it from wire, or a longer element if you make it from telescoping aluminum tubing.

Another problem is that theory says you must dress the feed line so that it is perpendicular to the half-wave radiator. This means you must support the coax feed line above

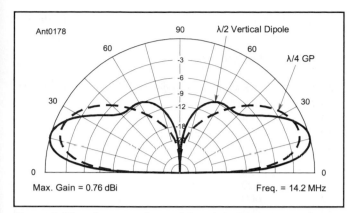

Figure 9.15 — A comparison of the elevation patterns for the two antennas in Figure 27. The peak gain of the HVD is about 1.5 dB higher than that for the quarter-wave ground-plane radiator with radials.

ground for some distance before bringing the coax down to ground level. A question immediately arises: How far must you go out horizontally with the feed line before going to ground level to eliminate common-mode currents that are radiated onto the coax shield? Such common-mode currents will affect the feed point impedance as well as the radiation pattern for the antenna system. Quite a bit of distortion in the azimuthal pattern can be created if common-mode currents aren't suppressed, usually by using a common-mode choke, also known as a current balun.

Constructing such a common-mode choke is very simple: ferrite beads of an approximate mix are slipped over the coax (before the connectors are soldered on or else they won't fit!) and taped in place. The only problem with this scheme is that

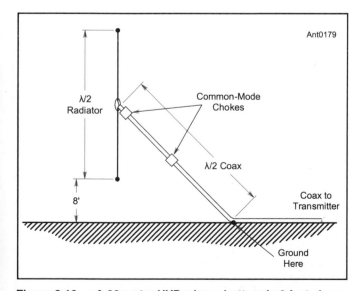

Figure 9.16 — A 20 meter HVD whose bottom is 8 feet above ground. This is fed with a λ/2 of RG-213 coax. This system uses a common-mode choke at the feed point and another λ/4 down the line. The resulting azimuthal radiation pattern is within 0.4 dB of being perfectly circular. The "wingspan" of this antenna system is 27 feet from the radiator to the point where the coax comes to ground level.

an additional support (some sort of "skyhook") is required to support the coax horizontally. Let's try to simplify the installation, by slanting the feed line coax down to ground from the feed point at a fairly steep angle of about 30° from vertical. See **Figure 9.16**.

Note that the bottom end of the coax in Figure 9.16 is grounded to a ground rod. This serves as a mechanical connection to hold the coax in place and it provides some protection against lightning strikes. Now, as a purely practical matter, just how picky are we being here? What if we skip the second common-mode choke and just use one at the feed point? The computer model predicts that there will be some distortion in the azimuthal pattern — about 1.1 dB worth. Whether this is serious is up to you. However, you may find other problems with common-mode currents on the coax shield — problems such as RF in the shack or variable SWR readings depending on the way coax is routed in the shack. The addition of three extra ferrite beads to suppress the common-mode currents is cheap insurance.

Later in this chapter we'll discuss shortened vertical antennas, ones arranged both as vertical dipoles and as vertical monopoles with radial systems. A variation on the HVD that is shortened through the use of capacitive loading is the *Compact Vertical Dipole (CVD)*. An article describing the CVD is included on the CD-ROM accompanying this book.

9.2.2. THE C-POLE

The antenna, designed by Brian Cake, KF2YN, consists of a vertical half-wave dipole that has been folded virtually in half and the feed point offset as shown in **Figure 9.17**. By erecting this just above ground level the ground currents are reduced dramatically over those of a λ/4 ground-mounted monopole. There is some induced ground current but it is quite small. The elevation radiation pattern for this antenna is virtually omni-directional. The design was originally published in the April 2004 issue of *QST*. The original article is included on this book's CD-ROM. The antenna's design is discussed in greater detail in *The Antenna Designer's Notebook* by the same author.

Construction is shown in **Figure 9.18** and dimensions for the HF amateur bands are given in **Table 9-2**. The author notes that using insulated wire or placing the antenna close to a structure will detune the antenna. Adjusting the length of the vertical wires is generally sufficient to restore proper operation.

Moving the feed point away from the voltage node at the antenna center increases the feed point impedance, and an exact match to 50 Ω at the center of the lower horizontal wire was obtained by shifting the position of the gap at the dipole ends. Unfortunately, doing this places the feed point at a position where there is a substantial common-mode potential. That is to say, the two antenna feed point terminals have the same potential on them relative to ground (in addition to the normal differential potential across the feed point), and this potential can be several hundred volts for an input power level of 100 W. If the coax is connected directly to the feed point, the natural resonance of the antenna is destroyed and

Table 9-2
Dimensions of C-pole Antennas
Wire diameter is 1/16-inch. Height of the lower horizontal wire is 12 inches to 24 inches and is non-critical.
See Figure 9.17 for the key to the dimensions.

Band (meters)	A (inches)	B (inches)	C (inches)	D (inches)	E (inches)	2:1 SWR bandwidth (kHz)
160	1666	924	994	60	80	58
80	840	460	360	30	40	120
60	591	322	249	20	26	250
40	450	240	190	20	20	260
30	320	167	139	14	14	360
20	177	85	84	8	40	400
15	124	60	60	4	20	600
10	87	46	37	4	20	800

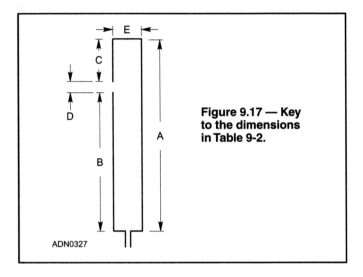

Figure 9.17 — Key to the dimensions in Table 9-2.

ADN0327

it becomes useless. The author specifies a balun to solve the problem as follows. The baluns are wound on FT-240-61 ferrite cores, and can use either twisted-pair feed line or coaxial cable wound through the core:

160 meters, 32 turns on two cores glued together to make a thick donut

80 meters, 32 turns on a single core

60 meters, 28 turns on a single core

40 meters, 23 turns on a single core

30 and 20 meters, 20 turns on a single core

17 meters and up, 15 turns on a single core, use FT-240-67 material

9.2.3 MONOPOLE VERTICALS WITH GROUND-PLANE RADIALS

For best performance the vertical portion of a ground-plane type of antenna should be λ/4 or more, but this is not an absolute requirement. With proper design, antennas as short as 0.1 λ or even less can be efficient and effective. Antennas shorter than λ/4 will be reactive and some form of loading and perhaps a matching network will be required.

If the radiator is made of wire supported by nonconducting

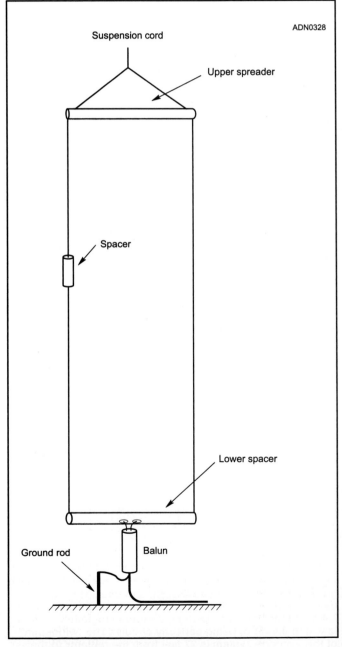

ADN0328

Figure 9.18 — C-pole construction details.

material, the *approximate* length for λ/4 resonance can be found from:

$$\ell_{feet} = \frac{234}{f_{MHz}} \qquad \text{(Eq 1)}$$

The same cautions about the effects of ground and wire or tubing diameter apply to this equation for verticals. For a tower, the resonant length will be shorter still. It is recommended that the builder start a few percent long and trim the antenna to length based on measurements taken with the antenna in place. (See the **Dipoles and Monopoles** chapter.)

The effect of ground characteristics on losses and elevation pattern is discussed in detail in the chapter **Effects of Ground**. The most important points made in that discussion are the effect of ground characteristics on the radiation pattern and the means for achieving low ground-loss resistance in a buried ground system. As ground conductivity increases, low-angle radiation improves. This makes a vertical very attractive to those who live in areas with good ground conductivity. If your QTH is on a saltwater beach, then a vertical would be very effective, even when compared to horizontal antennas at great height.

When a buried-radial ground system is used, the efficiency of the antenna will be limited by the loss resistance of the ground system. The ground can be a number of radial wires extending out from the base of the antenna for about λ/4. Driven ground rods, while satisfactory for electrical safety and for lightning protection, are of little value as an RF ground for a vertical antenna, except perhaps in marshy or beach areas. As pointed out, many long radials are desirable. In general, however, a large number of short radials are preferable to only a few long radials, although the best system would have 60 or more radials longer than λ/4. An elevated system of radials or a ground screen (*counterpoise*) may be used instead of buried radials, and can result in an efficient antenna. **Figure 9.19** and **Figure 9.20** illustrate the difference between buried and elevated radial systems and counterpoises. The reader is directed to the chapter **Effects of Ground** for a discussion of ground plane radial systems and counterpoises for vertical monopole antennas.

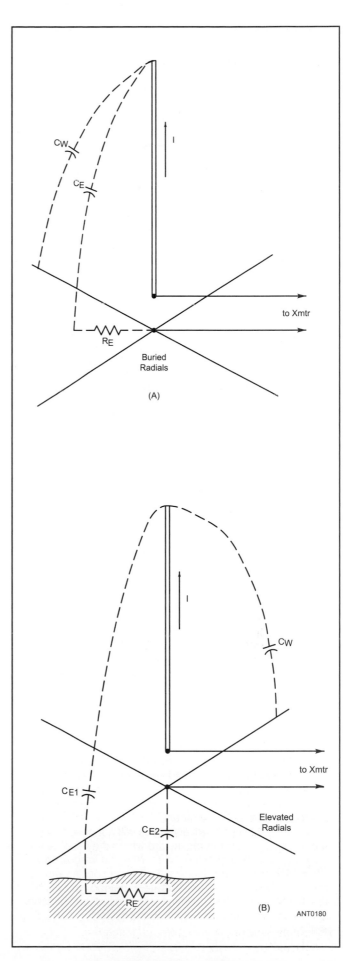

Figure 9.19 — How earth currents affect the losses in a short vertical antenna system. At A, the current through the combination of C_E and R_E may be appreciable if C_E is much greater than C_W, the capacitance of the vertical to the ground wires. This ratio can be improved (up to a point) by using more radials. By raising the entire antenna system off the ground, C_E (which consists of the series combination of C_{E1} and C_{E2}) is decreased while C_W stays the same. The radial system shown at B is sometimes called a *counterpoise*.

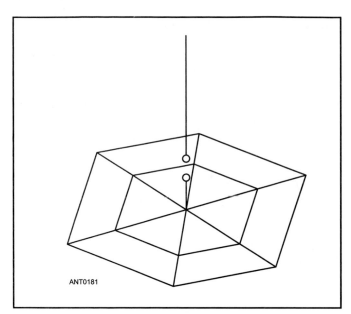

Figure 9.20 — Counterpoise, showing the radial wires connected together by cross wires. The length of the perimeter of the individual meshes should be < λ/4 to prevent undesired resonances. Sometimes the center portion of the counterpoise is made from wire mesh.

9.2.4 GROUND-PLANE ANTENNAS

The ground-plane antenna is a λ/4 vertical with four radials, as shown in **Figure 9.21**. The entire antenna is elevated above ground. A practical example of a 7-MHz ground-plane antenna is given in **Figure 9.22**. As explained earlier, elevating the antenna reduces the ground loss and lowers the radiation angle somewhat. The radials are sloped downward to

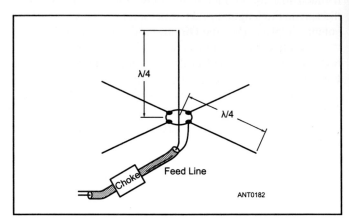

Figure 9.21 — The ground-plane antenna. Power is applied between the base of the vertical radiator and the center of the ground plane, as indicated in the drawing. Decoupling from the transmission line and any conductive support structure is highly desirable.

Radial Spacing

Figuring out how to space radials equally around a circle is explained in this sidebar. The information was originally published on the Towertalk reflector by Rod Ehrhart, WN8R, of DX Engineering.

Begin by determining the radius of the circle in which the radials will be installed. If your area is irregular, choose the minimum radial length. An example is the best way of illustrating the process:

If your minimum radial length is 25 feet, establish a circle that has a radius (r) of 25 feet from the antenna mount. The circumference (C) of that circle is $2\pi r$ or C = (2) × (3.14) × (25 feet), which equals 157 feet. If you have decided to install 60 radials (N = 60), the spacing (S) between each radial on the 25-foot radius circle is calculated as S = C / N or S = 157 feet / 60 radials = 2.6 feet or about 2 feet, 7 inches between each radial on the circle. Use string to draw the circle and measure 2 feet, 7 inches spacing around the circle. If the radial is longer than 25 feet, stretch it straight out from the antenna mount so that it crosses the circle at the marked point.

If you want to install 90 radials, then it would be 157 feet / 90 radials = 1.74 feet/radial, or a little less than 1 foot 9 inches between each radial wire on the circle at 25 feet from the antenna mount.

Working this out in advance, you will not need to worry about how far apart the radials are where they end, or trying to eye-ball their spacing. When filling an irregular area with radials, each one will have a different spacing where they end. By using this measurement method, you will be able to make all of the radials evenly spaced, and as long as they can be, for maximum antenna system performance.

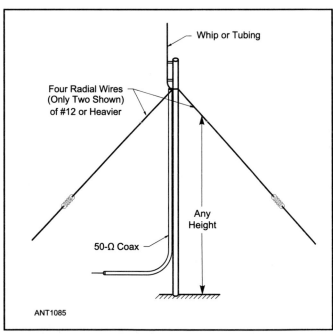

Figure 9.22 — A ground-plane antenna is effective for DX work on 7 MHz. Although its base can be any height above ground, losses in the ground underneath will be reduced by keeping the bottom of the antenna and the ground plane as high above ground as possible. Feeding the antenna directly with 50-Ω coaxial cable will result in a low SWR. The vertical radiator and the radials are all λ/4 long electrically. The radial's physical length will depend on their length-to-diameter ratios, the height over ground and the length of the vertical radiator, as discussed in text.

make the feed point impedance closer to 50 Ω.

The feed point impedance of the antenna varies with the height above ground, and to a lesser extent varies with the ground characteristics. **Figure 9.23** is a graph of feed point resistance (R_R) for a ground-plane antenna with the radials parallel to the ground. R_R is plotted as a function of height above ground. Notice that the difference between perfect ground and average ground ($\varepsilon = 13$ and $\sigma = 0.005$ S/m) is small, except when quite close to ground. Near ground R_R is between 36 and 40 Ω. This is a reasonable match for 50-Ω feed line but as the antenna is raised above ground R_R drops to approximately 22 Ω, which is not a very good match. The feed point resistance can be increased by sloping the radials downward, away from the vertical section.

The effect of sloping the radials is shown in **Figure 9.24**. The graph is for an antenna well above ground (> 0.3 λ). Notice that $R_R = 50$ Ω when the radials are sloped downward

at an angle of 45°, a convenient value. The resonant length of the antenna will vary slightly with the angle. In addition, the resonant length will vary a small amount with height above the ground. It is for these reasons, as well as the effect of conductor diameter, that some adjustment of the radial lengths is usually required. When the ground-plane antenna is used on the higher HF bands and at VHF, the height above ground is usually such that a radial sloping angle of 45° will give a good match to 50-Ω feed line.

The effect of height on R_R with a radial angle of 45° is shown in **Figure 9.25**. At 7 MHz and lower frequencies, it is seldom possible to elevate the antenna a significant portion of a wavelength and the radial angle required to match to 50-Ω line is usually of the order of 10° to 20°. To make the vertical portion of the antenna as long as possible, it may be better to accept a slightly poorer match and keep the radials parallel to ground.

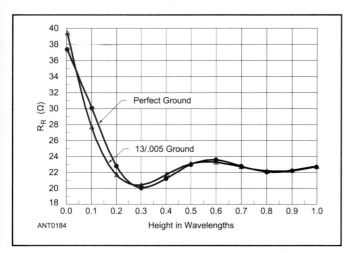

Figure 9.23 — Radiation resistance of a 4-radial ground-plane antenna as a function of height over ground. Perfect and average ground are shown. Frequency is 3.525 MHz. Radial angle (θ) is 0°.

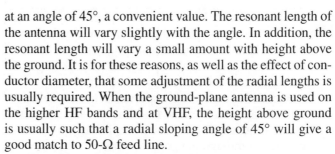

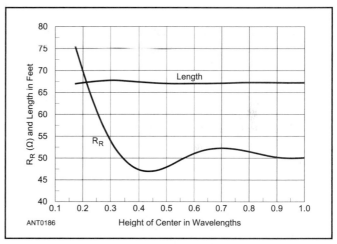

Figure 9.25 — Radiation resistance and resonant length for a 4-radial ground-plane antenna for various heights above average ground for radial droop angle θ = 45°.

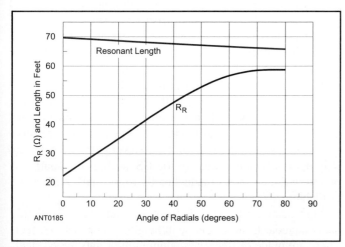

Figure 9.24 — Radiation resistance and resonant length for a 4-radial ground-plane antenna > 0.3 λ above ground as a function of radial droop angle (θ).

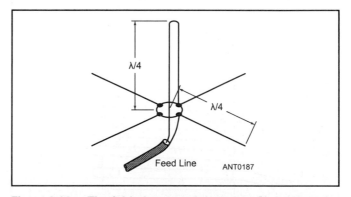

Figure 9.26 — The folded monopole antenna. Shown here is a ground plane of four λ/4 radials. The folded element may be operated over an extensive counterpoise system or mounted on the ground and worked against buried radials and the earth. As with the folded dipole antenna, the feed point impedance depends on the ratios of the radiator conductor sizes and their spacing.

The principles of the folded dipole discussed earlier can also be applied to the ground-plane antenna, as shown in **Figure 9.26**. This is the *folded monopole* antenna. The feed point resistance can be controlled by the number of parallel vertical conductors and the ratios of their diameters.

As mentioned earlier, it is important in most installations to isolate the antenna from the feed line and any conductive supporting structure. This is done to minimize the return current conducted through the ground. A return current on the feed line itself or the support structure can drastically alter the radiation pattern, usually for the worse. For these reasons, a balun (see the chapter **Transmission Line Coupling and Impedance Matching**) or other isolation scheme must be used. 1:1 baluns are effective for the higher bands but at 3.5 and 1.8 MHz commercial baluns often have too low a shunt inductance to provide adequate isolation. It is very easy to recognize when the isolation is inadequate. When the antenna is being adjusted while watching an isolated impedance or SWR meter, adjustments may be sensitive to your touching the instrument. After adjustment and after the feed line is attached, the SWR may be drastically different. When the feed line is inadequately isolated, the apparent resonant frequency or the length of the radials required for resonance may also be significantly different from what you expect.

In general, a choke balun inductance of 50 to 100 µH will be needed for 3.5 and 1.8-MHz ground-plane antennas. One of the easiest ways to make the required choke balun is to wind a length of coaxial cable into a coil as shown in **Figure 9.27**. For 1.8 MHz, 30 turns of RG-213 wound on a 14-inch length of 8-inch diameter PVC pipe will make a very good choke balun that can handle full legal power continuously. A smaller choke could be wound on 4-inch diameter plastic drain pipe using RG-8X or a Teflon insulated cable. The important point here is to isolate or decouple the antenna

from the feed line and support structure.

A full-size ground-plane antenna is often a little impractical for 3.5-MHz and quite impractical for 1.8 MHz, but it can be used at 7 MHz to good advantage, particularly for DX work. Smaller versions can be very useful on 3.5 and 1.8 MHz.

9.2.5 EXAMPLES OF VERTICALS

There are many possible ways to build a vertical antenna — the limits are set by your ingenuity. The primary problem is creating the vertical portion of the antenna with sufficient height. Some of the more common means are:

- A dedicated tower
- Using an existing tower with an HF Yagi on top
- A wire suspended from a tree limb or the side of a building
- A vertical wire supported by a line between two trees or other supports
- A tall pole supporting a conductor
- Flagpoles
- Light standards
- Irrigation pipe
- TV masts

If you have the space and the resources, the most straightforward means is to erect a dedicated tower for a vertical. While this is certainly an effective approach, many amateurs do not have the space or the funds to do this, especially if they already have a tower with an HF antenna on the top. The existing tower can be used as a top-loaded vertical, using shunt feed and a ground radial system. A system like this is shown in **Figure 9.28B**.

For those who live in an area with tall trees, it may be possible to install a support rope between two trees, or between a tree and an existing tower. (Under no circumstances should you use an active utility pole!) The vertical portion of the antenna can be a wire suspended from the support line to ground, as shown in Figure 9.28C. If top loading is needed, some or all of the support line can be made part of the antenna.

Your local utility company will periodically have older power poles that they no longer wish to keep in service. These are sometimes available at little or no expense. If you see a power line under reconstruction or repair in your area you might stop and speak with the crew foreman. Sometimes they will have removed older poles they will not use again and will have to haul them back to their shop for disposal. Your offer for local "disposal" may well be accepted. Such a pole can be used in conjunction with a tubing or whip extension such as that shown in Figure 9.28A. Power poles are not your only option. In some areas of the US, such as the southeast or northwest, tall poles made directly from small conifers are available.

Freestanding (unguyed) flagpoles and roadway illumination standards are available in heights exceeding 100 feet. These are made of fiberglass, aluminum or galvanized steel. All of these are candidates for verticals. Flagpole suppliers are listed under "Flags and Banners" in your Yellow Pages.

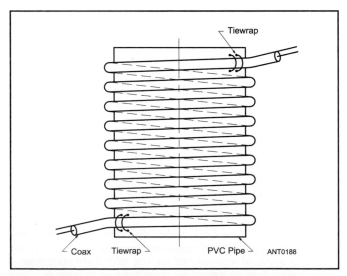

Figure 9.27 — A choke balun with sufficient impedance to isolate the antenna properly can be made by winding coaxial cable around a section of plastic pipe. Suitable dimensions are given in the text.

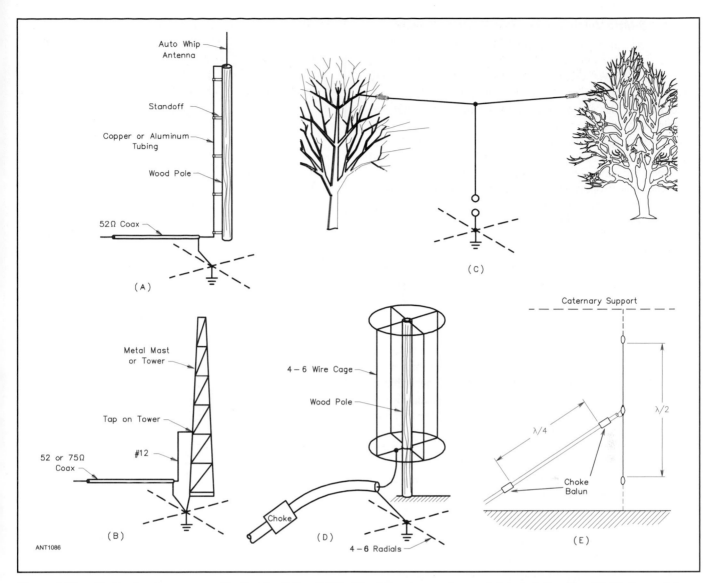

Figure 9.28 — Vertical antennas are effective for 3.5 or 7 MHz. The λ/4 antenna shown at A is fed directly with 50-Ω coaxial line, and the resulting SWR is usually less than 1.5 to 1, depending on the ground resistance. If a grounded antenna is used as at B, the antenna can be shunt fed with either 50- or 75-Ω coaxial line. The tap for best match and the value of C will have to be found by experiment. The line running up the side of the antenna should be spaced 6 to 12 inches from the antenna. If tall trees are available the antenna can be supported from a line suspended between the trees, as shown in C. If the vertical section is not long enough then the horizontal support section can be made of wire and act as top loading. A pole or even a grounded tower can be used with elevated radials if a cage of four to six wires is provided as shown in D. The cage surrounds the pole which may be wood or a grounded conductor.

For lighting standards (lamp posts), you can contact a local electrical hardware distributor. Like a wooden pole, a fiberglass flagpole does not require a base insulator, but metal poles do. Guy wires will be needed.

One option to avoid the use of guys and a base insulator is to mount the pole directly into the ground as originally intended and then use shunt feed. If you want to keep the pole grounded but would like to use elevated radials, you can attach a cage of wires (four to six) at the top as shown in Figure 9.28D. The cage surrounds the pole and allows the pole (or tower for that matter) to be grounded while allowing elevated radials to be used. The use of a cage of wires surrounding

the pole or tower is a very good way to increase the effective diameter. This reduces the Q of the antenna, thereby increasing the bandwidth. It can also reduce the conductor loss, especially if the pole is galvanized steel, which is not a very good RF conductor.

Aluminum irrigation tubing, which comes in diameters of 3 and 4 inches and in lengths of 20 to 40 feet, is widely available in rural areas. One or two lengths of tubing connected together can make a very good vertical when guyed with non-conducting line. It is also very lightweight and relatively easy to erect. A variety of TV masts are available which can also be used for verticals.

1.8 to 3.5-MHz Vertical Using an Existing Tower

A tower can be used as a vertical antenna, provided that a good ground system is available. The shunt-fed tower is at its best on 1.8 MHz, where a full λ/4 vertical antenna is rarely possible. Almost any tower height can be used. If the beam structure provides some top loading, so much the better, but anything can be made to radiate — if it is fed properly. Earl Cunningham, K6SE (SK) used a self-supporting, aluminum, crank-up, tilt-over tower, with a TH6DXX tribander mounted at 70 feet. Measurements showed that the entire structure has about the same properties as a 125-foot vertical. It thus works quite well as an antenna on 1.8 and 3.5 MHz for DX work requiring low-angle radiation.

Preparing the Structure

Usually some work on the tower system must be done before shunt-feeding is tried. If present, metallic guys should be broken up with insulators. They can be made to simulate top loading, if needed, by judicious placement of the first insulators. Don't overdo it; there is no need to "tune the radiator to resonance" in this way since a shunt feed is employed. If the tower is fastened to a house at a point more than about one-fourth of the height of the tower, it may be desirable to insulate the tower from the building. Plexiglas sheet, ¼-inch or more thick, can be bent to any desired shape for this purpose if it is heated in an oven and bent while hot.

All cables should be taped tightly to the tower, on the inside, and run down to the ground level. It is not necessary to bond shielded cables to the tower electrically, but there should be no exceptions to the down-to-the-ground rule.

A good system of buried radials is very desirable. The ideal would be 120 radials, each 250 feet long, but fewer and shorter ones must often suffice. You can lay them around corners of houses, along fences or sidewalks, wherever they can be put a few inches under the surface, or even on the ground. Aluminum clothesline wire may be used extensively in areas where it will not be subject to corrosion. Neoprene-covered aluminum wire will be better in highly acid soils. Contact with the soil is not important. Deep-driven ground rods and connection to underground copper water pipes may be helpful, if available, especially to provide some protection from lightning.

Installing the Shunt Feed

Principal details of the shunt-fed tower for 1.8 and 3.5 MHz are shown in **Figure 9.29**. Rigid rod or tubing can be used for the feed portion, but heavy gauge aluminum or copper wire is easier to work with. Flexible stranded #8 AWG copper wire is used at K6SE for the 1.8-MHz feed, because when the tower is cranked down, the feed wire must come down with it. Connection is made at the top, 68 feet, through a 4-foot length of aluminum tubing clamped to the top of the tower, horizontally. The wire is clamped to the tubing at the outer end, and runs down vertically through standoff insulators. These are made by fitting 12-inch lengths of PVC plastic water pipe over 3-foot lengths of aluminum tubing. These are clamped to the tower at 15- to 20-foot intervals, with the

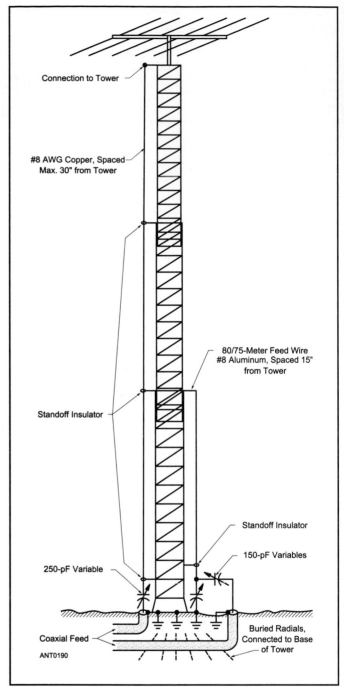

Figure 9.29 — Principal details of the shunt-fed tower at K6SE (SK). The 1.8-MHz feed, left side, connects to the top of the tower through a horizontal arm of 1-inch diameter aluminum tubing. The other arms have standoff insulators at their outer ends, made of 1-foot lengths of plastic water pipe. The connection for 3.5-4 MHz, right, is made similarly, at 28 feet, but two variable capacitors are used to permit adjustment of matching with large changes in frequency.

bottom clamp about 3 feet above ground. These lengths allow for adjustment of the tower-to-wire spacing over a range of about 12 to 36 inches, for impedance matching.

The gamma-match capacitor for 1.8 MHz is a 250-pF variable with about ⅛-inch plate spacing. This is adequate for power levels up to about 200 W. A large transmitting or a vacuum-variable capacitor should be used for high-power applications.

Tuning Procedure

The 1.8-MHz feed wire should be connected to the top of the structure if it is 75 feet tall or less. Mount the standoff insulators so as to have a spacing of about 24 inches between wire and tower. Pull the wire taut and clamp it in place at the bottom insulator. Leave a little slack below to permit adjustment of the wire spacing, if necessary.

Adjust the series capacitor in the 1.8-MHz line for minimum reflected power, as indicated on an SWR meter connected between the coax and the connector on the capacitor housing. Make this adjustment at a frequency near the middle of your expected operating range. If a high SWR is indicated, try moving the wire closer to the tower. Just the lower part of the wire need be moved for an indication as to whether reduced spacing is needed. If the SWR drops, move all insulators closer to the tower, and try again.

If the SWR goes up, increase the spacing. There will be a practical range of about 12 to 36 inches. If going down to 12 inches does not give a low SWR, try connecting the top a bit farther down the tower. If wide spacing does not make it, the omega match shown for 3.5 MHz should be tried. No adjustment of spacing is needed with the latter arrangement, which may be necessary with short towers or installations having little or no top loading.

The two-capacitor arrangement in the omega match is also useful for working in more than one 25-kHz segment of the 160 meter band. Tune up on the highest frequency, say 1990 kHz, using the single capacitor, making the settings of wire spacing and connection point permanent for this frequency. To move to the lower frequency, say 1810 kHz, connect the second capacitor into the circuit and adjust it for the new frequency. Switching the second capacitor in and out then allows changing from one segment to the other, with no more than a slight retuning of the first capacitor.

9.2.6 ELEVATED GROUND-PLANE ANTENNAS

This section describes a simple and effective means of using a grounded tower, with or without top-mounted antennas, as an elevated ground-plane antenna for 80 and 160 meters. It first appeared in a June 1994 *QST* article by Thomas Russell, N4KG.

From Sloper to Vertical

Recall the quarter-wavelength sloper, also known as the *half sloper*. (The half sloper is covered later in this chapter in more detail.) It consists of an isolated quarter wavelength of wire, sloping from an elevated feed point on a grounded tower. Best results are usually obtained when the feed point is somewhere below a top-mounted Yagi antenna. You feed a sloper by attaching the center conductor of a coaxial cable to the wire and the braid of the cable to the tower leg. Now, imagine four (or more) slopers, but instead of feeding each individually, connect them together to the center conductor of

Table 9-3
Effective Loading of Common Yagi Antennas

Antenna	Boom Length (feet)	S (area, ft²)	Equivalent Loading (feet)
3L 20	24	768	39
5L 15	26	624	35
4L 15	20	480	31
3L 15	16	384	28
5L 10	24	384	28
4L 10	18	288	24
3L 10	12	192	20
TH7	24	—	40 (estimated)
TH3	14	—	27 (estimated)

a single feed line. Voilà! Instant elevated ground plane.

Now, all you need to do is determine how to tune the antenna to resonance. With no antennas on the top of the tower, the tower can be thought of as a fat conductor and should be approximately 4% shorter than a quarter wavelength in free space. Calculate this length and attach four insulated quarter-wavelength radials at this distance from the top of the tower. For 80 meters, a feed point 65 feet below the top of an unloaded tower is called for. The tower guys must be broken up with insulators for all such installations. For 160 meters, 130 feet of tower above the feed point is needed.

What can be done with a typical grounded-tower-and-Yagi installation? A top-mounted Yagi acts as a large capacitance hat, top loading the tower. Fortunately, top loading is the most efficient means of loading a vertical antenna.

The examples in **Table 9-3** should give us an idea of how much top loading might be expected from typical amateur antennas. The values listed in the *Equivalent Loading* column tell us the approximate vertical height replaced by the antennas listed in a top-loaded vertical antenna. To arrive at the remaining amount of tower needed for resonance, subtract these numbers from the non-loaded tower height needed for resonance. Note that for all but the 10 meter antennas, the equivalent loading equals or exceeds a quarter wavelength on 40 meters. For typical HF Yagis, this method is best used only on 80 and 160 meters.

Construction Examples

Consider this example: A TH7 triband Yagi mounted on a 40-foot tower. The TH7 has approximately the same overall dimensions as a full-sized 3-element 20 meter beam, but has more interlaced elements. Its equivalent loading is estimated to be 40 feet. At 3.6 MHz, 65 feet of tower is needed without loading. Subtracting 40 feet of equivalent loading, the feed point should be 25 feet below the TH7 antenna.

Ten λ/4 (65-foot) radials were run from a nylon rope tied between tower legs at the 15-foot level, to various supports 10 feet high. Nylon cord was tied to the insulated, stranded, #18 AWG wire, without using insulators. The radials are all connected together and to the center of an exact half

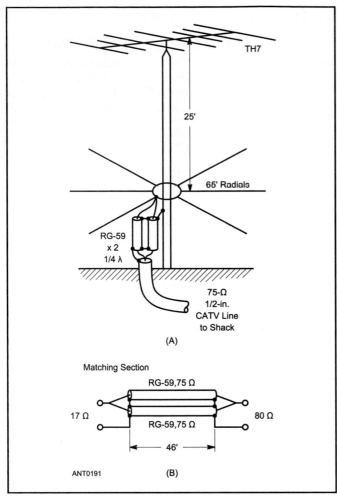

Figure 9.30 — At A, an 80 meter top-loaded, reverse-fed elevated ground plane, using a 40-foot tower carrying a TH7 triband Yagi antenna. At B, dimensions of the 3.6-MHz matching network, made from RG-59.

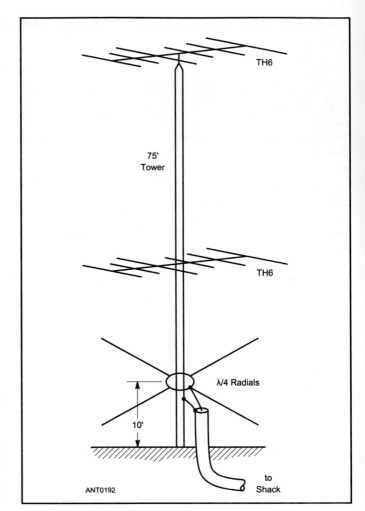

Figure 9.31 — A 160 meter antenna using a 75-foot tower carrying stacked triband Yagis.

wavelength (at 3.6 MHz) of RG-213 coax, which will repeat the antenna feed impedance at the other end. **Figure 9.30** is a drawing of the installation. The author used a Hewlett-Packard low-frequency impedance analyzer to measure the input impedance across the 80 meter band. An exact resonance (zero reactance) was seen at 3.6 MHz, just as predicted. The radiation resistance was found to be 17 Ω. The next question is, how to feed and match the antenna.

One good approach to 80 meter antennas is to tune them to the low end of the band, use a low-loss transmission line, and switch an antenna tuner in line for operation in the higher portions of the band. With a 50-Ω line, the 17-Ω radiation resistance represents a 3:1 SWR, meaning that an antenna tuner should be in-line for all frequencies. For short runs, it would be permissible to use RG-8 or RG-213 directly to the tuner. If you have a plentiful supply of low-loss 75-Ω CATV rigid coax, you can take another approach.

Make a quarter-wave (70 feet × 0.66 velocity factor = 46 feet) 37-Ω matching line by paralleling two pieces of RG-59 and connecting them between the feed point and a

run of the rigid coax to the transmitter. The magic of quarter-wave matching transformers is that the input impedance (R_i) and output impedance (R_o) are related by:

$$Z_0{}^2 = R_i \times R_o \qquad \text{(Eq 2)}$$

For $R_i = 17\ \Omega$ and $Z_0 = 37\ \Omega$, $R_o = 80\ \Omega$, an almost perfect match for the matching section made from 75-Ω CATV coax. The resulting 1.6:1 SWR at the transmitter is good enough for CW operation without a tuner.

160 Meter Operation

On the 160 meter band, a resonant quarter-wavelength requires 130 feet of tower above the radials. That's a pretty tall order. Subtracting 40 feet of top loading for a 3-element 20 meter or TH7 antenna brings us to a more reasonable 90 feet above the radials. Additional top loading in the form of more antennas will reduce that even more.

Another installation, using stacked TH6s on a 75-foot tower, is shown in **Figure 9.31**. The radials are 10 feet off the ground.

9.3 LOADING TECHNIQUES

9.3.1 LOADING VERTICAL ANTENNAS

On the lower frequencies it becomes increasingly difficult to accommodate a full λ/4 vertical height and full-sized λ/4 radials, or even worse, a full-sized half-wave vertical dipole (HVD). In fact, it is not absolutely necessary to make the antenna full size, whether it is an HVD, a grounded monopole antenna or a ground-plane type of monopole antenna. The size of the antenna can be reduced by half or even more and still retain high efficiency and the desired radiation pattern. This requires careful design, however. And if high efficiency is maintained, the operating bandwidth of the shortened antenna will be reduced because the shortened antenna will have a higher Q.

This translates into a more rapid increase of reactance away from resonance. The effect can be mitigated to some extent by using larger-diameter conductors. Even doing this however, bandwidth will be a problem, particularly on the 3.5 to 4-MHz band, which is very wide in proportion to the center frequency.

If we take a vertical monopole with a diameter of 2 inches and a frequency of 3.525 MHz and progressively shorten it from λ/4 in length, the feed point impedance and efficiency (using an inductor at the base to tune out the capacitive reactance) will vary as shown in **Table 9-4**. In this example perfect ground and conductor are assumed. Real ground will not make a great difference in the impedance but will introduce ground loss, which will reduce the efficiency further. Conductor loss will also reduce efficiency. In general, higher R_R will result in better efficiency.

The important point of Table 9-4 is the drastic reduction in radiation resistance R_R as the antenna gets shorter. This combined with the increasing loss resistance of the inductor (R_L) used to tune out the increasing base reactance (X_C) reduces the efficiency.

9.3.2 BASE LOADING A SHORT VERTICAL ANTENNA

The base of the antenna is a convenient point at which to add a loading inductor, but it is usually not the lowest loss point at which an inductor, of a given Q, could be placed.

There is an extensive discussion of the optimum location of the loading in a short vertical as a function of ground loss and inductor Q in the chapter **Mobile and Maritime HF Antennas**, which by necessity are electrically and physically short. This information should be reviewed before using inductive loading.

Available for download from **www.arrl.org/antennabook** is the program *MOBILE.EXE*. This is an excellent tool for designing short, inductively loaded antennas. In most cases, where top loading (discussed below) is not used, the optimum point is near or a little above the middle of the vertical section. Moving the loading coil from the base to the middle of the vertical antenna can make an important difference, increasing R_R and reducing the inductor loss. For example, in an antenna operating at 3.525 MHz, if we make L_1 = 34.9 feet (0.125 λ) the amount of loading inductor placed at the center is 25.2 μH. This resonates the antenna. In this configuration R_R will increase from 6.8 Ω (base loading) to 13.5 Ω (center loading). This substantially increases the efficiency of the antenna, depending on the ground loss and conductor resistances.

Instead of a lumped inductance being inserted at some point in the antenna, it is also possible to use "continuous loading," where the entire radiator is wound as a small diameter coil. The effect is to distribute the inductive loading all along the radiator. In this version of inductive loading the coil is the radiator. An example of a short vertical using this principle is given later in this chapter.

9.3.3 OTHER METHODS OF LOADING SHORT VERTICAL ANTENNAS

Inductive loading is not the only, or even the best, way to compensate for reduced antenna height. *Capacitive top loading* can also be used as indicated in **Figure 9.32** to bring a vertical monopole to resonance. **Table 9-5** gives information on a shortened 3.525-MHz vertical using top loading. The vertical portion (L_1) is made from 2 inch tubing. The top loading is also 2-inch tubing extending across the top like a T. The length of the top loading T ($\pm L_2$) is adjusted to resonate the antenna. Again, the ground and the conductors are assumed to be perfect in Table 9-5.

Table 9-4
Effect of Shortening a Vertical Radiator Below λ/4 Using Inductive Base Loading.
Frequency is 3.525 MHz and for the Inductor Q_L = 200. Ground and conductor losses are omitted.

Length (feet)	Length (λ)	R_R (Ω)	X_C (Ω)	R_L (Ω)	Efficiency (%)	Loss (dB)
14	0.050	0.96	−761	3.8	20	−7.0
20.9	0.075	2.2	−533	2.7	45	−3.5
27.9	0.100	4.2	−395	2.0	68	−1.7
34.9	0.125	6.8	−298	1.5	82	−0.86
41.9	0.150	10.4	−220	1.1	90	−0.44
48.9	0.175	15.1	−153	0.77	95	−0.22
55.8	0.200	21.4	−92	0.46	98	−0.09
62.8	0.225	29.7	−34	0.17	99	−0.02

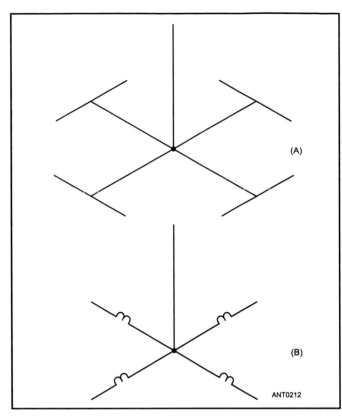

Figure 9.37 — Radials may be shortened by using either capacitive (A) or inductive (B) loading. In extreme cases both may be used but the operating bandwidth will be limited.

directly between the capacitance "hat" and the top of the antenna, can be added to resonate the antenna. An alternative would be to use linear loading in place of inductive loading. The previous section contained an example of end loading combined with linear loading.

Shortening Radials

Very often the space required by full-length radials is simply not available. Like the vertical portion of the antenna, the radials can also be shortened and loaded in very much the same way. An example of end loaded radials is given in **Figure 9.37A**. Radials half the usual length can be used with little reduction in efficiency but, as in the case of top loading, the antenna Q will be higher and the bandwidth reduced. As shown in Figure 9.37B, inductive loading can also be used. As long as they are not made too short (down to 0.1λ) loaded radials can be efficient — with careful design.

9.3.4 GENERAL RULES FOR LOADING VERTICAL ANTENNAS

The steps in designing an efficient short vertical antenna system are:
- Make the vertical section as long as possible.
- Make the diameter of the vertical section as large as possible. Tubing or a cage of smaller wires will work well.
- Provide as much top and/or bottom loading as possible.
- If the top/bottom loading is insufficient, resonate the

antenna with a high-Q inductor placed between the hat and the top of the antenna.
- For buried-ground systems, use as many radials (> 0.2 λ) as possible. 32 or more is best.
- If an elevated ground plane is used, use 4 to 8 radials, 5 or more feet above ground.
- If shortened radials must be used then capacitive loading is preferable to inductive loading.

9.3.5 LINEAR LOADING

Another alternative to inductive loading is *linear loading*. This little-understood method of shortening radiators can be applied to almost any antenna configuration — including parasitic arrays. Although commercial antenna manufacturers make use of linear loading in their HF antennas, relatively few hams have used it in their own designs. Linear loading can be used to advantage in many antennas because it introduces relatively little loss, does not degrade directivity patterns, and has low enough Q to allow reasonably good bandwidth. Some examples of linear-loaded antennas are shown in **Figure 9.38**.

Since the dimensions and spacing of linear-loading devices vary greatly from one antenna installation to another, the best way to employ this technique is to try a length of conductor 10% to 20% longer than the difference between the shortened antenna and the full-size dimension for the linear-loading device. Then use the "cut-and-try" method, varying both the spacing and length of the loading device to optimize the match. A hairpin at the feed point can be useful in achieving a 1:1 SWR at resonance.

Linear-Loaded Short Wire Antennas

More detail on linear loading is provided in this section,

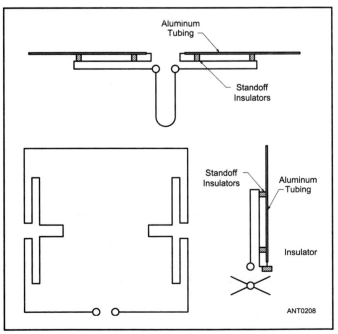

Figure 9.38 — Some examples of linear loading. The small circles indicate the feed points of the antennas.

which was originally presented in *The ARRL Antenna Compendium Vol 5* by John Stanford, NNØF. Linear loading can significantly reduce the required length for resonant antennas. For example, it is easy to make a resonant antenna that is as much as 30 to 40% shorter than an ordinary dipole for a given band. The shorter overall lengths come from bending back some of the wire. The increased self-coupling lowers the resonant frequency. These ideas are applicable to short antennas for restricted space or portable use.

Experiments

The results of the measurements are shown in **Figure 9.39** and are also consistent with values given by Rashed and Tai from an earlier paper. This shows several simple wire antenna configurations, with resonant frequencies and impedance (radiation resistance). The reference dipole has a resonant frequency f_0 and resistance R = 72 Ω. The f/f_0 values give the effective reduced frequency obtained with the linear loading in each case. For example, the two-wire linear-loaded dipole has its resonant frequency lowered to about 0.67 to 0.70 that of the simple reference dipole of the same length.

The three-wire linear-loaded dipole has its frequency reduced to 0.55 to 0.60 of the simple dipole of the same length. As you will see later, these values will vary with conductor diameter and spacing.

The two-wire linear-loaded dipole (Figure 9.39B) looks almost like a folded dipole but, unlike a folded dipole, it is open in the middle of the side opposite where the feed line is attached. Measurements show that this antenna structure has a resonant frequency lowered to about two-thirds that of the reference dipole, and R equal to about 35 Ω. A three-wire linear-loaded dipole (Figure 9.39C) has even lower resonant frequency and R about 25 to 30 Ω.

Linear-loaded monopoles (one half of the dipoles in Figure 9.39) working against a radial ground plane have similar resonant frequencies, but with only half the radiation resistance shown for the dipoles.

A Ladder-Line Linear-Loaded Dipole

Based on these results, NNØF next constructed a linear loaded dipole as in Figure 9.39B, using 24 feet of 1-inch ladder line (the black, 450-Ω plastic kind widely available) for the dipole length. He hung the system from a tree using nylon fishing line, about 4 feet from the tree at the top, and about 8 feet from the ground on the bottom end. It was slanted at about a 60° angle to the ground. This antenna resonated at 12.8 MHz and had a measured resistance of about 35 Ω. After the resonance measurements, he fed it with 1-inch ladder open-wire line (a total of about 100 feet to the shack).

For brevity, this is called a vertical *LLSD* (linear-loaded short dipole). A tuner resonated the system nicely on 20 and 30 meters. On these bands the performance of the vertical LLSD seemed comparable to his 120-foot long, horizontal center-fed Zepp, 30 feet above ground. In some directions where the horizontal, all-band Zepp has nulls, such as toward Siberia, the vertical LLSD was definitely superior. This system also resonates on 17 and 40 meters. However, from listening to various signals, NNØF had the impression that this length LLSD is not as good on 17 and 40 meters as the horizontal 120-foot antenna.

Using Capacitance End Hats

He also experimented with an even shorter resonant length by trying an LLSD with capacitance end-hats. The hats, as expected, increased the radiation resistance and lowered the resonant frequency. Six-foot long, single-wire hats were used on each end of the previous 24-foot LLSD, as shown in **Figure 9.40**. The antenna was supported in the same way as the previous vertical dipole, but the bottom-end

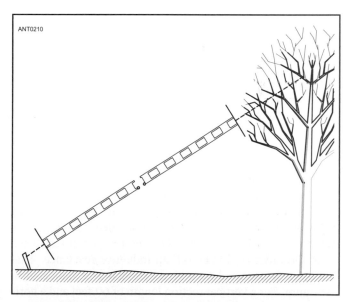

Figure 9.40 — Two-wire linear-loaded dipole with capacitance end hats. Main dipole length was constructed from 24 feet of "windowed" ladder line. The end-hat elements were stiff wires 6 feet long. The antenna was strung at about a 60° angle from a tree limb using monofilament fishing line. Measured resonant frequency and radiation resistance were 10.6 MHz and 50 Ω.

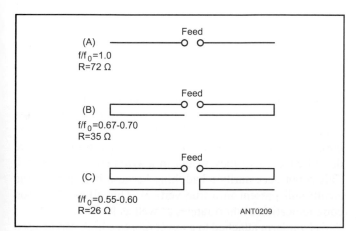

Figure 9.39 — Wire dipole antennas. The ratio f/f_0 is the measured resonant frequency divided by frequency f_0 of a standard dipole of same length. R is radiation resistance in ohms. At A, standard single-wire dipole. At B, two-wire linear-loaded dipole, similar to folded dipole except that side opposite feed line is open. At C, three-wire linear-loaded dipole.

hat wire was only inches from the grass. This system resonated at 10.6 MHz with a measured resistance of 50 Ω.

If the dipole section were lengthened slightly, by a foot or so, to about 25 feet, it should hit the 10.1-MHz band and be a good match for 50-Ω coax. It would be suitable for a restricted space, shortened 30 meter antenna. Note that this antenna is only about half the length of a conventional 30 meter dipole, needs no tuner, and has no losses due to traps. It does have the loss of the extra wire, but this is essentially negligible.

Any of the linear-loaded dipole antennas can be mounted either horizontally or vertically. The vertical version can be used for longer skip contacts — beyond 600 miles or so — unless you have rather tall supports for horizontal antennas to give a low elevation angle. Using different diameter conductors in linear-loaded antenna configurations yields different results, depending on whether the larger or small diameter conductor is fed. NNØF experimented with a vertical ground-plane antenna using a 10-foot piece of electrical conduit pipe (⅝ inch OD) and #12 AWG copper house wire.

Figure 9.41 shows the configuration. The radial ground system was buried a couple of inches under the soil and is not shown. Note that this is not a folded monopole, which would have either A or B grounded.

The two conductors were separated by 2 inches, using plastic spreaders held onto the pipe by stainless-steel hose clamps obtained from the local hardware store. Hose clamps intertwined at right angles were also used to clamp the pipe on electric fence stand-off insulators on a short 2 × 4 post set vertically in the ground.

The two different diameter conductors make the antenna characteristics change, depending on how they are configured. With the antenna bridge connected to the larger diameter conductor (point A in Figure 9.41), and point B unconnected, the system resonated at 16.8 MHz and had R = 35 Ω. With the bridge at B (the smaller conductor), and point A left unconnected, the resonance lowered to 12.4 MHz and

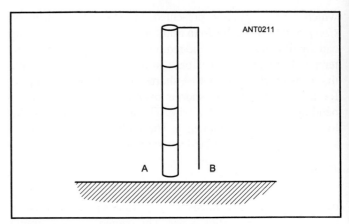

Figure 9.41 — Vertical ground-plane antenna with a 10-foot pipe and #12 AWG wire as the linear-loaded element. Resonant frequency and radiation resistance depend on which end (A or B) is fed. The other end (B or A) is *not* grounded. See text for details.

R was found to be about 24 Ω.

The resonant frequency of the system in Figure 9.41 can be adjusted by changing the overall height, or for increasing the frequency, by reducing the length of the wire. Note that a 3.8-MHz resonant ground plane can be made with height only about half that of the usual 67 feet required, if the smaller conductor is fed (point B in Figure 9.41). In this case, the pipe would be left unconnected electrically. The lengths given above can be scaled to determine a first-try attempt for your favorite band. Resonant lengths will, however, depend on the conductor diameters and spacing.

The same ideas hold for a dipole, except that the lengths should be doubled from those of the ground plane in Figure 9.41. The resistance will be twice that of the ground plane. Say, how about a shortened 40 meter horizontal beam to enhance your signal?

9.4 INVERTED-L ANTENNAS

The antenna shown in **Figure 9.42** is called an *inverted-L* antenna. It is simple and easy to construct and is a good antenna for the beginner or the experienced 1.8-MHz DXer. Because the overall electrical length is made somewhat greater than λ/4, the feed point resistance is on the order of 50 Ω, with an inductive reactance. That reactance is canceled by a series capacitor as indicated in the figure. For a vertical section length of 60 feet and a horizontal section length of 115 feet, the input impedance is ≈ 40 + j 300 Ω. Longer vertical or horizontal sections would increase the input impedance. The azimuthal radiation pattern is slightly asymmetrical with ≈1 to 2 dB increase in the direction opposite to the horizontal wire. This antenna requires a good buried ground system or elevated radials

and will have a 2:1 SWR bandwidth of about 50 kHz.

This antenna is a form of top-loaded vertical, where the top loading is asymmetrical. This results in both vertical and horizontal polarization because the currents in the top wire do not cancel like they would in a symmetrical-T vertical. This is not necessarily a bad thing because it eliminates the zenith null present in a true vertical. This allows for good communication at short ranges as well as for DX.

A yardarm attached to a tower or a tree limb can be used to support the vertical section. As with any vertical, for best results the vertical section should be as long as possible. A good ground system is necessary for good results — the better the ground, the better the results.

If you don't have the space for the inverted-L shown in

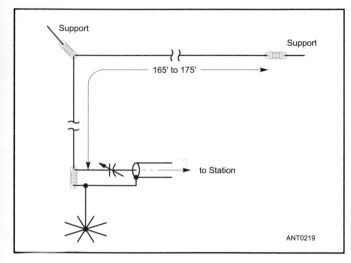

Figure 9.42 — The 1.8-MHz inverted-L. Overall wire length is 165 to 175 feet. The variable capacitor has a capacitance range from 100 to 800 pF, at 3 kV or more. Adjust antenna length and variable capacitor for lowest SWR.

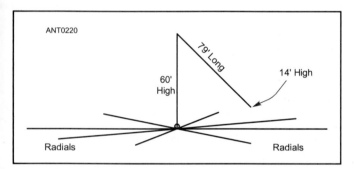

Figure 9.43— Sketch showing a modified 160 meter inverted-L, with a single supporting 60-foot high tower and a 79-foot long slanted top-loading wire. The feed point impedance is about 12 Ω in this system, requiring a quarter-wave matching transformer made of paralleled 50-Ω coaxes.

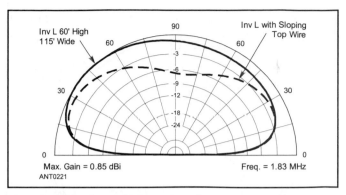

Figure 9.44 — Overlay of the elevation responses for the inverted-L antennas in Figure 9.42 (solid line) and Figure 9.43 (dashed line). The gains are very close for these two setups, provided that the ground radial system for the antenna in Figure 9.43 is extensive enough to keep ground losses low.

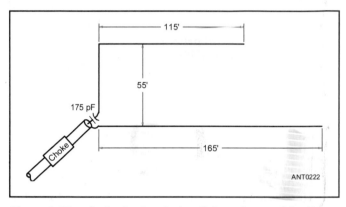

Figure 9.45 — A single elevated radial can be used for the inverted-L. This changes the directivity slightly. The series tuning capacitor is approximately 175 pF for this system.

Figure 9.42 (with its 115-foot horizontal section) and if you don't have a second tall supporting structure to make the top wire horizontal, consider sloping the top wire down toward ground. **Figure 9.43** illustrates such a setup, with a 60-foot high vertical section and a 79-foot sloping wire. As always, you will have to adjust the length of the sloping wire to fine-tune the resonant frequency. For a good ground radial system, the feed point impedance is about 12 Ω, which may be transformed to 50 Ω with a 25-Ω quarter-wave transformer consisting of two paralleled 50-Ω quarter-wave coaxes. The peak gain will decrease about 1 dB compared to the inverted-L shown in Figure 9.42. **Figure 9.44** overlays the elevation responses for average ground conditions. The 2:1 SWR bandwidth will be about 30 kHz, narrower than the larger system in Figure 9.42.

If the ground system suggested for Figures 9.42 and 9.43 is not practical, you can use a single elevated radial as shown in **Figure 9.45**. For the dimensions shown in the figure, $Z_i = 50 + j\,498\ \Omega$, requiring a 175-pF series resonating capacitor. The azimuthal radiation pattern is shown

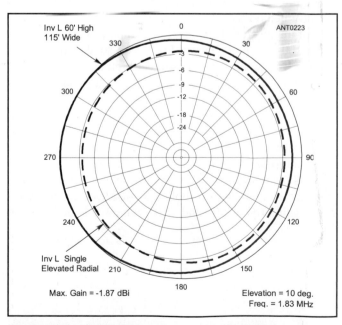

Figure 9.46 — Azimuthal pattern comparison for inverted-L antennas shown in Figure 9.42 (solid line) and the compromise, single-radial system in Figure 9.45 (dashed line). This is for a takeoff angle of 10°.

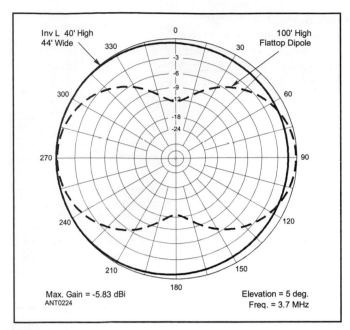

Figure 9.47 — Azimuthal pattern at a takeoff angle of 5° for an 80 meter version of the inverted-L (solid line) in Figure 9.42, compared to the response for a 100-foot high flattop dipole (dashed line).

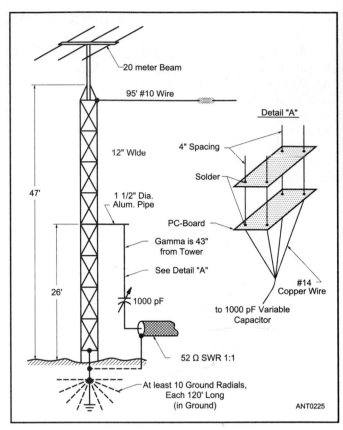

Figure 9.48 — Details and dimensions for gamma-match feeding a 50-foot tower as a 1.8-MHz vertical antenna. The rotator cable and coaxial feed line for the 14-MHz beam is taped to the tower legs and run into the shack from ground level. No decoupling networks are necessary.

in **Figure 9.46** compared to the inverted-L in Figure 9.42. Note that the 1 to 2 dB asymmetry is now in the direction of the horizontal wires, just the opposite of that for a symmetrical ground system. The 2:1 SWR bandwidth is about 40 kHz, assuming that the series capacitor is adjusted at 1.83 MHz for minimum SWR.

Figure 9.47 shows the azimuthal response at a 5° elevation angle for an 80 meter version of the inverted-L in Figure 9.42. The peak response occurs at an azimuth directly behind the direction in which the horizontal portion of the inverted-L points. For comparison, the response for a 100-foot high flattop dipole is also shown. The top wire of this antenna is only 40 feet high and the 2:1 SWR bandwidth is about 150 kHz wide with a good, low-loss ground-radial system.

Figure 9.47 illustrates that the azimuth response of an inverted-L is nearly omnidirectional. This gives such an antenna an advantage in certain directions compared to a flattop dipole, which is constrained by its supporting mounts (such as trees or towers) to favor fixed directions. For example, the flattop dipole in Figure 9.47 is at its weakest at azimuths of 90° and 270°, where it is down about

12 dB compared to the inverted-L. Hams who are fortunate enough to have high rotary dipoles or rotatable low-band Yagis have found them to be very effective antennas indeed.

9.4.1 TOWER-BASED INVERTED-L

Figure 9.48 shows the method used by Doug DeMaw, W1FB (SK), to gamma match his self-supporting 50-foot tower operating as an inverted-L. A wire cage simulates a gamma rod of the proper diameter. The tuning capacitor is fashioned from telescoping sections of 1¼ and 1½-inch aluminum tubing with polyethylene tubing serving as the dielectric. This capacitor is more than adequate for power levels of 100 W. The horizontal wire connected to the top of the tower provides the additional top loading.

9.5 HALF-SLOPER ANTENNAS

Sloping dipoles and λ/2 dipoles can be very useful antennas on the low bands. These antennas can have one end attached to a tower, tree or other structure and the other end near ground level, elevated high enough so that passersby can't contact them, of course. The following section gives a number of examples of these types of antennas.

Perhaps one of the easiest antennas to install is the λ/4 sloper shown in **Figure 9.49**. As pointed out above, a sloping λ/2 dipole is known among radio amateurs as a *sloper* or sometimes as a *full sloper*. If only one half of it is used, it becomes a *half sloper*. The performance of the two types of sloping antennas is similar — they exhibit some directivity in the direction of the slope and radiate vertically polarized energy at low angles respective to the horizon. The amount of directivity will range from 3 to 6 dB, depending upon the individual installation, and will be observed in the slope direction.

The main advantage of the half sloper over the full half wave-long sloping dipole is that its supporting tower needn't be as high. Both the half sloper and the full sloper place the feed point (the point of maximum current) high above lossy ground. But the half-sloper only needs half as much wire to build the antenna for a given amateur band. The disadvantage of the half sloper is that it is sometimes difficult or even impossible to obtain a low SWR when using coaxial-cable feed, especially without a good isolating choke balun. (See the section above on isolating ground-plane antennas.)

Other factors that affect the feed-impedance are tower height, height of the attachment point, enclosed angle between the sloper and the tower, and what is mounted atop the tower (HF or VHF beams). Further, the quality of the ground under the tower (ground conductivity, radials, etc) has a marked effect on the antenna performance. The final SWR can vary (after optimization) from 1:1 to as high as 6:1. Generally speaking, the closer the low end of the slope wire is to ground, the more difficult it will be to obtain a good match.

The half sloper can be an excellent DX type of antenna. Hams usually install theirs on a metal supporting structure such as a mast or tower. The support needs to be grounded at the lower end, preferably to a buried or on-ground radial system. If a nonconductive support is used, the outside of the coax braid becomes the return circuit and should be grounded at the base of the support. As a starting point you can attach the sloper so the feed point is approximately λ/4 above ground. If the tower is not high enough to permit this, the antenna should be fastened as high on the supporting structure as possible. Start with an enclosed angle of approximately 45°, as indicated in Figure 9.49. Cut the wire to the length determined from

$$\ell = \frac{260}{f_{MHz}}$$

This will allow sufficient extra length for pruning the wire for the lowest SWR. A metal tower or mast becomes an

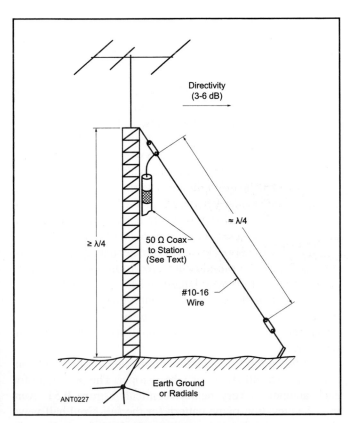

Figure 9.49 — The λ/4 "half sloper" antenna.

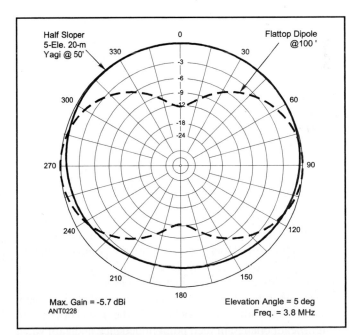

Figure 9.50 — Radiation pattern for a typical half sloper (solid line) mounted on a 50-foot high tower with a large 5-element 20 meter beam on the top compared to that for a flattop dipole (dashed line) at 100 feet. At a 5° takeoff angle typical for DX work on 80 meters, the two antennas are pretty comparable in the directions favored by the high dipole. In other directions, the half sloper has an advantage of more than 10 dB.

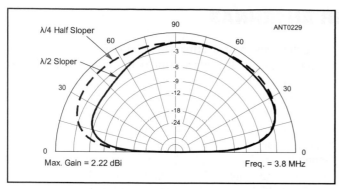

Figure 9.51 — Comparison of elevation patterns for a full-sized half wave sloper (solid line) on a 100-foot tower and a half sloper (dashed line) on a 50-foot tower with a 5-element 20 meter Yagi acting as a top counterpoise. The performance is quite comparable for these two systems.

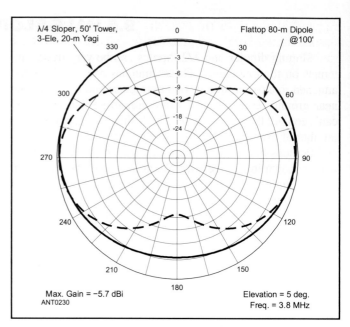

Figure 9.52 — Comparing the azimuthal response of a half sloper (solid line) on a 50-foot tower with a 3-element 20 meter Yagi on top to that of a flattop dipole (dashed line) at 100 feet. The two are again quite comparable at a 5° takeoff angle.

operating part of the half sloper system. In effect, it and the slope wire function somewhat like an inverted-V dipole antenna. In other words, the tower operates as the missing half of the dipole. Hence its height and the top loading (beams) play a significant role.

Detailed modeling indicates that a sufficiently large mass of metal (that is, a large, "Plumber's Delight" Yagi) connected to the top of the tower acts like enough of a "top counterpoise" that the tower may be removed from the model with little change in the essential characteristics of the half-sloper system. Consider an installation using a freestanding 50-foot tower with a large 5-element 20 meter Yagi on top. This Yagi is assumed to have a 40-foot boom oriented 90° to the direction of the slanted 80 meter half-sloper wire. The best SWR that could be reached by changing the length and slant angle for this sloper is 1.67:1, representing a feed point impedance of $30.1 - j\,2.7\;\Omega$. The peak gain at 3.8 MHz is 0.97 dBi at an elevation angle of 70°. **Figure 9.50** shows the azimuth-plane pattern for this half sloper, compared to a 100-foot high flattop dipole for reference, at an elevation angle of 5°.

Removing the tower from the model resulted in a feed point impedance of $30.1 - j\,1.5\;\Omega$ and a peak gain of 1.17 dBi. The tower is obviously not contributing much in this setup, since the mass of the large 20 meter Yagi is acting like an elevated counterpoise all by itself. It's interesting to rotate the boom of the model Yagi and observe the change in SWR that occurs on the half-sloper antenna. With the boom turned 90°, the SWR falls to 1.38:1. This level of SWR change could be measured with amateur-type instrumentation.

On the other hand, substituting a smaller 3-element 20 meter Yagi with an 18-foot boom in the model does result in significant change in feed point impedance and gain when the tower is removed from the model, indicating that the "counterpoise effect" of the smaller beam is insufficient by itself. Interestingly enough, the best SWR for the half sloper/tower and the 3-element Yagi (with its boom in line with the half sloper is 1.33:1), changing to 1.27:1 with the boom turned 90°. Such a small change in SWR would be difficult

to measure using typical amateur instrumentation.

In any case, the 50-Ω transmission line feeding a half sloper should be taped to the tower leg at frequent intervals to make it secure. The best method is to bring it to earth level, then route it to the operating position along the surface of the ground if it can't be buried. This will ensure adequate RF decoupling, which will help prevent RF energy from affecting the equipment in the station. Rotator cable and other feed lines on the tower or mast should be treated in a similar manner.

Adjustment of the half sloper is done with an SWR indicator in the 50-Ω transmission line. A compromise can usually be found between the enclosed angle and wire length, providing the lowest SWR attainable in the center of the chosen part of an amateur band. If the SWR "bottoms out" at 2:1 or lower, the system will work fine without using an antenna tuner, provided the transmitter can work into the load. Typical optimum values of SWR for 3.5 or 7-MHz half slopers are between 1.3:1 and 2:1. A 100-kHz bandwidth is normal on 3.5 MHz, with 200 kHz being typical at 7 MHz.

If the lowest SWR possible is greater than 2:1, the attachment point can be raised or lowered to improve the match. Readjustment of the wire length and enclosed angle may be necessary when the feed point height is changed. If the tower is guyed, the guy wires will need to be insulated from the tower and broken up with additional insulators to prevent resonance.

At this point you may be curious about which antenna is better — a full sloper or a half sloper. The peak gain for each antenna is very nearly identical. **Figure 9.51** overlays the elevation-plane pattern for the full-sized half wave sloper on a 100-foot tower and for the half sloper shown in

Figure 9.51 on a 50-foot tower with a 5-element 20 meter Yagi on top. The full-sized half wave sloper has more front-to-back ratio, but it is only a few dB more than the half sloper. **Figure 9.52** compares the azimuthal patterns at a 5° takeoff angle for a 100-foot high flattop dipole and a half-sloper system on a 50-foot tower with a 3-element 20 meter Yagi on top.

Despite the frustration some have experienced trying to achieve a low SWR with some half-sloper installations, many operators have found the half sloper to be an effective and low-cost antenna for DX work.

9.5.1 1.8-MHZ ANTENNA SYSTEMS USING TOWERS

The half sloper discussed above for 80 or 40 meter operation will also perform well on 1.8 MHz where vertically polarized radiators can achieve the low takeoff angles needed on Top Band. Prominent 1.8-MHz operators who have had success with the half sloper antenna suggest a minimum tower height of 50 feet. Dana Atchley, W1CF (SK), used the configuration

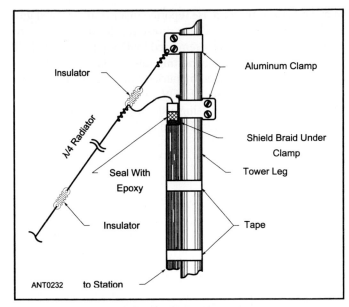

Figure 9.54 — Feed system used by W1FB for 1.8 MHz half sloper on a 50-foot self-supporting tower.

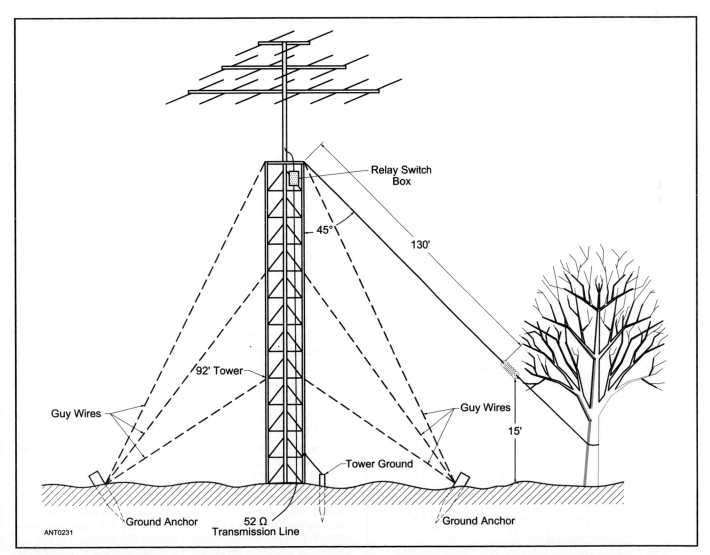

Figure 9.53 — The W1CF half sloper for 160 meters is arranged in this manner. Three monoband antennas atop the tower provide capacitive loading.

sketched in **Figure 9.53**. He reported that the uninsulated guy wires act as an effective counterpoise for the sloping wire. In **Figure 9.54** is the feed system used by Doug DeMaw, W1FB (SK), on a 50-foot self-supporting tower. The ground for the W1FB system is provided by buried radials connected to the tower base. Jack Belrose, VE2CV and DeMaw also described an interesting method of using a sloping wire to create a "half delta" usable on the lower HF bands. The system is described in the Sep 1982 *QST* article, "The Half-Delta Loop: A Critical Analysis and Practical Deployment" which is also available on this book's CD-ROM.

As described previously, a tower can also be used as a true vertical antenna, provided a good ground system is used. The shunt-fed tower is at its best on 1.8 MHz, where a full λ/4 vertical antenna is rarely possible. Almost any tower height can be used. An HF beam at the top provides some top loading.

9.6 ONE-WAVELENGTH LOOPS

A loop antenna one wavelength in circumference is a very effective antenna that is also very tolerant of changes in shape and orientation to fit available space and supports. A detailed discussion of how the loop antenna works is presented in the **Loop Antennas** chapter. This section presents several examples of loop antennas optimized for use on one band although they can be used on multiple bands with the use of an antenna tuner. In general, these designs can be scaled to work on other bands by multiplying all dimensions by the ratio of the design frequency to the new frequency = f_{design} / f_{new}.

9.6.1 A FULL-SIZE LOOP FOR 7 MHZ

This design is an effective but simple 7 MHz antenna that has a theoretical gain of approximately 1 dB over a dipole. Such a loop need not be square, as illustrated in **Figure 9.55A**. It can be trapezoidal, rectangular, circular, or some distorted configuration in between those shapes. For best results, however, you should attempt to make the loop as square as possible. The more rectangular the shape, the greater the cancellation of energy in the system, and the less effective it will be. In the limiting case, the antenna loses its identity as a loop and becomes a folded dipole.

You can feed the loop in the center of one of the vertical sides if you want vertical polarization. For horizontal polarization, you feed either of the horizontal sides at the center. Since optimum directivity occurs at right angles to the plane of the loop (or in more simple terms, broadside to the loop), you should hang the loop to radiate the maximum amount in some favored direction.

Figure 9.56A shows the azimuthal response at a takeoff angle of 15°, a typical angle for 40 meter DX, for vertical and horizontal feed systems over ground with "average" conductivity and dielectric constant. Figure 9.56A includes, for reference, the response of a flattop dipole 50 feet high. For DX work on 40 meters, the vertically polarized loop can perform as well as or substantially better than either a horizontally polarized loop or a flattop dipole, particularly in the azimuthal nulls of the dipole.

For the low elevation angles that favor DX work, the optimal feed point is at the center of one of the vertical wires. Feeding the loop at one of the corners at the bottom gives a compromise result for both local and DX work. The actual impedance is roughly the same at each point: bottom horizontal center, corner or vertical side center.

Figure 9.56B demonstrates how the gain for vertical polarization changes over different type of grounds: saltwater, very poor ground (conductivity = 1 mS/m, dielectric

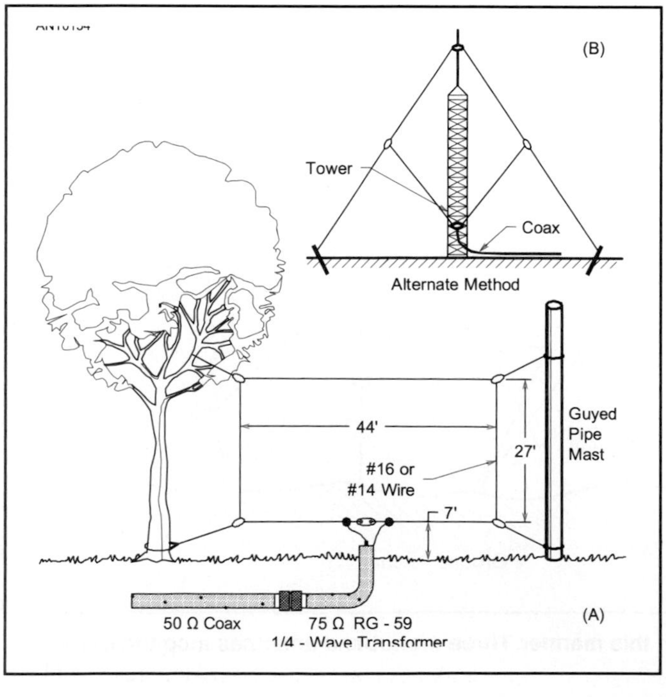

Figure 9.55 — At A, details of the rectangular full-wave loop. The dimensions given are for operation at 7.05 MHz. The height above ground was 7 feet in this instance, although improved performance should result if the builder can install the loop higher above ground without sacrificing length on the vertical sides. At B, illustration how a single supporting structure can be used to hold the loop in a diamond-shaped configuration. Feeding the diamond at the lower tip provides radiation in the horizontal plane. Feeding the system at either side will result in vertical polarization of the radiated signal.

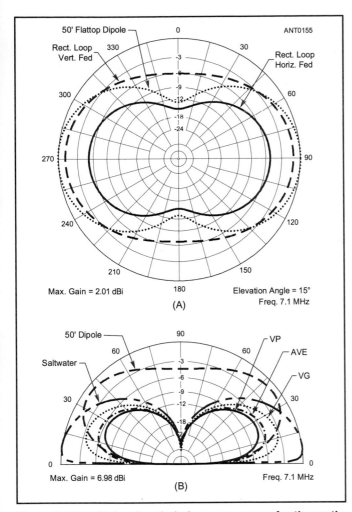

Figure 9.56 — At A, azimuthal plane responses for the vertically and horizontally polarized 7-MHz loop, compared to a flattop 50-foot high dipole, all at a takeoff angle of 15° for DX work. The solid line is for feeding the loop horizontally at the bottom; the dashed line is for feeding the loop vertically at a side, and the dotted line is for a simple flattop horizontal dipole at 50 feet in height. For DX work, the vertically polarized loop is an excellent performer.

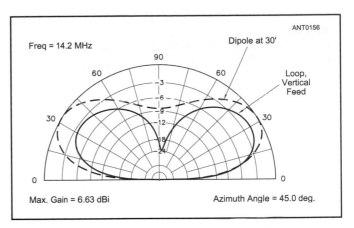

Figure 9.57 — Elevation-plane response of 7-MHz loop used on 14.2 MHz. This is for a feed point at the center of one of the two vertical wires. The dashed line is the response of a flattop 20-meter dipole at 30 feet in height for comparison.

The overall length of the wire used in a loop is determined in feet from the formula 1005/f (MHz). Hence, for operation at 7.125 MHz the overall wire length will be 141 feet. The matching transformer, an electrical ¼ λ of 75-Ω coax cable, can be computed by dividing 246 by the operating frequency in MHz, then multiplying that number by the velocity factor of the cable being used. Thus, for operation at 7.125 MHz, 246/7.125 MHz = 34.53 feet. If coax with solid polyethylene insulation is used, a velocity factor of 0.66 must be employed. Foam-polyethylene coax has a velocity factor of 0.80. Assuming RG-59 is used, the length of the matching transformer becomes 34.53 (feet) × 0.66 = 22.79 feet, or 22 feet, 9½ inches.

This same loop antenna in Figure 9.55A fed vertically may be used on the 14 and 21 MHz bands, although its pattern will not be as good as that on its fundamental frequency and you will have to use an open-wire transmission line to feed the loop for multiband use. **Figure 9.57** shows the response at the peak lobe of the loop, at a 45° angle to the plane of the loop, compared to the peak response for a simple half-wave 20 meter dipole, 30 feet high. The gain from a simple flattop dipole, mounted at 30 feet, will be superior to the loop operated on a harmonic frequency.

9.6.2 A HORIZONTALLY POLARIZED RECTANGULAR LOOP

This antenna design provides some gain over a dipole or inverted-V and can easily be constructed for use on the upper HF bands as shown in **Table 9-6**. The original design was created by Brian Beazley, K6STI, and described in the July 1994 *QST* article "A Gain Antenna for 28 MHz." To use the antenna on other bands, multiply each dimension by 28.4/f (MHz), where f is the desired operating frequency in MHz.

The loop develops 2.1 dB gain over a dipole at low radiation angles with the top mounted one wavelength or more above ground. The antenna is simple to feed — no matching network is necessary. When fed with 50-Ω coax, the SWR is close to 1:1 at the design frequency. The original antenna, designed for resonance at 28.4 MHz, presented less

constant = 5) very good (conductivity = 30 mS/m, dielectric constant = 20) and average ground (conductivity = 5 mS/m, dielectric constant = 13). Again, for reference a 50-foot high flattop dipole's elevation response is included. As has been mentioned previously in other chapters, a seaside location is a wonderful environment for verticals!

Just how you erect such a loop will depend on what is available in your backyard. Trees are always handy for supporting loop antennas. A disadvantage to the rectangular loop shown in Figure 9.55A is that two 34-foot high supports are needed, although in many instances your house may be high enough to serve as one of these supports. If you have a tower higher than about 50 feet, Figure 9.55B demonstrates how you can use it to support a diamond-shaped loop for 40 meters. The elevation and azimuthal responses are almost the same for either loop configuration, rectangular- or diamond-shaped.

Table 9-6
Loop Dimensions for 7 through 28 MHz Bands

Freq (MHz)	Side A (inches)	Side B (inches)	Side A (feet)	Side B (feet)
28.4	73.0	146.0	6.1	12.2
24.9	83.3	166.5	6.9	13.9
21.2	97.8	195.6	8.1	16.3
18.1	114.5	229.1	9.5	19.1
14.15	146.5	293.0	12.2	24.4
10.1	205.3	410.5	17.1	34.2
7.15	290.0	579.9	24.2	48.3

than 2:1 SWR from 28.0-28.8 MHz. At lower frequencies, the effects of ground will affect the antenna's resonant frequency and feed point impedance, but not drastically — be prepared to adjust the dimensions.

The antenna is made from #12 AWG wire (see **Figure 9.58**) and is fed at the center of the bottom wire. Coil the coax into a few turns about one foot in diameter near the feed point to provide a simple choke balun at 14 MHz and higher. (See the **Transmission Line Coupling and Impedance Matching** chapter for more information on choke baluns.) The antenna can be suspended from trees or supported on a mast with spreaders made of bamboo, fiberglass, wood, PVC or other non-conducting material. You can also use aluminum

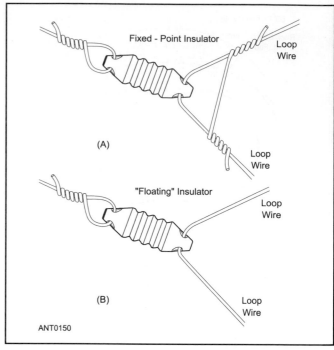

Figure 9.59 — Two methods of installing insulators at loop corners. The eyes of a floating insulator (B) should be smooth and have a large radius so that the loop wire does not make a sharp bend.

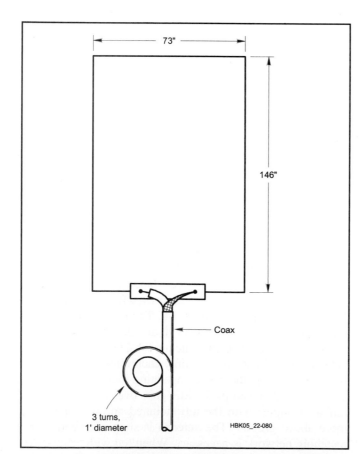

Figure 9.58 — Construction details of the 10 meter rectangular loop. See Table 9-6 for dimensions for other bands.

tubing both for support and conductors, but you may have to readjust the antenna dimensions for resonance.

Figure 9.59 shows two methods of supporting the loop wires with insulators. If Figure 9.59 is used, be sure the inside of the insulator eye is smooth and has a large radius or the loop wire will eventually break from repeated bending as it slides through the insulator.

The rectangular loop achieves gain by compressing its radiation pattern in the elevation plane. This happens because the top and bottom of the loop (where the current maxima are located) are farther apart than for a square loop. The antenna's beamwidth is slightly higher than that of a dipole (it's about the same as that of an inverted-V). A broad pattern is an advantage for a general-purpose, fixed antenna. The rectangular loop provides a bidirectional gain over a wide range of directions.

Mount the loop as high as possible. To provide 1.7 dB gain at low angles over an inverted-V, the top wire must be at least one wavelength high. The loop will work at lower heights, but its gain advantage disappears. For example, at $\frac{2}{3}\lambda$ the loop provides the same gain at low angles as an inverted-V.

9.6.3 A VERTICALLY POLARIZED DELTA LOOP FOR 14 MHZ

Two common methods of building a delta loop for the 14 MHz band are shown in **Figure 9.60**. (The design is from *Practical Wire Antennas* published by the RSGB.) Both radiate vertically-polarized signals and so ground quality will

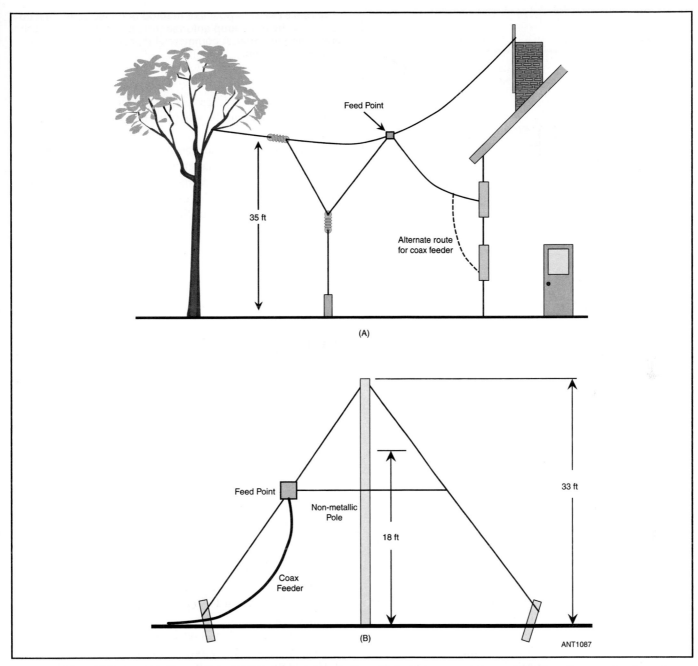

Feed Point

35 ft

Alternate route
for coax feeder

(A)

Feed Point

Non-metallic
Pole

18 ft

33 ft

Coax
Feeder

(B)

ANT1087

Figure 9.60 — A "flat top" delta loop for 14 MHz is shown at A. Suspended from two supports, its elevation angle of maximum radiation is approximately 20 degrees. The version at B uses only a single support but its effective height is lower than for A, raising the angle of peak signal.

have an effect on the antenna's efficiency. The total length of wire in the loop should be approximately 1005/f (MHz) = 71 feet for a resonant frequency of 14.15 MHz. For the optimum pattern, the loop should be equilateral with all three sides about the same length.

The antenna in Figure 9.60A has an effective height of about λ/2. The placement of the feed point at one of the upper corners configures the antenna to provide low-angle radiation for DX operation. The feed line should be suspended so that it runs directly away from the corner of the loop.

Figure 9.60B inverts the delta to use a single supporting mast or the antenna can be suspended from a tree. The

effective height of this antenna is much lower than the "flat-top" version in Figure 9.60A and so the elevation angle of maximum radiation will be higher. Nevertheless, the convenience of this configuration makes it a good choice for Field Day and portable operation. The orientation of the feed line is much less important in this configuration — it can simply drop vertically to the ground.

Figure 9.61 shows an example of how a feed point can be constructed. A commercial dipole center insulator with the built-in support point will also work well in this application. The antenna can be supported with lightweight fishing line or nylon cord. It is recommended that the lower corner

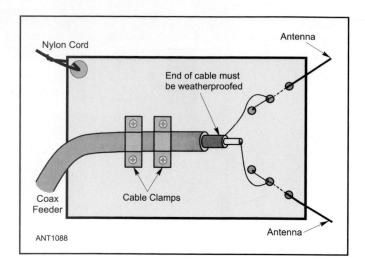

Figure 9.61 — One possible method of constructing a feed point for the delta loop antenna from polycarbonate or other insulating material. A commercial dipole center insulator can also be used.

Nylon Cord

Antenna

End of cable must be weatherproofed

Coax Feeder

Cable Clamps

Antenna

ANT1088

or corners be secured as well to prevent the antenna from moving too much in the wind. Insulators can be installed as in Figure 9.61.

The feed point impedance of both configurations will be 100-150 Ω and a quarter-wave matching section of feed line can be used to match the loop to 50 or 75-Ω feed line. A choke balun should be used at the feed point. (See the **Transmission Line Coupling and Impedance Matching** chapter for more information on quarter-wave matching sections and choke baluns.)

9.7 BIBLIOGRAPHY

Source material and more extended discussion of topics covered in this chapter can be found in the references given below.

ARRL's Wire Antenna Classics (Newington: ARRL, 1999).

D. Atchley, Jr., "Putting the Quarter-Wave Sloper to Work on 160," *QST*, Jul 1979, pp 19-20.

B. Beezley, "A Gain Antenna for 28 MHz," *QST*, Jul 1994, pp 70.

J. Belrose, "Transmission Line Low Profile Antennas," *QST*, Dec 1975, pp 19-25.

J. Belrose, "Terminated Folded Dipole," Technical Correspondence, *QST*, May 1994, p 88.

J. Belrose, "A Horizontal Loop for 80-Meter DX," *QST*, Aug 2002, pp 30-35.

J. Belrose and D. DeMaw, "The Half-Delta Loop: A Critical Analysis and Practical Deployment," *QST*, Sep 1982, pp 28-32.

L. Braskamp, AA6GL, "*MOBILE*, a Computer Program for Short HF Verticals," *The ARRL Antenna Compendium Vol 4* (Newington: ARRL, 1995), pp 92-96.

G. H. Brown, "The Phase and Magnitude of Earth Currents Near Radio Transmitting Antennas," *Proc. IRE*, Vol 23, No. 2, Feb 1935, pp 168-182.

G. H. Brown, R. F. Lewis and J. Epstein, "Ground Systems as a Factor in Antenna Efficiency," *Proc. IRE*, Vol 25, No. 6, Jun 1937, pp 753-787.

B. Cake, *The Antenna Designer's Notebook* (Newington: ARRL, 2009).

B. Cake, "The 'C Pole' — A Ground Independent Vertical Antenna," *QST*, Apr 2004, pp 37-39.

P. Carr, "A Two Band Half-Square Antenna with Coaxial Feed," *CQ*, Sep 1992, pp 40-45.

P. Carr, "A DX Antenna for 40 Meters," *CQ*, Sep 1994, pp 40-43.

P. Carr, "The N4PC Loop," *CQ*, Dec 1990, pp 11-15.

A. Christman, "Elevated Vertical Antennas for the Low Bands," *The ARRL Antenna Compendium Vol 5* (Newington: ARRL, 1996), pp 11-18.

D. DeMaw, "Additional Notes on the Half Sloper," *QST*, Jul 1979, pp 20-21.

D. DeMaw, L. Aurick, "The Full-Wave Delta Loop at Low Height," *QST*, Oct 1984, pp 24-26.

J. Devoldere, *Low Band DXing — 5th Edition* (Newington: ARRL, 2010).

P. Dodd, *The LF Experimenter's Source Book* (Potters Bar: RSGB, 1996).

A. C. Doty, Jr., J. A. Frey and H. J. Mills, "Efficient Ground Systems for Vertical Antennas," *QST*, Feb 1983, pp 9-12.

S. Ford, "*Low*fing on 1750 Meters," *QST*, Oct 1993, pp 67-68.

R. Fosberg, "Some Notes on Ground Systems for 160 Meters," *QST*, Apr 1965, pp 65-67.

J. Hall, "Off-Center-Loaded Dipole Antennas," *QST*, Sep 1974, pp 28-34.

J. Hallas, "The Fan Dipole as a Wideband and Multiband Antenna Element," *QST*, May 2005, pp 33-35.

J. Hallas, "A Close Look at the Terminated Folded Dipole Antenna," Getting on the Air, *QST*, Sep 2010, pp 51-52.

A. Harbach, "Broad-Band 80-Meter Antenna," *QST*, Dec 1980, pp 36-37.

H. Hawkins, "A Low-Budget, Rotatable 17 Meter Loop," *QST*, Nov 1997, p 35.

J. Heys, *Practical Wire Antennas* (Potters Bar: RSGB, 1989).

G. Hubbell, "Feeding Grounded Towers as Radiators," *QST*, Jun 1960, pp 32-33, 140, 142.

C. Hutchinson and R. D. Straw, *Simple and Fun Antennas for Hams* (Newington: ARRL, 2002).

P. H. Lee, *The Amateur Radio Vertical Antenna Handbook*,

1st edition (Port Washington, NY: Cowan Publishing Corp, 1974).

C. J. Michaels, "Some Reflections on Vertical Antennas," *QST*, July 1987, pp 15-19; feedback *QST*, Aug 1987, p 39.

More Wire Antenna Classics (Newington: ARRL, 1999).

I. Poole, *Practical Wire Antennas 2* (Potters Bar: RSGB, 2005).

Prediction of Sky-wave Field Strength at Frequencies Between About 150 and 1700 kHz, ITU Doc 3/14, Radiocommunication Study Groups, Feb 1995.

Rashed and Tai, "A New Class of Wire Antennas," 1982 International Symposium Digest, *Antennas and Propagation*, Vol 2, published by IEEE.

T. Russell, "Simple, Effective, Elevated Ground-Plane Antennas," *QST*, June 1994, pp 45-46

F. J. Schnell, "The Flagpole Deluxe," *QST*, Mar 1978, pp 29-32.

R. Severns, "A Wideband 80-Meter Dipole," *QST*, Jul 1995, pp 27-29.

J. Sevick, "The Ground-Image Vertical Antenna," *QST*, Jul 1971, pp 16-19, 22.

J. Sevick, "The W2FMI Ground-Mounted Short Vertical," *QST*, Mar 1973, pp 13-18, 41.

J. Sevick, "The Constant-Impedance Trap Vertical," *QST*, Mar 1974, pp 29-34.

J. Sevick, "Short Ground-Radial Systems for Short Verticals," *QST*, Apr 1978, pp 30-33.

J. Sevick, W2FMI, *Transmission Line Transformers* (Atlanta: Noble Publishing, 1996).

J. Stanford, NNØF, "Linear-Loaded Short Wire Antennas," *The ARRL Antenna Compendium Vol 5* (Newington: ARRL, 1996), pp 105-107.

Vertical Antenna Classics (Newington: ARRL, 1995)

A. D. Watt, *VLF Radio Engineering* (Pergamon Press, 1967) (out of print).

J. Weigl, *Sloper Antennas* (New York: CQ Communications, 2009).

TABLE OF CONTENTS

Chapter 10

Multiband HF Antennas

For operation on a number of bands below 30 MHz, it would be impractical for most amateurs to put up a separate antenna for each band. But this is not necessary — for example, a dipole one half-wavelength long on the lowest frequency band to be used can be operated readily on higher frequencies. In fact, most common antennas can be used on multiple bands through the use of antenna tuners and other techniques. What is usually referred to as a "multiband antenna," however, is one for which a method has been devised that allows the antenna to operate on a number of bands while still offering a good match to a transmission line, usually coaxial cable.

When a single physical antenna is used on different bands, one must be aware that the changing electrical heights and lengths lead to changes in the feed point impedance and the azimuth and the elevation patterns of the antenna as described in the chapters **Antenna Fundamentals** and **Dipoles and Monopoles**. For example, a horizontal wire antenna at an electrical height of $\lambda/2$ on 20 meters is $2\lambda/3$ high on 15 meters and $\lambda/4$ on 40 meters, leading to very different elevation patterns than if the antenna were at the same electrical height on all bands. Similarly, the elevation pattern and feed point impedance of a single vertical antenna will also change dramatically on different bands.

In fact, it is usually more effective to consider the installation as a "multiband antenna system" in which the antenna, feed line, and any impedance matching devices are considered together — as a package. By thinking about the performance of the antenna on different bands you can select a combination of system elements that result in good performance on all bands and not just one.

This chapter describes a number of antennas and antenna systems that are designed to be used on two or more of the HF bands. Separate chapters cover nonresonant **Long-Wire and Traveling Wave Antennas** as well as the popular **HF Yagi and Quad Antennas**. See the **Transmission Line Coupling and Impedance Matching** chapter for more information on using feed lines and impedance matching circuits.

Harmonic Radiation from Multiband Antennas

Since a multiband antenna is intentionally designed for operation on a number of different frequencies, any harmonics or spurious frequencies that happen to coincide with one of the antenna resonant frequencies will be radiated with very little, if any, attenuation. Particular care should be exercised, therefore, to prevent such harmonics from reaching the antenna.

Multiband antennas using tuned feed lines have a certain inherent amount of built-in protection against such radiation, since it is nearly always necessary to use a tuned coupling circuit (antenna tuner) between the transmitter and the feed line. This adds considerable selectivity to the system and helps to discriminate against frequencies other than the desired one.

Multiple dipoles and trap antennas do not have this feature, since the objective in design is to make the antenna show as nearly as possible the same resistive impedance in all the amateur bands the antenna is intended to cover. It is advisable to conduct tests with other amateur stations to determine whether harmonics of the transmitting frequency can be heard at a distance of, say, a mile or so. If they can, more selectivity should be added to the system since a harmonic that is heard locally, even if weak, may be quite strong at a distance because of propagation conditions.

10.1 SIMPLE WIRE ANTENNAS

10.1.1 RANDOM-WIRE ANTENNAS

The simplest multiband antenna is a random length of wire, attached directly to the output of a transmitter or antenna tuner. Power can be fed to the wire on practically any frequency using one or the other of the methods shown in **Figure 10.1**. If the wire is approximately 67 or 137 feet long (λ/4 or λ/2 on 80 meters) the end impedance will be high on the bands that are harmonics of 80 meters and it can be fed through a tuned circuit, as in **Figure 10.2**. Many antenna tuners have the option to feed an end-fed random wire in this way. Use an SWR meter between the transmitter and the matching network to adjust for minimum SWR.

If you have a rotatable beam antenna, in many cases it may be possible to use the beam's coaxial feed line as an antenna on HF. Connect the shield and center conductor together at the station end and use them as a random-length wire as in Figure 10.1. The beam at the far end will serve to end-load the wire as a capacitance hat.

The primary disadvantage of all such directly-fed systems is that the antenna system is composed of the random wire plus all of the station equipment enclosures and the station ground connection. The point at which the antenna is connected can be thought of as a randomly chosen feed point in an antenna that has one end tied to ground. As such, there is a good chance that you will have "RF hot spots" in your station because of the RF current in the antenna system.

RF voltages within the station can often be minimized by choosing an antenna and ground wire length so that the low feed point impedance at a current maximum occurs at or near the transmitter. A short connection (several feet or less) with heavy wire or strap to a ground rod or metallic water pipe that runs through ground may be sufficient on the lower bands but most ground connections are not short enough to minimize RF voltage by themselves. Regardless of how you address this issue, begin by connecting all equipment enclosures together to prevent significant voltages from existing between pieces of equipment.

Using an antenna wire length close to λ/4 (65 feet at

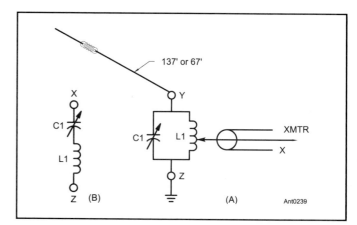

Figure 10.2 — If the antenna length is 137 feet, a parallel-tuned coupling circuit (A) can be used on each amateur band from 3.5 through 30 MHz, with the possible exception of the 10-, 18- and 24-MHz bands. C1 should be from 500-1000 pF with plate spacing capable of withstanding several hundred volts. L1 should be chosen to resonate with 20-80% of C1's maximum value. If the wire is 67 feet long, series tuning can be used on 3.5 MHz as shown at the left; parallel tuning will be required on 7 MHz and higher frequency bands. The L network shown in Figure 10.1B is also suitable for these antenna lengths.

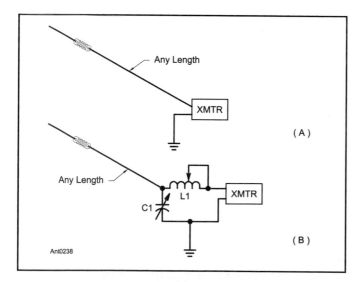

Figure 10.1 — At A, a random-length wire can be driven directly from the pi-network output of a vacuum-tube transmitter. At B, an L network (or antenna tuner) can be used with solid state transmitters that do not have tunable output networks. C1 should have plate spacing sufficient for at least several hundred volts; a maximum capacitance of 100 pF is sufficient if L1 is 20 to 25 μH. A suitable coil would consist of 30 turns of #12 AWG wire, 2½ inches diameter, 6 turns per inch. Bare wire should be used so the tap can be placed as required for loading the transmitter.

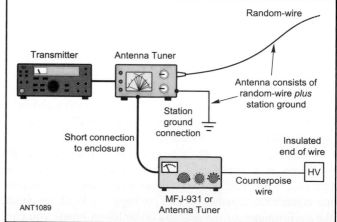

Figure 10.3 — An "artificial ground" can be used to tune a random length of wire to minimize RF voltage on station equipment enclosures.

3.6 MHz, 33 feet at 7.1 MHz), or an odd multiple of λ/4 (¾ λ is 195 feet at 3.6 MHz, 100 feet at 7.1 MHz, 50 feet at 14 MHz, etc) may be helpful. The goal is to place the antenna system's connection to the transmitter or antenna tuner at a point of low voltage. Obviously, this can be done for only one band even in the case of harmonically related bands, since the wire length that presents a current maximum at the transmitter will present a voltage maximum at two (or four) times that frequency.

Another possibility is to attach a counterpoise wire to the transmitter or antenna tuner enclosure. The counterpoise length is adjusted so that RF voltage on the station equipment is minimized. The length may or may not be λ/4 at the operating frequency since the impedance at the end of the antenna wire is unknown. Be prepared to experiment with different lengths. Different wires can be attached at different frequencies.

Another option is to use an "artificial ground" such as the MFJ-931 (**www.mfjenterprises.com**) as in **Figure 10.3** that tunes the counterpoise on different frequencies. It is also possible in many cases to use an ordinary 100-W antenna tuner to accomplish the same thing — tuning the random-length counterpoise to present a low impedance at the transmitter or antenna tuner enclosure.

If you do use a counterpoise, be sure to insulate the unattached end because like all unconnected ends of antennas, there will likely be enough RF voltage to cause an RF burn, particularly at 100 W or higher.

10.1.2 END-FED ANTENNAS

Another common antenna system for multiband operation is the *end-fed Zepp* antenna shown in **Figure 10.4**. The antenna length is λ/2 long at the lowest operating frequency. (This name came about because the first documented use of this sort of antennas was on the *Zeppelin* airships where the antenna was hung by one end and trailed below the airship.)

An antenna tuner with a balanced output can provide multiband coverage with an end-fed antenna with any length of open-wire feed line, as shown in Figure 10.4. Open-wire or window line with an impedance of 300 to 600 Ω is most often used.

The feed line length can be anything convenient, but odd multiples of λ/4 will transform the high feed point impedance to a lower value that is likely to be easier to transform to 50 Ω. (See "Tuned Feeders" below.) The asymmetrical placement of the feed line with respect to the antenna often results in common-mode current being picked up by the feed line. This results in radiation from the feed line portion of the system. (See "Feed Line Radiation" below.)

If you have room for only a 67-foot flattop and yet want to operate in the 3.5-MHz band, the two feed line wires can be tied together at the transmitter end and the entire system treated as a random-length wire fed directly, as in Figure 10.1.

10.1.3 CENTER-FED ANTENNAS

A center-fed single-wire antenna can be made to accept power and radiate it with high efficiency on any frequency higher than its fundamental resonant frequency and, with a reduction in efficiency and bandwidth, on frequencies as low as one half the fundamental.

In fact, it is not necessary for an antenna to be a full half-wavelength long at the lowest frequency. An antenna can be considerably shorter than ½ λ, even as short as ¼ λ, and still be a very efficient radiator. The use of such short antennas results in stresses, however, on other parts of the system (for example the antenna tuner and the transmission line) as discussed later on in this section.

The simplest and most flexible (and also least expensive) all-band antennas are those using parallel-wire feed lines to the center of the antenna, as in **Figure 10.5**. Because each half of the flattop is the same length, the feed line currents will be balanced at all frequencies unless, of course, imbalance is introduced by one half of the antenna being closer to ground (or a grounded object) than the other. To maintain balance of the current in each antenna leg and minimize common-mode current on the feed line, the feed line should be run at right angles to the antenna, preferably for a distance of at least λ/4 from the feed point.

Center feed is not only more desirable than end feed (described above) because of inherently better balance, but it generally also results in a lower standing wave ratio on the transmission line, provided a parallel-wire line having a

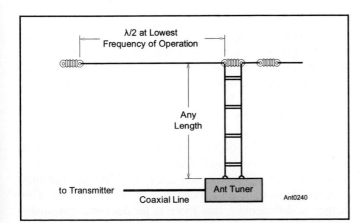

Figure 10.4 — An end-fed Zepp antenna for multiband use.

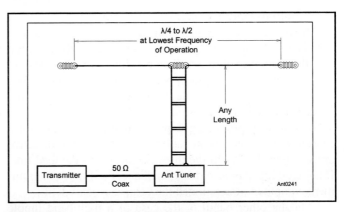

Figure 10.5 — A center-fed antenna system for multiband use.

characteristic impedance of 300 to 600 Ω is used. Ladder or window line is satisfactory for all but possibly high power installations (over 500 W), where heavier wire and wider spacing are desirable to handle the larger currents and voltages that may be present at high SWR.

The best type of antenna tuner to use in such an installation is a balanced type designed for coaxial feed line on the input and parallel-wire line on the output. An unbalanced tuner can also be used but because one wire of the output feed line is connected to the enclosure, RF current and voltages are more likely to be present in the station.

It is not recommended that coaxial feed line be used between the antenna tuner and antenna. At frequencies where the SWR is high, feed line loss in coaxial cable runs of more than 50 feet at HF can quickly become very high. (See the **Transmission Lines** chapter).

The length of the antenna is not critical, nor is the length of the line. As mentioned earlier, the length of the antenna can be considerably less than λ/2 and still be very effective. If the overall length is at least λ/4 at the lowest frequency, a quite usable system will result. Some experimentation will likely be necessary to find the length that works best at a specific location on the bands required.

Feed Line Radiation

Feed line radiation results when currents in a parallel-wire feed line are not balanced so that the radiation from each wire no longer cancels. This imbalance most commonly occurs when the feed line picks up energy radiated by the antenna on both wires at the same time. This creates *common-mode* current which re-radiates a signal just as an antenna does. (The equivalent situation for coaxial feed line is for the outer surface of the shield to pick up and re-radiate energy.)

Feed lines pick up the antenna's radiated signal when they are not symmetrically oriented with respect to the antenna and its radiated field. For example, a feed line that approaches a dipole at anything other than 90° will couple more strongly to the closer leg of the antenna. The closer the feed line is to one leg, the more energy it will pick up. Feed lines to an end-fed Zepp almost always carry common-mode current because they are connected at one end and not the middle. Common-mode feed line current and techniques for minimizing it are addressed in the chapter **Transmission Line Coupling and Impedance Matching**.

It should be emphasized that any radiation from a feed line is not "lost" energy and is not necessarily harmful. Whether or not feed line radiation is important depends entirely on the antenna system being used. For example, feed line radiation is not desirable when a directive array is being used. Such feed line radiation can distort the desired pattern of such an array, producing responses in unwanted directions. In other words, you want radiation only from the directive array, rather than from the directive array and the feed line. If the feed line passes close to appliances or home entertainment equipment, the radiated field can also cause RFI.

On the other hand, in the case of a multiband dipole where general coverage is desired, if the feed line happens to radiate, such energy could actually have a desirable effect. Antenna purists may dispute such a premise, but from a practical standpoint where you are not concerned with a directive pattern, much time and labor can be saved by ignoring possible feed line radiation.

Tuned Feeders

References are often made to "tuned feeders" meaning sections of feed line with a specific electrical length. The lengths act to transform load (antenna feed point) impedances as described in the **Transmission Lines** chapter. The most common application of a tuned feeder is with an end-fed antenna. A feed line that is any number of odd quarter-wavelengths long transforms a high impedance into a low impedance and so can be used to connect a 50-Ω transmitter to a high-impedance end-fed antenna. This only works at frequencies for which the feed line is the required electrical length, thus the term "tuned." Most tuned feeders are constructed from parallel-wire feed line to minimize loss from the high SWR in this application.

Tuned feeders can also create problems due to their length. For example, a feed line some multiple of λ/2 long connected to grounded equipment enclosures at one end also has a low impedance at the other end. That can cause trouble for an end-fed antenna with a high feed point impedance. Resonant feed line lengths (some multiple of λ/4 long) also tend to be effective at picking up energy from the antenna where it creates common-mode currents and re-radiated signals as discussed above.

10.1.4 THE 135-FOOT, 80 TO 10 METER DIPOLE

As mentioned previously, one of the most versatile antennas around is a simple dipole, center-fed with open-wire transmission line and used with an antenna tuner in the shack. A 135-foot long dipole hung horizontally between two trees or towers at a height of 50 feet or higher works very well on 80 through 10 meters. Such an antenna system has significant gain at the higher frequencies. (Other lengths reported to work well are 88 and 105 feet — don't be afraid to experiment.) The antenna can also be used on 1.8 MHz as a λ/4 antenna with some reduction in efficiency.

Flattop or Inverted V Configuration?

There is no denying that the inverted V mounting configuration is very convenient, since it requires only a single support. The flattop configuration, however, where the dipole is mounted horizontally, gives more gain at the higher frequencies. **Figure 10.6** shows the 80 meter azimuth and elevation patterns for two 135-foot long dipoles. The first is mounted as a flattop at a height of 50 feet over flat ground with a conductivity of 5 mS/m and a dielectric constant of 13, typical for average soil. The second dipole uses the same length of wire, with the center apex at 50 feet and the ends drooped down to be suspended 10 feet off the ground. This height is sufficient so that there is no danger to passersby from RF burns.

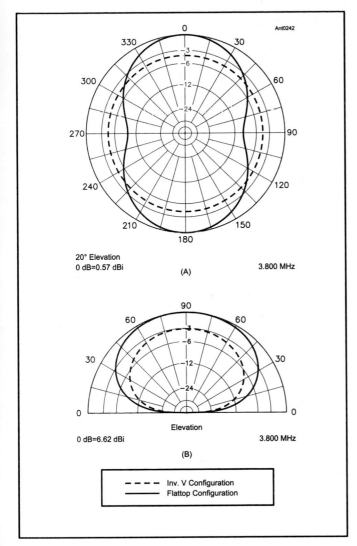

Figure 10.6 — Patterns on 80 meters for 135-foot, center-fed dipole erected as a horizontal flattop dipole at 50 feet, compared with the same dipole installed as an inverted V with the apex at 50 feet and the ends at 10 feet. The azimuth pattern is shown at A, where the dipole wire lies in the 90° to 270° plane. At B, the elevation pattern, the dipole wire comes out of the paper at a right angle. On 80 meters, the patterns are not markedly different for either flattop or inverted V configuration.

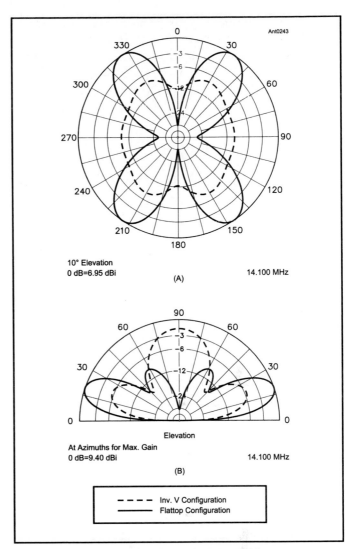

Figure 10.7 — Patterns on 20 meters for two 135-foot dipoles. One is mounted horizontally as a flattop and the other as an inverted V with 120° included angle between the legs. The azimuth pattern is shown in A and the elevation pattern is shown in B. The inverted V has about 6 dB less gain at the peak azimuths, but has a more uniform, almost omnidirectional, azimuthal pattern. In the elevation plane, the inverted V has a large high-angle lobe, making it a somewhat better antenna for local communication, but not quite so good for DX contacts at low elevation angles.

At 3.8 MHz, the flattop dipole has about 4 dB more peak gain than its drooping cousin. On the other hand, the inverted V configuration gives a pattern that is more omnidirectional than the flattop dipole, which has nulls off the ends of the wire. Omnidirectional coverage may be more important to net operators, for example, than maximum gain.

Figure 10.7 shows the azimuth and elevation patterns for the same two antenna configurations, but this time at 14.2 MHz. The flattop dipole has developed four distinct lobes at a 10° elevation angle, an angle typical for 20 meter skywave communication. The peak elevation angle gain of 9.4 dBi occurs at about 17° for a height of 50 feet above flat ground for the flattop dipole. The inverted V configuration is again nominally more omnidirectional, but the peak gain is

down some 6 dB from the flattop.

The situation gets even worse in terms of peak gain at 28.4 MHz for the inverted V configuration. Here the peak gain is down about 8 dB from that produced by the flattop dipole, which exhibits eight lobes at this frequency with a maximum gain of 10.5 dBi at about 7° elevation. See the comparisons in **Figure 10.8**.

Whatever configuration you choose to mount the 135-foot dipole, you will want to feed it with some sort of low-loss open-wire feed line. For example, 450-Ω window line is popular for this application. Be sure to twist the line once or twice per foot to keep it from twisting excessively in the wind. (Do not twist it so much that the wire spacing is reduced.) Make sure also that you provide some mechanical support

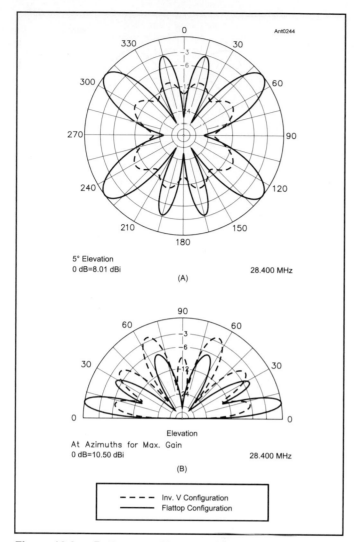

5° Elevation
0 dB=8.01 dBi
(A)
28.400 MHz

Elevation
At Azimuths for Max. Gain
0 dB=10.50 dBi
(B)
28.400 MHz

– – – – Inv. V Configuration
——— Flattop Configuration

Figure 10.8 — Patterns on 10 meters for same antenna configurations as in Figs 10.6 and 10.7. Once again, the inverted V configuration yields a more omnidirectional pattern, but at the expense of almost 8 dB less gain than the flattop configuration at its strongest lobes.

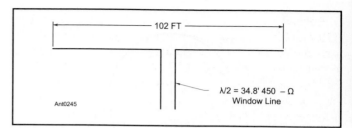

Figure 10.9 — The G5RV multiband antenna covers 3.5 through 30 MHz. Although many amateurs claim it may be fed directly with 50-Ω coax on several amateur bands, Louis Varney, its originator, recommends the use of a matching network on bands other than 14 MHz.

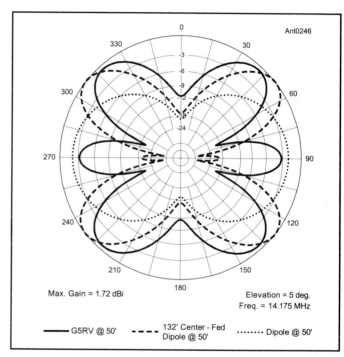

Max. Gain = 1.72 dBi

Elevation = 5 deg.
Freq. = 14.175 MHz

——— G5RV @ 50'   – – – 132' Center - Fed Dipole @ 50'   ······· Dipole @ 50'

Figure 10.10 — Azimuth pattern at a 5° elevation angle for a 102-foot long, 50-foot high G5RV dipole (solid line). For comparison, the response for a 132-foot long, center-fed dipole at 50 feet height (dashed line) and a 33-foot long half-wave 20 meter dipole at 50 feet (dotted line) are also shown. The longest antenna exhibits about 0.5 dB more gain than the G5RV, although the response is more omnidirectional for the G5RV — an advantage for a wire antenna that is not usually rotatable.

for the line at the junction with the dipole wires. This will prevent flexing of the transmission-line wire, since excessive flexing will result in breakage. (See the **Antenna Materials and Construction** chapter)

10.1.5 THE G5RV MULTIBAND ANTENNA

A variation on the center-fed antenna that does not require a lot of space, is simple to construct and low in cost is the G5RV. Designed in England by Louis Varney, G5RV (SK), some years ago, it has become quite popular in the US. (The original article by G5RV in the *RSGB Bulletin* is included on this book's CD-ROM.) The G5RV design is shown in **Figure 10.9**. The antenna may be used from 3.5 through 30 MHz. Although some amateurs claim it may be fed directly with 50-Ω coax on several amateur bands with a low SWR, Varney himself recommended the use of an antenna tuner on bands other than 14 MHz (see Bibliography). In fact,

an analysis of the G5RV feed point impedance shows there is no length of balanced line of any characteristic impedance that will transform the terminal impedance to the 50 to 75-Ω range on all bands. (Low SWR with coax feed and no matching network on bands other than 14 MHz may indicate excessive losses in the coax.)

Figure 10.10 shows the 20 meter azimuthal pattern for a G5RV at a height of 50 feet over flat ground, at an elevation angle of 5° that is suitable for DXing. For comparison, the response for two other antennas is also shown in Figure 10.10 — a standard half wave 20 meter dipole at

50 feet and a 132-foot long center-fed dipole at 50 feet. The G5RV on 20 meters is, of course, longer than a standard half wave dipole and it exhibits about 2 dB more gain compared to that dipole. With four lobes making it look rather like a four-leaf clover, the azimuth pattern is more omnidirectional than the two-lobed dipole. The 132-foot center-fed dipole is longer than the G5RV and it has about 0.5 dB more gain than the G5RV, also exhibiting four major lobes, along with two strong minor lobes in the plane of the wire. Overall, the azimuthal response for the G5RV is more omnidirectional than the comparison antennas.

The G5RV patterns for other frequencies are similar to those shown for the 135-foot dipole previously for other frequencies. Incidentally, you may be wondering why the pattern for a 132-foot dipole is shown in Figure 10.10, rather than the 135-foot dipole described earlier. The 132-foot overall length describes another antenna that we'll discuss in the next section on Windom antennas.

The portion of the G5RV antenna shown as horizontal in Figure 10.9 may also be installed in an inverted V dipole arrangement, subject to the same loss of peak gain mentioned above for the 135-foot dipole. Or instead, up to ⅙ of the total length of the antenna at each end may be dropped vertically or semi-vertically, or bent at a convenient angle to the main axis of the antenna, to cut down on the requirements for real estate.

10.1.6 THE WINDOM AND CAROLINA WINDOM

An antenna that enjoyed popularity in the 1930s and into the 1940s was what we now call the Windom. It was known at the time as a "single-feeder Hertz" antenna, after being described in September 1929 *QST* by Loren G. Windom, W8GZ (see Bibliography).

The Windom antenna, shown in **Figure 10.11**, is fed with a single wire, attached approximately 14% off center. In theory, this location provides a match for the single-wire transmission line, which is driven against an earth ground. Because the single-wire feed line is not inherently well balanced and because it is brought to the operating position, "RF in the shack" is a likely result of using this antenna. For that reason, the true single-feed-wire Windom antenna is rarely used although the name is often given to wires with non-centered feed points as described in the next section.

A recent variation is called the "Carolina Windom," apparently because two of the designers, Edgar Lambert, WA4LVB, and Joe Wright, W4UEB, lived in coastal North Carolina (the third, Jim Wilkie, WY4R, lived in nearby Norfolk, Virginia). One of the interesting parts about the Carolina Windom is that it turns a potential disadvantage — feed line radiation — into a potential advantage.

Figure 10.12 is a diagram of a flattop Carolina Windom, which uses a 50-foot wire joined with an 83-foot wire at the feed point insulator. This resembles the layout shown in Figure 10.11 for the original W8GZ Windom. The "Vertical Radiator" for the Carolina Windom is a 22-foot piece of RG-8X coax, with a "line Isolator" (current-type choke

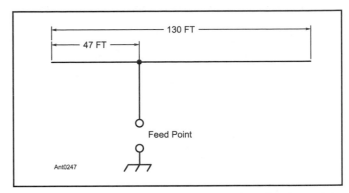

Figure 10.11 — The Windom antenna, cut for a fundamental frequency of 3.75 MHz. The single-wire feed line, connected 14% off center, is brought into the station and the system is fed against ground. The antenna is also effective on its harmonics.

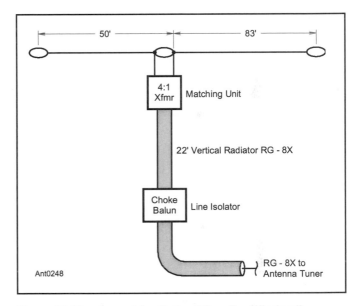

Figure 10.12 — Layout for flattop "Carolina Windom" antenna.

balun) at the bottom end and a 4:1 "matching unit" (impedance transformer) at the top. The system takes advantage of the asymmetry of the horizontal wires to purposely induce current onto the outer shield surface of the vertical coax section. Note that the matching unit is a voltage-type balun transformer, which purposely does not act like a common-mode current choke balun. You must use an antenna tuner with this system to present a 1:1 SWR to the transmitter on the amateur bands from 80 through 10 meters.

The radiation resulting from current induced onto the 22-foot vertical coax section tends to fill in the deep nulls that would be present if the 132 feet of horizontal wire were center fed. Over saltwater, the vertical radiator can give significant gain at the low elevation angles needed for DX work. Indeed, field reports for the Carolina Windom are most impressive for stations located near or on saltwater. Over average soil the advantage of the additional vertically polarized component is

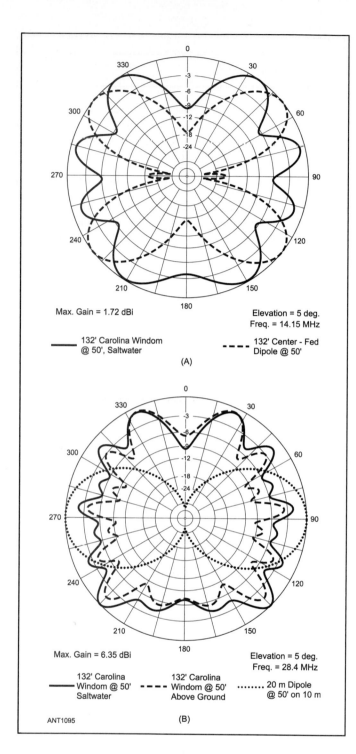

Max. Gain = 1.72 dBi

Elevation = 5 deg.
Freq. = 14.15 MHz

—— 132' Carolina Windom
@ 50', Saltwater

- - - 132' Center - Fed
Dipole @ 50'

(A)

Max. Gain = 6.35 dBi

Elevation = 5 deg.
Freq. = 28.4 MHz

—— 132' Carolina
Windom @ 50'
Saltwater

- - - 132' Carolina
Windom @ 50'
Above Ground

······ 20 m Dipole
@ 50' on 10 m

ANT1095

(B)

Figure 10.13 — At A, 20 meter azimuth patterns for a 132-foot long off-center fed Carolina Windom and a 132-foot long center-fed flattop dipole on 20 meters, both at a height of 50 feet above saltwater. The response for the Carolina Windom is more omnidirectional because the vertically polarized radiation from the 22-foot long vertical RG-8X coax fills in the deep nulls. At B, 10 meter azimuthal responses for a 132-foot long, 50-foot high Carolina Windom over saltwater (solid line) and over average ground (dashed line), compared to that for a 20 meter half-wave dipole at 50 feet (dotted line).

ham bands, use the minimum length of feed coax possible to hold down losses in the coax.

Figure 10.13B shows the azimuth responses for a 50-foot high flattop Carolina Windom on 28.4 MHz over saltwater and over average soil. The pattern for a 50-foot high, flattop 20 meter dipole operated on 28.4 MHz is also shown, since this 20 meter dipole can also be used as a multiband antenna, when fed with open-wire transmission line rather than with coax. Again, the Carolina Windom exhibits a more omnidirectional pattern, even if the pattern is somewhat lopsided at the bottom.

10.1.7 OFF-CENTER-FED (OCF) DIPOLES

The usual practice is to feed a λ/2 dipole in the center where the feed point impedance is low and makes a suitable match to coaxial cables. The dipole will accept energy from a feed point anywhere along its length, however, assuming that the source is matched to the higher impedance that is presented away from the center point. (As discussed in the **Dipoles and Monopoles** chapter, if the feed point is moved away from the center of the dipole, the impedance rises because current is dropping while voltage is rising.)

The *off-center-fed* dipole takes advantage of placing the feed point in a location along the dipole at which the impedance is similar on more than one band, generally in the neighborhood of 150-300 Ω. A suitable impedance matching device such as an impedance transformer is then used to reduce the feed point impedance to something closer to 50 Ω. Note that the feed point impedance of the antenna varies with height above ground and so will SWR.

Figure 10.14 shows an off-center-fed or *OCF* dipole.

not quite so evident. **Figure 10.13A** compares a 50-foot high Carolina Windom on 14 MHz over saltwater to a 50-foot high, 132-foot long, flattop center-fed dipole. The Carolina Windom has a more omnidirectional azimuthal pattern, a desirable characteristic in a 132-foot long wire antenna that is not normally rotated to favor different directions.

Another advantage of the Carolina Windom over a traditional Windom is that the coax feed line between the transmitter and common-mode choke balun does not radiate, meaning that there will be less "RF in the shack." Since the feed line is not always operating at a low SWR on various

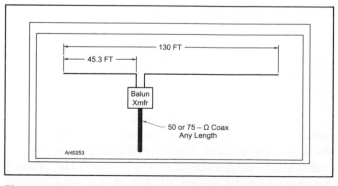

Figure 10.14 — The off-center-fed (OCF) dipole for 3.5, 7 and 14 MHz. A 1:4 or 1:6 balun is used at the feed point.

Because it is similar in appearance to the Windom of Figure 10.11, this antenna is often mistakenly called a "Windom," or sometimes a "coax-fed Windom." The two antennas are not the same, since the Windom is driven against an earth ground, while the OCF dipole is fed like a regular dipole — just not at its center. The extreme case of an OCF is the end-fed Zepp where the feed point is moved all the way to the end of the antenna.

The OCF dipole of Figure 10.14, fed ⅓ of its length from one end, may be used on its fundamental and even harmonics. Its free-space antenna-terminal impedance at 3.5, 7 and 14 MHz is on the order of 150 to 200 Ω. A 4:1 impedance transformer at the feed point should offer a reasonably good match to 50- or 75-Ω line, although some commercially made OCF dipoles use a 6:1 transformer. The usual caution is repeated here about height above ground affecting feed point impedance.

At the 6th harmonic, 21 MHz, the antenna is three wavelengths long and fed at a voltage maximum instead of a current maximum. The feed point impedance at this frequency is high, a few thousand ohms, so the antenna is unsuitable for use on this band.

Balun Requirements

Because the OCF dipole is not fed at the center of the radiator, the feed line is not placed symmetrically with respect to the antenna's radiated field. As a result, common-mode current will flow on the feed line, usually a coaxial cable. How much current flows depends on the impedance of the coaxial cable's outer surface which, in turn, depends on the orientation of the cable, how long it is, height above ground, and so forth. (Some of the common-mode current results from the slightly unequal impedances presented by the OCF legs but most of the shield current is induced by the asymmetric location in the antenna's field.)

Regardless of how the common-mode current is caused to flow on the feed line, it is generally viewed as undesirable and a current or choke balun is used to increase the impedance of coaxial cable's outer surface. Radiation from the feed line may not be a problem in your installation and may even improve the antenna's radiation pattern by filling in nulls. (See "Feed line radiation" above.) In that case, no balun is required. (Choke baluns are discussed in the chapter **Transmission Line Coupling and Impedance Matching**.)

10.1.8 MULTIPLE-DIPOLE ANTENNAS

The antenna system shown in **Figure 10.15A** consists of a group of center-fed dipoles, all connected in parallel at the point where the transmission line joins them. Each of the dipole elements is individually constructed to be an electrical λ/2 at different frequencies. This is often referred to as a "fan dipole," although that term is also applied to a dipole constructed as a bow-tie to increase operating bandwidth. (See the section "Broadband Dipoles" in the chapter **Single-Band MF and HF Antennas**.) The general idea is that the feed point impedance of the dipoles far from resonance will be high enough that nearly all of the signal power is applied to

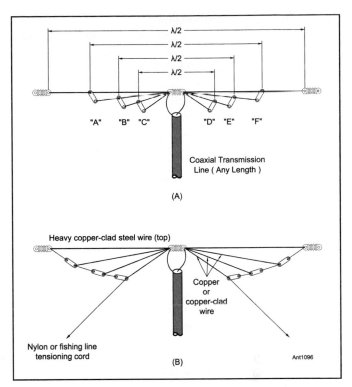

Figure 10.15 — At A, multiband antenna using paralleled dipoles all connected to a common low-impedance transmission line. The half-wave dimensions may be either for the centers of the various bands or selected to fit favorite frequencies in each band. Because of interaction among the various dipoles, the builder should expect to adjust lengths for resonance on each band. B shows a method of constructing the dipole that offers less interaction between the dipoles, making it easy to tune.

the resonant dipole which "ignores" the nonresonant dipoles.

In theory, the 4-wire antenna of Figure 10.15A can be used with a coaxial feed line on five bands. The four wires are prepared as parallel-fed dipoles for 3.5, 7, 14 and 28 MHz. The 7-MHz dipole is intended to be used on its 3rd harmonic for 21-MHz operation to cover a fifth band. However, in practice it has been found difficult to get a good match to coaxial line on all bands.

The λ/2 resonant length of any one dipole in the presence of the others is not the same as for a dipole by itself due to interaction and attempts to optimize all four lengths can become a frustrating procedure. The problem is compounded because the optimum tuning changes in a different antenna environment, so what works for one amateur may not work for another. The builder should start with a single dipole longer than resonance as discussed in the **Dipoles and Monopoles** chapter and be prepared to make repeated adjustments to the dipole lengths as more dipoles are added to the antenna.

Even if a perfect match cannot be obtained on all bands, many amateurs with limited antenna space are willing to accept the mismatch on some bands just so they can operate on those frequencies using a single coax feed line. The fewer dipoles that are used in parallel, the easier it will be to adjust them for the desired performance.

If an attempt is made to model the multi-wire dipole, take extra care to define the feed point construction carefully. As noted in the **Antenna Modeling** chapter, wires that are very close to each other or that join at small angles are hard to model so that the results reflect actual performance.

The multiple-dipole antenna can be fed with parallel-wire feed line and an antenna tuner but that negates the intended advantage of the design over a conventional single-wire nonresonant dipole — the use of a single coaxial feed line. The usual feed method is to use a coaxial feed line and a choke balun at the feed point as described in the chapter **Transmission Line Coupling and Impedance Matching**.

The separation between the dipoles for the various frequencies does not seem to be especially critical. One set of wires can be suspended from the next larger set, using insulating spreaders (of the type used for feed line spreaders) to give a separation of a few inches. Users of this antenna often run some of the dipoles at right angles to each other to help reduce interaction. Some operators use inverted V-mounted dipoles as guy wires for the mast that supports the antenna system. The top (and longest) dipole must support the weight of the rest of the antenna plus the feed line, so use heavy wire (copper-clad steel is the strongest) for the top antenna.

While the separation between dipoles does not seem to be especially critical to final performance, it does affect the amount of interaction between them that makes tuning each dipole difficult. A method of construction and tuning reported by Don Butler, N4UJW (**www.hamuniverse.com/multidipole.html**) is shown is Figure 10.15B. For dipoles in the 2-18 MHz range, separating the dipoles at the feed point by at least 5½ inches vertically and at the ends by 38 inches results in a final length closer than ±2% of a single dipole.

An interesting method of construction used successfully by Louis Richard, ON4UF, is shown in **Figure 10.16**. The antenna has four dipoles (for 7, 14, 21 and 28 MHz) constructed from 300-Ω twin lead. A single length of twin lead

makes two dipoles. Thus, two lengths, as shown in the sketch, serve to make dipoles for four bands. Be sure to use twin lead with copper-clad steel conductors because all of the weight, including that of the feed line, must be supported by the uppermost wire (450-Ω window line could also be used).

Two pieces of twin lead are first cut to a length suitable for the two halves of the longest dipole. Then one of the conductors in each piece is cut to proper length for the next band higher in frequency. The excess wire and insulation is stripped away. A second pair of lengths is prepared in the same manner, except that the lengths are appropriate for the next two higher frequency bands. (Note the potential for interaction between higher and lower-frequency dipoles that may alter the tuning of previously adjusted dipoles.)

A piece of thick plastic sheet (plexiglass, polycarbonate, or high-density polyethylene) drilled with holes for anchoring each wire serves as the central insulator. The shorter pair of dipoles is suspended the width of the ribbon below the longer pair by clamps also made of poly sheet. Intermediate spacers are made by sawing slots in pieces of poly sheet so they will fit the ribbon snugly.

The multiple-dipole principle can also be applied to vertical antennas. Parallel or fanned λ/4 elements of wire or tubing can be driven against ground or tuned radials from a common feed point.

Double-L Antenna

The Double-L antenna by Don Toman, K2LQ is a variation of the multi-wire dipole. (**www.yccc.org/Articles/double_l.htm**) Shown in **Figure 10.17**, the antenna is

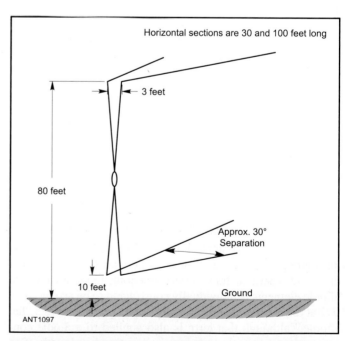

Figure 10.17 — The Double-L antenna by K2LQ is a pair of vertical dipoles with their ends bent to be parallel to the ground. The bottom horizontal wires should be at least 10 feet above ground. For single-band operation, install only a single dipole. The antenna works well as either a single-band or dual-band antenna.

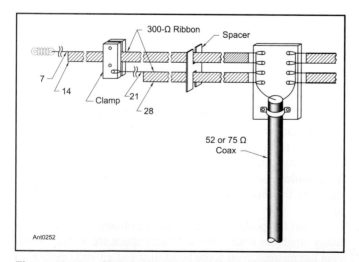

Figure 10.16 — Sketch showing how the twin-lead multiple-dipole antenna system is assembled. The excess wire and insulation are stripped away.

basically a vertical dipole with its ends bent to run horizontally over ground. It can be constructed as a single antenna for one band or a second dipole can be added to use the antenna on two bands.

Construction is not critical. The bottom wires should be at least 10 feet above ground and no radial system is required. If you do construct the dual-band version, the vertical wires are connected together at the feed point and separated by about 3 feet where they bend to become horizontal. The two horizontal sections are separated by about 30°. If the antennas are supported by a metal tower, the vertical section should be at least 3 feet from the tower.

The antenna is inherently unbalanced and may be tuned by removing or adding wire to the lower legs without dramatically affecting performance or feed point impedance. The dimensions given result in an SWR minimum near 1.83 MHz and 3.75 MHz.

10.1.9 TERMINATED FOLDED DIPOLE

A broad-banded variation of the folded dipole called the *terminated folded dipole (TFD)* adds a 600-Ω terminating resistor in the top conductor. The antenna is also called the *terminated tilted folded dipole* or *T2FD*. (See **Figure 10.18**) The function of the resistor is to act as a *swamping* load, reducing the higher feed point impedances over a wide frequency range. A TFD can be constructed to cover the entire 2 to 30 MHz range with SWR of 3:1 or less. The resistor dissipates some of the transmitter power (more than 50% at some frequencies!), but the improvement in SWR allows a coaxial feed line to be used without an impedance-matching unit. The increased convenience and installation outweigh the reduction in radiated signal. TD antennas are popular for emcomm operations and where only a single HF antenna can be installed and high performance is not required. A commercial version, the BWD-90, is available from B&W.

10.1.10 HORIZONTAL LOOP "SKYWIRE"

A horizontal full-wavelength loop is a very effective omnidirectional antenna for regional communications on its fundamental frequency where its radiation is a maximum at high angles. The loop is also useful on higher bands where the pattern begins to divide into multiple lobes at lower elevation angles.

While the feed point impedance might be reasonably low on some bands, using a coax feed line will result in significant losses on others. The best way to feed this versatile antenna is with parallel-wire window or ladder line using an antenna tuner in the shack.

The Loop Skywire is shown in **Figure 10.19**. The antenna has one wavelength of wire in its perimeter at the design or fundamental frequency. If you choose to calculate L_{total} in feet, the following equation should be used:

$$L_{total} = 1005 / f$$

where f equals the frequency in MHz.

Loop shapes other than a square are possible, but the larger the area enclosed by the loop, the better its performance will be. (A circle encloses the maximum area but this is rarely practical.) The Loop Skywire can also be operated as a vertical antenna with top-hat loading by tying both feed line conductors together at the antenna tuner. This method requires good station ground as described in the previous section on Random-Wire Antennas.

Although the loop can be made for any band or frequency of operation, the following two Loop Skywires are good performers. The 10-MHz band can also be used on both.

3.5-MHz Loop Skywire
(3.5-28 MHz loop and 1.8-MHz vertical)
Total loop perimeter: 272 feet
Square side length: 68 feet
7-MHz Loop Skywire
(7-28 MHz loop and 3.5-MHz vertical)
Total loop perimeter: 142 feet
Square side length: 35.5 feet

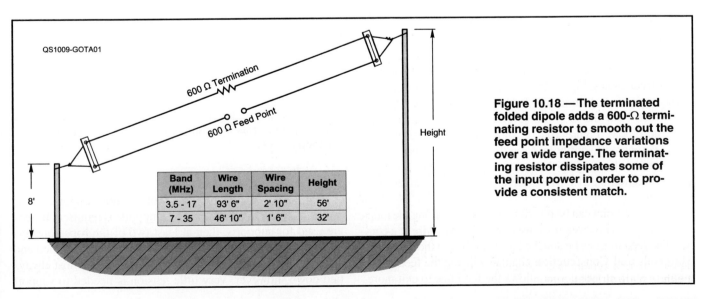

Band (MHz)	Wire Length	Wire Spacing	Height
3.5 - 17	93' 6"	2' 10"	56'
7 - 35	46' 10"	1' 6"	32'

Figure 10.18 — The terminated folded dipole adds a 600-Ω terminating resistor to smooth out the feed point impedance variations over a wide range. The terminating resistor dissipates some of the input power in order to provide a consistent match.

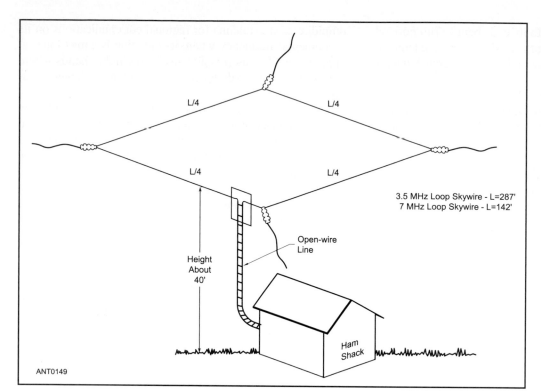

Figure 10.19 — A complete view of the Loop Skywire. The square loop is erected horizontally.

L/4   L/4

L/4   L/4

3.5 MHz Loop Skywire - L=287'
7 MHz Loop Skywire - L=142'

Open-wire Line

Height About 40'

Ham Shack

ANT0149

The actual total length can vary from the above by a few feet, as the length is not at all critical. Do not worry about tuning and pruning the loop to resonance as it will not make a significant difference in performance.

Bare #14 AWG wire is used in the loop. Copper-clad steel wire is recommended for the 3.5-MHz version. **Figure 10.20** shows the placement of the insulators at the loop corners. Two common methods are used to attach the insulators. Either lock or tie the insulator in place with a loop wire tie, as shown in Figure 10.20A, or leave the insulator free to "float" or slide along the wire, Figure 10.20B. Most loop users float at least two insulators. This allows pulling the slack out of the loop once it is in the air, and eliminates the need to have all the supports exactly placed for proper tension in each leg. Floating two opposite corners is recommended.

Figure 10.21A shows the azimuth performance on 7.2 MHz of a 142-foot long, 7-MHz Loop Skywire, 40 feet high at an elevation angle of 10°, compared to a regular flattop ½-λ dipole at a height of 30 feet. The loop comes into its own at higher frequencies. Figure 10.21B shows the response at 14.2 MHz, compared again to a ½-λ 14.2-MHz dipole at a height of 30 feet. Now the loop has several lobes that are stronger than the dipole. Figure 10.21C shows the response at 21.2 MHz, compared to a dipole. Now the loop has superior gain compared to the ½-λ dipole at almost any azimuth. In its favored direction on 21.2 MHz, the loop is 8 dB stronger than the dipole.

The feed point can be positioned anywhere along the loop that you wish. However, most users feed the Skywire at a corner. The feed line can be attached as described in the **Antenna Materials and Construction** chapter. Placing the feed point a foot or so from one corner allows the feed line to exit more

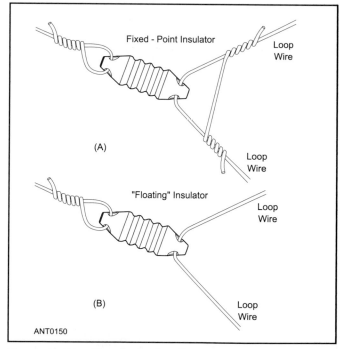

Fixed - Point Insulator

Loop Wire

(A)

Loop Wire

"Floating" Insulator

Loop Wire

(B)

Loop Wire

ANT0150

Figure 10.20 — Two methods of installing the insulators at the loop corners.

freely and keeps the feed line free of the loop support.

Generally a minimum of four supports is required. If trees are used for supports, then at least two of the ropes or guys used to support the insulators should be counterweighted and allowed to move freely. The feed line corner is almost always tied down, however. Very little tension is needed to support

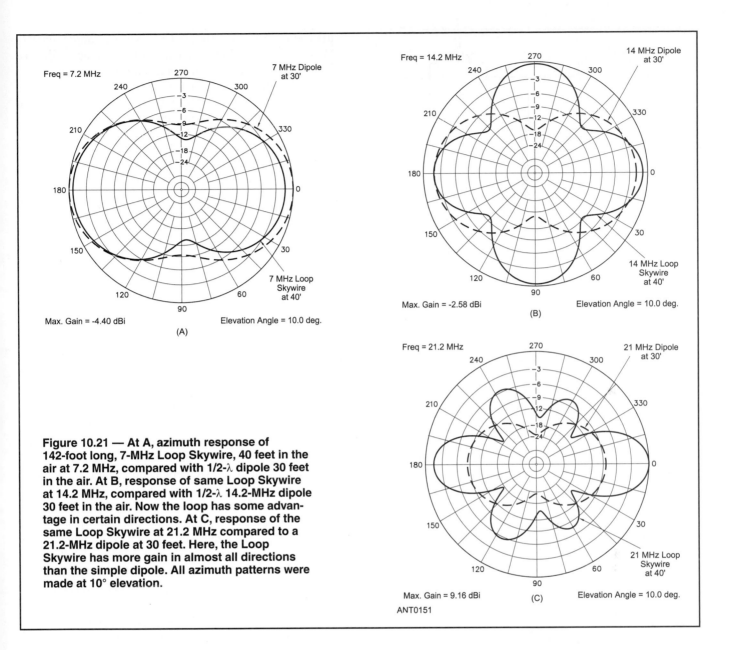

Figure 10.21 — At A, azimuth response of 142-foot long, 7-MHz Loop Skywire, 40 feet in the air at 7.2 MHz, compared with 1/2-λ dipole 30 feet in the air. At B, response of same Loop Skywire at 14.2 MHz, compared with 1/2-λ 14.2-MHz dipole 30 feet in the air. Now the loop has some advantage in certain directions. At C, response of the same Loop Skywire at 21.2 MHz compared to a 21.2-MHz dipole at 30 feet. Here, the Loop Skywire has more gain in almost all directions than the simple dipole. All azimuth patterns were made at 10° elevation.

the loop (far less than that for a dipole). Thus, counterweights are light. Several such loops have been constructed with bungee cords tied to three of the four insulators. This eliminates the need for counterweighting.

Recommended height for the antenna is 40 feet or more. Higher is better, especially if you wish to use the loop in the vertical mode. However, successful local and DX operation has been reported in several cases with the antenna at 20 feet.

10.2 TRAP ANTENNAS

By using tuned circuits of appropriate design strategically placed in a dipole, the antenna can be made to show what is essentially fundamental resonance at a number of different frequencies. The general principle is illustrated by **Figure 10.22**. The tuned circuits are also referred to as "traps" and so an antenna that uses tuned circuits to change its electrical configuration at different frequencies is called a "trap antenna" or a "trapped antenna."

Even though a trap antenna arrangement is a simple one,

an explanation of how a trap antenna works can be elusive. For some designs, traps are resonated in our amateur bands, and for others (especially commercially made antennas) the traps are resonant far outside any amateur band.

A trap in an antenna system can perform either of two functions, depending on whether or not it is resonant at the operating frequency. A familiar case is where the trap is parallel-resonant in an amateur band. For the moment, let us assume that dimension A in Figure 10.22 is 32 feet and

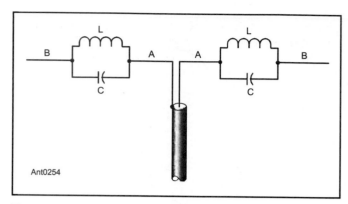

Figure 10.22 — A trap dipole antenna. This antenna may be fed with 50-Ω coaxial line. Depending on the L/C ratio of the trap elements and the lengths chosen for dimensions A and B, the traps may be resonant either in an amateur band or at a frequency far removed from an amateur band for proper two-band antenna operation.

that each L/C combination is resonant in the 7-MHz band. Because of its parallel resonance, the trap presents a high impedance at that point in the antenna system. The electrical effect at 7 MHz is that the trap behaves as an open circuit. It serves to separate the outside ends, the B sections, from the inner sections of the antenna. The result is easy to visualize — we now have an antenna system that is resonant in the 7-MHz band. Each 33-foot section (labeled A in the drawing) represents λ/4 with the trap acting as an open circuit. We therefore have a full-size 7-MHz antenna.

The second function of a trap, obtained when the frequency of operation is *not* the resonant frequency of the trap, is one of electrical loading. If the operating frequency is below the trap's resonant frequency, the trap behaves as an inductor; if above, as a capacitor. Inductive loading will electrically lengthen the antenna, and capacitive loading will electrically shorten the antenna.

Let's carry our assumption a bit further and try using the antenna we just considered at 3.5 MHz. With the traps resonant in the 7-MHz band, they will behave as inductors when operation takes place at 3.5 MHz, electrically lengthening the antenna. This means that the total length of sections A and B (plus the length of the inductor) may be something less than a physical λ/4 for resonance at 3.5 MHz. Thus, we have a two-band antenna that is shorter than full size on the lower frequency band. But with the electrical loading provided by the traps, the overall electrical length is λ/2. The total antenna length needed for resonance in the 3.5-MHz band will depend on the L/C ratio of the trap elements.

The key to trap operation away from resonance is its L/C ratio, the ratio of the value of L to the value of C. At resonance, however, within practical limitations the L/C ratio is immaterial as far as electrical operation goes. For example, in the antenna we've been discussing, it would make no difference for 7-MHz operation whether the inductor were 1 µH and the capacitor were 500 pF (the reactances would be just below 45 Ω at 7.1 MHz), or whether the inductor were

5 µH and the capacitor 100 pF (reactances of approximately 224 Ω at 7.1 MHz). But the choice of these values will make a significant difference in the antenna size for resonance at 3.5 MHz. In the first case, where the L/C ratio is 2000, the necessary length of section B of the antenna for resonance at 3.75 MHz would be approximately 28.25 feet. In the second case, where the L/C ratio is 50,000, this length need be only 24.0 feet, a difference of more than 15%.

The above example concerns a two-band antenna with trap resonance at one of the two frequencies of operation. On each of the two bands, each half of the dipole operates as an electrical λ/4. However, the same band coverage can be obtained with a trap resonant at, say, 5 MHz, a frequency quite removed from either amateur band. With proper selection of the L/C ratio and the dimensions for A and B, the trap will act to shorten the antenna electrically at 7 MHz and lengthen it electrically at 3.5 MHz. Thus, an antenna that is intermediate in physical length between being full size on 3.5 MHz and full size on 7 MHz can cover both bands, even though the trap is not resonant at either frequency. Again, the antenna operates with electrical λ/4 sections. Note that such nonresonant traps have less RF current flowing in the trap components, and hence trap losses are less than for resonant traps.

Additional traps may be added in an antenna section to cover three or more bands. Or a judicious choice of dimensions and the L/C ratio may permit operation on three or more bands with just a pair of identical traps in the dipole.

An important point to remember about traps is this. If the operating frequency is below that of trap resonance, the trap behaves as an inductor; if above, as a capacitor. The above discussion is based on dipoles that operate electrically as λ/2 antennas. This is not a requirement, however. Elements may be operated as electrical 3/2 λ, or even 5/2 λ, and still present a reasonable impedance to a coaxial feed line. In trap antennas covering several HF bands, using electrical lengths that are odd multiples of λ/2 is often done at the higher frequencies.

To further aid in understanding trap operation, let's now choose trap L and C components that each have a reactance of 20 Ω at 7 MHz. Inductive reactance is directly proportional to frequency, and capacitive reactance is inversely proportional. When we shift operation to the 3.5-MHz band, the inductive reactance becomes 10 Ω, and the capacitive reactance becomes 40 Ω. At first thought, it may seem that the trap would become capacitive at 3.5 MHz with a higher capacitive reactance, and that the extra capacitive reactance would make the antenna electrically shorter yet. Fortunately, this is not the case. The inductor and the capacitor are connected in parallel with each other.

$$Z = j\frac{X_L X_C}{X_L + X_C} \qquad \text{(Eq 1)}$$

where *j* indicates a reactive impedance component, rather than resistive. A positive result indicates inductive reactance, and a negative result indicates capacitive. In this 3.5-MHz case, with 40 Ω of capacitive reactance and 10 Ω of inductive, the equivalent series reactance is 13.3 Ω inductive. This inductive loading lengthens the antenna to an electrical λ/2 overall at 3.5 MHz, assuming the B end sections in Figure 10.22 are of the proper length.

With the above reactance values providing resonance at 7 MHz, X_L equals X_C, and the theoretical series equivalent is infinity. This provides the open-switch effect, disconnecting the antenna ends.

At 14 MHz, where $X_L = 40 \, \Omega$ and $X_C = 10 \, \Omega$, the resultant series equivalent trap reactance is 13.3 Ω capacitive. If the total physical antenna length is slightly longer than 3/2 λ at 14 MHz, this trap reactance at 14 MHz can be used to shorten the antenna to an electrical 3/2 λ. In this way, three-band operation is obtained for 3.5, 7 and 14 MHz with just one pair of identical traps. The design of such a system is not straightforward, however, because any chosen L/C ratio for a given total length affects the resonant frequency of the antenna on both the 3.5 and 14-MHz bands.

10.2.1 TRAP LOSSES

Since the tuned circuits have some inherent losses, the efficiency of a trap system depends on the unloaded Q values of the tuned circuits. Low-loss (high-Q) coils should be used, and the capacitor losses likewise should be kept as low as possible. With tuned circuits that are good in this respect — comparable with the low-loss components used in transmitter tank circuits, for example — the reduction in efficiency compared with the efficiency of a simple dipole is small, but tuned circuits of low unloaded Q can lose an appreciable portion of the power supplied to the antenna.

The commentary above applies to traps assembled from conventional components. The important function of a trap that is resonant in an amateur band is to provide a high isolating impedance, and this impedance is directly proportional to Q. Unfortunately, high Q restricts the antenna bandwidth, because the traps provide maximum isolation only at trap resonance.

10.2.2 FIVE-BAND W3DZZ TRAP ANTENNA

C. L. Buchanan, W3DZZ, created one of the first trap antennas for the five pre-1979 WARC amateur bands from 3.5 to 30 MHz. Dimensions are given in **Figure 10.23**. Only one set of traps is used, resonant at 7 MHz to isolate the inner (7-MHz) dipole from the outer sections. This causes the overall system to be resonant in the 3.5-MHz band. On 14, 21 and 28 MHz the antenna works on the capacitive-reactance principle just outlined. With a 75-Ω feed line, the SWR with this antenna is under 2:1 throughout the three highest frequency bands, and the SWR is comparable with that obtained with similarly fed simple dipoles on 3.5 and 7 MHz. (The complete article is available on this book's CD-ROM.)

Trap Construction

Traps frequently are built with coaxial aluminum tubes (usually with plastic tubing in-between them for insulation) for the capacitor, with the coil either self-supporting or wound on a form of larger diameter than the tubular capacitor. The coil is then mounted coaxially with the capacitor to form a unit assembly that can be supported at each end by the antenna wires. In another type of trap devised by William J. Lattin, W4JRW (see Bibliography at the end of this chapter), the coil is supported inside an aluminum tube and the trap capacitor is obtained in the form of capacitance between the coil and the outer tube. This type of trap is inherently weatherproof.

A simpler type of trap can be easily assembled from readily available components. A small transmitting-type ceramic "doorknob" capacitor is used, together with a length of commercially available coil material, these being supported by an ordinary ceramic or plastic antenna strain insulator 4¼ inches long. The circuit constants and antenna dimensions differ slightly from those of Figure 10.23, in order to bring the antenna resonance points closer to the centers of the various phone bands. Construction data are given in **Figure 10.24**. If a 10-turn length of inductor is used, a half turn from each end may be used to slip through the anchor holes in the insulator to act as leads.

The components used in these traps are sufficiently weatherproof in themselves so that no additional weatherproofing has been found necessary. However, if it is desired

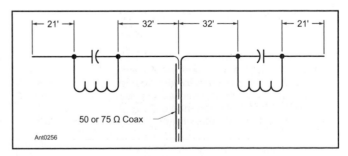

Figure 10.24 — Layout of multiband antenna using traps constructed as shown in Figure 10.25. The capacitors are 100 pF each, transmitting type, 5000-volt dc rating (Centralab 850SL-100N). Coils are 9 turns of #12 AWG wire, 2-1/2 inches diameter, 6 turns per inch (B&W 3029) with end turns spread as necessary to resonate the traps to 7.2 MHz. These traps, with the wire dimensions shown, resonate the antenna at approximately the following frequencies on each band: 3.9, 7.25, 14.1, 21.5 and 29.9 MHz (based on measurements by W9YJH).

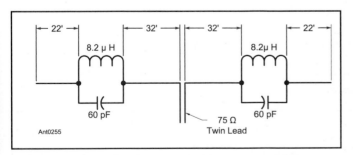

Figure 10.23 — Five-band (3.5, 7, 14, 21 and 28 MHz) trap dipole for operation with 75-Ω feed line at low SWR (C. L. Buchanan, W3DZZ). The balanced (parallel-conductor) line indicated is desirable, but 75-Ω coax can be substituted with a choke balun at the feed point to maintain symmetry. Dimensions given are for resonance (lowest SWR) at 3.75, 7.2, 14.15 and 29.5 MHz. Resonance is very broad on the 21-MHz band, with SWR less than 2:1 throughout the band.

to protect them from the accumulation of snow or ice, a plastic cover can be made by cutting two discs of plastic slightly larger in diameter than the coil, drilling at the center to pass the antenna wires, and cementing a plastic cylinder on the edges of the discs. The cylinder can be made by wrapping two turns or so of 0.02-inch plastic sheet around the discs, if no suitable ready-made tubing is available. Plastic drinking glasses and 2-liter soft-drink plastic bottles are easily adaptable for use as impromptu trap covers.

10.2.3 W8NX MULTIBAND, COAX-TRAP DIPOLES

Over the last 60 or 70 years, amateurs have used many kinds of multiband antennas to cover the traditional HF bands. The availability of the 30, 17 and 12 meter bands has expanded our need for multiband antenna coverage. This section is based on the August 1994 *QST* article "Two New Multiband Trap Dipoles" by Al Buxton, W8NX. This article and two others by the same author are included on this book's CD-ROM, providing designs for trap dipoles operating on all of the amateur bands below 30 MHz.

Two different antennas are described here. The first covers the traditional 80, 40, 20, 15 and 10 meter bands, and the second covers 80, 40, 17 and 12 meters. Each uses the same type of W8NX trap — connected for different modes of operation — and a pair of short capacitive stubs to enhance coverage. The W8NX coaxial-cable traps have two different modes: a high- and a low-impedance mode. The inner-conductor windings and shield windings of the traps are connected in series for both modes. However, either the low- or high-impedance point can be used as the trap's output terminal. For low-impedance trap operation, only the center conductor turns of the trap windings are used. For high-impedance operation, all turns are used, in the conventional manner for a trap. The short stubs on each antenna are strategically sized and located to permit more flexibility in adjusting the resonant frequencies of the antenna.

80, 40, 20, 15 and 10 meter Dipole

Figure 10.25 shows the configuration of the 80, 40, 20,

15 and 10 meter antenna. The radiating elements are made of #14 AWG stranded copper wire. The element lengths are the wire span lengths in feet. These lengths do not include the lengths of the pigtails at the balun, traps and insulators. The 32.3-foot-long inner 40 meter segments are measured from the eyelet of the input balun to the tension-relief hole in the trap coil form. The 4.9-foot segment length is measured from the tension-relief hole in the trap to the 6-foot stub. The 16.1-foot outer-segment span is measured from the stub to the eyelet of the end insulator.

The coaxial-cable traps are wound on PVC pipe coil forms and use the low-impedance output connection. The stubs are 6-foot lengths of ⅛-inch stiffened aluminum or copper rod hanging perpendicular to the radiating elements. The first inch of their length is bent 90° to permit attachment to the radiating elements by large-diameter copper crimp connectors. Ordinary #14 AWG wire may be used for the stubs, but it has a tendency to curl up and may tangle unless weighed down at the end. You should feed the antenna with 75-Ω coaxial cable using a choke balun.

This antenna may be thought of as a modified W3DZZ antenna due to the addition of the capacitive stubs. The length and location of the stub give the antenna designer two extra degrees of freedom to place the resonant frequencies within the amateur bands. This additional flexibility is particularly helpful to bring the 15 and 10 meter resonant frequencies to more desirable locations in these bands. The actual 10 meter resonant frequency of the original W3DZZ antenna is somewhat above 30 MHz, pretty remote from the more desirable low frequency end of 10 meters.

80, 40, 17 and 12 meter Dipole

Figure 10.26 shows the configuration of the 80, 40, 17 and 12 meter antenna. Notice that the capacitive stubs are attached immediately outboard after the traps and are 6.5 feet long, ½ foot longer than those used in the other antenna. The traps are the same as those of the other antenna, but are connected for the high-impedance parallel-resonant output mode. Since only four bands are covered by this antenna, it is easier to fine tune it to precisely the desired

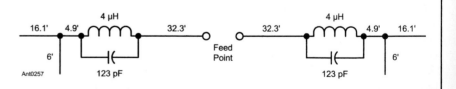

Figure 10.25 — A W8NX multiband dipole for 80, 40, 20, 15 and 10 meters. The values shown (123 pF and 4 µH) for the coaxial-cable traps are for parallel resonance at 7.15 MHz. The low-impedance output of each trap is used for this antenna.

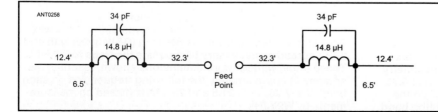

Figure 10.26 — A W8NX multiband dipole for 80, 40, 17 and 12 meters. For this antenna, the high-impedance output is used on each trap. The resonant frequency of the traps is 7.15 MHz.

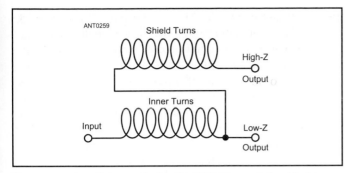

Figure 10.27 — Schematic for the W8NX coaxial-cable trap. RG-59 is wound on a 2⅜-inch OD PVC pipe.

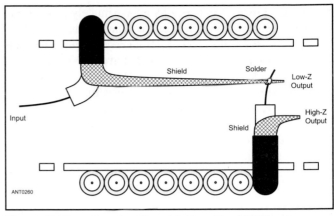

Figure 10.28 — Construction details of the W8NX coaxial-cable trap.

Figure 10.29 — Other views of a W8NX coax-cable trap.

frequency on all bands. The 12.4-foot tips can be pruned to a particular 17 meter frequency with little effect on the 12 meter frequency. The stub lengths can be pruned to a particular 12 meter frequency with little effect on the 17 meter frequency. Both such pruning adjustments slightly alter the 80 meter resonant frequency. However, the bandwidths of the antennas are so broad on 17 and 12 meters that little need for such pruning exists. The 40 meter frequency is nearly independent of adjustments to the capacitive stubs and outer radiating tip elements. Like the first antennas, this dipole is fed with a balun and 75-Ω feed line.

Figure 10.27 shows the schematic diagram of the traps. It explains the difference between the low and high-impedance modes of the traps. Notice that the high-impedance terminal is the output configuration used in most conventional trap applications. The low-impedance connection is made across only the inner conductor turns, corresponding to one-half of the total turns of the trap. This mode steps the trap's impedance down to approximately one-fourth of that of the high-impedance level. This is what allows a single trap design to be used for two different multiband antennas.

Figure 10.28 is a drawing of a cross-section of the coax trap shown through the long axis of the trap. Notice that the traps are conventional coaxial-cable traps, except for the added low-impedance output terminal. The traps are 8¾ close-spaced turns of RG-59 (Belden 8241) on a 2⅜-inch-OD PVC pipe (schedule 40 pipe with a 2-inch ID) coil form. The forms are 4⅛ inches long. Trap resonant frequency is very sensitive to the outer diameter of the coil form, so check it carefully. Unfortunately, not all PVC pipe is made with the same wall thickness. The trap frequencies should be checked with a dip meter and general-coverage receiver and adjusted to within 50 kHz of the 7150 kHz resonant frequency before installation. One inch is left over at each end of the coil forms to allow for the coax feed-through holes and holes for tension-relief attachment of the antenna radiating elements to the traps. Be sure to seal the ends of the trap coax cable to prevent moisture from entering the coaxial

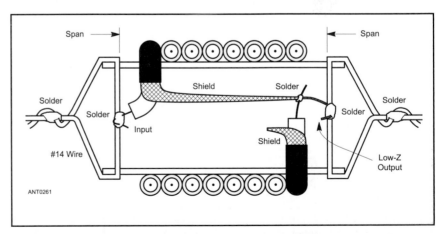

Figure 10.30 — Additional construction details for the W8NX coaxial-cable trap.

cable. (See the discussion on waterproofing in the **Building Antenna Systems and Towers** chapter.)

Also, be sure that you connect the 32.3-foot wire element at the start of the inner conductor winding of the trap. This avoids detuning the antenna by the stray capacitance of the coaxial-cable shield. The trap output terminal (which has the shield stray capacitance) should be at the outboard side of the trap. Reversing the input and output terminals of the trap will lower the 40 meter frequency by approximately 50 kHz, but there will be negligible effect on the other bands.

Figure 10.29 shows a coaxial-cable trap. Further details of the trap installation are shown in **Figure 10.30**. This drawing applies specifically to the 80, 40, 20, 15 and 10 meter antenna, which uses the low-impedance trap connections. Notice the lengths of the trap pigtails: 3 to 4 inches at each terminal of the trap. If you use a different arrangement, you must modify the span lengths accordingly. All connections can be made using crimp connectors rather than by soldering. Access to the trap's interior is attained more easily with a crimping tool than with a soldering iron.

Performance

The performance of both antennas has been very satisfactory. W8NX uses the 80, 40, 17 and 12 meter version because it covers 17 and 12 meters. (He has a tribander for 20, 15 and 10 meters.) The radiation pattern on 17 meters is that of a ³⁄₂-wave dipole. On 12 meters, the pattern is that of a ⁵⁄₂-wave dipole. At his location in Akron, Ohio, the antenna runs essentially east and west. It is installed as an inverted V, 40 feet high at the center, with a 120° included angle between the legs. Since the stubs are very short, they radiate little power and make only minor contributions to the radiation patterns. In theory, the pattern has four major lobes on 17 meters, with maxima to the northeast, southeast, southwest and northwest. These provide low-angle radiation into Europe, Africa, South Pacific, Japan and Alaska. A narrow pair of minor broadside lobes provides north and south coverage into Central America, South America and the polar regions.

There are four major lobes on 12 meters, giving nearly end-fire radiation and good low-angle east and west coverage. There are also three pairs of very narrow, nearly broadside, minor lobes on 12 meters, down about 6 dB from the major end-fire lobes. On 80 and 40 meters, the antenna has the usual figure-8 patterns of a half-wave-length dipole.

Both antennas function as electrical half-wave dipoles on 80 and 40 meters with a low SWR. They both function as odd-harmonic current-fed dipoles on their other operating frequencies, with higher, but still acceptable, SWR. The presence of the stubs can either raise or lower the input impedance of the antenna from those of the usual third and fifth harmonic dipoles. Again W8NX recommends that 75-Ω, rather than 50-Ω, feed line be used because of the generally higher input impedances at the harmonic operating frequencies of the antennas.

The SWR curves of both antennas were carefully measured using a 75 to 50-Ω transformer from Palomar Engineers inserted at the junction of the 75-Ω coax feed line and a 50-Ω SWR bridge. The transformer is required for accurate SWR measurement if a 50-Ω SWR bridge is used with a 75-Ω line. Most 50-Ω rigs operate satisfactorily with a 75-Ω line, although this requires different tuning and load settings in the final output stage of a vacuum tube amplifier or antenna tuner. The author uses the 75 to 50-Ω transformer only when making SWR measurements and at low power levels. The transformer is rated for 100 W, and when he runs his 1-kW PEP linear amplifier the transformer is taken out of the line.

Figure 10.31 gives the SWR curves of the 80, 40, 20, 15 and 10 meter antenna. Minimum SWR is nearly 1:1 on 80 meters, 1.5:1 on 40 meters, 1.6:1 on 20 meters, and 1.5:1 on 10 meters. The minimum SWR is slightly below 3:1 on 15 meters. On 15 meters, the stub capacitive reactance combines with the inductive reactance of the outer segment of the antenna to produce a resonant rise that raises the antenna input resistance to about 220 Ω, higher than that of the usual ³⁄₂-wavelength dipole. An antenna tuner may be required on

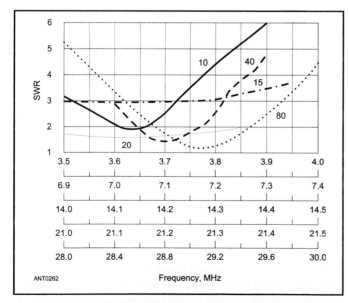

Figure 10.31 — Measured SWR curves for an 80, 40, 20, 15 and 10 meter antenna, installed as an inverted V with 40-ft apex and 120° included angle between legs.

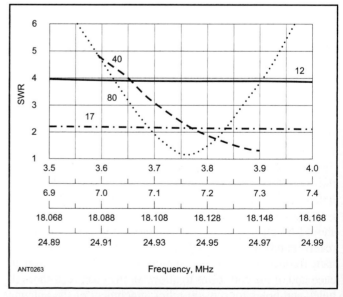

Figure 10.32 — Measured SWR curves for an 80, 40, 17 and 12 meter antenna, installed as an inverted V with 40-ft apex and 120° included angle between legs.

this band to keep a solid-state final output stage happy under these load conditions.

Figure 10.32 shows the SWR curves of the 80, 40, 17 and 12 meter antenna. Notice the excellent 80 meter performance with a nearly unity minimum SWR in the middle of the band. The performance approaches that of a full-size 80 meter wire dipole. The short stubs and the low-inductance traps shorten the antenna somewhat on 80 meters. Also observe the good 17 meter performance, with the SWR being only a little above 2:1 across the band.

But notice the 12 meter SWR curve of this antenna, which shows 4:1 SWR across the band. The antenna input resistance approaches 300 Ω on this band because the capacitive reactance of the stubs combines with the inductive reactance of the outer antenna segments to give resonant rises in impedance. These are reflected back to the input terminals. These stub-induced resonant impedance rises are similar to those on the other antenna on 15 meters, but are even more pronounced.

High SWR in coaxial cables longer than about 100 feet can lead to high feed line losses as shown in the **Transmission Lines** chapter. If you plan on operating this antenna with an SWR of greater than 3:1, make sure the amount of feed line loss is acceptable.

High voltages in the feed line should not cause too much concern. Even if the SWR is as high as 9:1 *no destructively high voltages will exist on the transmission line*. Recall that transmission-line voltages increase as the square root of the SWR in the line. Thus, 1 kW of RF power in 75-Ω line corresponds to 274 V line voltage for a 1:1 SWR. Raising the SWR to 9:1 merely triples the maximum voltage that the line must withstand to 822 V. This voltage is well below the 3700-V rating of RG-11, or the 1700-V rating of RG-59, the two most popular 75-Ω coax lines. Voltage breakdown in the traps is also very unlikely. As will be pointed out later, the operating power levels of these antennas are limited by RF power dissipation in the traps, not trap voltage breakdown or feed line SWR.

Trap Losses and Power Rating

Table 10-1 presents the results of trap Q measurements and extrapolation by a two-frequency method to higher frequencies above resonance. W8NX employed a Boonton Q meter for the measurements. Extrapolation to higher-frequency bands assumes that trap resistance losses rise with skin effect according to the square root of frequency, and that trap dielectric loses rise directly with frequency. Systematic measurement errors are not increased by frequency extrapolation. However, random measurement errors

increase in magnitude with upward frequency extrapolation. Results are believed to be accurate within 4% on 80 and 40 meters, but only within l0 to 15% at 10 meters. Trap Q is shown at both the high- and low-impedance trap terminals. The Q at the low-impedance output terminals is 15 to 20% lower than the Q at the high-impedance output terminals.

W8NX computer-analyzed trap losses for both antennas in free space. Antenna-input resistances at resonance were first calculated, assuming lossless, infinite-Q traps. They were again calculated using the Q values in Table 10-1. The radiation efficiencies were also converted into equivalent trap losses in decibels. **Table 10-2** summarizes the trap-loss analysis for the 80, 40, 20, 15 and 10 meter antenna and **Table 10-3** for the 80, 40, 17 and 12 meter antenna.

The loss analysis shows radiation efficiencies of 90% or more for both antennas on all bands except for the 80, 40, 20, 15 and 10 meter antenna when used on 40 meters. Here, the radiation efficiency falls to 70.8%. A 1-kW power level at 90% radiation efficiency corresponds to 50-W dissipation per trap. In W8NX's experience, this is the trap's survival limit for extended key-down operation. SSB power levels of 1 kW PEP would dissipate 25 W or less in each trap. This is well within the dissipation capability of the traps.

When the 80, 40, 20, 15 and 10 meter antenna is operated on 40 meters, the radiation efficiency of 70.8% corresponds to a dissipation of 146 W in each trap when 1 kW is delivered to the antenna. This is sure to burn out the traps — even if sustained for only a short time. Thus, the power should be limited to less than 300 W when this antenna is operated on 40 meters under prolonged key-down conditions such as RTTY. A 50% CW duty cycle would correspond to a 600-W power limit for normal 40 meter CW operation. Likewise, a 50% duty cycle for 40 meter SSB corresponds to a 600-W PEP power limit for the antenna.

The author knows of no analysis where the burnout wattage rating of traps has been rigorously determined. Operating experience seems to be the best way to determine trap burn-out ratings. In his own experience

---

Table 10-2
Trap Loss Analysis: 80, 40, 20, 15, 10 meter Antenna

Frequency (MHz)	3.8	7.15	14.18	21.3	28.6
Radiation Efficiency (%)	96.4	70.8	99.4	99.9	100.0
Trap Losses (dB)	0.16	1.5	0.02	0.01	0.003

Table 10-3
Trap Loss Analysis: 80, 40, 17, 12 meter Antenna

Frequency (MHz)	3.8	7.15	18.1	24.9
Radiation Efficiency (%)	89.5	90.5	99.3	99.8
Trap Losses (dB)	0.5	0.4	0.03	0.006

Table 10-1
Trap Q

Frequency (MHz)	3.8	7.15	14.18	18.1	21.3	24.9	28.6
High Z out (Ω)	101	124	139	165	73	179	186
Low Z out (Ω)	83	103	125	137	44	149	155

with these antennas, he's had no traps burn out, even though he operated the 80, 40, 20, 15 and 10 meter antenna on the critical 40 meter band using his AL-80A linear amplifier at the 600-W PEP output level. He did not make a continuous, key-down, CW operating test at full power purposely trying to destroy the traps!

Some hams may suggest using a different type of coaxial cable for the traps. The dc resistance of 40.7 Ω per 1000 feet of RG-59 coax seems rather high. However, W8NX has found no coax other than RG-59 that has the necessary inductance-to-capacitance ratio to create the trap characteristic reactance required for the 80, 40, 20, 15 and 10 meter antenna. Conventional traps with wide-spaced, open-air inductors and appropriate fixed-value capacitors could be substituted for the coax traps, but the convenience, weatherproof configuration and ease of fabrication of coaxial-cable traps is hard to beat.

10.3 MULTIBAND VERTICAL ANTENNAS

There are two basic types of vertical antennas; either type can be used in multiband configurations. The first is the ground-mounted vertical and the second, the ground plane. These antennas are described in detail in the chapter **Dipoles and Monopoles**.

The efficiency of any ground-mounted vertical depends a great deal on near-field earth losses. As pointed out in the chapter **Effects of Ground**, these near-field losses can be reduced or eliminated with an adequate radial system. Considerable experimentation has been conducted on this subject by Jerry Sevick, W2FMI (SK), and several important results were obtained. It was determined that a radial system consisting of 40 to 50 radials, 0.2 λ long, would reduce the earth losses to about 2 Ω when a λ/4 radiator was being used. These radials should be on the earth's surface, or if buried, placed not more than an inch or so below ground. Otherwise, the RF current would have to travel through the lossy earth before reaching the radials. In a multiband vertical system, the radials should be 0.2 λ long for the lowest band, that is, 55 feet long for 3.5-MHz operation. Any wire size may be used for the radials. The radials should fan out in a circle, radiating from the base of the antenna. A metal plate, such as a piece of sheet copper, can be used at the center connection.

The other common type of vertical is the ground-plane antenna. Normally, this antenna is mounted above ground with the radials fanning out from the base of the antenna. The vertical portion of the antenna is usually an electrical λ/4, as is each of the radials. In this type of antenna, the system of radials acts somewhat like an RF choke, to prevent RF currents from flowing in the supporting structure, so the number of radials is not as important a factor as it is with a ground-mounted vertical system. From a practical standpoint, the customary number of radials is four or five. In a multiband configuration, λ/4 radials are required for each band of operation with the ground-plane antenna.

This is not so with the ground-mounted vertical antenna, where the ground plane is relied upon to provide an image of the radiating section. Note that even quarter-wave-long radials are greatly detuned by their proximity to ground — radial resonance is not necessary or even possible. In the ground-mounted case, so long as the ground-screen radials are approximately 0.2 λ long at the lowest frequency, the length will be more than adequate for the higher frequency bands.

10.3.1 FULL-SIZE VERTICAL ANTENNAS

A vertical antenna should not be longer than about ¾ λ at the highest frequency to be used, however, if low-angle radiation is wanted. You can see why from reviewing the radiation patterns for dipoles in the chapter **Dipoles and Monopoles**. As the antenna lengthens, the pattern breaks up into lobes that are at high elevation angles for a vertical antenna. Nevertheless, an antenna that is λ/4 on the lower frequency of operation can still be useful over a 3:1 frequency range or even more if the high-angle radiation can be tolerated. For example, an 80 meter λ/4 vertical around 66 feet high is useful through the 30 meter band and a 25-foot vertical would be useful from about 10 MHz through the 28 MHz band.

In recent years, the 43-foot ground-mounted vertical antenna with an automatic antenna tuner mounted at the base of the antenna has become very popular as an all-band HF vertical, including 160 meters with the appropriate tuner. See **Figure 10.33**. While the elevation angle of maximum radiation begins to increase significantly above the 20 meter band, the combination of simplicity and clean appearance make up for the compromise. (A variation on this idea is the "flag-pole" antenna discussed in the **Stealth and Limited Space Antennas** chapter.) If the lower bands are not required, a 22-foot vertical is quite effective at and above 40 meters. The antennas can be constructed from aluminum tubing or as a fiberglass mast with wires inside or taped along the outside of the mast.

In lieu of using an automatic antenna tuner at the base of the vertical, several *QST* articles listed in the Bibliography serve as examples of how a single vertical antenna can be put to work on several bands. The referenced articles by Phil Salas, AD5X discuss matching the antenna's impedance on 160 and 80 meters.

10.3.2 SHORT VERTICAL ANTENNAS

A short vertical antenna (one less than λ/4 at the operating frequency) can be operated on several bands by loading it at the base, the general arrangement being similar to Figures 10.1 and 10.2. That is, for multiband operation the vertical can be handled by the same methods that are used for

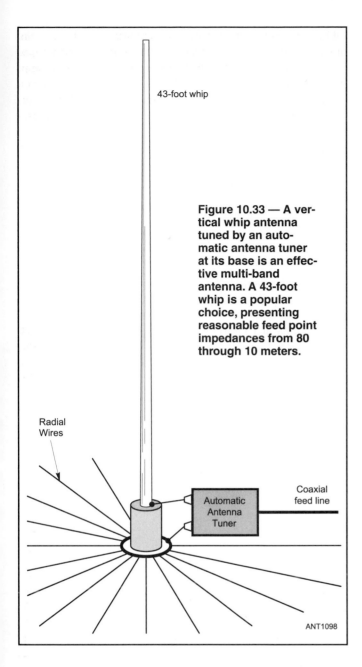

Figure 10.33 — A vertical whip antenna tuned by an automatic antenna tuner at its base is an effective multi-band antenna. A 43-foot whip is a popular choice, presenting reasonable feed point impedances from 80 through 10 meters.

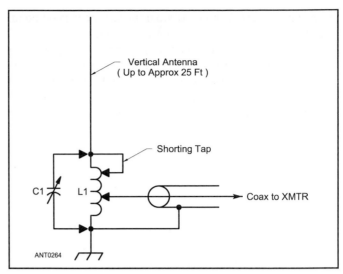

Figure 10.34 — Multiband vertical antenna system using base loading for resonating on 3.5 to 28 MHz. L1 should be wound with bare wire so it can be tapped at every turn, using #12 AWG wire. A convenient size is 2½ inches in diameter, 6 turns per inch (such as B&W 3029). Number of turns required depends on antenna and ground lead length, more turns being required as the antenna and ground lead are made shorter. For a 25-foot antenna and a ground lead of the order of 5 feet, L1 should have about 30 turns. The use of C1 is explained in the text. The smallest capacitance that will permit matching the coax cable should be used; a maximum capacitance of 100 to 150 pF will be sufficient in any case.

random-length wires.

Another method of feeding is shown in **Figure 10.34**. L1 is a loading coil, tapped to resonate the antenna on the desired band. A second tap permits using the coil as a transformer for matching a coax line to the transmitter. C1 is not strictly necessary, but may be helpful on the lower frequencies, 3.5 and 7 MHz, if the antenna is quite short. In that case C1 makes it possible to tune the system to resonance with a coil of reasonable dimensions at L1. C1 may also be useful on other bands as well, if the system cannot be matched to the feed line with a coil alone. (This is similar to the techniques described in the chapter **Mobile and Maritime HF Antennas**.)

The coil and capacitor should preferably be installed at the base of the antenna, but if this cannot be done a wire can be run from the antenna base to the nearest convenient location for mounting L1 and C1. The extra wire will of course be a part of the antenna, and since it may have to run through unfavorable surroundings it is best to avoid using it if at all possible. (Use the shortest possible ground connection both for efficiency and to avoid creating an unintended radiating element of the antenna system.)

This system is best adjusted with the help of an SWR indicator. Connect the coax line across a few turns of L1 and take trial positions of the shorting tap until the SWR reaches its lowest value. Then vary the feed line tap similarly; this should bring the SWR down to a low value. Small adjustments of both taps then should reduce the SWR to close to 1:1. If not, try adding C1 and go through the same procedure, varying C1 each time a tap position is changed.

10.3.3 TRAP VERTICALS

The trap principle described in Figure 10.21 for center-fed dipoles also can be used for vertical antennas. There are two principal differences. Only one half of the dipole is used, the ground connection taking the place of the missing half, and the feed point impedance is one half the feed point impedance of a dipole. Thus it is in the vicinity of 30 Ω (plus the ground-connection resistance), so 52-Ω cable should be used since it is the commonly available type that comes closest to matching.

Commercial multiband trap verticals such as the Hustler 4/5/6BTV series and the Hy-Gain AVQ series have been widely used for many years and provide effective performance as ground-mounted antennas when used with a good radial system.

Verticals advertised as "ground-independent" are intended to be mounted above ground. Models such as the Cushcraft R8 and R6000 and the Hy-Gain Patriot are end-fed systems that are electrically longer than λ/4 at the frequency of operation. They have a high feed point impedance that is reduced to 50 Ω with a matching network at the base of the antenna. These are particularly useful antennas for temporary stations and when restrictions prevent the installation of ground systems.

Most amateurs prefer to purchase multiband trap verticals because of the mechanical complexities and requirements to be self-supporting.

10.4 THE OPEN-SLEEVE ANTENNA

Although only recently adapted for the HF and VHF amateur bands, the open-sleeve antenna has been around since 1946. The antenna was invented by Dr J. T. Bolljahn, of Stanford Research Institute. This section on sleeve antennas summarizes material by Roger A. Cox, WBØDGF in previous editions. The complete article is available on this book's CD-ROM.

The basic form of the open-sleeve monopole is shown in **Figure 10.35**. The open-sleeve monopole consists of a base-fed central monopole with two parallel closely spaced parasitics, one on each side of the central element, and grounded at each base. The lengths of the parasitics are roughly one half that of the central monopole.

10.4.1 IMPEDANCE

The operation of the open sleeve can be divided into two modes, an antenna-mode and a transmission-line mode. This is shown in **Figure 10.36**.

The antenna-mode impedance, Z_A, is determined by the length and diameter of the central monopole. For sleeve lengths less than that of the monopole, this impedance is essentially independent of the sleeve dimensions.

The transmission-line mode impedance, Z_T, is determined by the characteristic impedance, end impedance, and length of the 3-wire transmission line formed by the central monopole and the two sleeve elements. The characteristic impedance, Z_c, can be determined by the element diameters and spacing if all element diameters are equal, and is found from

$$Z_c = 207 \log 1.59 \, (D/d) \qquad \text{(Eq 2)}$$

where
 D = spacing between the center of each sleeve element and the center of the driven element
 d = diameter of each element

This is shown graphically in **Figure 10.37**. However, since the end impedance is usually unknown, there is little need to know the characteristic impedance. The transmission-line mode impedance, Z_T, is usually determined by an educated guess and experimentation.

As an example, let us consider the case where the central monopole is λ/4 at 14 MHz. It would have an antenna mode impedance, Z_A, of approximately 52 Ω, depending upon the ground conductivity and number of radials. If two sleeve elements were added on either side of the central monopole, with each approximately half the height of the monopole and at a distance equal to their height, there would be very little effect on the antenna mode impedance, Z_A, at 14 MHz.

Also, Z_T at 14 MHz would be the end impedance transformed through a λ/8 section of a very high characteristic

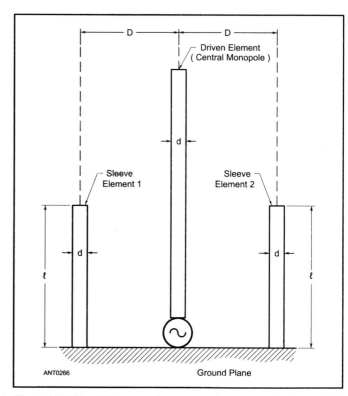

Figure 10.35 — Diagram of an open-sleeve monopole.

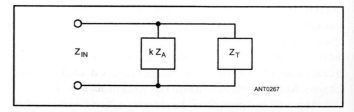

Figure 10.36 — Equivalent circuit of an open-sleeve antenna.

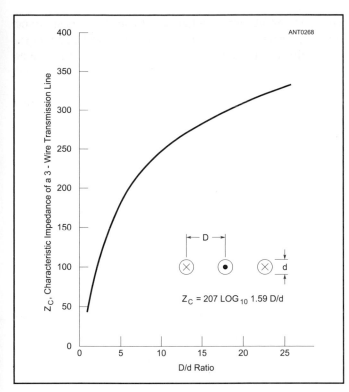

Figure 10.37 — Characteristic impedance of transmission-line mode in an open-sleeve antenna.

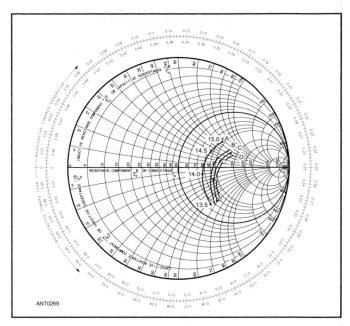

Figure 10.38 — Impedance of an open-sleeve monopole for the frequency range 13.5-15 MHz. Curve A is for a 14 MHz monopole alone. For curves B, C and D, the respective spacings from the central monopole to the sleeve elements are 8, 6 and 4 inches. See text for other dimensions.

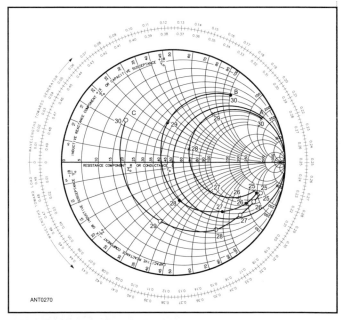

Figure 10.39 — Impedance of the open-sleeve monopole for the range 25-30 MHz. For curves A, B and C the spacings from the central monopole to the sleeve elements are 8, 6 and 4 inches, respectively.

impedance transmission line. Therefore, Z_T would be on the order of 500-2000 Ω resistive plus a large capacitive reactance component. This high impedance in parallel with 52 Ω would still give a resulting impedance close to 52 Ω.

At a frequency of 28 MHz, however, Z_A is that of an end-fed half-wave antenna, and is on the order of 1000-5000 Ω resistive. Also, Z_T at 28 MHz would be on the order of 1000 to 5000 Ω resistive, since it is the end impedance of the sleeve elements transformed through a quarter-wave section of a very high characteristic impedance three-wire transmission line. Therefore, the parallel combination of Z_A and Z_T would still be on the order of 500 to 2500 Ω resistive.

The actual impedance plots of a 14/28-MHz open-sleeve monopole appear in **Figures 10.38** and **10.39**. The length of the central monopole is 195.5 inches, and of the sleeve elements 89.5 inches. The element diameters range from 1.25 inches at the bases to 0.875 inch at each tip. The measured impedance of the 14-MHz monopole alone, curve A of Figure 10.38, is quite high. This is probably because of a very poor ground plane under the antenna. The addition of the sleeve elements raises this impedance slightly, curves B, C and D.

As curves A and B in Figure 10.39 show, an 8-inch sleeve spacing gives a resonance near 27.8 MHz at 70 Ω, while a 6-inch spacing gives a resonance near 28.5 MHz at 42 Ω. Closer spacings give lower impedances and higher resonances. The optimum spacing for this particular antenna would be somewhere between 6 and 8 inches. Once the

spacing is found, the lengths of the sleeve elements can be tweaked slightly for a choice of resonant frequency.

In other frequency combinations such as 10/21, 10/24, 14/21 and 14/24-MHz, spacings in the 6 to 10-inch range work very well with element diameters in the 0.5 to 1.25-inch range.

10.4.2 BANDWIDTH

The open-sleeve antenna, when used as a multiband antenna, does not exhibit broad SWR bandwidths unless the two bands are very close together. For example, **Figure 10.40** shows the return loss and SWR of a single 10-MHz vertical antenna. Its 2:1 SWR bandwidth is 1.5 MHz, from 9.8 to 11.3 MHz. Return loss and SWR are related as given by the following equation.

$$SWR = \frac{1+k}{1-k} \qquad \text{(Eq 3)}$$

where

$$k = 10^{\frac{R_L}{20}}$$

RL = return loss, dB

10.4.3 RADIATION PATTERN AND GAIN

The current distribution of the open-sleeve antenna where all three elements are nearly equal in length is nearly that of a single monopole antenna. If, at a particular frequency, the elements are approximately $\lambda/4$ long, the current distribution is sinusoidal.

If, for this and other length ratios, the chosen diameters

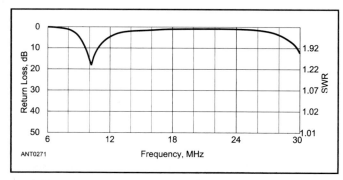

Figure 10.40 — Return loss and SWR of a 10 MHz vertical antenna. A return loss of 0 dB represents an SWR of infinity. The text contains an equation for converting return loss to an SWR value.

and spacings are such that the two sleeve elements approach an interelement spacing of $\lambda/8$, the azimuthal pattern will show directivity typical of two in-phase vertical radiators, approximately $\lambda/8$ apart. If a bidirectional pattern is needed, then this is one way to achieve it.

Spacings closer than this will produce nearly circular azimuthal radiation patterns. Practical designs in the 10 to 30 MHz range using 0.5 to 1.5-inch diameter elements will produce azimuthal patterns that vary less than ±1 dB.

If the ratio of the length of the central monopole to the length of the sleeves approaches 2:1, then the elevation pattern of the open-sleeve vertical antenna at the resonant frequency of the sleeves becomes slightly compressed. This is because of the in-phase contribution of radiation from the $\lambda/2$ central monopole.

The third, fifth, and seventh-order resonances of the sleeve elements and the central monopole element can be used, but their radiation patterns normally consist of high-elevation lobes, and the gain on the horizon is less than that of a $\lambda/4$ vertical.

10.4.4 CONSTRUCTION AND EVALUATION

The open-sleeve antenna lends itself very easily to home construction. For the open-sleeve vertical antenna, only a feed point insulator and a good supply of aluminum tubing are needed. No special traps or matching networks are required. The open-sleeve vertical can produce up to 3 dB more gain than a conventional $\lambda/4$ vertical. Further, there is no reduction in bandwidth, because there are no loading coils.

The open-sleeve design can also be adapted to horizontal dipole and beam antennas for HF, VHF and UHF. A good example of this is Hy-Gain's Explorer 14 triband beam which utilizes an open sleeve for the 10/15 meter driven element. The open-sleeve antenna is also very easy to model in computer programs such as *NEC* and *MININEC*, because of the open tubular construction and lack of traps or other intricate structures.

In conclusion, the open-sleeve antenna is an antenna experimenter's delight. It is not difficult to match or construct, and it makes an ideal broadband or multiband antenna.

10.5 THE COUPLED-RESONATOR DIPOLE

A variation of the open-sleeve system above is the coupled-resonator system described by Gary Breed, K9AY, in an article in *The ARRL Antenna Compendium, Vol 5*, entitled "The Coupled-Resonator Principle: A Flexible Method for Multiband Antennas." The following is condensed from that article.

In 1995, *QST* published two antenna designs that use an interesting technique to get multiband coverage in one antenna. Rudy Severns, N6LF, described a wideband 80 and 75 meter dipole using this technique (see the **Single Band MF and HF Antennas** chapter), and Robert Wilson,

AL7KK, showed us how to make a three-band vertical. Both of these antennas achieve multi-frequency operation by placing resonant conductors very close to a driven dipole or vertical — with no physical connection.

10.5.1 THE COUPLED-RESONATOR PRINCIPLE

As we all know, nearby conductors can interact with an antenna. Our dipoles, verticals and beams can be affected by nearby power lines, rain gutters, guy wires and other metallic materials. The antennas designed by Severns and Wilson use

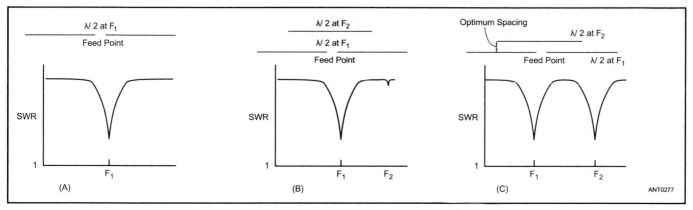

Figure 10.41 — At A, the SWR of a dipole over a wide frequency range. At B, a nearby conductor is just close enough to interact with the dipole. At C, when the second conductor is at the optimum spacing, the combination is matched at both frequencies.

this interaction intentionally, to combine the resonances of several conductors at a single feed point. While other names have been used, I call the behavior that makes these antennas work the coupled-resonator (C-R) principle.

Take a look at **Figure 10.41**, which illustrates the general idea. Each figure shows the SWR at the feed point of a dipole, over a range of frequencies. When this dipole is all alone, it will have a very low SWR at its half-wave resonant frequency (Figure 10.41A). Next, if we take another wire or tubing conductor and start bringing it close to the dipole, we will see a "bump" in the dipole's SWR at the resonant frequency of this new wire. See Figure 10.41B. We are beginning to the see the effects of interaction between the two conductors. As we bring this new conductor closer, we reach a point where the SWR "bump" has grown to a very deep dip — a low SWR. We now have a good match at both the original dipole's resonant frequency and the frequency of the new conductor, as illustrated in Figure 10.41C.

We can repeat this process for several more conductors at other frequencies to get a dipole with three, four, five, six, or more resonant frequencies. The principle also applies to verticals, so any reference to a dipole can be considered to be valid for a vertical, as well.

We can write a definition of the C-R principle this way: *Given a dipole (or vertical) at one frequency and an additional conductor resonant at another frequency, there is an optimum distance between them that results in the resonance of the additional conductor being imposed upon the original dipole, resulting in a low SWR at both resonant frequencies.*

Some History

In the late 1940s, the coaxial sleeve antenna was developed (**Figure 10.42**), covering two frequencies by surrounding a dipole or monopole with a cylindrical tube resonant at the higher of the desired frequencies. In the 1950s, Gonset briefly marketed a two-band antenna based on this design. Other experimenters soon determined that two conductors at the second frequency, placed on either side of the main dipole or monopole, would make a skeleton representation of a cylinder (Figure 10.42B). This is called the *open-sleeve antenna*. The Hy-Gain Explorer tribander uses this method in

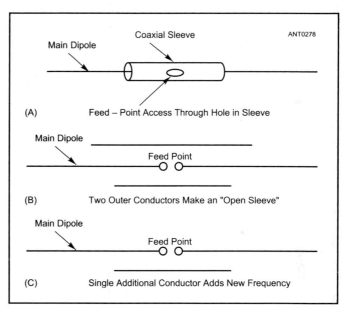

Figure 10.42 — Evolution of coupled-resonator antennas: At A, the *coaxial-sleeve* dipole; at B, the *open-sleeve* dipole; and at C, a *coupled-resonator* dipole, the most universal configuration.

its driven element to obtain resonance in the 10 meter band. Later on, a few antenna developers finally figured out that these extra conductors did not need to be added in pairs, and that a single conductor at each frequency could add the extra resonances (Figure 10.42C). This is the method used by Force 12 in some of their multiband antennas.

This is a perfect example of how science works. A specific idea is discovered, with later developments leading to an underlying general principle. The original coaxial-sleeve configuration is the most specific, being limited to two frequencies and requiring a particular construction method. The open-sleeve antenna is an intermediate step, showing that the sleeve idea is not limited to one configuration.

Finally, we have the coupled-resonator concept, which is the general principle, applicable in many different antenna configurations, for many different frequency combinations.

Severns's antenna uses it with a folded dipole, and Wilson uses it with a main vertical that is off-center fed. The author, K9AY used it with conventional dipoles and quarter-wave verticals. Other designers have used the principle more subtly, like putting the first director in a Yagi very close to the driven element, broadening the SWR bandwidth the same way Severns's design does with a dipole.

In the past, most open-sleeve or multiple-open-sleeve antennas built with this technique have also been called *open-sleeve* (or *multiple-open-sleeve*) antennas, a term taken from the history of their development. However, the term *sleeve* implies that one conductor must surround another. This is not really a physical or electrical description of the antenna's operation, therefore, K9AY suggests using the term *coupled-resonator*, which is the most accurate description of the general principle.

A Little Math

The interaction that makes the C-R principle work is not random. It behaves in a predictable, regular manner. K9AY derived an equation that shows the relationship between the driven element and the additional resonators for ordinary dipoles and verticals:

$$\frac{\log_{10} d}{\log_{10}(D/4)} = 0.54 \qquad \text{(Eq 4)}$$

where
  d = distance between conductors, measured in wavelengths at the frequency of the chosen additional resonator
  D = the diameter of the conductors, also in wavelengths at the frequency of the additional resonator.

Eq 4 assumes they are both the same diameter and that the feed point impedance at both frequencies is the same as a dipole in free space (72 Ω) or a quarter-wave monopole over perfect ground (36 Ω).

The equation only describes the impedance due to the additional resonator. The main dipole element is always part of the antenna, and it may have a fairly low impedance at the additional frequency. This is the case when the frequencies are close together, or when the main element is operating at its third harmonic. At these frequencies, the spacing distance must be adjusted so that the parallel combination of dipole and resonator results in the desired feed point impedance.

K9AY worked out two correction factors, one to cover a range of impedances and another for frequencies close together. These can be included in the basic equation, which is rearranged below to solve for the distance between the conductors:

$$d = 10^{0.54 \log_{10}(D/4)} \times \frac{Z_0 + 35.5}{109} \times \left[1 + e^{-[(((F_2/F_1)-1.1) \times 11.3)+0.1)]}\right]$$

$$\text{(Eq 5)}$$

C-R Element Spacing

K9AY's Eq 5 presented in the text does indeed yield a good "first-cut" value for the spacing between coupled-resonator elements. **Figure 10.A** shows the spacing, in inches, plotted against the ratio of frequencies, for two coupled resonator elements with different diameters, again expressed in inches. This is for an upper frequency of 28.4 MHz. Beyond a frequency ratio of about 1.5:1 (28.4:18.1 MHz), the spacing flattens out to a fixed distance between elements for each element diameter. For example, if 1/2-inch elements are used at 28.4 and 18.1 MHz, the spacing between the elements is about 3.75 inches.

EZNEC verifies Eq 5's computations. Note that a large number of segments are necessary for each element when they are closely spaced from each other, and the segments on the elements must be closely aligned with each other. Be sure to run the Average Gain test, as well as Segmentation tests. The modeler should also be aware that if mutually coupled resonators are placed along a horizontal boom (as they would be on multiband Yagis using coupled resonators), the higher-frequency elements will act like retrograde directors, producing some gain (or lack of gain, depending on the azimuth being investigated).

For example, in the *EZNEC* file **K9AY C-R 28-21-14 MHz 1 In.EZ**, using 1-inch diameter elements spaced 6 inches apart, if the 28-MHz element is placed 6 inches behind the 14-MHz driven element (with the 21-MHz element placed 6 inches ahead), on 28 MHz the system will have a F/B of 2.6 dB, favoring the rearward direction.

On 21 MHz, the system will exhibit a F/B of 1.6 dB, favoring the forward direction. Of course, there are systems where gain and F/B due to the C-R configuration may be put to good use, such as the multiband Yagis mentioned above. However, if the elements are spaced above/below the 14-MHz driven element there is no distortion of the dipole patterns.

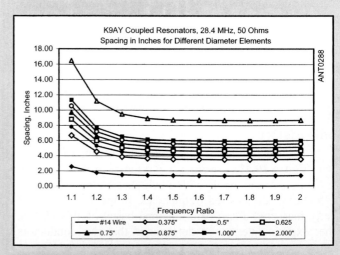

Figure 10.A — Graph of the spacing versus frequency ratio for two Coupled-Resonator elements at 28.4 MHz, for 50-Ω feed point impedance.

where

d and D are the same as in Eq 4 above.

Z_0 = the desired feed point impedance at the frequency of the additional resonator (between 20 and 120 Ω). For a vertical, multiply the desired impedance by two to get Z_0. If you want a 50-Ω feed, use 100 Ω for Z_0.

F_1 = the resonant frequency of the main dipole or vertical.

F_2 = the resonant frequency of the additional conductor. The ratio F_2/F_1 is more than 1.1.

e = 2.7183, the base of natural logarithms.

Eq 5 does not directly allow for conductors of unequal diameters, but it can be used as a starting point if you use the diameter of the driven dipole or vertical element for D in the equation.

10.5.2 CHARACTERISTICS OF COUPLED-RESONATOR (C-R) ANTENNAS

Here's the important stuff — what's different about C-R antennas, what are they good for and what are their drawbacks? The key points are:

- Multiband operation without traps, stubs or tuners
- Flexible impedance matching at each frequency
- Independent fine-tuning at each frequency (little interaction)
- Easily modeled using *MININEC* or *NEC*-based programs
- Pruning process same as a simple dipole
- Can accommodate many frequencies (seven or more)
- Virtually lossless coupling (high efficiency)
- Requires a separate wire or tubing conductor at each frequency
- Mechanical assembly requires a number of insulated supports
- Narrower bandwidth than equivalent dipole
- Capacitance requires slight lengthening of conductors

To begin with, the most obvious characteristic is that this principle can be used to add multiple resonant frequencies to an ordinary dipole or vertical, using additional conductors that are not physically connected. This gives us three variable factors: (1) the diameter of the conductor, (2) its length, and (3) its position relative to the main element.

Having the freedom to control these factors gives us the advantage of *flexibility*; we have a wide range of control over the impedance at each added frequency. Another advantage is that the behavior at each frequency is quite *independent*, once the basic design is in place. In other words, making fine-tuning adjustments at one frequency doesn't change the resonance or impedance at the other frequencies. A final advantage is *efficiency*. With conductors close together, and with a resonant target conductor, coupling is very efficient. Traps, stubs, and compensating networks found on other multiband antennas all introduce lossy reactive components.

There are two main disadvantages of C-R antennas. The first is the relative *complexity* of construction. Several conductors are needed, installed with some type of insulating spacers. Other multiband antennas have their complexities as well (such as traps that need to be mounted and tuned), but C-R antennas will usually be bulkier. The larger size generally means greater windload, which is a disadvantage to some hams.

The other significant disadvantage is *narrower bandwidth*, particularly at the highest of the operating frequencies. We can partially overcome this problem with large conductors that are naturally broad in bandwidth, and in some cases we might even use an extra conductor to put two resonances in one band. It is interesting to note that the pattern is opposite that of trap antennas. The C-R antenna gets narrower at the highest frequencies of operation, while trap antennas generally have narrowest bandwidth at their lowest frequencies.

There are two special situations that should be noted. First, when the antenna has a resonance near the frequency where the driven dipole is $\frac{3}{2} \lambda$ long ($\frac{3}{4} \lambda$ for a vertical), the dipole has a fairly low impedance. The spacing of the C-R element needs to be increased to raise its impedance so that the parallel combination of the main element and C-R element equals the desired impedance (usually 50 Ω). There is also significant antenna current in the part of the main dipole extending beyond the C-R section, contributing to the total radiation pattern. As a result, this particular arrangement radiates as three $\lambda/2$ sections in phase, and has about 3 dB gain and a narrower directional pattern compared to a dipole (**Figure 10.43**). This might be an advantage for antennas covering bands with a frequency ratio of about three, such as 3.5 and 10.1 MHz, 7 and 21 MHz, or 144 and 430 MHz.

The other special situation is when we want to add a new frequency very close to the resonant frequency of the main dipole. An antenna for 80 and 75 meters would be an

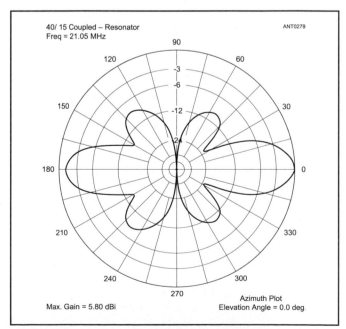

Figure 10.43 — Radiation pattern for the special case of a C-R antenna with the additional resonance at the third harmonic of the main dipole resonant frequency.

example of this. Again, the driven dipole has a fairly low impedance at the new frequency. Add the fact that coupling is very strong between these similar conductors and we find that a wide spacing is required to make the antenna work. A dipole resonant at 3.5 MHz and another wire resonant at 3.8 MHz will need to be 3 or 4 feet apart, while a 3.5 MHz and 7 MHz combination might only need to be spaced 4 or 5 inches.

Another useful characteristic of C-R antennas is that they are easily and accurately modeled by computer programs based on either *MININEC* or *NEC*, as long as you stay within each program's limitations. For example, Severns points out that *MININEC* does not handle folded dipoles very well, and *NEC* modeling is required. With ease of computer modeling, a precise answer isn't needed for the design equation given above. An approximate solution will provide a starting point that can quickly be adjusted for optimum dimensions.

The added resonators have an effect on the lengths of all conductors, due to the capacitance between the conductors. Capacitance causes antennas to look electrically shorter, so each element needs to be about 1% or 2% longer than a simple dipole at the same frequency. As a rule of thumb, use 477/f (in feet) instead of the usual 468/f when calculating dipole length, and 239/f instead of 234/f for a λ/4 vertical.

Summary

The coupled-resonator principle is one more weapon in the antenna designer's arsenal. It's not the perfect method for all multiband antennas, but what the C-R principle offers is an alternative to traps and tuners, in exchange for using more wire or aluminum. Although a C-R antenna requires more complicated construction, its main attraction is in making a multiband antenna that can be built with no compromise in matching or efficiency.

10.5.3 A C-R DIPOLE FOR 30/17/12 METERS

To show how a C-R antenna is designed, let's build a dipole to cover 30, 17 and 12 meters. We'll use #12 AWG wire, which has a diameter of 0.08 inches, and the main dipole will be cut for the 10.1 MHz band. From the equation above, the spacing between the main dipole and the 18-MHz resonator should be 2.4 inches for 72 Ω, or 1.875 inches for 50 Ω. At 24.9 MHz, the spacing to the resonator for that band should be 2.0 inches for 72 Ω, or 1.62 inches for 50 Ω. Of course, this antenna will be installed over real ground, not in free

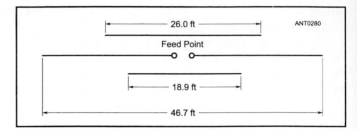

Figure 10.44 — Dimensions of a C-R dipole for the 30, 17 and 12 meter bands.

space, so these spacing distances may not be exact. Plugging these numbers into your favorite antenna-modeling program will let you optimize the dimensions for installation at the height you choose.

For those of you who like to work with real antennas, not computer-generated ones, the predicted spacing is accurate enough to build an antenna with minimum trial-and-error. You should use a nice round number just larger than the calculated spacing for 50 Ω. For this antenna, K9AY decided that the right spacing for the desired height would be 2 inches for the 18 MHz resonator and 1.8 inches for the 24.9 MHz resonator. For simplicity of construction, he just used 2 inches for both, figuring that the worst he would get is a 1.2:1 SWR if the numbers were a little bit off. Like all dipoles, the impedance varies with height above ground, but the 2-inch spacing results in an excellent match on the two additional bands, at heights of more than 25 feet.

The final dimensions of the dipole for 10.1, 18.068 and 24.89 MHz are shown in **Figure 10.44**. These are the final pruned lengths for a straight dipole installed at a height of about 40 feet. If you put up the antenna as an inverted V, you will need each wire to be a bit longer. Pruning this type of antenna is just like a dipole — if it's resonant too low in frequency, it's too long and the appropriate wire needs to be shortened. So, you can cut the wires just a little long to start with and easily prune them to resonance.

A final note: if you want to duplicate this antenna design, remember that the 2-inch spacing is just for #12 AWG wire! The required spacing for a C-R antenna is related to the conductor diameter. This same antenna built with #14 AWG wire needs under 1½-inch spacing, while a 1-inch aluminum-tubing version requires about 7-inch spacing.

10.6 HF LOG PERIODIC DIPOLE ARRAYS

The log periodic antenna whose theory is presented in the chapter **Log-Periodic Dipole Arrays** is intended to be used across a wide frequency range. Designs that cover two or more amateur bands are fairly common and rotatable LPDAs (Log Periodic Dipole Arrays) are popular antennas for 20 meters through the UHF bands.

This section presents a pair of LPDA designs — a fixed array of wire dipoles for the 3.5 and 7 MHz bands and a rotatable array for the five amateur bands from 14 through 30 MHz. In addition, the *QST* article "Practical High Performance HF Log Periodic Antennas" by Bill Jones, K8CU is provided on this book's CD-ROM for additional design information.

10.6.1 LPDAS FOR 3.5 OR 7 MHZ

These wire log-periodic dipole arrays for the lower HF bands are simple in design and easy to build. They are designed to have reasonable gain, be inexpensive and lightweight, and may be assembled with stock items found in large hardware stores. They are also strong — they can withstand a hurricane! These antennas were first described by John J. Uhl, KV5E, in *QST* for August 1986. **Figure 10.45** shows one method of installation. You can use the information here as a guide and point of reference for building similar LPDAs.

If space is available, the antennas can be rotated or repositioned in azimuth after they are completed. A 75-foot tower and a clear turning radius of 120 feet around the base of the tower are needed. The task is simplified if you use only three anchor points, instead of the five shown in Figure 10.45. Omit the two anchor points on the forward element, and extend the two nylon strings used for element stays all the way to the forward stay line.

Design of the Log-Periodic Dipole Arrays

Design constants for the two arrays are listed in **Tables 10-4** and **10-5**. The **Log-Periodic Dipole Arrays** chapter

has more information about the design procedure for arriving at the dimensions and other parameters of these arrays. The primary differences between these designs and one-octave upper HF arrays are the narrower frequency ranges and the use of wire, rather than tubing, for the elements. As design examples for the LPDA, you may wish to work through the step-by-step procedure and check your results against the values in Tables 10-4 and 10-5. You may also wish to compare these results with the output of an LPDA design software package such as *LPCAD*.

From the design procedure, the feeder wire spacings for the two arrays are slightly different, 0.58 inch for the 3.5-MHz array and 0.66 inch for the 7-MHz version. As

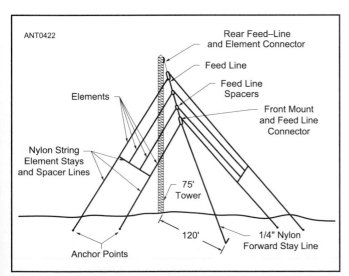

Figure 10.45 — Typical lower-HF wire 4-element log periodic dipole array erected on a tower.

Table 10-4
Design Parameters for the 3.5-MHz Single-Band LPDA

$f1 = 3.3$ MHz	Element lengths:
$f_n = 4.1$ MHz	$\ell 1 = 149.091$ feet
$B = 1.2424$	$\ell 2 = 125.982$ feet
$\tau = 0.845$	$\ell 3 = 106.455$ feet
$\sigma = 0.06$	$\ell 4 = 89.954$ feet
Gain = 5.9 dBi = 3.8 dBd	Element spacings:
$\cot \alpha = 1.5484$	$d_{12} = 17.891$ feet
$B_{ar} = 1.3864$	$d_{23} = 15.118$ feet
$B_s = 1.7225$	$d_{34} = 12.775$ feet
$L = 48.42$ feet	Element diameters
$N = 4.23$ elements (decrease to 4)	All = 0.0641 inches
Z_t = 6-inch short jumper	ℓ/diameter ratios:
$R_0 = 208\ \Omega$	$\ell/\text{diam}_4 = 16840$
$Z_{AV} = 897.8\ \Omega$	$\ell/\text{diam}_3 = 19929$
$\sigma' = 0.06527$	$\ell/\text{diam}_2 = 23585$
$Z_0 = 319.8\ \Omega$	$\ell/\text{diam}_1 = 27911$
Antenna feeder: #12 AWG wire spaced 0.58 inches	
Balun: 4:1	
Feed line: 52-Ω coax	

Table 10-5
Design Parameters for the 7-MHz Single-Band LPDA

$f1 = 6.9$ MHz	Element lengths:
$f_n = 7.5$ MHz	$\ell 1 = 71.304$ feet
$B = 1.0870$	$\ell 2 = 60.252$ feet
$\tau = 0.845$	$\ell 3 = 50.913$ feet
$\sigma = 0.06$	$\ell 4 = 43.022$ feet
Gain = 5.9 dBi = 3.8 dBd	Element spacings:
$\cot \alpha = 1.5484$	$d_{12} = 8.557$ feet
$B_{ar} = 1.3864$	$d_{23} = 7.230$ feet
$B_s = 1.5070$	$d_{34} = 6.110$ feet
$L = 18.57$ feet	Element diameters:
$N = 3.44$ elements (increase to 4)	All = 0.0641 inches
Z_t = 6-inch short jumper	ℓ/diameter ratios:
$R_0 = 208\ \Omega$	$\ell4/\text{diam}_4 = 8054$
$Z_{AV} = 809.3\ \Omega$	$\ell3/\text{diam}_3 = 9531$
$\sigma' = 0.06527$	$\ell2/\text{diam}_2 = 11280$
$Z_0 = 334.2\ \Omega$	$\ell1/\text{diam}_1 = 13349$
Antenna feeder: #12 AWG wire spaced 0.66 inches	
Balun: 4:1	
Feed line: 52-Ω coax	

a compromise toward the use of common spacers for both bands, a spacing of ⅝ inch is quite satisfactory. Surprisingly, the feeder spacing is not at all critical here from a matching standpoint, as may be verified from the equations in the **Log-Periodic Dipole Arrays** chapter. Increasing the spacing to as much as ¾ inch results in an R_0 SWR of less than 1.1:1 on both bands.

Constructing the Arrays

Construction techniques are the same for both the 3.5 and the 7-MHz versions of the array. Once the designs are completed, the next step is to fabricate the fittings; see **Figure 10.46** for details. Cut the wire elements and feed lines to the proper sizes and mark them for identification. After the wires are cut and placed aside, it will be difficult to remember which is which unless they are marked. When you have finished fabricating the connectors and cutting all of the wires, the antenna can be assembled. Use your ingenuity when building one of these antennas; it isn't necessary to duplicate these LPDAs precisely.

The elements are made of standard #14 AWG stranded copper wire. The two parallel-wire feed lines are made of #12 AWG solid copper-clad steel wire, such as Copperweld. Copperweld will not stretch when placed under tension. The front and rear connectors are cut from ½-inch thick polycarbonate sheeting, and the feed line spacers from ¼-inch acrylic sheeting.

Study the drawings carefully and be familiar with the way the wire elements are connected to the two feed lines, through the front, rear and spacer connectors. Details are sketched in **Figures 10.47** and **10.48**. Connections made in the way shown in the drawings prevent the wire from breaking. All of the rope, string, and connectors must be made of materials that can withstand the effects of tension and weathering. Use nylon rope and strings, the type that yachtsmen use. Figure 10.45 shows the front stay rope coming down to ground level at a point 120 feet from the base of a 75-foot tower. Space may not be available for this arrangement in all cases. An alternative installation technique is to put a pulley 40 feet up in a tree and run the front stay rope through the pulley and down to ground level at the base of the tree. The front stay rope will have to be tightened with a block and tackle at ground level.

Putting an LPDA together is not difficult if it is assembled in an orderly manner. It is easier to connect the elements to the feeder lines when the feed line assembly is stretched between two points. Use the tower and a block and tackle. Attaching the rear connector to the tower and assembling the LPDA at the base of the tower makes raising the antenna into place a much simpler task. Tie the rear connector securely to the base of the tower and attach the two feeder lines to it. Then thread the two feed line spacers onto the feed line. The spacers will be loose at this time, but will be positioned properly when the elements are connected. Now connect the front connector to the feed lines. A word of caution: Measure accurately and carefully! Double-check all measurements before you make permanent connections.

Connect the elements to the feeder lines through their respective plastic connectors, beginning with element 1, then element 2, and so on. Keep all of the element wires securely coiled. If they unravel, you will have a tangled mess of kinked wire. Recheck the element-to-feeder connections to ensure

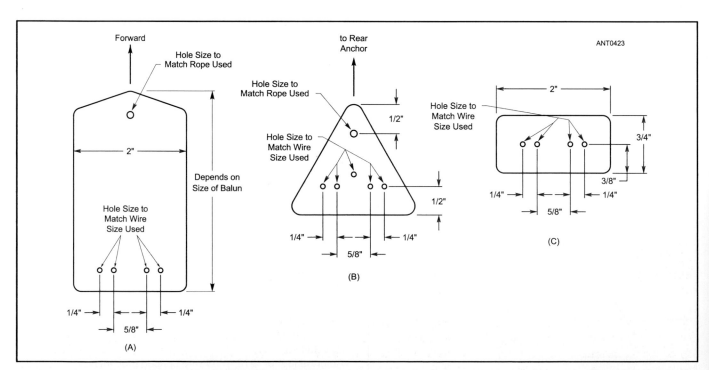

Figure 10.46 — Pieces for the LPDA that require fabrication. At A is the forward connector, made from ½-inch polycarbonate. At B is the rear connector, also made from ½-inch polycarbonate. At C is the pattern for the phase-line spacers, made from ¼-inch acrylic. Two spacers are required for the array.

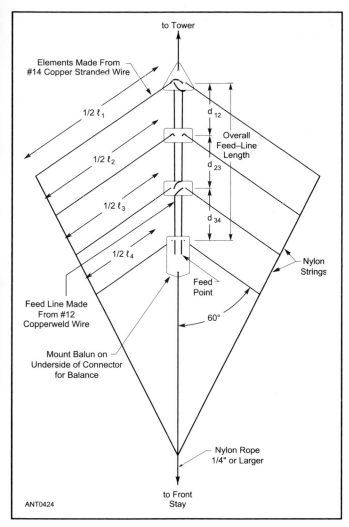

Figure 10.47 — The generic layout for the lower HF wire LPDA. Use a 4:1 balun on the forward connector. See Tables 10-4 and 10-5 for dimensions.

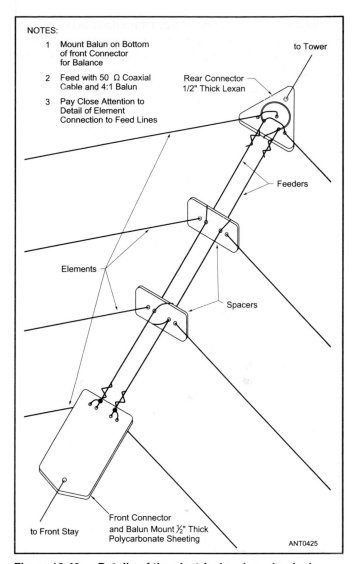

Figure 10.48 — Details of the electrical and mechanical connections of the elements to the phase-line. Knots in the nylon rope stay line are not shown.

proper and secure junctions. (See Figures 10.47 and 10.48.) Once you have completed all of the element connections, attach the 4:1 balun to the underside of the front connector. Connect the feeder lines and the coaxial cable to the balun.

You will need a separate piece of rope and a pulley to raise the completed LPDA into position. First secure the eight element ends with nylon string, referring to Figures 10.45 and 10.47. The string must be long enough to reach the tie-down points. Connect the front stay rope to the front connector, and the completed LPDA is now ready to be raised into position. While raising the antenna, uncoil the element wires to prevent their getting away and tangling up into a mess. Use care! Raise the rear connector to the proper height and attach it securely to the tower, then pull the front stay rope tight and secure it. Move the elements so they form a 60° angle with the feed lines, in the direction of the front, and space them properly relative to one another. By adjusting the end positions of the elements as you walk back and forth, you will be able to align all the elements properly. Now it is time to hook your rig to the system and make some contacts.

Performance

The reports received from these LPDAs were compared with an inverted-V dipole. All of the antennas are fixed; the LPDAs radiate to the northeast, and the dipole to the northeast and southwest. The apex of the dipole is at 70 feet, and the 40- and 80-meter LPDAs are at 60 and 50 feet, respectively. Basic array gain was apparent from many of the reports received. During pileups, it was possible to break in with a few tries on the LPDAs, yet it was impossible to break the same pileups using the dipole. The gain of the LPDAs is several dB over the dipole. For additional gain, experimenters may wish to try a parasitic director about $\frac{1}{8}\lambda$ ahead of the array. Director length and spacing from the forward LPDA element should be field-adjusted for maximum performance while maintaining the impedance match across each of the bands.

Wire LPDA systems offer many possibilities. They are easy to design and to construct: real advantages in countries where commercially built antennas and parts are not available at reasonable cost. The wire needed can be obtained in all parts of the world, and cost of construction is low. If damaged, the LPDAs can be repaired easily with pliers and solder. For those who travel on DXpeditions where space and weight are large considerations, LPDAs are lightweight but sturdy, and they perform well.

10.6.2 5-BAND LOG PERIODIC DIPOLE ARRAY

A rotatable log periodic array designed to cover the frequency range from 13 to 30 MHz is pictured in **Figure 10.49**. This is a large array having a free-space gain that varies from 6.6 to over 6.9 dBi, depending upon the operating portion of the design spectrum. This antenna system was originally described by Peter D. Rhodes, K4EWG, in November 1973 *QST*. A measured radiation pattern for the array appears in **Figure 10.50**.

The characteristics of this array are:
1) Half-power beamwidth, 43° (14 MHz)
2) Design parameter $\tau = 0.9$
3) Relative element spacing constant $\sigma = 0.05$
4) Boom length, L = 26 feet
5) Longest element $\lambda 1$ = 37 feet 10 inches.
6) Total weight, 116 pounds
7) Wind-load area, 10.7 square feet
8) Required input impedance (mean resistance), $R_0 = 72\ \Omega$, Z_t = 6-inch jumper #18 AWG wire
9) Average characteristic dipole impedance, Z_{AV}: 337.8 Ω

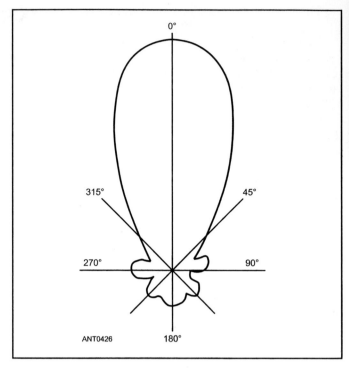

Figure 10.50 — Measured radiation pattern of the 13-30 MHz LPDA. The front-to-back ratio is about 14 dB at 14 MHz and increases to 21 dB at 28 MHz.

10) Impedance of the feeder, Z_0: 117.1 Ω
11) Feeder: #12 AWG wire, close spaced
12) With a 1:1 toroid balun at the input terminals and a 72-Ω coax feed line, the maximum SWR is 1.4:1.

The mechanical assembly uses materials readily available from most local hardware stores or aluminum supply houses. A complete set of tables and assembly drawings are included in the original article included on this book's CD-ROM.

Experimenters may wish to improve the performance of the array at both the upper and lower frequency ends of the design spectrum so that it more closely approaches the performance in the middle of the design frequency range. The most apt general technique for raising both the gain and the front-to-back ratio at the frequency extremes would be to circularize τ as described in the chapter **Log-Periodic Dipole Arrays**. However, other techniques may also be applied.

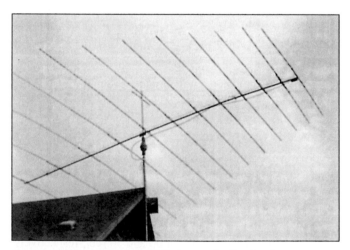

Figure 10.49 — The 13-30 MHz log periodic dipole array.

10.7 HF DISCONE ANTENNAS

The material in this section is adapted from an article by Daniel A. Krupp, W8NWF, in *The ARRL Antenna Compendium, Vol 5.* (Additional articles on discone antennas are referenced in the Bibliography or included on this book's CD-ROM.) The name "discone" is a contraction of the words "disc" and "cone." Although people often describe a discone by its design-center frequency (for example, a "20 meter discone"), discones work very well over a wide frequency range, as much as several octaves. **Figure 10.51** shows a typical discone, constructed of sheet metal for UHF use. On lower frequencies, the sheet metal may be replaced with closely spaced wires and/or aluminum tubing.

10.7.1 DISCONE BASICS

The dimensions of a discone are determined by the lowest frequency of use. The antenna produces a vertically polarized signal at a low-elevation angle and it presents a good match for 50-Ω coax over its operating range. One advantage of the discone is that its maximum current area is near the top of the antenna, where it can radiate away from ground clutter, reducing losses. The cone-like skirt of the discone radiates the signal — radiation from the disc on top is minimal. This is because the currents flowing in the skirt wires essentially all go in the same direction, while the currents in the disc elements oppose each other and cancel out. The discone's omnidirectional characteristics make it ideal for roundtable QSOs or for a net control station.

Electrical operation of this antenna is very stable, with no changes due to rain or accumulated ice. It is a self-contained antenna — unlike a traditional ground-mounted vertical radiator, the discone does not rely on a ground-radial system for efficient operation. However, just like any other vertical antenna, the quality of the ground in the Fresnel area will affect the discone's far-field pattern.

Both the disc and cone are inherently balanced for wind loading, so torque caused by the wind is minimal. The entire cone and metal mast or tower can be connected directly to ground for lightning protection.

Unlike a trap vertical or a triband beam, discone antennas are not adjusted to resonate at a particular frequency in a ham band or a group of ham bands. Instead, a discone functions as a sort of high-pass filter, efficiently radiating RF all the way from the low-frequency design cutoff to the high-frequency limits imposed by the physical design.

History of the Discone

The July 1949 and July 1950 issues of *CQ* magazine both contained excellent articles on discones. The first article, by Joseph M. Boyer, W6UYH, said that the discone was developed and used by the military during World War II. (See Bibliography.) The exact configuration of the top disc and cone was the brainchild of Armig G. Kandonian. Boyer described three VHF models, plus information on how to build them, radiation patterns, and most importantly, a detailed description of how they work. He referred to the discone as a

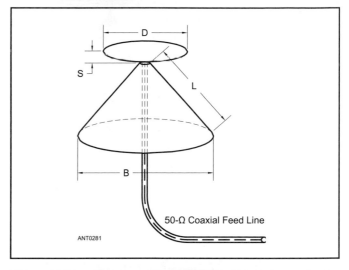

Figure 10.51 — Diagram of VHF/UHF discone, using a sheet-metal disc and cone. It is fed directly with 50-Ω coax line. The dimensions L and D, together with the spacing S between the disc and cone, determine the frequency characteristics of the antenna. L = 246 / f_{MHz} for the lowest frequency to be used. Diameter D should be from 0.67 to 0.70 of dimension L. The diameter at the bottom of the cone B is equal to L. The space S between disc and cone can be 2 to 12 inches, with the wider spacing appropriate for larger antennas.

type of "coaxial taper transformer."

The July 1950 article was by Mack Seybold, W2RYI. He described an 11-MHz version he built on his garage roof. The mast actually fit through the roof to allow lowering the antenna for service. Seybold stated that his 11-MHz discone would load up on 2 meters but that performance was down 10 dB compared to his 100-MHz Birdcage discone. He commented that this was caused by the relatively large spacing between the disc and cone. Actually, the performance degradation he found was caused by the wave angle lifting upward at high frequencies. The cone wires were electrically long, causing them to act like long wire antennas.

10.7.2 A-FRAME 20-10 METER DISCONE

W8NWF's first discone was designed to cover 20 through 10 meters without requiring an antenna tuner. The cone assembly uses 18-foot long wires, with a 60° included apex angle and a 12-foot diameter disc assembly. See **Figure 10.52**. The antenna was assembled on the ground, with the feed coax and all guys attached. Then with the aid of some friends, it was pulled up into position.

The author used a 40-foot tall wooden "A-frame" mast, made of three 22-foot-long 2×4s. He primed the mast with sealer and then gave it two coats of red barn paint to make it look nice and last a long time. The disc hub was a 12-inch length of 3-inch schedule-40 PVC plumbing pipe. The PVC is very tough, slightly ductile, and easy to drill and cut. PVC is well suited for RF power at the feed point of the antenna.

Three 12-foot by 0.375-inch OD pieces of 6061 alumi-

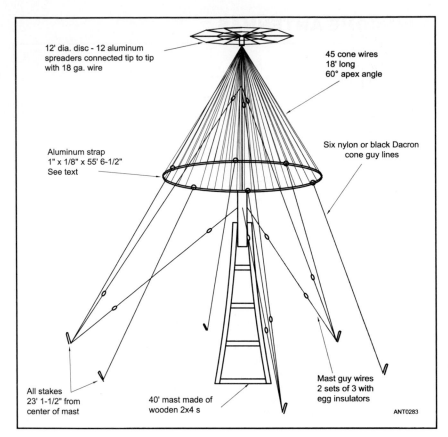

12' dia. disc - 12 aluminum spreaders connected tip to tip with 18 ga. wire

45 cone wires
18' long
60° apex angle

Aluminum strap
1" x 1/8" x 55' 6-1/2"
See text

Six nylon or black Dacron cone guy lines

All stakes
23' 1-1/2" from center of mast

40' mast made of wooden 2x4 s

Mast guy wires
2 sets of 3 with egg insulators

ANT0283

Figure 10.52 — Detailed drawing of the A-frame discone for 14 to 30 MHz. The disc assembly at the top of the A-frame is 12 feet in diameter. There are 45 cone wires, each 18 feet long, making a 60° included angle of the cone.

num, with 0.058-inch wall thickness, were used for the 12-foot diameter top disc. These were cut in half to make the center portions of the six telescoping spreaders. Four twelve foot by 0.250-inch OD (0.035-inch wall thickness) tubes were cut into 12 pieces, each 40 inches long. This gave extension tips for each end of the six spreaders.

10.7.3 40-10 METER DISCONE

When an opportunity arose to buy a 64-foot self-supporting TV tower, W8NWF jumped at the chance to implement a full 7 to 30-MHz discone. His new tower had eight sections, each eight feet long. Counting the overlap between sections, the cone wires would come off the tower at about the 61.5-foot mark. See **Figure 10.53**.

W8NWF took some liberties with the design of this larger discone compared to the first one, which he had done strictly "by the book." The first change was to make the cone wires 70 feet long, even though the formula said they should be 38 feet long. Further, the cone wires would not be connected together at the bottom. With the longer cone wires, he felt that 75 and 80-meter operation might be a possibility.

The second major change was to widen the apex angle out from 60° to about 78°. Modeling said this should produce a flatter SWR over the frequency spectrum and would also give a better guy system for the tower.

The topside disc assembly would be 27 feet in diameter

and have 16 radial spreaders, using telescoping aluminum tubing tapering from 5/8 to 1/2 to 3/8 inches OD. All spreaders were made from 0.058-inch wall thickness 6063-T832 aluminum tubing, available from Texas Towers and other suppliers. A section of 10-inch PVC plumbing pipe would be used as the hub for construction of the disc assembly.

On the air tests proved to be very satisfying. Loading up on 40 meters was easy — the SWR was 1:1 across the entire band. W8NWF can work all directions very well and receives excellent signal reports from DX stations. When he switches to his long (333 foot) center-fed dipole for comparison, he finds the dipole is much noisier and that received signals are weaker. During the daytime, nearby stations (less than about 300 to 500 miles) can be louder with the dipole, but the discone can work them just fine also.

The author happily reports that this antenna even works well on 75 meters. As you might expect, it doesn't present a 1:1 match. However, the SWR is between 3.5:1 and 5.5:1 across the band. W8NWF uses an antenna tuner to operate the discone on 75. It seems to get out as well on 75 as it does on 40 meters.

The SWR on 30 meters is about 1.1:1. On 20 meters the SWR runs from 1.05:1 at 14.0 MHz to 1.4:1 at 14.3 MHz. The SWR on the 17, 15, 12 and 10-meter bands varies, going up to a high of 3.5:1 on 12 meters.

From modeling using *NEC/Wires* by K6STI, W8NWF verified that the low-angle performance for the bigger antenna is worse than that for the smaller discone on the upper frequencies. See **Figure 10.54** for an elevation-pattern comparison on 10 meters for both antennas, with average ground constants. The azimuth patterns are simply circles. Radiation patterns produced by antenna modeling programs are very helpful to determine what to expect from an antenna.

The smaller discone, which was built by the book, displays good, low-angle lobes on 20 through 10 meters. The frequency range of 14 through 28 MHz is an octave's worth of coverage. It met his expectations in every way by covering this frequency span with low SWR and a low angle of radiation.

The bigger discone, with a modified cone suitable for use on 75 meters, presents a little different story. The low-angle lobe on 40 meters works well, and 75-meter performance also is good, although an antenna tuner is necessary on this band. The 30-meter band has a good low-angle lobe but secondary high-angle lobes are starting to hurt performance. Note that 30 meters is roughly three times the design frequency of the cone. On 20 and 17 meters there still are good low-angle lobes but more and more power is wasted in high-angle lobes.

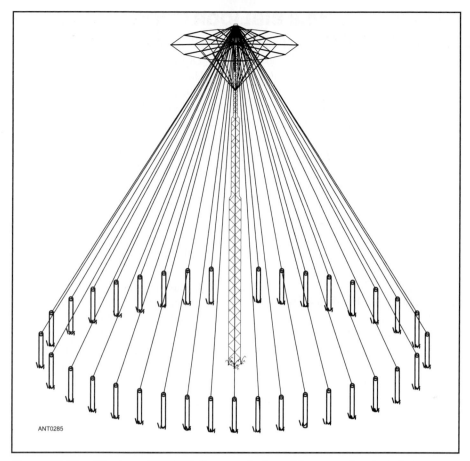

Figure 10.53 — The large W8NWF discone, designed for operation from 7 to 14 MHz, but useable with a tuning network in the shack for 3.8 MHz.

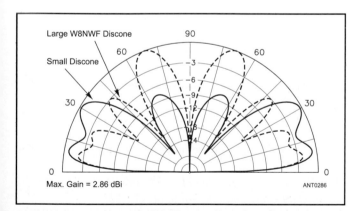

Figure 10.54 — Computed patterns showing elevation response of small discone at 28.5 MHz compared to that of the larger discone at 28.5 MHz. The cone wires are clearly too long for efficient operation on 10 meters, producing unwanted high-angle lobes that rob power from the desirable low-elevation angles.

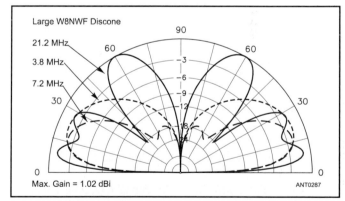

Figure 10.55 — Computed elevation-response patterns for the larger W8NWF discone for 3.8, 7.2 and 21.2 MHz operation. Again, as in Figure 10.54, the pattern degrades at 21.2 MHz, although it is still reasonably efficient, if not optimal.

The operation on 15, 12, and 10 meters continues to worsen for the larger discone. The message here is that although a discone may have a decent SWR as high as 10 times the design frequency, its radiation pattern is not necessarily good for low-angle communications. See **Figure 10.55** for a comparison of elevation patterns for 3.8, 7.2 and 21.2 MHz on the larger discone.

A discone antenna built according to formula will work predictably and without any adjustments. One can modify the antenna's cone length and apex angle without fear of rendering it useless. The broadband feature of the discone makes it attractive to use on the HF bands. The low angle of radiation makes DX a real possibility and the discone is also much less noisy on receive than a dipole.

10.8 BIBLIOGRAPHY

Source material and more extended discussion of topics covered in this chapter can be found in the references given below and in the textbooks listed at the end of Chapter 2, **Antenna Fundamentals**.

H. B. Barkley, *The Open-Sleeve As A Broadband Antenna*, Technical Report No. 14, U.S. Naval Postgraduate School, Monterey, CA, Jun 1955.

W. M. Bell, "A Trap Collinear Antenna," *QST*, Aug 1963, pp 30-31.

J. S. Belrose, "The HF Discone Antenna," *QST*, Jul 1975, pp 11-14, 56.

J. Belrose and P. Bouliane, "The Off-Center-Fed Dipole Revisited: A Broadband, Multiband Antenna," *QST*, Aug 1990, pp 28-34.

J. Belrose, "Technical Correspondence: Terminated Folded Dipole," *QST,* May 1994, pp 88-89.

H. J. Berg, "Multiband Operation with Paralleled Dipoles," *QST*, Jul 1956, pp 42-43.

E. L. Bock, J. A. Nelson and A. Dorne, "Sleeve Antennas," *Very High Frequency Techniques*, H. J. Reich, ed. (New York: McGraw-Hill, 1947), Chap 5.

J. T. Bolljahn and J. V. N. Granger, "Omnidirectional VHF and UHF Antennas," *Antenna Engineering Handbook* , H. Jasik, ed. (New York: McGraw-Hill, 1961) pp 27-32 through 27-34.

J. M. Boyer, "Discone — 40 to 500 Mc Skywire," *CQ*, July 1949, p 11.

G. A. Breed, "Multi-Frequency Antenna Technique Uses Closely-Coupled Resonators," *RF Design*, November 1994. US Patent 5,489,914, "Method of Constructing Multiple-Frequency Dipole or Monopole Antenna Elements Using Closely-Coupled Resonators," Gary A. Breed, Feb 6, 1996.

G. H. Brown, "The Phase and Magnitude of Earth Currents Near Radio Transmitting Antennas," *Proc. IRE*, Vol 23, No. 2, Feb 1935, pp 168-182.

G. H. Brown, R. F. Lewis and J. Epstein, "Ground Systems as a Factor in Antenna Efficiency," *Proc. IRE*, Vol 25, No. 6, Jun 1937, pp 753-787.

C. L. Buchanan, "The Multimatch Antenna System," *QST*, Mar 1955. pp 22-23, 155.

R. A. Cox, "The Open-Sleeve Antenna," *CQ*, Aug 1983, pp 13-19.

G. Countryman, "An Experimental All-Band Nondirectional Transmitting Antenna," *QST*, Jun 1949, pp 54-55.

D. DeMaw, "Lightweight Trap Antennas — Some Thoughts," *QST*, Jun 1983, pp 15-18.

W. C. Gann, "A Center-Fed 'Zepp' for 80 and 40," *QST*, May 1966, pp 15-17.

D. Geiser, "An Inexpensive Multiband VHF Antenna," *QST*, Dec 1978, pp 28-29.

A. Greenberg, "Simple Trap Construction for the Multiband Antenna," *QST*, Oct 1956, pp 18-19, 120.

G. L. Hall, "Trap Antennas," Technical Correspondence, *QST*, Nov 1981, pp 49-50.

J. Hallas, "Getting On the Air: The Terminated Folded Dipole," *QST*, Sep 2010, pp 51-52.

W. Hayward, "Designing Trap Antennas," Technical Correspondence, *QST*, Aug 1976, p 38.

D. Hollander, "A Big Signal from a Small Lot," *QST*, Apr 1979, pp 32-34.

R. H. Johns, "Dual-Frequency Antenna Traps," *QST*, Nov 1983, pp 27-30.

W. Jones, "Practical High Performance HF Log Periodic Antennas," *QST*, Sep 2002, pp 31-37.

A. G. Kandoian, "Three New Antenna Types and Their Applications," *Proc IRE*, Vol 34, Feb 1946, pp 70W-75W.

R. W. P. King, *Theory of Linear Antennas* (Cambridge, MA: Harvard Univ Press, 1956), pp 407-427.

W. J. Lattin, "Multiband Antennas Using Decoupling Stubs," *QST*, Dec 1960, pp 23-25.

W. J. Lattin, "Antenna Traps of Spiral Delay Line," *QST*, Nov 1972, pp 13-15.

M. A. Logan, "Coaxial-Cable Traps," Technical Correspondence, *QST*, Aug 1985, p 43.

J. R. Mathison, "Inexpensive Traps for Wire Antennas," *QST*, Feb 1977, p 18.

L. McCoy, "An Easy-to-Make Coax-Fed Multiband Trap Dipole," *QST*, Dec 1964, pp 28-30.

M. Mims, "The All-Around 14-mc. Signal Squirter," *QST*, Dec 1935, pp 12-17.

G. E. O'Neil, "Trapping the Mysteries of Trapped Antennas," *Ham Radio*, Oct 1981, pp 10-16.

W. I. Orr, editor, "The Low-Frequency Discone," *Radio Handbook*, 14th Edition, (Editors and Engineers, 1956), p 369.

W. I. Orr, "Radio FUNdamentals," The Open-Sleeve Dipole, *CQ*, Feb 1995, pp 94-96.

E. W. Pappenfus, "The Conical Monopole Antenna," *QST*, Nov 1966, pp 21-24.

P. D. Rhodes, "The Log-Periodic Dipole Array," *QST*, Nov 1973, pp 16-22.

P. D. Rhodes, "The Log-Periodic V Array," *QST*, Oct 1979, pp 40-43.

P. D. Rhodes, "The K4EWG Log Periodic Array," *The ARRL Antenna Compendium, Vol 3*, pp 118-123

L. Richard, "Parallel Dipoles of 300-Ohm Ribbon," *QST*, Mar 1957, p 14.

P. Salas, "160 and 80 Meter Matching Network for Your 43 Foot Vertical — Part 1 and Part 2," *QST*, Dec 2009, p 30-32, and Jan 2010, pp 34-35.

W. Sandford, Jr., "A Modest 45-Foot DX Vertical for 160, 80, 40, and 30 Meters," *QST*, Sep 1981, pp 27-31. Also see Feedback, Nov 1981, p 50.

R. R. Schellenbach, "Try the 'TJ'," *QST*, Jun 1982, pp 18-19.

R. R. Schellenbach, "The JF Array," *QST*, Nov 1982, pp 26-27. Also see Technical Correspondence, *QST*, Apr 1983, p 39.

R. Severns, "A Wideband 80 meter Dipole," *QST*, Jul 1995, pp 27-29.

T. H. Schiller, Force 12, US Patent 5,995,061, "No loss, multi-band, adaptable antenna," Nov 30, 1999.

H. Scholle and R. Steins, "Eine Doppel-Windom Antenna fur Acht Bander," *cq-DL*, Sep 1983, p 427. (In English: *QST*, Aug 1990, pp 33-34.)

M. Seybold, "The Low-Frequency Discone," *CQ*, July 1950, p 13.

D. P. Shafer, "Four-Band Dipole with Traps," *QST*, Oct 1958, pp 38-40.

R. C. Sommer, "Optimizing Coaxial-Cable Traps," *QST*, Dec 1984, pp 37-42.

S. Stearns, "All About the Discone Antenna: Antenna of Mysterious Origin and Superb Broadband Performance," *QEX*, Jan/Feb 2007, pp 37-44.

J. J. Uhl, "Construct a Wire Log-Periodic Dipole Array for 80 or 40 Meters," *QST*, Aug 1986, pp 21-24.

L. Varney, "The G5RV Multiband Antenna . . . Up-to-Date," *The ARRL Antenna Compendium, Vol 1* (Newington: ARRL, 1985), p 86.

R. Wilson, "The Offset Multiband Trapless Antenna (OMTA)," *QST*, Oct 1995, pp 30-32. Also see Feedback, Dec 1995, p 79.

L. G. Windom, "Notes on Ethereal Adornments," *QST*, Sep 1929, pp 19-22, 84.

TABLE OF CONTENTS

Chapter 11

HF Yagi and Quad Antennas

11.1 YAGI ANTENNAS

Along with the dipole and the quarter-wave vertical, radio amateurs throughout the world make extensive use of the Yagi antenna, more accurately referred to as a Yagi array. Hidetsugu Yagi and Shintaro Uda, two Japanese university professors, invented the Yagi in the 1920s. Uda did much of the developmental work while Yagi introduced the array to the world outside Japan through his writings in English. Although the antenna should properly be called a *Yagi-Uda* array, it is commonly referred to simply as a *Yagi*.

The Yagi is a type of end-fire multielement array as described in the **Multielement Arrays** chapter. At the minimum, it consists of a single *driven element* and a single *parasitic element*. These elements are placed parallel to each other on a supporting boom some distance apart. This arrangement is known as a 2-element Yagi. The parasitic element is termed a *reflector* when it is placed behind the driven element, opposite to the direction of maximum radiation, and is called a *director* when it is placed ahead of the driven element. See **Figure 11.1**. In the VHF and UHF spectrum, Yagis employing 30 or more elements are not uncommon, with a single reflector and multiple directors. See the **VHF and UHF Antenna Systems** chapter for details on VHF and UHF Yagis. Large HF arrays may employ 10 or more elements and will be covered in this chapter.

11.1.1 HOW A YAGI WORKS — AN OVERVIEW

The gain and directional pattern of a Yagi array is determined by the relative amplitudes and phases of the currents induced into all the parasitic elements. Unlike directly driven multielement arrays in which the designer must compensate for mutual coupling between elements, proper Yagi operation *relies on* mutual coupling. The current in each parasitic element is determined by its spacing from both the driven element and other parasitic elements, and by the tuning of the element itself. Both length and diameter affect element tuning.

The following discussion is quite over-simplified but

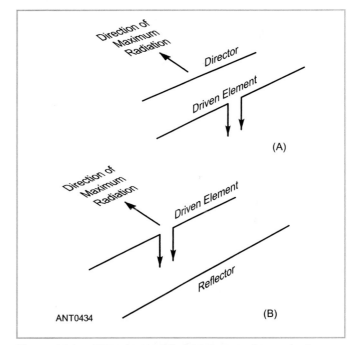

Figure 11.1 — Two-element Yagi systems using a single parasitic element. At A the parasitic element acts as a director, and at B as a reflector. The arrows show the direction in which maximum radiation takes place.

serves to illustrate the basic process by which the Yagi antenna creates its radiation pattern. Begin with a dipole driven element resonant at the operating frequency and a single parasitic element configured as a reflector, slightly longer than the driven element. Current in the driven element creates a radiated electromagnetic field (the *direct field*) that induces a current in the parasitic element. That induced current causes a *re-radiated field* just as if the current was caused by a transmitter connected to the element. The re-radiated field combines with the direct field from the driven element to create the antenna's radiation pattern.

Three things determine the phase relationship between the current in the reflector and in the driven element. First, the direct field at the reflector slightly lags the field at the driven element because the direct field must travel from the driven element to the reflector. Second, the induced current is 180° out of phase with the direct field at the location of the reflector. Third, the reflector element is slightly longer than a resonant length and so its self-impedance is inductive, creating additional phase lag in the induced current relative to the direct field.

The combination of phase lags due to the direct field's travel time, the 180° phase inversion for induced current, and the reflector's inductance cause the re-radiated field to partially cancel with the direct field from the driven element along a line from the driven element through the reflector. (Imagine the boom extending beyond the reflector — that is the line being referred to.) This creates the rear null in the Yagi radiation pattern. Similarly, the fields reinforce each other in the opposite direction to the forward direction as shown in Figure 11.1.

The situation is reversed in the case of a director element. The phase lag from travel time and the inversion in the induced current act the same as for the reflector. The director element is slightly shorter than resonant however and so has a capacitive self-impedance, creating a phase lead. The combination results in the fields reinforcing in the forward direction and cancelling in the opposite direction.

Two-element Yagis are useful antennas but even more directivity (gain) can be obtained by adding additional parasitic elements. Additional reflectors are rarely used because field cancellation to the rear of the antenna leaves too little field for them to improve directivity. Thus, multiple directors are used to increase directivity as you will see in practical Yagi designs later in the chapter.

The actual situation is of course far more complicated than this simplistic view of Yagi operation. In a real Yagi, the mutual coupling between all elements must be considered, including between the parasitic elements. This makes determining the optimum spacing and element length for a desired radiation pattern quite involved mathematically and best left to software modeling programs.

11.1.2 YAGI MODELING

For about 50 years amateurs and professionals created Yagi array designs largely by "cut and try" experimental techniques. In the early 1980s, Jim Lawson, W2PV (SK),

described in detail for the amateur audience the fundamental mathematics involved in modeling Yagis. His book *Yagi Antenna Design* (now out of print) is highly recommended for serious antenna designers as is his series of articles in *Ham Radio* (see Bibliography). The advent of powerful microcomputers and sophisticated computer antenna modeling software in the mid 1980s revolutionized the field of Yagi design for the radio amateur. In a matter of minutes, a computer can try 100,000 or more different combinations of element lengths and spacings to create a Yagi design tailored to meet a particular set of high-performance parameters. To explore this number of combinations experimentally, a human experimenter would take an unimaginable amount of time and dedication and the process would no doubt suffer from considerable measurement errors. With the computer tools available today, an antenna can be designed, constructed and then put up in the air, with little or no tuning or pruning required.

A very popular modeling program for amateur use today is *EZNEC* by Roy Lewallen, W7EL. *EZNEC* is well-suited to model Yagi antennas. A special version of the software, *EZNEC-ARRL*, is included with this book. There are several Yagi models included with the software. *EZNEC* and *EZNEC-ARRL* are discussed in the **Antenna Modeling** chapter.

The *YW* Modeling Program

Included on this book's CD-ROM, the *YW* modeling program developed by Dean Straw, N6BV, is designed to evaluate monoband Yagi antennas. (*YW* stands for *Yagi for Windows*.) *YW* results compare very closely with Brian Beezley's *YO* or *YA* programs (no longer sold in the amateur market) and with *NEC*-based programs, such as *EZNEC*, *NEC-Win Plus* or *NEC-4*. *YW* is a special-purpose program, designed strictly for monoband Yagis. It has the advantage of running many times more quickly than general-purpose programs such as *NEC* but it has some attendant limitations.

YW evaluations over ground are done over flat "perfect" ground. Mutual impedances between Yagi elements and the ground are not specifically taken into account in *YW*, so calculations for antennas mounted less than approximately λ/8 above ground are likely to be inaccurate. Antennas mounted in the presence of other nearby antennas or mounted very low to the ground are the specialties of method-of-moment programs like *EZNEC*. Despite these caveats, *YW* will get you very close to a final design — one where you can simply cut the elements and expect that your Yagi will work as advertised.

11.2 YAGI PERFORMANCE PARAMETERS

There are three main parameters used to characterize the performance of a particular Yagi — *forward gain*, *pattern* and *drive impedance/SWR*. Another important consideration is mechanical strength. It is very important to recognize that each of the three electrical parameters should be characterized over the frequency band of interest in order to be meaningful. Neither the gain, the SWR nor the pattern measured at a single frequency gives very much insight

into the overall performance of a particular Yagi.

Poor designs have even been known to reverse their directionality over a frequency band, while other designs have excessively narrow SWR bandwidths, or gain that peaks excessively in the band. Finally, an antenna's ability to survive the wind and ice conditions expected in one's geographical location is an important consideration in any design. Much of this chapter will be devoted to describing detailed Yagi designs that are optimized for a good balance between gain, pattern and SWR over various amateur bands, and that are designed to survive strong winds and icing.

11.2.1 YAGI GAIN

Like any other antenna, the gain of a Yagi must be stated in comparison to some standard of reference. Designers of phased vertical arrays often state gain referenced to a single, isolated vertical element. See the section on "Phased Array Techniques" in the chapter **Multielement Arrays**.

Many antenna designers prefer to compare gain to that of an *isotropic radiator in free space*. This is a theoretical antenna that radiates equally well in all directions, and by definition, it has a gain of 0 *dBi* (dB isotropic). Many radio amateurs, however, are comfortable using a dipole as a standard reference antenna, mainly because it is *not* a theoretical antenna.

In free space, a dipole does not radiate equally well in all directions — it has a figure-eight azimuth pattern, with deep nulls off the ends of the wire. In its favored directions, a free-space dipole has 2.15 dB gain compared to the isotropic radiator. You may see the term *dBd*, meaning gain referenced to a dipole in free space. Subtract 2.15 dB from gain in dBi to convert to gain in dBd.

Assume for a moment that we take a dipole out of "free space," and place it one wavelength above the ocean, whose saltwater makes an almost perfect ground. At an elevation angle of 15°, where sea water-reflected radiation adds in phase with direct radiation, the dipole has a gain of about 6 dB, compared to its gain when it was in free space, isolated from any reflections. This and other related effects are addressed in the chapter **Effects of Ground**.

It is perfectly legitimate to say that this dipole has a gain of 6 dBd, although the term "dBd" (meaning "dB dipole") makes it sound as though the dipole somehow has gain over itself! Always remember that gain expressed in dBd (or dBi) refers to the *counterpart antenna in free space*. The gain of the dipole over saltwater in this example can be rated at either 6 dBd (over a dipole in free space), or as 8.15 dBi (over an isotropic radiator in free space). Each frame of reference is valid, as long as it is used consistently and clearly. In this chapter we will often switch between Yagis in free space and Yagis over ground. To prevent any confusion, gains will be stated in dBi.

Yagi free-space gain ranges from about 5 dBi for a small 2-element design to about 20 dBi for a 31-element long-boom UHF design. The length of the boom is the main factor determining the gain a Yagi can deliver. Gain as a function of boom length will be discussed in detail after the sections below defining antenna response patterns and SWR characteristics.

11.2.2 RADIATION PATTERN MEASUREMENTS

Figure 11.2 compares the E-plane and H-plane pattern of a 3-element Yagi in free space to those of a dipole and an isotropic radiator. (See the **Antenna Fundamentals** chapter for definitions and conventions associated with measurement of radiation patterns.) These patterns were generated using *NEC-2* modeling software. Figure 11.2A shows that this 3-element Yagi in free space exhibits 7.28 dBi of gain (referenced to isotropic), and has 5.13 dB gain over a free-space dipole. For this particular antenna, the half-power beamwidth is about 66°.

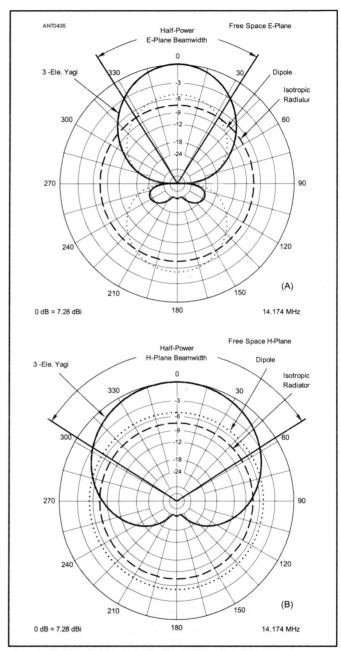

Figure 11.2 — E-Plane (electric field) and H-Plane (magnetic field) response patterns for 3-element 20 meter Yagi in free space. At A the E-Plane pattern for a typical 3-element Yagi is compared with a dipole and an isotropic radiator. At B the H-Plane patterns are compared for the same antennas. The Yagi has an E-Plane half-power beamwidth of 66°, and an H-Plane half-power beamwidth of about 120°. The Yagi has 7.28 dBi (5.13 dBd) of gain. The front-to-back ratio, which compares the response at 0° and at 180°, is about 35 dB for this Yagi. The front-to-rear ratio, which compares the response at 0° to the largest lobe in the rearward 180° arc behind the antenna, is 24 dB, due to the lobes at 120° and 240°.

Front-to-Back Ratio

Again as seen in Figure 11.2A, this antenna's front-to-back ratio is 34 dB comparing response at 180° to that in the forward direction at 0°. (The ratio of the forward response to the averaged response over the entire 180° rearward section is called the *front-to-rear ratio*.) In Figure 11.2A there are two sidelobes, at 120° and at 240°, which are about 24 dB below the peak response at 0°. Since interference can come from any direction, not only directly off the back of an antenna, these kinds of sidelobes limit the ability to discriminate against rearward signals. The term *worst-case front-to-rear ratio* is used to describe the worst-case rearward lobe in the 180°-wide sector behind the antenna's main lobe. In this case, the worst-case front-to-rear ratio is 24 dB.

In the rest of this chapter the worst-case front-to-rear ratio will be used as a performance parameter, and will be abbreviated as "F/R." For a dipole or an isotropic radiator, Figure 11.2A demonstrates that F/R is 0 dB. Figure 11.2B depicts the H-field response for the same 3-element Yagi in free space, again compared to a dipole and an isotropic radiator in free space. Unlike the E-field pattern, the H-field pattern for a Yagi does not have a null at 90°, directly over the top of the Yagi. For this 3-element design, the H-field half-power beamwidth is approximately 120°.

Figure 11.3 compares the azimuth and elevation patterns for a horizontally polarized 6-element 14-MHz Yagi with a 60-foot boom mounted one wavelength over ground to a dipole at the same height. As with any horizontally polarized antenna, the height above ground is the main factor determining the peaks and nulls in the elevation pattern of each antenna. Figure 11.3A shows the E-field pattern, which has now been labeled as the Azimuth pattern. This antenna has a half-power azimuthal beamwidth of about 50°, and at an elevation angle of 12° it exhibits a forward gain of 16.02 dBi, including about 5 dB of ground reflection gain over relatively poor ground, with a dielectric constant of 13 and conductivity of 5 mS/m. In free space this Yagi has a gain of 10.97 dBi.

The H-field elevation response of the 6-element Yagi has a half-power beamwidth of about 60° in free space, but as shown in Figure 11.3B, the first lobe (centered at 12° in elevation) has a half-power beamwidth of only 13° when the antenna is mounted one wavelength over ground. The dipole at the same height has a very slightly larger first-lobe half-power elevation beamwidth of 14°, since its free-space H-field response is omnidirectional.

Note that the free-space H-field directivity of the Yagi suppresses its second lobe over ground (at an elevation angle of about 40°) to 8 dBi, while the dipole's response at its second lobe peak (at about 48°) is at a level of 9 dBi.

The shape of the azimuthal pattern for a Yagi operated over real ground will change slightly as the Yagi is placed closer and closer to ground. Generally, however, the azimuth pattern doesn't depart significantly from the free-space pattern until the antenna is less than 0.5 λ high. This is just over 17 feet high at 28.4 MHz and just below 35 feet at 14.2 MHz — heights that are not difficult to achieve for most amateurs. Some advanced modeling programs can optimize Yagis at the exact installation height.

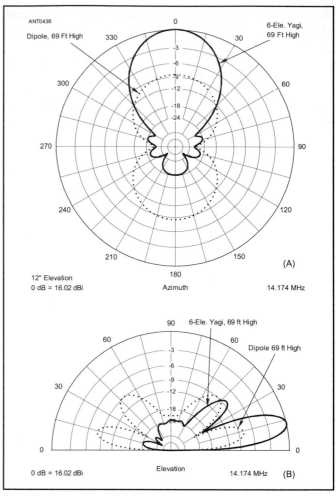

Figure 11.3 — Azimuth pattern for 6-element 20 meter Yagi on 60-foot long boom, mounted 60 feet over ground. At A, the azimuth pattern at 12° elevation angle is shown, compared to a dipole at the same height. Peak gain of the Yagi is 16.04 dBi, or just over 8 dB compared to the dipole. At B, the elevation pattern for the same two antennas is shown. Note that the peak elevation pattern of the Yagi is compressed slightly lower compared to the dipole, even though they are both at the same height over ground. This is most noticeable for the Yagi's second lobe, which peaks at about 40°, while the dipole's second lobe peaks at about 48°. This is due to the greater free-space directionality of the Yagi at higher angles.

11.2.3 FEED POINT IMPEDANCE AND SWR

The impedance at the feed point of the driven element in a Yagi is affected not only by the tuning of the driven element itself, but also by the spacing and tuning of nearby parasitic elements, and to a lesser extent by the presence of ground. In some designs that have been tuned solely for maximum gain, the driven-element impedance can fall to very low levels, sometimes less than 5 Ω. This can lead to excessive losses due to conductor resistance, especially at VHF and UHF. In a Yagi that has been optimized solely for gain, conductor losses are usually compounded by large excursions in impedance levels with relatively small changes in frequency. The SWR can thus change dramatically over a band and can create additional losses in the feed line. **Figure 11.4** illustrates the SWR over the 28 to 28.8 MHz portion of the 10 meter amateur band for a 5-element Yagi on a 24-foot boom, tuned for maximum forward gain at a spot frequency of 28.4 MHz. Its SWR curve is contrasted to that of a Yagi designed for a good compromise of gain, SWR and F/R.

Even professional antenna designers have difficulty accurately measuring forward gain. On the other hand, SWR can easily be measured by professional and amateur alike.

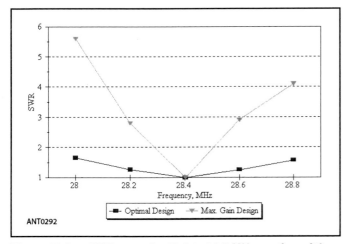

Figure 11.4 — SWR over the 28.0 to 28.8 MHz portion of the 10 meter band for two different 3-element Yagi designs. One is designed strictly for maximum gain, while the second is optimized for F/R pattern and SWR over the frequency band. A Yagi designed only for maximum gain usually suffers from a very narrow SWR bandwidth.

Few manufacturers would want to advertise an antenna with the narrow-band SWR curve shown in Figure 11.4!

Direct Feed Yagis

By carefully adjusting the position and tuning of the Yagi elements by using modeling software it is possible to create an antenna design for which the feed point impedance is close to 50 Ω and can be fed directly with coaxial cable. The tradeoff is a usually a small amount of gain but such *direct feed* designs are still relatively uncommon as commercial products. (Mosley Electronics (**www.mosley-electronics.com**) has offered direct feed beams for many years.) In addition, direct feed designs require that the driven element be insulated from the boom

There is some confusion about whether a choke balun is required for direct feed beams. If such a balun is *not* used and the feed line is positioned so as to couple strongly to the antenna, then the subsequent re-radiation from the outside of the feed line shield could fill in the nulls of the pattern and reduce both front-to-back and front-to-side performance. Forward gain is rarely affected significantly by feed line re-radiation

If the coupling is strong enough, the balance of the driven element could be affected so the use of a choke balun might be prudent but is not an absolute requirement. If maximum front-to-back and front-to-side performance is important to you or if feed line common-mode current causes problems in the station, then a choke balun should be used as described in the **Transmission Line Coupling and Impedance Matching** chapter.

11.3 MONOBAND YAGI PERFORMANCE OPTIMIZATION

11.3.1 YAGI DESIGN GOALS

The previous section discussing driven-element impedance and SWR hinted at possible design trade-offs among gain, pattern and SWR, especially when each parameter is considered over a frequency band rather than at a spot frequency. Trade-offs in Yagi design parameters can be a matter of personal taste and operating style. For example, one operator might exclusively operate the CW portions of the HF bands, while another might only be interested in the Phone portions. Another operator may want a good pattern in order to discriminate against signals coming from a particular direction; someone else may want the most forward gain possible, and may not care about responses in other directions.

There are only a few variables available to adjust when one is designing a Yagi to meet certain design goals. The variables are:
1) The physical length of the boom
2) The number of elements on the boom
3) The spacing of each element along the boom
4) The tuning of each element
5) The type of matching network used to feed the array.

For elements that are created from telescoping tubing sections, the lengths of individual sections (called the taper schedule) affects antenna performance as well. Taper schedule is usually varied in order to provide mechanical strength

and is not considered a primary electrical design variable.

Extensive computer modeling of Yagis indicates that the parameter that must be compromised most to achieve wide bandwidths for front-to-rear ratio and SWR is forward gain. However, not much gain must be sacrificed for good F/R and SWR coverage, especially on long-boom Yagis. Although 10 and 7-MHz Yagis are not rare, the HF bands from 14 to 30 MHz are where Yagis are most often found, mainly due to the mechanical difficulties involved with making sturdy antennas for lower frequencies. The highest HF band, 28.0 to 29.7 MHz, represents the largest percentage bandwidth of the upper HF bands, at almost 6%. It is difficult to try to optimize in one design the main performance parameters of gain, worst-case F/R ratio and SWR over this large a band. Many commercial designs thus split up their 10 meter designs into antennas covering one of two bands: 28.0 to 28.8 MHz, and 28.8 to 29.7 MHz. For the amateur bands below 10 meters, optimal designs that cover the entire band are more easily achieved.

The performance requirements for Yagis used at VHF and UHF are similar to those of HF Yagis but place more emphasis on reduction of side lobes due to the importance of lowering received noise above 30 MHz. In addition, there are differences in feed point matching and considerations of losses are handled differently. These topics are addressed in the **VHF and UHF Antenna Systems** chapter. The remainder of this chapter will focus on HF designs unless specifically noted otherwise.

11.3.2 GAIN AND BOOM LENGTH

As pointed out earlier, the gain of a Yagi is largely a function of the length of the boom. As the boom is made longer, the maximum gain potential rises. For a given boom length, the number of elements populating that boom can be varied, while still maintaining the antenna's gain, provided of course that the elements are tuned properly. In general, putting more elements on a boom gives the designer added flexibility to achieve desired design goals, especially to broaden the response across a frequency band.

Figure 11.5A is an example illustrating gain versus frequency for three different types of 3-element Yagis on 8-foot booms. The three antennas were designed for the lower end of the 10 meter band, 28.0 to 28.8 MHz, based on the following different design goals:

Antenna 1: Maximum mid-band gain, regardless of F/R or SWR across the band

Antenna 2: SWR less than 2:1 over the frequency band; best compromise gain, with no special consideration for F/R over the band.

Antenna 3: "Optimal" case: F/R greater than 20 dB, SWR less than 2:1 over the frequency band; best compromise gain.

Figure 11.5B shows the F/R over the frequency band for these three designs, and Figure 11.5C shows the SWR curves over the frequency band. Antenna 1, the design that strives strictly for maximum gain, has a poor SWR response over the band, as might be expected after the previous section discussing SWR. The SWR is 10:1 at 28.8 MHz and rises to 22:1 at 29 MHz. At 28 MHz, at the low end of the band, the SWR of the maximum-gain design is more than 6:1. Clearly, designing for maximum gain alone produces an unacceptable design in terms of SWR bandwidth. The F/R for Antenna 1 reaches a high point of about 20 dB at the low-frequency end of the band, but falls to only 3 dB at the high-frequency end.

Antenna 2, designed for the best compromise of gain while the SWR across the band is held to less than 2:1, achieves this goal, but at an average gain sacrifice of 0.7 dB compared to the maximum gain case. The F/R for this design is just under 15 dB over the band. This design is fairly typical of many amateur Yagi designs before the advent of computer modeling and optimization programs. SWR can easily be measured, and experimental optimization for forward gain is a fairly straightforward procedure. By contrast, overall pattern optimization is not a trivial thing to achieve experimentally, particularly for antennas with more than four or five elements.

Antenna 3, designed for an optimum combination of F/R, SWR and gain, compromises forward gain an average of 1.0 dB compared to the maximum gain case, and about 0.4 dB compared to the compromise gain/SWR case. It achieves its design objectives of more than 20 dB F/R over the 28.0 to 28.8 MHz portion of the band, with an SWR less than 2:1 over that range.

Figure 11.6A shows the free-space gain versus frequency for the same three types of designs, but for a bigger 5-element

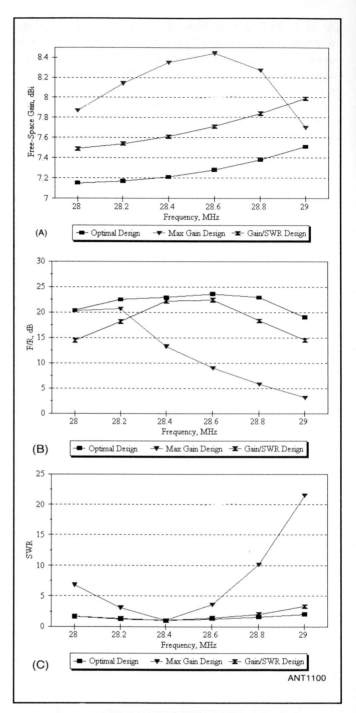

Figure 11.5 — Comparisons of three different 3-element 10 meter Yagi designs using 8-foot booms. At A, gain comparisons are shown. The Yagi designed for the best compromise of gain and SWR sacrifices an average of about 0.5 dB compared to the antenna designed for maximum gain. The Yagi designed for optimal F/R, gain and SWR sacrifices an average of 1.0 dB compared to the maximum-gain case, and about 0.4 dB compared to the compromise gain and SWR case. At B, the front-to-rear ratio is shown for the three different designs. The antenna designed for optimal combination of gain, F/R and SWR maintains a F/R higher than 20 dB across the entire frequency range, while the antenna designed strictly for gain has a F/R of 3 dB at the high end of the band. At C, the three antenna designs are compared for SWR bandwidth. At the high end of the band, the antenna designed strictly for gain has a very high SWR.

10 meter Yagi on a 20-foot boom. Figure 11.6B shows the variation in F/R, and Figure 11.6C shows the SWR curves versus frequency. Once again, the design that concentrates solely on maximum gain has a poor SWR curve over the band, reaching just over 6:1 toward the high end of the band. The difference in gain between the maximum gain case and the optimum design case has narrowed for this size of boom to an average of under 0.5 dB. This comes about because the designer has access to more variables in a 5-element design than he does in a 3-element design, and he can stagger-tune the various elements to spread the response out over the whole band.

Figure 11.7A, **B** and **C** show the same three types of designs, but for a 6-element Yagi on a 36-foot boom. The SWR bandwidth of the antenna designed for maximum gain has improved compared to the previous two shorter-boom examples, but the SWR still rises to more than 4:1 at 28.8 MHz, while the F/R ratio is pretty constant over the band, at a mediocre 11 dB average level. While the antenna designed for gain and SWR does hold the SWR below 2:1 over the band, it also has the same mediocre level of F/R performance as does the maximum-gain design.

The optimized 36-foot boom antenna achieves an excellent F/R of more than 22 dB over the whole 28.0 to 28.8 MHz band. Again, the availability of more elements and more space on the 36-foot long boom gives the designer more flexibility in broad-banding the response over the whole band, while sacrificing only 0.3 dB of gain compared to the maximum-gain design.

Figure 11.8A, **B**, and **C** show the same three types of 10 meter designs, but now for a 60-foot boom, populated with eight elements. With eight elements and a very long boom on which to space them out, the antenna designed solely for maximum gain can achieve a much better SWR response across the band, although the SWR does rise to more than 7:1 at the very high end of the band. The SWR remains less than 2:1 from 28.0 to 28.7 MHz, much better than for shorter-boom, maximum-gain designs. The worst-case F/R ratio is never better than 19 dB, however, and remains around 10 dB over much of the band. The antenna designed for the best compromise gain and SWR loses only about 0.1 dB of gain compared to the maximum-gain design, but does little better in terms of F/R across the band.

Contrasted to these two designs, the antenna optimized for F/R, SWR and gain has an outstanding pattern, exhibiting an F/R of more than 24 dB across the entire band, while keeping the SWR below 2:1 from 28.0 to 28.9 MHz. It must sacrifice an average of only 0.4 dB compared to the maximum gain design at the low end of the band, and actually has more gain than the maximum gain and gain/SWR designs at the high-frequency end of the band.

The conclusion drawn from these and many other detailed comparisons is that designing strictly for maximum mid-band gain yields an inferior design when the antenna is examined over an entire frequency band, especially in terms of SWR. Designing a Yagi for both gain and SWR will yield antennas that have mediocre rearward patterns, but that lose relatively

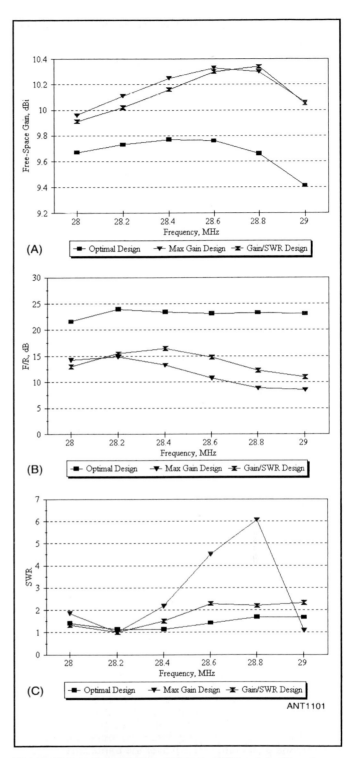

(A)

(B)

(C)

ANT1101

Figure 11.6 — Comparisons of three different designs for 5-element 10 meter Yagis on 20-foot booms. At A, the gain of three different 5-element 10 meter Yagi designs are graphed. The difference in gain between the three antennas narrows because the elements can be stagger-tuned to spread the response out better over the desired frequency band. The average gain reduction for the fully optimized antenna design is about 0.5 dB. At B, the optimal antenna displays better than 22 dB F/R over the band, while the Yagi designed for gain and SWR displays on average 10 dB less F/R throughout the band. At C, the SWR bandwidth is compared for the three Yagis. The antenna designed strictly for forward gain has a poor SWR bandwidth and a high peak SWR of 6:1 at 28.8 MHz.

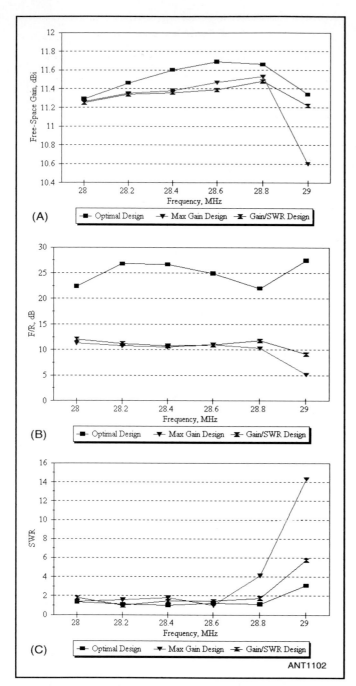

(A)

(B)

(C)

ANT1102

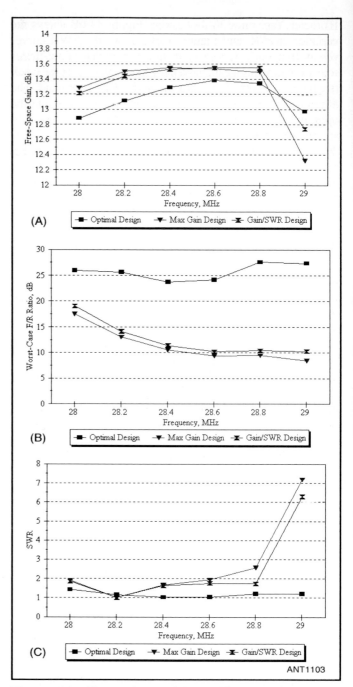

(A)

(B)

(C)

ANT1103

Figure 11.7 — Comparisons of three different 6-element 10 meter Yagi designs on 36-foot booms. At A, gain is shown over the band. With more elements and a longer boom, the tuning can be staggered even more to make the antenna gain more uniform over the band. This narrows the gain differential between the antenna designed strictly for maximum gain and the antenna designed for an optimal combination of F/R and gain. The average difference in gain is about 0.2 dB throughout the band. At B, the F/R performance over the band is shown for the three antenna designs. The antenna designed for optimal performance maintains an average of almost 15 dB better F/R over the whole band compared to the other designs. At C, the SWR bandwidth is compared. Again, the antenna designed strictly for maximum gain exhibits a high SWR of 4:1 at 28.8 MHz, and rises to more than 14:1 at 29.0 MHz.

Figure 11.8 — Comparisons of three different 8-element 10 meter Yagi designs using 60-foot booms. At A, gain is shown over the frequency band. With even more freedom to stagger-tune elements and a very long boom on which to place them, the average antenna gain differential over the band is now less than 0.2 dB between the three design cases. At B, an excellent 24 dB F/R for the optimal design is maintained over the whole band, compared to the average of about 12 dB for the other two designs. At C, the SWR differential over the band is narrowed between the three designs, again because there are more variables available to broaden the bandwidth.

little gain compared to the maximum gain case, at least for designs with more than three elements.

However, designing a Yagi for an optimal combination of F/R, SWR and gain results in a loss of gain less than 0.5 dB compared to designs designed only for gain and SWR. **Figure 11.9** summarizes the forward gain achieved for the three different design types versus boom length, as expressed in wavelength.

Except for the 2-element designs, the Yagis described in the rest of this chapter have the following design goals over a desired frequency band:

1) Front-to-rear ratio over the frequency band of more than 20 dB

2) SWR over the frequency band less than 2:1

3) Maximum gain consistent with points 1 and 2 above

Just for fun and to illustrate what an imaginative antenna designer can do with modeling software, **Figure 11.10** shows the gain versus boom length for theoretical 20 meter Yagis that have been designed to meet the three design goals above. The 31-element design for 14 MHz would be wondrous to behold. Sadly, it is unlikely that anyone will build one, considering that the boom would be 724 feet long! However, such a design *does* become practical when scaled to 432 MHz. In fact, a K1FO 22-element and a K1FO 31-element Yagi described in the **VHF and UHF Antenna Systems** chapter are the prototypes for the theoretical 14-MHz long-boom designs.

11.3.3 OPTIMIZED DESIGNS AND ELEMENT SPACING

Two-Element Yagis

Many hams consider a 2-element Yagi to give "the most bang for the buck" among various Yagi designs, particularly for portable operations such as Field Day. A 2-element Yagi has about 4 dB of gain over a simple dipole (sometimes jokingly called a "one-element Yagi") and gives a modest F/R of

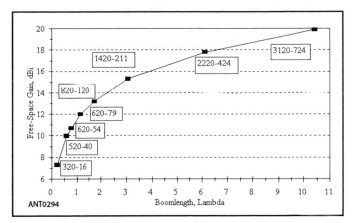

Figure 11.10 — Theoretical gain versus boom length for 20 meter Yagis designed for optimal combination of F/R, SWR and gain across the entire 14.0 to 14.35 MHz band. The theoretical gain approaches 20 dBi for a gigantic 724-foot boom, populated with 31 elements. Such a design on 20 meters is not too practical, of course, but can readily be achieved on a 24-foot boom on 432 MHz.

about 10 dB to help with rejection of interference on receive. By comparison, going from a 2-element to a 3-element Yagi increases the boom length by about 50% and adds another element, a 50% increase in the number of elements — for a gain increase of about 1 dB and another 10 dB in F/R.

Element Spacing in Larger Yagis

One of the more interesting results of computer modeling and optimization of high-performance Yagis with four or more elements is that a distinct pattern in the element spacings along the boom shows up consistently. This pattern is relatively independent of boom length, once the boom is longer than about 0.3 λ.

The reflector, driven element and first director of these optimal designs are typically bunched rather closely together, occupying together only about 0.15 to 0.20 λ of the boom. This pattern contrasts sharply with older designs, where the amount of boom taken up by the reflector, driven element and first director was typically more than 0.3 λ. **Figure 11.11** shows the element spacings for an optimized 6-element, 36-foot boom, 10 meter design, compared to a W2PV 6-element design with constant spacing of 0.15 λ between all elements.

A problem arises with such a bunching of elements toward the reflector end of the boom — the wind loading of the antenna is not equal along the boom. Unless properly compensated, such new-generation Yagis will act like wind vanes, punishing and often breaking, the rotators trying to turn, or hold, them in the wind. One successful solution to wind-vaning has been to employ "dummy elements" made of PVC pipe. These non-conducting elements — called *torque compensators* — are placed on the boom close to the last director so the wind load is equalized at the mast-to-boom bracket. Flat plates can also be installed on the boom to oppose the turning force from the elements.

Along with an unbalanced wind load, the weight balance

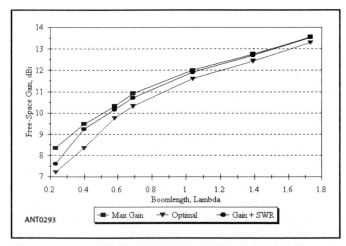

Figure 11.9 — Gain versus boom length for three different 10 meter design goals. The goals are: (1) designed for maximum gain across band, (2) designed for a compromise of gain and SWR, and (3) designed for optimal F/R, SWR and gain across 28.0 to 28.8 MHz portion of 10 meter band. The gain difference is less than 0.5 dB for booms longer than approximately 0.5 λ.

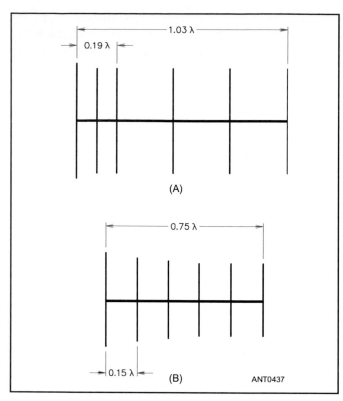

Figure 11.11 — Tapering spacing versus constant element spacing. At A, illustration of how the spacing of the reflector, driven element and first director (over the first 0.19 λ of the boom) of an optimally designed Yagi is bunched together compared to the Yagi at B, which uses constant 0.15 λ spacing between all elements. The optimally designed antenna has more than 22 dB F/R and an SWR less than 1.5:1 over the frequency band 28.0 to 28.8 MHz.

element and first director, modern optimal Yagi designs are not overly sensitive to small changes in either element length or spacing. In fact, these antennas can be constructed from design tables without excessive concern about close dimensional tolerances. In the HF range up to 30 MHz, building the antennas to the nearest ⅛-inch results in performance remarkably consistent with the computations, without any "tweaking" or fine-tuning when the Yagi is on the tower.

11.3.4 ELEMENT TUNING

Element tuning (or *self-impedance*) is a complex function of the effective electrical length of each element and the effective diameter of the element. In turn, the effective length and diameter of each element is related to the taper schedule (if telescoping aluminum tubing is used, the most common method of construction), the length of each telescoping section, the type and size of mounting bracket used to secure the element to or through the boom, and the size of the Yagi boom itself. Note especially that Yagis constructed using wire elements will perform very differently compared to the same antenna constructed with elements made of telescoping aluminum tubing.

The process by which a modern Yagi is designed usually starts out with the selection of the longest boom possible for a given installation. A suitable number of elements of a given taper schedule are then placed on this boom, and the gain, pattern and SWR are calculated over the entire frequency band of interest to the designer. Once an electrical design is chosen, the designer must then ensure the mechanical integrity of the antenna design. This involves verifying the integrity of the boom and each element in the face of the wind and ice loading expected for a particular location. The chapter **Antenna Materials and Construction** discusses the details of tapered telescoping aluminum elements for the upper HF bands. In addition, the ARRL book *Physical Design of Yagi Antennas*, by Dave Leeson, W6NL, describes the mechanical design process for all portions of a Yagi antenna very thoroughly, and is highly recommended for serious Yagi builders. (This book is now out of print.)

point is likely to be different than wind load balance point. The solution is generally to place a small amount of lead or iron inside one end of the boom in order to balance the antenna weight.

Despite the relatively close spacing of the reflector, driven

11.4 MONOBAND YAGI DESIGNS

The detailed Yagi design tables that follow are for two taper schedules for HF Yagis covering the 14 through 30-MHz amateur bands. The heavy-duty elements are designed to survive at least 120-mph winds without icing, or 85-mph winds with ¼-inch radial ice. The medium-duty elements are designed to survive winds greater than 80 mph, or 60-mph winds with ¼-inch radial ice.

For 10.1 MHz, the elements shown are capable of surviving 105-mph winds, or 93-mph winds with ¼-inch radial ice. For 7.1 MHz the elements shown can survive 93-mph winds, or 69-mph winds with ¼-inch radial ice. For these two lower frequency bands, the elements and the booms needed are very large and heavy. Mounting, turning and keeping such antennas in the air is not a trivial task.

Each element is mounted above the boom with a heavy rectangular aluminum plate by means of U-bolts with saddles, as shown in **Figure 11.12A**. This method of element mounting is rugged and stable, and because the element is mounted away from the boom, the amount of element detuning due to the presence of the boom is minimal. The element dimensions given in each table already take into account any element detuning due to the boom-to-element mounting plate. For each element, the length of the tip determines the tuning, since the inner tubes are fixed in diameter and length.

The element-to-boom mounting plates are modeled as a short section of element equivalent to a cylinder with an effective diameter given for each antenna. These dimensions to simulate the effect of the mounting plate are incorporated in the files for the *YW* (*Yagi for Windows*) computer modeling program on the CD-ROM accompanying this book.

The second column in each design table shows the spacing of each element relative to the next element in line on the boom, starting at the reflector, which itself is defined as being at the 0.000-inch reference point on the boom. The boom for antennas less than 30 feet long can be constructed of 2-inch OD tubing with 0.065-inch wall thickness. Designs larger than 30 feet long should use 3-inch OD heavy-wall tubing for the boom. Because each boom has extra space at each end, the reflector is actually placed 3 inches from the end of the boom. For example, in the 310-08H.YW design (a 10 meter Yagi with 3 elements on an 8-foot boom), the driven element is placed 36 inches ahead of the reflector, and the director is placed 54 inches ahead of the driven element.

The next columns give the lengths for the variable tips for the heavy-duty and then the medium-duty elements. In the example above for the 310-08H.YW Yagi, the heavy-duty reflector tip, made out of ½-inch OD tubing, sticks out 66.750 inches from the ⅝-inch OD tubing. Note that each telescoping piece of tubing overlaps 3 inches inside the piece into which it fits, so the overall length of ⅛-inch OD tubing is 69.750 inches long for the reflector. The medium-duty reflector tip has 71.875 inches protruding from the ⅝-inch OD tube, and is 74.875 inches long overall. As previously stated, the dimensions are not extremely critical, although measurement accuracy to ⅛ inch is desirable.

(A)

(B)

Figure 11.12 — Typical construction techniques for an HF Yagi. Photo A shows a typical element-to-boom clamp. U-bolts are used to hold the element to the plate and muffler clamps hold the plate to the boom. Photo B shows a hairpin match on a driven element insulated from a mounting plate that is attached to the boom with muffler clamps and saddles. Outdoor-rated gray PVC conduit sleeves insulate the element from the mounting plate. U-bolts hold the element on the plate. The feed line is connected to the two screws to which the hairpin inductor is attached. Note that the hairpin inductor's center point is attached to the boom at an electrically neutral point. All mounting hardware should be galvanized or stainless steel. The latter requires the use of an anti-seize compound to prevent thread galling.

The last row in each variable tip column shows the length of one-half of the "dummy element" torque compensator used to correct for uneven wind loading along the boom. This compensator is made from 2.5 inches OD PVC water pipe mounted to an element-to-boom plate like those used for each element. The compensator is mounted 12 inches behind the last director, the first director in the case of the 3-element 310-08H.YW antenna. Note that the heavy-duty elements require a correspondingly longer torque compensator than do the medium-duty elements.

Half Elements

Each design shows the dimensions for *one-half* of each element, mounted on *one side* of the boom. The other half of each element is symmetrical, mounted on the other side of the boom. The use of a tubing sleeve inside the center portion of the element is recommended, so that the element is not crushed by the mounting U-bolts. Unless otherwise noted, each section of tubing is made of 6061-T6 aluminum tubing, with a 0.058-inch wall thickness. This wall thickness ensures that the next standard size of tubing can telescope with it. Each telescoping section is inserted 3 inches into the larger tubing, and is secured by one of the methods shown in the **Antenna Materials and Construction** chapter, which also includes generic half-element designs rated for specific wind- and ice-loading conditions.

Matching System

Each antenna is designed with a driven-element length appropriate for a hairpin or *beta match* network. The driven-element's length may require slight readjustment for best match, particularly if a different matching network is used. *Do not change* either the lengths or the telescoping tubing schedule of the parasitic elements — they have been optimized for best performance and will not be affected by tuning of the driven element! (See the **Transmission Line Coupling and Impedance Matching** chapter for information on other types of matching systems.)

Figure 11.12B is a photograph of the driven element for a 2-element 17 meter Yagi built by Chuck Hutchinson, K8CH, for the ARRL book *Simple and Fun Antennas for Hams*. The aluminum tubing on each side of the boom was 1-inch OD, and the two pieces were mechanically joined together with a ¾-inch OD fiberglass insulator. Chuck wound electrical tape over the insulator to protect the fiberglass from the sun's UV.

Three-inch lengths of 1-inch UV-resistant PVC conduit, split lengthwise, to make the grey outer insulators for the driven element. The aluminum plates came from DX Engineering, as did the stainless steel U-bolts and saddle clamps. These saddles ensured that the elements don't rotate on the 2-inch OD boom in heavy winds.

You can see the bolts used to pin the center fiberglass insulator to the aluminum tubing, while also providing an electrical connection for the #12 AWG hairpin inductor wire and for the feed line coax). Note that the center of the hairpin is connected to the boom using a grounding lug. The center of the hairpin inductor is electrically neutral and may be connected to boom to provide dc grounding and a measure of protection from static buildup.

11.4.1 10 METER YAGIS

Figure 11.13 describes the electrical performance of eight optimized 10 meter Yagis with boom lengths between 6 to 60 feet. The end of each boom includes 3 inches of space for the reflector and last-director (or driven element for the 2-element designs) mounting plates. Figure 11.13A shows the free-space gain versus frequency for each antenna; Figure 11.13B shows the front-to-rear ratio, and Figure 11.13C shows the SWR versus frequency. Each antenna with three or more elements was designed to cover the lower half of the 10 meter band from 28.0 to 28.8 MHz, with SWR less than 2:1 and F/R better than 20 dB over that range.

Figure 11.13D shows the taper schedule for two types of 10 meter elements. The heavy-duty design can survive 125-mph winds with no icing, and 88-mph winds with ¼-inch of radial ice. The medium-duty design can handle 96-mph winds with no icing, and 68-mph winds with ¼-inch of radial ice.

The element-to-boom mounting plate for these Yagis is a 0.250-inch thick flat aluminum plate, 4 inches wide by 4 inches long. Each element except for the insulated driven element, is centered on the plate, held by two stainless-steel U-bolts with saddles. Another set of U-bolts with saddles is used to secure the mounting plate to the boom. The mounting plate has an effective diameter of 2.405 inches for the heavy-duty element and 2.310 inches for the medium-duty element. The equivalent length on each side of the boom is 2 inches.

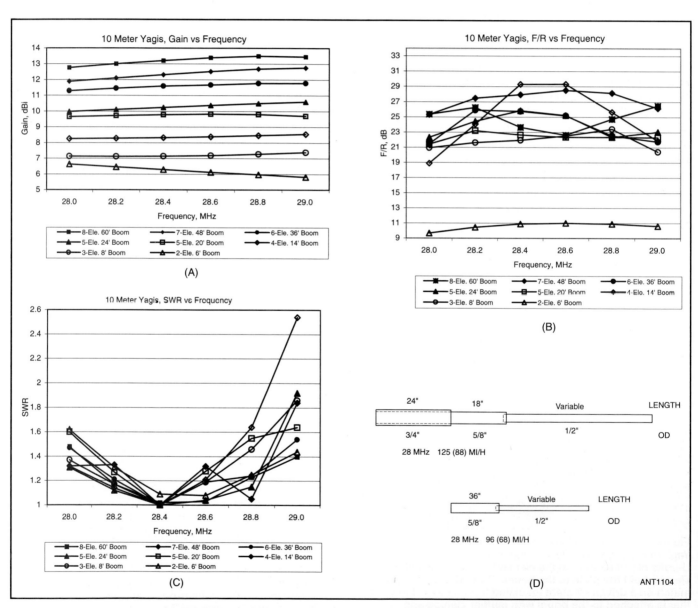

Figure 11.13 — Gain, F/R and SWR performance versus frequency for optimized 10 meter Yagis. At A, gain is shown versus frequency for eight 10 meter Yagis whose booms range from 6 feet to 60 feet long. Except for the 2-element design, these Yagis have been optimized for better than 20 dB F/R and less than 2:1 SWR over the frequency range 28.0 to 28.8 MHz. At B, front-to-rear ratio for these antennas is shown versus frequency, and at C, SWR is shown over the frequency range. At D, the taper schedule is shown for heavy-duty and for medium-duty 10 meter elements. The heavy-duty elements can withstand 125-mph winds without icing, and 88-mph winds with ¼-inch radial ice. The medium-duty elements can survive 96-mph winds without icing, and 68-mph winds with ¼-inch radial ice. The wall thickness for each telescoping section of 6061-T6 aluminum tubing is 0.058 inches, and the overlap at each telescoping junction is 3 inches.

Table 11-1

Optimized 10 meter Yagi Designs

Two-element 10 meter Yagi, 6 foot boom

Element	Spacing	*Heavy-Duty Tip*	*Medium-Duty Tip*
File Name		210-06H.YW	210-06M.YW
Reflector	0.000"	66.000"	71.500"
Driven Element	66.000"	57.625"	63.000"

Three-element 10 meter Yagi, 8 foot boom

Element	Spacing	*Heavy-Duty Tip*	*Medium-Duty Tip*
File Name		310-08H.YW	310-08M.YW
Reflector	0.000"	66.750"	71.875"
Driven Element	36.000"	57.625"	62.875"
Director 1	54.000"	53.125"	58.500"
Compensator	12" behind Dir. 1	19.000"	18.125"

Four-element 10 meter Yagi, 14 foot boom

Element	Spacing	*Heavy-Duty Tip*	*Medium-Duty Tip*
File Name		410-14H.YW	410-14M.YW
Reflector	0.000"	66.000"	72.000"
Driven Element	36.000"	58.625"	63.875"
Director 1	36.000"	57.000"	62.250"
Director 2	90.000"	47.750"	53.125"
Compensator	12" behind Dir. 2	22.000"	20.500"

Five-element 10 meter Yagi, 24 foot boom

Element	Spacing, inches	*Heavy-Duty Tip*	*Medium-Duty Tip*
File Name		510-24H.YW	510-24M.YW
Reflector	0.000"	65.625"	70.750"
Driven Element	36.000"	58.000"	63.250"
Director 1	36.000"	57.125"	62.375"
Director 2	99.000"	55.000"	60.250"
Director 3	111.000"	50.750"	56.125"
Compensator	12" behind Dir. 3	28.750"	26.750"

Six-element 10 meter Yagi, 36 foot boom

Element	Spacing, inches	*Heavy-Duty Tip*	*Medium-Duty Tip*
File Name		610-36H.YW	610-36M.YW
Reflector	0.000"	66.500"	71.500"
Driven Element	37.000"	58.500"	64.000"
Director 1	43.000"	57.125"	62.375"
Director 2	98.000"	54.875"	60.125"
Director 3	127.000"	53.875"	59.250"
Director 4	121.000"	49.875"	55.250"
Compensator	12" behind Dir. 4	32.000"	29.750"

Seven-element 10 meter Yagi, 48 foot boom

Element	Spacing, inches	*Heavy-Duty Tip*	*Medium-Duty Tip*
File Name		710-48H.YW	710-48M.YW
Reflector	0.000"	65.375"	70.500"
Driven Element	37.000"	59.000"	64.250"
Director 1	37.000"	57.500"	62.750"
Director 2	96.000"	54.875"	60.125"
Director 3	130.000"	52.250"	57.625"
Director 4	154.000"	52.625"	58.000"
Director 5	116.000"	49.875"	55.250"
Compensator	12" behind Dir. 5	35.750"	33.750"

Eight-element 10 meter Yagi, 60 foot boom

Element	Spacing, inches	*Heavy-Duty Tip*	*Medium-Duty Tip*
File Name		810-60H.YW	810-60M.YW
Reflector	0.000"	65.000"	70.125"
Driven Element	42.000"	58.000"	63.500"
Director 1	37.000"	57.125"	62.375"
Director 2	87.000"	55.375"	60.625"
Director 3	126.000"	53.250"	58.625"
Director 4	141.000"	51.875"	57.250"
Director 5	157.000"	52.500"	57.875"
Director 6	121.000"	50.125"	55.500"
Compensator	12" behind Dir. 6	59.375"	55.125"

These 10 meter Yagi designs are optimized for > 20 dB F/R, and SWR < 2:1 over frequency range from 28.000 to 28.800 MHz, for heavy-duty elements (125 mph wind survival) and for medium-duty (96 mph wind survival). For coverage from 28.8 to 29.7 MHz, subtract 2.000 inches from end of each element, but leave element spacings the same as shown here. Only element tip dimensions are shown, and all dimensions are inches. See Fig 11.13D for element telescoping tubing schedule. Torque compensator element is made of 2.5" OD PVC water pipe placed 12 inches behind last director. Dimensions shown for compensators is one-half of total length, centered on boom.

11.4.2 12 METER YAGIS

Figure 11.14 describes the electrical performance of seven optimized 12 meter Yagis with boom lengths between 6 to 54 feet. The end of each boom includes 3 inches of space for the reflector and last director (or driven element) mounting plates. The narrow frequency range of the 12 meter band allows the performance to be optimized easily. Figure 11.14A shows the free-space gain versus frequency for each antenna; Figure 11.14B shows the front-to-rear ratio, and Figure 11.14C shows the SWR versus frequency. Each antenna with three or more elements was designed to cover the narrow 12 meter band from 24.89 to 24.99 MHz, with SWR less than 2:1 and F/R better than 20 dB over that range.

Figure 11.14D shows the taper schedule for two types of 12 meter elements. The heavy-duty design can survive 123-mph winds with no icing, and 87-mph winds with ¼ inch of radial ice. The medium-duty design can handle 85-mph winds with no icing, and 61-mph winds with ¼ inch of radial ice.

The element-to-boom mounting plate for these Yagis is a 0.375 inch thick flat aluminum plate, 5 inches wide by 6 inches long. The mounting plate has an effective diameter of 2.945 inches for the heavy-duty element, and 2.857 inches for the medium-duty element. The equivalent length on each side of the boom is 3 inches. As usual, the torque compensator is mounted 12 inches behind the last director.

11.4.3 15 METER YAGIS

Figure 11.15 describes the electrical performance of eight optimized 15 meter Yagis with boom lengths between 6 feet to a spectacular 80 feet. The end of each boom includes 3 inches of space for the reflector and last director (or driven

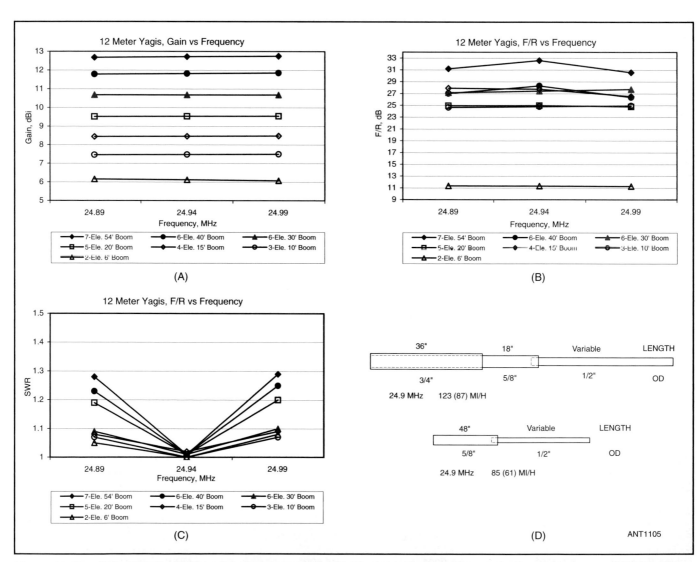

Figure 11.14 — Gain, F/R and SWR performance versus frequency for optimized 12 meter Yagis. At A, gain is shown versus frequency for seven 12 meter Yagis whose booms range from 6 feet to 54 feet long. Except for the 2-element design, these Yagis have been optimized for better than 20 dB F/R and less than 2:1 SWR over the narrow 12 meter band 24.89 to 24.99 MHz. At B, front-to-rear ratio for these antennas is shown versus frequency, and at C, SWR over the frequency range is shown. At D, the taper schedule for heavy-duty and for medium-duty 12 meter elements is shown. The heavy-duty elements can withstand 123-mph winds without icing, and 87-mph winds with ¼-inch radial ice. The medium-duty elements can survive 85-mph winds without icing, and 61-mph winds with ¼-inch radial ice. The wall thickness for each telescoping section of 6061-T6 aluminum tubing is 0.058 inches, and the overlap at each telescoping junction is 3 inches.

Table 11-2

Optimized 12 meter Yagi Designs

Two-element 12 meter Yagi, 6 foot boom

Element	Spacing	Heavy-Duty Tip	Medium-Duty Tip
File Name		212-06H.YW	212-06M.YW
Reflector	0.000"	67.500"	72.500"
Driven Element	66.000"	59.500"	65.000"

Three-element 12 meter Yagi, 10 foot boom

Element	Spacing, inches	Heavy-Duty Tip	Medium-Duty Tip
File Name		312-10H.YW	312-10M.YW
Reflector	0.000"	69.000"	73.875"
Driven Element	40.000"	60.250"	65.250"
Director 1	74.000"	54.000"	59.125"
Compensator	12" behind Dir. 1	13.625"	12.000"

Four-element 12 meter Yagi, 15 foot boom

Element	Spacing, inches	Heavy-Duty Tip	Medium-Duty Tip
File Name		412-15H.YW	412-15M.YW
Reflector	0.000"	66.875"	71.875"
Driven Element	46.000"	61.000"	66.000"
Director 1	46.000"	58.625"	63.750"
Director 2	82.000"	50.875"	56.125"
Compensator	12" behind Dir. 2	16.375"	14.500"

Five-element 12 meter Yagi, 20 foot boom

Element	Spacing, inches	Heavy-Duty Tip	Medium-Duty Tip
File Name		512-20H.YW	512-20M.YW
Reflector	0.000"	69.750"	74.625"
Driven Element	46.000"	62.250"	67.000"
Director 1	46.000"	60.500"	65.500"
Director 2	48.000"	55.500"	60.625"
Director 3	94.000"	54.625"	59.750"
Compensator	12" behind Dir. 3	22.125"	19.625"

Six-element 12 meter Yagi, 30 foot boom

Element	Spacing, inches	Heavy-Duty Tip	Medium-Duty Tip
File Name		612-30H.YW	612-30M.YW
Reflector	0.000"	68.125"	73.000"
Driven Element	46.000"	61.750"	66.750"
Director 1	46.000"	60.250"	65.250"
Director 2	73.000"	52.375"	57.625"
Director 3	75.000"	57.625"	62.750"
Director 4	114.000"	53.625"	58.750"
Compensator	12" behind Dir. 4	30.000"	26.250"

Six-element 12 meter Yagi, 40 foot boom

Element	Spacing, inches	Heavy-Duty Tip	Medium-Duty Tip
File Name		612-40H.YW	612-40M.YW
Reflector	0.000"	67.000"	71.875"
Driven Element	46.000"	60.125"	65.500"
Director 1	46.000"	57.375"	62.500"
Director 2	91.000"	57.375"	62.500"
Director 3	157.000"	57.000"	62.125"
Director 4	134.000"	54.375"	59.500"
Compensator	12" behind Dir. 4	36.500"	31.625"

Seven-element 12 meter Yagi, 54 foot boom

Element	Spacing, inches	Heavy-Duty Tip	Medium-Duty Tip
File Name		712-54H.YW	712-54M.YW
Reflector	0.000"	68.000"	73.000"
Driven Element	46.000"	60.500"	65.500"
Director 1	46.000"	56.750"	61.875"
Director 2	75.000"	58.000"	63.125"
Director 3	161.000"	55.625"	60.750"
Director 4	174.000"	56.000"	61.125"
Director 5	140.000"	53.125"	58.375"
Compensator	12" behind Dir. 5	43.125"	37.500"

These 12 meter Yagi designs were optimized for > 20 dB F/R, and SWR < 2:1 over frequency range from 24.890 to 24.990 MHz, for heavy-duty elements (123 mph wind survival) and for medium-duty (85 mph wind survival). Only element tip dimensions are shown, and all dimensions are inches. See Fig 11.14D for element telescoping tubing schedule. Torque compensator element is made of 2.5" OD PVC water pipe placed 12" behind last director. Dimensions shown for compensators is one-half of total length, centered on boom.

Table 11-3
Optimized 15 meter Yagi Designs

Two-element 15 meter Yagi, 6 foot boom

Element	Spacing	Heavy-Duty Tip	Medium-Duty Tip
File Name		215-06H.YW	215-06M.YW
Reflector	0.000"	62.000"	85.000"
Driven Element	66.000"	51.000"	74.000"

Three-element 15 meter Yagi, 12 foot boom

Element	Spacing	Heavy-Duty Tip	Medium-Duty Tip
File Name		315-12H.YW	315-12M.YW
Reflector	0.000"	62.000"	84.250"
Driven Element	48.000"	51.000"	73.750"
Director 1	92.000"	43.500"	66.750"
Compensator	12" behind Dir. 1	34.750"	37.625"

Four-element 15 meter Yagi, 18 foot boom

Element	Spacing	Heavy-Duty Tip	Medium-Duty Tip
File Name		415-18H.YW	415-18M.YW
Reflector	0.000"	61.000"	83.500"
Driven Element	56.000"	51.500"	74.500"
Director 1	56.000"	48.000"	71.125"
Director 2	98.000"	36.625"	60.250"
Compensator	12" behind Dir. 2	20.875"	18.625"

Five-element 15 meter Yagi, 24 foot boom

Element	Spacing	Heavy-Duty Tip	Medium-Duty Tip
File Name		515-24H.YW	515-24M.YW
Reflector	0.000"	62.000"	84.375"
Driven Element	48.000"	52.375"	75.250"
Director 1	48.000"	47.875"	71.000"
Director 2	52.000"	47.000"	70.125"
Director 3	134.000"	41.000"	64.375"
Compensator	12" behind Dir. 3	40.250"	35.125"

Six-element 15 meter Yagi, 36 foot boom

Element	Spacing	Heavy-Duty Tip	Medium-Duty Tip
File Name		615-36H.YW	615-36M.YW
Reflector	0.000"	61.000"	83.375"
Driven Element	53.000"	52.000"	75.000"
Director 1	56.000"	49.125"	72.125"
Director 2	59.000"	45.125"	68.375"
Director 3	116.000"	47.875"	71.000"
Director 4	142.000"	42.000"	65.375"
Compensator	12" behind Dir. 4	45.500"	39.750"

Seven-element 15 meter Yagi, 48 foot boom

Element	Spacing	Heavy-Duty Tip	Medium-Duty Tip
File Name		615-48H.YW	615-48M.YW
Reflector	0.000"	62.000"	84.000"
Driven Element	48.000"	52.000"	75.000"
Director 1	48.000"	51.250"	74.125"
Director 2	125.000"	48.000"	71.125"
Director 3	190.000"	45.500"	68.750"
Director 4	161.000"	42.000"	65.375"
Compensator	12" behind Dir. 4	51.500"	45.375"

Seven-element 15 meter Yagi, 60 foot boom

Element	Spacing	Heavy-Duty Tip	Medium-Duty Tip
File Name		715-60H.YW	715-60M.YW
Reflector	0.000"	59.750"	82.250"
Driven Element	48.000"	52.000"	75.000"
Director 1	48.000"	52.000"	74.875"
Director 2	93.000"	49.500"	72.500"
Director 3	173.000"	44.125"	67.375"
Director 4	197.000"	45.500"	68.750"
Director 5	155.000"	41.750"	65.125"
Compensator	12" behind Dir. 5	58.500"	51.000"

Eight-element 15 meter Yagi, 80 foot boom

Element	Spacing	Heavy-Duty Tip	Medium-Duty Tip
File Name		815-80H.YW	815-80M.YW
Reflector	0.000"	62.000"	84.000"
Driven Element	56.000"	52.500"	75.500"
Director 1	48.000"	51.500"	74.375"
Director 2	115.000"	48.375"	71.500"
Director 3	164.000"	45.750"	69.000"
Director 4	202.000"	43.125"	66.500"
Director 5	206.000"	44.750"	68.000"
Director 6	163.000"	40.875"	64.250"
Compensator	12" behind Dir. 6	95.000"	83.375"

These 15 meter Yagi designs are optimized for > 20 dB F/R, and SWR < 2:1 over entire frequency range from 21.000 to 21.450 MHz, for heavy-duty elements (124 mph wind survival) and for medium-duty (86 mph wind survival). Only element tip dimensions are shown. See Fig 11.15D for element telescoping tubing schedule. All dimensions are in inches. Torque compensator element is made of 2.5" OD PVC water pipe placed 12" behind last director, and dimensions shown for compensators is one-half of total length, centered on boom.

element) mounting plates. Figure 11.15A shows the free-space gain versus frequency for each antenna; Figure 11.15B shows the worst-case front-to-rear ratio, and Figure 11.15C shows the SWR versus frequency. Each antenna with three or more elements was designed to cover the full 15 meter band from 21.000 to 21.450 MHz, with SWR less than 2:1 and F/R ratio better than 20 dB over that range.

Figure 11.15D shows the taper schedule for two types of 15 meter elements. The heavy-duty design can survive 124-mph winds with no icing, and 90-mph winds with ¼ inch of radial ice. The medium-duty design can handle 86-mph winds with no icing, and 61-mph winds with ¼ inch of radial ice.

The element-to-boom mounting plate for these Yagis is a 0.375-inch thick flat aluminum plate, 5 inches wide by 6 inches long. The mounting plate has an effective diameter of 3.0362 inches for the heavy-duty element, and 2.9447 inches for the medium-duty element. The equivalent length on each side of the boom is 3 inches. As usual, the torque compensator is mounted 12 inches behind the last director.

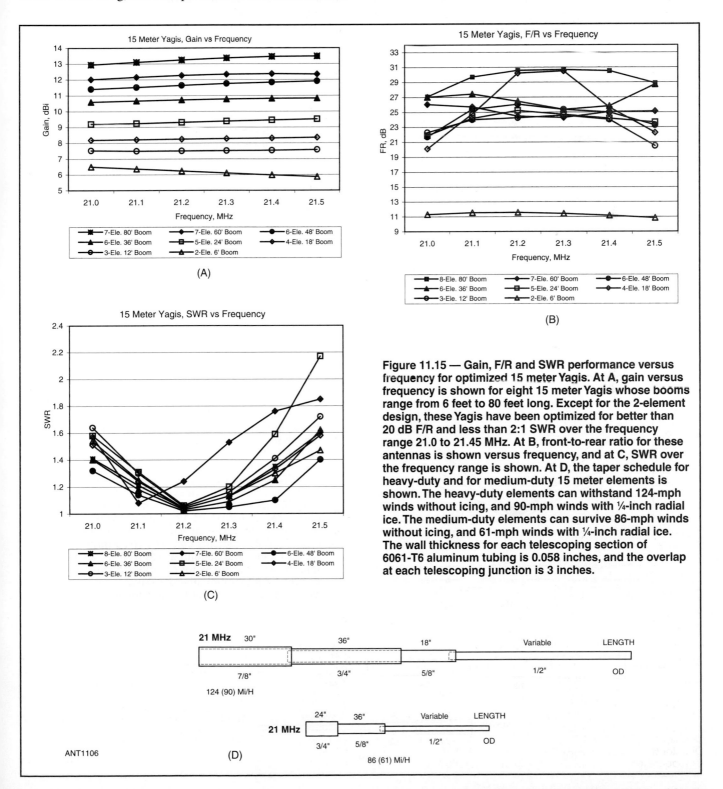

Figure 11.15 — Gain, F/R and SWR performance versus frequency for optimized 15 meter Yagis. At A, gain versus frequency is shown for eight 15 meter Yagis whose booms range from 6 feet to 80 feet long. Except for the 2-element design, these Yagis have been optimized for better than 20 dB F/R and less than 2:1 SWR over the frequency range 21.0 to 21.45 MHz. At B, front-to-rear ratio for these antennas is shown versus frequency, and at C, SWR over the frequency range is shown. At D, the taper schedule for heavy-duty and for medium-duty 15 meter elements is shown. The heavy-duty elements can withstand 124-mph winds without icing, and 90-mph winds with ¼-inch radial ice. The medium-duty elements can survive 86-mph winds without icing, and 61-mph winds with ¼-inch radial ice. The wall thickness for each telescoping section of 6061-T6 aluminum tubing is 0.058 inches, and the overlap at each telescoping junction is 3 inches.

11.4.4 17 METER YAGIS

Figure 11.16 describes the electrical performance of six optimized 17 meter Yagis with boom lengths between 6 to a heroic 60 feet. As usual, the end of each boom includes 3 inches of space for the reflector and last director (or driven element) mounting plates. Figure 11.16A shows the free-space gain versus frequency for each antenna; Figure 11.16B shows the worst-case front-to-rear ratio, and Figure 11.16C shows the SWR versus frequency. Each antenna with three or more elements was designed to cover the narrow 17 meter band from 18.068 to 18.168 MHz, with SWR less than 2:1 and F/R ratio better than 20 dB over that range.

Figure 11.16D shows the taper schedule for two types of 17 meter elements. The heavy-duty design can survive 123-mph winds with no icing, and 83-mph winds with ¼-inch of radial ice. The medium-duty design can handle 83-mph winds with no icing, and 59-mph winds with ¼ inch of radial ice.

The element-to-boom mounting plate for these Yagis is a 0.375-inch thick flat aluminum plate, 6 inches wide by 8 inches long. The mounting plate has an effective diameter of 3.5122 inches for the heavy-duty element, and 3.3299 inches for the medium-duty element. The equivalent length on each side of the boom is 4 inches. As usual, the torque compensator is mounted 12 inches behind the last director.

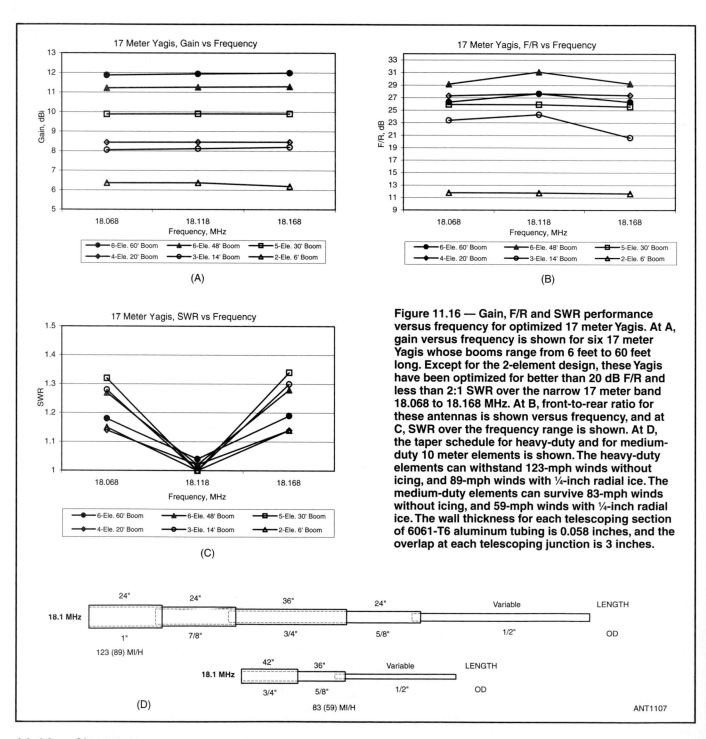

Figure 11.16 — Gain, F/R and SWR performance versus frequency for optimized 17 meter Yagis. At A, gain versus frequency is shown for six 17 meter Yagis whose booms range from 6 feet to 60 feet long. Except for the 2-element design, these Yagis have been optimized for better than 20 dB F/R and less than 2:1 SWR over the narrow 17 meter band 18.068 to 18.168 MHz. At B, front-to-rear ratio for these antennas is shown versus frequency, and at C, SWR over the frequency range is shown. At D, the taper schedule for heavy-duty and for medium-duty 10 meter elements is shown. The heavy-duty elements can withstand 123-mph winds without icing, and 89-mph winds with ¼-inch radial ice. The medium-duty elements can survive 83-mph winds without icing, and 59-mph winds with ¼-inch radial ice. The wall thickness for each telescoping section of 6061-T6 aluminum tubing is 0.058 inches, and the overlap at each telescoping junction is 3 inches.

Table 11-4
Optimized 17 meter Yagi Designs

Two-element 17 meter Yagi, 6 foot boom

Element	Spacing	Heavy-Duty Tip	Medium-Duty Tip
File Name		217-06H.YW	217-06M.YW
Reflector	0.000"	61.000"	89.000"
Driven Element	66.000"	48.000"	76.250"

Three-element 17 meter Yagi, 14 foot boom

Element	Spacing	Heavy-Duty Tip	Medium-Duty Tip
File Name		317-14H.YW	317-14M.YW
Reflector	0.000"	61.500"	91.500"
Driven Element	65.000"	52.000"	79.500"
Director 1	97.000"	46.000"	73.000"
	12" behind Dir. 1	12.625"	10.750"

Four-element 17 meter Yagi, 20 foot boom

Element	Spacing	Heavy-Duty Tip	Medium-Duty Tip
File Name		417-20H.YW	417-20M.YW
Reflector	0.000"	61.500"	89.500"
Driven Element	48.000"	54.250"	82.625"
Director 1	48.000"	52.625"	81.125"
Director 2	138.000"	40.500"	69.625"
Compensator	12" behind Dir. 2	42.500"	36.250"

Five-element 17 meter Yagi, 30 foot boom

Element	Spacing	Heavy-Duty Tip	Medium-Duty Tip
File Name		517-30H.YW	517-30M.YW
Reflector	0.000"	61.875"	89.875"
Driven Element	48.000"	52.250"	80.500"
Director 1	52.000"	49.625"	78.250"
Director 2	93.000"	49.875"	78.500"
Director 3	161.000"	43.500"	72.500"
Compensator	12" behind Dir. 3	54.375"	45.875"

Six-element 17 meter Yagi, 48 foot boom

Element	Spacing	Heavy-Duty Tip	Medium-Duty Tip
File Name		617-48H.YW	617-48M.YW
Reflector	0.000"	63.000"	90.250"
Driven Element	52.000"	52.500"	80.500"
Director 1	51.000"	45.500"	74.375"
Director 2	87.000"	47.875"	76.625"
Director 3	204.000"	47.000"	75.875"
Director 4	176.000"	42.000"	71.125"
Compensator	12" behind Dir. 4	68.250"	57.500"

Six-element 17 meter Yagi, 60 foot boom

Element	Spacing	Heavy-Duty Tip	Medium-Duty Tip
File Name		617-60H.YW	617-60M.YW
Reflector	0.000"	61.250"	89.250"
Driven Element	54.000"	54.750"	83.125"
Director 1	54.000"	52.250"	80.750"
Director 2	180.000"	46.000"	74.875"
Director 3	235.000"	44.625"	73.625"
Director 4	191.000"	41.500"	70.625"
Compensator	12" behind Dir. 4	62.875"	53.000"

These 17 meter Yagi designs are optimized for > 20 dB F/R, and SWR < 2:1 over entire frequency range from 18.068 to 18.168 MHz, for heavy-duty elements (123 mph wind survival) and for medium-duty (83 mph wind survival). Only element tip dimensions are shown. All dimensions are in inches. Torque compensator element is made of 2.5" OD PVC water pipe placed 12" behind last director, and dimensions shown for compensators is one-half of total length, centered on boom.

11.4.5 20 METER YAGIS

Figure 11.17 describes the electrical performance of eight optimized 20 meter Yagis with boom lengths between 8 to a giant 80 feet. As usual, the end of each boom includes 3 inches of space for the reflector and last director (driven element) mounting plates. Figure 11.17A shows the free-space gain versus frequency for each antenna; Figure 11.17B shows the front-to-rear ratio, and Figure 11.17C shows the SWR versus frequency. Each antenna with three or more elements was designed to cover the complete 20 meter band from 14.000 to 14.350 MHz, with SWR less than 2:1 and F/R ratio better than 20 dB over that range.

Figure 11.17D shows the taper schedule for two types of 20 meter elements. The heavy-duty design can survive 122-mph

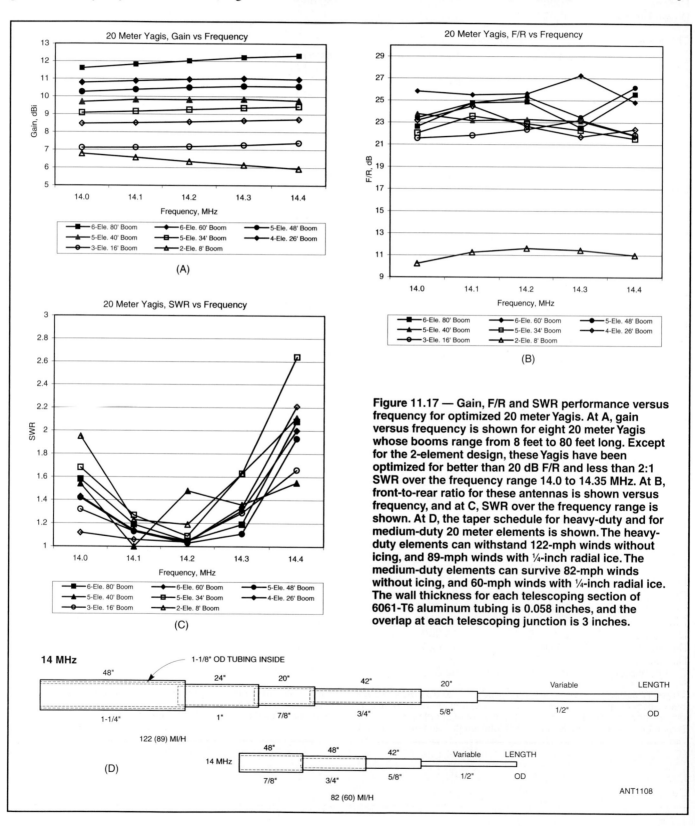

(A)

(B)

(C)

Figure 11.17 — Gain, F/R and SWR performance versus frequency for optimized 20 meter Yagis. At A, gain versus frequency is shown for eight 20 meter Yagis whose booms range from 8 feet to 80 feet long. Except for the 2-element design, these Yagis have been optimized for better than 20 dB F/R and less than 2:1 SWR over the frequency range 14.0 to 14.35 MHz. At B, front-to-rear ratio for these antennas is shown versus frequency, and at C, SWR over the frequency range is shown. At D, the taper schedule for heavy-duty and for medium-duty 20 meter elements is shown. The heavy-duty elements can withstand 122-mph winds without icing, and 89-mph winds with ¼-inch radial ice. The medium-duty elements can survive 82-mph winds without icing, and 60-mph winds with ¼-inch radial ice. The wall thickness for each telescoping section of 6061-T6 aluminum tubing is 0.058 inches, and the overlap at each telescoping junction is 3 inches.

(D)

ANT1108

Table 11-5

Optimized 20 meter Yagi Designs

Two-element 20 meter Yagi, 8 foot boom

Element	Spacing	*Heavy-Duty Tip*	*Medium-Duty Tip*
File Name		220-08H.YW	220-08M.YW
Reflector	0.000"	66.000"	80.000"
Driven Element	90.000"	46.000"	59.000"

Three-element 20 meter Yagi, 16 foot boom

Element	Spacing	*Heavy-Duty Tip*	*Medium-Duty Tip*
File Name		320-16H.YW	320-16M.YW
Reflector	0.000"	69.625"	81.625"
Driven Element	80.000"	51.250"	64.500"
Director 1	106.000"	42.625"	56.375"
Compensator	12" behind Dir. 1	33.375"	38.250"

Four-element 20 meter Yagi, 26 foot boom

Element	Spacing	*Heavy-Duty Tip*	*Medium-Duty Tip*
File Name		420-26H.YW	420-26M.YW
Reflector	0.000"	65.625"	78.000"
Driven Element	72.000"	53.375"	65.375"
Director 1	60.000"	51.750"	63.875"
Director 2	174.000"	38.625"	51.500"
Compensator	12" behind Dir. 2	54.250"	44.250"

Five-element 20 meter Yagi, 34 foot boom

Element	Spacing	*Heavy-Duty Tip*	*Medium-Duty Tip*
File Name		520-34H.YW	520-34M.YW
Reflector	0.000"	68.625"	80.750"
Driven Element	72.000"	52.250"	65.500"
Director 1	71.000"	45.875"	59.375"
Director 2	68.000"	45.875"	59.375"
Director 3	191.000"	37.000"	51.000"
Compensator	12" behind Dir. 3	69.250"	56.250"

Five-element 20 meter Yagi, 40 foot boom

Element	Spacing	*Heavy-Duty Tip*	*Medium-Duty Tip*
File Name		520-40H.YW	520-40M.YW
Reflector	0.000"	68.375"	80.500"
Driven Element	72.000"	53.500"	66.625"
Director 1	72.000"	51.500"	64.625"
Director 2	139.000"	48.375"	61.750"
Director 3	191.000"	38.000"	52.000"
Compensator	12" behind Dir. 3	69.750"	56.750"

Five-element 20 meter Yagi, 48 foot boom

Element	Spacing	*Heavy-Duty Tip*	*Medium-Duty Tip*
File Name		520-48H.YW	520-48M.YW
Reflector	0.000"	66.250"	78.500"
Driven Element	72.000"	53.000"	66.000"
Director 1	88.000"	50.500"	63.750"
Director 2	199.000"	47.375"	60.875"
Director 3	211.000"	39.750"	53.625"
Compensator	12" behind Dir. 3	70.325"	57.325"

Six-element 20 meter Yagi, 60 foot boom

Element	Spacing	*Heavy-Duty Tip*	*Medium-Duty Tip*
File Name		620-60H.YW	620-60M.YW
Reflector	0.000"	67.000"	79.250"
Driven Element	84.000"	51.500"	65.000"
Director 1	91.000"	45.125"	58.750"
Director 2	130.000"	41.375"	55.125"
Director 3	210.000"	46.875"	60.375"
Director 4	199.000"	39.125"	53.000"
Compensator	12" behind Dir. 4	72.875"	59.250"

Six-element 20 meter Yagi, 80 foot boom

Element	Spacing	*Heavy-Duty Tip*	*Medium-Duty Tip*
File Name		620-80H.YW	620-80M.YW
Reflector	0.000"	66.125"	78.375"
Driven Element	72.000"	52.375"	65.500"
Director 1	122.000"	49.125"	62.500"
Director 2	229.000"	44.500"	58.125"
Director 3	291.000"	42.625"	56.375"
Director 4	240.000"	38.750"	52.625"
Compensator	12" behind Dir. 4	78.750"	64.125"

These 20 meter Yagi designs are optimized for > 20 dB F/R, and SWR < 2:1 over entire frequency range from 14.000 to 14.350 MHz, for heavy-duty elements (122 mph wind survival) and for medium-duty (82 mph wind survival). Only element tip dimensions are shown. See Fig 11.17 for element telescoping tubing schedule. All dimensions are in inches. Torque compensator element is made of 2.5" OD PVC water pipe placed 12" behind last director, and dimensions shown for compensators is one-half of total length, centered on boom.

winds with no icing, and 89-mph winds with $\frac{1}{4}$ inch of radial ice. The medium-duty design can handle 82-mph winds with no icing, and 60-mph winds with ¼ inch of radial ice.

The element-to-boom mounting plate for these Yagis is a 0.375-inch thick flat aluminum plate, 6 inches wide by 8 inches long. The mounting plate has an effective diameter of 3.7063 inches for the heavy-duty element, and 3.4194 inches for the medium-duty element. The equivalent length on each side of the boom is 4 inches. As usual, the torque compensator is mounted 12 inches behind the last director.

11.4.6 30 METER YAGIS

Figure 11.18 describes the electrical performance of three optimized 30 meter Yagis with boom lengths between 15 to 34 feet. Because of the size and weight of the elements alone for Yagis on this band, only 2-element and 3-element designs are described. The front-to-rear ratio requirement for the 2-element antenna is relaxed to be greater than 10 dB over the band from 10.100 to 10.150 MHz, while that for the 3-element designs is kept at greater than 20 dB over that frequency range.

As usual, the end of each boom includes 3 inches of space for the reflector and last director mounting plates. Figure 11.18A shows the free-space gain versus frequency for each antenna; Figure 11.18B shows the worst-case front-to-rear ratio, and Figure 11.18C shows the SWR versus frequency.

Figure 11.18D shows the taper schedule for the 30 meter

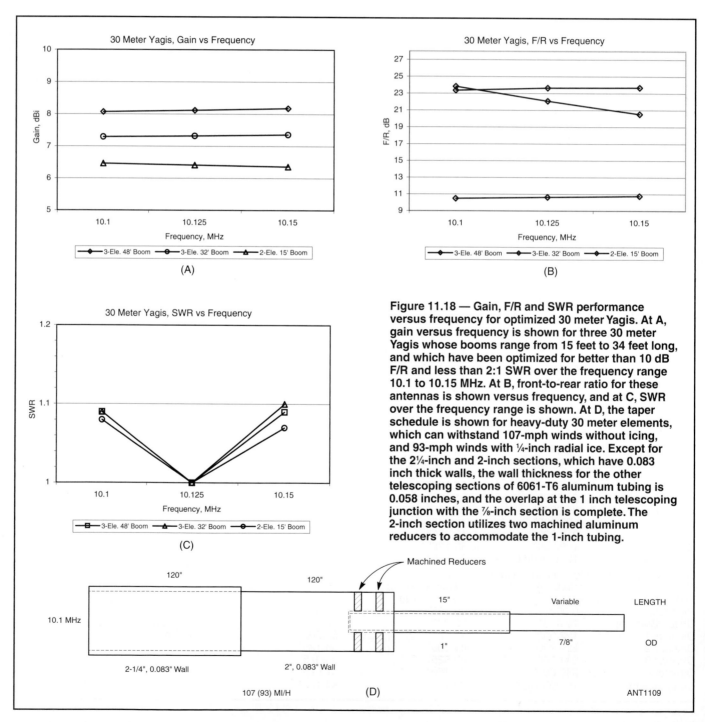

Figure 11.18 — Gain, F/R and SWR performance versus frequency for optimized 30 meter Yagis. At A, gain versus frequency is shown for three 30 meter Yagis whose booms range from 15 feet to 34 feet long, and which have been optimized for better than 10 dB F/R and less than 2:1 SWR over the frequency range 10.1 to 10.15 MHz. At B, front-to-rear ratio for these antennas is shown versus frequency, and at C, SWR over the frequency range is shown. At D, the taper schedule is shown for heavy-duty 30 meter elements, which can withstand 107-mph winds without icing, and 93-mph winds with ¼-inch radial ice. Except for the 2¼-inch and 2-inch sections, which have 0.083 inch thick walls, the wall thickness for the other telescoping sections of 6061-T6 aluminum tubing is 0.058 inches, and the overlap at the 1 inch telescoping junction with the ⅞-inch section is complete. The 2-inch section utilizes two machined aluminum reducers to accommodate the 1-inch tubing.

elements. Note that the wall thickness of the first two sections of tubing is 0.083 inches, rather than 0.058 inches. This heavy-duty element design can survive 107-mph winds with no icing, and 93-mph winds with ¼ inch of radial ice.

The element-to-boom mounting plate for these Yagis is a 0.500-inch thick flat aluminum plate, 6 inches wide by 24 inches long. The mounting plate has an effective diameter of 4.684 inches. The equivalent length on each side of the boom is 12 inches. These designs require no torque compensator.

11.4.7 40 METER YAGIS

Figure 11.19 describes the electrical performance of three optimized 40 meter Yagis with boom lengths between 20 to 48 feet. Like the 30 meter antennas, because of the size and weight of the elements for a 40 meter Yagi, only 2-element and 3-element designs are described. The front-to-rear ratio requirement for the 2-element antenna is relaxed to be greater than 10 dB over the band from 7.000 to 7.300 MHz, while the goal for the 3-element designs is 20 dB over the frequency range of 7.000 to 7.200 MHz. It is exceedingly difficult to hold the F/R greater than 20 dB over the entire 40 meter band without sacrificing excessive gain with a 3-element design.

As usual, the end of each boom includes 3 inches of space for the reflector and last director mounting plates. Figure 11.19A shows the free-space gain versus frequency for each antenna;

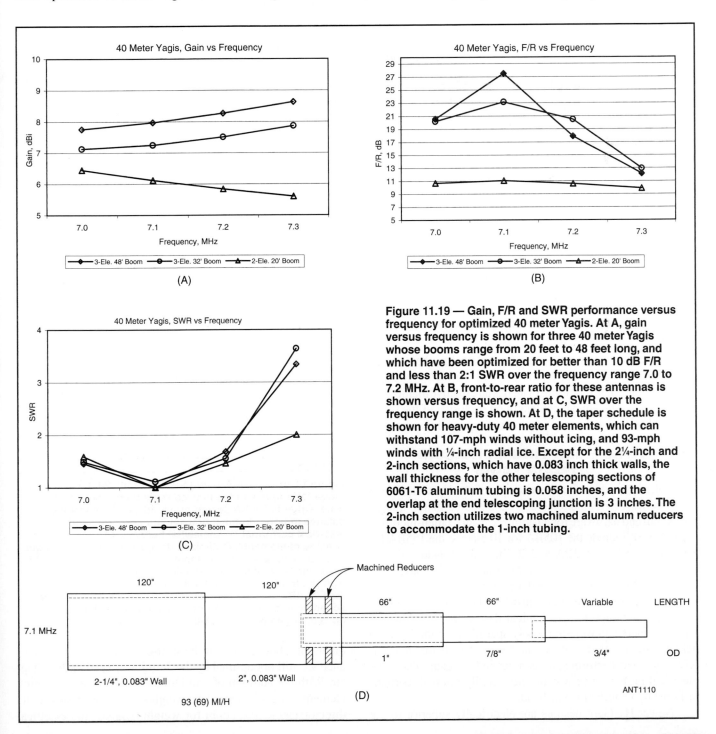

Figure 11.19 — Gain, F/R and SWR performance versus frequency for optimized 40 meter Yagis. At A, gain versus frequency is shown for three 40 meter Yagis whose booms range from 20 feet to 48 feet long, and which have been optimized for better than 10 dB F/R and less than 2:1 SWR over the frequency range 7.0 to 7.2 MHz. At B, front-to-rear ratio for these antennas is shown versus frequency, and at C, SWR over the frequency range is shown. At D, the taper schedule is shown for heavy-duty 40 meter elements, which can withstand 107-mph winds without icing, and 93-mph winds with ¼-inch radial ice. Except for the 2¼-inch and 2-inch sections, which have 0.083 inch thick walls, the wall thickness for the other telescoping sections of 6061-T6 aluminum tubing is 0.058 inches, and the overlap at the end telescoping junction is 3 inches. The 2-inch section utilizes two machined aluminum reducers to accommodate the 1-inch tubing.

Table 11-6
Optimized 30 meter Yagi Designs

Two-element 30 meter Yagi, 15 foot boom

Element	Spacing	Heavy-Duty Tip
File Name		230-15H.YW
Reflector	0.000"	50.250"
Driven Element	174.000"	14.875"

3-element 30 meter Yagi, 22 foot boom

Element	Spacing	Heavy-Duty Tip
File Name		330-22H.YW
Reflector	0.000	59.375
Driven Element	135.000	35.000
Director 1	123.000	19.625

Three-element 30 meter Yagi, 34 foot boom

Element	Spacing	Heavy-Duty Tip
File Name		330-34H.YW
Reflector	0.000"	53.750"
Driven Element	212"	29.000"
Director 1	190"	14.500"

These 30 meter Yagi designs are optimized for > 10 dB F/R, and SWR < 2:1 over entire frequency range from 10.100 to 10.150 MHz for heavy-duty elements (105 mph wind survival). Only element tip dimensions are shown. See Fig 11.18D for element telescoping tubing schedule. All dimensions are in inches. No torque compensator element is required.

Table 11-7
Optimized 40 meter Yagi Designs

Two-element 40 meter Yagi, 20 foot boom

Element	Spacing	Heavy-Duty Tip
File Name		240-20H.YW
Reflector	0.000"	85.000"
Driven Element	234.000"	35.000"

Three-element 40 meter Yagi, 32 foot boom

Element	Spacing	Heavy-Duty Tip
File Name		340-32H.YW
Reflector	0.000"	90.750"
Driven Element	196.000"	55.875"
Director 1	182.000"	33.875"

Three-element 40 meter Yagi, 48 foot boom

Element	Spacing	Heavy-Duty Tip
File Name		340-48H.YW
Reflector	0.000"	81.000"
Driven Element	300.000"	45.000"
Director 1	270.000"	21.000"

These 40 meter Yagi designs are optimized for > 10 dB F/R, and SWR < 2:1 over low-end of frequency range from 7.000 to 7.200 MHz, for heavy-duty elements (95 mph wind survival). Only element tip dimensions are shown. See Fig 11.19D for element telescoping tubing schedule. All dimensions are in inches. No wind torque compensator is required.

Figure 11.19B shows the front-to- rear ratio, and Figure 11.19C shows the SWR versus frequency.

Figure 11.19D shows the taper schedule for the 40 meter elements. Note that the wall thickness of the first two sections of tubing is 0.083 inches, rather than 0.058 inches. This element design can survive 93-mph winds with no icing, and 69-mph winds with ¼ inch of radial ice.

The element-to-boom mounting plate for these Yagis is a 0.500-inch thick flat aluminum plate, 6 inches wide by 24 inches long. The mounting plate has an effective diameter of 4.684 inches. The equivalent length on each side of the boom is 12 inches. These designs require no torque compensator.

11.4.8 MODIFYING MONOBAND HY-GAIN YAGIS

Enterprising amateurs have long used the Hy-Gain "Long John" series of HF monobanders as a source of top-quality aluminum and hardware for customized Yagis. Often-modified older models include the 105BA for 10 meters, the 155BA for 15 meters, and the 204BA and 205BA for 20 meters. Newer Hy-Gain designs, the 105CA, 155CA and 205CA, have been redesigned by computer for better performance.

Hy-Gain antennas have historically had an excellent reputation for superior mechanical design. In the older designs the elements were purposely spaced along the boom to achieve good weight balance at the mast-to-boom bracket, with electrical performance as a secondary goal. Thus, the electrical performance was not necessarily optimal, particularly over an entire amateur band.

Newer Hy-Gain designs are electrically superior to the

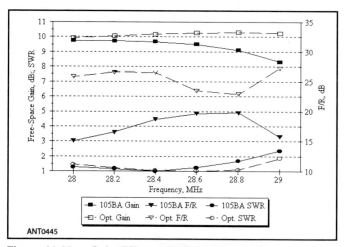

Figure 11.20 — Gain, F/R and SWR over the 28.0 to 28.8 MHz range for original and optimized Yagis using Hy-Gain hardware. Original 105BA design provided excellent weight balance at boom-to-mast bracket, but compromised the electrical performance somewhat because of non-optimum spacing of elements. Optimized design requires wind torque-balancing compensator element, and compensating weight at director end of boom to rebalance weight. The F/R ratio over the frequency range for the optimized design is more than 23 dB. Each element uses the original Hy-Gain taper schedule and element-to-boom clamp, but the length of the tip is changed per Table 11-8.

older ones, but because of the strong concern for weight balance are still not optimal by the definitions used in this chapter. With the addition of wind torque-compensation dummy elements, and with extra lead weights where necessary at the director end of the boom for weight-balance, the electrical

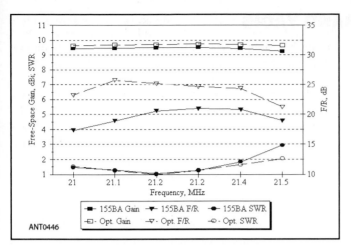

ANT0446

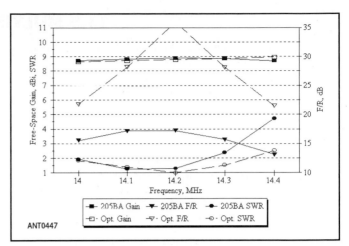

ANT0447

Figure 11.21 — Gain, F/R and SWR over the 21.0 to 21.45 MHz band for original and optimized Yagis using Hy-Gain hardware. Original 155BA design provided excellent weight balance at boom-to-mast bracket, but compromised the electrical performance somewhat because of non-optimum spacing of elements. Optimized design requires wind torque-balancing compensator element, and compensating weight at director end of boom to rebalance weight. The F/R ratio over the frequency range for the optimized design is more than 22 dB. Each element uses the original Hy-Gain taper schedule and element-to-boom clamp, but the length of the tip is changed per Table 11-9.

Figure 11.22 — Gain, F/R and SWR over the 14.0 to 14.35 MHz band for original and optimized Yagis using Hy-Gain hardware. Original 205BA design provided good weight balance at boom-to-mast bracket, but compromised the electrical performance because of non-optimum spacing of elements. Optimized design requires wind torque-balancing compensator element, and compensating weight at director end of boom to rebalance weight. The F/R ratio over the frequency range for the optimized design is more than 23 dB, while the original design never went beyond 17 dB of F/R. Each element uses the original Hy-Gain taper schedule and element-to-boom clamp, but the length of the tip is changed per Table 11-10.

Table 11-8

Optimized Hy-Gain 20 meter Yagi Designs

Optimized 204BA, Four-element 20 meter Yagi, 26 foot boom

Element	Spacing	Element Tip
File Name		BV204CA.YW
Reflector	0.000"	56.000"
Driven Element	85.000"	52.000"
Director 1	72.000"	61.500"
Director 2	149.000"	50.125"

Optimized 205CA, Five-element 20 meter Yagi, 34 foot boom

Element	Spacing	Element Tip
File Name		BV205CA.YW
Reflector	0.000"	62.625"
Driven Element	72.000"	53.500"
Director 1	72.000"	63.875"
Director 2	74.000"	61.625"

Table 11-9

Optimized Hy-Gain 15 meter Yagi Designs

Optimized 155BA, Five-element 15 meter Yagi, 24 foot boom

Element	Spacing	Element Tip
File Name		BV155CA.YW
Reflector	0.000"	64.000"
Driven Element	48.000"	65.500"
Director 1	48.000"	63.875"
Director 2	82.750"	61.625"
Director 3	127.250"	55.000"

Table 11-10

Optimized Hy-Gain 10 meter Yagi Designs

Optimized 105BA, Five-element 10 meter Yagi, 24 foot boom

Element	Spacing, inches	Element Tip
File Name		BV105CA.YW
Reflector	0.000"	44.250"
Driven Element	40.000"	53.625"
Director 1	40.000"	52.500"
Director 2	89.500"	50.500"
Director 3	112.250"	44.750"

performance can be enhanced, using the same proven mechanical parts.

Figure 11.20 shows the computed gain, F/R ratio and SWR for a 24-foot boom, 10 meter optimized Yagi (modified 105BA) using Hy-Gain hardware. **Figure 11.21** shows the same for a 26-foot boom 15 meter Yagi (modified 155BA), and **Figure 11.22** shows the same for a 34-foot boom (modified 205BA) 20 meter Yagi. **Tables 11-8** through **11-10** show

dimensions for these designs. The original Hy-Gain taper schedule is used for each element. Only the length of the end tip (and the spacing along the boom) is changed for each element.

11.5 MULTIBAND YAGIS

So far, this chapter has discussed monoband Yagis — that is, Yagis designed for a single Amateur Radio frequency band. Because hams have operating privileges on more than one band, multiband coverage has always been very desirable.

Interlacing Elements

In the late 1940s, some experimenters tried interlacing Yagi elements for different frequencies on a single boom, mainly to cover the 10 and 20 meter bands (at that time the 15 meter band wasn't yet available to hams). The experimenters discovered that the mutual interactions between different elements tuned to different frequencies are very difficult to handle.

Adjusting a lower-frequency element usually results in interaction with higher-frequency elements near it. In effect, the lower-frequency element acts like a retrograde reflector, throwing off the effectiveness of the higher-frequency directors nearby. Element lengths and the spacing between elements can be changed to improve performance of the higher-frequency Yagi, but the resulting compromise is rarely equal to that of an optimized monoband Yagi. A reasonable compromise for portable operation was developed by VE7CA and is described in the **Portable Antennas** chapter.

Trap Multibanders

Multiband Yagis using a single boom can also be made using traps. Traps allow an element to have multiple resonances. The **Multiband Antennas** chapter provides details on trap designs. The general function is very similar to trap dipoles in which the traps act as open circuits or reactances that change the electrical length of the element at different frequencies.

Commercial vendors have sold trap antennas to hams since the 1950s and surveys show that after simple wire dipoles and multiband verticals, trap triband Yagis are the most popular antennas in the Amateur Radio service.

The originator of the trap tribander was Chester Buchanan, W3DZZ, in his March 1955 *QST* article, "The Multimatch Antenna System." On 10 meters this rather unusual tribander used two reflectors (one dedicated and one with traps) and two directors (one dedicated and one with traps). On 20 and 15 meters three of the five elements were active using traps. The W3DZZ tribander employed 12 traps overall, made with heavy wire and concentric tubular capacitors to hold down losses in the traps. Each trap was individually fine-tuned after construction before mounting it on an element.

Another example of a homemade tribander was the 26-foot boom 7-element 20/15/10 meter design described by Bob Myers, W1XT (ex-W1FBY) in December 1970 *QST*. The W1FBY tribander used only two sets of traps in the driven element, with dedicated reflectors and directors for each frequency band. Again, the traps were quite robust in

this design to minimize trap losses, using $^7/_{16}$-inch aluminum tubing for the coils and short pieces of RG-8 coax as high-voltage tuning capacitors.

Relatively few hams actually build tribanders for themselves, mainly because of the mechanical complexity and the close tolerances required for such antennas. The traps themselves must be constructed quite accurately for reproducible results, and they must be carefully weatherproofed for long life in rain, snow, and often polluted or corrosive atmospheres.

Traps, like any lumped-constant circuit, have some amount of loss which can be minimized with careful design. The primary compromise incurred in a trap multiband Yagi is the fixed element spacing on all bands. The usual tribander design is optimized for the middle band while the spacing is a bit too long for the highest band and a bit too short for the lowest band. Nevertheless, trap tribanders provide good performance in a compact package.

Christmas Tree Stacks

Another possible method for achieving multiband coverage using monoband Yagis is to stack them in a "Christmas tree" arrangement as in **Figure 11.23**. For an installation covering 20, 15 and 10 meters, you could mount the 20 meter monobander on the rotating mast just at the top of the tower. Then perhaps 9 feet above that you would mount the 15 meter monobander, followed by the 10 meter monoband Yagi 7 feet further up on the mast. Another configuration would be to place the 10 meter Yagi in between the lower 20 meter and upper 15 meter Yagis. Whatever the arrangement, the antenna in the middle of such a Christmas-tree always suffers the most interaction from the lowest-frequency Yagi.

Dave Leeson, W6NL, mentions that the 10 meter Yagi in a closely stacked Christmas Tree (15 meters at the top, 10 meters in the middle, and 20 meters at the bottom of the rotating mast) loses "substantial gain" because of serious interaction with the 20 meter antenna. (N6BV and K1VR calculated that the free-space gain in the W6NL stack drops to 5 dBi, compared to about 9 dBi with no surrounding antennas.) Monobanders are *definitely not* universally superior to tribanders in multiband installations.

Forward Staggering

Some hams have built multiband Yagis on a common boom, using a technique called *forward staggering*. This means that that most (or all) of the higher-frequency elements are placed in front of any lower-frequency elements — in other words, most of the elements are not interlaced. Richard Fenwick, K5RR, described his triband Yagi design in September 1996 *QEX* magazine. This uses forward-stagger and open-sleeve design techniques and was optimized using several sophisticated modeling programs.

Fenwick's tribander used a 57-foot, 3-inch OD boom to hold 4 elements on 20 meters, 4 elements on 15 meters and

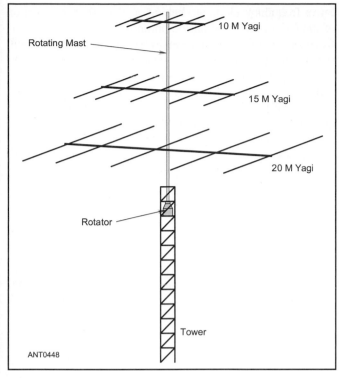

Figure 11.23 — "Christmas Tree" stack of 20/15/10 meter Yagis spaced vertically on a single rotating mast.

5 elements on 10 meters. **Figure 11.24** shows the element placement for the K5RR tribander. Most hams, of course, don't have the real-estate or the large rotator needed to turn such a large, but elegant solution to the interaction problem!

Force 12 C-3 "Multi-Monoband" Triband Yagi

Antenna manufacturer Force 12 also uses forward-stagger layouts and patented combinations of open- and closed-sleeve drive techniques extensively in their product line of multiband antennas, which they call "multi-monoband Yagis." **Figure 11.25** shows the layout for the popular Force 12 C-3 triband Yagi. The C-3 uses no traps, thereby avoiding any losses due to traps. The C-3 consists of three 2-element Yagis on an 18-foot boom, using full-sized elements designed to withstand high winds. (There is a pair of 10 meter driven elements for coverage of the full band.)

The C-3 feed system employs open-sleeves, where the 20 meter driver element is fed with coax through a common-mode current balun and parasitically couples to the closely spaced 15 meter driver and the two 10 meter driven elements to yield a feed point impedances close to 50 Ω on all three bands. Open-sleeve dipoles are discussed in the **Multiband Antennas** chapter.

Note the use of the forward-stagger technique in the C-3, especially on 10 meters. To reduce interaction with the

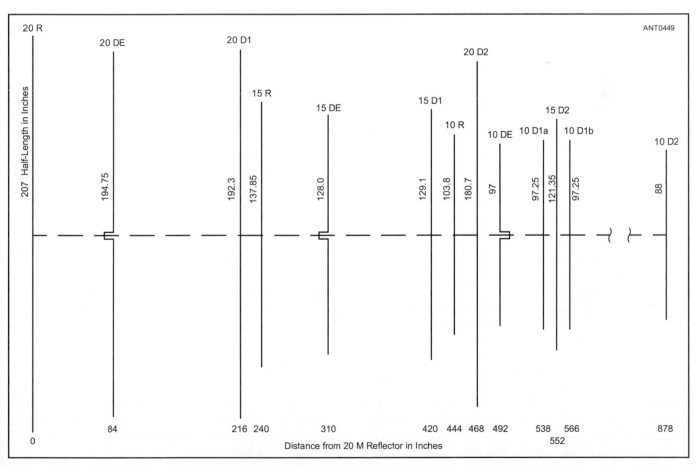

Figure 11.24 — Dimensions of K5RR's trap-less tribander using "forward stagger" and open-sleeve techniques to manage interaction between elements for different frequencies.

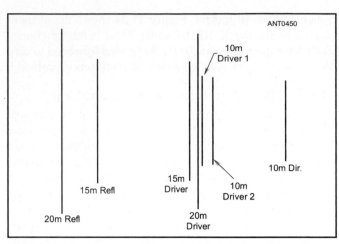

Figure 11.25 — Layout of Force 12 C3 multiband Yagi. Note that the 10 meter (driver/director) portion of the antenna is "forward staggered" ahead of the 15 meter (reflector/driver) portion, which in turn is placed ahead of the 20 meter (reflector/driver) portion. The antenna is fed at the 20 meter driver, which couples parasitically to the 15 meter driver and the two 10 meter drivers.

lower-frequency elements behind it, the 10 meter portion of the C-3 is mounted on the boom ahead of all the lower-frequency elements with the main 10 meter parasitic element (#7) acting as a director. The lower-frequency elements behind the 10 meter section act as retrograde reflectors, gaining some improvement of the gain and pattern compared to a monoband 2-element Yagi. A simplified *EZNEC* model of the C-3 is included on the CD-ROM accompanying this book.

On 15 meters, the main parasitic element (#2) is a dedicated reflector, but the other elements ahead on the boom act like retrograde directors to improve the gain and pattern somewhat over a typical 2-element Yagi with a reflector. On 20 meters, the C-3 is a 2-element Yagi with a dedicated reflector (#1) at the back end of the boom.

The exact implementation of any Yagi, of course, depends on the way the elements are constructed using telescoping aluminum tubing. The C-3 type of design is no exception.

11.6 SHORTENING YAGI ELEMENTS

Almost any technique that can be used to reduce the physical length of a dipole can also be used to shorten the physical length of a Yagi element. The tradeoffs are additional mechanical complexity and reduced performance with respect to forward gain and SWR bandwidth. As with shortened dipoles and monopoles, placement of the loading structures is critical to obtaining good performance and careful modeling is required. (Caution should be used in modeling wires that are very close to each other, junctions of large-diameter conductors, and other complex mechanical arrangements.)

Linear Loading

The most common size-reducing technique is *linear loading* and it can be applied to Yagis as well as dipoles and verticals. An example of linear loading for a dipole was presented by Lew Gordon, K4VX, in his July 2002 *QST* article. A very similar example of linear loading for a 2-element 20 meter Yagi can be found in a June 1976 *QST* article by Cole Collings, WØYNF.

Linear loading essentially consists of folding the antenna into a zig-zag pattern. Each back-and-forth folded segment radiates very little because the field from each of the folded conductors partially cancels that of the adjacent conductors. Nevertheless, the folding does extend the electrical length of the antenna. The effective length of the

folded antenna is somewhat longer than if the section remained unfolded.

The Hy-Gain 402BA 2-element 40 meter Yagi was a popular linearly-loaded antenna with 46-foot elements. A full-size element on 40 meters is approximately 65 feet long, so linear loading provided a substantial reduction in size.

End Loading and Inductor Loading

The technique of adding capacitance hats near the end of an antenna to lower its resonant frequency is most often encountered in vertical ground-plane antennas for the lower HF bands. The technique can also be put to good use on HF Yagis as seen in the Cushcraft (**www.cushcraftamateur. com**) MA5B mini-beam for 20/17/15/12/10 meters. The capacitance hats on this multiband Yagi play a major role in reducing the longest element to a bit over 17 feet long — just over λ/4 on 20 meters.

The elements of the MA5B also use traps and that also helps reduce length by inserting inductance into the element below the trap's resonant frequency. The Cushcraft XM240 2-element 40 meter Yagi also uses a combination of capacitance hats and coils to reduce element size.

Inductors on large Yagis for 75/80 meters are used similarly to base loading in verticals. The same general concerns apply with the inductance and placement of the coil, as well as losses in the coil.

11.7 THE MOXON RECTANGLE

L.B. Cebik, W4RNL (SK), has written extensively about the *Moxon rectangle*, an antenna invented by Les Moxon, G6XN (SK), derived from a design by VK2ABQ. The Moxon rectangle beam takes less space horizontally than a conventional 2-element Yagi design, yet it offers nearly the same amount of gain and a superior front-to-back ratio. And as an additional benefit, the drive-point impedance is close to 50 Ω, so that it doesn't need a matching section.

For example, rather than a "wingspan" of 17 feet for the reflector in a conventional 2-element 10 meter Yagi, the Moxon rectangle is 13 feet wide, a saving of almost 25%. The Moxon rectangle W4RNL created for *The ARRL Antenna Compendium, Vol 6,* had an SWR less than 2:1 from 28.0 to 29.7 MHz, with a gain over ground of 11 dBi. It had a F/B of 15 dB at 28.0 MHz, more than 20 dB at 28.4 MHz, and 12 dB at 29.7 MHz.

The Moxon rectangle relies on controlling the spacing (hence controlling the coupling) between the ends of the driven element tips and the ends of the reflector tips, which are both bent toward each other. See **Figure 11.26** which shows the general outline for W4RNL's 10 meter aluminum Moxon rectangle. The tips of the elements are kept a fixed distance from each other by PVC spacers. The closed rectangular mechanical assembly gives some rigidity to the design, keeping it stable in the wind. W4RNL described other Moxon rectangle designs using wire elements in June 2000 *QST.*

11.7.1 40 METER MOXON RECTANGLE

Dave Leeson, W6NL, has modified the Cushcraft XM240 2-element 40 meter Yagi to a Moxon Rectangle design shown in **Figure 11.27**. The W6NL Moxon Yagi is a high efficiency design that uses cross elements to provide both loading and the Moxon coupling. The upgrade of the

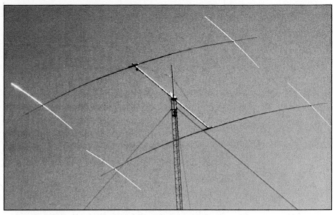

Figure 11.27 — A Cushcraft XM240 2-element 40 meter Yagi is modified by W6NL to become a Moxon Rectangle. The antenna is mechanically strengthened during the modification, as well. (Photo by Dave Leeson, W6NL)

XM240 to the W6NL Moxon consists of replacing the loading coil LCA sections with four new assemblies, each consisting of two new sections and the new tee loading element. The remaining parts are original Cushcraft.

The antenna has a gain of more than 10 dBi (including ground reflections) and a high front-to-back ratio (not specified by the designer). As is usual for Moxon designs, the SWR bandwidth is very good — more than 300 kHz with an SWR of less than 1.5:1.

Modifying the XM240 is described in detail in W6NL's design article, "Construction of W6NL Moxon on Cushcraft XM240," included on the CD-ROM for this book. The mechanical strength of the antenna is also improved as part of the modification procedure.

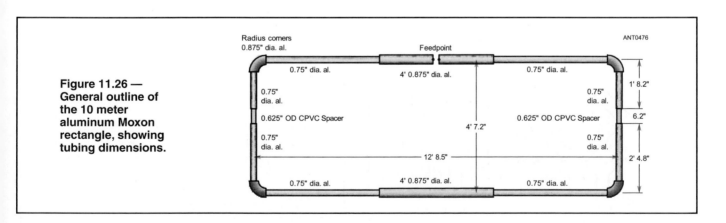

Figure 11.26 — General outline of the 10 meter aluminum Moxon rectangle, showing tubing dimensions.

11.8 QUAD ANTENNAS

The previous section discussed Yagi arrays as systems of approximately half-wave dipole elements that are coupled together mutually. You can also employ other kinds of elements using the same basic principles of analysis. For example, loops of various types may be combined into directive arrays. A popular type of parasitic array using loops is the *quad antenna*, in which loops having a perimeter of about one wavelength are used in much the same way as half-wave dipole elements in the Yagi antenna.

Clarence Moore, W9LZX, created the quad antenna in the early 1940s while he was at the Missionary Radio Station HCJB in Quito, Ecuador. He developed the quad to combat the effects of corona discharge at high altitudes. The problem at HCJB was that their large Yagi was literally destroying itself by melting its own element tips. This occurred due to the huge balls of corona it generated in the thin atmosphere of the high Andes Mountains. Moore reasoned correctly that closed loop elements would generate less high voltage — and hence less corona — than would the high impedances at the ends of a half-wave dipole element.

Figure 11.28 shows the original version of the two-element quad, with a driven element and a parasitic reflector. The square loops may be mounted either with the corners lying on horizontal and vertical lines, as shown at the left, or with two sides horizontal and two vertical (right). The feed points shown for these two cases will result in horizontal polarization, which is commonly used.

Quad designers may want to look up a copy of Bill Orr, W6SAI's *All About Cubical Quads* (now out of print) for a variety of design notes and ideas. Similarly, R. P. Haviland, W4MB's series of quad-related articles in *Ham Radio* and *QEX* are also worth reading. (See Bibliography.)

11.8.1 QUADS VERSUS YAGIS

Since its invention, there has been controversy whether the quad is a better performer than a Yagi. The three main electrical performance parameters of a Yagi are gain, response patterns (front-to-rear ratio, F/R) and feed point impedance/SWR. Proper analysis of a quad also involves checking all these parameters across the entire frequency range over which you intend to use it. Both a quad and a Yagi are classified as "parasitic, end-fire arrays." Modern antenna modeling by computer shows that monoband Yagis and quads with the same boom lengths and optimized for the same performance parameters have gains within about 1 dB of each other, with the quad slightly ahead of the Yagi.

Figure 11.29 plots the three parameters of gain, front-to-rear ratio (F/R) and SWR over the 14.0 to 14.35-MHz band for two representative antennas — a monoband three-element quad and a monoband four-element Yagi. Both of these have 26-foot booms and both are optimized for the best compromise of gain, F/R and SWR across the whole band.

While the quad in Figure 11.29 consistently exhibits about 0.5 dB more gain over the whole band, its F/R pattern toward the rear isn't quite as good as the Yagi's over that span of frequencies. This quad attains a maximum F/R of 25 dB at 14.1 MHz, but it falls to 17 dB at the bottom end of the band and 15 dB at the top. On the other hand, the Yagi's F/R stays consistently above 21 dB across the whole 20 meter band. The quad's SWR rises to just under 3:1 at the top end of the band, but stays below 2:1 from 14.0 to almost 14.3 MHz. The Yagi's SWR remains lower than 1.5:1 over the whole band.

The reason the Yagi in Figure 11.29 has more consistent responses for gain, F/R and SWR across the whole 20 meter band is that it has an additional parasitic element, giving two additional variables to play with — that is, the length of that

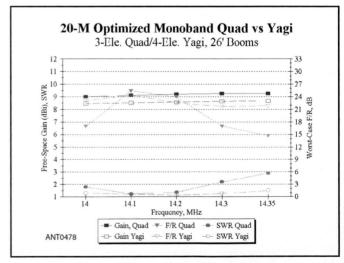

Figure 11.29 — Comparison of gain, F/R and SWR over the 14.0 to 14.35-MHz range for an optimized three-element quad and an optimized three-element Yagi, both on 26-foot booms. The quad exhibits almost 0.5 dB more gain for the same boom length, but doesn't have as good a rearward pattern over the whole frequency range compared to the Yagi. This is evidenced by the F/R curve. The quad's SWR curve is also not quite as flat as the Yagi. The quad's design emphasizes gain more than the other two parameters.

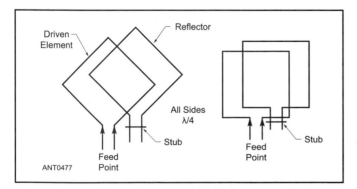

Figure 11.28 — The basic two-element quad antenna, with driven-element loop and reflector loop. The driven loops are electrically one wavelength in circumference (¼ wavelength on a side); the reflectors are slightly longer. Both configurations shown give horizontal polarization. For vertical polarization, the driven element should be fed at one of the side corners in the arrangement at the left, or at the center of a vertical side in the "square" quad at the right.

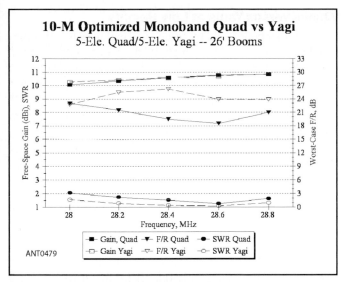

Figure 11.30 — Comparison of gain, F/R and SWR over the 28.0 to 28.8-MHz range for an optimized five-element quad and an optimized five-element Yagi, both on 26-foot booms. The gain advantage of the quad is about 0.25 dB at the low end of the band. The F/R is more peaked in frequency for the quad, however, than the Yagi.

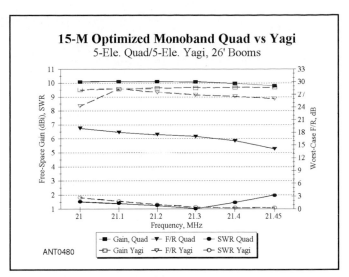

Figure 11.31 — Comparison of gain, F/R and SWR over the 21.0 to 21.45-MHz range for an optimized 5-element quad and optimized 5-element Yagi, both on 26-foot booms. The quad enjoys a gain advantage of about 0.5 dB over most of the band. Its rearward pattern is not as good as the Yagi, which remains higher than 24 dB across the whole range, compared to the quad, which remains in the 16-dB average range.

additional element and the spacing of that element from the others on the boom.

Yagi advocates point out that it is easier to add extra elements to a Yagi, given the mechanical complexities of adding another element to a quad. Extra parasitic elements give a designer more flexibility to tailor all performance parameters over a wide frequency range. Quad designers have historically opted to optimize strictly for gain and, as stated before, they can achieve as much as 1 dB more gain than a Yagi with the same length boom. But in so doing, a quad designer typically has to settle for front-to-rear patterns that are peaked over more narrow frequency ranges. The 20 meter quad plots in Figure 11.29 actually represent an even-handed approach, where the gain is compromised slightly to obtain a more consistent pattern and SWR across the whole band.

Figure 11.30 plots gain, F/R and SWR for two 10 meter monoband designs: a five-element quad and a five-element Yagi, both placed on 26-foot booms. The quad now has the same degrees of freedom as the Yagi, and as a consequence the pattern and SWR are more consistent across the range from 28.0 to 28.8 MHz. The quad's F/R remains above about 18.5 dB from 28.0 to 28.8 MHz. Meanwhile, the Yagi maintains an F/R of greater than 22 dB over the same range, but has almost 0.8 dB less gain compared to the quad at the low end of the band, eventually catching up at the high end of the band. The SWR for the quad is just over 2:1 at the bottom of the band, but remains less than 2:1 up to 28.8 MHz. The SWR on the Yagi remains less than 1.6:1 over the whole band.

Figure 11.31 shows the performance parameters for two 15 meter monoband designs: a five-element quad and a five-element Yagi, both on 26-foot booms. The quad is still the leader in gain, but has a less optimal rearward pattern and a somewhat less flat SWR curve than the Yagi. One thing

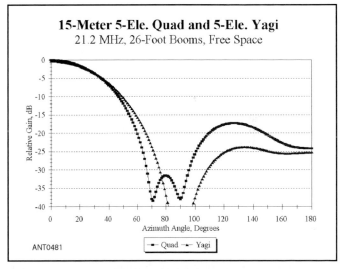

Figure 11.32 — Comparing the pattern of the 15 meter quad and Yagi shown in Figure 11.31. The quad has a slightly narrower frontal beamwidth (it has 0.5 dB more gain than the Yagi), but has higher "rear quartering" sidelobes at about 125° (with a twin sidelobe, not shown, at 235°). These sidelobes limit the worst-case front-to-rear (F/R) to about 17 dB, while the F/B (at 180°, directly at the back of the quad) is more than 24 dB for each antenna.

should be noted in Figures 11.29-11.31. The F/R pattern on the Yagi is largely determined by the response at the 180° point, directly in back of the frontal lobe. This point is usually referred to when discussing the "front-to-back ratio."

The quad on the other hand has what a sailor might term "quartering lobes" (referring to the direction toward the "quarterdeck" at the stern of a sailing vessel) in

Table 11-11

Dimensions for Optimized Monoband Quads in Figs 11.29, 11.30 and 11.31, on 26-Foot Booms

	14.2 MHz	21.2 MHz	28.4 MHz
Reflector	73' 9"	49' 6"	37' 3"
R-DE Spacing	17' 8"	7'	6' 4"
Driven Element	71' 8"	47' 6"	35' 9"
DE-D1 Spacing	8' 3"	5'	5' 6"
Director 1	68' 7"	46' 8"	34' 8"
D1-D2 Spacing	—	6' 8"	6' 9"
Director 2	—	46' 10"	35' 2"
D2-D3 Spacing	—	7' 4"	7' 5"
Director 3	—	45' 8"	34' 2"
Feed method	Direct 50 Ω	Direct 50 Ω	Direct 50 Ω

the rearward pattern. These quartering lobes are often worse than the response at 180°, directly in back of the main beam. **Figure 11.32** overlays the free-space E-Field responses of the 15 meter quad and Yagi together. At 21.2 MHz, the quad actually has a front-to-back ratio (F/B) of about 24 dB, excellent in anyone's book. The Yagi at 180° has a F/B of about 25 dB, again excellent.

However, at an azimuth angle of about 125° (and at 235° azimuth on the other side of the main lobe) the quad's "quartering lobe" is down only some 17 dB, setting the worst-case F/R at 17 dB also. As explained in the sections on Yagis, the reason F/R is more important than just the F/B is that on receive, signals can come from any direction, not just from directly behind the main beam.

Table 11-1 lists the dimensions for the three computer-optimized monoband quads shown in Figures 11.29, 11.30, and 11.31.

Cubical versus Concentric Quads

First — no quad is truly "cubical" in the sense of the distance between the elements being the same as the side of an element. That would place the elements λ/4 apart which is too widely spaced for good performance. The term "cubical quad" generally applies to multiband quads that maintain the same electrical spacing between elements on each band whereas "concentric quad" refers to a set of elements mounted on the spreaders in one plane, concentric to each other. (The two quad antennas shown in this chapter are concentric quads.)

The cubical quad with its consistent electrical spacing has a very slight performance advantage on the higher frequency bands but requires a special spreader mount at the center of the boom to hold the spreaders in the required tilted configuration as seen in the Gem Quad at **www.gemquad.com**. In fact, the boom of a true cubical quad is only inches long since the spreaders meet near the center. The cubical quad's spreaders, being both diagonal and tilted, must be a few percent longer than the planar spreaders of the concentric quad.

Quads Versus Yagis at Low Heights

Another belief held by some quad enthusiasts is that they need not be mounted very high off the ground to give excellent DX performance. Quads are somehow supposed to be greatly superior to a Yagi at the same height above ground. Unfortunately, this is mainly wishful thinking.

Figure 11.33 compares the same two 10 meter antennas as in Figure 11.30, but this time with each one mounted on a 50-foot tower over flat ground, rather than in theoretical free space. The quad does indeed have slightly more gain than a Yagi with the same boom length, as it has in free space. This is evidenced by the very slight compression of the quad's main lobe, but is more obvious when you look at the third lobe, which peaks at about 53° elevation. In effect, the quad squeezes some energy out of its second and third lobes and adds that to the first lobe. However, the difference in gain compared to the Yagi is only 0.8 dB for this particular quad design at a 9° elevation angle. And while it's true that every dB counts, you can also be certain that on the air you wouldn't be able to tell the difference between the two antennas. After all, a 10- to 20-dB variation in the level of signals is pretty common because of fading at HF.

11.8.2 MULTIBAND QUADS

On the other hand, one of the valid reasons quads have remained popular over the years is that antenna homebrewers can build multiband quads far more easily than they can construct multiband Yagis. In effect, all you have to do with a quad is add more wire to the existing support arms. It's not quite as simple as that, of course, but the idea of ready expandability

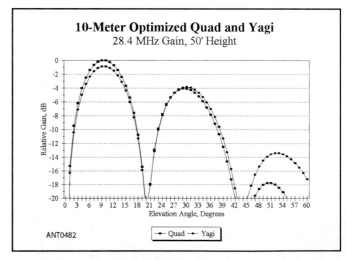

Figure 11.33 — A comparison on 10 meters between an optimized five-element quad and an optimized five-element Yagi, both mounted 50 feet high over flat ground and both employing 26-foot booms. There is no appreciable difference in the peak elevation angle for either antenna. In other words, a quad does not have an appreciable elevation-angle advantage over a Yagi mounted at the same boom height. Note that the quad achieves its slightly higher gain by taking energy from higher-angle lobes and concentrating that energy in the main elevation lobe. This is a process that is similar to what happens with stacked Yagis.

for other bands is very appealing to experimenters.

Like the Yagi, the quad does suffer from interactions between wires of different frequencies, but the degree of interaction between bands is usually less for a quad. The higher-frequency bands are the ones that often suffer most from any interaction, for both Yagis and quads. For example, the 10 and 15 meter bands are usually the ones affected most by nearby 20 meter wires in a triband quad, while the 20 meter elements are not affected by the 10 or 15 meter elements.

Modern computer modeling software can help you counteract at least some of the interaction by allowing you to do virtual "retuning" of the quad on the computer screen — rather than clinging precariously to your tower fiddling with wires. However, the programs (such as *NEC-2* or *EZNEC*) that can model three-dimensional wire antennas such as quads typically run far more slowly than those designed for monoband Yagis (such as *YW* included with this book). This makes optimizing rather tedious, but you use the same considerations for tradeoffs between gain, pattern (F/R) and SWR over the operating bandwidth as you do with monoband Yagis.

11.8.3 BUILDING A QUAD

The parasitic element shown in Figure 11.28 is tuned in much the same way as the parasitic element in a Yagi antenna. That is, the parasitic loop is tuned to a lower frequency than the driven element when the parasitic is to act as a reflector, and to a higher frequency when it is to act as a director. Figure 11.28 shows the parasitic element with an adjustable tuning stub, a convenient method of tuning since the resonant frequency can be changed simply by changing the position of the shorting bar on the stub. In practice, it has been found that the length around the loop should be approximately 3.5% greater than the self-resonant length if the element is a reflector, and about 3.0% shorter than the self-resonant length if the parasitic element is a director. Approximate formulas for the loop lengths in feet are:

$$\text{Driven Element} = \frac{1008}{f_{MHz}}$$

$$\text{Reflector} = \frac{1045}{f_{MHz}}$$

$$\text{Director} = \frac{977}{f_{MHz}}$$

These are valid for quad antennas intended for operation below 30 MHz and using uninsulated #14 AWG stranded copper wire. At VHF, where the ratio of loop circumference to conductor diameter is usually relatively small, the circumference must be increased in comparison to the wavelength. For example, a one-wavelength loop constructed of ¼-inch tubing for 144 MHz should have a circumference about 2% greater than in the above equation for the driven element.

Element spacings on the order of 0.14 to 0.2 free-space wavelengths are generally used. You would employ the smaller spacings for antennas with more than two elements, where the structural support for elements with larger spacings tends

to become challenging. The feed point impedances of antennas having element spacings on this order have been found to be in the 40- to 60-Ω range, so the driven element can be fed directly with coaxial cable with only a small mismatch.

For spacings on the order of 0.25 wavelength (physically feasible for two elements, or for several elements at 28 MHz) the impedance more closely approximates the impedance of a driven loop alone — that is, 80 to 100 Ω. The feed methods described in the **Transmission Line Coupling and Impedance Matching** chapter can be used, just as in the case of the Yagi.

Feeding the Multiband Quad

There are two approaches to feeding a multiband quad with several driven elements. If the driven elements are all on one set of spreaders the *combined feed* ties all of the elements together at a single feed point. This allows the use of a single feed line but creates a great deal of interaction between harmonically-related elements, reducing gain and F/B dramatically as described by L.B. Cebik in "Feeding the 5-Band Quad" (see Bibliography). Using separate feed lines to each driven element results in much less interaction and preserves the quad's performance.

A compromise that allows the use of a single feed line to the shack but separate feed lines for each element is to use a remote coax switch such as the Ameritron RCS-4 or RCS-8V (**www.ameritron.com**). The coax switch can be mounted on the antenna boom or mast and short feed lines run from the switch to the elements. The editor used just such a configuration for a number of years for a five-band 2-element quad with good results.

The impedance of the multiband quad driven elements varies quite a bit from the free-space value of a single loop. Cebik's article mentioned above shows that the feed point impedance varies from close to 50 Ω on 10 meters (the innermost element) to more than 100 Ω on 20 meters (the outermost element). If multiple feed lines are used, quarter-wave matching sections as described in the **Transmission Line Coupling and Impedance Matching** chapter can be used to provide an acceptable SWR.

Mechanical Construction Issues

The most obvious problem related to quad antennas is the ability to build a structurally sound system. If high winds or heavy ice are a normal part of the environment, special precautions are necessary if the antenna is to survive a winter season.

Both multiband quad arrays use fiberglass spreaders. Bamboo is a suitable substitute (if economy is of great importance). However, the additional weight of the bamboo spreaders over fiberglass is an important consideration. A typical 12-foot bamboo pole weighs about 2 pounds; the fiberglass type weighs less than a pound. By multiplying the difference times 8 for a two-element array, times 12 for a three-element antenna, and so on, it quickly becomes apparent that fiberglass is worth the investment if weight is an important factor. Properly treated, bamboo has a useful life of three or four

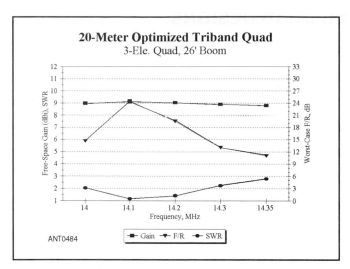

Figure 11.36 — Computed performance of the triband, five-element quad over the 20 meter band. The direct 50-Ω feed system holds the SWR below 2.8: 1 across the whole band. This could be improved with a gamma-match system tuned to 14.1 MHz if the builder really desires a low SWR. The F/R peaks at 14.1 MHz and remains above 10 dB across the whole band.

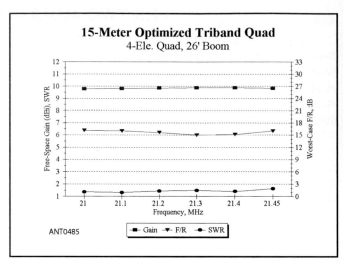

Figure 11.37 — Computed performance of the triband, five-element quad over the 15 meter band. There is some degree of interaction with the 20 meter elements, limiting the worst-case F/R to about 15 dB. The gain and SWR curves are relatively flat across the band.

of the five elements, and the higher-frequency bands dictate the spacing because they are more critical.

Each of the parasitic loops is closed (ends soldered together) and requires no tuning. **Figure 11.35** shows the physical layout of the triband quad. **Figure 11.36** plots the computed free-space gain, front-to-rear ratio and SWR response across the 20 meter band. With only a few degrees of freedom in tuning and spacing of the three elements, it is impossible to spread the response out to cover the entire 20 meter band. The compromise design results in a rearward pattern that varies from a worst-case of just under 10 dB at the high end of the band, to a peak F/R of just under 19 dB at 14.2 MHz, in the phone portion of the band. The F/R is about 11 dB at the low end of the band.

The SWR remains under 3:1 for the entire 20 meter band, rising to 2.8:1 at the high end. The feed system for this triband quad consists of three separate 50-Ω coax lines, one per driven element, together with a relay switchbox mounted to the boom so that a single coax can be used back to the operating position. Each feed line uses a ferrite-bead balun to control common-mode currents and preserve the radiation pattern and each coax going to the switchbox is cut to be an electrical three-quarter wavelength on 15 meters. This presents a short at the unused driven elements since modeling indicated that the 15 meter band is adversely affected by the presence of the 20 meter driven element if it is left open-circuited. If you use RG-213 coax, the ¾-λ electrical length of each feed line is 23 feet long at 21.2 MHz. This is sufficient physical length to reach each driven element from the switchbox.

Figure 11.37 shows the free-space response for the 15 meter band. The rearward response is roughly 15 dB across the band. This is a result of the residual interaction

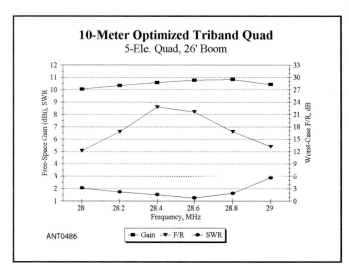

Figure 11.38 — Computed performance of the triband, five-element quad over the 10 meter band. The F/R is higher than 12 dB across the band from 28.0 to 29.0 MHz, but the SWR rises at the top end of the band beyond 2:1. The free-space gain is higher than 10 dBi across the band.

between the 20 meter elements on 15 meters, and no further tuning could improve the F/R. Note how flat the SWR curve is. This SWR characteristic is what gives the quad the reputation of being "wideband." A flat SWR curve, however, is not necessarily a good indicator of optimal performance for directional antennas like quads or Yagis, particularly multiband designs where compromises must be made by physical necessity.

Figure 11.38 shows the characteristics of the 10 meter portion of the two-element triband quad. The response favors the low-phone band, with the F/R falling to about 12 dB at the low end of the frequency range and rising to just about 23 dB at 28.4 MHz. The SWR curve is once again relatively flat across the major portion of the band up to 28.8 MHz.

Construction

A 3-foot length of steel angle stock, 1 inch per side, is used to interconnect the pairs of spreader arms. The steel is drilled at the center to accept a muffler clamp of sufficient size to clamp the assembly to the boom. The fiberglass is clamped to the steel angle stock with stainless steel hose clamps, two per pole. Each quad-loop spreader frame consists of two assemblies of the type shown in **Figure 11.39**.

Connecting the wires to the fiberglass is shown in **Figure 11.40**. The model described here has no holes in the spreader arms; the wires are attached to each arm with a few layers of plastic electrical tape and then wrapped approximately 20 times in a crisscross fashion with 1/8-inch diameter nylon string, followed by more electrical tape for UV protection, as shown in **Figure 11.41**.

The wire loops are left open at the bottom of each driven element where the feed line coaxes are attached. All of the parasitic elements are continuous loops of wire; the solder joint is at the base of the diamond.

Although you could run three separate coax cables down to the shack, we suggest that you install a relay box at the

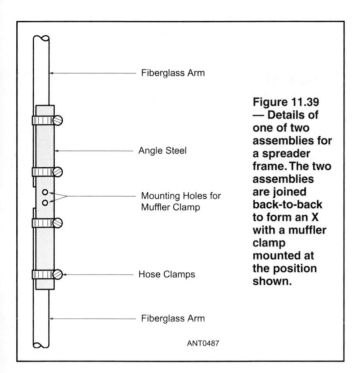

Figure 11.39 — Details of one of two assemblies for a spreader frame. The two assemblies are joined back-to-back to form an X with a muffler clamp mounted at the position shown.

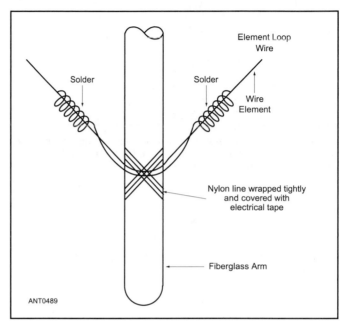

Figure 11.41 — An alternative method of assembling the wire of a quad loop to the spreader arm.

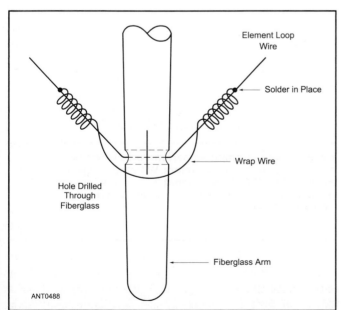

Figure 11.40 — A method of assembling a corner of the wire loop of a quad element to the spreader arm.

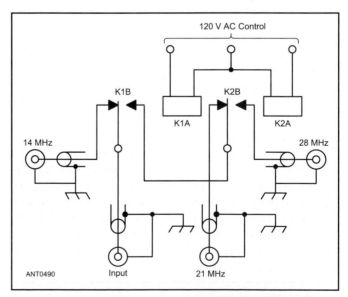

Figure 11.42 — Suitable circuit for relay switching of bands for the three-band quad. A three-wire control cable is required. K1, K2 — any type of relay suitable for RF switching, coaxial type not required (Potter and Brumfield MR11A acceptable; although this type has double-pole contacts, mechanical arrangements of most single-pole relays make them unacceptable for switching of RF).

Figure 11.43 — The relay box is mounted on the boom near the center. Each of the spreader-arm fiberglass poles is attached to steel angle stock with hose clamps.

center of the boom. A three-wire control system may be used to apply power to the proper relay for changing bands. The circuit diagram of a typical configuration is presented in **Figure 11.42** and its installation is shown in **Figure 11.43**.

11.9.2 A TWO-ELEMENT, 8-FOOT BOOM PENTABAND QUAD

This two-element pentaband (20/17/15/12/10 meter) quad uses the same construction techniques as its big brother above. Since only two elements are used, the boom can be less robust for this antenna, at 2 inches diameter rather than 3 inches. Those who like really rugged antennas can still use the 3-inch diameter boom, of course.

This quad is very similar to those sold commercially by vendors such as Cubex who also sell hard-to-find parts for quads such as spreaders and the spiders that mount the spreaders to the boom. Readers may also want to review the article on improving the 2-element quad by Mees (see Bibliography).

Table 11-13 lists the element dimensions for the pentaband quad. The following plots show the performance for each of the five bands covered. The feed system for the pentaband quad uses five, direct 50-Ω coaxes, one to each driven element. These five coaxes are cut to be ¾-λ electrically on 10 meters (17 feet, 2 inches for RG-213 at 28.4 MHz). In this design the 10 meter band is the one most affected by the presence of the other driven elements if they are left

un-shorted. The ¾-λ lines open-circuited at the switchbox are long enough physically to reach all elements from a centrally mounted switchbox. This length assumes that the switchbox open-circuits the unused coaxes. If the switchbox short-circuits unused coaxes (as several commercial switchboxes do), then use ½-λ long lines to feed all five driven elements (11 feet, 5 inches for RG-213 at 28.4 MHz).

The SWR curves do not necessarily go down to 1:1 because of this simple, direct feed system. If anyone is bothered by this, of course they can always implement individual matching systems, such as gamma matches. Most amateurs would agree that such a degree of complexity is not warranted. The worst-case SWR is less than 2.3:1 on each band, even with direct feed on 20 meters. With typical lengths of coaxial feed line from the shack to the switchbox at the antenna, say 100 feet of RG-213, the SWR at the transmitter would be less than 2.0:1 on all bands due to losses in the feed line.

Figure 11.44 shows the computed responses for the pentaband quad over the 20 meter band. With only two degrees of freedom (spacing and element tuning) there is not much that can be done to spread the response out over the entire 20 meter band. Nonetheless, the performance over the band is still pretty reasonable for an antenna this small. The F/R pattern peaks at 19 dB at 14.1 MHz and falls to about 10 dB at either end of the band. The free-space gain varies from about 7.5 dBi to just above 6 dBi, comparable to a short-boom

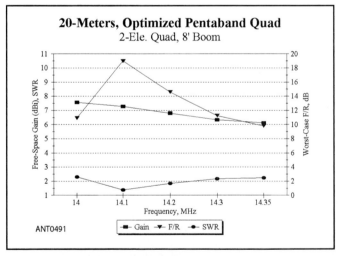

Figure 11.44 — Computed performance of the pentaband two-element quad on 20 meters. With the simple direct-feed system, the SWR rises to about 2.3:1 at the low end of the band. A gamma match can bring the SWR down to 1:1 at 14.1 MHz, if desired.

Table 11-13
Five-Band Two-Element Quad on 8-Foot Boom

	14.2 MHz	18.1 MHz	21 MHz	24.9 MHz	28.4 MHz
Reflector	72' 4"	56' 4"	48' 6"	40' 11¼"	37' 5½"
R-DE Spacing	8'	8'	8'	8'	8'
Driven Element	69' 10½"	54' 10½"	46' 7"	39' 10½"	34' 6"

three-element Yagi. The SWR curve remains below 2.3:1 across the band. If you were to employ a gamma match tuned at 14.1 MHz, you could limit the peak SWR to less than 2.0:1, and this would still occur at 14.0 MHz.

On 17 meters, **Figure 11.45** shows that the other elements are affecting 18 MHz, even with element-length optimization. Careful examination of the current induced on the other elements shows that the 20 meter driven element is interacting on 18 MHz, deteriorating the pattern and gain slightly. Even still, the performance on 17 meters is reasonable, especially for a five-band quad on an 8-foot boom.

On 15 meters, the interactions seems to have been contained, as **Figure 11.46** demonstrates. The F/R peaks at 21.1 MHz, at 19 dB and remains better than 12 dB past the top of the band. The SWR curve is low across the whole band.

On 12 meters, the interaction between bands is minor, leading to the good results shown in **Figure 11.47**. The SWR change across this band is quite flat, which isn't surprising given the narrow bandwidth of the 12 meter band.

On 10 meters, the interaction seems to have been tamed well by computer-tuning of the elements. The F/R remains higher than about 14 dB from 28 to 29 MHz. The SWR remains below 2.2:1 up to about 28.8 MHz, while the gain is relatively flat across the band at more than 7.2 dBi in free space. See **Figure 11.48**.

Overall, this pentaband quad is physically compact and yet it provides good performance across all five bands. It is competitive with commercial Log Periodic Dipole Array (LPDA) designs and triband Yagi designs that employ longer booms.

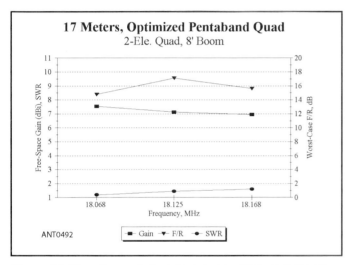

ANT0492

Figure 11.45 — Computed performance of the pentaband two-element quad on 17 meters. There is some interaction with the other elements, but overall the performance is satisfactory on this band.

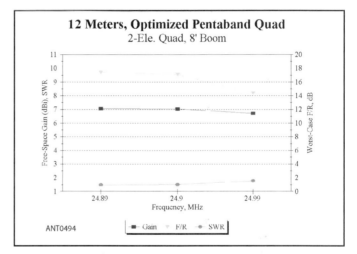

ANT0494

Figure 11.47 — Computed performance of the pentaband two-element quad on 12 meters.

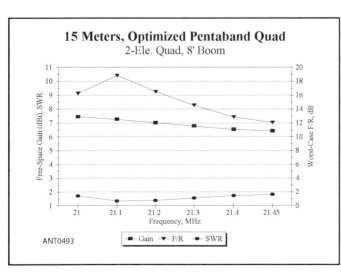

ANT0493

Figure 11.46 — Computed performance of the pentaband two-element quad on 15 meters. The performance is acceptable across the whole band.

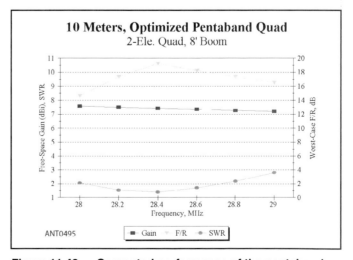

ANT0495

Figure 11.48 — Computed performance of the pentaband two-element quad on 10 meters. The SWR curve is slightly above the target 2:1 at the low end of the band and rises to about 2.2:1 at 28.8 MHz. This unlikely to be a problem, even with rigs with automatic power-reduction due to SWR, since the SWR at the input of a typical coax feed line will be lower than that at the antenna due to losses in the line.

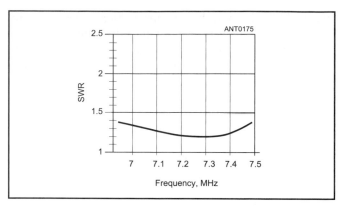

Figure 12.11 — Measured SWR curve across the 40 meter band for the N6LF Double Extended Zepp.

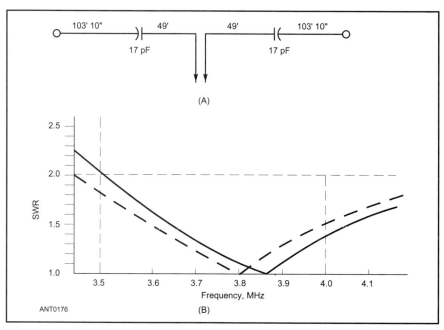

Figure 12.12 — 75/80 meter modified Double Extended Zepp, designed using *NEC Wires*. At A, a schematic is shown for the antenna. At B, an SWR curve is shown across the 75/80 meter band. The solid line shows the measured curve for the W7ISV antenna, which was pruned to place the SWR minimum higher in the band. The dashed curve shows the computed response when the SWR minimum is set to 3.8 MHz.

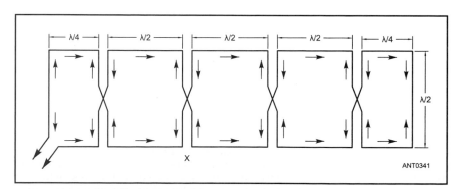

Figure 12.13 — Typical Sterba array, an 8-element version.

A silicone sealant was used and then both ends covered with coax seal, finally wrapping it with plastic tape. The solder balls indicated on the drawing are to prevent wicking of moisture through the braid and the stranded center conductor. This is a small but important point if long service out in the weather is expected. An even better way to protect the capacitor would be to enclose it in a short piece of PVC pipe with end caps, as shown in Figure 12.10B.

Note that all RG-8 type cables do not have exactly the same capacitance per foot and there will also be some end effect adding to the capacitance. If possible the capacitor should be trimmed with a capacitance meter. It isn't necessary to be too exact — the effect of varying the capacitance ±10% was checked and the antenna still worked fine.

The results proved to be close to those predicted by the computer model. **Figure 12.11** shows the measured value for SWR across the band. These measurements were made with a Bird directional wattmeter. The worst SWR is 1.35:1 at the low end of the band.

Dick Ives, W7ISV, erected an 80 meter version of the antenna, shown in **Figure 12.12A**. The series capacitors are 17 pF. Since he isn't interested in CW, Dick adjusted the length for the lowest SWR at the high end of the band, as shown in the SWR curve (Figure 12.12B). The antenna could have been tuned somewhat lower in frequency and would then provide an SWR less than 2:1 over the entire band, as indicated by the dashed line.

This antenna provides wide bandwidth and moderate gain over the entire 75/80 meter band. Not many antennas will give you that with a simple wire structure.

12.1.6 THE STERBA CURTAIN

Two collinear arrays can be combined to form the Sterba array, often called the Sterba curtain. An 8-element example of a Sterba array is shown in **Figure 12.13**. The four λ/4 elements joined on the ends are equivalent to two λ/2 elements. The two collinear arrays are spaced λ/2 and the λ/4 phasing lines connected together to provide λ/2 phasing lines. This arrangement has the advantage of increasing the gain for a given length and also increasing the E-plane directivity, which is no longer circular. An additional advantage of this array is that the wire forms a closed loop. For installations where icing is a problem a low voltage dc or low frequency (50 or 60 Hz) ac current can be passed through the wire to heat it for deicing. The heating current is isolated from RF by decoupling chokes. This is standard practice in commercial installations.

The number of sections in a Sterba array can be extended as far as desired but more than four or five are rarely used because of the slow increase in gain with extra elements, the narrow H-plane directivity and the appearance of multiple sidelobes. When fed at the point indicated the impedance is about 600 Ω. The antenna can also be fed at the point marked X. The impedance at this point will be about 1 kΩ. The gain of the 8-element array in Figure 12.13 will be between 7 to 8 dB over a single element. A 10 meter Sterba curtain is described in the article, "Curtains for You," by Jim Cain, K1TN, that is included on this book's CD-ROM.

12.2 PARALLEL BROADSIDE ARRAYS

To obtain broadside directivity with parallel elements the currents in the elements must all be in-phase. At a distant point lying on a line perpendicular to the axis of the array and also perpendicular to the plane containing the elements, the fields from all elements add up in phase. The situation is similar to four parallel λ/2 dipoles fed together as a broadside array.

Broadside arrays of this type theoretically can have any number of elements. However, practical limitations of construction and available space usually limit the number of broadside parallel elements. These practical aspects of building a dipole curtain are illustrated in the article "A Dipole Curtain for 15 and 10 Meters" by Mike Loukides, W1JQ, in the Aug 2003 QST article on this book's CD-ROM.

12.2.1 POWER GAIN

The power gain of a parallel-element broadside array depends on the spacing between elements as well as on the number of elements. The way in which the gain of a two-element array varies with spacing is shown in **Figure 12.14**. The greatest gain is obtained when the spacing is in the vicinity of 0.67 λ.

The theoretical gains of broadside arrays having more than two elements are approximately as follows:

No. of Parallel Elements	dB Gain with λ/2 Spacing	dB Gain with 3λ/4 Spacing
3	5.7	7.2
4	7.1	8.5
5	8.1	9.4
6	8.9	10.4

The elements must, of course, all lie in the same plane and all must be fed in-phase.

12.2.2 DIRECTIVITY

The sharpness of the directive pattern depends on spacing between elements and number of elements. Larger element spacing will sharpen the main lobe, for a given number of elements, up to a point as was shown in Figure 12.1. The two-element array has no minor lobes when the spacing is λ/2, but small minor lobes appear at greater spacings. When three or more elements are used the pattern always has minor lobes.

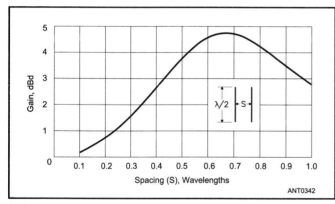

Figure 12.14 — Gain as a function of the spacing between two parallel elements operated in-phase (broadside).

12.3 OTHER FORMS OF BROADSIDE ARRAYS

For those who have the available room, multielement arrays based on the broadside concept have something to offer. The antennas are large but of simple design and non-critical dimensions; they are also very economical in terms of gain per unit of cost.

Large arrays can often be fed at several different points. However, the pattern symmetry may be sensitive to the choice of feed point within the array. Nonsymmetrical feed points will result in small asymmetries in the pattern but these are not usually of great concern.

Arrays of three and four elements are shown in **Figure 12.15**. In the 3-element array with λ/2 spacing at A, the array is fed at the center. This is the most desirable point in that it tends to keep the power distribution among the elements uniform. However, the transmission line could alternatively be connected at either point B or C of Fig-

ure 12.15A, with only slight skewing of the radiation pattern.

When the spacing is greater than λ/2, the phasing lines must be 1 λ long and are not transposed between elements. This is shown Figure 12.15B. With this arrangement, any element spacing up to 1 λ can be used, if the phasing lines can be folded as suggested in the drawing.

The 2-element array at C is fed at the center of the system to make the power distribution among elements as uniform as possible. However, the transmission line could be connected at either point B, C, D or E. In this case the section of phasing line between B and D must be transposed to make the currents flow in the same direction in all elements. The 4-element array at C and the 3-element array at B have approximately the same gain when the element spacing in the array at B is 3λ/4.

An alternative feeding method is shown in Figure 12.15D. This system can also be applied to the 3-element arrays, and will result in better symmetry in any case. It is necessary only to move the phasing line to the center of each element, making connection to both sides of the line instead of one only.

The free-space pattern for a 4-element array with λ/2 spacing is shown in **Figure 12.16**. This is also approximately the pattern for a 3-element array with 3λ/4 spacing.

Larger arrays can be designed and constructed by following the phasing principles shown in the drawings. No accurate figures are available for the impedances at the various feed points indicated in Figure 12.15. You can estimate it to be in the vicinity of 1 kΩ when the feed point is at a junction between the phasing line and a λ/2 element, becoming

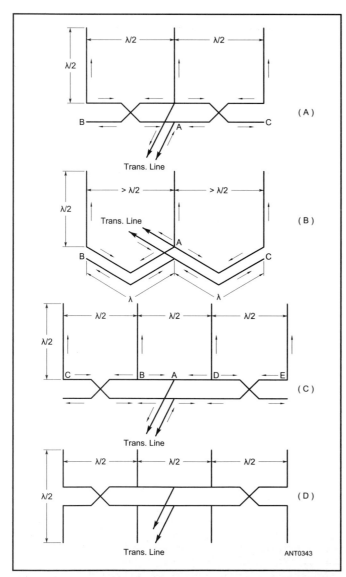

Figure 12.15 — Methods of feeding 3- and 4-element broadside arrays with parallel elements.

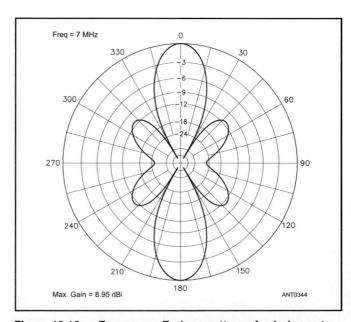

Figure 12.16 — Free-space E-plane pattern of a 4-element broadside array using parallel elements (Figure 12.15). This corresponds to the horizontal directive pattern at low wave angles for a vertically polarized array over ground. The axis of the elements lies along the 90°-270° line.

smaller as the number of elements in the array is increased. When the feed point is midway between end-fed elements as in Figure 12.15C, the feed point impedance of a 4-element array is in the vicinity of 200 to 300 Ω, with 600-Ω open-wire phasing lines. The impedance at the feed point with the antenna shown at D should be about 1.5 kΩ.

12.3.1 NON-UNIFORM ELEMENT CURRENTS

The pattern for a 4-element broadside array shown in Figure 12.16 has substantial sidelobes. This is typical for arrays more than λ/2 wide when equal currents flow in each element. Sidelobe amplitude can be reduced by using non-uniform current distribution among the elements. Many possible current amplitude distributions have been suggested. All of them have reduced current in the outer elements and greater current in the inner elements. This reduces the gain somewhat but can produce a more desirable pattern. One of the common current distributions is called binomial current grading. In this scheme the ratio of element currents is set equal to the coefficients of a polynomial. For example:

$$1 x + 1, \Rightarrow 1, 1$$
$$(x+1)^2 = 1x^2 + 2x + 1, \Rightarrow 1, 2, 1$$
$$(x+1)^3 = 1x^3 + 3x^2 + 3x + 1, \Rightarrow 1, 3, 3, 1$$
$$(x+1)^4 = 1x^4 + 4x^3 + 6x^2 + 6x + 1, \Rightarrow 1, 4, 6, 4, 1$$

In a 2-element array the currents are equal, in a 3-element array the current in the center element is twice that in the outer elements, and so on.

12.3.2 HALF-SQUARE ANTENNA

On the low-frequency bands (40, 80 and 160 meters) it becomes increasingly difficult to use λ/2 elements because of their size. The half-square antenna is a 2-element broadside array with λ/4-high vertical elements and λ/2 horizontal spacing. See **Figure 12.17**. The free-space H-plane pattern for this array is shown in **Figure 12.18**. The antenna gives modest (4.2 dBi) but useful gain and has the advantage of only λ/4 height. Like all vertically polarized antennas, real-world performance depends directly on the characteristics of the ground surrounding it.

The half-square can be fed either at the point indicated or at the bottom end of one of the vertical elements using a voltage-feed scheme, such as for the Bobtail curtain described below. The feed point impedance is in the region of 50 Ω when fed at a corner as shown in Figure 12.17. The SWR bandwidth is typically quite narrow as shown in the following design examples.

Variations on the Half-Square Antenna

The following section was originally presented in *The ARRL Antenna Compendium Vol 5*, by Rudy Severns, N6LF.

A simple modification to a standard dipole is to add two λ/4 vertical wires, one at each end, as shown in **Figure 12.19**. This makes a *half-square antenna*. The antenna can be fed at one corner (low-impedance, current fed) or at the lower end

of one of the vertical wires (high-impedance, voltage fed). Other feed arrangements are also possible.

The "classical" dimensions for this antenna are λ/2 (131 feet at 3.75 MHz) for the top wire and λ/4 (65.5 feet) for the vertical wires. However, there is nothing sacred

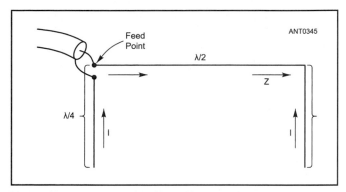

Figure 12.17 — Layout for the half-square antenna.

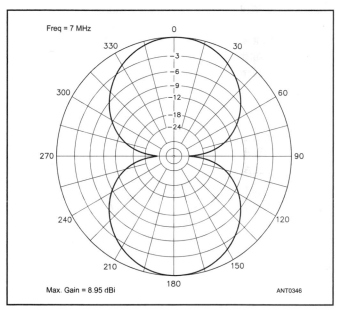

Figure 12.18 — Free-space E-plane directive pattern for the half-square antenna.

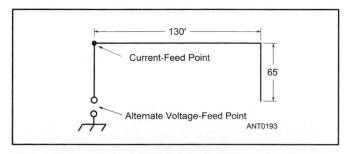

Figure 12.19 — Typical 80 meter half-square, with λ/4-high vertical legs and a λ/2-long horizontal leg. The antenna may be fed at the bottom or at a corner. When fed at a corner, the feed point is a low-impedance, current-feed. When fed at the bottom of one of the wires against a small ground counterpoise, the feed point is a high-impedance, voltage-feed.

about these dimensions! They can vary over a wide range and still obtain nearly the same performance.

This antenna is two λ/4 verticals, spaced λ/2, fed in-phase by the top wire. The current maximums are at the top corners. The theoretical gain over a single vertical is 3.8 dB. An important advantage of this antenna is that it does not require the extensive ground system and feed arrangements that a conventional pair of phased λ/4 verticals would.

Comparison to a Dipole

In the past, one of the things that has turned off potential users of the half-square on 80 and 160 meters is the perceived need for λ/4 vertical sections. This forces the height to be >65 feet on 80 meters and >130 feet on 160 meters. That's not really a problem. If you don't have the height there are several things you can do. For example, just fold the ends in, as shown in **Figure 12.20**. This compromises the performance surprisingly little.

It is helpful to compare the examples given in Figures 12.19 and 12.20 to dipoles at the same height. Two heights, 40 and 80 feet, and average, very good and sea water grounds, were used for this comparison. It is also assumed

that the lower end of the vertical wires had to be a minimum of 5 feet above ground.

At 40 feet the half-square is really mangled, with only 35-foot long (≈ λ/8) vertical sections. The elevation-plane comparison between this antenna and a dipole of the same height is shown in **Figure 12.21**. Over average ground the half-square is superior below 32° and at 15° is almost 5 dB better. That is a worthwhile improvement. If you have very good soil conductivity, like parts of the lower Midwest and South, then the half-square will be superior below 38° and at 15° will be nearly 8 dB better. For those fortunate few with saltwater frontal property the advantage at 15° is 11 dB! Notice also that above 35°, the response drops off rapidly. This is great for DX but is not good for local work.

Figure 12.22 shows the azimuthal-plane pattern for the 80 meter half-square antenna in Figure 12.20, but this time compared with the response of a flattop horizontal dipole that is 100 feet high. These comparisons are for average ground and are for an elevation angle of 5°. The message here is that the lower your dipole and the better your ground, the more you have to gain by switching from a dipole to a half-square. The half-square antenna looks like a good bet for DXing.

Changing the Shape of the Half Square

Just how flexible is the shape? There are several common distortions of practical importance. Some have very little effect but a few are fatal to the gain. Suppose you have either more height and less width than called for in the standard version or more width and less height, as shown in **Figure 12.23A**.

The effect on gain from this type of dimensional variation is given in **Table 12-1**. For a top length (L_T) varying between 110 and 150 feet, where the vertical wire lengths

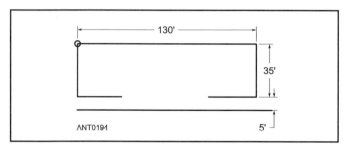

Figure 12.20 — An 80 meter half-square configured for 40-foot high supports. The ends have been bent inward to reresonate the antenna. The performance is compromised surprisingly little.

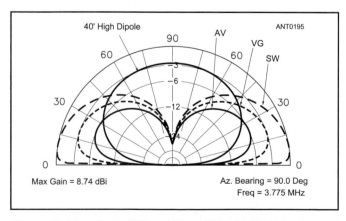

Figure 12.21 — Comparison of 80 meter elevation response of 40-foot high, horizontally polarized dipole over average ground and a 40-foot high, vertically polarized half-square, over three types of ground: average (conductivity σ = 5 mS/m, dielectric constant ε = 13), very good (σ = 30 mS/m, ε = 20) and salt water (σ = 5000 mS/m, ε = 80). The quality of the ground clearly has a profound effect on the low-angle performance of the half-square. Even over average ground, the half-square outperforms the low dipole below about 32°.

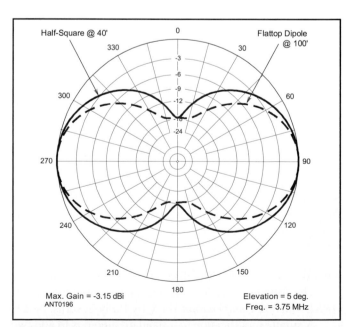

Figure 12.22 — 80 meter azimuth patterns for shortened half-square antenna (solid line) compared with flattop dipole (dashed line) at 100 feet height. Average ground is assumed for these cases.

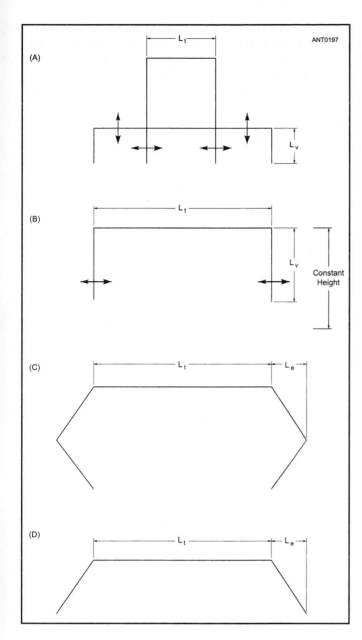

Figure 12.23 — Varying the horizontal and vertical lengths of a half-square. At A, both the horizontal and vertical legs are varied, while keeping the antenna resonant. At B, the height of the horizontal wire is kept constant, while its length and that of the vertical legs is varied to keep the antenna resonant. At C, the length of the horizontal wire is varied and the legs are bent inwards in the shape of "vees." At D, the ends are sloped outward and the length of the flattop portion is varied. All these symmetrical forms of distortion of the basic half-square shape result in small performance losses.

Table 12-1
Variation in Gain with Change in Horizontal Length, with Vertical Height Readjusted for Resonance (see Figure 12.23A)

L_T (feet)	L_V (feet)	Gain (dBi)
100	85.4	2.65
110	79.5	3.15
120	73.7	3.55
130	67.8	3.75
140	61.8	3.65
150	56	3.05
155	53	2.65

Table 12-2
Variation in Gain with Change in Horizontal Length, with Vertical Length Readjusted for Resonance, but Horizontal Wire Kept at Constant Height (see Figure 12.23B)

L_T (feet)	L_V (feet)	Gain (dBi)
110	78.7	3.15
120	73.9	3.55
130	68	3.75
140	63	3.35
145	60.7	3.05

Table 12-3
Gain for Half-Square Antenna, Where Ends Are Bent Into V-Shape (see Figure 12.23C)

Height ⇒ L_T (feet)	H=40 feet L_V (feet)	H=40 feet Gain (dBi)	H=60 feet L_e (feet)	H=60 feet Gain (dBi)
40	57.6	3.25	52.0	2.75
60	51.4	3.75	45.4	3.35
80	45.2	3.95	76.4	3.65
100	38.6	3.75	61.4	3.85
120	31.7	3.05	44.4	3.65
140	—	—	23	3.05

(L_V) readjusted to resonate the antenna, the gain changes only by 0.6 dB. For a 1-dB change the range of L_T is 100 to 155 feet, a pretty wide range.

Another variation results if we vary the length of the horizontal top wire and readjust the vertical wires for resonance, while keeping the top at a constant height. See Figure 12.23B. **Table 12-2** shows the effect of this variation on the peak gain. For a range of L_T = 110 to 145 feet, the gain changes only 0.65 dB.

The effect of bending the ends into a V shape, as shown in Figure 12.23C, is given in **Table 12-3**. The bottom of the antenna is kept at a height of 5 feet and the top height (H) is either 40 or 60 feet. Even this gross deformation has only a relatively small effect on the gain. Sloping the ends outward as shown in Figure 12.23D and varying the top length also has only a small effect on the gain. While this is good news because it allows you dimension the antenna to fit different QTHs, not all distortions are so benign.

Suppose the two ends are not of the same height, as illustrated in **Figure 12.24**, where one end of the half-square is 20 feet higher than the other. The elevation-plane radiation pattern for this antenna is shown in **Figure 12.25** compared to a dipole at 50 feet. This type of distortion does affect the pattern. The gain drops somewhat and the zenith null goes away. The nulls off the end of the antenna also go away, so that there is some end-fire radiation. In this example the difference in height is fairly extreme at 20 feet. Small differences of 1 to 5 feet do not affect the pattern seriously.

If the top height is the same at both ends but the length

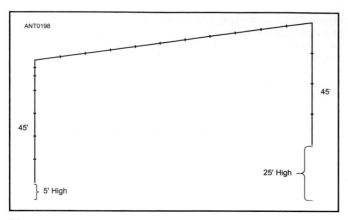

Figure 12.24 — An asymmetrical distortion of the half-square antenna, where the bottom of one leg is purposely made 20 feet higher than the other. This type of distortion does affect the pattern!

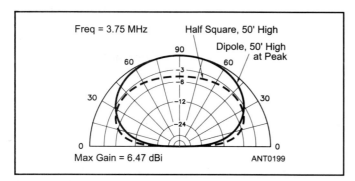

Figure 12.25 — Elevation pattern for the asymmetrical half-square compared with pattern for a 50-foot high dipole. This is over average ground, with a conductivity of 5 mS/m and a dielectric constant of 13. Note that the zenith-angle null has filled in and the peak gain is lower compared to conventional half-square over the same kind of ground.

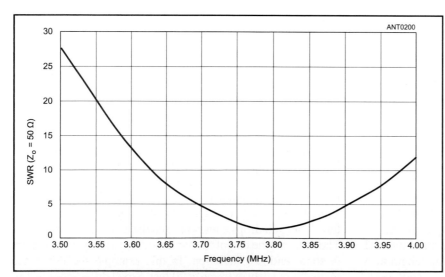

Figure 12.26 — Variation of SWR with frequency for current-fed half-square antenna. The SWR band- width is quite narrow.

of the vertical wires is not the same, then a similar pattern distortion can occur. The antenna is very tolerant of symmetrical distortions but it is much less accepting of asymmetrical distortion.

What if the length of the wires is such that the antenna is not resonant? Depending on the feed arrangement, that may or may not matter. We will look at that issue later on, in the section on patterns versus frequency. The half-square antenna, like the dipole, is very flexible in its proportions.

Half-Square Feed Point Impedance

There are many different ways to feed the half-square. Traditionally the antenna has been fed either at the end of one of the vertical sections, against ground, or at one of the upper corners as shown in Figure 12.19.

For voltage feed at the bottom against ground, the impedance is very high, on the order of several thousand ohms. For current feed at a corner, the impedance is much lower and is usually close to 50 Ω. This is very convenient for direct feed with coax.

The half-square is a relatively high-Q antenna (Q ≈ 17). **Figure 12.26** shows the SWR variation with frequency for this feed arrangement. An 80 meter dipole is not particularly wideband either, but a dipole will have less extreme variation in SWR than the half-square.

Patterns Versus Frequency

Impedance is not the only issue when defining the bandwidth of an antenna. The effect on the radiation pattern of changing frequency is also a concern. For a voltage-fed half-square, the current distribution changes with frequency. For an antenna resonant near 3.75 MHz, the current distribution is nearly symmetrical. However, above and below resonance the current distribution increasingly becomes asymmetrical. In effect, the open end of the antenna is constrained to be a voltage maximum but the feed point can behave less as a voltage point and more like a current maximum. This allows the current distribution to become asymmetrical.

The effect is to reduce the gain by −0.4 dB at 3.5 MHz and by −0.6 dB at 4 MHz. The depth of the zenith null is reduced from −20 dB to −10 dB. The side nulls are also reduced. Note that this is exactly what happened when the antenna was made physically asymmetrical. Whether the asymmetry is due to current distribution or mechanical arrangements, the antenna pattern will suffer.

When current feed at a corner is used, the asymmetry introduced by off-resonance operation is much less, since both ends of the antenna are open circuits and constrained to be voltage maximums. The resulting gain reduction is only −0.1 dB. It is interesting that the sensitivity of the pattern to changing frequency depends on the feed scheme used.

Of more concern for corner feed is the effect of the transmission line. The usual instruction is to simply feed the antenna using coax, with the shield connected to vertical wire and the center conductor to the top wire. Since the shield of the coax is a conductor, more or less parallel with the radiator, and is in the immediate field of the antenna, you might expect the pattern to be seriously distorted by this practice. This arrangement seems to have very little effect on the pattern. The greatest effect is when the feed line length was near a multiple of $\lambda/2$. Such lengths should be avoided.

Of course, you may use a choke balun at the feed point if you desire. This might reduce the coupling to the feed line even further but it doesn't appear to be worth the trouble. In fact, if you use an antenna tuner in the shack to operate away from resonance with a very high SWR on the transmission line, a balun at the feed point would take a beating.

Voltage-Feed at One End of Antenna: Matching Schemes

Several straightforward means are available for narrowband matching. However, broadband matching over the full 80 meter band is much more challenging. Voltage feed with a parallel-resonant circuit and a modest local ground, as shown in **Figure 12.27**, is the traditional matching scheme for this antenna. Matching is achieved by resonating the circuit at the desired frequency and tapping down on the inductor in Figure 12.27A or using a capacitive divider (Figure 12.27B). It is also possible to use a $\lambda/4$ transmission-line matching scheme, as shown in Figure 12.27C.

If the matching network shown in Figure 12.27B is used,

typical values for the components would be: L = 15 µH, C1 = 125 pF and C2 = 855 pF. At any single point the SWR can be made very close to 1:1 but the bandwidth for SWR < 2:1 will be very narrow at <100 kHz. Altering the L-C ratio doesn't make very much difference. The half-square antenna has a well-earned reputation for being narrowband.

12.3.3 BOBTAIL CURTAIN

The antenna system in **Figure 12.28**, called a Bobtail curtain, was originally described by Woodrow Smith, W6BCX, in 1948 (see Bibliography for this and other articles on the Bobtail.) It uses the principles of co-phased verticals to produce a broadside, bidirectional pattern providing approximately 5.1 dB of gain over a single $\lambda/4$ element. The antenna performs as three in-phase, top-fed vertical radiators approximately $\lambda/4$ in height and spaced approximately $\lambda/2$. It is most effective for low-angle signals and makes an excellent long-distance antenna for 1.8, 3.5 or 7 MHz.

The three vertical sections are the actual radiating components, but only the center element is fed directly. The two horizontal parts, A, act as phasing lines and contribute very little to the radiation pattern. Because the current in the center element must be divided between the end sections, the current distribution approaches a binomial 1:2:1 ratio. The radiation pattern is shown in **Figure 12.29**.

The vertical elements should be as vertical as possible. The height for the horizontal portion should be slightly greater than B, as shown in Figure 12.28. The tuning network is resonant at the operating frequency. The L/C ratio should be fairly low to provide good loading characteristics. As a starting point, a maximum capacitor value of 75 to 150 pF is recommended, and the inductor value is determined by C and the operating frequency. The network is first tuned to resonance and then the tap point is adjusted for the best match.

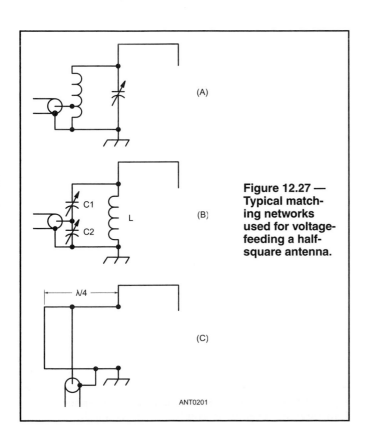

Figure 12.27 — Typical matching networks used for voltage-feeding a half-square antenna.

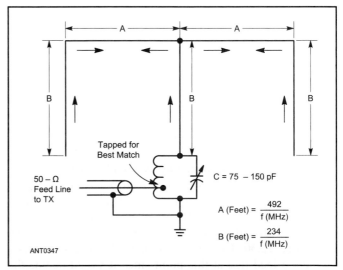

$$A \text{ (Feet)} = \frac{492}{f \text{ (MHz)}}$$

$$B \text{ (Feet)} = \frac{234}{f \text{ (MHz)}}$$

Figure 12.28 — The Bobtail curtain is an excellent low-angle radiator having broadside bidirectional characteristics. Current distribution is represented by the arrows. Dimensions A and B (in feet, for wire antennas) can be determined from the equations.

Table 12-4
Bruce Array Length, Impedance and Gain as a Function of Number of Elements

Number Elements	Gain Over λ/2 Vertical Dipole	Gain over λ/4 Ground-Plane	Array Length Wavelengths	Approx. Feed Z, Ω
2	1.2 dB	1.9 dB	¼	130
3	2.8 dB	3.6 dB	½	200
4	4.3 dB	5.1 dB	¾	250
5	5.3 dB	6.1 dB	1	300

Figure 12.32 call for section lengths = 1.05 λ/4. The need to use slightly longer elements to achieve resonance is common in large wire arrays. A quad loop behaves in the same manner. This is quite different from wire dipoles, which are typically shortened by 2-5% to achieve resonance.

Figure 12.33 shows the variations in gain and pattern for 2 to 5-element 80 meter Bruce arrays. **Table 12-4** lists the gain over a vertical λ/2 dipole, a 4-radial ground-plane vertical and the size of the array. The gain and impedance parameters listed are for free space. Over real ground the patterns and gain will depend on the height above ground and the ground characteristics. Copper loss using #12 AWG conductors is included.

Worthwhile gain can be obtained from these arrays, especially on 80 and 160 meters, where any gain is hard to come by. The feed point impedance is for the center of a vertical section. From the patterns in Figure 12.33 you can see that sidelobes start to appear as the length of the array is increased beyond 3λ/4. This is typical for arrays using equal

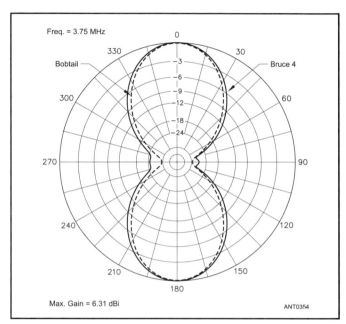

Figure 12.34 — Comparison of free space patterns of a 4-element Bruce array (solid line) and a 3-element Bobtail curtain (dashed line).

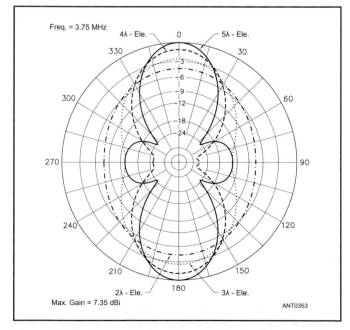

Figure 12.33 — 80 meter free-space E-plane directive patterns for the Bruce arrays shown in Figure 12.32. The 5-element's pattern is a solid line; the 4-element is a dashed line; the 3-element is a dotted line, and the 2-element version is a dashed-dotted line.

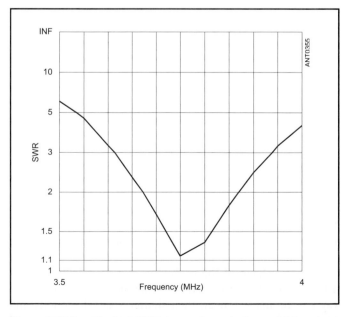

Figure 12.35 — Typical SWR curve for a 4-element 80 meter Bruce array.

currents in the elements.

It is interesting to compare the Bobtail curtain (Figure 12.28) with a 4-element Bruce array. **Figure 12.34** compares the radiation patterns for these two antennas. Even though the Bruce is shorter (3λ/4) than the Bobtail (1 λ), it has slightly more gain. The matching bandwidth is illustrated by the SWR curve in **Figure 12.35**. The 4-element Bruce has over twice the match bandwidth (200 kHz) than does the Bobtail (75 kHz in Figure 12.30). Part of the gain difference is due to the binomial current distribution — the center element has twice the current as the outer elements in the Bobtail. This reduces the gain slightly so that the 4-element Bruce becomes competitive. This is a good example of using more than the minimum number of elements to improve performance or to reduce size. On 160 meters the 4-element Bruce will be 140 feet shorter than the Bobtail, a significant reduction. If additional space is available for the Bobtail (1 λ) then a 5-element Bruce could be used, with a small increase in gain but also introducing some sidelobes.

The 2-element Bruce and the half-square antennas are both 2-element arrays. However, since the spacing between radiators is greater in the half-square (λ/2) the gain of the half-square is about 1 dB greater. If space is available, the half-square would be a better choice. If there is not room for a half-square then the Bruce, which is only half as long (λ/4), may be a good alternative. The 3-element Bruce, which has the same length (λ/2) as the half-square, has about 0.6 dB

more gain than the half-square and will have a wider match bandwidth.

The Bruce antenna can be fed at many different points and in different ways. In addition to the feed points indicated in Figure 12.32, you may connect the feed line at the center of any of the vertical sections. In longer Bruce arrays, feeding at one end will result in some current imbalance among the elements but the resulting pattern distortion is small. Actually, the feed point can be anywhere along a vertical section. One very convenient point is at an outside corner. The feed point impedance will be higher (about 600 Ω). A good match for 450-Ω ladder-line can usually be found somewhere on the vertical section. It is important to recognize that feeding the antenna at a voltage node (dots in Figure 12.32) by breaking the wire and inserting an insulator, completely changes the current distribution. This will be discussed in the section on end-fire arrays.

A Bruce can be fed unbalanced against ground or against a counterpoise as shown in **Figure 12.36**. Because it is a vertically polarized antenna, the better the ground system, the better the performance. As few as two elevated radials can be used as shown in Figure 12.36B, but more radials can also be used to improve the performance, depending on local ground constants. The original development of the Bruce array in the late 1920s used this feed arrangement.

12.3.5 FOUR-ELEMENT BROADSIDE ARRAY

The 4-element array shown in **Figure 12.37** is commonly known as the Lazy H. It consists of a set of two collinear elements and a set of two parallel elements, all operated in-phase to give broadside directivity. The gain and directivity will depend on the spacing, as in the case of a simple parallel-element broadside array. The spacing may be chosen between the limits shown on the drawing, but spacings below 3λ/8 are

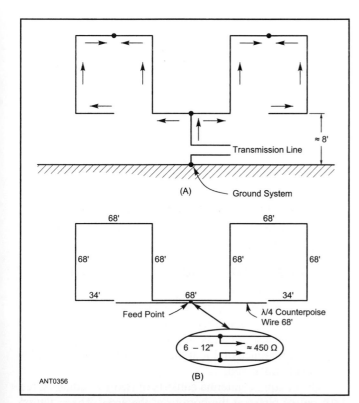

Figure 12.36 — Alternate feed arrangements for the Bruce array. At A, the antenna is driven against a ground system and at B, it uses a two-wire counterpoise.

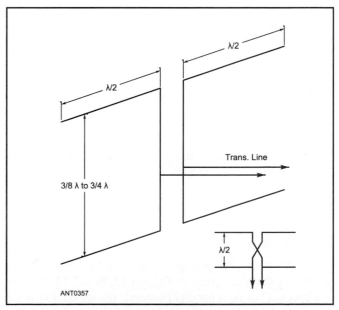

Figure 12.37 — Four-element broadside array ("lazy H") using collinear and parallel elements.

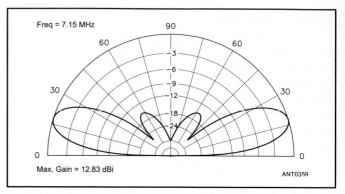

Figure 12.39 — Vertical pattern of the 4-element broadside antenna of Figure 12.37, when mounted with the elements horizontal and the lower set λ/4 above flat ground. Stacked arrays of this type give best results when the lowest elements are at least λ/2 high. The gain is reduced and the wave angle raised if the lowest elements are too close to ground.

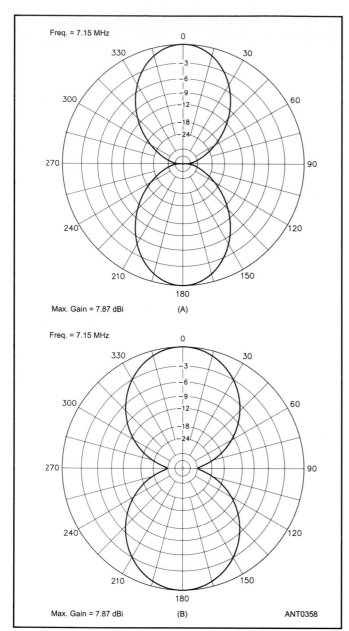

Figure 12.38 — Free-space directive diagrams of the 4-element antenna shown in Figure 12.37. At A is the E-plane pattern. The axis of the elements lies along the 90°-270° line. At B is the free-space H-plane pattern, viewed as if one set of elements is above the other from the ends of the elements.

not worthwhile because the gain is small. Estimated gains compared to a single element are:

3λ/8 spacing — 4.2 dB
λ/2 spacing — 5.8 dB
5λ/8 spacing — 6.7 dB
3λ/4 spacing — 6.3 dB

Half-wave spacing is generally used. Directive patterns for this spacing are given in **Figures 12.38** and **12.39**. With λ/2 spacing between parallel elements, the impedance at the junction of the phasing line and transmission line is resistive and in the vicinity of 100 Ω. With larger or smaller spacing

the impedance at this junction will be reactive as well as resistive. Matching stubs are recommended in cases where a non-resonant line is to be used. They may be calculated and adjusted as described in the **Transmission Line Coupling and Impedance Matching** chapter.

The system shown in Figure 12.37 may be used on two bands having a 2-to-1 frequency relationship. It should be designed for the higher of the two frequencies, using 3λ/4 spacing between parallel elements. It will then operate on the lower frequency as a simple broadside array with 3λ/8 spacing.

An alternative method of feeding is shown in the small diagram in Figure 12.37. In this case the elements and the phasing line must be adjusted exactly to an electrical half wavelength. The impedance at the feed point will be resistive and on the order of 2 kΩ.

A variation of this antenna called the "extended Lazy H" makes an effective broadside antenna on its fundamental and several higher bands. It is a good Field Day antenna if the supports are available for the lower elements to be at least λ/4 above the ground. It can be used with a tuner on all HF bands and as a top-loaded vertical by connecting the feed line conductors together and driving it against a ground system. A version for 7, 14, and 21 MHz is described in "The Extended Lazy H Antenna," by Walter Salmon in Oct 1955 *QST* and included on this book's CD-ROM.

12.3.6 THE BI-SQUARE ANTENNA

A development of the lazy H, known as the bi-square antenna, is shown in **Figure 12.40**. The gain of the bi-square is somewhat less than that of the lazy-H, but this array is attractive because it can be supported from a single pole. It has a circumference of 2 λ at the operating frequency, and is horizontally polarized.

The bi-square antenna consists of two 1 λ radiators, fed 180° out-of-phase at the bottom of the array. The radiation resistance is 300 Ω, so it can be fed with either 300- or 600-Ω line. The free space gain of the antenna is about

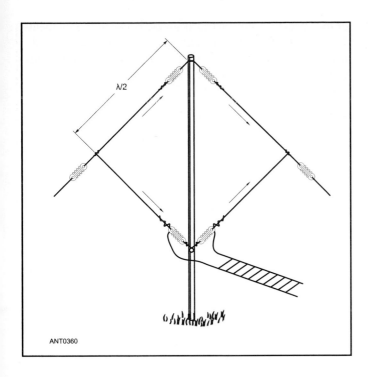

ANT0360

Figure 12.40 — The bi-square array. It has the appearance of a loop, but is not a true loop because the conductor is open at the top. The length of each side, in feet, is 480/f (MHz).

5.8 dBi, which is 3.7 dB more than a single dipole element. Gain may be increased by adding a parasitic reflector or director. Two bi-square arrays can be mounted at right angles and switched to provide omnidirectional coverage. In this way, the antenna wires may be used as part of the guying system for the pole.

Although it resembles a loop antenna, the bi-square is not a true loop because the ends opposite the feed point are open. However, identical construction techniques can be used for the two antenna types. Indeed, with a means of remotely closing the connection at the top for lower frequency operation, the antenna can be operated on two harmonically related bands. As an example, an array with 17 feet per side can be operated as a bi-square at 28 MHz and as a full-wave loop at 14 MHz. For two-band operation in this manner, the side length should favor the higher frequency. The length of a closed loop is not as critical.

12.4 END-FIRE ARRAYS

The term end-fire covers a number of different methods of operation, all having in common the fact that the maximum radiation takes place along the array axis, and that the array consists of a number of parallel elements in one plane. End-fire arrays can be either bidirectional or unidirectional. In the bidirectional type commonly used by amateurs there are only two elements, and these are operated with currents 180° out-of-phase. Even though adjustment tends to be complicated, unidirectional end-fire driven arrays have also seen amateur use, primarily as a pair of phased, ground-mounted $\lambda/4$ vertical elements. Extensive discussion of this array is contained in the **Multielement Arrays** chapter.

Horizontally polarized unidirectional end-fire arrays see little amateur use except in log-periodic arrays (described in the **Log-Periodic Dipole Arrays** chapter). Instead, horizontally polarized unidirectional arrays usually have parasitic elements (described in the **HF Yagi and Quad Antennas** chapter) and are called Yagis.

12.4.1 TWO-ELEMENT END-FIRE ARRAY

In a 2-element array with equal currents out-of-phase, the gain varies with the spacing between elements as shown in **Figure 12.41**. The maximum gain occurs in the neighborhood of 0.1 λ spacing. Below that the gain drops rapidly due to conductor loss resistance.

The feed point resistance for either element is very low at the spacings giving greatest gain, as shown in the **Multielement Arrays** chapter. The spacings most frequently

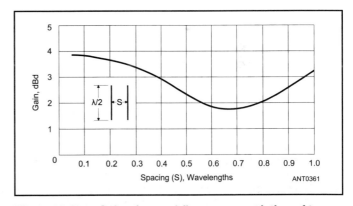

Figure 12.41 — Gain of an end-fire array consisting of two elements fed 180° out-of-phase, as a function of the spacing between elements. Maximum radiation is in the plane of the elements and at right angles to them at spacings up to $\lambda/2$, but the direction changes at greater spacings.

used are $\lambda/8$ and $\lambda/4$, at which the resistances of center-fed $\lambda/2$ elements are about 9 and 32 Ω, respectively.

The effect of conductor resistance on gain for various spacings is shown in **Figure 12.42**. Because current along the element is not constant (it is approximately sinusoidal), the resistance shown is the equivalent resistance (R_{eq}) inserted at the center of the element to account for the loss distributed along the element.

The equivalent resistance of a $\lambda/2$ element is one half the

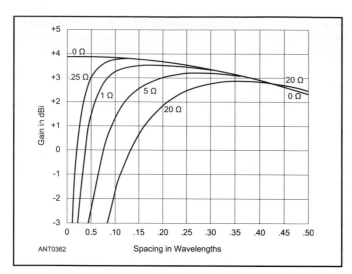

Figure 12.42 — Gain over a single element of two out-of-phase elements in free space as a function of spacing for various loss resistances.

ac resistance (R_{ac}) of the complete element. R_{ac} is usually $\gg R_{dc}$ due to skin effect. For example, a 1.84 MHz dipole using #12 AWG copper wire will have the following R_{eq}:

Wire length = 267 feet

$R_{dc} = 0.00159\ [\Omega/\text{foot}] \times 267\ [\text{feet}] = 0.42\ \Omega$

$F_r = R_{ac}/R_{dc} = 10.8$

$R_{eq} = (R_{dc}/2) \times F_r = 2.29\ \Omega$

For a 3.75 MHz dipole made with #12 AWG wire, R_{eq} = 1.59 Ω. In Figure 12.42, it is clear that end-fire antennas made with #12 AWG or smaller wire will limit the attainable gain because of losses. There is no point in using spacings much less than $\lambda/4$ if you use wire elements. If instead you use elements made of aluminum tubing then smaller spacings can be used to increase gain. However, as the spacing is reduced below $\lambda/4$ the increase in gain is quite small even with good conductors. Closer spacings give little gain increase but can drastically reduce the operating bandwidth due to the rapidly increasing Q of the array.

Unidirectional End-Fire Arrays

Two parallel elements spaced $\lambda/4$ apart and fed equal currents 90° out-of-phase will have a directional pattern in the plane at right angles to the plane of the array. See **Figure 12.43**. The maximum radiation is in the direction of the element in which the current lags. In the opposite direction the fields from the two elements cancel.

When the currents in the elements are neither in-phase nor 180° out-of-phase, the feed point resistances of the elements are not equal. This complicates the problem of feeding equal currents to the elements, as discussed in the **Multielement Arrays** chapter.

More than two elements can be used in a unidirectional end-fire array. The requirement for unidirectivity is that there must be a progressive phase shift in the element currents equal

to the spacing, in electrical degrees, between the elements. The amplitudes of the currents in the various elements also must be properly related. This requires binomial current distribution. In the case of three elements, this requires that the current in the center element be twice that in the two outside elements, for 90° ($\lambda/4$) spacing and element current phasing. This antenna has an overall length of $\lambda/2$. The directive diagram is shown in **Figure 12.44**. The pattern is similar to that

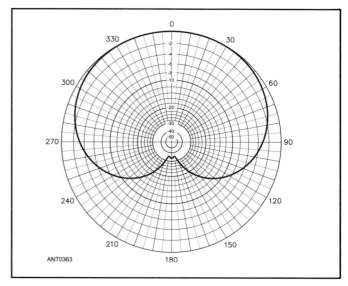

Figure 12.43 — Representative H-plane pattern for a 2-element end-fire array with 90° spacing and phasing. The elements lie along the vertical axis, with the uppermost element the one of lagging phase. Dissimilar current distributions are taken into account.

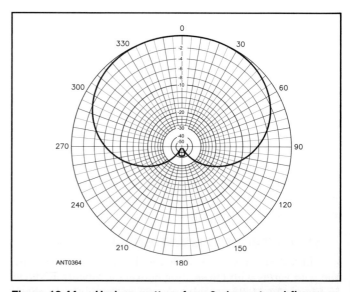

Figure 12.44 — H-plane pattern for a 3-element end-fire array with binomial current distribution (the current in the center element is twice that in each element). The elements are spaced $\lambda/4$ apart along the 0°-180° axis. The center element lags the lower element by 90°, while the upper element lags the lower element by 180° in phase. Dissimilar current distributions are taken into account.

of Figure 12.43, but the 3-element binomial array has greater directivity, evidenced by the narrower half-power beamwidth (146° versus 176°). Its gain is 1.0 dB greater.

12.4.2 THE W8JK ARRAY

John Kraus, W8JK (SK), described his bidirectional flat-top W8JK beam antenna in 1940. See **Figure 12.45**. (His June 1982 *QST* article "The W8JK Recap and Update" is included on the CD-ROM for this book.) Two $\lambda/2$ elements are spaced $\lambda/8$ to $\lambda/4$ and driven 180° out-of-phase. The free-space radiation pattern for this antenna, using #12 AWG copper wire, is given in **Figure 12.46**. The pattern is representative of spacings between $\lambda/8$ and $\lambda/4$ where the gain varies less than 0.5 dB. The gain over a dipole is about 3.3 dB (5.4 dBi referenced to an isotropic radiator),

a worthwhile improvement. The feed point impedance (including wire resistance) of each element is about 11 Ω for $\lambda/8$ spacing and 33 Ω for $\lambda/4$ spacing. The feed point impedance at the center connection will depend on the length and Z_0 of the connecting transmission line.

Kraus gave a number of other variations for end-fire arrays, some of which are shown in **Figure 12.47**. The ones fed at the center (A, C and E) are usually horizontally polarized flat-top beams. The end-fed versions (B, D and F) are usually

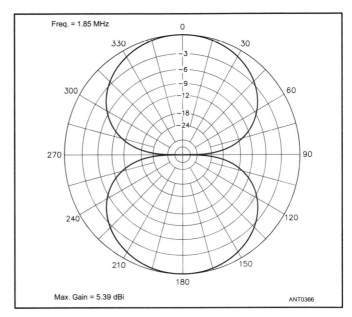

Figure 12.46 — Free-space E-plane pattern for the 2-element W8JK array.

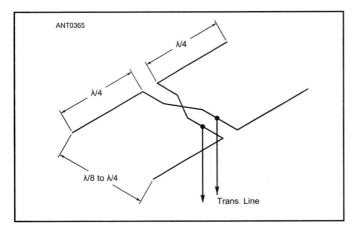

Figure 12.45 — A 2-element W8JK array.

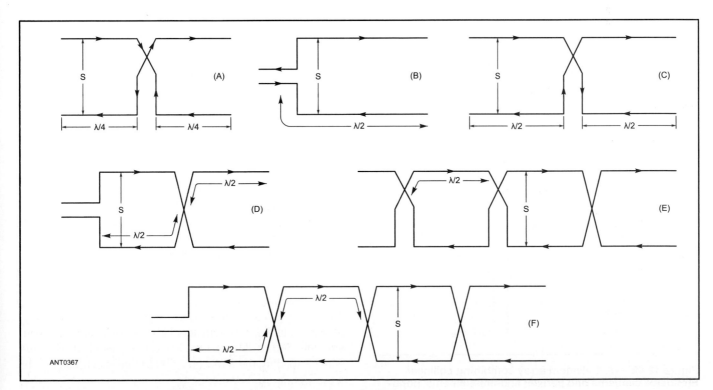

Figure 12.47 — Six other variations of W8JK "flat-top beam" antennas.

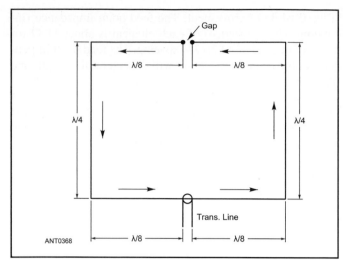

Figure 12.48 — A 2-element end-fire array with reduced height.

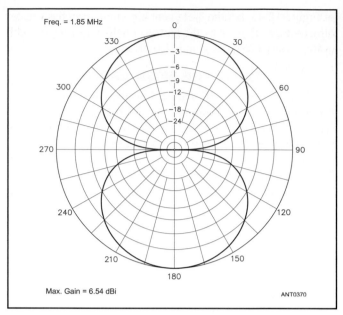

Figure 12.50 — Free-space E-plane pattern for the antenna shown in Figure 12.49, with λ/8 spacing. The elements are parallel to the 90°-270° line in this diagram. Less than a 1° change in half-power beamwidth results when the spacing is changed from λ/8 to λ/4.

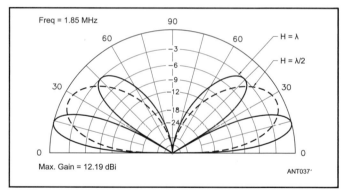

Figure 12.51 — Elevation-plane pattern for the 4-element antenna of Figure 12.49 when mounted horizontally at two heights over flat ground. Solid line = 1 λ high; dashed line = λ/2 high.

vertically polarized, where the feed point can be conveniently near ground.

A practical variation of Figure 12.47B is given in **Figure 12.48**. In this example, the height is limited to λ/4 so the ends can be bent over as shown, producing a 2-element Bruce array. This reduces the gain somewhat but allows much shorter supports, an important consideration on the low bands. If additional height is available, then you can achieve some additional gain. The upper ends can be bent over to fit the available height. The feed point impedance will greater than 1 kΩ.

The article "Building the W8JK" by Suggs (see Bibliography) shows how to build a W8JK beam that covers 20 through 6 meters.

12.4.3 FOUR-ELEMENT END-FIRE AND COLLINEAR ARRAYS

The array shown in **Figure 12.49** combines collinear in-phase elements with parallel out-of-phase elements to give

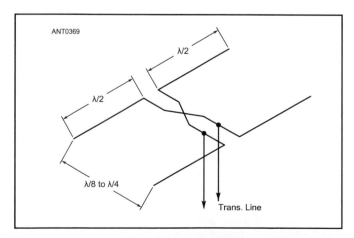

Figure 12.49 — A 4-element array combining collinear broadside elements and parallel end-fire elements, popularly known as a two-section W8JK array.

both broadside and end-fire directivity. It is a two-section W8JK. The approximate free-space gain using #12 AWG copper wire is 4.9 dBi with λ/8 spacing and 5.4 dBi with λ/4 spacing. Directive patterns are given in **Figure 12.50** for free space, and in **Figure 12.51** for heights of 1 λ and λ/2 above flat ground.

The impedance between elements at the point where the phasing line is connected is of the order of several thousand ohms. The SWR with an unmatched line consequently is quite high, and this system should be constructed with open-wire line (500 or 600 Ω) if the line is to be resonant. With λ/4 element spacing the SWR on a 600 Ω line is estimated to be in the vicinity of 3 or 4:1.

To use a matched line, you could connect a closed

stub 3λ/16 long at the transmission-line junction shown in Figure 12.49. The transmission line itself can then be tapped on this matching section at the point resulting in the lowest line SWR. This point can be determined by trial.

This type of antenna can be operated on two bands having a frequency ratio of 2 to 1, if a resonant feed line is used. For example, if you design for 28 MHz with λ/4 spacing between elements, you can also operate on 14 MHz as a simple 2-element end-fire array having λ/8 spacing.

Combination Driven Arrays

You can readily combine broadside, end-fire and collinear elements to increase gain and directivity, and this is in fact usually done when more than two elements are used in an array. Combinations of this type give more gain, in a given amount of space, than plain arrays of the types just described. Since the combinations that can be worked out are almost endless, this section describes only a few of the simpler types.

The accurate calculation of the power gain of a multi-element array requires a knowledge of the mutual impedances between all elements, as discussed in earlier sections. For approximate purposes it is sufficient to assume that each set (collinear, broadside, end-fire) will have the gains as given earlier, and then simply add up the gains for the combination. This neglects the effects of cross-coupling between sets of elements. However, the array configurations are such that the mutual impedances from cross-coupling should be relatively small, particularly when the spacings are λ/4 or more, so the estimated gain should be reasonably close to the actual gain. Alternatively, an antenna modeling program, such as *EZNEC*, can give good estimates of all parameters for a real-world antenna, providing that you take care to model all applicable parameters.

12.4.4 FOUR-ELEMENT DRIVEN ARRAYS

The array shown in **Figure 12.52** combines parallel elements with broadside and end-fire directivity. The smallest array (physically) — 3λ/8 spacing between broadside and λ/8 spacing between end-fire elements — has an estimated gain of 6.5 dBi and the largest — 3λ/4 and λ/4 spacing, respectively — about 8.4 dBi. Typical directive patterns for a λ/4 × λ/2 array are given in **Figures 12.53** and **12.54**.

The impedance at the feed point will not be purely resistive unless the element lengths are correct and the phasing lines are exactly λ/2 long. (This requires somewhat less than λ/2 spacing between broadside elements.) In this case the impedance at the junction is estimated to be over 10 kΩ. With other element spacings the impedance at the junction will be reactive as well as resistive, but in any event the SWR will be quite large. An open-wire line can be used as a resonant line, or a matching section may be used for non-resonant operation.

12.4.5 EIGHT-ELEMENT DRIVEN ARRAYS

The array shown in **Figure 12.55** is a combination of collinear and parallel elements in broadside and end-fire directivity. Common practice in a wire antenna is to use λ/2

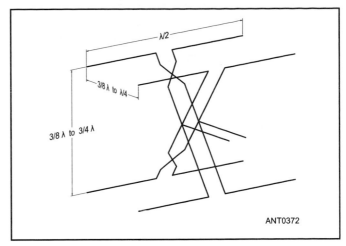

Figure 12.52 — Four-element array combining both broadside and end-fire elements.

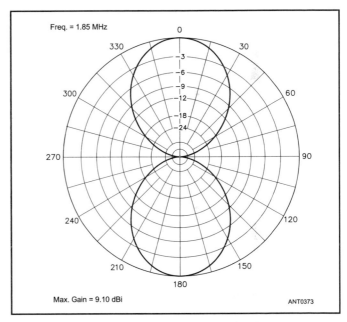

Figure 12.53 — Free-space H-plane pattern of the 4-element antenna shown in Figure 12.52.

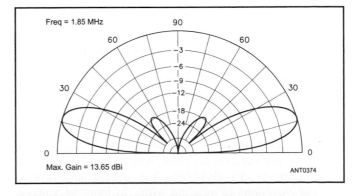

Figure 12.54 — Vertical pattern of the antenna shown in Figure 12.52 at a mean height of 3λ/4 (lowest elements λ/2 above flat ground) when the antenna is horizontally polarized. For optimum gain and low wave angle the mean height should be at least 3λ/4.

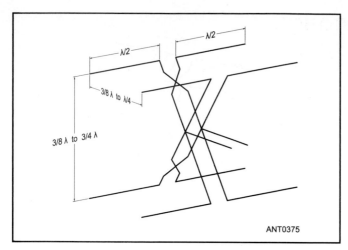

Figure 12.55 — Eight-element driven array combining collinear and parallel elements for broadside and end-fire directivity.

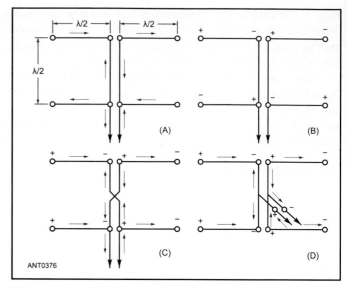

Figure 12.56 — Methods of checking the phase of currents in elements and phasing lines.

spacing for the parallel broadside elements and λ/4 spacing for the end-fire elements. This gives a free-space gain of about 9.1 dBi. Directive patterns for an array using these spacings are similar to those of Figures 12.53 and 12.54, but are somewhat sharper.

The SWR with this arrangement will be high. Matching stubs are recommended for making the lines non-resonant. Their position and length can be determined as described in the chapter **Transmission Line Coupling and Impedance Matching**.

This system can be used on two bands related in frequency by a 2-to-1 ratio, providing it is designed for the higher of the two, with 3λ/4 spacing between the parallel broadside elements and λ/4 spacing between the end-fire elements. On the lower frequency it will then operate as a 4-element antenna of the type shown in Figure 12.52, with 3λ/8 broadside spacing and λ/8 end-fire spacing. For two-band operation a resonant transmission line must be used.

12.4.6 PHASING ARROWS IN ARRAY ELEMENTS

In the antenna diagrams of preceding sections, the relative direction of current flow in the various antenna elements and connecting lines was shown by arrows. In laying out any antenna system it is necessary to know that the phasing lines are properly connected; otherwise the antenna may have entirely different characteristics than anticipated. The phasing may be checked either on the basis of current direction or polarity of voltages. There are two rules to remember:

1) In every λ/2 section of wire, starting from an open end, the current directions reverse. In terms of voltage, the polarity reverses at each λ/2 point, starting from an open end.

2) Currents in transmission lines always must flow in opposite directions in adjacent wires. In terms of voltage, polarities always must be opposite.

Examples of the use of current direction and voltage

polarity are given at A and B, respectively, in **Figure 12.56**. The λ/2 points in the system are marked by small circles. When current in one section flows toward a circle, the current in the next section must also flow toward it, and vice versa. In the 4-element antenna shown at A, the current in the upper right-hand element cannot flow toward the transmission line because then the current in the right-hand section of the phasing line would have to flow upward and thus would be flowing in the same direction as the current in the left-hand wire. The phasing line would simply act like two wires in parallel in such a case. Of course, all arrows in the drawing could be reversed, and the net effect would be unchanged.

C shows the effect of transposing the phasing line. This transposition reverses the direction of current flow in the lower pair of elements, as compared with A, and thus changes the array from a combination collinear and end-fire arrangement into a collinear-broadside array.

The drawing at D shows what happens when the transmission line is connected at the center of a section of phasing line. Viewed from the main transmission line, the two parts of the phasing line are simply in parallel, so the half wavelength is measured from the antenna element along the upper section of phasing line and thence along the transmission line. The distance from the lower elements is measured in the same way. Obviously, the two sections of phasing line should be the same length. If they are not, the current distribution becomes quite complicated; the element currents are neither in-phase nor 180° out-of-phase, and the elements at opposite ends of the lines do not receive the same current. To change the element current phasing at D into the phasing at A, simply transpose the wires in one section of the phasing line. This reverses the direction of current flow in the antenna elements connected to that section of phasing line.

12.5 BIBLIOGRAPHY

J. Cain, "Curtains for You," *QST*, Oct 1991, pp 26-30. See also Feedback in Dec 1991 *QST*, p 73. This article also appears in *ARRL's Wire Antenna Classics*.

L.B. Cebik, "Some Notes on Two-Element Horizontal Phased Arrays," in four parts, *NCJ*, Nov/Dec 2001, pp 4-10; Jan/Feb 2002, pp 4-9; Mar/Apr 2002, pp 3-8; and May/Jun 2002, pp 3-8.

D. Cooper, "The Bi-Square Array," *Ham Radio*, May 1990, pp 42-44.

J. Haigwood, "The Extended Double Zepp Revisited," *QST*, Sep 2006, pp 35-36.

H. Jasik, *Antenna Engineering Handbook*, 1st ed. (New York: McGraw-Hill, 1961). Later editions are edited by Richard C. Johnson.

H. Kennedy, "The N4GG Array", *QST*, Jul 2002, pp 35-39.

J. D. Kraus, *Antennas*, 2nd ed. (New York: McGraw-Hill Book Co., 1988).

J. D. Kraus, "The W8JK Antenna Recap and Update," *QST*, Jun 1982, pp 11-14.

R. Johnson, *Antenna Engineering Handbook*, 3rd ed. (New York: McGraw-Hill Inc., 1993). This is a later edition of the volume by the same name edited by H. Jasik.

E. A. Laport, *Radio Antenna Engineering* (New York: McGraw-Hill Book Co, 1952).

M. Loukides, "A Dipole Curtain for 15 and 10 Meters," *QST*, Aug 2003, pp 34-38.

H. Romander, "The Extended Double-Zepp Antenna," *QST*, Jun 1938, pp 12-16. This article also appears in *More Wire Antenna Classics*, published by ARRL.

W. Salmon, "The Extended Lazy H Antenna," *QST*, Oct 1955, p 20.

W. Smith, "Bet My Money on a Bobtail Beam," *CQ*, Mar 1948, pp 21-23.

W. Smith, "The Bobtail Curtain and Inverted Ground Plane, Part One," *Ham Radio*, Feb 1983, pp 82-86.

W. Smith, "Bobtail Curtain Follow-Up: Practical DX Signal Gain" *Ham Radio*, Mar 1983, pp 28-30.

D. Suggs, "Building the W8JK Beam," *QST*, Sep 2005, pp 31-35.

R. Zavrel, "The Multiband Extended Double Zepp and Derivative Designs," *QEX*, Jul/Aug 1999, pp 34-40.

R. Zimmerman, "A Simple 50-Ohm Feed for W8JK Beams," *QST*, Jun 1999, pp 41-42, 47. See also Feedback in Jul 1999 *QST*, p 63.

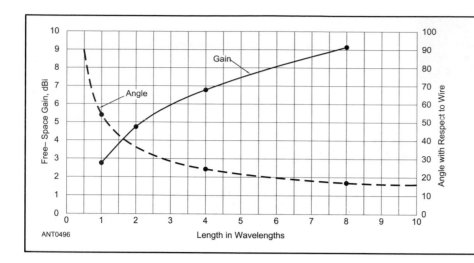

Figure 13.1 — Theoretical gain of a long-wire antenna, in dBi, as a function of wire length. The angle, with respect to the wire, at which the radiation intensity is maximum also is shown.

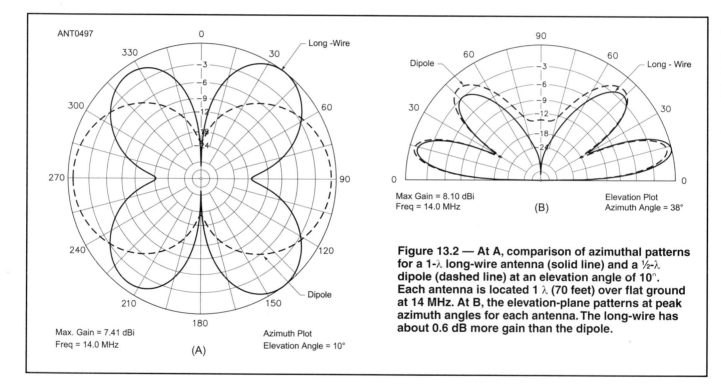

Max. Gain = 7.41 dBi
Freq = 14.0 MHz

Azimuth Plot
Elevation Angle = 10°

(A)

Max Gain = 8.10 dBi
Freq = 14.0 MHz

Elevation Plot
Azimuth Angle = 38°

(B)

Figure 13.2 — At A, comparison of azimuthal patterns for a 1-λ long-wire antenna (solid line) and a ½-λ dipole (dashed line) at an elevation angle of 10°. Each antenna is located 1 λ (70 feet) over flat ground at 14 MHz. At B, the elevation-plane patterns at peak azimuth angles for each antenna. The long-wire has about 0.6 dB more gain than the dipole.

reason for this is that the fields radiated by elementary lengths of wire along the antenna do not combine, at a distance, in as simple a fashion as the fields from half-wave dipoles used in other types of directive arrays.

There is no point in space, for example, where the distant fields from all points along the wire are exactly in phase (as they are, in the optimum direction, in the case of two or more collinear or broadside dipoles when fed with in-phase currents). Consequently, the field strength at a distance is always less than would be obtained if the same length of wire were cut up into properly phased and separately driven dipoles. As the wire is made longer, the fields combine to form increasingly intense main lobes, but these lobes do not develop appreciably until the wire is several wavelengths long. See **Figure 13.1**.

The longer the antenna, the sharper the lobes become,

and since it is really a hollow cone of radiation about the wire in free space, it becomes sharper in both planes. Also, the greater the length, the smaller the angle with the wire at which the maximum radiation lobes occur. There are four main lobes to the directive patterns of long-wire antennas; each makes the same angle with respect to the wire.

Figure 13.2A shows the azimuthal radiation pattern of a 1-λ long-wire antenna, compared with a ½-λ dipole. Both antennas are mounted at the same height of 1 λ above flat ground (70 feet high at 14 MHz, with a wire length of 70 feet) and both patterns are for an elevation angle of 10°, an angle suitable for long-distance communication on 20 meters. The long-wire in Figure 13.2A is oriented in the 270° to 90° direction, while the dipole is aligned at right angles so that its characteristic figure-8 pattern goes left-to-right. The 1-λ long-wire has about 0.6 dB more gain than the dipole, with four main lobes as compared to the two lobes from the dipole.

You can see that the two lobes on the left side of Figure 13.2A are about 1 dB down compared to the two lobes on the right side. This is because the long-wire here is fed at the left-hand end in the computer model. Energy is radiated as a wave travels down the wire and some energy is also lost to ohmic resistance in the wire and the ground. The forward-going wave then reflects from the open-circuit at the right-hand end of the wire and reverses direction, traveling toward the left end, still radiating as it travels. An antenna operating in this way has much the same characteristics as a transmission line that is terminated in an open circuit — that is, it has standing waves on it. Unterminated long-wire antennas are often referred to as standing wave antennas. As the length of a long-wire antenna is increased, a moderate front-to-back ratio results, about 3 dB for very long antennas.

Figure 13.2B shows the elevation-plane pattern for the long-wire and for the dipole. In each case the elevation pattern is at the azimuth of maximum gain — at an angle of 38° with respect to the wire-axis for the long-wire and at 90° for the dipole. The peak elevation for the long-wire is very slightly lower than that for the dipole at the same height above ground, but not by much. In other words, the height above ground is the main determining factor for the shape of the main lobe of a long-wire's elevation pattern, as it is for most horizontally polarized antennas.

The shape of the azimuth and elevation patterns in Figure 13.2 might lead you to believe that the radiation pattern is simple. **Figure 13.3** is a 3-D representation of the pattern from a 1-λ long-wire that is 1 λ high over flat ground. Besides the main low-angle lobes, there are strong lobes at higher angles. Things get even more complicated when the length of the long-wire increases.

Directivity

Because many points along a long wire are carrying currents in different phases (with different current amplitudes as well), the field pattern at a distance becomes more complex as the wire is made longer. This complexity is manifested in a series of minor lobes, the number of which increases with the wire length. The intensity of radiation from the minor lobes is frequently as great as, and sometimes greater than, the radiation from a half-wave dipole. The energy radiated in the minor lobes is not available to improve the gain in the major lobes, which is another reason why a long-wire antenna must be long to give appreciable gain in the desired directions.

Figure 13.4 shows an azimuthal-plane comparison between a 3-λ (209 feet long) long-wire and the comparison ½-λ dipole. The long-wire now has eight minor lobes besides the four main lobes. Note that the angle the main lobes make with respect to the axis of the long-wire (also left-to-right in Figure 13.4) becomes smaller as the length of the long-wire increases. For the 3-λ long-wire, the main lobes occur 28° off the axis of the wire itself.

Other types of simple driven and parasitic arrays do not have minor lobes of any great consequence. For that reason they frequently seem to have much better directivity than long-wire antennas, because their responses in undesired directions are well down from their response in the desired direction. This is the case even if a multielement array and a long-wire antenna have the same peak gain in the favored direction. **Figure 13.5** compares the same 3-λ long-wire with a 4-element Yagi and a ½-λ dipole, again both at the same height as the long-wire. Note that the Yagi has only a single

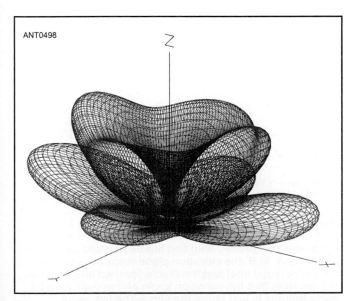

Figure 13.3 — A 3-D representation of the radiation pattern for the 1-λ long-wire shown in Figure 13.2. The pattern is obviously rather complex. It gets even more complicated for wires longer than 1 λ.

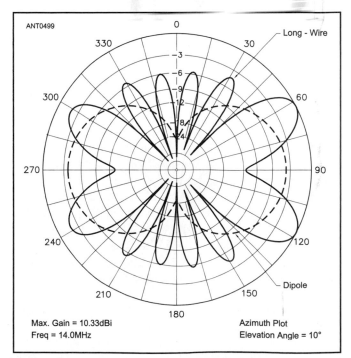

ANT0499

Max. Gain = 10.33dBi
Freq = 14.0MHz

Azimuth Plot
Elevation Angle = 10°

Figure 13.4 — An azimuthal-plane comparison between a 3-λ (209 feet long) long-wire (solid line) and the comparison ½-λ dipole (dashed line) at 70 feet high (1 λ) at 14 MHz.

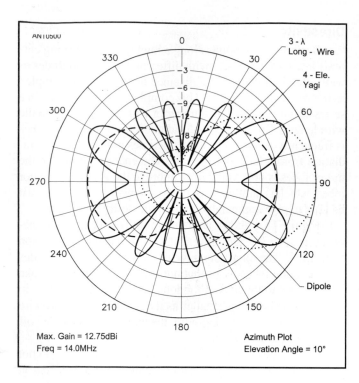

Max. Gain = 12.75dBi
Freq = 14.0MHz

Azimuth Plot
Elevation Angle = 10°

Figure 13.5 — A comparison between the 3-λ long-wire (solid line) in Figure 13.4, a 4-element 20-meter Yagi on a 26-foot boom (dotted line), and a ½-λ dipole (dashed line), again at a height of 70 feet. The main lobes of the long-wire are very narrow compared to the wide frontal lobe of the Yagi. The long-wire exhibits an azimuthal pattern that is more omnidirectional in nature than a Yagi, particularly when the narrow, deep nulls in the long-wire's pattern are filled-in due to irregularities in the terrain under its long span of wire.

rear lobe, down about 21 dB from its broad main lobe, which has a 3-dB beamwidth of 63°. The 3-dB beamwidth of the long-wire's main lobes (at a 28° angle from the wire axis) is far more narrow, at only 23°.

For amateur work, particularly with directive antennas that cannot be rotated, the minor lobes of a long-wire antenna have some advantages. Although the nulls in the computer model in Figure 13.5 are deeper than 30 dB, they are not so dramatic in actual practice. This is due to irregularities

in the terrain that inevitably occur under the span of a long wire. In most directions the long-wire antenna will be as good as a half-wave dipole, and in addition will give high gain in the most favored directions, even though that is over narrow azimuths.

Figure 13.6A compares the azimuth responses for a 5-λ long-wire (350 feet long at 14 MHz) to the same 4-element Yagi and dipole. The long-wire now exhibits 16 minor lobes in addition to its four main lobes. The peaks of these sidelobes are down about 8 dB from the main lobes and they are stronger than the dipole, making this long-wire antenna effectively omnidirectional. Figure 13.6B shows the elevation pattern of the 5-λ long-wire at its most effective azimuth compared to a dipole. Again, the shape of the main lobe is mainly determined by the long-wire's height above ground, since the peak angle is only just a bit lower than the peak angle for the dipole. The long-wire's elevation response breaks up into numerous lobes above the main lobes, just as it does in the azimuth plane.

For the really ambitious, **Figure 13.7** compares the performance for an 8-λ (571 feet) long-wire antenna with a 4-element Yagi and the ½-λ dipole. Again, in actual practice, the nulls would tend to be filled in by terrain irregularities,

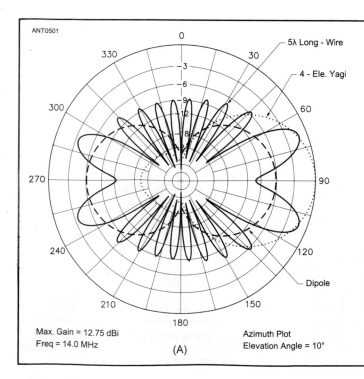

Max. Gain = 12.75 dBi
Freq = 14.0 MHz

Azimuth Plot
Elevation Angle = 10°

(A)

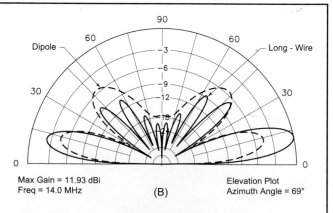

Max Gain = 11.93 dBi
Freq = 14.0 MHz

(B)

Elevation Plot
Azimuth Angle = 69°

Figure 13.6 — At A, the azimuth responses for a 5-λ long-wire (350 feet long at 14 MHz — solid line) to the same 4-element Yagi (dotted line) and dipole (dashed line) as in Figure 13.5. At B, the elevation-plane responses for the long-wire (solid line) and the dipole (dashed line) by themselves. Note that the elevation angle giving peak gain for each antenna is just about the same. The long-wire achieves gain by compressing mainly the azimuthal response, squeezing the gain into narrow lobes; not so much by squeezing the elevation pattern for gain.

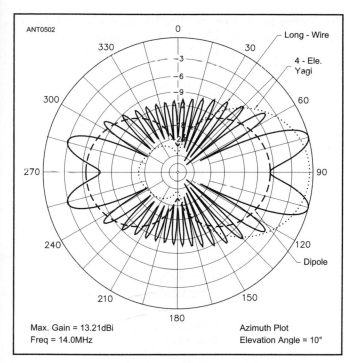

Figure 13.7 — The azimuthal-plane performance for an 8-λ (571 feet) long-wire antenna (solid line), compared with a 4-element Yagi (dotted line) and a ½-λ dipole (dashed line).

so a very long antenna like this would be a pretty potent performer.

Calculating Length

In this chapter, lengths are discussed in terms of wavelengths. Throughout the preceding discussion the frequency in the models was held at 14 MHz. Remember that a long-wire that is 4 λ long at 14 MHz is 8 λ long at 28 MHz.

There is nothing very critical about wire lengths in an antenna system that will work over a frequency range including several amateur bands. The antenna characteristics change very slowly with length, except when the wires are short (around one wavelength, for instance). There is no need to try to establish exact resonance at a particular frequency for proper antenna operation.

The formula for determining the lengths for harmonic wires is:

$$\text{Length (feet)} = \frac{984\,(N - 0.025)}{f\,(\text{MHz})} \qquad \text{(Eq 1)}$$

where N is the antenna length in wavelengths. In cases where precise resonance is desired for some reason (for obtaining a resistive load for a transmission line at a particular frequency, for example) it is best established by trimming the wire length until the standing-wave ratio on the line is minimum.

Tilted Wires

In theory, it is possible to maximize gain from a long-wire antenna by tilting it to favor a desired elevation take-off angle. Unfortunately, the effect of real ground under the antenna negates the possible advantages of tilting, just as it

does when a Yagi or other type of parasitic array is tilted from horizontal. You would do better keeping a long-wire antenna horizontal, but raising it higher above ground, to achieve more gain at low takeoff angles.

13.1.3 FEEDING LONG WIRES

A long-wire antenna is normally fed at the end or at a current maximum where feed point impedance is relatively low. Since a current maximum changes to a minimum when the antenna is operated at any even multiple of the frequency for which it is designed, a long-wire antenna will operate as a true long wire on all bands only when it is fed at the end where feed point impedance is always high.

A common method of feeding a long-wire is to use a resonant open-wire line. This system will work on all bands down to the one, if any, at which the antenna is only a half-wave long. Any convenient line length can be used if you match the transmitter to the line's input impedance using an antenna tuner. Using coaxial cable to feed long wires directly can lead to excessive losses if the SWR is high and so open-wire line is the usual choice.

Two arrangements for using nonresonant lines are given in **Figure 13.8**. The one at A is useful for one band only since the matching section must be a quarter-wave long, approximately, unless a different matching section is used for each band. In B, the λ/4 transformer (Q-section) impedance can be designed to match the antenna to the line. You can determine the value of radiation resistance using a modern modeling program or you can actually measure the feed point impedance. Although it will work as designed on only one band, the antenna can be used on other bands by treating the line and matching transformer as a resonant line. In this case, as mentioned earlier, the antenna will not radiate as a true long wire on even multiples of the frequency for which the matching system is designed.

The end-fed arrangement, although the most convenient when tuned feeders are used, has the disadvantage that there is

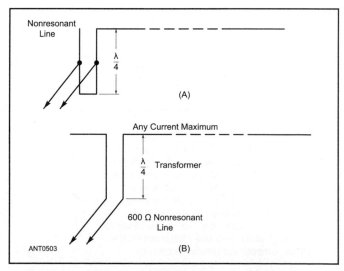

Figure 13.8 — Methods for feeding long single-wire antennas.

likely to be a considerable antenna current on the line. In addition, the antenna reactance changes rapidly with frequency. Consequently, when the wire is several wavelengths long, a relatively small change in frequency — a fraction of the width of a band — may require major changes in the adjustment of the antenna tuner. Also, the line becomes unbalanced at all frequencies between those at which the antenna is resonant. This leads to a considerable amount of radiation from the line. The unbalance can be overcome by using multiple long wires in a V or rhombic shape, as described below.

13.2 COMBINATIONS OF LONG WIRES

The directivity and gain of long wires may be increased by using two wires placed in relation to each other such that the fields from both combine to produce the greatest possible field strength at a distant point. The principle is similar to that used in designing multielement arrays.

13.2.1 PARALLEL WIRES

One possible method of using two (or more) long wires is to place them in parallel, with a spacing of ½ λ or so, and feed the two in phase. In the direction of the wires the fields will add in phase. However, the takeoff angle is high directly in the orientation of the wire, and this method will result in rather high-angle radiation even if the wires are several wavelengths long. With a parallel arrangement of this sort the gain should be about 3 dB over a single wire of the same length, at spacings in the vicinity of ½ wavelength.

13.2.2 THE V-BEAM ANTENNA

Instead of using two long wires parallel to each other, they may be placed in the form of a horizontal V, with the included angle between the wires equal to twice the angle made by the main lobes referenced to the wire axis for a single wire of the same physical length. For example, for a leg length of 5 λ, the angle between the legs of a V should be about 42°, twice the angle of 21° of the main lobe referenced to the long-wire's axis. See Figure 13.6A.

The plane directive patterns of the individual wires combine along a line in the plane of the antenna and bisecting the V, where the fields from the individual wires reinforce each other. The sidelobes in the azimuthal pattern are suppressed by about 10 dB, so the pattern becomes essentially bidirectional. See **Figure 13.9**.

The included angle between the legs is not particularly critical. This is fortunate, especially if the same antenna is used on multiple bands, where the electrical length varies directly with frequency. This would normally require different included angles for each band. For multiband V-antennas, a compromise angle is usually chosen to equalize performance. **Figure 13.10** shows the azimuthal pattern for a

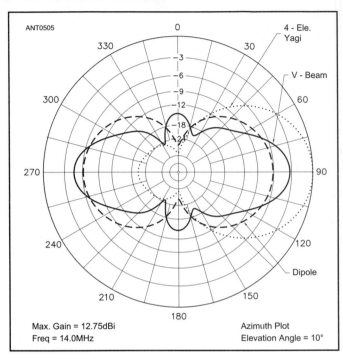

Figure 13.10 — Azimuthal-plane pattern at 10° elevation angle for a 14-MHz V-beam (solid line) with 1-λ legs (68.5 feet long), using an included angle of 75° between the legs. The V-beam is mounted 1 λ above flat ground, and is compared with a ½-λ dipole (dashed line) and a 4-element 20-meter

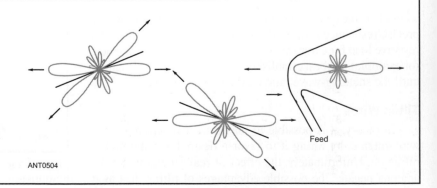

Figure 13.9 — Two long wires and their respective patterns are shown at the left. If these two wires are combined to form a V with an angle that is twice that of the major lobes of the wires and with the wires excited out of phase, the radiation along the bisector of the V adds and the radiation in the other directions tends to cancel.

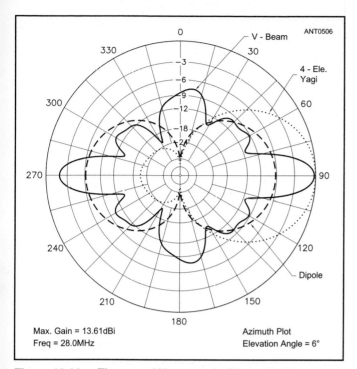

Figure 13.11 — The same V-beam as in Figure 13.10 at 28 MHz (solid line), at an elevation angle of 6°, compared to a 4-element Yagi (dotted line) and a dipole (dashed line). The V-beam's pattern is very narrow, at 18.8° at the 3-dB points, requiring accurate placement of the supports poles to aim the antenna at the desired geographic target.

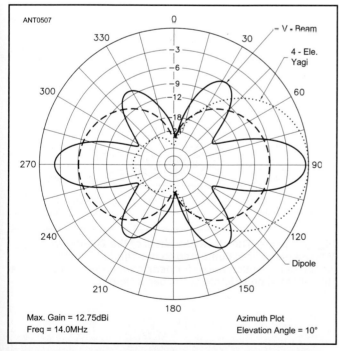

Figure 13.12 — Azimuthal pattern for a V-beam (solid line) with 2-λ legs (137 feet at 14 MHz), with an included angle of 60° between them. The height is 70 feet, or 1 λ, over flat ground. For comparison, the response for a 4-element Yagi (dotted line) and a dipole (dashed line) are shown. The 3-dB beamwidth has decreased to 23.0°.

V-beam with 1-λ legs, with an included angle of 75° between the legs, mounted 1 λ above flat ground. This is for a 10° elevation angle. At 14 MHz the antenna has two 70-foot high, 68.5-foot long legs, separated at their far ends by 83.4 feet. For comparison, the azimuthal patterns for the same 4-element Yagi and ½-λ dipole used previously for the long-wires are overlaid on the same plot. The V has about 2 dB more gain than the dipole but is down some 4 dB compared to the Yagi, as expected for relatively short legs.

Figure 13.11 shows the azimuthal pattern for the same antenna in Figure 13.10, but at 28 MHz and at an elevation angle of 6°. Because the legs are twice as long electrically at 28 MHz, the V-beam has compressed the main lobe into a narrow beam that now has a peak gain equal to the Yagi, but with a 3-dB beamwidth of only 18.8°. Note that you could obtain about 0.7 dB more gain at 14 MHz, with a 1.7-dB degradation of gain at 28 MHz, if you increase the included angle to 90° rather than 75°.

Figure 13.12 shows the azimuthal pattern for a V-beam with 2-λ legs (137 feet at 14 MHz), with an included angle of 60° between them. As usual, the assumed height is 70 feet, or 1 λ at 14 MHz. The peak gain for the V-beam is just about equal to that of the 4-element Yagi, although the 3-dB nose beamwidth is narrow, at 23°. This makes setting up the geometry critical if you want to maximize gain into a particular geographic area. While you might be able to get away with using convenient trees to support such an antenna, it's far more likely that you'll have to use carefully located towers to make sure the beam is aimed where you expect it to be pointed.

For example, in order to cover all of Europe from San Francisco, an antenna must cover from about 11° (to Moscow) to about 46° (to Portugal). This is a range of 35° and signals from the V-beam in Figure 13.12 would be down some 7 dB over this range of angles, assuming the center of the beam is pointed exactly at a heading of 28.5°. The 4-element Yagi on the other hand would cover this range of azimuths more consistently, since its 3-dB beamwidth is 63°.

Figure 13.13 shows the same V-beam as in Figure 13.12, but this time at 28 MHz. The peak gain of the main lobe is now about 1 dB stronger than the 4-element Yagi used as a reference, and the main lobe has two nearby sidelobes that tend to broaden out the azimuthal response. At this frequency the V-beam would cover all of Europe better from San Francisco.

Figure 13.14 shows a V-beam with 3-λ (209 feet at 14 MHz) legs with an included angle of 50° between them. The peak gain is now greater than that of a 4-element Yagi, but the 3-dB beamwidth has been reduced to 17.8°, making aiming the antenna even more critical. **Figure 13.15** shows the same V-beam at 28 MHz. Here again, the main lobe has nearby sidelobes that broaden the effective azimuth to cover a wider area.

Figure 13.16 shows the elevation-plane response for the same 209-foot leg V-beam at 28 MHz (3-λ at 14 MHz), compared to a dipole at the same height of 70 feet. The higher-gain V-beam suppresses higher-angle lobes, essentially

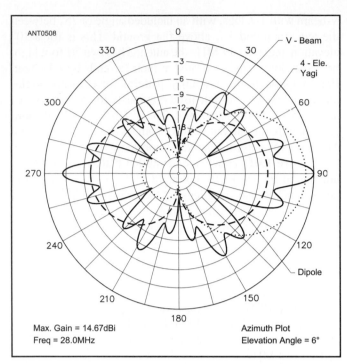

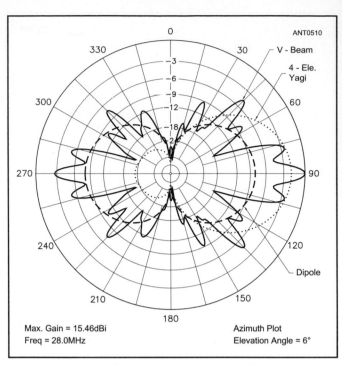

Figure 13.13 — The same 2-λ-per-leg V-beam (solid line) as in Figure 13.12, but at 28 MHz and at a 6° takeoff elevation angle. Two sidelobes have appeared flanking the main lobe, making the effective azimuthal pattern wider at this frequency.

Figure 13.15 — The same 209-foot-per-leg V-beam as Figure 13.14, but at 28 MHz. Again, the two close-in sidelobes tend to spread out the azimuthal response some at 28 MHz.

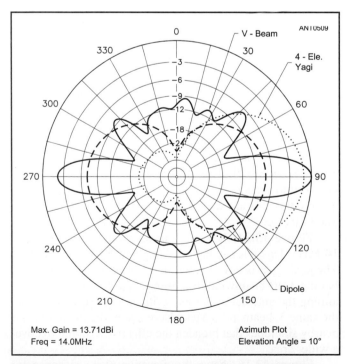

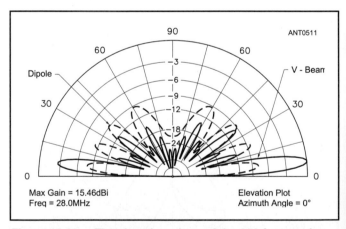

Figure 13.16 — The elevation-plane of the 209-foot-per-leg V-beam (solid line) compared to the dipole (dashed line). Again, the elevation angle for peak gain corresponds well to that of the simple dipole at the same height.

Figure 13.14 — A V-beam (solid line) with 3-λ (209 feet at 14 MHz) legs using an included angle of 50° between them, compared to a 4-element Yagi (dotted line) and a dipole (dashed line). The 3-dB beamwidth has now decreased to 17.8°.

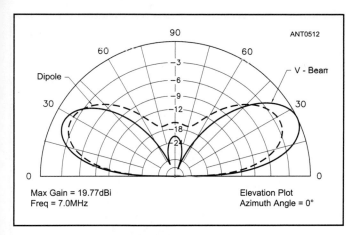

Figure 13.17 — Elevation pattern for the same 209-foot-per-leg V-beam (solid line), at 7 MHz, compared to a 40-meter dipole (dashed line) at the same height of 70 feet.

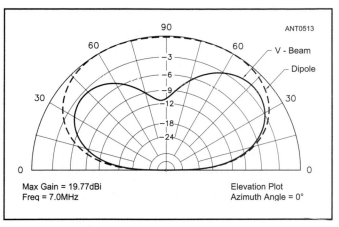

Figure 13.18 — Elevation pattern for the same 209-foot-per-leg V-beam (solid line), at 3.5 MHz, compared to an 80-meter dipole at 70 feet (dashed line).

stealing energy from them and concentrating it in the main beam at 6° elevation.

The same antenna can be used at 3.5 and 7 MHz. The gain will not be large, however, because the legs are not very long at these frequencies. **Figure 13.17** compares the V-beam versus a horizontal ½-λ 40-meter dipole at 70 feet. At low elevation angles there is about 2 dB of advantage on 40 meters. **Figure 13.18** shows the same type of comparison for 80 meters, where the 80 meter dipole is superior at all angles.

Other V Combinations

A gain increase of about 3 dB can be had by stacking two V-beams one above the other, a half wavelength apart, and feeding them with in-phase currents. This will result in a lowered angle of radiation. The bottom V should be at least a quarter wavelength above the ground, and preferably a half wavelength. This arrangement will narrow the elevation pattern and it will also have a narrow azimuthal pattern.

The V antenna can be made unidirectional by using a second V placed an odd multiple of a quarter wavelength in back of the first and exciting the two with a phase difference of 90°. The system will be unidirectional in the direction of the antenna with the lagging current. However, the V reflector is not normally employed by amateurs at low frequencies because it restricts the use to one band and requires a fairly elaborate supporting structure. Stacked Vs with driven reflectors could, however, be built for the 200- to 500-MHz region without much difficulty.

Feeding the V Beam

The V-beam antenna is most conveniently fed with tuned open wire feeders with an antenna tuner, since this permits multiband operation. Although the length of the wires in a V-beam is not at all critical, it is important that both wires be the same electrical length. If a single band matching solution is desired, probably the most appropriate matching system is that using a stub or quarter-wave matching section.

13.3 THE RESONANT RHOMBIC ANTENNA

The diamond-shaped or rhombic antenna shown in **Figure 13.19** can be looked upon as two acute-angle V-beams placed end-to-end. This arrangement is called a resonant rhombic. The leg lengths of the resonant rhombic must be an integral number of half wavelengths to avoid reactance at its feed point.

The resonant rhombic has two advantages over the simple V-beam. For the same total wire length it gives somewhat greater gain than the V-beam. A rhombic with 3 λ on a leg, for example, has about 1 dB gain over a V antenna with 6 wavelengths on a leg. **Figure 13.20** compares the azimuthal pattern at a 10° elevation for a resonant rhombic with 3 λ legs on 14 MHz, compared to a V-beam with 6 λ legs at the same height of 70 feet. The 3-dB nose beamwidth of the resonant rhombic is only 12.4° wide, but the

gain is very high at 16.26 dBi.

The directional pattern of the rhombic is less frequency sensitive than the V when the antenna is used over a wide frequency range. This is because a change in frequency causes the major lobe from one leg to shift in one direction while the lobe from the opposite leg shifts the other way. This automatic compensation keeps the direction the same over a considerable frequency range. The disadvantage of the rhombic as compared with the V-beam is that an additional support is required. Some authors also report success with "half-rhombics" oriented vertically over ground with and without a counterpoise. (See Bibliography entry for Orr.)

The same factors that govern the design of the V-beam apply in the case of the resonant rhombic. The optimal apex angle A in Figure 13.19 is the same as that for a V having an

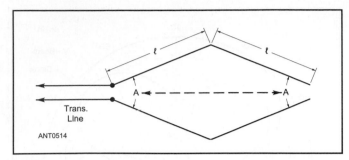

Figure 13.19 — The resonant rhombic or diamond-shaped antenna. All legs are the same length, and opposite angles of the diamond are equal. Length ℓ is an integral number of half wavelengths for resonance.

equal leg length. The diamond-shaped antenna also can be operated as a terminated antenna, as described later in this chapter, and much of the discussion in that section applies to the resonant rhombic as well.

The resonant rhombic has a bidirectional pattern, with minor lobes in other directions, their number and intensity depending on the leg length. In general, these sidelobes are suppressed better with a resonant rhombic than with a V-beam. When used at frequencies below the VHF region, the rhombic antenna is always mounted with the plane containing the wires horizontal. The polarization in this plane, and also in the perpendicular plane that bisects the rhombic, is horizontal. At 144 MHz and above, the dimensions are such that the antenna can be mounted with the plane containing the wires vertical if vertical polarization is desired.

When the rhombic antenna is to be used on several HF amateur bands, it is advisable to choose the apex angle, A, on the basis of the leg length in wavelengths at 14 MHz. Although the gain on higher frequency bands will not be quite as favorable as if the antenna had been designed for the higher frequencies, the system will still work well at the low angles that are necessary at such frequencies.

The resonant rhombic has lots of gain, but you must not forget that this gain comes from a radiation pattern that is very narrow. This requires careful placement of the supports

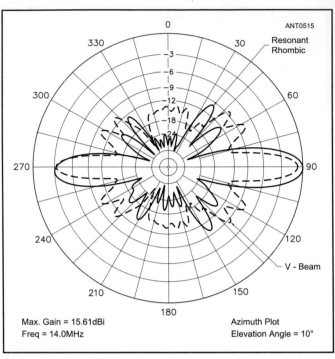

Max. Gain = 15.61dBi
Freq = 14.0MHz

Azimuth Plot
Elevation Angle = 10°

Figure 13.20 — Azimuthal-plane pattern of resonant (unterminated) rhombic (solid line) with 3-λ legs on 14 MHz, at a height of 70 feet above flat ground, compared with a 6-λ per leg V-beam (dashed line) at the same height. Both azimuthal patterns are at a takeoff angle of 10°. The sidelobes for the resonant rhombic are suppressed to a greater degree than those for the V-beam.

for the resonant rhombic to cover desired geographic areas. This is definitely not an antenna that allows you to use just any convenient trees as supports!

Even if you cannot place its corners exactly, the rhombic can still give good performance. (See the Bibliography entry for Hallas.) The main lobe broadens and peak gain is lower but the author found it to be a very effective antenna.

The resonant rhombic antenna can be fed in the same way as the V-beam. Resonant feeders are necessary if the antenna is to be used in several amateur bands.

13.4 TERMINATED LONG-WIRE ANTENNAS

All the antenna systems considered so far in this chapter have been based on operation with standing waves of current and voltage along the wire. Although most hams use antenna designs based on using resonant wires, resonance is by no means a necessary condition for the wire to radiate and intercept electromagnetic waves efficiently, as discussed in the **Antenna Fundamentals** chapter. The result of using nonresonant wires is reactance at the feed point, unless the antenna is terminated with a resistive load.

In **Figure 13.21**, suppose that the wire is parallel with the ground (horizontal) and is terminated by a load Z equal to its characteristic impedance, Z_{ANT}. The wire and its image in the

ground create a transmission line. The load Z can represent a receiver matched to the line. The *terminating resistor* R is also equal to the Z_{ANT} of the wire. A wave coming from direction X will strike the wire first at its far end and sweep across the wire at some angle until it reaches the end at which Z is connected. In so doing, it will induce voltages in the antenna, and currents will flow as a result. The current flowing toward Z is the useful output of the antenna, while the current flowing backwards toward R will be absorbed in R. The same thing is true of a wave coming from the direction X'. In such an antenna there are no standing waves, because all received power is absorbed at either end.

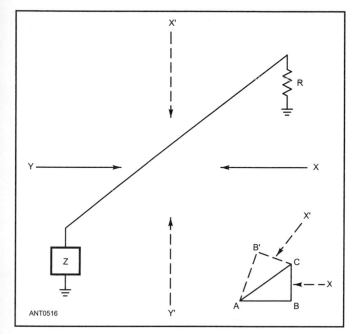

Figure 13.21 — Layout for a terminated long-wire antenna.

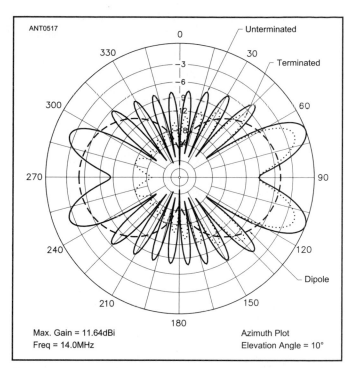

Figure 13.22 — Azimuthal-plane pattern for 5-λ long-wire antenna at 14 MHz and 70 feet above flat ground. The solid line shows the long-wire terminated with 600-Ω to ground, while the dashed line is for the same antenna unterminated. For comparison, the response for a ½-λ dipole is overlaid with the two other patterns. You can see that the terminated long-wire has a good front-to-back pattern, but it loses about 2 dB in forward gain compared to the unterminated long-wire.

The greatest possible power will be delivered to the load Z when the individual currents induced as the wave sweeps across the wire all combine properly on reaching the load. The currents will reach Z in optimum phase when the time required for a current to flow from the far end of the antenna to Z is exactly one-half cycle longer than the time taken by the wave to sweep over the antenna. A half cycle is equivalent to a half wavelength greater than the distance traversed by the wave from the instant it strikes the far end of the antenna to the instant that it reaches the near end. This is shown by the small drawing, where AC represents the antenna, BC is a line perpendicular to the wave direction, and AB is the distance traveled by the wave in sweeping past AC. AB must be one-half wavelength shorter than AC. Similarly, AB' must be the same length as AB for a wave arriving from X'.

A wave arriving at the antenna from the opposite direction Y (or Y'), will similarly result in the largest possible current at the far end. However, since the far end is terminated in R, which is equal to Z, all the power delivered to R by the wave arriving from Y will be absorbed in R. The current traveling to Z will produce a signal in Z in proportion to its amplitude. If the antenna length is such that all the individual currents arrive at Z in such phase as to add up to zero, there will be no current through Z. At other lengths the resultant current may reach appreciable values. The lengths that give zero amplitude are those which are odd multiples of ¼ λ, beginning at ¾ λ. The response from the Y direction is greatest when the antenna is any even multiple of ½ λ long; the higher the multiple, the smaller the response.

Directional Characteristics

Figure 13.22 compares the azimuthal pattern for a 5-λ long 14-MHz long-wire antenna, 70 feet high over flat ground, when it is terminated and when it is unterminated. The rearward pattern when the wire is terminated with a 600 Ω resistor is reduced about 15 dB, with a reduction in gain in the forward direction of about 2 dB.

For a shorter leg length in a terminated long-wire antenna, the reduction in forward gain is larger — more energy is radiated by a longer wire before the forward wave is absorbed in the terminating resistor. The azimuthal patterns for terminated and unterminated V-beams with 2-λ legs are overlaid for comparison in **Figure 13.23**. With these relatively short legs the reduction in forward gain is about 3.5 dB due to the terminations, although the front-to-rear ratio approaches 20 dB for the terminated V-beam. Each leg of this terminated V-beam use a 600-Ω non-inductive resistor to ground. Each resistor would have to dissipate about one-quarter of the transmitter power. For average conductor diameters and heights above ground, the Z_{ANT} of the antenna is of the order of 500 to 600 Ω.

13.4.1 THE TERMINATED RHOMBIC ANTENNA

The highest development of the long-wire antenna is the *terminated rhombic*, shown schematically in **Figure 13.24**. It consists of four conductors joined to form a diamond, or *rhombus*. All sides of the antenna have the same length and the opposite corner angles are equal. The antenna can be

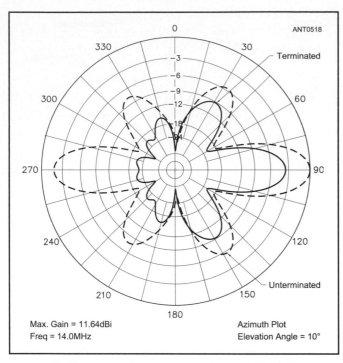

Figure 13.23 — The azimuthal patterns for a shorter-leg V-beam (2-λ legs) when it is terminated (solid line) and unterminated (dashed line). With shorter legs, the terminated V-beam loses about 3.5 dB in forward gain compared to the unterminated version, while suppressing the rearward lobes as much as 20 dB.

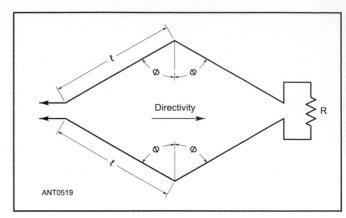

Figure 13.24 — The layout for a terminated rhombic antenna.

considered as being made up of two V antennas placed end to end and terminated by a noninductive resistor to produce a unidirectional pattern. The terminating resistor is connected between the far ends of the two sides, and is made approximately equal to the characteristic impedance of the antenna as a unit. The rhombic may be constructed either horizontally or vertically, but is practically always constructed horizontally at frequencies below 54 MHz, since the pole height required is considerably less. Also, horizontal polarization is equally, if not more, satisfactory at these frequencies over most types of soil.

The basic principle of combining lobes of maximum radiation from the four individual wires constituting the rhombus or diamond is the same in either the terminated type or the resonant type described earlier in this chapter.

Tilt Angle

In dealing with the terminated rhombic, it is a matter of custom to talk about the tilt angle (φ in Figure 13.24), rather than the angle of maximum radiation with respect to an individual wire. **Figure 13.25** shows the tilt angle as a function of the antenna leg length. The curve marked "0°" is used for a takeoff elevation angle of 0°; that is, maximum radiation in the plane of the antenna. The other curves show the proper tilt angles to use when aligning the major lobe with a desired takeoff angle. For a 5° takeoff angle, the difference in tilt angle is less than 1° for the range of lengths shown.

The broken curve marked "optimum length"

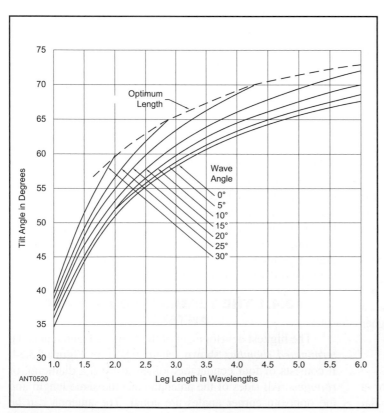

Figure 13.25 — Rhombic-antenna design chart. For any given leg length, the curves show the proper tilt angle to give maximum radiation at the selected takeoff angle. The broken curve marked "optimum length" shows the leg length that gives the maximum possible output at the selected takeoff angle. The optimum length as given by the curves should be multiplied by 0.74 to obtain the leg length for which the takeoff angle and main lobe are aligned.

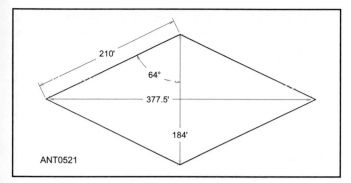

Figure 13.26 — Rhombic antenna dimensions for a compromise design between 14- and 28-MHz requirements, as discussed in the text. The leg length is 6 λ at 28 MHz, 3 λ at 14 MHz.

shows the leg length at which maximum gain is obtained at any given takeoff angle. Increasing the leg length beyond the optimum will result in less gain, and for that reason the curves do not extend beyond the optimum length. Note that the optimum length becomes greater as the desired takeoff angle decreases. Leg lengths over 6 λ are not recommended because the directive pattern becomes so sharp that the antenna performance is highly variable with small changes in the angle, both horizontal and vertical, at which an incoming wave reaches the antenna. Since these angles vary to some extent in ionospheric propagation, it does not pay to attempt to try for too great a degree of directivity.

Multiband Design

When a rhombic antenna is to be used over a considerable frequency range, a compromise must be made in the tilt angle. **Figure 13.26** gives the design dimensions of a suitable compromise for a rhombic that covers the 14 to 30 MHz range well. **Figure 13.27** shows the azimuth and elevation patterns for this antenna at 14 MHz, at a height of 70 feet over flat ground. The comparison antenna in this case is a 4-element Yagi on a 26-foot boom, also 70 feet above flat ground. The rhombic has about 2.2 dB more gain, but its azimuthal pattern is 17.2° wide at the 3 dB points, and only 26° at the –20 dB points! On the other hand, the Yagi has a 3-dB beamwidth of 63°, making it far easier to aim at a distant geographic location. Figure 13.27B shows the elevation-plane patterns for the same antennas above. As usual, the peak angle for either horizontally polarized antenna is determined mainly by the height above ground.

The peak gain of a terminated rhombic is less than that of an unterminated resonant rhombic. For the rhombic of Figure 13.26, the reduction in peak gain is about 1.5 dB. **Figure 13.28** compares the azimuthal patterns for this rhombic with and without an 800-Ω termination.

Figure 13.29 shows the azimuth and elevation patterns for the terminated rhombic of Figure 13.26 when it is operated at 28 MHz. The main lobe becomes very narrow, at 6.9° at the 3-dB points. However, this is partially compensated for by the appearance of two sidelobes each side of the main beam. These tend to spread out the main pattern some. Again, a 4-element Yagi at the same height is used for comparison.

Termination

Although the difference in the gain is relatively small with terminated or unterminated rhombics of comparable design, the terminated antenna has the advantage that over a wide frequency range it presents an essentially resistive and constant load to the transmitter. In a sense, the power

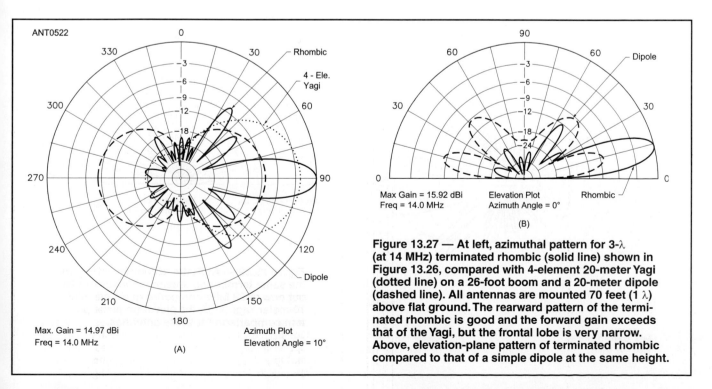

Figure 13.27 — At left, azimuthal pattern for 3-λ (at 14 MHz) terminated rhombic (solid line) shown in Figure 13.26, compared with 4-element 20-meter Yagi (dotted line) on a 26-foot boom and a 20-meter dipole (dashed line). All antennas are mounted 70 feet (1 λ) above flat ground. The rearward pattern of the terminated rhombic is good and the forward gain exceeds that of the Yagi, but the frontal lobe is very narrow. Above, elevation-plane pattern of terminated rhombic compared to that of a simple dipole at the same height.

dissipated in the terminating resistor can be considered power that would have been radiated in the other direction had the resistor not been there. Therefore, the fact that some of the power (about one-third) is used up in heating the resistor does not mean that much actual loss in the desired direction.

The characteristic impedance of an ordinary rhombic antenna, looking into the input end, is in the order of 700 to 800 Ω when properly terminated in a resistance at the far end. The terminating resistance required to bring about the matching condition usually is slightly higher than the input impedance because of the loss of energy through radiation by the time the far end is reached. The correct value usually will be found to be of the order of 800 Ω, and should be determined experimentally if the flattest possible antenna is desired. However, for average work a noninductive resistance of 800 Ω can be used with the assurance that the operation will not be far from optimum.

The terminating resistor must be practically a pure resistance at the operating frequencies; that is, its inductance and capacitance should be negligible. Ordinary wire-wound resistors are not suitable because they have far too much inductance and distributed capacitance. Small carbon resistors have satisfactory electrical characteristics but will not dissipate more than a few watts and so cannot be used, except when the transmitter power does not exceed 10 or 20 watts or when the antenna is to be used for reception only. The special resistors designed either for use as dummy antennas or for terminating rhombic antennas should be used in other cases. To allow a factor of safety, the total rated power dissipation of the resistor or resistors should be equal to half the power output of the transmitter.

To reduce the effects of stray capacitance it is desirable to use several units, say three, in series even when one alone will safely dissipate the power. The two end units should be identical and each should have one fourth to one third the total resistance, with the center unit making up the difference. The units should be installed in a weatherproof housing at the end of the antenna to protect them and to permit mounting

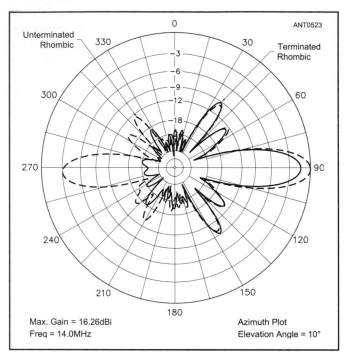

Figure 13.28 — Comparison of azimuthal patterns for terminated (solid line) and unterminated (dashed line) rhombic antennas, using same dimensions as Figure 13.26 at a frequency of 14 MHz. The gain tradeoff is about 1.5 dB in return for the superior rearward pattern of the terminated antenna.

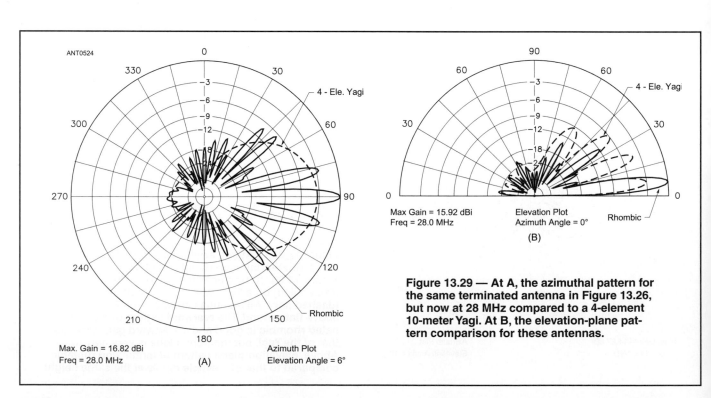

Figure 13.29 — At A, the azimuthal pattern for the same terminated antenna in Figure 13.26, but now at 28 MHz compared to a 4-element 10-meter Yagi. At B, the elevation-plane pattern comparison for these antennas.

without mechanical strain. The connecting leads should be short so that little extraneous inductance is introduced.

Alternatively, the terminating resistance may be placed at the end of an 800-Ω line connected to the end of the antenna. This will permit placing the resistors and their housing at a point convenient for adjustment rather than at the top of the pole. Resistance wire may be used for this line, so that a portion of the power will be dissipated before it reaches the resistive termination, thus permitting the use of lower wattage lumped resistors.

If the rhombic is to be used on a single-band, Hallas (see the Bibliography) presents an interesting method of using an antenna tuner and a more common 50-Ω dummy load to create a "tunable load" that can be adjusted for the best performance.

Multi-Wire Rhombics

The input impedance of a rhombic antenna constructed as in Figure 13.26 is not quite constant as the frequency is varied. This is because the varying separation between the wires causes the characteristic impedance of the antenna to vary along its length. The variation in Z_{ANT} can be minimized by a conductor arrangement that increases the capacitance per unit length in proportion to the separation between the wires.

The method of accomplishing this is shown in **Figure 13.30**. Three conductors are used, joined together at the ends but with increasing separation as the junction between legs is approached. For HF work the spacing between the wires at the center is 3 to 4 feet, which is similar to that used in commercial installations using legs several wavelengths long. Since all three wires should have the same length, the

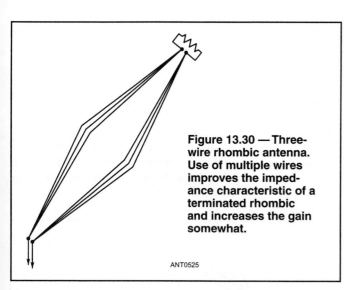

Figure 13.30 — Three-wire rhombic antenna. Use of multiple wires improves the impedance characteristic of a terminated rhombic and increases the gain somewhat.

ANT0525

top and bottom wires should be slightly farther from the support than the middle wire. Using three wires in this way reduces the Z_{ANT} of the antenna to approximately 600 Ω, thus providing a better match for practical open-wire line, in addition to smoothing out the impedance variation over the frequency range.

A similar effect (although not quite as favorable) is obtained by using two wires instead of three. The 3-wire system has been found to increase the gain of the antenna by about 1 dB over that of a single-conductor version.

Front-to-Back Ratio

It is theoretically possible to obtain an infinite front-to-back ratio with a terminated rhombic antenna, and in practice very large values can be had. However, when the antenna is terminated in its characteristic impedance, the infinite front-to-back ratio can be obtained only at frequencies for which the leg length is an odd multiple of a quarter wavelength. The front-to-back ratio is smallest at frequencies for which the leg length is a multiple of a half wavelength.

When the leg length is not an odd multiple of a quarter-wave at the frequency under consideration, the front-to-back ratio can be made very high by decreasing the value of terminating resistance slightly. This permits a small reflection from the far end of the antenna, which cancels out the residual response at the input end. With large antennas, the front-to-back ratio may be made very large over the whole frequency range by experimental adjustment of the terminating resistance. Modification of the terminating resistance can result in a splitting of the back null into two nulls, one on either side of a small lobe in the back direction. Changes in the value of terminating resistance thus permit steering the back null over a small horizontal range so that signals coming from a particular spot not exactly to the rear of the antenna may be minimized.

Methods of Feed

If the broad frequency characteristic of the terminated rhombic antenna is to be utilized fully, the feeder system must be similarly broadbanded. Open-wire transmission line of the same characteristic impedance as that shown at the antenna input terminals (approximately 700 to 800 Ω) may be used. Data for the construction of such lines is given in the chapter on **Transmission Lines**. While the usual matching stub can be used to provide an impedance transformation to more satisfactory line impedances, this limits the operation of the antenna to a comparatively narrow range of frequencies centering about that for which the stub is adjusted. Probably a more satisfactory arrangement would be to use a coaxial transmission line and a broadband transformer balun at the antenna feed point.

13.5 PROJECT: FOUR-WIRE STEERABLE V BEAM FOR 10 THROUGH 40 METERS

A simple arrangement of four wires can be used to work multiple bands and have antenna gain in different directions without using a rotator. A version of this antenna was described in *QST* (see Bibliography entry for Colvin) and is included in ARRL's *Wire Antenna Classics*. That version had wires 584 feet long. In this version, built by Sam Moore, NX5Z, each wire is only 106 feet long. Many DX stations have had great success with this type of antenna.

Antenna Characteristics

An unterminated V beam gain pattern is bidirectional with two main gain lobes 180° apart if the leg lengths are at least a wavelength long. In **Figure 13.31**, a long wire antenna at the left is shown to have a gain pattern of four major lobes. Another long wire antenna positioned 45° from the first is also shown. If these are combined to form a V, it has the gain pattern as shown to the right in Figure 13.31.

In this design, four 106 foot wires are spaced at 45°. The length of the wire is not as important as that they all be the same length. The author installed his V beam with the apex and relay control box at a height of 40 feet with the wire ends 10 feet off the ground in a sloping V configuration. This V beam's gain approximates that of a three element Yagi on 10, 12, 15 and 17 meters and is within a few dB on 20 meters. The antenna provides useful operation on 30 and 40 meters,

with essentially an omnidirectional pattern on 40. The beam direction is controlled by simply switching two switches in the station.

This antenna may also be built with wire lengths as short as 60 feet to more easily fit on a city lot. There will be a small decrease in gain. The V beam gain increases with the length of the wires. The longer the wires, the greater the gain. As the wire lengthens, however, the beamwidth narrows. The gains and beamwidths of 106 and 60 foot versions are shown in **Table 13-1**, based on *EZNEC* analysis. (*EZNEC-ARRL* is provided with this book and discussed in the **Antenna Modeling** chapter.) As a reference, the typical two element Yagi has 6 to 7 dBi gain while a three element Yagi can be expected to have a 7.5 to 8.1 dBi gain, depending on design, especially boom length.

The azimuth pattern looking down on a V beam is shown in **Figure 13.32**. If the height of the V beam is less than ½ wavelength, the gain pattern will distort and make the antenna more omnidirectional.

To reduce the gain lobe to the rear of the V beam you can terminate the wire ends with a resistor. An unterminated version has gain in both directions. If terminated, the antenna would need eight wires instead of four to have gain in all directions.

Since this antenna may be used for multiband operation, the gain waveform changes somewhat depending on the frequency of operation. The higher the frequency, the greater the gain, since the frequency to wire length ratio changes. For example, if your V beam is 1 wavelength long at 20 meters, it is 2 wavelengths long at 10 meters, thus causing greater gain and narrower beamwidth as shown in Table 13-1. While essentially bidirectional on the upper bands, there is a 1 to 2 dB front to back ratio, with the maximum signal to the open end of the V. The beamwidth shown in Table 1 is of the front beam, with the rear

Table 1
Gain and Beamwidth of the V Beam on Each Band

Frequency (MHz)	Gain at 106' (dBi)	3 dB Beamwidth at 106' (°)	Gain at 60' (dBi)	3 dB Beamwidth at 60' (°)
7.15	1.9*	Omnidirectional	2.4*	Omnidirectional
10.12	3.6	133	3.7*	Omnidirectional
14.15	6.7	71	4.1	137
18.11	8.5	42	4.1	136
21.2	9.1	33	6.0	63
24.93	9.7	28	6.1	61
28.3	10.7	23	7.3	40

*Essentially omnidirectional with maximum gain nearly perpendicular to the wire bisector.

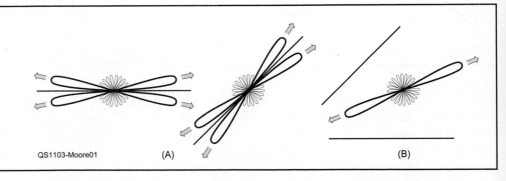

Figure 13.31 — The azimuth patterns of two long wire antennas are shown at (A). If the two are combined in phase to form a V, the resulting pattern is shown at (B).

QS1103-Moore01   (A)   (B)

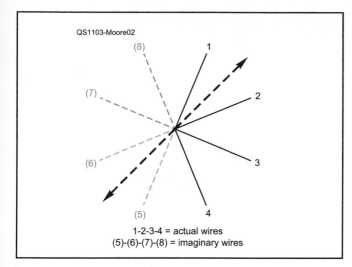

Figure 13.32 — The selectable azimuth looking down on the V beam. The arrow shows directions of maximum radiation with wires 1 and 2 connected.

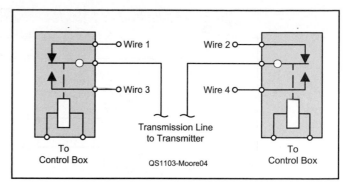

Figure 13.34 — Schematic diagram of the relay box used to remotely select the V beam wires.

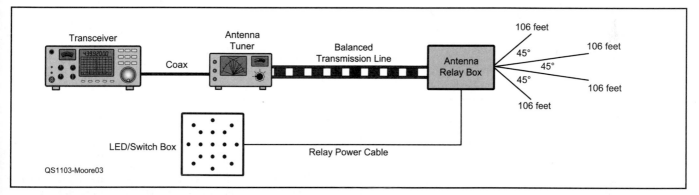

Figure 13.33 — The block diagram of the V beam system. The antenna tuner must be able to accept balanced transmission line and a built-in or external 4:1 balun is necessary.

beam generally somewhat narrower. A horizontal, rather than sloping, V beam will be more symmetrical.

The block diagram of the V beam system is shown in **Figure 13.33**. The antenna tuner must be able to accept balanced transmission line and a built in or external 4:1 balun is necessary. The author made a homebrew air core external 4:1 balun using 1 inch PVC pipe and used a small automatic antenna tuner.

Controls and Indicators

The LED switch box supplies power to the relays in the antenna relay box at the center of the V beam via a three wire cable such as three wire electrical zip cord. Smaller wires would work.

The relay box schematic is shown in **Figure 13.34**. Only two switches are needed to power relays 1 and 2. Relay 1 switches between wire 1 and 3 and relay 2 switches between wire 2 and 4. Note that wire 4 is used in combination with wire 1 instead of (imaginary) wire 5. This obtuse angle yields

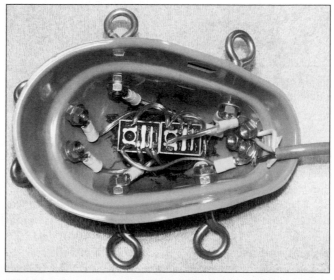

Figure 13.35 — Relay box assembled in a power entry PVC cover.

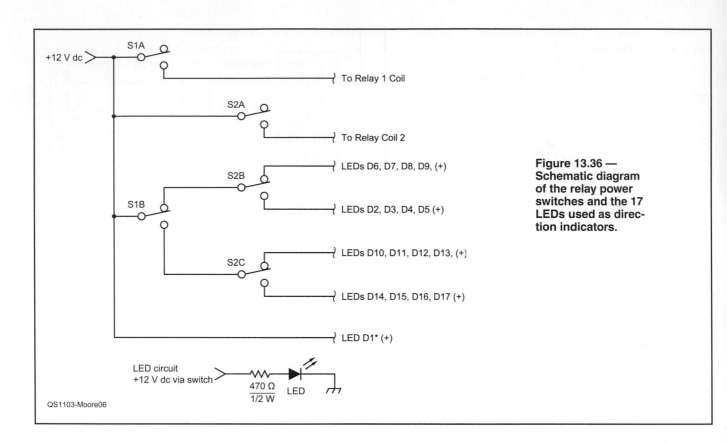

Figure 13.36 — Schematic diagram of the relay power switches and the 17 LEDs used as direction indicators.

QS1103-Moore06

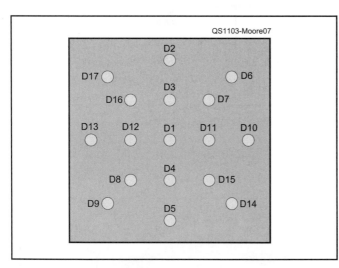

QS1103-Moore07

Figure 13.37 — Top view of the indicator panel showing LED placement.

Figure 13.38 — The V beams are supported by a mast and a standard PVC power-entry cover. Relays are used to switch between the beams and are controlled through a separate control cable.

the about same gain and waveform as wire 4 to 5 would have offered, without having to string another wire. **Figure 13.35** shows an assembled relay box in a power entry PVC cover.

The schematic in **Figure 13.36** shows the relay power switches and the 17 LED connections. LED and relay common connections go to a 12 V return. A top view of the LEDs is shown in **Figure 13.37**. The LED switch box illuminated LEDs indicate the direction of greatest gain. Note LED 1 is always on, since it's used in all directions. The other 4 LEDs in a particular row, in a bingo board pattern, are connected and supplied with +12 V dc via switch 1 or 2, depending on wires chosen. Use a 3-pole switch for S2, or use two closely spaced DPDT switches and switch them at the same time.

The assembled control head is mounted as shown in **Figure 13.38**. Total cost is around $50, not counting the balun and balanced transmission line. For the four wires, the author used electric fence wire, which accepted solder surprisingly well. You can buy a ¼ mile roll of electric fence wire inexpensively at agricultural supply stores. You may also have a few necessary parts in your junk box.

13.6 BIBLIOGRAPHY

Source material and more extended discussion of topics covered in this chapter can be found in the references given below.

E. Bruce, "Developments in Short-Wave Directive Antennas," *Proc IRE*, Aug 1931.

E. Bruce, A. C. Beck and L. R. Lowry, "Horizontal Rhombic Antennas," *Proc IRE*, Jan 1935.

P. S. Carter, C. W. Hansel and N. E. Lindenblad, "Development of Directive Transmitting Antennas by R.C.A. Communications," *Proc IRE*, Oct 1931.

L. Colvin, DL4ZC (W6KG), "Multiple V Beams," *QST*, Aug 1956.

J. Devoldere, ON4UN, *Low-Band DXing* (Newington: ARRL, 2010).

J. Hallas, W1ZR, "Achieving Near Perfection with the Imperfect Rhombic," *QST*, Nov 2004, pp 28-32.

A. E. Harper, *Rhombic Antenna Design* (New York: D. Van Nostrand Co, Inc).

E. A. Laport, "Design Data for Horizontal Rhombic Antennas," *RCA Review*, Mar 1952.

G. M. Miller, *Modern Electronic Communication* (Englewood Cliffs, NJ: Prentice Hall, 1983).

S. Moore, NX5Z, "A Four Wire Steerable V Beam for 10 through 40 Meters," *QST*, Mar 2011, pp 30-33.

J. H. Mullaney, Capt., W4HGU, "The Half-Rhombic Antenna," *QST*, Jan 1946, pp 28-31.

M. Orr, AA2PE, "The Tilted Half-Rhombic Antenna," *Antenna Compendium, Vol 4*, ARRL, 1999, pp 5-10 through 5-13.

F. E. Terman, *Radio Engineering*, Second Edition (New York: McGraw-Hill, 1937).

TABLE OF CONTENTS

Chapter 14

HF Antenna System Design

This chapter combines information from previous editions into a condensed discussion of HF antenna system design. An amateur just beginning to build an HF station may be more interested in trying out different types of antennas and gaining experience with selecting, building and installing them. Later on, as experience is gained and specific goals are formed, the process of system design becomes important.

No single book can provide a step-by-step procedure for designing antenna systems — there are too many different needs and operating styles. What can be done, however, is to give an overview of the process by which system-level issues are identified and dealt with. Tools such as propagation prediction and antenna modeling software will be discussed from

the antenna system perspective. Methods of using antennas to meet certain goals, such as stacking Yagis and using near vertical incidence skywave propagation (NVIS), will be covered.

By thinking about your "antenna farm" as a system — whether a single antenna in a tree or a multiple-tower contest station — you will be able to make better use of your time and materials and have more success on the air.

We will begin with an overview of the system design process and how to approach it. The next step is a section covering the use of propagation prediction tools as a means of assessing the coverage of an antenna system. Then the effects of local terrain on antenna system planning and performance are covered. The final sections address the use of vertical stacks of Yagi antennas to control elevation angle.

14.1 SYSTEM DESIGN BASICS

The most important time spent in putting together an antenna system is the time spent in planning. Later in this chapter the section on Local Terrain will present steps needed to evaluate how your local terrain can affect HF communications. You will need to compare the patterns resulting from your own terrain to the statistically relevant elevation angles needed for coverage of various geographic areas. (The elevation-angle statistics were discussed in the **Radio Wave Propagation** chapter and are located on the CD-ROM included with this book, as is the terrain-assessment program *HFTA*.)

The implicit assumptions in using propagation data and terrain analysis are (1) that you know where you want to talk

to, and (2) that you'd like the most effective system possible. At the start of such a theoretical analysis, cost is no object. Practical matters, like cost or the desires of your spouse, can come later! After all, you're just checking out all the possibilities. If nothing else, you will use the methodology in this chapter to evaluate any property you are considering buying so that you can build your "dream station."

By using the techniques and tools available in this book, you can rationally and logically plan an antenna system that will be best suited for your own particular conditions. Now, however, you have to get practical. Thinking through and planning the installation can save a lot of time, money and frustration.

One often overlooked part of successful antenna system design (and station design, too) is the keeping of a station notebook. Make sure you save and organize the various computer files and documents associated with your system design. Being able to revisit the steps leading to a decision — successful or unsuccessful — is very important. Important data from measurements or tests should always be clearly labeled and stored so that you can find it later. Think of each page or file as a brick in the grand structure you are building. No one ever regrets having kept good records!

While no one can tell you the exact steps you should take in developing your own master plan, this section, prepared originally by Chuck Hutchinson, K8CH, should help you with some ideas.

14.1.1 DESIRES AND LIMITATIONS

Begin planning by spelling out your communications desires and the limitations placed on them. Engineers call these "requirements" and "constraints" — all successful projects begin with clearly understanding and recording them. What bands are you interested in? Who (or where) do you want to talk to? When do you operate? How much time and money are you willing to spend on an antenna system? What physical limitations affect your master plan?

From the answers to the above questions, begin to formulate goals — short, intermediate and long range. Be realistic about those goals. Remember that there are three station effectiveness factors that are under your control. These are: operator skill, equipment in the shack, and the antenna system. There is no substitute for developing operating skills. Some tradeoffs are possible between shack equipment and antennas. For example, a high-power amplifier can compensate for a less than optimum antenna but only for transmitted signals. By contrast, a better antenna has advantages for receiving as well as for transmitting.

Consider your limitations. Are there regulatory restrictions on antennas in your community? Are there any deed restrictions or covenants that apply to your property? Do other factors (finances, family considerations, other interests, and so forth) limit the type or height of antennas that you can erect? All of these factors must be investigated because they play a major role determining the type of antennas you erect.

Chances are that you won't be able to immediately do all you desire. Think about how you can budget your resources over a period of time. Your resources are your money, your time available to work, materials you may have on hand, friends that are willing to help, etc. One way to budget is to concentrate your initial efforts on a given band or two. If your major interest is in chasing DX, you might want to start with a very good antenna for the 14-MHz band. A simple multiband antenna could initially serve for other frequencies. Later you can add better antennas for those other bands.

14.1.2 SITE PLANNING

A map of your property or proposed antenna site can be of great help as you begin to consider alternative antennas.

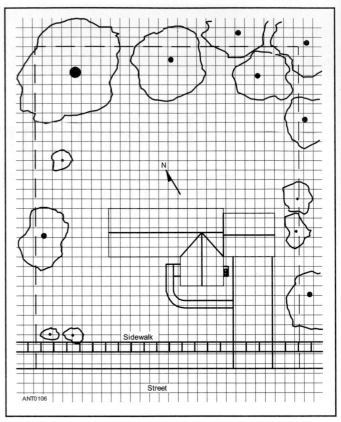

Figure 14.1 — A site map such this one is a useful tool for planning your antenna installation.

You'll need to know the size and location of buildings, trees and other major objects in the area. Be sure to note compass directions on your map. Graph or quadrille paper (or a simple CAD program) can be very useful for this purpose. See **Figure 14.1** for an example. It's a good idea to make a few photocopies of your site map so you can mark on the copies as you work on your plans. If you create a master map with CAD software, you can create and save lots of alternatives for comparisons and evaluations.

Use your map to plan antenna layouts and locations of any supporting towers or masts. If your plan calls for more than one tower or mast, think about using them as supports for wire antennas. As you work on a layout, be sure to think in three dimensions even though the map shows only two.

Be sensitive to your neighbors. A 70-foot guyed tower in the front yard of a house in a residential neighborhood is not a good idea (and probably won't comply with local ordinances!). You probably will want to locate that tower in the back yard.

Be sure to include restrictions and hazards on the map. For example, you may have set-back requirements from property lines for any structure on your property, such as a tower. You may not be allowed to intrude on neighboring "air space" with antenna elements. Power lines and other hazards such as buried utilities should be on your map, as well. It's just as important to identify where antennas can't go as where they can.

As discussed in the **Building Antenna Systems and Towers** chapter, consider access needs when laying out your system. If you will be putting up towers, consider how a backhoe or concrete truck can get to the location of the tower base. You'll need to allow space for towers that fold over or that are tipped up for installation, too.

14.1.3 INITIAL ANALYSIS

Use the information in this chapter, antenna modeling software and propagation evaluation tools to analyze antenna patterns in both horizontal and vertical planes toward geographic areas of interest.

Use antenna modeling tools to help you evaluate what type of antenna might be suitable to your own particular style of operating. Do you want a Yagi with a lot of rejection of received signals from the rear? Let's say that terrain analysis shows that you need an antenna at least 50 feet high. Do you really need a steel tower, or would a simple dipole in the trees serve your communication needs just fine? How about a vertical in your backyard? Would that be inconspicuous enough to suit your neighbors and your own family, yet still get you on the air?

If you want to work DX, you'll want antennas that radiate energy at low as well as intermediate angles. An antenna pattern is greatly affected by the presence of ground and by the local topography of the ground. Therefore, be sure to consider what effect ground will have on the antenna pattern at the height you are considering. A 70-foot high antenna is approximately ½, 1, 1½ and 2 wavelengths high on 7, 14, 21 and 28 MHz respectively. Those heights are useful for long-distance communications. The same 70-foot height represents only λ/4 at 3.5 MHz, however. Most of the radiated energy from a dipole at that height would be concentrated straight up. This condition is not great for long-distance communication, but can still be useful for some DX work and excellent for short-range communications.

Lower antenna heights can be useful for certain types of communications — see the section on NVIS communications later in this chapter, for example. However, for most amateur operation it is generally true that "the higher, the better" as far as communications effectiveness is concerned. This general rule of thumb, of course, should be tempered by an exact analysis of your local terrain. Being located at the top of a steep hill can mean that you can use lower tower heights to achieve good coverage.

There may be cases where it is not possible to install low-frequency dipoles λ/4 or more above the ground. A vertical antenna with many radials is a good choice for long-distance communications. You may want to install both a dipole and a vertical for the 3.5- or 7-MHz bands. On the 1.8-MHz band, unless extremely tall supports are available, a vertical antenna is likely to be the most useful for DXing. You can then choose the antenna that performs best for a given set of conditions. A low dipole will generally work better for shorter-range communications, while the vertical will generally be the better performer over longer distances.

Consider the azimuthal pattern of fixed antennas. You'll want to orient any fixed antennas to favor the directions of greatest interest to you.

14.1.4 BUILDING A SYSTEM PLAN

At this point, you will enter a repeated sequence of "design-model-adjust" as you evaluate the plan. You should start with modeling and then compare the results to those "desires" you wrote down at the beginning. With each round of modeling and comparison, your antenna system will be improved.

As you refine your system design, you can also build the long-term plan for construction of the antenna system. Chances are that you can divide the actual construction of your system into a series of phases or steps. By keeping the long-range plan in mind you will be able to make better decisions at every step of the way toward achieving your goals!

Say, for example, that you have lots of room and that your long-range plan calls for a pair of towers, one 100-feet high, and the other 70-feet high, to support monoband Yagi antennas. The towers will also support a horizontal 3.5-MHz dipole, for DX work. On your map you've located them so the 80 meter dipole will be broadside to Europe. You decide to build the 70-foot tower with a triband beam and 80 and 40 meter inverted-V dipoles to begin the project.

In your master plan you design the guys, anchors and all hardware for the 70-foot tower to support the load of stacked 4-element 10 and 15 meter monobanders Yagis. So you make sure you buy a heavy-duty rotator and the stout mast needed for the monoband antennas later because you have a long-range plan for them. Thus you avoid having to buy, and then sell, a medium-duty rotator and lighter weight tower materials later on when you upgrade the station. You could have saved money in the long run by putting up a monoband beam for your favorite band, but you decided that for now it is more important to have a beam on 14, 21 and 28 MHz, so you choose a commercial triband Yagi.

The second step of your plan calls for installing the second tower and stacking a 2-element 40 meter and a 4-element 20 meter monoband Yagi on it. You also plan to replace the tribander on the 70-foot tower with stacked 4-element 10 and 15 meter monoband Yagis. Although this is still a "dream system" you can now apply some of the modeling techniques discussed earlier in this chapter to determine the overall system performance.

14.1.5 MODELING INTERACTIONS

In this next step of analysis we're going to assume that you have sufficient real estate to separate the 70- and 100-foot towers by 150 feet so that you can easily support an 80 meter dipole between them. We'll also assume that you want the 80 meter dipole to have its maximum response at a heading of 45° into Europe from your location in Newington, Connecticut. The dipole will also have a lobe facing 225° toward the USA and New Zealand, making it a good antenna for both domestic contacts and DX work. Note that it is important to model interactions for the full system even if you don't plan on building all of it right away.

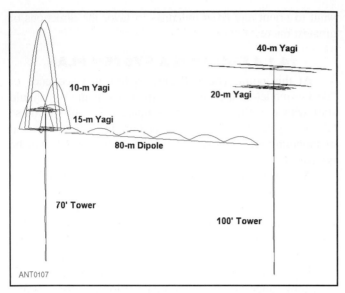

Figure 14.2 — Layout for two-tower antenna system, at 70 and 100 feet high and 150 feet apart. The 70-foot tower has a 4-element 10 meter Yagi at 80 feet on a 10-foot rotating mast and a 4-element 15 meter Yagi at 70 feet. An 80 meter dipole goes from the 70-foot tower to the 100-foot tower, which holds a 2-element 40 meter Yagi at 110 feet and a 4-element 20 meter Yagi at 100 feet. In this figure all the rotatable Yagis are facing the direction of Europe and the currents on the 15 meter Yagi are shown. Note the significant amount of current induced on the nearby 80 meter dipole that will cause a re-radiated signal!

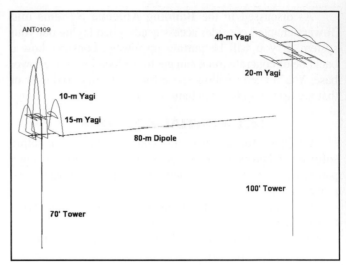

Figure 14.4 — The layout and 15 meter currents when the Yagis on the 100-foot tower are pointed toward the 70-foot tower. The 15 meter Yagi has been rotated to face the direction of the 100-foot tower (toward the Caribbean).

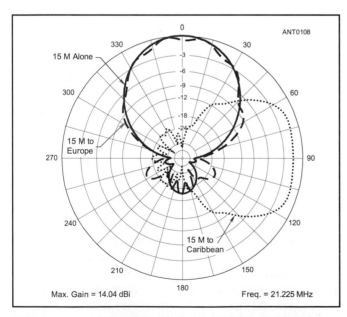

Figure 14.3 — An overlay of azimuth patterns. The solid line is the radiation pattern for the 15 meter Yagi all by itself. The dashed line is the pattern for the 15 meter Yagi, as affected by all the other antennas. The dotted line is the pattern for the 15 meter Yagi when it is pointed toward the Caribbean, with the Yagis on the 100-foot tower pointed toward the 70-foot tower. The peak response of the 15 meter Yagi has dropped by about 1.5 dB.

This helps avoid "mid-course corrections."

Let's examine the interactions that occur between the rotatable Yagis for 10, 15, 20 and 40 meters. See **Figure 14.2**, which purposely exaggerates the magnitude of the currents on the 4-element 15 meter Yagi mounted at 70 feet. Here, both sets of Yagis have been rotated so that they are pointing into Europe. There is a small amount of current radiated onto the 10 meter antenna but virtually no current is radiated onto the 40 and 20 meter Yagis. This is good.

However, significant current is picked up by the 80 meter dipole. This undesired current and the subsequent reradiated signal affects the radiation pattern of the 15 meter antenna, as shown in **Figure 14.3**, which overlays the pattern of the 4-element 15 meter Yagi by itself with that of the Yagi interacting with the other antennas. You can see "ripples" in the azimuthal response of the 15 meter Yagi due to the effects of the 80 meter dipole's re-radiation. The magnitude of the ripples is about 1 dB at worst, so they don't seriously affect the forward pattern (into Europe), but the rearward lobes are degraded somewhat, to just below 20 dB.

Figure 14.3 also shows the worst-case situation for the 15 meter Yagi. Here, the 15 and 10 meter stack has been turned clockwise 90°, facing the Caribbean, while the 40 and 20 meter Yagis on the 100-foot tower have been turned counter-clockwise 90° (in the direction of Japan) to face the 70-foot tower holding the 10/15 meter Yagis. You can see the layout and the currents in **Figure 14.4**. Now the 40 and 20 meter Yagis re-radiate some 15 meter energy and reduce the maximum gain by about 1.5 dB. Note that in this direction the 80 meter dipole no longer has 15 meter energy radiated onto it by the 15 meter Yagi.

The shape of the patterns will change depending on whether you specify "current" or "voltage" sources in the models for the other antennas, since this effectively opens up or shorts the feed points at the other antennas so far as

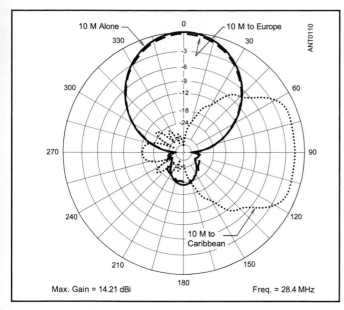

Figure 14.5 — The radiation patterns for the 10 meter Yagi. The solid line is the 10 meter Yagi by itself. The dashed line is for the same Yagi, with all other antenna interactions. The dotted line shows the worst-case pattern, with the stacked Yagis on the 100-foot tower facing the 70-foot tower and the 10 meter Yagi pointed toward the Caribbean. Again, the peak response of the 10 meter Yagi has dropped about 1.5 dB in the worst-case situation.

15 meter energy is concerned. In practice, this means that the interaction between antennas will vary somewhat depending on the length of the feed lines going to each antenna and whether each feed line is open-circuited or short-circuited when it is not in use.

You can now see that interactions between various antennas pointing in different directions can be significant in a real-world antenna system. In general, higher frequency antennas are affected by re-radiation from lower-frequency antennas, rather than the other way around. Thus the presence of a 10 or 15 meter stack does not affect the 20 meter Yagi at all.

Modeling can also help determine the minimum stacking distance required between monoband Yagis on the same rotating mast. In this case, stacking the 10 and 15 meter monobanders 10 feet apart holds down interaction between them so that the pattern and gain of the 10 meter Yagi are not impacted adversely. **Figure 14.5** demonstrates this in the European direction, where the patterns for the 10 meter beam by itself looks very clean compared to the same Yagi separated by 10 feet from the 15 meter Yagi below it. The worst-case situation is pointing toward the Caribbean, when the 40 and 20 meter stack is facing the 70-foot tower. This drops the 10 meter gain down about 1.5 dB from maximum, indicating significant interaction is occurring.

In this situation you might find it best to place the 70-foot tower in the direction closest to the Caribbean if this direction is very important to you. Doing so will, however, cause the pattern in the direction of the Far East to be affected on

10 and 15 meters. You have the modeling tools necessary to evaluate various configurations to achieve whatever is most important to you.

14.1.6 COMPROMISES

Because of limitations, most amateurs are never able to build their dream antenna system. This means that some compromises must be made. Do not, under any circumstances, compromise the safety of an antenna installation. Follow the manufacturer's recommendations for tower assembly, installation and accessories. Make sure that all hardware is being used within its ratings.

Guyed towers are frequently used by radio amateurs because they cost less than more complicated unguyed or free-standing towers with similar ratings. Guyed towers are fine for those who can climb or those with a friend who is willing to climb. But you may want to consider an antenna tower that folds over or one that cranks up (and down). Some towers crank up (and down) and fold over too. See **Figure 14.6**. That makes for convenient access to antennas for adjustments and maintenance without climbing. Crank-up towers also offer another advantage. They allow antennas to be lowered during periods of no operation, for aesthetic reasons or during periods of high winds.

A well-designed monoband Yagi should outperform a multiband Yagi. In a monoband design the best adjustments can be made for gain, front-to-rear ratio (F/R) and matching, but only for a single band. In a multiband design, there are always tradeoffs in these properties for the ability to operate on more than one band. Nevertheless, a multiband antenna has many advantages over two or more single band antennas. A multiband antenna requires less heavy-duty hardware, requires only one feed line, takes up less space and it costs less.

Apartment dwellers face much greater limitations in their choice of antennas. For most, the possibility of a tower is only a dream. (One enterprising ham made arrangements to purchase a top-floor condominium from a developer. The arrangements were made before construction began, and the plans were altered to include a roof-top tower installation.) For apartment and condominium dwellers, the situation is still far from hopeless. The chapters **Stealth and Limited Space Antennas** and **Portable Antennas** present ideas for consideration.

14.1.7 SYSTEM DESIGN EXAMPLES

You can plan according to the preceding sections to put together modest or very large antenna systems. The process may sound intimidating but the hardest part is usually just getting started! At this point, some simple examples might be instructive and encourage you to start planning.

Antenna System Example #1

What might a ham put together for antennas when he or she wants to try a little of everything, and has a modest budget? Let's suppose that the goals are (1) low cost, (2) no tower, (3) coverage of all HF bands and the repeater portion of one VHF band and (4) the possibility of working some DX.

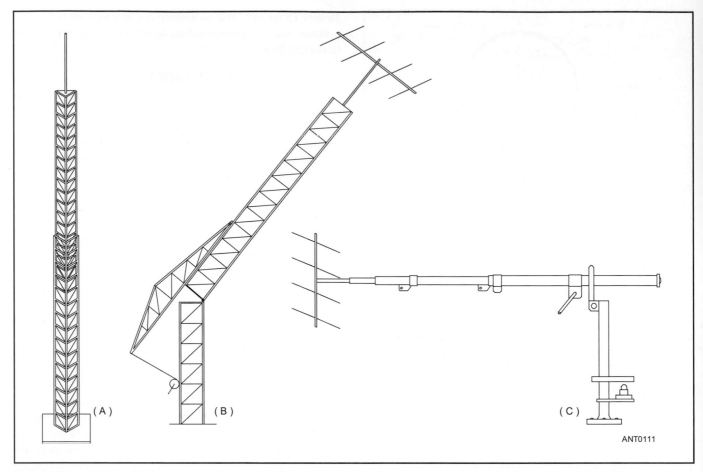

Figure 14.6 — Alternatives to a guyed tower are shown here. At A, the crank-up tower permits working on antennas at reduced height. It also allows antennas to be lowered during periods of no operation. Motor-driven versions are available. The fold-over tower at B and the combination at C permit working on antennas at ground level.

After studying the pages of this book, the station owner decides to first put up a 135-foot center-fed antenna. High trees in the back yard will serve as supports to about 50 feet. This antenna will cover all the HF bands by using a balanced feeder and an antenna tuner. It should be good for DX contacts on 10 MHz and above and will probably work okay for DX contacts on the lower bands. However, her plan calls for a ground-mounted vertical and radial system for 3.5 and 7 MHz to enhance the DX possibilities on those bands. For VHF, a chimney-mounted vertical is included.

Antenna System Example #2

A licensed couple has bigger ambitions. Goals for their station are (1) a good setup for DX on 14, 21 and 28 MHz, (2) moderate cost, (3) one tower, (4) ability to work some DX on 1.8, 3.5 and 7 MHz, and (5) no need to cover the CW portion of the bands.

After considering the options, the couple decides to install a 65-foot guyed tower. A large commercial triband Yagi will be mounted on top of the tower. The center of a trap dipole tuned for the phone portion of the 3.5- and 7-MHz bands will be supported by a wooden yardarm installed at the 60-foot level of the tower, with ends drooping down to form an inverted-V. An inverted-L for 1.8 MHz starts near ground

level and goes up to a similar yardarm on the opposite side of the tower. The horizontal portion of the inverted L runs away from the tower at right angles to the trap dipole. Later, the husband will experiment with sloping antennas for 3.5 MHz. If those experiments are not successful, a λ/4 vertical will be used on that band.

14.1.8 EMPIRICAL TESTING

Part of system design is "closing the loop" and evaluating the performance of what you have designed. If the performance is as expected, that validates your planning and design approach. If the performance isn't as expected, find out why and use that as a learning experience to improve your skills.

Unfortunately, many amateurs do not know how to evaluate performance scientifically or compare one antenna with another. Typically, they will put up one antenna and try it out on the air to see how it "gets out" in comparison with a previous antenna. This is obviously a very poor evaluation method because there is no way to know if the better or worse reports are caused by changing band conditions, different S meter characteristics or any of several other factors that could influence the reports received.

Many times the difference between two antennas or between two different locations for identical antennas amounts

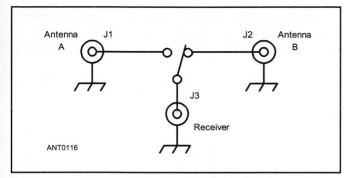

Figure 14.7 — When antennas are compared on fading signals, the time delay involved in disconnecting and reconnecting coaxial cables is too long for accurate measurements. A simple slide switch will do well for switching coaxial lines at HF. The four components can be mounted in a tin can or any small metal box. Leads should be short and direct. J1 through J3 are coaxial connectors.

to only a few decibels, a difference that is hard to discern unless instantaneous switching between the two is possible. Those few decibels are not important under strong signal conditions, of course, but when the going gets rough a few dB can make the difference between solid copy and no possibility of real communication.

Very little in the way of test equipment is needed for casual antenna evaluation, other than a communications receiver. You can even do a qualitative comparison by ear, if you can switch antennas instantaneously. Differences of less than 2 dB, however, are still hard to discern. The same is true of S meter readings. Signal strength differences of less than a decibel are usually difficult to see. If you want to measure that last fraction of a decibel, you should use a good ac voltmeter

at the receiver audio output (with the AGC turned off).

In order to compare two antennas, switching the co-axial transmission line from one to the other is necessary. No elaborate coaxial switch is needed; even a simple double-throw toggle or slide switch will provide more than 40 dB of isolation at HF. See **Figure 14.7**. Switching by means of manually connecting and disconnecting coaxial lines is not recommended because that takes too long. Fading can cause signal-strength changes during the changeover interval.

Whatever difference shows up in the strength of the received signal will be the difference in performance between the two antennas in the direction of that signal. For this test to be valid, both antennas must have nearly the same feed point impedance, a condition that is reasonably well met if the SWR is below 2:1 on both antennas.

On ionospheric propagated signals (sky wave) there will be constant fading, and for a valid comparison it will be necessary to take an average of the difference between the two antennas. Occasionally, the inferior antenna will deliver a stronger signal to the receiver, but in the long run the law of averages will put the better antenna ahead.

Of course with a ground-wave signal, such as that from a station across town, there will be no fading problems. A ground-wave signal will enable the operator to properly evaluate the antenna under test in the direction of the source. The results will be valid for ionospheric-propagated signals at low elevation angles in that direction. On 28 MHz, all sky-wave signals arrive and leave at low angles. But on the lower bands, particularly 3.5 and 7 MHz, we often use signals propagated at high elevation angles, almost up to the zenith. For these angles a ground-wave test between local stations may not provide a proper evaluation of the antenna, and use of sky wave signals becomes necessary.

14.2 PROPAGATION AND COVERAGE

The section "Elevation Angles for HF Communication" in the **Radio Wave Propagation** chapter is an excellent introduction to the use of propagation prediction software such as *IONCAP* and *VOACAP* to assess the coverage of an HF antenna at different frequencies for a wide range of solar conditions. The CD-ROM included with this book includes a set of elevation angle statistics derived from these tools that you can use when designing your antenna system. The author of that elevation angle data and the editor of this book's previous edition, Dean Straw, N6BV, compiled a new and expanded set of data that is available from Radioware (**www.radio-ware.com**) at reasonable cost. The data set has been expanded to more than 240 locations around the world in all 40 CQ zones and covers the five primary HF amateur bands (80 through 10 meters) for 24 hours at six levels of solar activity. These tables show signal strength in S units for easier use by amateurs.

As you plan your antenna system, it is strongly recom-

mended that you become familiar with at least one propagation prediction tool and undertake a study of propagation at your location to the areas of the world with which you want to communicate. Two descriptions of using propagation information are presented as examples of how understanding propagation can inform your antenna system design choices.

14.2.1 ELEVATION ANGLES FOR LOW-BAND DXING

In the chapter **Effects of Ground**, the importance was noted of matching the elevation response of your antennas as closely as possible to the range of elevation angles needed for communication with desired geographic areas. **Figure 14.8** shows the statistical 40 meter elevation angles needed over the entire 11-year solar cycle to cover the path from Boston, Massachusetts, to all of Europe. These angles range from 1° (at 9.6% of the time when the 40 meter band is open to Europe) to 28° (at 0.3% of the time). Creating an antenna

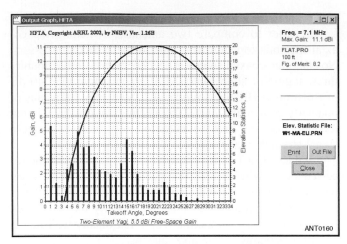

Figure 14.8 — Screen capture from HFTA (HF Terrain Assessment) program showing elevation response for 100-foot high dipole over flat ground on 7.1 MHz, with bargraph overlay of the statistical elevation angles needed over the whole 11-year solar cycle from New England (Boston) to all of Europe. Even a 100-foot high antenna cannot cover all the necessary angles.

system that concentrates the radiated energy at these low elevation angles is crucial to work DX on the bands below 10 MHz.

Figure 14.8 also overlays the elevation pattern response of a 100-foot high flattop dipole on the elevation-angle statistics, illustrating that even at this height the coverage is hardly optimum to cover all the necessary elevation angles. While Figure 14.8 is dramatic in its own right, the data can be viewed in another way that emphasizes even more the importance of low elevation angles. **Figure 14.9** plots the *cumulative distribution function*, the total percentage of time 40 meters is open from Boston to Europe, at or below each

elevation angle. For example, Figure 14.9 says that 40 meters is open to Europe from Boston 50% of the time at an elevation angle of 9° or less. The band is open 90% of the time at an elevation angle of 19° or less.

Figure 14.10 plots the 40 meter elevation-angle data for six major geographic areas around the world from Boston. In general, the overall range of elevation angles for far-distant locations is smaller, and the angles are lower than for closer-in areas. For example, from Boston to southern Asia (India), 50% of the time the takeoff angles are 4° or less. On the path to Japan from Boston, the takeoff angles is less than or equal to 6° about 70% of the time. These are low angles indeed.

Figure 14.11 shows similar data for the 40 meter band from San Francisco, California, to the rest of the world. The path to southern Africa from the US West Coast is a very long-distance path, open some 65% of the time it is open at angles of 2° or less! The 40 meter path to Japan involves takeoff angles of 10° or less more than 50% of the time. If you are fortunate enough to have a 100-foot high flattop dipole for 40 meters, at a takeoff angle of 10° the response would be down about 3 dB from its peak level at 20°. At an elevation angle of 5° the response would be about 8 dB down from peak. You can see why the California stations located on mountain tops do best on 40 meters for DXing.

Figure 14.12 shows the same percentage-of-time data for the 80 meter band from Boston to the world. Into Europe from Boston, the 80 meter elevation angle is 13° or less more than 50% of the time. Into Japan from Boston, 90% of the

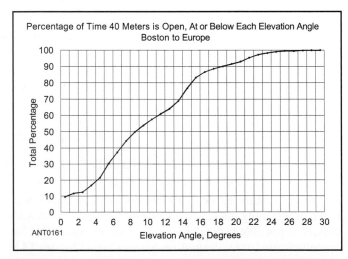

Figure 14.9 — Another way of looking at the elevation statistics from Figure 14.8. This shows the percentage of time the 40 meter band is open, at or below each elevation angle, on the path from Boston to Europe. For example, the band is open 50% of the time at an angle of 9° or lower. It is open 90% of the time at an angle of 19° or lower.

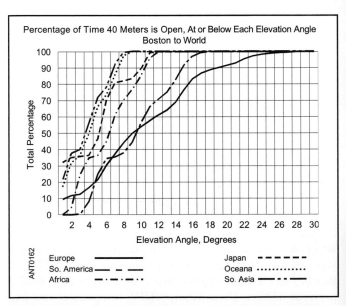

Figure 14.10 — The percentage of time the 40 meter band is open, at or below each elevation angle, for various DX paths from Boston: to Europe, South America, southern Africa, Japan, Oceania and south Asia. The angles are predominantly quite low. For example, on the path from Boston to Japan, 90% of the time when the 40 meter band is open, it is open at elevation angles less than or equal to 10°. Achieving good performance at these low takeoff angles requires very high horizontally polarized antennas, or efficient vertically polarized antennas.

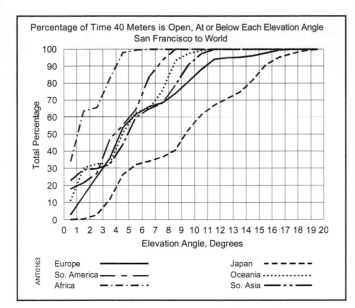

Figure 14.11 — The 40 meter statistics from the West Coast: from San Francisco to the rest of the DX world. Here, 90% of the time the path to Europe is open, it is at takeoff angles less than or equal to 11°. No wonder the hams living on mountain tops do best into Europe from the West Coast.

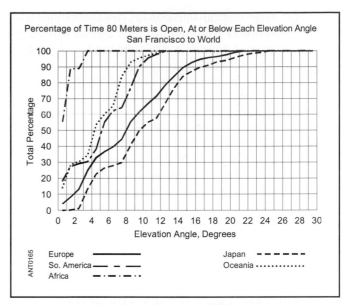

Figure 14.13 — From San Francisco to the rest of the world on 80 meters: 90% of the time on the path to Japan, the takeoff angle is less than or equal to 17°; 50% of the time the angle is less than or equal to 10°; 25% of the time the angle is less than or equal to 6°. A horizontally polarized antenna would have to be 600 feet above flat ground to be optimum at 6°!

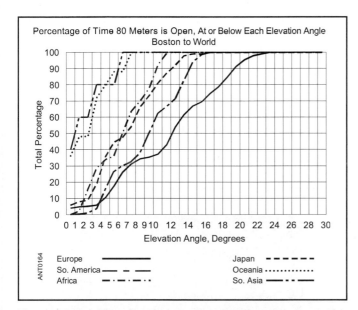

Figure 14.12 — The situation on 80 meters from Boston to the rest of the DX world. Into Europe, 90% of the time the elevation angle is less than or equal to 20°. Into Japan from Boston, 90% of the time the angle is less than or equal to 12°.

time the band is open is at a takeoff angle of 13° or less. (Note that these elevation statistics are computed for "undisturbed" ionospheric conditions. There are times when the incoming angles are affected by geomagnetic storms, and generally speaking the elevation angles rise under these conditions.)

Figure 14.13 shows the 80 meter data from San Francisco to the world. Low elevation angles dominate in this graph and high horizontal antennas would be necessary to optimal

coverage. In fact, 50% of the time for all paths, the elevation angle is less than 10°.

14.2.2 NVIS COMMUNICATION

Not all hams are interested in working stations thousands of miles from them. Traffic handlers and rag chewers may, in fact, only be interested in *nearby* communications — perhaps out to 600 miles from their location. In such cases, the low elevation angles needed for effective DXing may be completely ineffective in providing the required short-range coverage.

For example, a ham in Boston may want to talk with his brother-in-law in Cleveland, Ohio, a path that is just over 550 miles away. Or an operator in Buffalo, New York, may be the net control station (NCS) for a regional net involving the states of New York and New Jersey. She needs to cover distances up to about 300 miles away.

Depending on the time of day, the most appropriate ham frequencies needed for nearby communications are the 40 and 80/75 meter bands, with 160 meters also a possibility during the night hours, particularly during low portions of the sunspot cycle. The elevation angles involved in such nearby distances are usually high, even almost directly overhead for distances beyond ground-wave coverage (which may be as short as a few miles on 40 meters). For example, the distance between the Massachusetts cities of Boston and Worcester is about 40 miles. On 40 meters, 40 miles is beyond ground-wave coverage. So you will need sky-wave signals that use the ionosphere to communicate between these two cities, where the elevation angle is 83° — very nearly straight up.

Hams using vertical antennas for communications with nearby stations may well find that their signals will be below the noise level typical on the lower bands, especially if they aren't running maximum legal power. Such relatively short-range paths involve what is called *NVIS*, "Near Vertical Incidence Skywave," a fancy name for HF communication systems covering nearby geographic areas. The US military discusses NVIS out to about 500 miles, encompassing the territory a brigade might cover. Elevation angles needed to cover distances from 0 to 500 miles range from about 40° to 90°. This also covers the circumstances involved in amateur communications, particularly in emergency situations.

The following section is adapted from the article "What's the Deal About NVIS?" by Dean Straw, N6BV, that appeared in December 2005 *QST*. This article used an example of a hypothetical earthquake in San Francisco to analyze HF emergency communication requirements.

Ham Radio Response in Natural Disasters

One of San Francisco's somewhat less endearing nicknames is "the city that waits to die." When the *Big Earthquake* does come, you can be assured that all the cell phones and the land-line telephones will be totally jammed, making calling in or out of the San Francisco Bay Area virtually impossible. The same thing occurred in Manhattan on September 11, 2001. The Internet will also be severely affected throughout northern California because of its trunking via the facilities of the telephone network. Commercial electricity will be out in wide areas because power lines will be down.

If the repeaters on the hills around the San Francisco Bay Area haven't been damaged by the shaking itself, there will be some ham VHF/UHF voice coverage in the intermediate area, at least until the backup batteries run down. But

Table 14-1
Average Elevation Angles for Target Destinations from San Francisco

Location	Distance (Miles)	Average Elevation Angle (Degrees)
San Jose, CA	43	80
Sacramento, CA	75	78
Fresno, CA	160	63
Reno, NV	185	60
Los Angeles	350	44
San Diego	450	42
Portland, OR	530	30
Denver, CO	950	18
Dallas, TX	1500	8

connecting to the dysfunctional telephone system will be difficult at best through amateur repeaters.

With little or no telephone coverage, an obvious need for ham radio communications to aid disaster relief would be from San Francisco to Sacramento, the state capital. Sacramento is 75 miles northeast of the Bay Area, well outside VHF/UHF coverage, so amateur HF will be required on this radio circuit. On-the-ground communications directly between emergency personnel (including the armed-forces personnel who will be brought into the rescue and rebuilding effort) will often be difficult on VHF/UHF since San Francisco is a hilly place. So HF will probably be needed even for short distance, operator-to-operator or operator-to-communications center work. Throughout the city, portable HF stations will have to be quickly set up and staffed to provide such communications.

Hams used to half jokingly call short range HF

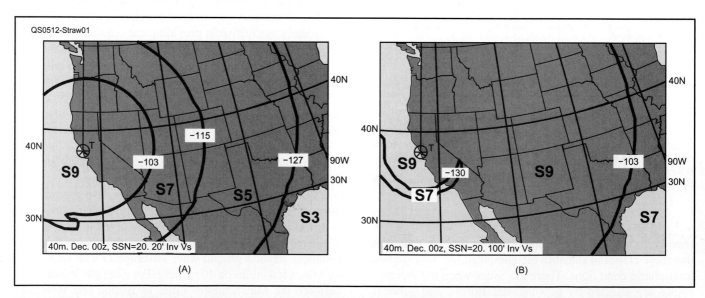

Figure 14.14 — At A, Predicted 40 meter geographic coverage plot for a 100 W transmitter in December at 0000 UTC (near sunset), for a SSN (Smoothed Sunspot Number) of 20. The antennas used are 20-foot-high inverted V dipoles. At B, 40 meter coverage for same date and time, but for 100-foot-high flattop dipoles. Most of California is well covered with S9 signals in both cases, but there is more susceptibility in the higher dipole case to thunderstorm crashes coming from outside California, for example from Arizona or even Texas. Such noise can interfere with communications inside California.

communications on 40 and 80 meters "cloud warming." This is an apt description, because the takeoff angles needed to launch HF signals up into the ionosphere and then down again to a nearby station are almost directly upward. **Table 14-1** lists the distance and takeoff angles from San Francisco to various cities around the western part of the USA. The distance between San Francisco and Sacramento is about 75 miles, and the optimum takeoff angle is about 78°. Launching such a high-angle signal is best done using horizontally polarized antennas mounted relatively close to the ground, such as low dipoles.

Geographic Coverage for NVIS

Figure 14.14A shows the geographic area coverage around San Francisco for a 100-W station on 7.2 MHz using an inverted V dipole. The center of this antenna is 20 feet above flat ground and the ends are 8 feet high. An actual implementation of such an antenna could be as an 80 meter inverted V, fed in parallel with a 40 meter inverted V dipole

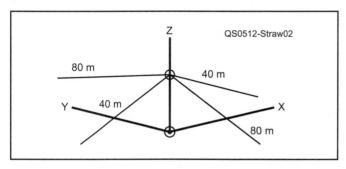

Figure 14.15 — Layout for two band inverted V dipoles for 40 and 80 meters. The two dipoles are fed together at the center and are laid out at right angles to each other to minimize interaction between them. Each end of both dipoles is kept 8 feet above ground for personal safety.

at a 90° angle. See **Figure 14.15**. The 8-foot height puts the ends high enough to prevent RF burns to humans (or most animals). The low height of the antenna above ground means that the azimuthal pattern is omnidirectional for high elevation angles.

Figure 14.14 was generated using the *VOAAREA* program, part of the *VOACAP* propagation-prediction suite, for the month of December. This was for 0000 UTC, close to sundown, for a low period of solar activity (Smoothed Sunspot Number, SSN of 20). The receiving stations were also assumed to be using identical inverted-V dipoles.

You can see that almost the whole state of California is covered with S9 signals, minus only a thin slice of land near the Mexican border in the southeast portion of the state, where the signal drops to S7. Signals from Texas are predicted to be only S5 or less in strength. Signals (or thunderstorm static) coming from, say, Louisiana would be several S units weaker than signals from central Texas.

Now take a look at Figure 14.14B. Here, the date, time and solar conditions remain the same, but now the antennas are 100-foot high flattop dipoles. California is still blanketed with S9 signals, save for an interesting crescent-shaped slice near Los Angeles, where the signal drops down to S7. Close investigation of this intriguing drop in signal strength reveals that the necessary elevation angle, 44°, from San Francisco to this part of southern California falls in the first null of the 100-foot high antenna's elevation pattern. See **Figure 14.16**, which shows the elevation patterns for five 40 meter antennas at different heights. In the null at a 44° takeoff angle, the 100-foot high dipole is just about equal to a 2-foot high dipole. We'll discuss 2-foot high dipoles in more detail later.

For most of California, the problem with 100-foot high 40 meter antennas is that interfering signals from Texas, Colorado or Washington State will *also* be S9 in San Francisco. So will static crashes coming from thunderstorms

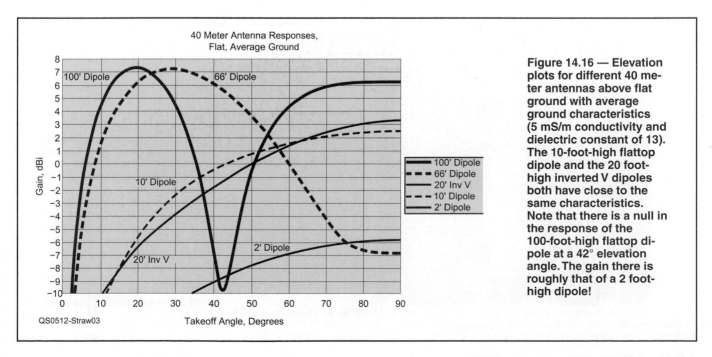

Figure 14.16 — Elevation plots for different 40 meter antennas above flat ground with average ground characteristics (5 mS/m conductivity and dielectric constant of 13). The 10-foot-high flattop dipole and the 20 foot-high inverted V dipoles both have close to the same characteristics. Note that there is a null in the response of the 100-foot-high flattop dipole at a 42° elevation angle. The gain there is roughly that of a 2 foot-high dipole!

Figure 14.17 — The distribution of lightning strikes across the USA for August 10, 2005 from 2200 to 0000 UTC, in the afternoon California time. There are lots of lightning strikes in the US during the summer — 60,898 of them in this two-hour period! (Courtesy Vaisala Lightning Explorer.)

all over the West and much of the Gulf Coast. See **Figure 14.17**, which shows a typical distribution of thunderstorms across the US in the late afternoon, California time, in mid-August. There certainly are a lot of thunderstorms raging around the country in the summer.

The signal-to-noise and signal-to-interference ratios for a 20-foot high inverted V dipole will be superior for medium-range distances, say out to 500 miles from the center, compared to a 100-foot high antenna. The 20-foot high antenna can discriminate against medium-angle thunderstorm noise in the late afternoon coming from the Arizona desert, although it wouldn't help much for thunderstorms in the Sierra Nevada in central Nevada, which are arriving in San Francisco at high angles, along with the desired NVIS signals.

This is the essence of what NVIS means. NVIS exploits the difference in elevation pattern responses of low horizontally polarized antennas compared to higher horizontal antennas, or even verticals. Over the years, many hams have been lead to believe that higher is always better. This is not quite so true for consistent coverage of medium or short distance signals!

If NVIS only involved putting up a low horizontally polarized antenna on 40 meters the story would end here. However, real cloud warming is more complicated. It also involves the intelligent choice of more than just one operating frequency to achieve reliable all day, all-night communications coverage.

Figure 14.18 shows the signal strength predicted using *VOACAP* for the 350-mile path from San Francisco to Los Angeles for the month of December for a period of low solar activity (SSN of 20). The antennas used in this case are 10-foot high dipoles, just for some variety. These act almost like 20-foot high Inverted V dipoles. December at a low SSN was chosen as a worst-case scenario because the *winter solstice* occurs on December 21. This is the day that has the fewest hours of daylight in the year. (Contrast this with the *summer solstice*, on June 21, which has the most hours of daylight in the year.) Note that the upper signal limit in Figure 14.18 is "S10" — a fictitious quantity that allows easier graphing. S10 is equivalent to S9+, or at least S9+10 dB.

The 40 meter curve in Figure 14.18 shows that the MUF (maximum usable frequency) actually drops below

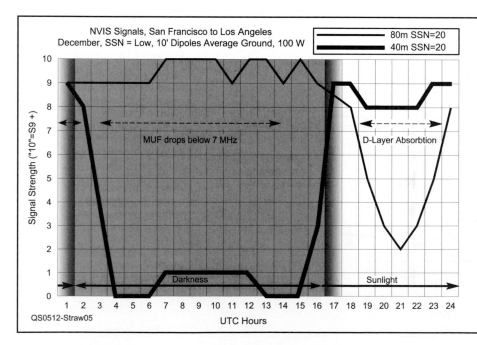

Figure 14.18 — VOACAP calculations for a 350 mile path from San Francisco to Los Angeles, using 10 foot-high flattop dipoles. This plot shows the signal strength in S units ("S10" = S9+10) for a worst-case month/SSN combination — winter solstice, in December, for a low level of solar activity (SSN = 20). The 40 meter signal drops to a very low level during the night because the MUF drops well below 7.2 MHz. The 80 meter signal drops in the afternoon because of D-layer absorption. For 24-hour communications on this path, the rule of thumb is to select 40 meters during the day and 80 meters during the night.

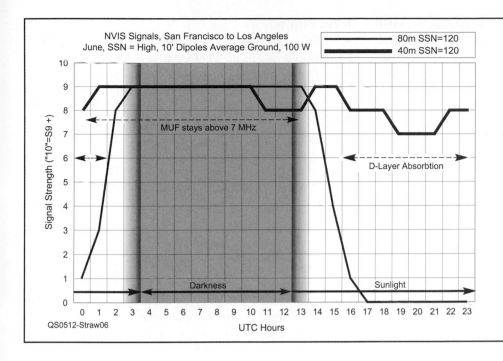

Figure 14.19 — Signal strengths for the San Francisco to Los Angeles path for a worst-case month/SSN combination — summer solstice, in June, for a high level of solar activity (SSN = 120). Now 80 meters drops out more dramatically during the daylight hours, due to increased D-layer absorption. At this high level of solar activity, 40 meters remains open 24 hours with reasonable signal levels. However, the NVIS rule-of-thumb still holds: Use 40 meters during the day; 80 meters at night.

the 7.2 MHz amateur band after sunset. The signal becomes quite weak for about 14 hours during the night, from about 0300 to 1700 UTC. In a period of low solar activity the 40 meter band thus becomes strictly a *daytime band* on this medium-distance path.

The 80 meter curve in Figure 14.18 shows strong signals after dusk, through the night and up until about an hour after sunrise. After sunrise, 80 meters starts to suffer absorption in the D layer of the ionosphere and hence the signal strength drops. Here, 80 meters is a true *nighttime band*.

Let's see what happens from San Francisco to Los Angeles during a period of high solar activity (SSN of 120)

during the summer solstice in June. **Figure 14.19** shows that 40 meters now stays open all hours of the day due to the greater number of hours of sunlight in June and because the ionosphere becomes more highly ionized by higher solar activity. Meanwhile, 80 meters still remains a nighttime band during these conditions on this path.

Now, let's look at a shorter-distance path — our 75-mile emergency communications path from San Francisco to Sacramento. We'll again use June during the summer solstice, at a high level of solar activity (SSN of 120) because this represents another worst-case scenario. **Figure 14.20** shows that 40 meters remains open on this path all day, dropping to

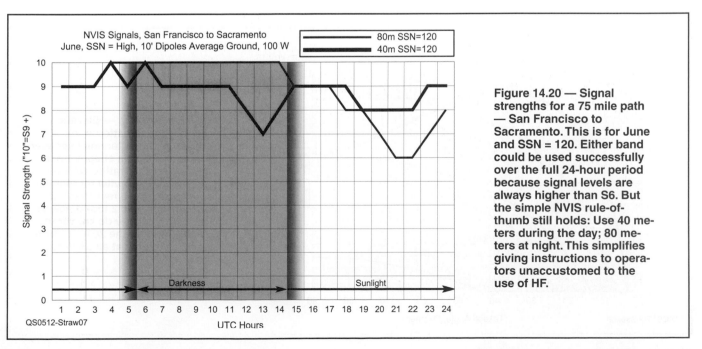

Figure 14.20 — Signal strengths for a 75 mile path — San Francisco to Sacramento. This is for June and SSN = 120. Either band could be used successfully over the full 24-hour period because signal levels are always higher than S6. But the simple NVIS rule-of-thumb still holds: Use 40 meters during the day; 80 meters at night. This simplifies giving instructions to operators unaccustomed to the use of HF.

a lower signal level just before sunrise. At sunrise, the MUF drops close to 7.2 MHz. 80 meters is still mainly a nighttime band to Sacramento, even though it does yield workable signal levels even during the daylight hours. However, 40 meters is better from 1200 to 0400 UTC, so 40 would be still the right daytime band for this path during the day.

Choosing the Right NVIS Frequency

You can see that a pattern is developing here for efficient NVIS short/medium-distance communications out to 500 miles:

■ You should pick a frequency on 40 meters during the day.

■ You should pick a frequency on 80 meters during the night.

■ You should choose an antenna that emphasizes moderate to high elevation angles, from 40° to almost directly overhead at 90°.

"What about 60 meters?" you might ask. The characteristics on 60 meters fall in between 40 and 80 meters, although it resembles 40 meters more closely. With characteristics close to that of 40, but with only five channels available and a 50-W power limit, the 60 meter band is of low utility for serious NVIS use.

What about 160 meters? For 100-W level radios, even at the worst-case month or during low solar activity, the critical frequency doesn't fall below 3.8 MHz often enough to destroy the ability to communicate, even for short distances. That is a relief, considering that installing a 160 meter half-wave dipole involves a 255-foot wingspan, and it would need to be elevated at least 30 feet in the center. A short loaded vertical such as a 160 meter mobile whip would have poor response at the high elevation angles needed for NVIS. You could probably put a monster 160 meter horizontal dipole up at a permanent location, but hauling such a thing around in the field would not be an easy task.

NVIS Strategy

You could pose the question about whether NVIS is an operating *mode* or whether it is actually an operating *strategy*. We maintain that NVIS is a strategy. It involves choosing both appropriate frequencies and then appropriate antennas for those frequencies. Figure 14.20 does show that on short-distance paths, such as between San Francisco and Sacramento, you could stay on 80 meters all day and night. But if you have to give a single rule-of-thumb to operators who are not very experienced at operating HF, we would tell them to operate on the higher frequency band during the day and on the lower frequency band at night.

Antenna Height for NVIS

Some NVIS aficionados have advocated placing dipoles only a few feet over ground, something akin to saying, "If low is good for NVIS, then lower must be even better." Now we are not claiming that a very low antenna *won't* work in specific instances — for example, covering a small state such as Rhode Island or even just the San Francisco Bay Area.

It certainly is convenient to mount a 40 meter dipole on some 2-foot high red traffic cones! You should be very skeptical, however, about the ability of such antennas to cover all of a large state, such as California or Texas, especially on 80 meters. **Figure 14.21** shows the computed elevation responses for a number of 80 meter antennas, including a 2-foot-high dipole.

Figure 14.22B shows the 80 meter geographic coverage plot for 2-foot-high flattop dipoles, compared with the plot in Figure 14.22A for 20-foot-high inverted V dipoles on both ends of the path. The 2-foot-high dipoles produce about two S-units less signal across all of California than the 20-foot-high inverted V dipoles, at 0300 UTC in December, with an SSN of 20. The reason is that a low dipole will suffer more losses in the ground under it.

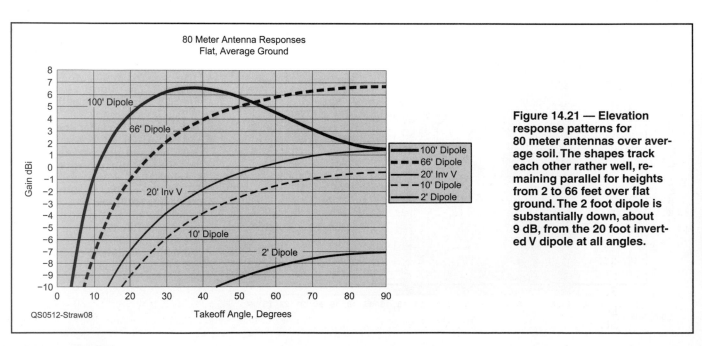

Figure 14.21 — Elevation response patterns for 80 meter antennas over average soil. The shapes track each other rather well, remaining parallel for heights from 2 to 66 feet over flat ground. The 2 foot dipole is substantially down, about 9 dB, from the 20 foot inverted V dipole at all angles.

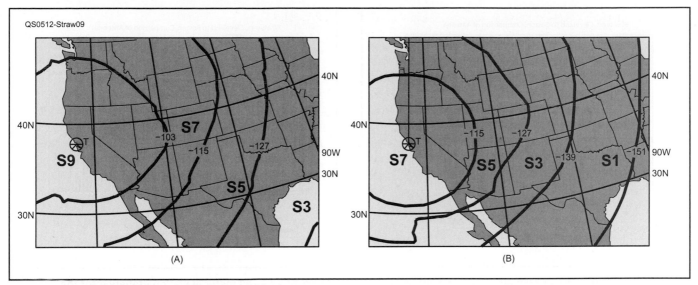

Figure 14.22 — Geographic coverage plots for December, SSN = 20, 0300 UTC. At A, antennas are 20-foot-high inverted V dipoles over Average soil. At B, antennas are 2-foot-high flattop dipoles over Average soil. The response for the 2-foot-high antennas is down about 2 S Units, 8 to 12 dB for a typical communications receiver.

The differential between California signals and possible interfering signals from, say, New Mexico, is predicted to be four S-units, the same as it is for the higher inverted V dipole at 20 feet. Thus there is no real advantage in terms of signal-to-interference ratio or signal-to-noise ratio (for thunderstorm static crashes) for either height. This is because the shape of all the response curves in Figure 14.21 below 20 feet essentially track each other in parallel.

However, the lower the antenna, the lower the transmitted signal strength. Physics remain physics. And if you are in an emergency situation operating on batteries, you could reduce power from 100 W to 10 W with a 20-foot high inverted-V antenna and still maintain the same signal strength as a 2-foot high dipole at 100 W.

Low NVIS Antennas and Local Power Line Noise

Some advocates of really low antennas have stated that the received noise is much lower than that received from higher antennas, and this therefore leads to better signal-to-noise ratios (SNR). How much this is true depends on the source of the noise. If the noise comes from distant thunderstorms, then the SNR advantage going to a 2-foot antenna from a 20-foot-high one is insignificant, as Figure 14.22 indicates.

If noise is from an arcing insulator on a HV power line half a mile away, that noise will arrive at the antenna as a ground-wave signal. We calculate that the 2-foot antenna receives 4.4 dB less noise by ground-wave than a 20-foot-high inverted V dipole. However, at an incoming elevation angle of 45° — suitable for a signal going from Los Angeles to San Francisco — the signal would be down 7.1 dB on the low dipole compared to the higher antenna. The net loss in SNR for the 2-foot-high dipole is thus 7.1– 4.4 or 2.7 dB. Close, but no cigar. Summarizing about really low NVIS antennas:

■A 2-foot-high dipole yields weaker signals, but without an SNR advantage compared to its more elevated brethren.

■A 2-foot-high dipole is a lot easier to trip over at night. We would call this a "knee biter."
■You (and your dog) can easily get RF burns from an antenna that is only 2 feet off the ground.

This is not a winning strategy to make friends or QSOs, it seems. But still, a really low dipole may serve your short-range communication needs just fine. But remember, that just as "higher is better" isn't universally true for NVIS (or even longer range) applications, "lower is better" isn't a panacea either.

Elevation Angles for Moderate Distances on 75/80 Meters

Figure 14.23 shows the elevation angles statistics for a 75 meter, 550-mile path from Boston to Cleveland, together with overlays of the elevation patterns for several different types of antennas. These elevation statistics cover all parts of the 11-year solar cycle for this path. The responses for the popular G5RV antenna (see the **Multiband Antennas** chapter) are shown for two different heights above flat ground: 50 and 100 feet. An 80 meter half-wave sloper ("full sloper") and an 80 meter ground-plane antenna are also shown. All antenna patterns are for "average ground" constants of 5 mS/m conductivity and a dielectric constant of 13.

At the statistically most significant takeoff angles around 50°, the two horizontally polarized G5RV antennas are about equal. At the second-highest elevation peak near 30°, the 100-foot G5RV has about a 4-dB advantage over its lower counterpart. The full sloper has comparable performance to the 100-foot high G5RV from 1° to about 20° and then gradually rises to its peak at angles higher than 70°. The full sloper is superior to the 50-foot horizontal G5RV at low takeoff elevation angles. The 80 meter ground plane has a deep null directly overhead. At an elevation angle of 70° it is down

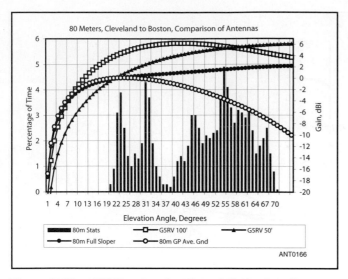

Figure 14.23 — 80/75 meter elevation statistics for all portions of the 11-year solar cycle for the path from Cleveland, Ohio, to Boston, Massachusetts, together with the elevation responses for four different multiband antennas. The 100-foot high horizontally polarized G5RV performs well over the entire range of necessary takeoff elevation angles.

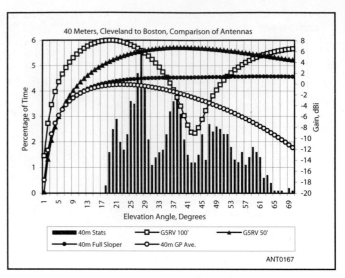

Figure 14.24 — 40 meter elevation statistics for the Cleveland to Boston path, together with elevation patterns for four antennas. Here, the 100-foot high horizontally polarized G5RV would have a null in the middle of the range of elevation angles needed for consistent performance on this path. For multiband use on this path to relatively nearby stations, the 50-foot high horizontal antenna would be a better choice than the 100-foot high antenna.

some 16 dB compared to the 50-foot high horizontal G5RV.

The advantage of antennas suitable for high-angle radiation was vividly demonstrated during a 75 meter QSO one fall evening between N6BV/1 in southern New Hampshire and W1WEF in central Connecticut. This involved a distance of about 100 miles and W1WEF was using his Four Square vertical array. Although W1WEF's signal was S9 on the Four Square, N6BV/1 suggested an experiment. Instead of connecting the so-called "dump power" connector on his Comtek ACB-4 hybrid phasing coupler to a 50-Ω dummy load (the normal configuration), W1WEF switched the dump power to his 100-foot high 80 meter horizontal dipole. W1WEF's signal came up more than 20 dB! The approximately 100-W of power that would otherwise be "wasted" in the dummy load was converted to useful signal.

Elevation Angles for Moderate Distances on 40 Meters

Figure 14.24 shows the situation for the 40 meter band, from Boston to Cleveland, together with the same antennas used for 80 meters in Figure 14.23. Note that the 100-foot high horizontally polarized G5RV has about a 16-dB null at an elevation angle of 43°. This doesn't affect things for low elevation angles, but it certainly has a profound effect on signals arriving between about 30° to 60°, especially when compared to the 50-foot high horizontal G5RV. The 40 meter full sloper beats out the high horizontal antenna from about 35° to 50°. And the ground plane is obviously not the antenna of choice for this moderate-range path from Boston to Cleveland, although it is still a good

performer on longer-distance paths, with their low takeoff angles.

A 100-foot high multiband dipole is about ⅜-λ high on 75/80 meters. It is an excellent antenna for general-purpose local and DXing operation. But the same dipole used on 40 meters becomes ¾-λ high. At that height, the nulls in its elevation pattern give large holes in coverage for nearby 40 meter contacts. Many operators have found that a 40- to 50-foot high dipole on 40 meters gives them far superior performance for close-in QSOs, when compared to a high dipole, or even a high 2-element 40 meter Yagi.

NVIS Summary

The use of NVIS strategies to cover close-in and intermediate distance communications within about 600 miles involves the intelligent choice of low HF frequencies. As a rule-of-thumb for ham band NVIS, 40 meters is recommended for use during the day; 80 meters during the night.

NVIS involves the choice of antennas suitable for this strategy. Horizontally polarized dual-band 80 and 40 meter flattop dipoles that are mounted higher than about 10 feet high will work adequately for portable operations. Dual-band 80 and 40 meter inverted V dipoles supported 20 feet above the ground at the center can also work well in portable operations.

Single-band 40 meter flattop antennas about 30 feet high and 80 meter flattop antennas about 60 feet high can do a good job for fixed locations.

14.3 EFFECTS OF LOCAL TERRAIN

The following material is condensed from an article by R. Dean Straw, N6BV, in July 1995 *QEX* magazine and updated for this edition. *HFTA* (IIF Terrain Assessment) and supporting data files are included on this book's CD-ROM. *HFTA* is the latest version of the *YT* program included with earlier editions of *The ARRL Antenna Book*.

Prior to the introduction of this material, the last major study that appeared in the amateur literature on the subject of local terrain as it affects DX operation appeared in four *QST* "How's DX" columns, by Clarke Greene, K1JX, from October 1980 to January 1981. Greene's work was an update of a landmark series of 1966 *QST* articles entitled "Station Design for DX," by Paul Rockwell, W3AFM. The long-range profiles of several prominent, indeed legendary, stations in Rockwell's articles are fascinating: W3CRA, W4KFC and W6AM. (The articles by Rockwell are included on this book's CD-ROM.)

14.3.1 CHOOSING A QTH FOR DX

The subject of how to choose a QTH for working DX has fascinated hams since the beginning of amateur operations. No doubt, Marconi probably spent a lot of time wandering around Newfoundland looking for a great radio QTH before making the first transatlantic transmission. Putting together a high-performance HF station for contesting or DXing has always followed some pretty simple rules. First, you need the perfect QTH, preferably on a rural mountaintop or at least on top of a hill. Even better yet, you need a mountaintop surrounded by seawater! Then, after you have found your dream QTH, you put up the biggest antennas you possibly can, on the highest towers you can afford. Then you work all sorts of DX — sunspots willing, of course.

The only trouble with this straightforward formula for success is that it doesn't always work. Hams fortunate enough to be located on mountain tops with really spectacular drop-offs often find that their highest antennas don't do very well, especially on 15 or 10 meters, but often even on 20 meters. When they compare their signals with nearby locals in the flatlands, they sometimes (but not always) come out on the losing end, especially when sunspot activity is high.

On the other hand, when the sunspots drop into the cellar, the high antennas on the mountaintop are usually the ones crunching the pileups — but again, not always. So, the really ambitious contest aficionados, the guys with lots of resources and infinite enthusiasm, have resorted to putting up antennas at all possible heights, on a multitude of towers.

There is a more scientific way to figure out where and how high to put your antennas to optimize your signal during all parts of the 11-year solar cycle. We advocate the system approach to HF antenna system design, in which you need to know the following:

1) The range of elevation angles necessary to get from point A to point B

2) The elevation patterns for various types and configurations of antennas

3) The effect of local terrain on elevation patterns for horizontally polarized antennas.

14.3.2 REQUIRED RANGE OF ELEVATION ANGLES

Up until 1994, *The ARRL Antenna Book* contained only a limited amount of information about the elevation angles needed for communication throughout the world. In the 1974 edition, Table 1-1 in the Wave Propagation chapter was captioned: "Measured vertical angles of arrival of signals from England at receiving location in New Jersey."

What the caption didn't say was that Table 1-1 was derived from measurements made during 1934 by Bell Labs. The highest frequency data seemed pretty shaky, considering that 1934 was the low point of Cycle 17. Neither was this data applicable to any other path, other than the one from New Jersey to England. Nonetheless, many amateurs located throughout the US tried to use the sparse information in Table 1-1 as the only rational data they had for determining how high to mount their antennas. (If they lived on hills, they made estimates of the effect of the terrain, assuming that the hill was adequately represented by a long, unbroken slope. More on this later.)

In 1993 ARRL HQ embarked on a major project to tabulate the range of elevation angles from all regions of the US to important DX QTHs around the world. This was accomplished by running many thousands of computations using the *IONCAP* computer program. *IONCAP* has been under development for more than 40 years by various agencies of the US government and is considered the standard of comparison for propagation programs by many agencies, including the Voice of America, Radio Free Europe, and more than 100 foreign governments throughout the world. *IONCAP* is a real pain in the neck to use, but it is the standard of comparison.

The calculations were done for all levels of solar activity, for all months of the year, and for all 24 hours of the day. The results were gathered into some very large databases, from which special custom-written software extracted detailed statistics. The results appeared in summary form in Tables 4 through 13 printed in Chapter 23, Radio Wave Propagation, of the 17th Edition and in more detail on the diskette included with that book. (This book, the 22nd Edition, contains even more statistical data, for more areas of the world, on the accompanying CD-ROM. The author has also made available an expanded set of data through Radioware.)

Figure 14.25 shows the full range of elevation angles (represented as vertical bars) for the 20 meter path from New England (centered on Newington, Connecticut) to all of Europe. This is for all openings, in all months, over the entire 11-year solar cycle. The most likely elevation angle occurs at 5° for about 13% of the times when the 20 meter band is open to Europe from New England. The band is open from 4° to 6° a total of about 34% of the times the band is open. There is a secondary peak between 10° to 12°, occurring for a total of about 25% of the times the band is open.

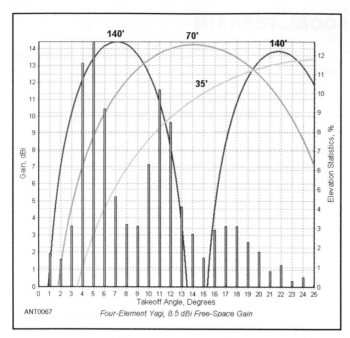

Figure 14.25 — Graph showing 20 meter percentage of all openings from New England to Europe versus elevation angles, together with overlay of elevation patterns over flat ground for three 20 meter antenna systems. The most statistically likely angle at which the band will be open is 5°, although at any particular hour, day, month and year, the actual angle will likely be different. Note the deep null exhibited by the 140-foot high antenna centered at 14°.

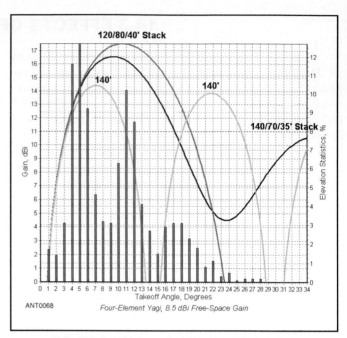

Figure 14.26 — Graph showing results of stacking antennas at different heights on the same tower to cover a wider range of elevation angles, in this case for the path from Connecticut (W1) to all of Europe on 20 meters. The optimized stack at 120/80/40 feet covers the needed range of elevation angles better than the stack at 140/70/35 feet or the single Yagi at 140 feet.

Overlaid on Figure 14.25 along with the elevation-angle statistics are the elevation-plane responses for three different horizontally polarized Yagi beams, all over flat ground. The first is mounted 140 feet high, 2 λ in terms of wavelength. The second Yagi is mounted 70 feet high (at 1 λ) and the third is 35 feet (0.5 λ). The 140-foot high antenna has a deep null at 15°, but it also has the highest response (13.4 dBi) of the three at the statistical peak elevation angle of 5°. However, at 12° — where the band is open some 9% of the time — the 140-foot high Yagi is down 4 dB compared to the 70-foot antenna.

The 70-foot high Yagi arguably covers the overall range best, since it has no disastrous nulls in the 1° to 25° range, where most of the action is occurring on 20 meters. At 5°, however, its response is only 8.8 dBi, 4.6 dB down from the 140-foot high antenna at that angle. The 35-foot antenna peaks above 26° in elevation angle, and is down some 10.4 dB compared to the 140-foot antenna at 5°. Obviously, no single antenna covers the complete range of elevation angles needed.

Note that the highest Yagi has a strong *second lobe* peaking at 22°. Let's say that you could select between two antennas, one at 140 and one at 70 feet, and that the incoming angle for a particular distant station is 22°. You might be fooled into thinking that the incoming angle is around 6°, favoring the first peak of the higher antenna, when in truth the angle is relatively high. The 70-foot antenna's response

would be lower at 22° than the higher one, but only because the 140-foot antenna is operating on its second lobe. (What would clinch a determination of the correct incoming angle — 6° or 22° — would be the response of the 35-foot high Yagi, which would be close to its peak at 22°, while it would be very far down at 6°.)

Now, we must emphasize that these elevation angles are *statistical entities* — in other words, just because 5° is the "statistically most likely angle" for the 20 meter path from New England to Europe doesn't mean that the band will be open at 11° at any particular hour, on a particular day, in a particular month, in any particular year. In fact, however, experience agrees with the *IONCAP* computations: the 20 meter path to Europe usually opens at a low angle in the New England morning hours, rising to about 11° during the afternoon, when the signals remain strongest throughout the afternoon until the evening in New England.

What would happen if we were to feed all three Yagis at 140, 70 and 35 feet in-phase as a stack? **Figure 14.26** shows this situation, along with a more highly optimized stack at 120, 80 and 40 feet that better covers the overall range of elevation angles from Connecticut to Europe.

Now see **Figure 14.27**, which uses the same 120/80/40-foot stack of 20 meter antennas as in Figure 14.26, but this time from Seattle, Washington, to Europe. For comparison, the response of a single 4-element Yagi at 100 feet over flat ground is also shown in Figure 14.27. Just because 5° is the

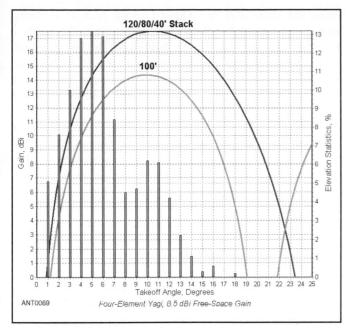

Figure 14.27 — Graph showing 20 meter percentage of all openings, this time from Seattle, WA, to Europe, together with an overlay of elevation patterns over flat ground for two 20 meter antenna systems. The statistically most likely angle on this path is 5°, occurring about 13% of the time when the band is actually open. Higher antennas predominate on this low-angle path.

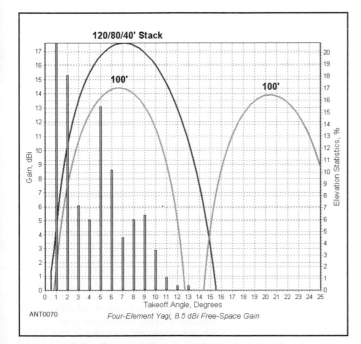

Figure 14.28 — Graph showing 15 meter percentage of all openings from Chicago to Southern Africa, together with overlay of elevation patterns over flat ground for two 15 meter antenna systems. On this long-distance, low-angle path, higher antennas are again most effective.

statistically most prevalent angle (occurring some 13% of the time) from Seattle to Europe on 20 meters, this doesn't mean that the actual angle *at any particular moment in time* might not be 10°, or even 2°. The statistics for W7 to Europe say that 5° is the most likely angle, but 20 meter signals from Europe arrive at angles ranging from 1° to 18°. Note that this range of angles is quite a bit less than from W1 to Europe, which is much closer geographically to Europe than is the Pacific Northwest coast of the US. If you design an antenna system to cover all possible angles needed to talk to Europe from Seattle (or from Seattle to Europe) on 20 meters, you would need to cover the full range from 1° to 18° equally well.

Similarly, if you wish to cover the full range of elevation angles from Chicago to Southern Africa on 15 meters, you would need to cover 1° to 13°, even though the most statistically likely signals arrive at 1°, for 21% of the time when that the band is open for that path. See **Figure 14.28**.

It is important to recognize that Figures 14.25 through 14.28 are for flat ground. When the antennas are mounted over irregular local terrain, things get much more complicated. First, however, we'll discuss general-purpose antenna modeling programs as they try to model real terrain.

14.3.3 DRAWBACKS OF COMPUTER MODELS OVER REAL TERRAIN

Modern general-purpose antenna modeling programs such as *NEC* or *MININEC* (or their commercially upgraded equivalents, such as *NEC-Win Plus*, *EZNEC* and *EZNEC ARRL*) can accurately model almost any type of antenna commonly used by radio amateurs. In addition, there are specialized programs specifically designed to model Yagis efficiently, such as *YO* or *YW* (Yagi for *Windows*, bundled on the CD-ROM with this book) or *YagiMax*. These programs however are all unable to model antennas accurately over anything other than *purely flat ground*.

While both *NEC* and *MININEC* can simulate irregular ground terrain, they do so in a decidedly crude manner, employing step-like concentric rings of height around an antenna. The documentation for *NEC* and *MININEC* both clearly state that diffraction off these steps is not modeled. Common experience among serious modelers is that the warnings in the manuals are worth heeding.

Although you can analyze and even optimize antenna designs using free-space or flat-earth ground models, it is *diffraction* that makes the real world a very, very complicated place. This should be clarified — diffraction is hard, even tortuous, to analyze properly, but it makes analysis of real world results far more believable than a flat-world reflection model does.

14.3.4 RAY-TRACING OVER UNEVEN LOCAL TERRAIN

The Ray-Tracing Technique

First, let's look at a simple ray-tracing procedure involving only horizontally polarized reflections, with no diffractions. From a specified height on the tower, an antenna shoots "rays" (just as though they were bullets) in 0.25° increments from +35° above the horizon to –35° below the horizon. Each ray is traced over the foreground terrain to see if it hits the ground at any point on its travels in the direction of interest. If it does hit the ground, the ray is reflected following the classical law of reflection. That is, the outgoing angle equals the incoming angle, reflected through the normal to the slope of the surface. Once the rays exit into the ionosphere, the individual contributions are vector-summed to create the overall far-field elevation pattern.

The next step in terrain modeling involves adding *diffractions* as well as reflections. At the Dayton antenna forum in 1994, Jim Breakall, WA3FET, gave a fascinating and tantalizing lecture on the effect of foreground terrain. Later Breakall, Dick Adler, K3CXZ, Joel Young and a group of other researchers published an extremely interesting paper entitled "The Modeling and Measurement of HF Antenna Skywave Radiation Patterns in Irregular Terrain" in the July 1994 *IEEE Transactions on Antennas and Propagation*. They described in rather general terms the modifications they made to the *NEC-BSC* program. They showed how the addition of a ray-tracing reflection and diffraction model to the simplistic stair-stepped reflection model in regular *NEC* gave far more realistic results. For validation, they compared actual pattern measurements made on a site in Utah (with an overflying helicopter) to computed patterns made using the modified *NEC* software. However, because the US Navy funded this work the software remained for a long time a military secret.

Thumbnail History of the Uniform Theory of Diffraction

It is instructive to look briefly at the history of how *Geometric Optics* (GO) evolved (and still continues to evolve) into the *Uniform Theory of Diffraction* (UTD). The following is summarized from the historical overview in one book found to be particularly useful and comprehensive on the subject of UTD: *Introduction to the Uniform Geometrical Theory of Diffraction*, by McNamara, Pistorius, and Malherbe.

Many years before the time of Christ, the ancient Greeks studied optics. Euclid is credited with deriving the law of reflection about 300 BC. Other Greeks, such as Ptolemy, were also fascinated with optical phenomena. In the 1600s, a Dutchman named Snell finally figured out the law of refraction, resulting in *Snell's law*. By the early 1800s, the basic world of classical optics was pretty well described from a mathematical point of view, based on the work of a number of individuals.

As its name implies, classical geometric optical theory deals strictly with geometric shapes. Of course, the importance of geometry in optics shouldn't be minimized — after all, we wouldn't have eyeglasses without geometric optics. Mathematical analysis of shapes utilizes a methodology that traces the paths of straight-line *rays* of light. (Note that the paths of rays can also be likened to the straight-line paths of particles.) In classical geometric optics, however, there is no mention of three important quantities: phase, intensity and polarization. Indeed, without phase, intensity or polarization, there is no way to deal properly with the phenomenon of *interference*, or its cousin, *diffraction*. These phenomena require theories that deal with *waves* rather than rays.

Wave theory has also been around for a long time, although not as long as geometry. Workers like Hooke and Grimaldi had recorded their observations of interference and diffraction in the mid 1600s. Huygens had used elements of wave theory in the late 1600s to help explain refraction. By the late 1800s, the work of Lord Rayleigh, Sommerfeld, Fresnel, Maxwell and many others led to the full mathematic characterization of all electromagnetic phenomena, light included.

Unfortunately, ray theory doesn't work for many problems, at least ray theory in the classical optical form. The real world is a lot more jagged, pointy and fuzzy in shape than can be described in a totally rigorous mathematic fashion. Some properties of the real world are most easily explained on the micro level using electrons and protons as conceptual objects, while other macro phenomena (like resonance, for example) are more easily explained in terms of waves. To get a handle on a typical real-world physical situation, a combination of classical ray theory and wave theory was needed.

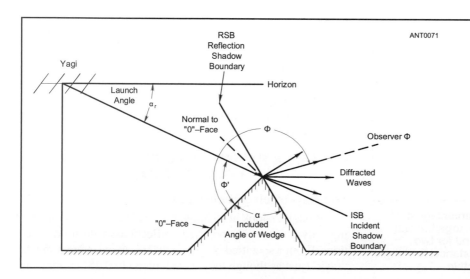

Figure 14.29 — Diagram showing diffraction mechanism of ray launched at angle α_r below the horizon at a diffraction wedge, whose included angle is α. Referenced to the incident face (the o-face as it is called in UTD terminology), the incoming angle is ϕ' (phi prime). The wedge creates an infinite number of diffracted waves. Shown is one whose angle referenced to the o-face is ϕ, the so-called observation angle in UTD terminology.

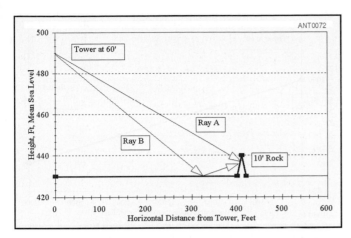

Figure 14.30 — Hypothetical terrain exhibiting so-called "10-foot rock effect." The terrain is flat from the tower base out to 400 feet, where a 10-foot high rock is placed. Note that this forms a diffraction wedge, but that it also blocks direct waves trying to shoot through it to the flat surface beyond, as shown by Ray A. Ray B reflects off the flat surface before it reaches the 10-foot rock, but it is blocked by the rock from proceeding further. A simple Geometric Optics (GO) analysis of this terrain without taking diffraction into account will result in the elevation response shown in Figure 14.31.

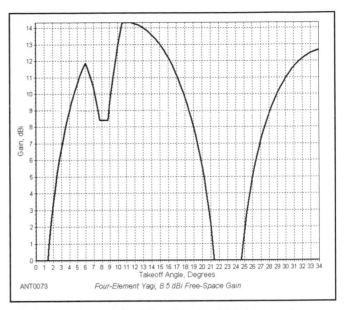

Figure 14.31 — Elevation response for rays launched at terrain in Figure 14.30 from a height of 60 feet using a 4-element Yagi. This was computed using a simple Geometrical Optics (GO) reflection-only analysis. Note the hole in the response between 6° to 10° in elevation. It is not reasonable for a 10-foot high rock to create such a disturbance at 21 MHz!

The breakthrough in the combination of classical geometric optics and wave concepts came from J. B. Keller of Bell Labs in 1953, although he published his work in the early 1960s. In the very simplest of terms, Keller introduced the notion that shooting a ray at a diffraction *wedge* causes wave interference at the tip, with an infinite number of diffracted waves emanating from the diffraction point. Each diffracted wave can be considered to be a point source radiator at the place of generation, the diffraction point. Thereafter, the paths of individual waves can be traced as though they were individual classical optic rays again. What Keller came up with was a reasonable mathematical description of what happens at the tip of the diffraction wedge.

Figure 14.29 is a picture of a simple diffraction wedge, with an incoming ray launched at an angle of α_r, referenced to the horizon, impinging on it. The diffraction wedge here is considered to be perfectly conducting, and hence impenetrable by the ray. The wedge generates an infinite number of diffracted waves, going in all directions not blocked by the wedge itself. The amplitudes and phases of the diffracted waves are determined by the interaction at the wedge tip, and this in turn is governed by the various angles associated with the wedge. Shown in Figure 14.29 are the included angle α of the wedge, the angle ϕ' of the incoming ray (referenced to the incoming surface of the wedge), and the observed angle ϕ of one of the outgoing diffracted waves, also referenced to the wedge surface.

The so-called *shadow boundaries* are also shown in Figure 14.29. The Reflection-Shadow Boundary (RSB) is the angle beyond which no further reflections can take place for a given incoming angle. The Incident-Shadow Boundary (ISB) is that angle beyond which the wedge's face blocks any

incident rays from illuminating the observation point.

Keller derived the amplitude and phase terms by comparing the classical Geometric Optics (GO) solution with the exact mathematical solution calculated by Sommerfeld for a particular case where the boundary conditions were well known — an infinitely long, perfectly conducting wedge illuminated by a plane wave. Simply speaking, whatever was left over had to be diffraction terms. Keller combined these diffraction terms with GO terms to yield the total field everywhere.

Keller's new theory became known as the *Geometric Theory of Diffraction* (abbreviated henceforth as GTD). The beauty of GTD was that in the regions where classical GO predicted zero fields, the GTD "filled in the blanks," so to speak. For example, see **Figure 14.30**, showing the terrain for a hypothetical case, where a 60-foot high 4-element 15 meter Yagi illuminates a wide, perfectly flat piece of ground. A 10-foot high rock has been placed 400 feet away from the tower base in the direction of outgoing rays. **Figure 14.31** shows the elevation pattern predicted using reflection-only GO techniques. Due to blockage of the direct wave (A) trying to shoot past the 10-foot high rock, and due to blockage of (B) reflections from the flat ground in front of the rock by the rock, there is a *hole* in the smooth elevation pattern.

Now, doesn't it defy common sense to imagine that a single 10-foot high rock will really have such an effect on a 15 meter signal? Keller's GTD took diffraction effects into account to show that waves do indeed sneak past and over the rock to fill in the pattern. The whole GTD scheme is very clever indeed.

However, GTD wasn't perfect. Keller's GTD predicts some big spikes in the pattern, even though the overall shape of the elevation pattern is much closer to reality than a simple GO reflection analysis would indicate. The region right at the RSB and ISB shadow boundaries is where problems are found. The GO terms go to zero at these points because of blockage by the wedge, while Keller's diffraction terms tend to go to infinity at these very spots. In mathematical terms this is referred to as a *caustic problem*. Nevertheless, despite these nasty problems at the ISB and RSB, the GTD provided a remarkably better solution to diffraction problems than did classical GO.

In the early 1970s, a group at Ohio State University under R. G. Kouyoumjian and P. H. Pathak did some pivotal work to resolve this caustic problem, introducing what amounts to a clever "fudge factor" to compensate for the tendency of the diffraction terms at the shadow boundaries to go to infinity. They introduced what is known as a *transition function*, using a form of Fresnel integral. Most importantly, the Ohio State researchers also created several *FORTRAN* computer programs to compute the amplitude and phase of diffraction components. Now computer hackers could get to work!

The ARRL program that finally resulted is called *HFTA*, standing for "HF Terrain Assessment." (The earlier DOS version of *HFTA* was known as *YT*, standing for "Yagi Terrain.") As the name suggests, *HFTA* analyzes the effect of local terrain on HF propagation through the ionosphere. It is designed for horizontally polarized Yagis, although it will model the effects of a simple flattop dipole also. The accurate appraisal of the effect of terrain on vertically polarized signals is a far more complex problem than for horizontally polarized waves, and *HFTA* doesn't do verticals. (*HFTA* is included on this book's CD-ROM.)

14.3.5 SIMULATION EXAMPLES

We want to focus first on some simple results, to show that the computations do make some sense by presenting some simulations over simple terrains. We've already described the "10-foot rock at 400 feet" situation, and showed where a simple GO reflection analysis is inadequate to the task without taking diffraction effects into account.

Simple Terrain Examples

Now look at the simple case shown in **Figure 14.32**, where a very long, continuous down-slope from the tower base is shown. Note that the scales used for the X- and Y-axes are different: the Y-axis changes 300 feet in height (from 800 to 1100 feet), while the X-axis goes from 0 to 3000 feet. This exaggerates the apparent steepness of the downward slope, which is actually a rather gentle slope, at $\tan^{-1} (1000 - 850) / (3000 - 0) = -2.86°$. In other words, the terrain falls 150 feet in height over a range of 3000 feet from the base of the tower.

Figure 14.33 shows the computed elevation response for this terrain profile, for a 4-element horizontally polarized Yagi on a 60-foot tower. The response is compared to that of an identical Yagi placed 60 feet above flat ground. Compared to the "flatland" antenna, the hilltop antenna has an elevation

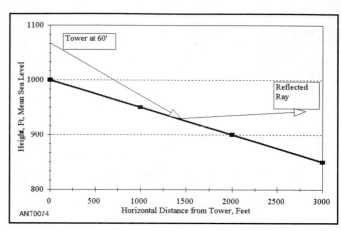

Figure 14.32 — A long, gentle downward-sloping terrain. This terrain has no explicit diffraction points and can be analyzed using simple GO reflection techniques.

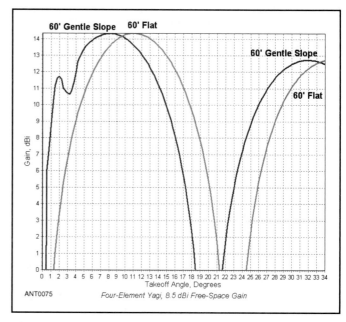

Figure 14.33 — Elevation response for terrain shown in Figure 14.32, using a 4-element 15 meter Yagi, 60 feet high. Note that the shape of the response is essentially shifted toward the left, toward lower elevation angles, by the angle of the sloping ground. For reference, the response for an identical Yagi placed over flat ground is also shown.

response shifted over by almost 3° toward the lower elevation angles. In fact, this shift is directly due to the –2.86° slope of the hill. Reflections off the slope are tilted by the slope. In this situation there is a single diffraction at the bottom of the gentle slope at 3000 feet, where the program assumes that the terrain becomes flat.

Look at **Figure 14.34**, which shows another simple terrain profile, called a "Hill-Valley" scenario. Here, the 60-foot high tower stands on the edge of a gentle hill overlooking a long valley. Once again the slope of the hill is exaggerated by the different X and Y-axes. **Figure 14.35** shows the computed

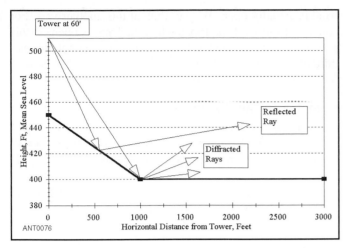

Figure 14.34 — "Hill-Valley" terrain, with reflected and diffracted rays.

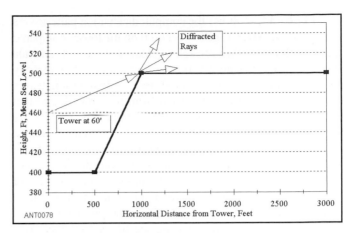

Figure 14.36 — "Hill-Ahead" terrain, shown with diffracted rays created by illumination of the edge of the plateau at the top of the hill.

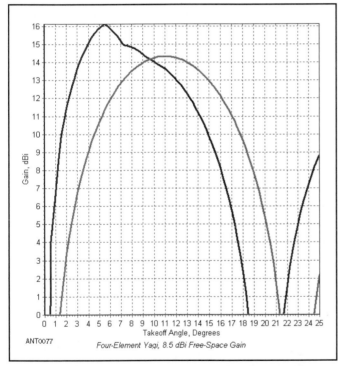

Figure 14.35 — Elevation response computed by HFTA program for single 4-element 15 meter Yagi at 60 feet above "Hill-Valley" terrain shown in Figure 14.34. Note that the slope has caused the response in general to be shifted toward lower elevation angles. At 5° elevation, the diffraction components add up to increase the gain slightly above the amount a GO-only analysis would indicate.

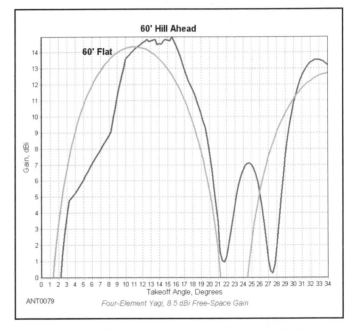

Figure 14.37 — Elevation response computed by HFTA for "Hill-Ahead" terrain shown in Figure 14.36. Now the hill blocks direct rays and also precludes possibility of any constructive reflections. Above 10°, diffraction components add up together with direct rays to create the response shown.

elevation response at 21.2 MHz for a 4-element Yagi on a 60-foot high tower at the edge of the slope.

Once again, the pattern is overlaid with that of an identical 60-foot-high Yagi over flat ground. Compared to the flatland antenna, the hilltop antenna's response above 9° in elevation is shifted by almost 3° toward the lower elevation angles. Again, this is due to reflections off the downward

slope. From 1° to 9°, the hilltop pattern is enhanced even more compared to the flatland antenna, this time by diffraction occurring at the bottom of the hill.

Now let's see what happens when there is a hill ahead in the direction of interest. **Figure 14.36** depicts such a situation, labeled "Hill-Ahead." Here, at a height of 400 feet above mean sea level, the land is flat in front of the tower, out to a distance 500 feet, where the hill begins. The hill then rises 100 feet over the range 500 to 1000 feet away from the tower base. After that, the terrain is a plateau, at a constant 500 feet elevation.

Figure 14.37 shows the computed elevation pattern for a 4-element 21-MHz Yagi 60-feet high on the tower, compared again with an overlay for an identical 60-foot high antenna over flat ground. The hill blocks low-angle waves directly radiated from the antenna from 0° to 2.3°. In addition, waves that would normally be reflected from the ground, and that would normally add in phase from about 2.3° to 12°, are blocked by the hill also. Thus the signal at 8° is down almost 5 dB from the signal over flat ground, all due to the effect of the hill. Diffracted waves start kicking in once the direct wave rises enough above the horizon to illuminate the top edge of the hill. These diffracted waves tend to augment elevation angles above about 12°, which reflected waves can't reach.

Is there is any hope for someone in such a lousy QTH for DXing? **Figure 14.38** shows the elevation response for a truly heroic solution. This involves a stack of four 4-element Yagis, mounted at 120, 90, 60 and 30 feet on the tower. Now, the total gain at low angles is just about comparable to that from a single 4-element Yagi mounted over flat ground. Where there's a ham, there is a way!

At 5° elevation, four diffraction components add up (there are zero reflection components) to achieve the far-field pattern. This seems reasonable, because each of the four antennas is illuminating the diffraction point separately and we know that none of the four antennas can *see over* the hill directly to produce a reflection at a low launch angle.

At an elevation angle of 5°, 15 meter signals arrive from Europe to New England about 13% of the total time when the

band is actually open. We can look at this another way. For about two-thirds of the times when the band is open on this path, the incoming angle is between 3° to 12°. For about one-third of the time, signals arrive above 10°, where the "heroic" four-stack is really beginning to come into its own.

Complex Terrain Example

The results for simple terrains look reasonable; let's try a more complicated real-world situation. **Figure 14.39** shows the terrain from the New Hampshire N6BV/1 QTH toward Japan. The terrain was complex, with 52 different points *HFTA* identifies as diffraction points. **Figure 14.40** shows a labeled *HFTA* output for three different types of antennas on 20 meters: a stack at 120 and 60 feet, the 120-foot antenna by itself, and then a 120/60-foot stack over flat ground, for reference. The elevation-angle statistics for New England to Japan are overlaid on the graph also, making for a very complicated looking picture — it is a *lot* easier to decipher the lines on the color monitor, by the way, than on a black-and-white printer.

Comparison of the same 120/60-foot stacks over irregular terrain and flat ground is useful to show where the terrain itself is affecting the elevation response. The flatland stack has more gain in the region of 3° to 7° than the same stack over the N6BV/1 local terrain toward Japan. On the other hand, the N6BV/1 local terrain boosts signals in the range of 8° to about 12°. This demonstrates the conservation of energy — you may gain a stronger signal at certain elevation angles, but you will lose gain at others. In this case, the N6BV/1 station always felt "weak" toward Japan on 20 meters, because the dominant angles are low.

Examination of the detailed data output from *HFTA* shows that at an elevation angle of 5°, there are 6159 diffraction components. There are many, many signals bouncing around off the terrain on their trip to Japan! Note that because

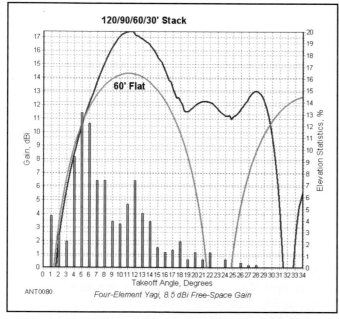

Figure 14.38 — Elevation response of "heroic effort" to surmount the difficulties imposed by hill in Figure 14.36. This effort involves a stack of four 4-element Yagis in a stack starting at 120 feet and spaced at 30-foot increments on the tower. The response is roughly equivalent to a single 4-element Yagi at 60 feet above flat ground, hence the characterization as being a "heroic effort." The elevation-angle statistics from New England to Europe are overlaid on the graph for reference.

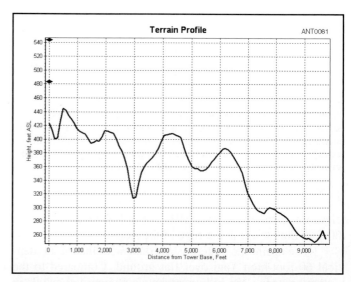

Figure 14.39 — Terrain of N6BV/1 in Windham, NH, toward Japan. HFTA identifies 52 different points where diffraction can occur.

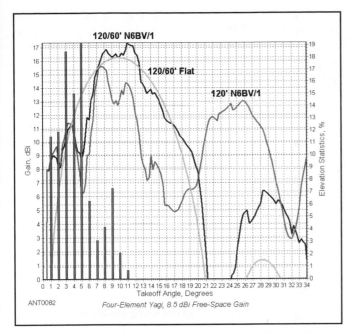

Figure 14.40 — Elevation responses computed by HFTA for N6BV/1 terrain shown in Figure 14.39, for a stack of two 4-element 20 meter Yagis at 120 and 60 feet, together with the response for a single Yagi at 120 feet and a 120/60-foot stack over flat ground for reference. Due to the response, many diffraction and reflection components is quite complicated!

of blockage of some parts of the terrain, the 60-foot high Yagi cannot illuminate all the diffraction points, while the higher 120-foot Yagi is able to see these diffraction points.

It is fascinating to reflect on the thought that received signals coming down from the ionosphere to the receiver are having encounters with the terrain, but from the opposite direction. It's not surprising, given these kinds of interactions, that transmitting and receiving might not be totally reciprocal.

The 120/60-foot stack in Figure 14.40 achieves its peak gain of 17.3 dBi at 11° elevation, where it is about 3 dB stronger than the single Yagi at 120 feet. It maintains this 3-dB advantage over most of the range of incoming signals from Japan. This difference in performance between the stack and each antenna by itself was observed many times on the air. Much of the time when comparisons are being made, however, the small differences in signal are difficult to measure meaningfully, especially when the fading varies signals by 20 dB or so during a typical QSO. It should be noted that the stack usually exhibited less fading compared to each antenna by itself.

14.3.6 USING *HFTA*

Manually Generating a Terrain Profile

The *HFTA* program uses two distinct algorithms to generate the far-field elevation pattern. The first is a simple reflection-only Geometric Optics (GO) algorithm. The second is the diffraction algorithm using the Uniform Theory of Diffraction (UTD). These algorithms work with a digitized representation of the terrain profile for a single azimuthal direction — for example, toward Japan or toward Europe.

You can generate a terrain file manually using a topographic map and a ruler or a pair of dividers. The HFTA.PDF file (accessed by clicking on the HELP button) and on the accompanying CD-ROM gives complete instructions on how to create a terrain file manually (or automatically). The manual process is simple enough in concept. Mark on your US Geological Survey 7.5-minute map the exact location of your tower. You will find 7.5-minute maps available from some local sources, such as large hardware stores, but the main contact point is the U.S. Geological Survey (**nationalmap.gov**). Many countries outside the USA have topographic charts also. Most are calibrated in meters. To use these with *HFTA*, you will have to convert meters to feet by multiplying meters by 3.28 or else inserting a single line at the very beginning of the disk file, saying "meters" for *HFTA* to recognize meters automatically.

Mark off a pencil line from the tower base, in the azimuthal direction of interest, perhaps 45° from New England to Europe, or 335° to Japan. Then measure the distance from the tower base to each height contour crossed by the pencil line. Enter the data at each distance/height into an ASCII computer file, whose filename extension is "PRO," standing for *profile*.

Figure 14.41 shows a portion of the USGS paper map for the N6BV/1 QTH in Windham, NH, along with lines scribed in several directions toward various parts of Europe and the Far East. Note that the elevation heights of the intermediate contour lines are labeled manually in pencil in order to make sense of things. It is very easy to get confused unless you do this!

The terrain model used by *HFTA* assumes that the terrain is represented by flat *plates* connecting the elevation points in the *.PRO file with straight lines. The model is two dimensional, meaning that range and elevation are the only data for a particular azimuth. In effect, *HFTA* assumes that the width of a terrain plate is wide relative to its length. Obviously, the world is three-dimensional. If your shot in a particular direction involves aiming your Yagi down a canyon with steep walls, then it's pretty likely that your actual elevation pattern will be different from what *HFTA* tells you. The signals must careen horizontally from wall to wall, in addition to being affected by the height changes of the terrain. *HFTA* isn't designed to do canyons.

To get a true 3-D picture of the full effects of terrain, a terrain model would have to show azimuth, along with range and elevation, point-by-point for about two miles in every direction around the base of the tower. After you go through the pain of creating a profile for a single azimuth, you'll appreciate the immensity of the process if you were to try to create a full 360° 3D profile manually.

Terrain Data from the Internet

At one time digitized terrain data commonly available from the Internet didn't have sufficient resolution to be accurate enough for *HFTA*. Nowadays, the complete, accurate set of USGS topographic 7.5-minute maps are available at no cost on the Internet (**nationalmap.gov**). You can use a

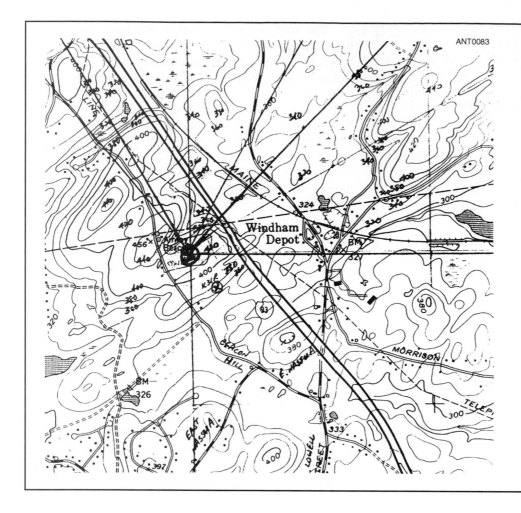

ANT0083

Figure 14.41 — A portion of USGS 7.5-minute topographic map, showing N6BV/1 QTH, together with marks in direction of Europe and Japan from tower base. Note that the elevation contours were marked by hand to help eliminate confusion. This required a magnifying glass and a steady hand!

program called *MicroDEM*, written by Professor Peter Guth at the US Naval Academy, to quickly and easily produce terrain data files suitable for *HFTA* from topographic data files. Dr Guth and the US Naval Academy have published *MicroDEM* for downloading at no cost at **www.usna.edu/User/oceano/pguth/website/microdem/microdem.htm**. It should be noted that besides automatically creating terrain profiles for *HFTA*, *MicroDEM* is a full-featured mapping program on its own.

There are presently three on-line sources of digital elevation data:

- DEM (USGS Digital Elevation Model, corresponding to the 7.5-minute "quadrangle" printed topographic maps used for years by hams and hikers).
- NED (USGS "seamless") topographic data that doesn't require "merging" together different 7.5-minute maps in order to cover sufficient geography for a 4400-meter radius around a tower.
- SRTM (Shuttle Radar Topology Mission). USGS/NOAA SRTM data covers about 80% of the world, but for security reasons has been limited to a resolution of about 30 meters.

Detailed instructions for using *MicroDEM* with these three digital-map data sources are in the Help file for *HFTA* (HFTA.PDF), which you can access from the *HFTA* main

window by clicking on the HELP button. **Figure 14.42** shows a screen capture of the *MicroDEM* program for the N6BV/1 location in New Hampshire for an azimuth of 45° into Europe. The black/white rendering of the screen capture doesn't do justice to the same information in color. The computed terrain profile is plotted in the window at the right of Figure 14.42 and the data file is shown in the inset window at the top right.

Using *MicroDEM* and on-line USGS topographic map data, you can also automatically create up to 360 terrain profiles with as little as 1° spacing of azimuths in a few seconds. (Specifying a 1° spacing is really overkill; most operators choose to create 72 profiles with 5° spacing.) On a topographic DEM (digital elevation model) map that covers the geographic area of interest, you simply specify the latitude and longitude of a tower's location — found using a GPS receiver — and then ask *MicroDEM* for a VIEWSHED. See the *HFTA* HELP file for the details.

Compare this automated several-second *MicroDEM* process to creating manual profiles on a paper topographic map. It can take up to an hour of meticulous measurements to manually create a single terrain profile.

Algorithm for Ray-Tracing the Terrain

Once a terrain profile is created, there are a number of

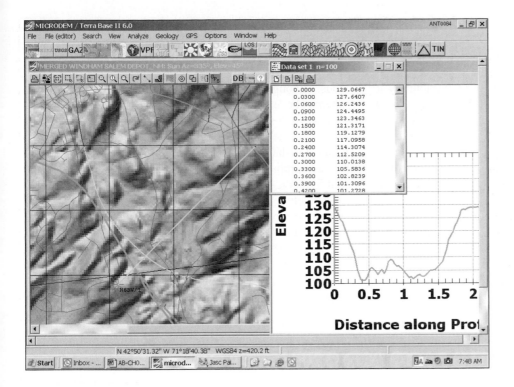

Figure 14.42 — A screen-capture of the *MicroDEM* program, showing the topographic map for the same terrain shown in Figure 14.41, together with the computed terrain profile along an azimuth of 45° on the path toward Europe from the N6BV/1 location in Windham, NH.

mechanisms that *HFTA* takes into account as a ray travels over that terrain:

1) Classical ray reflection, with Fresnel ground coefficients.

2) Direct diffraction, where a diffraction point is illuminated directly by an antenna, with no intervening terrain features blocking the direct illumination.

3) When a diffracted ray is subsequently reflected off the terrain.

4) When a reflected ray encounters a diffraction point and causes another series of diffracted rays to be generated.

5) When a diffracted ray hits another diffraction point, generating another whole series of diffractions.

Certain unusual, bowl-shaped terrain profiles, with sheer vertical faces, can conceivably cause signals to reflect or diffract in a backward direction, only to be reflected back again in the forward direction by the sheer-walled terrain to the rear. *HFTA* does not accommodate these interactions, mainly because to do so would increase the computation time too much. It only evaluates terrain in the forward direction along one azimuth of interest.

Figure 14.43 shows a portion of an *HFTA* screen capture in the direction toward Europe from the N6BV/1 location in New Hampshire on 21.2 MHz. It compares the results for a 90/60/30-foot stack of TH7DX tribanders to the same stack over flat land, and to a single antenna at 70 feet over flat ground. The 70-foot single antenna represents a pretty typical station on 15 meters. The terrain produces excellent gain at lower elevation angles compared to the same stack over flat ground. The stack is very close to or superior to the single 70-foot high Yagi at all useful elevation angles. Terrain can indeed exhibit a profound effect on the launch of signals into the ionosphere — for good or for bad.

HFTA's Internal Antenna Model

The operator selects the antenna used inside *HFTA* to be anything from a dipole to an 8-element Yagi. The default assumes a simple cosine-squared mathematic response, equivalent to a 4-element Yagi in free space. *HFTA* traces rays only in the forward direction from the tower along the azimuth

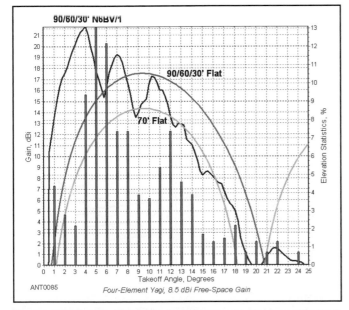

Figure 14.43 — The 21-MHz elevation response for a stack of three TH7DX Yagis mounted on a single tower at 90/60/30 feet, at the N6BV/1 QTH for a 45° azimuth toward Europe. The terrain focuses the energy at low elevation angles compared to the same stack over flat ground. This illustrates once again the conservation of energy: Energy squeezed down into low elevation angles is stolen from other, higher, angles.

of interest. This keeps the algorithms reasonably simple and saves computing time.

HFTA considers each antenna in a stack as a separate *point source*. The simulation begins to fall apart if a traveling wave type of antenna like a rhombic is used, particularly if the terrain changes under the antenna — that is, the ground is not flat under the entire antenna. For a typical Yagi, even a long-boom one, the point-source assumption is reasonable. The internal antenna model also assumes that the Yagi is horizontally polarized. *HFTA* does not do vertically polarized antennas, as discussed previously. The documentation for *HFTA* also cautions the user to work with practical spacings between stacked Yagis — 0.5 λ or more because *HFTA* doesn't explicitly model mutual coupling between Yagis in a stack.

HFTA compares well with the measurements for the horizontal antennas described earlier by Jim Breakall, WA3FET, using a helicopter in Utah. Breakall's measure-ments were done with a 15-foot high horizontal dipole.

More About *HFTA* Frequency Coverage

HFTA can be used on frequencies higher than the HF bands, although the graphical resolution is only 0.25°. The patterns above about 100 MHz thus look rather grainy. The UTD is a *high-frequency-asymptotic* solution, so in theory the results become more realistic as the frequency is raised. Keep in mind too that *HFTA* is designed to model launch angles for skywave propagation modes, including E- and F-layer, and even Sporadic-E. Since by definition the ionospheric launch angles include only those above the horizon, direct line-of-sight UHF modes involving negative launch angles are not considered in *HFTA*.

See the HFTA.PDF documentation file for further details on the operation of *HFTA*. This file, as well as sample terrain profiles for some *big-gun* stations, is located on the CD-ROM accompanying this book.

14.4 STACKING YAGIS AND SWITCHING SYSTEMS

The preceding sections illustrate the importance of controlling the elevation angle of an antenna's radiation pattern at HF. In addition, the wide variations also illustrate that a single antenna, no matter how much gain it produces, at a single height is often inadequate in maintaining effective communications over the desired path. For example, during a DX band opening on the upper HF bands the initial signals usually appear at very low elevation angles. Later, as the opening strengthens and spreads, signals at higher elevation angles are the strongest. Finally, as the band closes to that area, signals will again be the strongest at low angles. Being able to select the right elevation angle at the right time is important to sustained success in DXing or contest operation.

In HF amateur stations, the most common arrangement to control elevation angle is a vertical stack of identical Yagis on a single tower. This arrangement is commonly called a *vertical stack*. At VHF and UHF, amateurs sometimes employ collinear stacks, where identical Yagis are stacked side-by-side at the same height. This arrangement is called a *horizontal stack*, and is not usually found at HF, because of the severe mechanical difficulties involved with large, rotatable side-by-side arrays. In addition, whereas on HF a primary goal is being able to control the elevation angle of the radiation pattern for the optimum ionospheric path, on VHF and UHF it is more important to narrow the azimuthal width of the array's main lobe and minimize side lobes to improve the signal-to-noise ratio of very weak signals on both ends of the path.

Figure 14.44 illustrates the two different stacking arrangements. In either case, the individual Yagis making up the stack are generally fed in phase. There are times, however, when individual antennas in a stacked array are purposely fed out of phase in order to emphasize a particular elevation pattern. See the **Repeater Antenna Systems** chapter for such a case where elevation pattern steering is implemented for a repeater station.

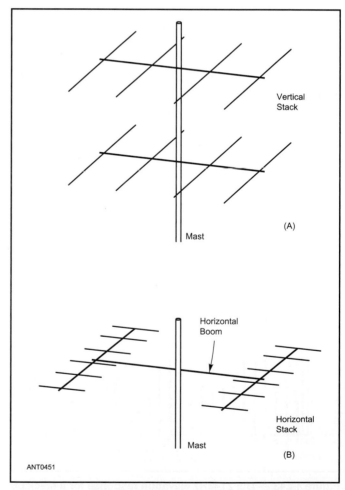

Figure 14.44 — Stacking arrangements. At A, two Yagis are stacked vertically (broadside) on the same mast. At B, two Yagis are stacked horizontally (collinear) side-by-side. At HF the vertical stack is more common because of mechanical difficulties involved with large HF antennas stacked side-by-side, whereas at VHF and UHF the horizontal stack is common.

Let's look at the reasons hams stack Yagis:

- For more gain
- For a wider elevation footprint in a target geographical area
- For azimuthal diversity — two or more directions at once
- For less fading
- For less precipitation static

14.4.1 STACKS AND GAIN

Figure 14.45 compares the elevation responses for three antenna systems of 4-element 15 meter Yagis. The response for the single Yagi at a height of 120 feet peaks at an elevation of about 5°, with a second peak at 17° and a third at 29°. When operated by itself, the 60-foot high Yagi has its first peak at about 11° and its second peak beyond 34°.

The basic principle of a vertically stacked HF array is that it takes energy from higher-angle lobes and concentrates that energy into the main elevation lobe. The main lobe of the 120/60-foot stack peaks about 7° and is about 2 dB stronger than either the 60- or 120-foot antenna by itself. The shape of the left-hand side of the stack's main lobe is determined mainly by the 120-foot antenna's response. The right-hand side of the stack's main lobe is "stretched" rightward (toward higher angles) mainly by the 60-foot Yagi, while the shape follows the curve of the 120-foot Yagi.

Look at the second and third lobes of the stack, which appear about 18° and 27°. These are about 14 dB down from the stack's peak gain, showing that energy has indeed been extracted from them. By contrast, look at the levels of the second and third lobes for the individual Yagis at 60 and 120 feet. These higher-angle lobes are almost as strong as the first lobes.

The stack squeezes higher-angle energy into its main elevation lobe, while maintaining the frontal lobe azimuth pattern of a single Yagi. This is the reason why many state-of-the-art contest stations are stacking arrays of relatively short-boom antennas, rather than stacking long-boom, higher-gain Yagis. A long-boom HF Yagi narrows the azimuthal pattern (and the elevation pattern too), making pointing the antenna more critical and making it more difficult to spread a signal over a wide azimuthal area, such as all of Europe and Asiatic Russia at one time.

14.4.2 STACKS AND WIDE ELEVATION COVERAGE

Detailed studies using sophisticated computer models of the ionosphere have revealed that coverage of a wide range of elevation angles is necessary to ensure consistent DX or contest coverage on the HF bands. These studies have been conducted over all phases of the 11-year solar cycle, and for numerous transmitting and receiving QTHs throughout the world.

The chapter **Radio Wave Propagation** covers these studies in more detail, and the CD-ROM accompanying this book contains a huge number of elevation-angle statistical tables for locations all around the world. The *HFTA* (HF Terrain Assessment) program on the CD-ROM can not only compute antenna elevation patterns over irregular local terrain, but it can compare them directly to the elevation-angle statistics for a particular target geographic area.

A 10 Meter Example

Figure 14.46 shows the 10 meter elevation-angle statistics for the New England path from Boston, Massachusetts, to all of the continent of Europe. The statistics are overlaid with the computed elevation response for three individual 4-element Yagis, at three heights: 90, 60 and 30 feet above flat ground. In terms of wavelength, these heights are 2.60 λ, 1.73 λ and 0.86 λ high.

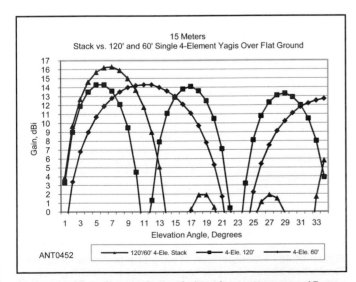

Figure 14.45 — Comparison of elevation patterns on 15 meters for a stack of 4-element Yagis at 120 and 60 feet and individual Yagis at those two heights. The shape of the stack's response is determined mainly by that of the top antenna.

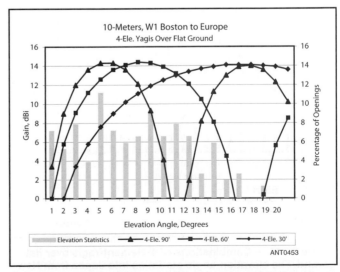

Figure 14.46 — Comparison of elevation patterns and elevation-angle statistics for individual 10-meter TH7DX tribanders mounted over flat ground aiming from New England to Europe. No single antenna can cover the wide range of angles needed — from 1° to 18°.

You can see that the 90-foot high Yagi covers the lower elevation angles best, but it has a large null in its response centered at about 11°. This null puts a big hole in the coverage for some 22% of all the times the 10 meter band is open to Europe. At those angles where the 90-foot Yagi exhibits a null, the 60-foot Yagi would be effective, and so would the 30-foot Yagi. If that is the only antenna you have, the 90-foot high Yagi would be too high for good coverage of Europe from New England.

The peak statistical elevation angle into Europe is 5°, and this occurs about 11% of all the times the 10 meter band is open to Europe from Boston. At an elevation of 5° the 30-foot high Yagi would be down almost 7 dB compared to the 90-foot high Yagi, but at 11° the 90-foot Yagi would be more than 22 dB down from the 30-foot Yagi. There is no single height at which one Yagi can optimally cover all the necessary elevation angles, especially to a large geographic area such as Europe — although the 60-foot high antenna is arguably the best compromise for a single height. To cover all the possibilities to Europe, however, you need a 10 meter antenna system that can cover equally well the entire range of elevation angles from 1° to 18°.

Figure 14.47 compares elevation-angle statistics for two 10 meter paths from New England to Europe and to Japan. The elevation angles needed for communications with the Far East are very low. Overlaid on Figure 14.47 for comparison are the elevation responses over flat ground for three different antenna systems, using identical 4-element Yagis:
- Three Yagis, stacked at 90, 60 and 30 feet
- Two Yagis, stacked at 70 and 40 feet
- One Yagi at 90 feet.

The best coverage of all the necessary angles on 10 meters to Europe is with the stack of three Yagis at 90/60/30 feet.

The two-Yagi stack at 70 and 40 feet comes in a close second to Europe, and for elevation angles higher than about 9° the 70/40-foot stack is actually superior to the 90/60/30-foot stack.

Both of the stacks illustrated here give a wider *elevation footprint* than any single antenna, so that all the angles can be covered automatically without having to switch from higher to lower antennas manually. This is perhaps the major benefit of using stacks, but not the only one, as we'll see.

To Japan, the necessary range of elevation angles is considerably smaller than that needed to a larger geographic target area like Europe. The 90/60/30-foot stack is still best on the basis of having higher gain at low angles, although the two-Yagi stack at 70 and 40 feet is a good choice too. Note that the single 90-foot high Yagi's performance is very close to the 70/40-foot stack of two Yagis at low angles, but the two-Yagi stack is superior to the single 90-foot antenna for angles higher than about 5° on 10 meters.

A 15 Meter Example

The situation is similar on 15 meters from New England to Europe. On 15 meters, the range of angles needed to fully cover Europe is 1° to 28°. This large range of angles makes covering all the angles even more challenging. Ken Wolff, K1EA, a devoted contest operator and the author of the famous *CT* contest logging program, put it very clearly when he wrote in the bulletin for the Yankee Clipper Contest Club:

"Suppose you have 15 meter Yagis at 120 feet and 60 feet, but can feed only one at a time. A 15 meter beam at 120 feet has its first maximum at roughly 5° and the first minimum at 10°. The Yagi at 60 feet has a maximum at 10° and a minimum at 2°. At daybreak, the band is just opening, signals are arriving at 3° or less and the high Yagi outperforms the

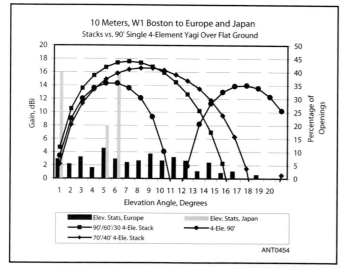

Figure 14.47 — Combinations of 4-element Yagis over flat ground. The elevation-angle statistics into Japan from New England (Boston) are represented by the black vertical bars, while the grey vertical bars represent the elevation-angle statistics to Europe. The 90/60/30-foot stack has the best elevation footprint into Japan, although the 70/40-foot stack performs well also.

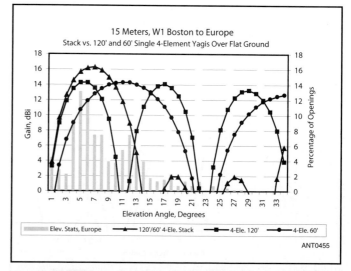

Figure 14.48 — Comparison of elevation patterns for K1EA's illustration about 15 meter Yagis mounted over flat ground, with elevation-angle statistics to Europe added. The stack at 120 and 60 feet yields a better footprint over the range of 3° to 11° at its half-power points, better than either antenna by itself.

low one by 5-10 dB. Late in the morning, western Europeans are arriving at angles of 10° or more, while UA6 is still arriving at 4-5°. Western Europe can be 20-30 dB louder on the low antenna than the high! What to do? Stack 'em!"

Figure 14.48 illustrates K1EA's scenario, showing the elevation statistics to Europe from Massachusetts and the elevation responses for a 120- and a 60-foot high, 4-element Yagi, both over flat ground, together with the response for both antennas operated as a vertical stack. The half-power beamwidth of the stack's main lobe is 6.9°, while that for the 120-foot antenna by itself is 5.5° and that for the 60-foot antenna by itself is 11.1°. The half-power beamwidth numbers by themselves can be deceiving, mainly because the stack starts out with a higher gain. A more meaningful observation is that the stack has equal to or more gain than either of the two individual antennas from 1° to about 10°.

Is such a stack of 15 meter Yagis at 120 and 60 feet optimal for the New England to Europe path? No, it isn't, as we'll explore later, but the stack is clearly better than either antenna by itself for the scenario K1EA outlined above.

A 20 Meter Example

Take a look now at **Figure 14.49**, which overlays elevation-angle statistics for Europe (gray vertical bars) and Japan (black vertical bars) from Boston on 20 meters, plus the elevation responses for four different sets of antennas mounted over flat ground. Just for emphasis, the highest antenna is a 200-foot high 4-element Yagi. It is clearly too high for complete coverage of all the needed angles into Europe. A number of New England operators have verified that this is true — a really high Yagi will open the 20 meter band to

Europe in the morning and may shut it down in the afternoon, but during the middle of the day the high antenna gets soundly beaten by lower antennas.

To Japan, however, from New England the range of angles needed narrows considerably on 20 meters, from 1° to only 11°. For these angles, the 200-foot Yagi is the best antenna to work Japan from New England on 20 meters.

This is true provided that the antenna is aiming out over flat ground. The actual, generally irregular, terrain in various directions can profoundly modify the takeoff angles favored by an antenna system, particularly on steep hills. There will be more discussion on this important topic later on.

14.4.3 ELIMINATING DEEP NULLS

Now, let's look closely at some other 20 meter antennas in Figure 14.46, the ones at 120 and 60 feet. At an elevation angle of 8° the difference in elevation response between the 60- and 120-foot high Yagis is just over 3 dB. Can you really notice a change of 3 dB on the air? Signals on the HF bands often rise and fall quickly due to fading, so differences of 2 or 3 dB are difficult to discern. Consequently, the difference between a Yagi at 120 feet and one at 60 feet may be difficult to detect at elevation angles covered well by both antennas. But a *deep null* in the elevation response is very noticeable.

Back in 1990, when Dean Straw, N6BV, put up his 120-foot tower in Windham, New Hampshire, his first operational antenna was a 5-element triband Yagi, with 3 elements on 40 and 4 elements on both 20 and 15 meters. Just as the sun was going down on a late August day Straw finished connecting the feed line in the shack. The antenna seemed to be playing like it should, with a good SWR curve and a good pattern when it was rotated. So N6BV/1 called a nearby friend, John Dorr, K1AR, on the telephone and asked him to get on the air to make some signal comparisons on 20 meters into Europe.

Straw was shocked that every European they worked that evening said his signal was several S units weaker than K1AR's. Dorr was using a 4-element 20 meter monobander at 90 feet, which at first glance should have been comparable to Straw's 4-element antenna at 120 feet. But N6BV really shouldn't have been so shocked — in New England, the elevation angles from Europe late in the day on 20 meters are almost always higher than 11°, and that is true for the entire solar cycle.

The N6BV/1 station was located on a small hill, while K1AR was located on flat terrain toward Europe. The elevation response for N6BV/1's 120-foot high Yagi fell right into a deep null at 11°. This was later confirmed many times in the following eight years that the N6BV/1 station was operational. During the early morning opening on 20 meters into Europe, the top antenna was always very close to or equal to the stack of three TH7DX tribanders at 90/60/30 feet on the same tower. But in the afternoon the top antenna was *always* decidedly worse than the stack, so much so that Straw often wondered whether something had gone wrong with the top antenna!

So what's the moral to this short tale? It's simple: *The gain you can achieve, while useful, is not so important as the deep nulls you can avoid by using a stack.*

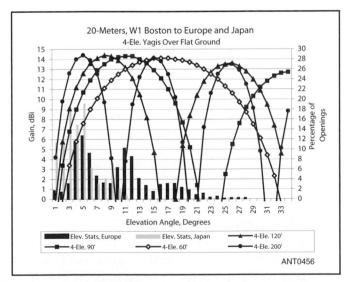

Figure 14.49 — Comparison of elevation patterns for individual 20 meter Yagis over flat ground, compared with the range of elevation angles needed on this band from New England to Europe (gray bars) and to Japan (black bars). For fun, the response of a 200-foot high Yagi is included — this antenna is far too high to cover the needed range of angles to Europe because of its deep nulls at critical angles, like 10°. But the 200 footer is great into Japan!

14.4.4 STACKING DISTANCES BETWEEN YAGIS

So far, we've examined stacks as a means of achieving more gain over an individual Yagi, while also matching the antenna system's response to the range of elevation angles needed for particular propagation paths. Most importantly, we seek to avoid nulls in the elevation response. Earlier we asked whether a 120/60-foot stack was optimal for the path from New England to Europe on 15 meters. Let's examine how the stacking distance between individual antennas affects the performance of a stack.

Figure 14.50 shows overlays of various combinations of 15 meter Yagis. Just for reference, a plot for a single 60-foot high Yagi is also included. Let's start by looking at the most widely spaced stack in the group: the 120/30-foot stack. Here, the spacing is obviously too large, since the second lobe is actually stronger than the first lobe. In terms of wavelength, the 90-foot spacing between antennas in this stack is 1.94 λ, a large spacing indeed.

There is a great deal of folklore and superstition among amateurs about stacking distances for HF arrays. For years, high-performance stacked Yagi arrays have been used for weak-signal DXing on the VHF and UHF bands. The most extreme example of weak-signal work is EME work (Earth-Moon-Earth, also called *moonbounce*) because of the huge path losses incurred on the way to and from the Moon. The most successful arrays used for moonbounce have low sidelobe levels and very narrow frontal lobes that give huge amounts of gain. The low sidelobes help minimize received noise, since the receive levels for signals that do manage to bounce off the Moon and return to Earth are exceedingly weak.

But HF operation is different from moonbounce in that rigorously trying to minimize high-angle lobes is far less crucial at HF, where we've already shown that the main goal is to achieve gain over a wide elevation-plane footprint without any disastrous nulls in the pattern. The gain gradually increases as spacing in terms of wavelength is increased between individual Yagis in a stack, and then decreases slowly once the spacing is greater than about 1.0 λ. The difference in gain between spacings of 0.5 λ to 1.0 λ for a stack of typical HF Yagis amounts to only a fraction of a decibel. Stacking distances on the order of 0.6 λ to 0.75 λ give best gain commensurate with good patterns.

While the stack at 120/60 feet in Figure 14.50 doesn't have the second-lobe-stronger problem the 120/30-foot stack has — 60 feet between antennas is 1.29 λ, again outside the normal range of HF stack spacings. As a consequence, the 120/60-foot stack doesn't cover the range of elevation angles as well as it could, and is inferior to both the 90/60/30-foot stack and the 120/90/60/30-foot stack. The 120/60-foot two-Yagi stack needs at least one more antenna placed in-between to spread out the elevation-range coverage and to provide more gain.

It could be debated, but the 90/60/30-foot stack seems optimal for coverage of all the angles into Europe from New England on 15 meters. Note that the 30-foot spacing between Yagis is 0.65 λ on 21.2 MHz, right in the middle of the range of typical stack spacings.

Switching Out Yagis in the Stack

Still, the extra gain that is available at low elevation angles from a 120/90/60/30-foot high, four-Yagi stack in Figure 14.50 is alluring. For those statistically possible, but less likely, occasions when the elevation angle is higher than about 12°, it would be advantageous to switch out the top 120-foot Yagi and operate with only the lower three Yagis in a stack. (This also allows the top antenna to be rotated in another direction, an aspect we'll explore later.) There are even times when the incoming angles are really high and when the top two antennas might be switched out to create a 60/30-foot stack. Later in this chapter we'll present circuitry for such stack switching.

Stacking Distance and Lobes at HF

Let's look a little more closely at how a stack achieves gain and a wide elevation footprint. **Figure 14.51** shows a rectangular X-Y graph of the elevation response from 0° to 180° for two 3-element 15 meter Yagis (with 12-foot booms) spaced 30 feet apart (0.65 λ at 21.2 MHz), but mounted at two different heights: 95/65 and 85/55 feet. The rectangular plot gives more resolution than is possible on a polar plot. Note that the heights shown represent typical stacking heights on 15 meters — there's nothing magic about these choices. The

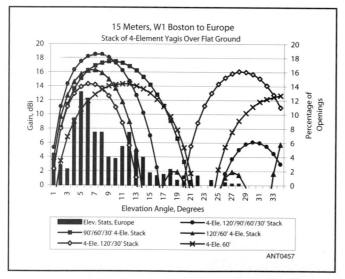

Figure 14.50 — Various stacks toward Europe from New England for 15 meters. The stack at 120 and 30 feet is clearly suboptimal, since the second lobe is higher than the first lobe. The 120/60-foot stack is better in this regard, but is still not as good a performer as the 90/60/30-foot stack. It's debatable whether going to four Yagis in the 120/90/60/30-foot stack is a good idea because it drops below the performance of the 90/60/30-foot stack at about 10° in elevation. The exact distance between practical HF Yagis is not critical to obtain the benefits of stacking. For a stack of tribanders at 90, 60 and 30 feet, the distance in wavelengths between individual antennas is 0.87 λ at 28.5 MHz, 0.65 λ at 21.2 MHz, and 0.43 λ at 14.2 MHz.

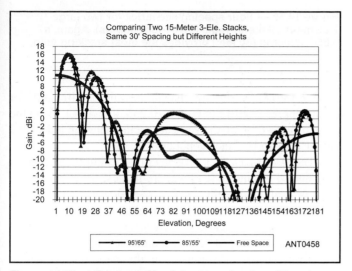

Figure 14.51 — Rectangular plot comparing two 15-meter stacks of 3-element Yagis — each antenna is spaced 30 feet from its partner, but at different heights. The lobes are a complicated function of the antenna height, not the spacing, since that remains constant.

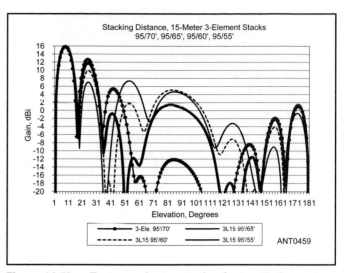

Figure 14.52 — Four spacing scenarios for two 3-element 15-meter Yagis. Things get very complicated. The optimal spacing in terms of stacking gain is 30 feet, which is 0.65 λ. The near-overhead lobes turn out to be ugly looking, but unimportant for skywave propagation.

free-space H-Plane pattern for the 30-foot spaced stack is also shown for reference.

The worst-case overhead elevation lobe, which ranges from about 60° to 120° in elevation (±30° from straight overhead at 90°), is about 14.7 dB down for the 95/65-foot stack. The overhead lobe peaks broadly at an elevation angle of about 82°. The overhead lobe for the lower 85/55-foot stack occurs at an elevation of about 64°, where it is 19 dB down.

The F/B for both 3-element sets of heights is about 15 dB, well down from the excellent 32 dB F/B for each Yagi by itself. The degradation of F/B is mainly due to mutual coupling to its neighbor in the stack.

The ground-reflection pattern in effect "modulates" the free-space pattern of the individual Yagi, but in a complex and not always intuitive manner. This is quite evident for the 85/55-foot stack at near-overhead angles. In this region things become complicated indeed, because the fourth and fifth lobes due to ground reflections are interacting with the free-space pattern of the stack.

Because the spacing remains constant at 30 feet for these pairs of antennas, however, the main determinant for the upper-elevation angle lobes is the distance of the horizontally polarized antennas above the ground, not the spacing between them.

Changing the Stack Spacing

Figure 14.52 demonstrates just how complicated things get for four different spacing scenarios. Here, the lower Yagi in the stack is moved down in 5-foot increments from the 95/70 feet level, to 95/65, 95/60 and 95/55 feet. The closest spacing, 25 feet in the 95/70-foot stack, yields nominally the "cleanest" pattern in the overhead region from 60° to 120°. The worst-case overhead lobe for the 95/70-foot stack is down 28 dB from peak. The F/B is again about 15 dB.

The worst case overhead lobe for the widest spacing,

40 feet in the 95/55-foot stack, is about 11 dB down from peak. The F/B has increased marginally, but is still only about 16 dB. It is difficult to pinpoint directly whether the spacing or the height above ground is the major determinant for the various lobe amplitudes for the 3-element stack. We'll soon look closely at whether the overhead lobe is important or not for HF work.

Longer Boom Length and Stack Spacing

Figure 14.53 shows the same type overlay of elevation plots, but this time for two 7-element 15 meter Yagis on gigantic 64-foot booms. These Yagis are also spaced 30 feet apart (0.65 λ at 21.2 MHz), mounted at the same four sets of heights in Figure 14.52. As you'd expect, the free-space elevation pattern for a stacked pair of 7-element Yagis on 64-foot booms is narrower than that for a stacked pair of 3-element Yagis on 12-foot booms. The intrinsic F/B of the longer Yagi is also better than the F/B of the shorter antenna. As a result, all lobes beyond the main lobe of the stacked 7-element pair are lower for both sets of heights than their 3-element counterparts. The worst-case overhead lobe for the 7-element 95/65-foot pair is about 22 dB down at 76° and the F/B at 172° is greater than 21 dB for all four sets of heights.

Table 14-2 summarizes the main performance characteristics for four sets of stacked Yagis. The first entry for each boom length is for the Yagi by itself at a height of 95 feet. Stacked configurations are next listed in order of gain. The column labeled "Worst lobe, dB re Peak" is the amplitude of the second lobe due to ground reflections, and the elevation angle of that second lobe is listed as well.

Besides the 3- and 7-element designs discussed above, we've also added 4- and 5-element designs in Table 14-2. Over the range of stacking distances between 20 and 40 feet on 15 meters (0.43 λ to 0.86 λ), the peak gain for the 3-element stacks changes less than 0.75 dB, with the

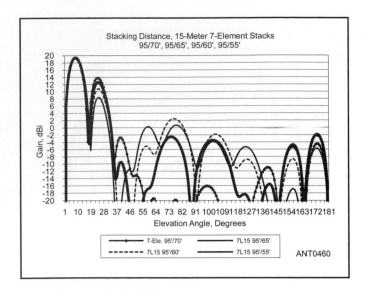

Figure 14.53 — Four spacing scenarios for two large 7-element 15-meter Yagis (on 64-foot booms). Again, a 0.65-λ spacing (30 feet) provides the most stacking gain.

(0.43 λ to 0.86 λ) doesn't change the gain significantly for boom lengths from 12 to 64 feet (0.26 λ to 1.38 λ). From the point of view of gain, the vertical spacing between individual antennas in an HF stack is not critical.

The worst-case lobes (generally speaking, the second lobe due to ground reflections) are highest for a Yagi operated by itself. After all, a single Yagi doesn't benefit from the redistribution of energy from higher-angle lobes into the main lobe that a stack gives. Thus, the 3-element, 12-foot boom Yagi by itself at 95 feet would have a second lobe at 21° that is only 0.9 dB down from the main lobe, while the stack of two such antennas with 30-foot (0.65 λ) spacing at 95/65 feet would have a second lobe down 4.5 dB. As the spacing between antennas in a vertical stack increases, the second lobe is suppressed more, up to 8.7 dB with 40-foot (0.86 λ) spacing.

Since the free-space elevation pattern for a 3-element Yagi is wider than that for a 7-element Yagi, the second lobe due to ground reflection will be somewhat reduced. This is true for all longer-boom antennas operating by themselves over ground. Used in stacks, the second lobe's amplitude will vary depending on spacing between antennas, but they range only about 6 dB.

The front-to-back ratio will also tend to increase with longer boom lengths on a properly designed Yagi. Table 14-2 shows that the F/B is somewhat better for closer spacings between antennas in a stack, a rather non-intuitive result, considering that the mutual coupling should be greater for closer antennas. For example, the 5-element Yagi stack with 20-foot spacing has a exceptional F/B of 34.3 dB, compared to a F/B of 21.4 dB with the 30-foot spacing distance that gives nominally the most gain. High values of F/B, however, rarely hold over a wide frequency range because of the very critical phasing relationships necessary to get a deep null, so the difference between 34.3 and 21.4 dB would rarely be noticeable in practice.

The near-overhead lobe structure (between 60° to 120° in elevation) tends also to be lower for smaller stack spacings — for all boom lengths — peaking in this

30-foot spacing exhibiting the highest gain. The differences between peak gains versus stacking distance become smaller as the boom length increases. For example, for the 64-foot boom Yagi, the gain varies 19.39 – 19.08 = 0.31 dB for stack spacings from 20 to 40 feet.

In other words, changing the spacing from 20 to 40 feet

Table 14-2
Example, Spacing Between 15-Meter Yagis

Antenna	Peak Gain (dBi)	Worst Lobe (dB re Peak)	Worst Lobe Angle (°)	F/B (dB)	Overhead Lobe (dB re Peak)
3 Elements, 12 Foot Boom					
By itself 95'	13.2	–0.9	21	28.8	–17.5
95'/65' (Δ 30')	16.08	–4.5	25	14.9	–14.7
95'/60' (Δ 35')	16.01	–6.2	24	15.1	–10.9
95'/70' (Δ 25')	15.81	–3.2	24	14.8	–28
95'/55' (Δ 40')	15.71	–8.7	24	16.4	–11
95'/75' (Δ 20')	15.34	–2.3	23	16.3	–17.2
4 Elements, 18 Foot Boom					
By itself 95'	13.92	–1	21	28.3	–20.4
95'/65' (Δ 30')	16.63	–4.5	23	18.5	–17.3
95'/60' (Δ 35')	16.6	–6.2	24	18.2	–13.1
95'/55' (Δ 40')	16.36	–8.7	24	19.8	–13.2
95'/70' (Δ 25')	16.36	–3.3	24	20.4	–31.8
95'/75' (Δ 20')	15.92	–2.5	23	25.9	–19
5 Elements, 23 Foot Boom					
By itself 95'	14.26	–1.1	21	27.9	–22.3
95'/65' (Δ 30')	16.86	–4.6	24	20.8	–19
95'/60' (Δ 35')	16.86	–6.3	24	20.7	–14.4
95'/55' (Δ 40')	16.67	–8.8	24	23.5	–14.4
95'/70' (Δ 25')	16.59	–3.4	24	24.9	–34.4
95'/75' (Δ 20')	16.18	–2.6	23	34.3	–20.2
7 Elements, 64 Foot Boom					
By itself 95'	17.93	–2.2	21	28.9	–17.1
95'/65' (Δ 30')	19.39	–6.9	24.3	21.4	–21.9
95'/60' (Δ 35')	19.38	–8.6	24	21.4	–16.9
95'/55' (Δ 40')	19.29	–10.9	24	25.0	–18.6
95'/70' (Δ 25')	19.26	–5.5	23	24	–35.3
95'/75' (Δ 20')	19.08	–4.6	23	27	–23.4

example at a spacing of 25 feet for the boom lengths considered here. Since the peak gain actually occurs with smaller spacing between Yagis in this 7-element stack, even relatively large and messy looking overhead lobes are not subtracting from the stacking gain. In the next section we'll now examine whether this overhead lobe is important or not.

Stacking Distances for Multiband Yagis

By definition, a stack of multiband Yagis (such as a "tribander" covering 20/15/10 meters) has a constant vertical spacing between antennas in terms of feet or meters, but not in terms of wavelength. Tribanders are no different than monobanders in terms of optimal spacing between individual antennas. Again, the difference in gain between spacings of 0.5 λ and 1.0 λ for a stack of triband Yagis amounts to only a fraction of a decibel. Furthermore, the main practical constraint that limits choice of stacking distances between any kind of Yagis, multiband or monoband, is the spacing between guy wire sets on the tower itself.

Summary — Stacking Distances

In short, let us summarize that there is nothing magical about stacking distances for practical HF Yagis — a good rule-of-thumb is a stacking distance of 0.65 λ. This is 23 feet on 10 meters, 30 feet on 15 meters and 45 feet on 20 meters for monoband stacks. Practically speaking, however, you've only got limited places where you can mount antennas on the tower — mainly where guy wires allow you to place them. This is especially applicable if you wish to rotate lower antennas on the tower, where you must clear the guys from above the antenna.

14.4.5 RADIATION OUTSIDE THE MAIN LOBE

The Importance of Higher-Angle Lobes

We've already shown that the exact spacing between HF Yagis is not critical for stacking gain. Further, the heights (and hence spacing) of the individual Yagis in a stack interact in a complicated fashion to determine higher-angle lobes.

Let's examine the relevance of such higher-angle lobes for stacked HF Yagis, this time in terms of interference reduction on receive. As the **Radio Wave Propagation** chapter points out, few DX signals arrive at elevation angles greater than about 30°. In fact, DX signals only propagate at elevation angles in the range from 1° to 30° on all the bands where operators might reasonably expect to stack Yagis — nominally from 7 to 29.7 MHz.

You should remember that the definition of the *critical frequency* for HF propagation is the highest frequency for which a wave launched directly overhead at 90° elevation is reflected back down to Earth, rather than being lost into outer space. The maximum critical frequency for extremely high levels of solar flux is about 15 MHz. In other words, high overhead angles do not propagate signals on the upper HF bands.

However, some domestic signals do arrive at relatively high elevation angles. Let's look at some scenarios where higher angles might be encountered and how the elevation patterns of typical HF stacks affect these signals. Let's examine a situation where a medium-range interfering station is on the same heading as a more distant target station.

We'll examine a typical scenario involving stations in Atlanta, Boston and Paris. The heading from Atlanta to Paris is 49°, the same heading as Atlanta to Boston. In other words, the Atlanta station would have to transmit over (and listen through) a Boston station for communication with Paris. The distance between Atlanta and Boston is about 940 miles, while the distance from Atlanta to Paris is about 4350 miles. Ground wave signals obviously cannot travel either of these distances at 21 MHz (ground wave coverage is less than about 10 miles at this frequency), and so the propagation between Atlanta to Boston and Atlanta to Paris will be entirely by means of the ionosphere.

Let's evaluate the situation on 15 meters in the month of October. We'll assume a smoothed sunspot number (SSN) of 100 and that each station puts 1500 W of power into theoretical isotropic antennas that have +10 dBi of gain at all elevation and azimuth angles. [We use such theoretical isotropic antennas because they make it easier to work in *VOACAP*. We will factor in real-world stacks later.] *VOACAP* predicts that the signal from Boston will be S9 + 8 dB in Atlanta at 1400 UTC, arriving at an elevation angle of 21.3° on a single F2 hop. This elevation angle is higher than commonly encountered angles for DX signals, but it is still far away from near-overhead angles.

The signal from Paris into Atlanta is predicted to be about S6 for the same theoretical isotropic antennas, at an incoming elevation angle of 6.4° on three F2 hops. The S6 level validates the rule-of-thumb that each extra hop loses approximately 10 dB of signal strength, assuming that each S unit is about 4 dB, typical for modern receivers.

Now look at **Figure 14.54**, which shows the response for a stack of 3-element Yagis at 90/60/30 feet over flat ground, along with the response for a similar stack of 7-element Yagis. Again, we'll assume that all three stations are using such 3-element 90/60/30-foot stacks. The stations in Atlanta and Boston point their stacks into Europe and the Parisian station points his stack toward the USA. The gain of the Atlanta array at 6.4° into Paris will be about 16 dBi, or 6 dB more than the isotropic array with its +10 dBi of gain selected for use in *VOACAP*. Similarly, the French station's transmitted signal will enjoy a 6 dB gain advantage over the isotropic array used in the *VOACAP* calculation, and thus the French signal into Atlanta will now be S6 + 12 dB, or about S9.

By comparison, the interfering signal from Boston into Atlanta will be reduced by the rearward pattern of his array, which will launch a signal at 180° – 21.3° = 158.7° in elevation at the single F2 mode from Boston to Atlanta. From Figure 14.51, the Boston station's gain at this rearward elevation is going to drop from the isotropic's +10 dBi of gain down to –11 dBi, a drop of 21 dB. The signal into the Atlanta receiver will also be reduced by the pattern of the Atlanta array on receive, which has a gain of about 0 dBi at 21.3°, compared

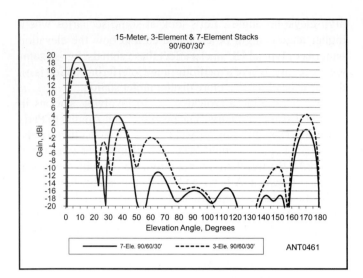

Figure 14.54 — Stacks of three 3-element and 7-element Yagis on 15 meters at 90/60/30 feet heights. The F/B for the 7-element stack is superior to the 3-element stack mainly because the F/B is intrinsically better for the long-boom design.

to the isotropic's +10 dBi gain at 6.4°, a net drop of 10 dB.

Thus, the Boston station's signal will drop by about 21 + 10 = 31 dB, bringing the interfering signal from Boston, which would be S9 + 8 dB for isotropic antennas, down to about S3 due to the combined effects of the arrays. This is a very significant reduction in interference. But you will note that the reduction has nothing to do with the near-overhead lobes, dealing as it does with the trailing edge of the main lobe and the F/B lobe.

Higher Elevation Angles

Now let's evaluate a station that is even closer to Boston, say a station in Philadelphia. The heading from Philadelphia to Paris is 53° and the distance is 3220 miles. On the same day in October as above, *VOACAP* predicts a signal strength of S8 from Paris to Philadelphia, at a 2.7° elevation angle on two F2 hops. Again, the *VOACAP* computations assume isotropic antennas with +10 dBi gain at all three stations. The gain of the 3-element stacks at both ends of the circuit at 2.7° is also about +10 dBi, so the signal level from Paris to Philadelphia would be S8 with the 3-element stacks.

Now *VOACAP* computes the elevation angle from Philadelphia to Boston as 56.3°, on one F_2 hop launched at an azimuth of 53°, well within the azimuthal beamwidth of the stack. *VOACAP* says the predicted signal strength for isotropic antennas with +10 dBi of gain is less than S1!

What's happening here? Boston and Philadelphia are within the "skip" region on 21 MHz and signals are skipping right over Boston from Philadelphia (and vice versa). Actual signals would be much weaker than they would be with theoretical isotropic antennas because of the actual patterns of the transmitting and receiving stacks. At an elevation angle of 56.3° the receiving stack would have a gain of –10 dBi, while at an elevation of 180° – 56.3° = 123.7° the transmitting stack would be down to –10 dBi as well. The net reduction for the

stacks compared to isotropics with +10 dBi gain each would be 40 dB, putting the interfering signal well into the receiver noise.

You can safely say that near-overhead angles don't enter into the picture, simply because signals at intermediate distances are in the ionospheric skip zone and interfering signals are very weak in that zone already.

Even in situations where having a poor front-to-back ratio might be beneficial — because it alerts stations tuning across your signal that you are occupying that frequency — the ionosphere doesn't cooperate for intermediate-distance signals that are in the skip zone. Often two stations may be on the same frequency without either knowing that the other is there.

Ground Wave and Stacks

What happens, you might wonder, for ground-wave signals? Let's look at a situation where the interfering station is in the same direction as the desired target, but is only 5 miles away. Unfortunately, his signal is S9 + 50 dB. Even reducing the level by 30 dB, a huge number, is still going to make his signal 20 dB stronger than signals from your desired target location! There is not much you can do about ground-wave signals and fretting about optimizing stack heights to discriminate against local signals is generally futile.

14.4.6 REAL-WORLD TERRAIN AND STACKS

So far, the stacking examples shown have been for flat ground. Things can become a lot more complicated when you deal with real-world irregular terrains! **Figure 14.55** shows the *HFTA*-computed 20 meter elevation responses toward Europe (at an azimuth of 45°) for three antennas at the N6BV/1 location in Windham, New Hampshire. Overlaid as a bar graph are the elevation-angle statistics for the path to all of Europe from New England (Massachusetts). The stack at 90/60/30 feet clearly covers all the angles needed best at 14 MHz. The N6BV/1 120-foot Yagi has a severe null in the region from about 7° to about 20°, with the deepest part of that null occurring at about 13° and is roughly comparable to the 90/60/30-foot stack between 2° to 7°.

In practice, the 120-foot Yagi was indeed comparable to the stack during morning openings to Europe on 20 meters, when the elevation angles are typically about 5°. In the New England afternoon, when the elevation angles typically rise to about 11°, the 120-foot Yagi was always distinctly inferior to the stack.

For reference, the response of a single 120-foot high Yagi over flat ground is also shown. Note that the N6BV 120-foot high Yagi has about 3 dB more gain at a 5° takeoff angle than does its flatland counterpart. This additional gain is due to the focusing effects of the local terrain, which had about a 3° downward slope toward Europe.

Figure 14.56 shows the *HFTA*-computed 15 meter elevation responses toward Europe for the 90/60/30-foot stack at 90/60/30 feet at N6BV/1, compared to the same 120-foot high Yagi and a 90/60/30-foot stack, but this time over flat ground. Again, the N6BV/1 terrain toward Europe has a

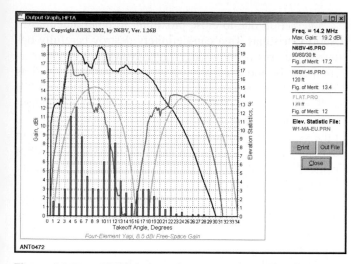

Figure 14.55 — *HFTA* screen shot showing how complicated things become when real-world irregular terrain is analyzed. This is the 20-meter elevation pattern for the N6BV/1 station location in Windham, NH, for the 90/60/30-foot stack of triband TH7DX Yagis and a 4-element Yagi at 120 feet on the same tower. For comparison, the response of a 120-foot Yagi over flat ground is also included.

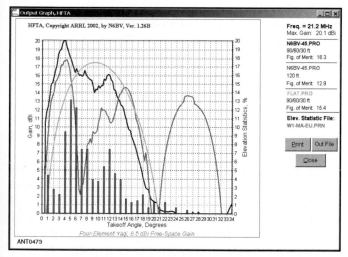

Figure 14.56 — *HFTA* screen shot showing the 15-meter elevation pattern for the N6BV/1 station location in Windham, NH, for the 90/60/30-foot stack of triband TH7DX Yagis and a 4-element Yagi at 120 feet on the same tower. For comparison, the response of a 120-foot Yagi over flat ground is also included.

significant effect on the gain of the stack compared to that of an identical stack over flat ground. In fact, the peak gain of 20.1 dBi at a 4° elevation angle is close to moon-bounce levels.

Optimizing Over Local Terrain

There are only a small number of possibilities to optimize an installation over local terrain:
- Change the antenna height(s) above ground.
- Stack two (or more) Yagis.
- Change the spacing between stacked Yagis.

- Move the tower back from a cliff (or a hill).
- BIP/BOP (Both In Phase/Both Out of Phase).

The *HFTA* program on the CD-ROM accompanying this book can be used, together with Digital Elevation Model (DEM) topographic data available on the Internet, to evaluate all these options.

It is sometimes very surprising to compare elevation responses for different towers located at various points on the same property, particularly when that property is located in the mountains. **Figure 14.57** shows the computed elevation responses for three 100-foot high 14-MHz Yagis over three terrains toward Europe: from the North tower at K1KI's location in West Suffield, Connecticut, from the South tower at K1KI, and over flat ground. The elevation response from

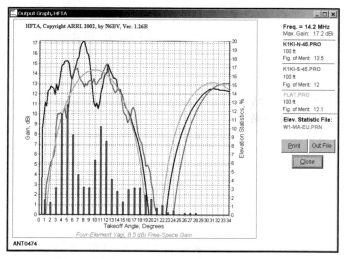

Figure 14.57 — *HFTA* screen shot showing the 20-meter elevation pattern for K1KI's North and South towers, with 100-foot high 4-element Yagis pointing into Europe at an azimuth of 45°. The responses are surprisingly different for two towers separated by only 600 feet.

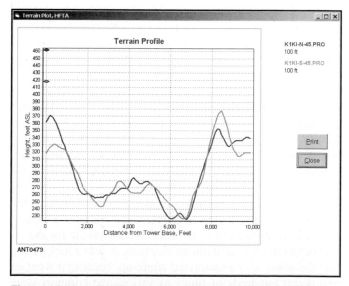

Figure 14.58 — K1KI's terrain profiles for the North and South towers at an azimuth of 45° into Europe.

the South tower follows that over flat ground well, while the response from the North tower is quite a bit stronger at low elevation angles — about 1.5 dB on average, as the Figure of Merit shows from *HFTA*.

Figure 14.58 shows the reason why this happens — the terrain from the North tower slopes down quickly toward Europe, while the terrain from the South tower goes out almost 900 feet before starting to fall off. These two towers are about 600 feet apart.

14.4.7 STACKING TRIBANDERS

Enterprising amateurs have built stacked tribander arrays even with full recognition that they are compromise antennas when compared one-on-one against monoband Yagis. Bob Mitchell, N5RM, is a prominent example, with his so-called "TH28DX" array of four TH7DX tribanders on a 145-foot-high rotating tower. Mitchell employed a rather complex system of relay-selected tuned networks to choose either the upper stacked pair, the lower stacked pair or all four antennas in stack. Others in Texas have also had good results with their tribander stacks. Contester Tom Owens, K7RI, has very successfully used a pair of stacked KT-36XA tribanders for years.

A major reason why tribanders were used is that over the years both amateurs have had good results using TH6DXX or TH7DX antennas. They are ruggedly built, mechanically and electrically, and their 24-foot long booms are long enough to produce significant gain, despite trap-loss compromises. Trap losses estimated at approximately 0.5 dB are not high enough to be of serious concern. A long-boom tribander like the TH6DXX or TH7DX also has enough space to employ elements dedicated to different bands, so the compromises in element spacing usually found on short-boom 3 or 4-element tribanders can be avoided.

Another factor in favor of tribanders is the serious interaction that can result from stacking monoband antennas closely together on one mast in a Christmas Tree configuration. N6BV's worst experience was with the ambitious 10 through 40 meter Christmas Tree at W6OWQ in the early 1980s. This installation used a Tri-Ex SkyNeedle tubular crank-up tower with a rotating 10-foot-long heavy-wall mast. The antenna suffering the greatest degradation was the 5-element 15 meter Yagi, sandwiched 5 feet below the 5-element 10 meter Yagi at the top of the mast, and 5 feet above the full-sized 3-element 40 meter Yagi, which also had five 20 meter elements interlaced on its 50-foot boom.

The front-to-back ratio on 15 meters was at best about 12 dB, down from the 25+ dB measured with the bottom 40/20 meter Yagi removed. No amount of fiddling with element spacing, element tuning or even orientation of the 15 meter boom with respect to the other booms (at 90° or 180°, for example) improved its performance. Further, the 20 meter elements had to be lengthened by almost a foot *on each end of each element* in order to compensate for the effect of the interlaced 40 meter elements. It was a lucky thing that the tower was a motorized crank-up, because it went up and down hundreds of times as various experiments were attempted!

Interaction due to close proximity to other antennas in a short Christmas Tree can definitely destroy carefully optimized patterns of individual Yagis. Nowadays, such interaction can be modeled using a computer program such as *EZNEC* or *NEC*. A gain reduction of as much as 2 to 3 dB can easily result due to close vertical spacing of monobanders, compared to the gain of a single monoband antenna mounted in the clear. Curiously enough, at times such a reduction in gain can be found even when the front-to-back ratio is not drastically degraded, or when the front-to-back occasionally is actually *improved*.

If you plan on stacking monoband Yagis — for example, putting 15 and 20 meter Yagis on a single tower, do make sure you model the system to see if any interactions occur. You may be quite surprised.

Finally, triband antennas make for less mechanical complexity than do an equivalent number of monobanders. There were five Yagis on the N6BV/1 tower, yielding gain from 40 to 10 meters, as opposed to using 12 or 13 monobanders on the tower.

Simple Tribander Stacks

All this discussion of large stacks of many antennas is simply out of the question for most amateurs. However, many hams already have a tribander on top of a moderately tall tower, typically at a height of about 70 feet. It is not terribly difficult to add another, identical tribander at about the 40-foot level on such a tower. The second tribander can be pointed in a fixed direction of particular interest (such as Europe or Japan), or it can be rotated around the tower on a side mount or a Ring Rotor. If guy wires get in the way of rotation, the antenna can usually be arranged so that it is fixed in a single direction.

Insulate the guy wires at intervals to ensure that they don't shroud the lower antenna electrically. A simple feed system consists of equal-length runs of surplus ½-inch 75-Ω hardline (or more expensive 50-Ω hardline, if you are really obsessed by SWR) from the shack up the tower to each antenna. Each tribander is connected to its respective hardline feeder by means of an equal length of flexible coaxial cable, with a ferrite choke balun, so that the antenna can be rotated.

Down in the shack, the two runs of hardline can simply be switched in and out of parallel to select the upper antenna only, the lower antenna only, or the two antennas as a stack. See **Figure 14.59**. Any impedance differences can be handled as stated previously, simply by retuning the linear amplifier, or by means of the internal antenna tuner (included in most modern transceivers) when the transceiver is run barefoot. The extra performance experienced in such a system will be far greater than the extra decibel or two that modeling calculates.

14.4.8 STACKING DISSIMILAR YAGIS

So far we have been discussing vertical stacks of identical Yagis. Less commonly, hams have successfully stacked dissimilar Yagis. For example, consider a case where two 5-element 10 meter Yagis are placed 46 and 25 feet above

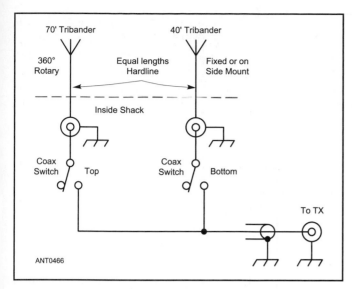

Figure 14.59 — Simple feed system for 70/40-foot stack of tribanders. Each tribander is fed with equal lengths of 0.5-inch 75-Ω Hardline cables (with equal lengths of flexible coax at the antenna to allow rotation), and can be selected singly or in parallel at the operator's position in the shack. Again, no special provision is made in this system to equal SWR for any of the combinations.

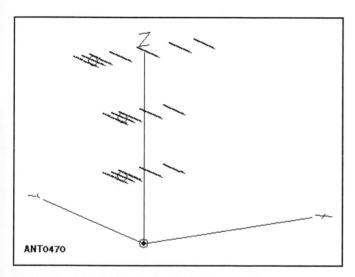

Figure 14.60 — Stacking dissimilar Yagis. In this case a 7-element 10-meter Yagi is stacked over two 5-element Yagis. Note the displacement of the 7-element Yagi's driven element compared to the position of the two 5-element Yagis. This leads to an undesired phase shift for the higher antenna.

flat ground, with a 7-element 10 meter Yagi at 68 feet on the same tower. See **Figure 14.60**, which is a schematic of the layout for this stack. Note that the driven element for the top 7-element Yagi is well behind the vertical plane of the driven elements for the two 5-element Yagis. This offset distance must be compensated for with a phase shift in the drive system for the top Yagi.

Figure 14.61 shows the elevation-pattern responses for uncompensated (equal-length feed lines) and the compensated

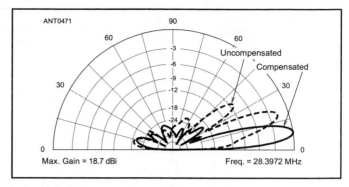

Figure 14.61 — Comparison of elevation responses for 7/5/5-element 10-meter stacks, with and without compensation for driven-element offset.

(additional 150° of phase shift to top Yagi) stacks. These patterns were computed using *EZNEC ARRL*, which is included with this book. Not only is about 1.7 dB of maximum gain lost, but the peak elevation angle is shifted upward by 11° from the optimal takeoff angle of 8° — where some 10 dB of gain is also lost. Without compensation, this is a severe distortion of the stack's elevation pattern.

For RG-213 coax, the extra length needed to provide an additional 150° of phase shift = 150°/360° λ = 0.417 λ = 9.53 feet at 28.4 MHz. This was computed using the program *TLW* (Transmission Line for *Windows*) included on the CD-ROM accompanying this book.

It is not always possible to compensate for dissimilar Yagis in a stack with a simple length of extra coax, so you should be sure to model such combinations to make sure that they work properly. A safe alternative, of course, is to stack only identical Yagis, feeding all of them with equal lengths of coax to ensure in-phase operation.

14.4.9 THE WXØB APPROACH TO STACK SWITCHING

Earlier we mentioned how useful it would be to switch various antennas in or out of a stack, depending on the elevation angles that need to be emphasized at that moment. Jay Terleski, WXØB, of Array Solutions (**www.arraysolutions. com**) has designed switchable matching systems, called *StackMatches*, for stacks of monoband or multiband Yagis. This has become the standard method of switching for stacks of Yagi antennas, whether monoband or triband. (A description of two other systems used by N6BV/1 and K1VR is included on this book's CD-ROM.)

The StackMatch uses a 50-Ω to 22.25-Ω broadband transmission-line transformer to match combinations of up to three Yagis in a stack. See **Figure 14.62** for a schematic of the StackMatch. For selection of any 50-Ω Yagi by itself, no matching transformer is needed and Relay IN routes RF directly to the common bus going to Relay 1, 2 and 3. For selection of two Yagis together the parallel impedance is 50/2 = 25 Ω and Relay IN routes RF to the matching transformer. The SWR is 25/22.25 = 1.1:1. For three Yagis used together, the parallel impedance is 50/3 = 16.67 Ω, and

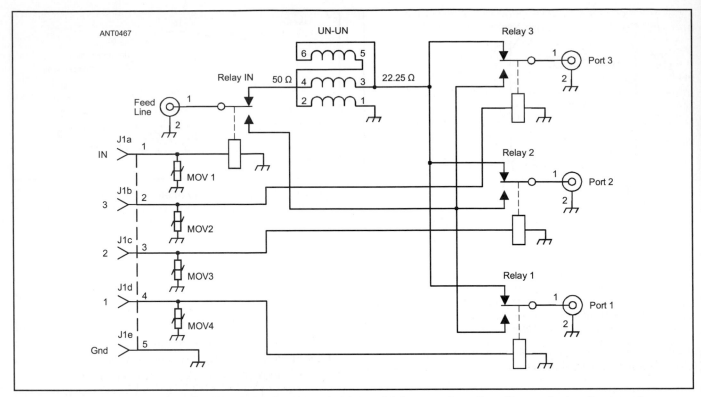

Figure 14.62 — Schematic of WXØB's StackMatch 2000 switchbox, which uses a broadband transmission line transformer using trifilar #12 enamel-insulated wires. (*Courtesy Array Solutions.*)

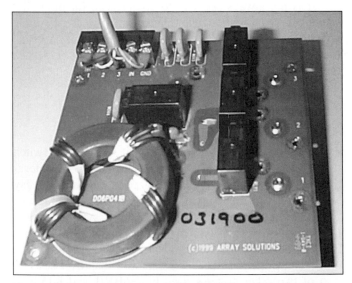

Figure 14.63 — Inside view of StackMatch. (*Photo courtesy Array Solutions.*)

the SWR is 22.25/16.67 = 1.3:1.

The broadband transformer consists of four trifilar turns of #12 enamel-insulated wire wound on a Ferrite Corporation FT-240 2.4-inch OD core made of #61 material (μ = 125). WXØB uses 10-A relays enclosed in plastic cases to do the RF switching, selected by a control box at the operating position. (10-A relays can theoretically handle 10 A^2 × 50 Ω = 5000 W.) **Figure 14.63** shows a photo of the transmission-line

transformer and StackMaster PCB.

The control/indicator box uses a diode matrix to switch various combinations of antennas in/out of the stack. Three LEDs lined up vertically on the front panel indicate which antennas in a stack are selected.

14.4.10 MISCELLANEOUS TOPICS

Stacks and Fading

The following is derived from an article by Fred Hopengarten, K1VR, and Dean Straw, N6BV, in a February 1994 *QST* article. Using stacked Hy-Gain TH7DXs or TH6DXXs at their respective stations, they have solicited a number of reports from stations, mainly in Europe, to compare various combinations of antennas in stacks and as single antennas. The peak gain of the stack is usually just a little bit higher than that for the best of the single antennas, which is not surprising. Even a large stack has no more than about 6 dB of gain over a single Yagi at a height favoring the prevailing elevation angle. Fading on the European path can easily be 20 dB or more, so it is very confusing to try to make definitive comparisons. They have noticed over many tests that the stacks are much less susceptible to fading compared to single Yagis. Even within the confines of a typical SSB bandwidth, frequency-selective fading occasionally causes the tonal quality of a voice to change on both receive and transmit, often dramatically becoming fuller on the stacks, and tinnier on the single antennas. This doesn't happen all the time, but is often seen. They have also observed often that the depth of a fade is less, and the period of fading is longer, on the stacks compared to single antennas.

Exactly *why* stacks exhibit less fading is a fascinating subject, for which there exist a number of speculative ideas, but little hard evidence. Some maintain that stacks outperform single antennas because they can afford *space diversity* effects, where by virtue of the difference in physical placement one antenna will randomly pick up signals that another one in another physical location might not hear.

This is difficult to argue with, and equally difficult to prove scientifically. A more plausible explanation about why stacked Yagis exhibit superior fading performance is that their narrower frontal elevation lobes can discriminate against undesired propagation modes. Even when band conditions favor, for example, a very low 3° elevation angle on 10 or 15 meters from New England to Western Europe, there are signals, albeit weaker ones, that arrive at higher elevation angles. These higher-angle signals have traveled longer distances on their journey through the ionosphere, and thus their signal levels and their phase angles are different from the signals traversing the primary propagation mode. When combined with the dominant mode, the net effect is that there is both destructive and constructive fading. If the elevation response of a stacked antenna can discriminate against signals arriving at higher elevation angles, then in theory the fading will be reduced. Suffice it to say: In practice, stacks do reduce fading.

Stacks and Precipitation Static

The top antenna in a stack is often much more affected by rain or snow precipitation static than is the lower antenna. N6BV and K1VR have observed this phenomenon, where signals on the lower antenna by itself are perfectly readable, while S9+ rain static is rendering reception impossible on the higher antenna or on the stack. This means that the ability to select individual antennas in a stack can sometimes be extremely important for reasons unrelated to elevation angle.

Stacks and Azimuthal Diversity

Azimuthal diversity is a term coined to describe the situation where one of the antennas in a stack is purposely pointed in a direction different from the main direction of the stack. During most of the time in a DX contest from the East Coast, the lower antennas in a stack are pointed into Europe, while the top antenna is often rotated toward the Caribbean or Japan. In a stack of three identical Yagis, the first-order effect of pointing one antenna in a different direction is that one-third of the transmitter power is diverted from the main target area. This means that the peak gain is reduced by 1.8 dB, not a very large amount considering that signals are often 10 to 20 dB over S9 anyway when the band is open from New England to Europe.

Figure 14.64 shows the 3D pattern of a pair of 4-element Yagis fed in-phase at 95 and 65 feet, but where the lower antenna has been rotated 180° to fire in the –X direction. The backwards lobe peaks at a higher elevation angle because the antenna doing the radiating in this direction is lower on the

tower. The forward lobe peaks at a lower angle because its main radiator is higher.

"BIP/BOP" Operation

The contraction "BIP" means "both in-phase," while "BOP" means "both out-of-phase." BIP/BOP refer to stacks containing two Yagis, although the term is commonly used for stacks containing more than two Yagis. In theory, feeding a stack with the antennas out-of-phase will shift the elevation response higher than in-phase feeding.

Figure 14.65 shows a rectangular plot comparing BIP/

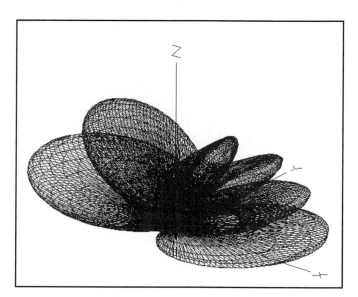

Figure 14.64 — 3D representation of the pattern for two 4-element 15-meter Yagis, with the top antenna at 95 and the bottom at 65 feet, but pointed in the opposite direction.

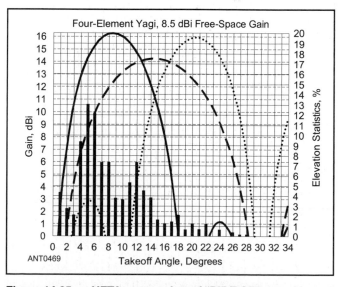

Figure 14.65 — *HFTA* screen shot of "BIP/BOP" operation of two 4-element 15-meter Yagis at 93 and 46 feet above flat ground. The elevation response in BOP (both out-of-phase) operation is shifted higher, peaking at about 21°, compared to the BIP (both in-phase) operation where the peak is at 8°. The dashed line is response of single Yagi at 46 feet.

BOP operation of two 3-element 15 meter Yagis at heights of 2 λ and 1 λ (93 and 46 feet) over flat ground. The BOP pattern is the higher-angle lobe and the two lobes cross over about 14°. The maximum amplitude of the BOP stack's gain is about ½ dB less than the BIP pair. For reference, the pattern of a single 46-foot high Yagi is overlaid on the pattern for the stacks.

The most common method for feeding one Yagi 180° out-of-phase is to include an extra electrical half wavelength of feed line coax going to one of the antennas. This method obviously works on a single frequency band and thus is not applicable to stacks of multiband Yagis, such as tribanders. For such multiband stacks, feeding only the lower antenna(s) — by switching out higher antenna(s) in the stack — is a practical method for achieving better coverage at medium or high elevation angles.

TABLE OF CONTENTS

Chapter 15

VHF and UHF Antenna Systems

A good antenna system is one of the most valuable assets available to the VHF/UHF enthusiast. Compared to an antenna of lesser quality, an antenna that is well designed, is built of good quality materials, and is well maintained, will increase transmitting range, enhance reception of weak signals and reduce interference problems. The work itself building antennas is by no means the least attractive part of the job. Even with high-gain antennas, experimentation is greatly simplified at VHF and UHF because the antennas are a physically manageable size. Setting up a home antenna range is within the means of most amateurs, and much can be learned about the nature and adjustment of antennas. No large investment in test equipment is necessary.

15.1 DESIGN FACTORS AT AND ABOVE VHF

The fundamental principles of antenna systems are the same at VHF and UHF as at HF. There is no magic dividing line at 50 MHz that suddenly changes the way antenna system components operate. However, factors that may be insignificant at HF must be taken into account at higher frequencies as the wavelength of the signals drops, dielectric loss increases, and skin depth shrinks. Similarly, techniques that may be impractical at HF such as dishes and long-boom Yagis with 20 elements can be put to work at VHF and higher frequencies. Instead of repeating the theory presented in other chapters, this section will identify areas that must be treated differently than at HF and give guidelines for how to approach the problem.

15.1.1 ANTENNAS

As on HF, the first step in choosing the right antenna is figuring out what you want it to do. Most VHF/UHF falls into one of two categories — weak-signal and local or regional repeater communication. Weak-signal operating on CW, SSB, and increasingly various digital modes, benefits from horizontally polarized, rotatable antennas with narrow beamwidths and minimum sidelobes. Satellite operation on CW and SSB goes farther and adds elevation control and circular polarization to the list. FM repeater and simplex operation uses vertical polarization for both directional and omnidirectional antennas. Simple ground-plane and low-gain omnidirectional antennas are common.

Just the polarization issue alone can have a dramatic effect as an antenna cross-polarized to an incoming signal receives up to 20 dB less signal than if the antenna and signal polarization are the same. Similarly, a narrow-beamwidth rotatable antenna can be a poor choice if the goal is to use several nearby repeaters that are located in different directions from the station. As a result, it is not uncommon for an amateur station to include both types — a horizontally polarized beam and a vertically polarized omnidirectional antenna — for VHF and UHF operation.

Gain

At VHF and UHF, it is possible to build Yagi antennas with very high gain — 15 to 20 dBi — on a physically manageable boom. Such antennas then can be combined in arrays of two, four, six, eight or more antennas. These arrays are attractive for EME, tropospheric scatter or other weak-signal communications modes where the path loss is very high.

Collinear antennas such as Franklin arrays become much more manageable at and above 2 meters with gains of 6 to 12 dBi in a single, vertical package similar in size to a 10 meter ground plane antenna. The collinear dipole array is very popular as a repeater antenna (see the **Repeater Antenna**

Systems chapter) with potential gains of up to 9 dBd for eight dipole arrays as described by Belrose. (See Bibliography.)

Reflectors, horns and dishes offer even higher gains (and narrower patterns) at UHF and microwave frequencies. A medium-sized dish can develop up to 30 dBi gain at 10 GHz, for example, turning 1 W of power into an EIRP of 1 kW!

Radiation Patterns

Antenna radiation can be made omnidirectional, bidirectional, practically unidirectional, or anything between these configurations. A VHF net operator may find an omnidirectional system almost a necessity, but it may be a poor choice otherwise. Noise pickup and other interference problems are greater with such omnidirectional antennas, and omnidirectional antennas having some gain are especially bad in these respects. Maximum gain and low radiation angle are usually prime interests of the weak-signal DX aspirant. A clean pattern, with lowest possible pickup and radiation off the sides and back, may be important in high-activity areas, or where the noise level is high.

Frequency Response

The ability to use an entire VHF band may be important in some types of operation. Modern Yagis can achieve performance over a remarkably wide frequency range, providing that the boom length is long enough and enough elements are used to populate the boom. Modern Yagi designs in fact are competitive with directly driven collinear arrays of similar size and complexity. The primary performance parameters of gain, front-to-rear ratio and SWR can be optimized over all the VHF or UHF amateur bands readily, with the exception of the full 6 meter band from 50.0 to 54.0 MHz, which is an 8% wide bandwidth. A Yagi can be easily designed to cover any 2 MHz portion of the 6 meter band with superb performance.

Height Gain

In general, higher is better in VHF and UHF antenna installations. Raising the antenna over nearby obstructions may make dramatic improvements in coverage. Within reason, greater height is almost always worth its cost, but height gain (see the **Radio Wave Propagation** chapter) must be balanced against increased transmission line loss. This loss can be considerable, and it increases with frequency. The best available line may not be very good if the run is long in terms of wavelengths. Line loss considerations as discussed in the **Transmission Lines** chapter are important in antenna planning.

Physical Size

A given antenna design for 432 MHz has the same gain as the same design for 144 MHz, but being only one-third as large intercepts only one-ninth as much energy in receiving. In other words, the antenna has less pickup efficiency at 432 MHz. To be equal in communication effectiveness, the 432-MHz array should be at least equal in *size* to the 144-MHz antenna, which requires roughly three times as many elements. With all the extra difficulties involved in using the higher frequencies effectively, it is best to keep antennas as large as possible for these bands.

Polarization

Whether to position antenna elements vertically or horizontally has been widely debated since early VHF pioneering days. Tests have shown little evidence about which polarization sense is most desirable. On long propagation paths there is no consistent advantage either way. Shorter paths tend to yield higher signal levels with horizontally polarized antennas over some kinds of terrain. Man-made noise, especially ignition interference, also tends to be lower with horizontal antennas. These factors make horizontal polarization somewhat more desirable for weak-signal communications. On the other hand, vertically polarized antennas are much simpler to use in omnidirectional systems and in mobile operation.

Vertical polarization was widely used in early VHF operation, but horizontal polarization gained favor when directional arrays started to become widely used. The major use of FM and repeaters, particularly in the VHF/UHF bands, has tipped the balance in favor of vertical antennas in mobile and repeater use. Horizontal polarization predominates in other communication on 50 MHz and higher frequencies. An additional loss of 20 dB or more can be expected when cross-polarized antennas are used.

15.1.2 TRANSMISSION LINES

Transmission line principles are covered in detail in the **Transmission Lines** chapter. Techniques that apply to VHF and UHF operation are dealt with in greater detail here. As at HF, RF is carried principally via coaxial cables at VHF/UHF although parallel-wire transmission lines (window-line or twin-lead) are used on the VHF and low UHF bands. Certain aspects of these lines characterize them as good or bad for use above 50 MHz. At 10 GHz and higher frequencies, waveguide becomes feasible for amateur use. At VHF and higher frequencies, the primary consideration for transmission lines is loss, which increases dramatically with frequency.

While not in widespread use at VHF/UHF today, properly built parallel-wire line can operate with very low loss in VHF and UHF installations. A total line loss under 2 dB per 100 feet at 432 MHz can easily be obtained. A line made of #12 AWG wire, spaced ¾ inch or more with Teflon spreaders and run essentially straight from antenna to station, can be better than anything but the most expensive coax. Such line can be home-made or purchased at a fraction of the cost of coaxial cables, with comparable loss characteristics. Careful attention must be paid to efficient impedance matching if the benefits of this system are to be realized. A similar system for 144 MHz can easily provide a line loss under 1 dB.

Small coax such as RG-58 or RG-59 should never be used in VHF operation if the length of the run is more than a few feet. Lines of ½-inch diameter (RG-8 or RG-11) work fairly well at 50 MHz, and are acceptable for 144-MHz runs of 50 feet or less. These lines are somewhat better if they employ foam instead of ordinary PE dielectric material but still very lossy.

Aluminum-jacket *hardline* or Heliax coaxial cables with large inner conductors and foam insulation are well worth their cost. Hardline can sometimes be obtained for free from local cable TV operators as "end runs" — pieces at the end of a roll. The most common CATV cable is ½-inch OD 75-Ω hardline. Matched-line loss for this cable is about 1.0 dB/100 feet at 146 MHz and 2.0 dB/100 feet at 432 MHz. Less commonly available from CATV companies is the ¾-inch 75-Ω hardline, sometimes with a black self-healing hard plastic covering. This line has 0.8 dB of loss per 100 feet at 146 MHz, and 1.6 dB loss per 100 feet at 432 MHz. There will be small additional losses for either line if 75-to-50-Ω transformers are used at each end. The **Transmission Line Coupling and Impedance Matching** chapter describes synchronous transmission line transformers for converting between 50- and 75-Ω lines on a single band. Hardline must not be bent too sharply, because it will kink.

Commercial connectors for hardline are expensive but provide reliable connections with full waterproofing. They are often available at very reasonable prices via Internet auction and for-sale sites including adapters to UHF and other connector types. Enterprising amateurs have homebrewed low-cost connectors. If they are properly waterproofed, connectors and hardline can last almost indefinitely. See the **Transmission Lines** chapter for details on hardline connectors.

Beware of any "bargains" in coax for VHF or UHF use. Feed line loss can be compensated to some extent by increasing transmitter power but once lost, a weak signal can never be recovered in the receiver.

Effects of weather on transmission lines should not be ignored. Well-constructed open-wire line works optimally in nearly any weather, and it stands up well. Twinlead is almost useless in heavy rain, wet snow or icing. The best grades of coax are completely impervious to weather — they can be run underground, fastened to metal towers without insulation and bent into any convenient position with no adverse effects on performance.

15.1.3 IMPEDANCE MATCHING

Impedance matching is covered in detail in the **Transmission Line Coupling and Impedance Matching** chapter. The various technical aspects of impedance matching are similar at HF and above 50 MHz but the electrical size of the various components can be a primary factor in the choice of methods. Only the matching devices used in practical construction examples later in this chapter are discussed in detail here. This should not rule out consideration of other methods, however.

Impedance matching at the antenna takes on more importance at VHF and UHF because of feed line loss. At HF, the moderate additional feed line loss caused by an impedance mismatch at the antenna can be tolerated and the impedance matched to 50 Ω at the transmitter with an antenna tuner. At VHF and above, with feed line loss much higher, even moderate SWR can result in unacceptable additional losses. Thus, impedance matching is usually done at the antenna so that

the minimum matched-line loss is obtained. For that reason, antenna tuners are not usually employed on the bands above 50 MHz.

Universal Stub

As its name *universal stub* implies, the double-adjustment stub of **Figure 15.1A** is useful for many matching purposes. The stub length is varied to resonate the system and the transmission line attachment point is varied until the transmission line and stub impedances are equal. In practice this involves moving both the sliding short and the point of line connection for zero reflected power, as indicated on an SWR bridge connected in the line.

The universal stub allows for tuning out any small reactance present in the driven part of the system. It permits matching the antenna to the line without knowledge of the actual impedances involved. The position of the short

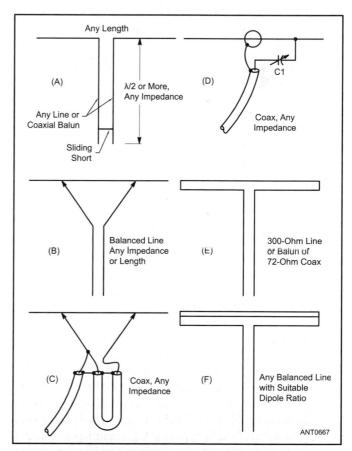

Figure 15.1 — Matching methods commonly used at VHF. The universal stub, A, combines tuning and matching. The adjustable short on the stub and the points of connection of the transmission line are adjusted for minimum reflected power on the line. In the delta match, B and C, the line is fanned out and connected to the dipole at the point of optimum impedance match. Impedances need not be known in A, B or C. The gamma match, D, is for direct connection of coax. C1 tunes out inductance in the arm. A folded dipole of uniform conductor size, E, steps up antenna impedance by a factor of four. Using a larger conductor in the unbroken portion of the folded dipole, F, gives higher orders of impedance transformation.

yielding the best match gives some indication of the amount of reactance present. With little or no reactive component to be tuned out, the stub must be approximately ½ λ from the load toward the short.

The stub should be made of stiff bare wire or rod, spaced no more than ¹⁄₂₀ λ apart. Preferably it should be mounted rigidly, on insulators. Once the position of the short is determined, the center of the short can be grounded, if desired, and the portion of the stub no longer needed can be removed.

It is not necessary that the stub be connected directly to the driven element. It can be made part of a parallel-wire line as a device to match coaxial cable to the line. The stub can be connected to the lower end of a delta match or placed at the feed point of a phased array. Examples of these uses are given later.

Delta Match

Probably the most basic impedance matching device is the *delta match*, fanned ends of an parallel-wire line tapped onto a ½ λ antenna at the point of the most-efficient power transfer. This is shown in Figure 15.1B. Both the side length and the points of connection either side of the center of the element must be adjusted for minimum reflected power on the line, but as with the universal stub, you needn't know the impedances. The delta match makes no provision for tuning out reactance, so the universal stub is often used as a termination for it.

At one time, the delta match was thought to be inferior for VHF applications because of its tendency to radiate if improperly adjusted. The delta has come back into favor now that accurate methods are available for measuring the effects of matching. It is very handy for phasing multiple-bay arrays with open-wire lines, and its dimensions in this use are not particularly critical. It should be checked out carefully in applications like that of Figure 15.1C, where no tuning device is used.

Gamma and T Matches

An application of the same principle allowing direct connection of coax is the *gamma match*, Figure 15.1D. Because the RF voltage at the center of a ½ λ dipole is zero, the outer conductor of the coax is connected to the element at this point. This may also be the junction with a metallic or wooden boom. The inner conductor, carrying the RF current, is tapped out on the element at the matching point. Inductance of the arm is tuned out by means of C1, resulting in electrical balance. Both the point of contact with the element and the setting of the capacitor are adjusted for zero reflected power, with a bridge connected in the coaxial line.

The capacitance can be varied until the required value is found, and the variable capacitor replaced with a fixed unit of that value. C1 can be mounted in a waterproof box. The maximum required value should be about 100 pF for 50 MHz and 35 to 50 pF for 144 MHz.

The capacitor and arm can be combined in one coaxial assembly, with the arm connected to the driven element by means of a sliding clamp and the inner end of the arm sliding

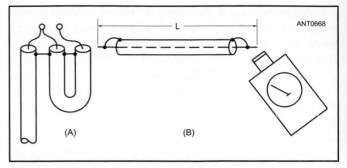

Figure 15.2 — Conversion from unbalanced coax to a balanced load can be done with a ½-λ, coaxial balun at A. Electrical length of the looped section should be checked with a dip meter, with the ends shorted, as at B. The ½-λ balun gives a 4:1 impedance step-up.

inside a sleeve connected to the center conductor of the coax. An assembly of this type can be constructed from concentric pieces of tubing, insulated by a plastic or heat-shrink sleeve. RF voltage across the capacitor is low when the match is adjusted properly, so with a good dielectric, insulation presents no great problem. The initial adjustment should be made with low power. A clean, permanent high-conductivity bond between arm and element is important, since the RF current is high at this point.

Because it is inherently somewhat unbalanced, the gamma match can sometimes introduce pattern distortion, particularly on long-boom, highly directive Yagi arrays. The *T-match*, essentially two gamma matches in series creating a balanced feed system, has become popular for this reason. A coaxial balun like that shown in **Figure 15.2** is used from the 200 Ω balanced T-match to the unbalanced 50 Ω coaxial line going to the transmitter. See the K1FO Yagi designs later in this chapter for details on practical use of a T-match. A ferrite bead choke balun as described below can be used with a gamma match to decouple the outer surface of the feed line.

Folded Dipole

As described in the **Dipoles and Monopoles** chapter, if a single conductor of uniform size is folded to make a ½ λ dipole as shown in Figure 15.1E, the impedance is stepped up four times. Such a folded dipole can be fed directly with 300-Ω line with no appreciable mismatch. If a 4:1 balun is used, the antenna can be fed with 75-Ω coaxial cable. (See balun information presented below.) Higher step-up impedance transformation can be obtained if the unbroken portion is made larger in cross-section than the fed portion, as shown in Figure 15.1F.

Hairpin Match

The feed point resistance of most multielement Yagi arrays is less than 50 Ω. If the driven element is split and fed at the center, it may be shortened from its resonant length to add capacitive reactance at the feed point. Then, shunting the feed point with a wire loop resembling a *hairpin* causes a step-up of the feed point resistance. The hairpin match (described in the **Transmission Line Coupling and Impedance Matching** chapter) is used together with a 4:1 coaxial balun in the 50 MHz arrays described later in this chapter.

15.1.4 BALUNS

Conversion from balanced loads to unbalanced lines (or vice versa) can be performed with electrical circuits, or their equivalents made of coaxial cable. A balun made from flexible coax is shown in Figure 15.2A. The looped portion is an electrical ½ λ. The physical length depends on the velocity factor of the line used, so it is important to check its resonant frequency as shown in Figure 15.2B. The two ends are shorted, and the loop at one end is coupled to a dip meter coil. This type of balun gives an impedance step-up of 4:1 (typically 50 to 200 Ω, or 75 to 300 Ω).

Coaxial baluns that yield 1:1 impedance transformations are shown in **Figure 15.3**. The coaxial sleeve, open at the top and connected to the outer conductor of the line at the lower end (A) is the preferred type. At B, a conductor of approximately the same size as the line is used with the outer conductor to form a ¼ λ stub. Another piece of coax, using only the outer conductor, will serve this purpose. Both baluns are intended to present an infinite impedance to any RF current that might otherwise flow on the outer surface of the coax shield.

Ferrite bead choke or current baluns become less attractive at VHF and higher frequencies due to the properties of

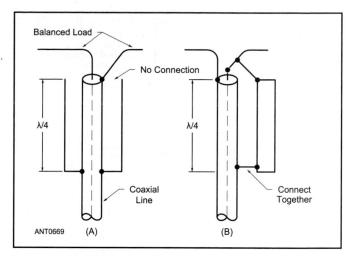

Figure 15.3 — The balun conversion function, with no impedance transformation, can be accomplished with ¼-λ lines, open at the top and connected to the coax outer conductor at the bottom. The coaxial sleeve at A is preferred.

the ferrite material. However, bead-type choke baluns using type 31, 43, and 61 material can be effective at 50 MHz and even 144 MHz. For 144 MHz and higher frequency bands, coaxial baluns are the usual choice.

15.2 BASIC ANTENNAS FOR VHF AND UHF

Local operation with mobile stations and handheld radios requires an antenna with wide coverage capabilities and a generally omnidirectional pattern. Most mobile operation uses FM and the polarization used with this mode is generally vertical. Some simple vertical systems are described below. Additional material on antennas of this type is presented in the **Mobile VHF and UHF Antennas** chapter.

15.2.1 GROUND-PLANE ANTENNAS

For the FM operator living in the primary coverage area of a repeater, the ease of construction and low cost of a ¼ λ ground-plane antenna make it an ideal choice. Three different types of construction are detailed in the following section; the choice of construction method depends upon the materials at hand and the desired style of antenna mounting. (Note that while UHF connectors are not generally recommended for use on the upper VHF bands and at UHF, they will work fine as a base for ground-plane antennas. It is their uncontrolled impedance above 100 MHz that causes problems in transmission lines but as part of an antenna, their impedance is accounted for when trimming the antenna for minimum SWR.)

The 144-MHz model shown in **Figure 15.4** uses a flat piece of sheet aluminum, to which radials are connected

with machine screws. A 45° bend is made in each of the radials. This bend can be made with an ordinary bench vise. An SO-239 chassis connector is mounted at the center of the aluminum plate with the threaded part of the connector facing down. The vertical portion of the antenna is made of #12 AWG copper wire soldered directly to the center pin of the SO-239 connector.

The 222-MHz version, **Figure 15.5**, uses a slightly different technique for mounting and sloping the radials. In this case the corners of the aluminum plate are bent down at a 45° angle with respect to the remainder of the plate. The four radials are held to the plate with machine screws, lock washers and nuts. A mounting tab is included in the design of this antenna as part of the aluminum base. A compression type of hose clamp could be used to secure the antenna to a mast. As with the 144-MHz version, the vertical portion of the antenna is soldered directly to the SO-239 connector.

A very simple method of construction, shown in **Figure 15.6** and **Figure 15.7**, requires nothing more than an SO-239 connector and some #4-40 hardware. A small loop formed at the inside end of each radial is used to attach the radial directly to the mounting holes of the coaxial connector. After the radial is fastened to the SO-239 with #4-40 hardware, a large soldering iron or propane torch is used to solder

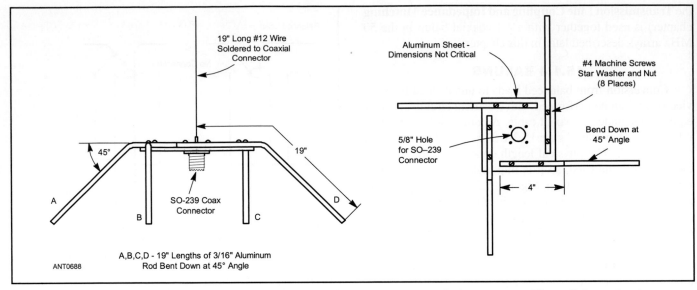

Figure 15.4 — These drawings illustrate the dimensions for the 144-MHz ground-plane antenna. The radials are bent down at a 45° angle.

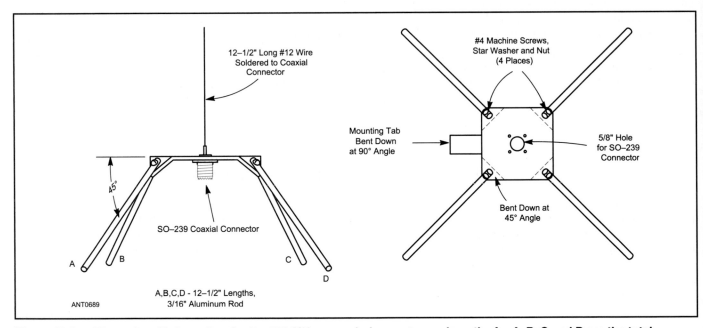

Figure 15.5 — Dimensional information for the 222-MHz ground-plane antenna. Lengths for A, B, C and D are the total distances measured from the center of the SO-239 connector. The corners of the aluminum plate are bent down at a 45° angle rather than bending the aluminum rod as in the 144-MHz model. Either method is suitable for these antennas.

the radial and the mounting hardware to the coaxial connector. The radials are bent to a 45° angle and the vertical portion is soldered to the center pin to complete the antenna. The antenna can be mounted by passing the feed line through a mast of ¾-inch ID plastic or aluminum tubing. A compression hose clamp can be used to secure the PL-259 connector, attached to the feed line, in the end of the mast. Dimensions for the 144-, 222- and 440-MHz bands are given in Figure 15.6.

If these antennas are to be permanently mounted outside, waterproof the antenna by applying a small amount of sealant around the areas of the center pin of the connector to prevent

the entry of water into the connector and coax line. The coax connector should be waterproofed as well. Techniques and materials for waterproofing are described in the **Building Antenna Systems and Towers** chapter.

15.2.2 THE J-POLE ANTENNA

The J-Pole is a half-wave antenna that is end-fed at its bottom. Since the radiator is longer than that of a ¼-wave ground-plane antenna, the vertical lobe is compressed down toward the horizon and it has about 1.5 dB of gain compared to the ground-plane configuration. The stub-matching section

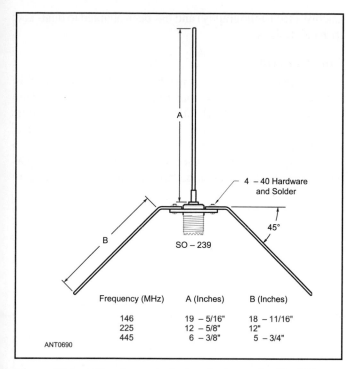

Figure 15.6 — Simple ground-plane antenna for the 144-, 222- and 440-MHz bands. The vertical element and radials are ³⁄₃₂- or ¹⁄₁₆-inch brass welding rod. Although ³⁄₃₂-inch rod is preferred for the 144-MHz antenna, #10 or #12 AWG copper wire can also be used.

Frequency (MHz)	A (Inches)	B (Inches)
146	19 – 5/16"	18 – 11/16"
225	12 – 5/8"	12"
445	6 – 3/8"	5 – 3/4"

ANT0690

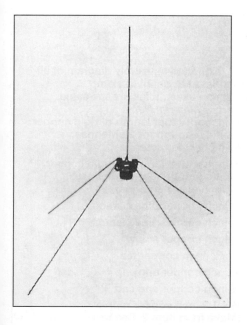

Figure 15.7 — A 440-MHz ground-plane constructed using only an SO-239 connector, no. 4-40 hardware and ¹⁄₁₆-inch brass welding rod.

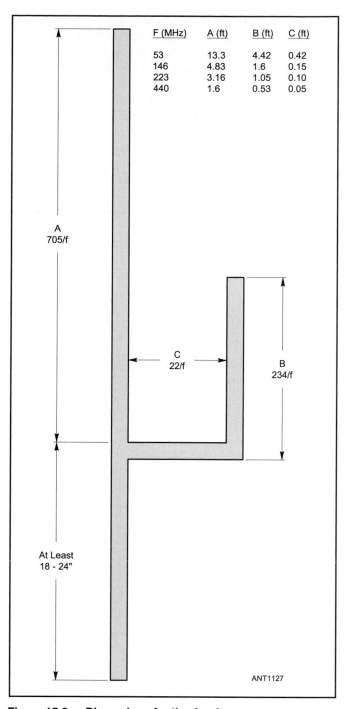

F (MHz)	A (ft)	B (ft)	C (ft)
53	13.3	4.42	0.42
146	4.83	1.6	0.15
223	3.16	1.05	0.10
440	1.6	0.53	0.05

A 705/f

C 22/f

B 234/f

At Least 18 - 24"

ANT1127

Figure 15.8 — Dimensions for the J-pole.

used to transform the high impedance at the end of a half-wave antenna to 50 Ω is shorted at the bottom, making the antenna look like the letter "J," and giving the antenna its name.

Rigid copper tubing, fittings and assorted hardware can be used to make a rugged J-pole antenna for the VHF bands through 440 MHz. When copper tubing is used, the entire assembly can be soldered together, ensuring electrical integrity, and making the whole antenna weatherproof. A general-purpose set of dimensions for the J-pole is provided in **Figure 15.8** along with a table of dimensions for 53 MHz, 146 MHz, 223 MHz, and 440 MHz. The 53-MHz version is somewhat large for this construction method and the 440 MHz version a little small. Note that the inside dimensions of the matching section are between the outside surfaces of the tubing, not center-to-center. For placing the feed point, start with the feed point approximately as high above the bottom of the matching section as the tubing spacing.

The J-Pole can be fed directly from 50-Ω coax through a choke balun. The feed line can be made into a choke balun by forming it into a 3-turn coil about 8 inches in diameter and held together with electrical tape. If the balun is not used, the outer surface of the coaxial cable will become part of the antenna, making tuning difficult and highly dependent on cable placement. In addition, radiation from the current flowing on the feed line can distort the pattern of the antenna, leading to poor performance by breaking up the low-elevation main lobe expected from this design.

There are many J-pole designs available online and in the ARRL's online archive of *QST* articles at **www.arrl.org**. One of the more popular variants is known as the "Copper Cactus" (see Bibliography) and has been adapted to dual- and tri-band designs.

Construction

No special hardware or machined parts are used in this antenna, nor are insulating materials needed, since the antenna is always at dc ground. The following design came from an article by Michael Hood, KD8JB, in *The ARRL Antenna Compendium, Vol. 4.*

Copper and brass is used exclusively in this antenna. These metals get along together, so dissimilar metal cor-

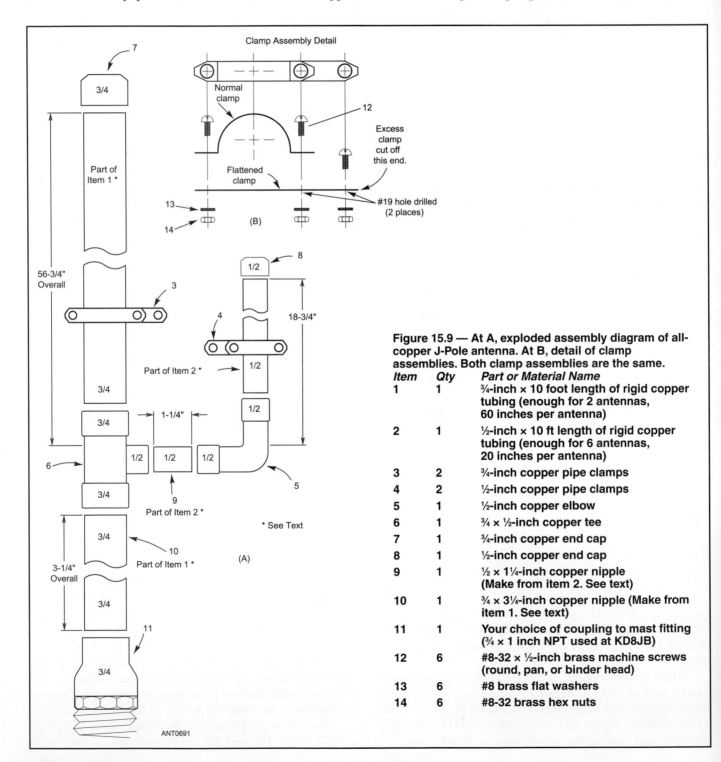

Figure 15.9 — At A, exploded assembly diagram of all-copper J-Pole antenna. At B, detail of clamp assemblies. Both clamp assemblies are the same.

Item	Qty	Part or Material Name
1	1	¾-inch × 10 foot length of rigid copper tubing (enough for 2 antennas, 60 inches per antenna)
2	1	½-inch × 10 ft length of rigid copper tubing (enough for 6 antennas, 20 inches per antenna)
3	2	¾-inch copper pipe clamps
4	2	½-inch copper pipe clamps
5	1	½-inch copper elbow
6	1	¾ × ½-inch copper tee
7	1	¾-inch copper end cap
8	1	½-inch copper end cap
9	1	½ × 1¼-inch copper nipple (Make from item 2. See text)
10	1	¾ × 3¼-inch copper nipple (Make from item 1. See text)
11	1	Your choice of coupling to mast fitting (¾ × 1 inch NPT used at KD8JB)
12	6	#8-32 × ½-inch brass machine screws (round, pan, or binder head)
13	6	#8 brass flat washers
14	6	#8-32 brass hex nuts

rosion is eliminated. Both metals solder well, too. See **Figure 15.9**. Cut the copper tubing to the lengths indicated. Item 9 is a 1¼-inch nipple cut from the 20-inch length of ½-inch tubing. This leaves 18¾ inches for the ¼-λ matching stub. Item 10 is a 3¼-inch long nipple cut from the 60-inch length of ¾-inch tubing. The ¾-wave element should measure 56¾ inches long. Remove burrs from the ends of the tubing after cutting, and clean the mating surfaces with sandpaper, steel wool or emery cloth.

After cleaning, apply a very thin coat of flux to the mating elements and assemble the tubing, elbow, tee, end caps and stubs. Solder the assembled parts with a propane torch and rosin-core solder. Wipe off excess solder with a damp cloth, being careful not to burn yourself. The copper tubing will hold heat for a long time after you've finished soldering. After soldering, set the assembly aside to cool.

Flatten one each of the ½-inch and ¾-inch pipe clamps. Drill a hole in the flattened clamp as shown in Figure 15.9A. Assemble the clamps and cut off the excess metal from the flattened clamp using the unmodified clamp as a template. Disassemble the clamps.

Assemble the ½-inch clamp around the ¼-wave element and secure with two of the screws, washers, and nuts as shown in Figure 15.9B. Do the same with the ¾-inch clamp around the ¾-wave element. Initially set the clamps to a spot about 4 inches above the bottom of the "J" on their respective elements. Tighten the clamps only finger tight, since you'll need to move them when tuning.

Tuning

Before tuning, mount the antenna vertically, about 5 to 10 feet from the ground. A short TV mast on a tripod works well for this purpose. When tuning VHF antennas, keep in mind that they are sensitive to nearby objects — such as your body. Attach the feed line to the clamps on the antenna, and make sure all the nuts and screws are at least finger tight. It really doesn't matter to which element (¾-wave element or stub) you attach the coaxial center lead. KD8JB has done it both ways with no variation in performance. Tune the antenna by moving the two feed point clamps equal distances a small amount each time until the SWR is a minimum at the desired frequency. The SWR will be close to 1:1. (Stand clear of the antenna when measuring the SWR and include the choke balun in the feed line when making measurements.)

Final Assembly

The final assembly of the antenna will determine its long-term survivability. Perform the following steps with care. After adjusting the clamps for minimum SWR, mark the clamp positions with a pencil and then remove the feed line and clamps. Apply a very thin coating of flux to the inside of the clamp and the corresponding surface of the antenna element where the clamp attaches. Install the clamps and tighten the clamp screws.

Solder the feed line clamps where they are attached to the antenna elements. Now, apply a small amount of solder around the screw heads and nuts where they contact the clamps. Don't get solder on the screw threads! Clean away excess flux with a noncorrosive solvent. After final assembly and erecting/mounting the antenna in the desired location, attach the feed line and secure with the remaining washer and nut. Weatherproof this joint as described in the **Building Antenna Systems and Towers** chapter.

15.2.3 COLLINEAR ARRAYS

The information given earlier in this chapter pertains mainly to parasitic arrays, but the collinear array is worthy of consideration in VHF/UHF operation. Two types of collinear arrays are commonly used by amateurs; the *transposed-coaxial array* and the *collinear dipole array*.

Collinear arrays tend to be tolerant of construction tolerances, making them easy to build and adjust for VHF and UHF applications. The use of many collinear driven elements was once popular in very large phased arrays, such as those required in moonbounce (EME) communications, but computer-optimized Yagi arrays have largely replaced them. A collinear array of four dipoles is a popular repeater antenna as described in the chapter **Repeater Antenna Systems**.

Collinear Transposed-Coax Arrays

The most popular collinear array is the omnidirectional array of half-wave dipoles constructed of transposed sections of coaxial cable as shown in **Figure 15.10**. The original array of this type is the Franklin array shown in Figure 15.10A. The phase-reversing stubs allow multiple half-wave sections to operate in phase, creating gain at right angles to the antenna. An example of this array is the popular Cushcraft Ringo Ranger series of omnidirectional VHF and UHF antennas.

While the phasing stubs make the Franklin array inconvenient for vertical stacking of more than two elements, a derivative of this array uses transposed sections of coaxial cable as in Figure 15.10B. The phasing stub is created by the inside of each coaxial section. The outer surface of the coaxial shield forms the radiating element. The resulting antenna can be enclosed in a PVC or fiberglass tube, such as the Comet GP-series of VHF/UHF omnidirectional antennas.

The practical limit for gain in this type of array is about 10 dBi. A choke balun or other method of decoupling such as a set of λ/4 radials is required at the feed point of the array to prevent current from being induced on the outer surface of the coaxial feed line.

Collinear Omnidirectional Array for 70 cm

Figure 15.11 shows the basic construction of a transposed-coax array for the 70 cm band with dimensions in millimeters for accuracy. The λ/4 whip at the end of the array is optional. The gain of this array is approximately 9 dBi (slightly less without the whip). The original design of this antenna is credited to the Radio Amateur Society of Norwich (**www.rason.org**). More information is available via the "Projects" page of the RASON website.

The physical length of each λ/2 section of coax must account for the velocity factor of the cable which should be measured accurately before cutting any cable. Once the

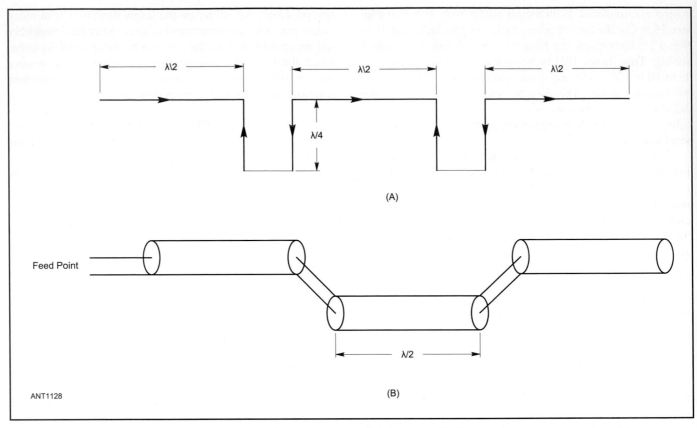

Figure 15.10 — The most popular collinear array is the omnidirectional array of half-wave dipoles constructed of transposed sections of coaxial cable.

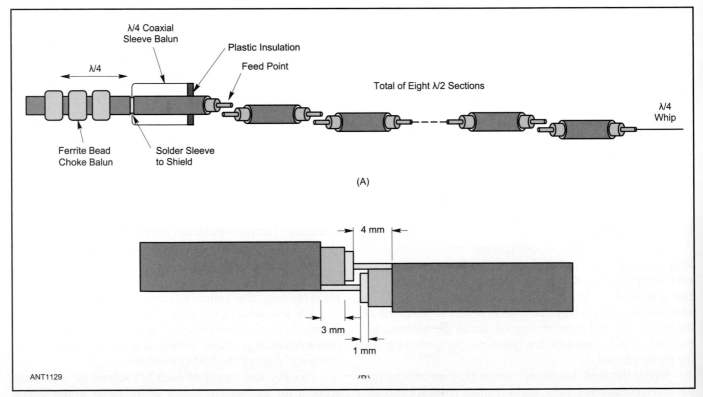

Figure 15.11 — Basic construction of a transposed-coax array for the 70 cm band. Dimensions are given in millimeters for accuracy.

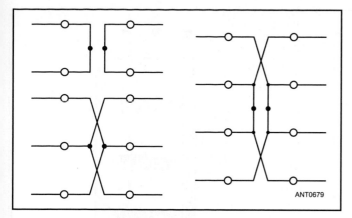

Figure 15.12 — Element arrangements for 8-, 12- and 16-element collinear arrays. Elements are ½ λ long and spaced ½ λ. Parasitic reflectors, omitted here for clarity, are 5% longer and 0.2 λ behind the driven elements. Feed points are indicated by black dots. Open circles show recommended support points. The elements can run through wood or metal booms, without insulation, if supported at their centers in this way. Insulators at the element ends (points of high RF voltage) detune and unbalance the system.

physical length of λ/2 has been determined, add 8 mm to allow for creating the 4 mm connecting surfaces on each end. For a VF = 0.66, the λ/2 sections should be 223 mm long plus 8 mm for a total of 231 mm. RG-58, RG-8, RG-8X or RG-213 can be used for this antenna. Do not remove the outer jacket from the cable other than at the connecting ends as this will allow the individual braid strands to loosen, reducing the shield's effectiveness as a continuous conductor.

Use a 169 mm segment of #16 AWG copper wire for

the top whip section. A λ/4 coaxial sleeve balun is attached at the feed point of the antenna. (See the **Transmission Line Coupling and Impedance Matching** chapter.) The balun is made from copper tubing that is soldered to the shield of the feed line using strips of brass or copper shim. If ⅝-inch tubing is used, the length should be 160 mm. The feed line should be centered in the balun tubing by using small pieces of plastic inserted between the coax jacket and the tubing's inner surface. Approximately λ/4 beyond the end of the balun's closed end add an additional choke balun of three type 43 ferrite beads (choose the ID to fit the feed line coax). The entire antenna should be enclosed in a length of PVC or fiberglass tubing to protect it from the weather. If necessary for mechanical stability, support the antenna sections with a length of wooden dowel or plastic rod, secured with electrical tape.

Large Collinear Dipole Arrays

Bidirectional curtain arrays of four, six and eight half waves in phase are shown in **Figure 15.12**. Usually reflector elements are added, normally at about 0.2 λ behind each driven element, for more gain and a unidirectional pattern. Such parasitic elements are omitted from the sketch in the interest of clarity.

The feed point impedance of two half waves in phase is high, typically 1000 Ω or more. When they are combined in parallel and parasitic elements are added, the feed impedance is low enough for direct connection to open wire line or twin-lead, connected at the points indicated by black dots. With coaxial line and a balun, it is suggested that the universal stub match, Figure 15.1A, be used at the feed point. All elements should be mounted at their electrical centers, as indicated by

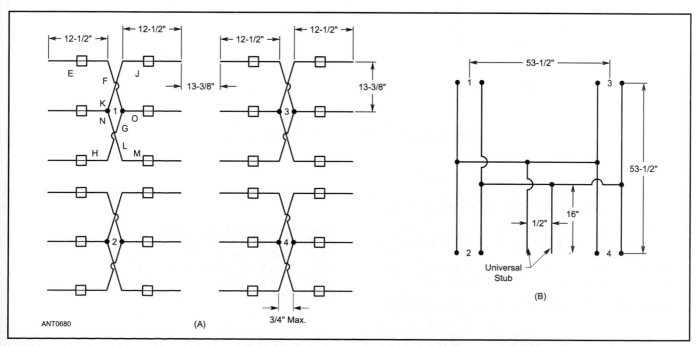

Figure 15.13 — Large collinear arrays should be fed as sets of no more than eight driven elements each, interconnected by phasing lines. This 48-element array for 432 MHz (A) is treated as if it were four 12-element collinear antennas. Reflector elements are omitted for clarity. The phasing harness is shown at B. Squares represent supporting insulators.

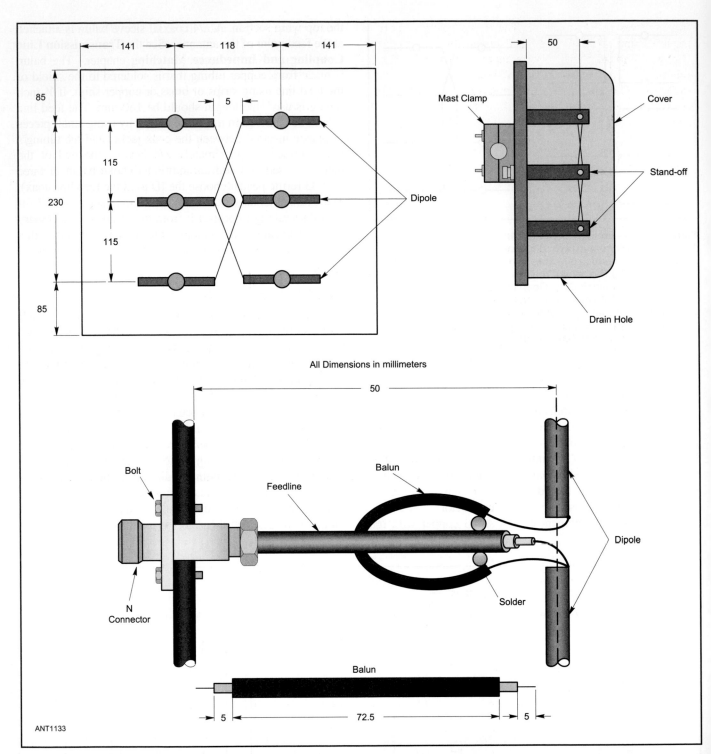

All Dimensions in millimeters

Figure 15.14 — Details of the F5JIO 23 cm collinear array.

ANT1133

Parts list
Reflector — 400 mm × 400 mm (340 mm min), 2.5 mm
  thick aluminum sheet
Standoffs — Teflon or PVC, 60 mm L × 20 mm D (qty 6)
Dipoles — brass, silver plated (opt), 108 mm L × 6 mm D
  (qty 6)
Phasing rods — Wire, silver plated (opt), 2 mm D (qty 4)

Connector — N-type receptacle
Feed line — semi-rigid coax 50-Ω approx 4 mm D
Balun — same type as feed line, 92.5 mm L
Bolt — M3 × 8 mm, stainless steel (qty 4)
Cover — plastic food container
Mast clamp from TV antenna

open circles in Figure 15.12. The framework can be metal or insulating material. The metal supporting structure is entirely behind the plane of the reflector elements. Sheet-metal clamps can be cut from scraps of aluminum for this kind of assembly. Collinear elements of this type should be mounted at their centers (where the RF voltage is zero), rather than at their ends, where the voltage is high and insulation losses and detuning can be harmful.

Collinear arrays of 32, 48, 64 and even 128 elements can give outstanding performance. Any collinear array should be fed at the center of the system, to ensure balanced current distribution. This is very important in large arrays, where sets of six or eight driven elements are treated as "sub arrays," and are fed through a balanced harness. The sections of the harness are resonant lengths, usually of open wire line. The 48-element collinear array for 432 MHz in **Figure 15.13** illustrates this principle.

A reflecting plane, which may be sheet metal, wire mesh, or even closely spaced elements of tubing or wire, can be used in place of parasitic reflectors. To be effective, the plane reflector must extend on all sides to at least ¼ λ beyond the area occupied by the driven elements. The plane reflector provides high F/B ratio, a clean pattern, and somewhat more gain than parasitic elements, but large physical size limits it to use above 420 MHz. An interesting space-saving possibility lies in using a single plane reflector with elements for two different bands mounted on opposite sides. Reflector spacing from the driven element is not critical. About 0.2 λ is common.

Wideband 23 cm Collinear Array

This design for a wideband beam by F5JIO is taken from the RSGB publication *Antennas for VHF and Above*. In the development of the antenna F5JIO consulted *Rothammel*, the German antenna reference text which gives the following guidelines for the reflector plane:

■ For the best F/B ratio, the reflector should extend at least half a wavelength beyond the perimeter of the curtain on all sides.

■ If made of wire or mesh instead of solid sheet metal to reduce wind loading surface area, the wire pitch should be 1 λ or less.

■ A reflector plane spaced ⅝ λ behind the radiator adds a maximum gain of up to 7 dB, but a spacing of 0.1 to 0.3 λ provides a better F/B ratio.

■ If spaced at least 0.3 λ behind the curtain, the reflector plane does not affect the feed point impedance of the array.

Details for the matching of the antenna can be seen in the **Figure 15.14**. With the antenna dimensions given, the feed point impedance of each dipole pair is approximately 600 Ω balanced. There are three pairs in parallel which divides this impedance by three to give 200 Ω, and a 4:1 coaxial balun transforms this to provide an excellent match to 50-Ω coax which is unbalanced. Note that as each dipole is supported at its voltage node, the insulators need to be of good quality.

The construction of the antenna is fairly straightforward, although reasonable care and precision are required. Being a 23 cm band antenna, it is quite small and therefore wind loading is not normally a problem and this makes a solid reflector feasible. This then means that the plate used as the reflector can be used as the support for the other components. During construction it is necessary to bend the phasing rods slightly so that they do not touch at the cross-over points. Then, for weather protection, a plastic food container can used as a radome. This can be used as the RF absorption appears to be negligible and it is much cheaper than a Teflon equivalent.

15.3 YAGIS AND QUADS AT VHF AND UHF

Without doubt, the Yagi is king of home-station VHF and UHF antennas for weak-signal operating and for long-distance repeater and simplex operation. Today's best designs are computer optimized. The **HF Yagi and Quad Antennas** chapter describes the parameters associated with Yagi antennas. Except for somewhat tighter dimensional tolerances needed at VHF and UHF, the properties that make a good Yagi at HF also are needed on the higher frequencies. Conversely, due to the shorter wavelengths above 50 MHz, high-performance designs that would be impractical at HF are easily achievable at VHF and UHF. A variety of designs are presented following the discussion of stacking Yagis.

15.3.1 STACKING YAGIS

Where suitable provision can be made for supporting them, two Yagis mounted one above the other and fed in phase can provide better performance than one long Yagi with the same theoretical or measured gain. The pair occupies a much smaller turning space for the same gain, and their wider elevation coverage can provide excellent results. The wide azimuthal coverage for a vertical stack often results in QSOs that might be missed with a single narrow-beam long-boom Yagi pointed in a different direction. On long ionospheric paths, a stacked pair occasionally may show an *apparent* gain much greater than the measured 2 to 3 dB of stacking gain. (See also the extensive section on stacking Yagis in the **HF Antenna System Design** chapter.)

Optimum vertical spacing for Yagis with booms longer than 1 λ or more is about 1 λ (984/50.1 = 19.64 feet), but this may be too much for many builders of 50-MHz antennas to handle. Worthwhile results can be obtained with as little as ½ λ (10 feet), but ⅝ λ (12 feet) is markedly better. The difference between 12 and 20 feet, however, may not be worth the added structural problems involved in the wider spacing, at least at 50 MHz. The closer spacings give lower measured gain, but the antenna patterns are cleaner in both azimuth and elevation than with 1 λ spacing. Extra gain with wider spacings is usually the objective on 144 MHz and higher-frequency bands, where the structural problems are not as severe.

Yagis can also be stacked in the same plane (collinear elements) for sharper azimuthal directivity. A spacing of ⅝ λ between the ends of the inner elements yields the maximum gain within the main lobe of the array.

If individual antennas of a stacked array are properly designed, they look like noninductive resistors to the phasing system that connects them. The impedances involved can thus be treated the same as resistances in parallel.

Three sets of stacked dipoles are shown in **Figure 15.15**.

Whether these are merely dipoles or the driven elements of Yagi arrays makes no difference for the purpose of these examples. Two 300 Ω antennas at A are 1 λ apart, resulting in a paralleled feed point impedance of 150 Ω at the center. (Actually it is slightly less than 150 Ω because of coupling between bays, but this can be neglected for illustrative purposes.) This value remains the same regardless of the impedance of the phasing line. Thus, any convenient line can be used for phasing, as long as the *electrical* length of each line is the same.

The velocity factor of the line must be taken into account as well. As with coax, this is subject to so much variation that it is important to make a resonance check on the actual line used. The method for doing this is shown in Figure 15.2B. A ½ λ line is resonant both open and shorted, but the shorted

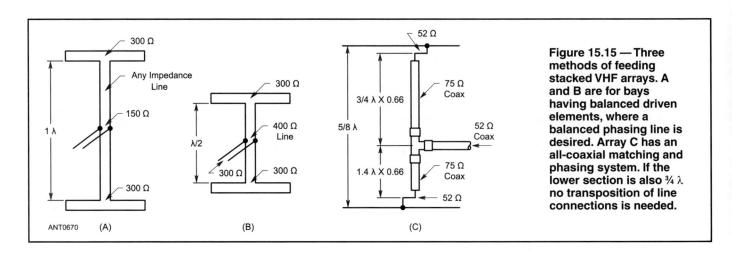

Figure 15.15 — Three methods of feeding stacked VHF arrays. A and B are for bays having balanced driven elements, where a balanced phasing line is desired. Array C has an all-coaxial matching and phasing system. If the lower section is also ¾ λ no transposition of line connections is needed.

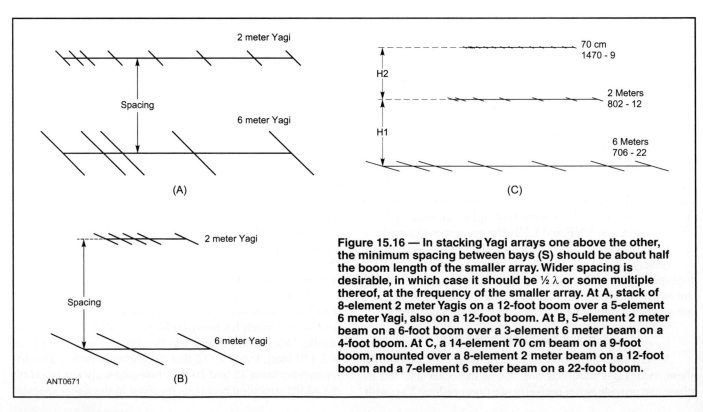

Figure 15.16 — In stacking Yagi arrays one above the other, the minimum spacing between bays (S) should be about half the boom length of the smaller array. Wider spacing is desirable, in which case it should be ½ λ or some multiple thereof, at the frequency of the smaller array. At A, stack of 8-element 2 meter Yagis on a 12-foot boom over a 5-element 6 meter Yagi, also on a 12-foot boom. At B, 5-element 2 meter beam on a 6-foot boom over a 3-element 6 meter beam on a 4-foot boom. At C, a 14-element 70 cm beam on a 9-foot boom, mounted over a 8-element 2 meter beam on a 12-foot boom and a 7-element 6 meter beam on a 22-foot boom.

condition (both ends) is usually the more convenient test condition.

The impedance transforming property of a ¼-λ line section can be used in combination matching and phasing lines, as shown in Figure 15.15B and C. At B, two bays spaced ½ λ apart are phased and matched by a 400-Ω line, acting as a double-Q section, so that a 300-Ω main transmission line is matched to two 300-Ω bays. The two halves of this phasing line could also be ¾-λ or ⁵⁄₄-λ long, if such lengths serve a useful mechanical purpose. (An example is the stacking of two Yagis where the desirable spacing is more than ½ λ.)

A double-Q section of coaxial line is illustrated in Figure 15.15C. This is useful for feeding stacked bays that were designed for 50-Ω feed. A spacing of ⁵⁄₈ λ is useful for small Yagis, and this is the equivalent of a full electrical wavelength of solid-dielectric coax such as RG-11.

If one phasing line is electrically ¼ λ and ¾ λ on the other, the connection to one driven element should be reversed with respect to the other to keep the RF currents in the elements in phase — the gamma match is located on opposite sides of the driven elements in Figure 15.15C. If the number of ¼ λ lengths is the same on either side of the feed point, the two connections should be in the same position, and not reversed. Practically speaking however, you can ensure proper phasing by using exactly equal lengths of line from the same roll of coax. This ensures that the velocity factor for each line is identical.

One marked advantage of coaxial phasing lines is that they can be wrapped around the vertical support, taped or grounded to it, or arranged in any way that is mechanically convenient. The spacing between bays can be set at the most desirable value, and the phasing lines placed anywhere necessary.

Stacking Yagis for Different Frequencies

In stacking horizontal Yagis one above the other on a single rotating support, certain considerations apply when the bays are for different bands. As a very general rule of thumb, the minimum desirable spacing is half the boom length of the higher frequency Yagi.

For example, assume the stacked two-band array of **Figure 15.16A** is for 50 and 144 MHz. This vertical arrangement is commonly referred to as a *Christmas tree*, because it resembles one. The 50 MHz Yagi has 5 elements on a 12-foot boom. It tends to look like "ground" to the 8-element 144 MHz Yagi on a 12-foot boom directly above it. [The exact Yagi designs for the examples used in this section are located on the CD-ROM accompanying this book. They may be evaluated as monoband Yagis using the *YW* (Yagi for *Windows*) program also supplied on the CD-ROM. In each case the bottom Yagi in the stack (at the top of the tower) is assumed to be 20 feet high.]

SWR Change in a Multi-Frequency Stack

Earlier editions of *The ARRL Antenna Book* stated that the feed point impedance of the higher-frequency antenna

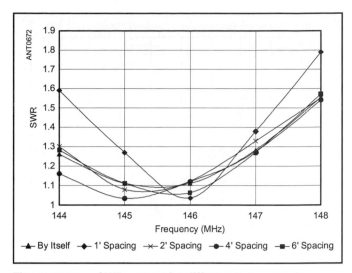

Figure 15.17 — SWR curves for different boom spacing between 8-element 2 meter Yagi on 12-foot boom, over a 5-element 6 meter Yagi on a 12-foot boom. For spacings greater than 1 foot between the booms, differences between the SWR curves are difficult to discern.

would likely be affected the most by the proximity of the lower-frequency Yagi. Modern computer modeling programs reveal that while the feed point SWR can indeed be affected, by far the greatest degradation is in the forward gain and rearward pattern of the higher-frequency Yagi when the booms are closely spaced. In fact, the SWR curve is usually not affected enough to make it a good diagnostic indicator of interaction between the two Yagis.

Figure 15.17 shows an overlay of the SWR curves across the 2 meter band for four configurations: an 8-element 2 meter Yagi by itself, and then over a 5-element 6 meter Yagi with spacings between the booms of 1, 2, 4 and 6 feet. The SWR curves are similar — it would be difficult to see any difference between these configurations using typical amateur SWR indicators for anything but the very closest (1-foot) spacing. For example, the SWR curve for the 2-foot spacing case is virtually indistinguishable from that of the Yagi by itself, while the forward gain has dropped more than 0.6 dB because of interactions with the 6 meter Yagi below it.

Gain and Pattern Degradation Due to Stacking

Figure 15.18 shows four overlaid rectangular plots of the azimuth response from 0° to 180° for the 8-element 2 meter Yagi described above, spaced 1, 2, 4 and 6 feet over a 5-element 6 meter beam. The rectangular presentation gives more detail than a polar plot. The most closely spaced configuration (with 1-foot spacing between the booms) shows the largest degradation in the forward gain, a drop of 1.7 dB. The worst-case front-to-rear ratio for the 6-foot spacing is 29.0 dB, while it is 36.4 dB for the 1-foot spacing — actually better than the F/R for the 8-element 2 meter Yagi by itself. Performance change due to the nearby presence of other Yagis can be enormously complicated (and sometimes is not intuitive as well).

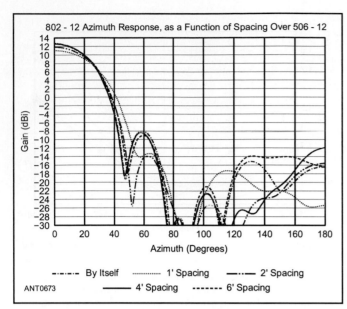

Figure 15.18 — Plots of the 8-element 2 meter Yagi's azimuth response from 0° to 180° for spacing distances from 1 to 6 feet. The sidelobe at about 60° varies about 6 dB over the range of boom spacings, while the shape of worst-case F/R curve varies considerably due to interactions with the lower 6 meter beam. The gain for the 1-foot spacing is degraded by more than 3 dB compared to the 2 meter antenna by itself.

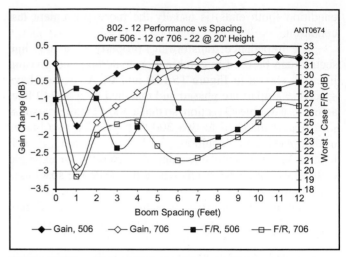

Figure 15.19 — Plot of 8-element 2 meter Yagi's gain and worst-case F/R as a function of distance over two types of 6 meter beams, one on a 12-foot boom and the other on a 22-foot boom. Beyond a spacing of about 5 feet the performance is degraded a minimal amount.

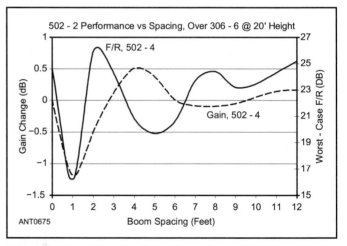

Figure 15.20 — Plot of gain and worst-case F/R of a 5-element 2 meter Yagi on a 4-foot boom as a function of distance over a 3-element 6 meter beam on a 6-foot boom. Beyond a spacing of about 3 feet the performance is degraded a minimal amount.

What happens when a different kind of 6 meter Yagi is mounted below the 8-element 2 meter Yagi? **Figure 15.19** compares the change in forward gain and the worst-case F/R performance as a function of spacing between the booms for two varieties of 6 meter Yagis: the 5-element design on a 12-foot boom and a 7-element Yagi on a 22-foot boom. The spacing of "0 feet" represents the 8-element 2 meter Yagi when it is used alone, with no other antenna nearby. This sets the reference expectations for gain and F/R.

The most severe degradation occurs for the 1-foot spacing, as you might imagine, for both the 12 and 22-foot boom lengths. Over the 5-element 6 meter Yagi, the 2 meter gain doesn't recover to the reference level of the 8-element 2 meter beam by itself until the spacing is greater than 9 feet. However, the gain is within 0.25 dB of the reference level for spacings of 3 feet or more. Interestingly, the F/R is higher than that of the 2 meter antenna by itself for the 1, 2 and 5-foot spacings and for spacings greater than 11 feet. The 2 meter F/R in the presence of the 12-foot 5-element 6 meter Yagi remains above 20 dB for spacings beyond 1 feet.

Overall, the 2 meter beam performs reasonably well for spacings of 3 feet or more over the 5-element 6 meter Yagi. Put another way, the 2 meter beam's performance is degraded only slightly for boom spacings greater than 3 feet. A spacing of 3 feet is less than the old rule of thumb that the minimum spacing between booms be greater than one-half the boom length of the higher-frequency Yagi, which in this case is 6 feet long.

For the 7-element 6 meter Yagi, the 2 meter gain recovers

to the reference level for spacings beyond 7 feet, but the F/R is degraded below the reference level for all spacings shown in Figure 15.19. If we use a gain reduction criterion of less than 0.25 dB and a 20-dB F/R level as the minimum acceptable level, then the spacing must be 5 feet or more over the larger 6 meter Yagi. Again, this is less than the rule of thumb that the minimum spacing between booms be greater than one-half the boom length of the higher-frequency Yagi.

Now, let's try a smaller setup of 2 and 6 meter Yagis stacked vertically in a Christmas-tree configuration to see if the rule of thumb for spacing the booms still holds. **Figure 15.20** shows the performance curves versus boom spacing for a 5-element 2 meter Yagi on a 4-foot boom stacked over a 3-element 6 meter Yagi on a 6-foot boom. Again, the 1-foot spacing produces a substantial gain reduction of about 1.3 dB compared to the reference gain when the 2 meter Yagi is used by itself. Beyond a boom spacing of 3 feet the 2 meter gain drops less than 0.25 dB from the reference level of the 2 meter Yagi by itself and the F/R remains above about 20 dB. In this example, the simple rule of thumb that the minimum spacing between booms be greater than half the boom length (half of 4 feet) of the higher-frequency Yagi does not hold up. However, the same minimum spacing of 3 feet we found for the larger 2 meter Yagi remains true. Three feet spacing is almost 0.5 λ between the booms at the higher frequency.

Adding a 70 cm Yagi to the Christmas Tree

Let's get more ambitious and set up a larger VHF/UHF Christmas tree, with a 14-element 70 cm Yagi on a 9-foot boom at the top, mounted 5 feet over an 8-element 2 meter Yagi on a 12-foot boom. At the bottom of the stack (at the top of the tower) is either the 5-element 6 meter beam on a 12-foot boom, or a 7-element 6 meter beam on a 22-foot boom. See Figure 15.16C. As before, we will vary the spacing between the 70 cm Yagi and the 2 meter Yagi below it to assess the interactions that degrade the 70 cm performance.

Figure 15.21 compares the change in gain and F/R curves as a function of boom spacings between the 70 cm and 2 meter Yagis for the two different 6 meter Yagis (with a fixed distance of 5 feet between the 2 meter and 6 meter Yagis). In this example, the 70 cm Yagi was designed to be an intrinsic 50-Ω feed, where the F/R has been compromised

to some extent. Still, the F/R is greater than 20 dB when the 70 cm Yagi is used by itself.

For spacings greater than 4 feet between the 70 cm and 2 meter booms, the 70 cm gain is equal to or even slightly greater than that of the 70 cm antenna by itself. The increase of gain indicates that the elevation pattern of the 70 cm antenna is slightly compressed by the presence of the other Yagis below it. The F/R stays above at 19.5 dB for spacings greater than or equal to 4 feet. This falls just below our desired lower limit of 20 dB, but it is highly doubtful that anyone would notice this 0.5-dB drop in actual operation. A spacing of 4 feet between booms falls under the rule of thumb that the minimum spacing be at least half the boom length of the higher-frequency Yagi, which in this case is 9 feet.

What should be obvious in this discussion is that you should model the exact configuration you plan to build to avoid unnecessary performance degradation.

Stacking Same-Frequency Yagis

This subject has been examined in some detail in the **HF Antenna System Design** chapter. The same basic principles hold at VHF and UHF as they do on HF. That is, the gain increases gradually with increasing spacing between the booms, and then falls off gradually past a certain spacing distance.

At HF, you should avoid nulls in the antenna's elevation response — so that you can cover all the angles needed for geographic areas of interest. At VHF/UHF, propagation is usually at low elevation angles for most propagation modes, and signals are often extremely weak. Thus, achieving maximum gain is the most common design objective for a VHF/UHF stack. Of secondary importance is the cleanliness of the beam pattern, to discriminate against interference and noise sources.

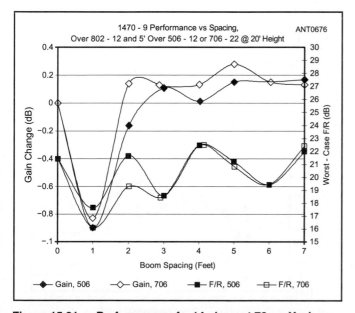

Figure 15.21 — Performance of a 14-element 70 cm Yagi on a 9-foot boom, mounted a variable distance over an 8-element 2 meter Yagi on a 12-foot boom, which is mounted 5 feet above either a 5-element 6 meter Yagi on a 12-foot boom or a 7-element 6 meter Yagi on a 22-foot boom. Beyond a spacing of about 4 feet, the performance of the 70 cm beam is degraded a minimal amount.

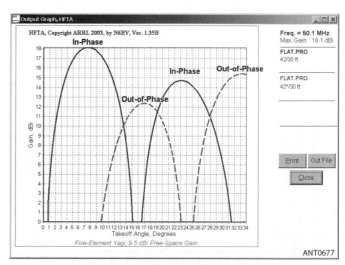

Figure 15.22 — *HFTA* comparison plots of the elevation responses for two 5-element 6 meter Yagis mounted at 42 and 30 feet above flat ground, when they are fed in-phase and out-of-phase. By switching the phasing (adding a half-wavelength of coax to one of the antennas), the elevation angle can be controlled to enhance performance when a sporadic-E cloud is nearly overhead.

Six meter sporadic-E can sometimes occur at high elevation angles, especially if the E_s cloud is overhead, or nearly overhead. Since sporadic-E is exactly that, *sporadic*, it's not a good design practice to try to cover a wide range of elevation angles, as you must often do at HF to cover large geographic areas. On 6 meters, you can change to high-angle coverage when necessary. For example, you might switch to a separate Yagi mounted at a low height, or you might provide means to feed stacked antennas out-of-phase. **Figure 15.22** shows an *HFTA* (HF Terrain Assessment) plot of two 5-element 6 meter Yagis, fed either in-phase or out-of-phase to cover a much wider range of elevation angles than the in-phase stack alone.

Figure 15.23A shows the change in gain for four 2 meter stacked designs, as a function of the spacing in wavelengths between the booms. The 3-element Yagi is mounted on a 2-foot boom (occupying 0.28 λ of that boom). The 5-element Yagi is on a 4-foot boom (0.51 λ of the boom), while the 8-element Yagi is on a 12-foot boom (1.72 λ of boom). The biggest antenna in the group has 16 elements, on a 27-foot boom (4.0 λ of boom). This range of boom lengths pretty much covers the practical range of antennas used by hams.

The stack of two 3-element Yagis peaks at 3.2 dB of additional gain over a single Yagi for 0.75 λ spacing between the booms. Further increases in spacing see the gain change gradually drop off. Figure 15.23B shows the worst-case F/R of the four stacks, again as a function of boom length. The F/R of a single 3-element Yagi is just over 24 dB, but in the presence of the second 3-element Yagi in the stack, the F/R of the pair oscillates between 15 to 26 dB, finally remaining consistently over the desired 20-dB level for spacings greater than about 1.7 λ, where the gain has fallen about 0.6 dB from the peak possible gain. A boom spacing of 1.7 λ at 146 MHz is 11.5 feet. Thus you must compromise in choosing the boom spacing between achieving maximum gain and the best pattern.

The increase in gain of the stack of two 5-element Yagis peaks at a spacing of about 1 λ (6.7 feet), where the F/R is an excellent 25 dB. Having more elements on a particular length of boom aids in holding a more consistent F/R in the presence of the second antenna.

The gain increase for the bigger stack of 8-element Yagis peaks at a spacing of about 1.5 λ (10.1 feet), where the F/R is more than 27 dB. The 16-element Yagi's gain increase is 2.6 dB for a spacing of about 2.25 λ (15.2 feet), where the F/R remains close to 25 dB. The stacking distance of 15.2 feet for an antenna with a 27-foot long boom may be a real challenge physically, requiring a very sturdy rotating mast to withstand wind pressures without bending.

These examples show that the exact spacing between booms is not overly critical, since the gain varies relatively slowly around the peak. Figure 15.23A shows that the boom spacing needed to achieve peak gain from a stack increases when higher-gain (longer-boom) individual antennas are used in that stack. It also shows that the increase in maximum gain from stacking decreases for long-boom antennas. Figure 15.23B shows that beyond boom spacings of about 1 λ, the F/R pattern holds well for Yagi designs with booms longer than about 0.5 λ, which is about 4 feet at 146 MHz.

The plots in Figure 15.23 are representative of typical modern Yagis. You could simply implement these designs as is, and you'll achieve good results. However, we recommend that you model any specific stack you design, just to make sure. Since the boom spacings are displayed in terms of wavelength, you can extend the results for 2 meters to other bands, provided that you use properly scaled Yagi designs to the other bands too.

You can even tweak the element dimensions and spacings of each Yagi used in a stack to optimize the rearward pattern for a particular stacking distance. This strategy can work out well at VHF/UHF, where stacks are often configured for best gain (and pattern) and are "hard-wired" with fixed lengths of feed lines permanently joined together at the junctions.

This is in contrast to the situation at HF (and even on 6 meters). The HF operator usually wants flexibility to select individual Yagis (or combinations of Yagis) from the stack, to match the array's takeoff angle with ionospheric propagation

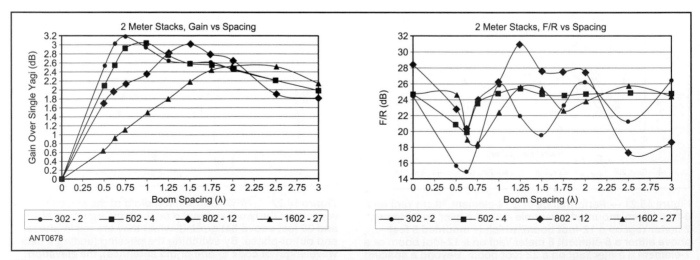

Figure 15.23 — Performance of two different 2 meter Yagis (5 elements on 4-foot boom and 8 elements on 12-foot boom) fed in-phase, as a function of spacing between the booms. Note that the distance is measured in wavelengths.

conditions. The designer of a flexible HF stack thus usually doesn't try to redo the element lengths and spacings of the Yagis to optimize a particular stack.

Stacking Stacks of Different-Frequency Yagis

The investment in a tower is usually substantial, and most hams want to put as many antennas as possible on a tower, provided that interaction between the antennas can be held to a reasonable level. Really ambitious weak-signal VHF/UHF enthusiasts may want "stacked stacks" — sets of stacked Yagis that cover different bands. For example, a VHF contester might want a stack of two 8-element 2 meter Yagis mounted on the same rotating mast as a stack of two 5-element 6 meter Yagis. Let's assume that the boom length of the 8-element 2 meter Yagis is 12 feet (1.78 λ). We'll assume a boom length of 12 feet (0.61 λ) for the 5-element 6 meter Yagis.

From Figure 15.23, we find the stacking distance between the 8-element 2 meter beams for peak gain and good pattern is 1.5 λ, or 10 feet, but adequate performance can be had for a boom spacing of 0.75 λ, which is 5 feet on 2 meters.

The boom spacing for two 5-element 6 meter beams is 1 λ for peak stacking gain, but a compromise of 0.625 λ (12 feet) still yields an acceptable gain increase of 2 dB over a single Yagi. The overall height of the rotating mast sticking out of the top of the tower is thus set by the 0.625 λ stacking distance on 6 meters, at 12 feet. In-between the 6 meter Yagis at the bottom and top of the rotating mast we will mount the 2 meter Yagi stack. With only 12 feet available on the mast, the spacing for symmetric placement of the two 2 meter Yagis in-between the 6 meter Yagis dictates a distance of only 4 feet between the 2 meter beams. This is less than optimal.

The performance of the 2 meter stack in this "stack within a stack" is affected by the close spacing, but the interactions are not disastrous. The stacking gain is 1.62 dB more than the gain for a single 8-element 2 meter Yagi and the F/R remains above 20 dB across the 2 meter band.

On 6 meters, the stacking gain for two 5-element 6 meter Yagis spaced 12 feet apart is 2.2 dB more than the gain of a single Yagi, while the F/R pattern remains about 20 dB over the weak-signal portion of the 6 meter band. As described in the **HF Antenna System Design** chapter, stacking gives more advantages than merely a gain increase, and 6 meter propagation does require coverage of a range of elevation angles because much of the time ionospheric modes are involved.

Increasing the length of the rotating mast to 18 feet sticking out of the top of the tower will increase performance, particularly on 2 meters. The stacking gain on 6 meters will increase to 2.3 dB while the F/R decreases to 18.5 dB, modest changes both. The 18-foot mast allows the 2 meter Yagis to be spaced 6 feet from each other and 6 feet away from both top and bottom 6 meter antennas. The stacking gain goes to 2.14 dB and the F/R approaches 27 dB in the weak-signal portion of the 2 meter band.

Whether the modest increase in stacking gain is worth the cost and mechanical complexity of stacking two 2 meter Yagis between a stack of 6 meter Yagis is a choice left to the operator. Certainly the cost and weight of a rotating mast that is 20 feet long (18 feet out of the top of the tower and 2 feet down inside the tower), a mast that must be sturdy enough to support the antennas in high winds without bending, should give pause to even the most enthusiastic 6 meter weak-signal operator.

15.3.2 YAGIS FOR 50 MHZ

Boom length often proves to be the deciding factor when one selects a Yagi design. **Table 15-1** shows three 6 meter Yagis designed for convenient boom lengths (6, 12 and 22 feet). The 3-element, 6-foot boom design has 8.0 dBi gain in free space; the 12 foot boom, 5-element version has 10.1 dBi gain, and the 22-foot, 7 element Yagi has a gain of 11.3 dBi. All antennas exhibit better than 22 dB front-to-rear ratio and cover 50 to 51 MHz with better than 1.7:1 SWR.

A beam designed for FM operation higher in the band is described by the August 2007 *QST* article "A Short Boom,

Table 15-1
Optimized 6 Meter Yagi Designs

	Spacing Between Elements (inches)	Seg1 OD Length (inches)	Seg2 OD Length (inches)	Midband Gain F/R
306-06				
OD		0.750	0.625	
Refl.	0	36	23.500	7.9 dBi
D.E.	24	36	16.000	27.2 dB
Dir. 1	42	36	15.500	
506-12				
OD		0.750	0.625	
Refl.	0	36	24.000	10.1 dBi
D.E.	24	36	17.125	24.7 dB
Dir. 1	12	36	19.375	
Dir. 2	44	36	18.250	
Dir. 3	58	36	15.375	
706-22				
OD		0.750	0.625	
Refl.	0	36	25.000	11.3 dBi
D.E.	27	36	17.250	29.9 dB
Dir. 1	16	36	18.500	
Dir. 2	51	36	15.375	
Dir. 3	54	36	15.875	
Dir. 4	53	36	16.500	
Dir. 5	58	36	12.500	

Figure 15.24 — The element to boom clamp. U bolts are used to hold the element to the plate, and 2-inch galvanized muffler clamps hold the plates to the boom.

Wideband 3 Element Yagi for 6 Meters," by L.B. Cebik, W4RNL (SK). Cebik describes two additional 3-element Yagis for 6 meters — one optimized for gain and F/B and the other optimized for bandwidth — in the February 2000 *QST* article, "2X3 = 6." Both articles are included on this book's CD-ROM.

Half-element lengths and spacings are given in the table. Elements can be mounted to the boom as shown in **Figure 15.24**. Two muffler clamps hold each aluminum plate to the boom, and two U bolts fasten each element to the plate, which is 0.25 inch thick and 4 × 4 inches square. Stainless steel is the best choice for hardware, but galvanized hardware can be substituted. Automotive muffler clamps do not work well in this application because they are not galvanized and quickly rust once exposed to the weather. Please note that the element lengths shown in Table 15-1 are half the overall element lengths. See the **Antenna Materials and Construction** chapter for practical details of telescoping aluminum elements.

The driven element is mounted to the boom on a Bakelite or G-10 fiberglass plate of similar dimension to the other mounting plates. A 12-inch piece of Plexiglas rod is inserted into the driven element halves. The Plexiglas allows the use of a single clamp on each side of the element and also seals the center of the elements against moisture. Self-tapping screws are used for electrical connection to the driven element.

Refer to **Figure 15.25** for driven-element and hairpin match details. A bracket made from a piece of aluminum is used to mount the three SO-239 connectors to the driven element plate. A 4:1 transmission line balun connects the two element halves, transforming the 200 Ω resistance at the hairpin match to 50 Ω at the center connector. Note that the electrical length of the balun is λ/2, but the physical length will be shorter due to the velocity factor of the particular coaxial cable used. The hairpin is connected directly across the element halves. The exact center of the hairpin is electrically neutral and should be fastened to the boom. This has the advantage of placing the driven element at dc ground potential.

The hairpin match requires no adjustment as such. However, you may have to change the length of the driven element slightly to obtain the best match in your preferred portion of the band. Changing the driven-element length will not adversely affect antenna performance. *Do not adjust the lengths or spacings of the other elements — they are optimized already.* If you decide to use a gamma match, add 3 inches to each side of the driven element lengths given in the table for all antennas.

15.3.3 UTILITY YAGIS FOR 144 MHZ AND 432 MHZ

There are many applications for Yagis on 144 MHz that do not require high gain or tightly-controlled pattern. In fact, for casual operating, a beamwidth that is too narrow can actually prevent a station from hearing weak signals not in the main lobe of the antenna. For meteor scatter and other applications (see the sidebar, "Meteor Scatter: How Much Antenna is Too Much?") where the opening comes from an unknown azimuth, a wider beamwidth is preferred. Rover

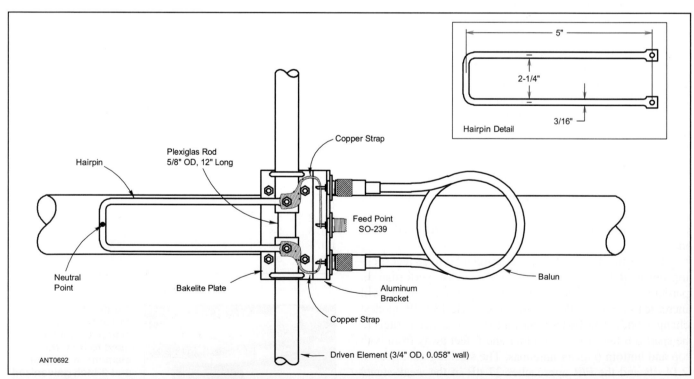

**Figure 15.25 — This shows how the driven element and feed system are attached to the boom. The phasing line is coiled and taped to the boom. The center of the hairpin loop may be connected to the boom electrically and mechanically if desired.
Phasing-line lengths:
For cable with 0.80 velocity factor — 7 ft, 10⅝ inches**　　　　**For cable with 0.66 velocity factor — 6 ft, 5¾ inches**

Meteor Scatter: How Much Antenna is Too Much?

Can an antenna be too big or have too much gain? Perhaps surprisingly, in some circumstances the answer is a definite "Yes."

High gain means narrow beamwidth. Even supposing that a sharp beam can be directed just as desired, you may sometimes want your transmitter to illuminate a larger range of directions, or to receive signals with reasonable gain over a larger range. Such situations can exist even for point-to-point communication — for example, when station A tries to work station B, at a known location some 800 to 1200 km away, on a VHF band using meteor scatter.

The most probable path geometries for random meteor scatter are offset by angles of about 8° to 16° either side of the great circle path. Smaller offsets apply to the longest paths, on the order of 2200 to 2400 km; paths less than 1000 km have optimum offsets near the high end of the range. The largest number of meteor-scatter reflections will occur when stations A and B use antenna beamwidths that overlap throughout most of the potentially useful scattering volume. This implies beamwidths at least twice the offset angle: around 32° for 800 km paths, or 16° for the longest feasible paths. Of course, antennas with higher gain and narrower beams may yield stronger signals, when they produce any at all; but for efficient completion of their desired contact, A and B may be interested in getting *more* meteor reflections, rather than *stronger* ones.

A Yagi antenna with 30° beamwidth has boom length of about 3 wavelengths and gain of 13 dBd. Three wavelengths at 50 MHz is nearly 60 feet, so few if any amateur antennas for this band are likely to be "too large" for effective meteor-scatter use. At 144 MHz, however, Yagis of 5 wavelengths and more are quite practical. Their beamwidths will be significantly less than 30°, so they will be sub-optimal for meteor-scatter contacts at moderate distances.

Real-world amateur meteor scatter experience confirms the picture outlined above. For meteor scatter out to 1600 km on the 2 meter band, an optimized 10 to 12 element Yagi (length 1.8 to 2.5 λ) is probably close to the optimum antenna. Takeoff angles for meteor scatter are no more than about 15°, so a vertical stack of two such Yagis (which would have the same beamwidth in azimuth) would be even better. Horizontal stacking of a pair, or a 2 × 2 box of four such Yagis, would work well beyond about 1600 km, but would be sub-optimal at shorter distances. On the longest feasible meteor-scatter paths, beyond about 1800 km, the rule-of-thumb once again becomes "bigger is better." Note that for these long paths the optimum takeoff angle has fallen to less than 3°, so antenna height in excess of 5 λ (about 35 feet at 144 MHz) is also important. — *Joe Taylor, K1JT*

Table 15-2
2 Meter OWA Yagi Dimensions

Element	Element Length (inches)	Reflector Spacing (inches)	Element Diameter (inches)
Reflector	40.52	—	0.1875
Driver	39.70	10.13	0.5000
Director 1	37.36	14.32	0.1875
Director 2	36.32	25.93	0.1875
Director 3	36.32	37.28	0.1875
Director 4	34.96	54.22	0.1875

and portable stations often find the lighter weight and shorter boom length of the smaller antennas easier to handle.

Utility Yagi for 144 MHz

The following material is a summary of the design presented by L.B. Cebik, ,W4RNL (SK) in the December 2004 *QST* article "Building a Medium-Gain, Wide-Band, 2 Meter Yagi." (The complete article is included on this book's CD-ROM.)

The 6-element Yagi presented here is a derivative of the "optimized wideband antenna" (OWA) designs developed for HF use by NW3Z and WA3FET. **Figure 15.26** shows the general structure of the beam and **Figure 15.27** gives the free-space E-plane pattern. If mounted with the elements horizontal, the E-plane pattern would be the azimuthal pattern.

Oversimplifying the design somewhat, the reflector and first director largely set the feed point impedance. The next two directors contribute to setting the operating bandwidth. The final director sets the gain.

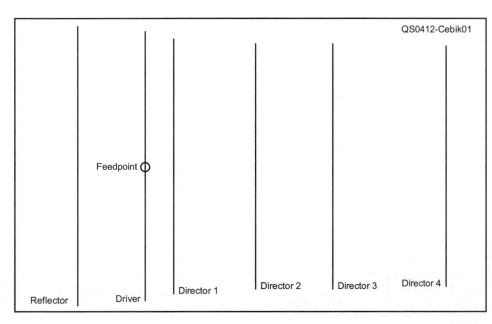

QS0412-Cebik01

Feedpoint

Reflector Driver Director 1 Director 2 Director 3 Director 4

Figure 15.26 — The general structure of the 2 meter, 6-element OWA Yagi. See Table 15-2 for dimensions.

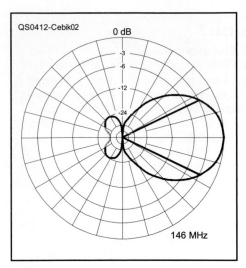

Figure 15.27 — E-plane (horizontal azimuth) pattern of the 2 meter, 6-element OWA Yagi in free space at mid-band — 146 MHz. The antenna exhibits a gain of about 10.2 dBi, consistent across the 2 meter band.

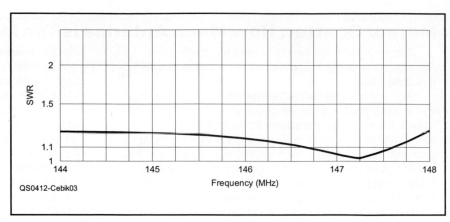

Figure 15.28 — The SWR for the OWA 2 meter Yagi from 144 to 148 MHz as modeled by *NEC-4*.

Designed using *NEC-4*, the antenna's six elements are arranged on a 56-inch boom **Table 15-2** gives the specific dimension for the antenna. The parasitic elements are all 3/16-inch aluminum rod while the driver uses ½-inch aluminum tubing for reasons of construction. Dimensions for the beam with an alternate driver or the use of ⅛-inch elements is given in the original article.

The OWA design provides about 10.2 dBi of free-space gain with better than 20 dB F/B across the entire 2 meter band. The horizontal beamwidth is considerably wider if the beam is mounted with the elements vertical for use on FM.

One significant feature of the OWA design is its direct 50-Ω feed point impedance that requires no matching network. Of course, a common-mode choke balun (see the **Transmission Line Coupling and Impedance Matching** chapter) is desirable. The SWR as shown in **Figure 15.28** is very flat across the band and never exceeds 1.3:1. The SWR and pattern consistency together create a very useful utility antenna for 2 meters.

Utility Yagi for 432 MHz

The following design was developed by Zack Lau, W1VT and described in his "RF" column "A Small 70-cm Yagi" in the July/August 2001 *QEX*. The complete article is included on this book's CD-ROM.

This six-element Yagi was designed for a wide bandwidth — in gain, F/B and SWR. Its gain was measured at 8.5 dBd during the 1995 Eastern States VHF/UHF Conference — with little gain variation between 417 and 446 MHz. The SWR is almost as broad, with better than 1.4:1 SWR between 422 and 446 MHz. The measured gain and return loss curves are shown in **Figure 15.29**. The short 30-inch boom is small enough to fit in the trunk of a compact

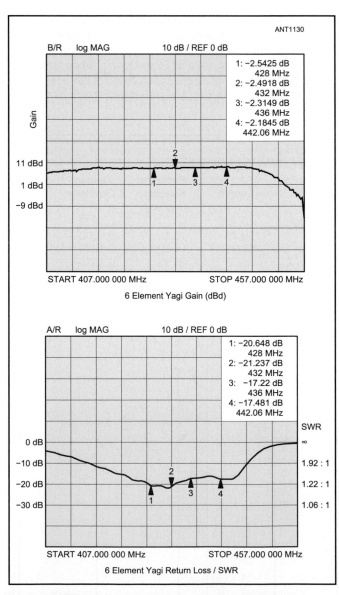

Figure 15.29 — Gain and SWR measurements for the 70 cm Yagi.

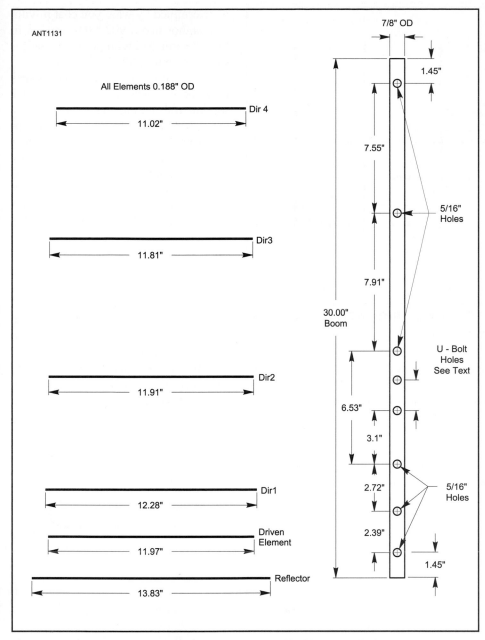

All Elements 0.188" OD

ANT1131

Dir 4 — 11.02"

Dir3 — 11.81"

Dir2 — 11.91"

Dir1 — 12.28"

Driven Element — 11.97"

Reflector — 13.83"

7/8" OD

1.45"

7.55"

5/16" Holes

7.91"

30.00" Boom

U - Bolt Holes See Text

6.53"

3.1"

2.72"

5/16" Holes

2.39"

1.45"

Figure 15.30 — Rough scale drawing of the 70 cm Yagi boom and elements.

Table 15-3
432-MHz Yagi Dimensions

Spacing	Cumulative Boom Length	Element Length
0		13.832
2.394	2.394	11.968
2.715	5.109	12.284
6.528	11.637	11.908
7.907	19.544	11.810
7.546	27.09	11.01

Dimensions in inches.

sedan, perfect for portable or emergency operation. The F/B bandwidth is also very good, with over 20 dB of F/B between 424 and 450 MHz, according to a *Yagi Analyzer* computer model.

Even if you only intend to use this antenna for 432-MHz SSB or 436-MHz satellite operation, the extra bandwidth is useful when it rains. Heavy rain causes antenna elements to resonate lower in frequency. This is much worse if the antenna is tweaked for maximum gain. Yagis typically have a low-pass gain response. The gain falls off rapidly past the maximum-gain point. Thus, while the maximum gain is around 442 MHz, the gain is significantly lower at 457 MHz, while only a little bit lower at 427 MHz.

The optimized design is shown in **Figure 15.30** and the element lengths and placement are given in **Table 15-3**. The element lengths are adjusted to work with a particular boom and mounting arrangement. Changing the boom or element mounting may require adjusting the element lengths. The antenna uses a simple T-match, as simpler gamma matches have a poor reputation on this band. A T-matched Yagi is more likely to have a symmetrical radiation pattern. The feed system shown in the complete article on the CD-ROM is a copy of that used in the K2RIW Yagi. A half-wave balun made out of semi-rigid UT-141 coax steps up the impedance to 200 Ω. Similarly, he T match steps up the impedance of the driven element to 200 Ω.

15.3.4 CHEAP YAGIS BY WA5VJB

The following material is adapted from an online paper by Kent Britain, WA5VJB, entitled "Controlled Impedance 'Cheap' Antennas." The paper is available from **www.wa5vjb.com/references.html**. The simplified feed uses the structure of the antenna itself for impedance matching. The antennas were designed with *YagiMax*, tweaked in *NEC*, and the driven elements experimentally determined on the antenna range. The result is a family of Yagis with good performance that can be built very inexpensively.

Construction of the antennas is straightforward. The boom is ¾-inch square, or ½-inch by ¾-inch wood. To

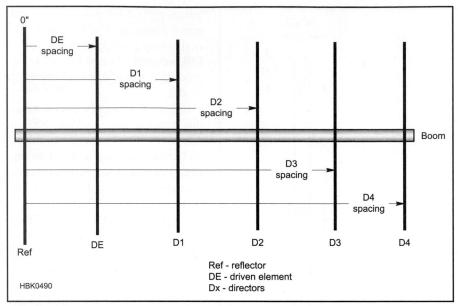

Figure 15.31 — Element spacing for the Cheap Yagis. Refer to Tables 15-4 to 15-10 for exact dimensions for the various bands.

is determined by what you coat it with. The author had a 902-MHz version in the air varnished with polyurethane for two years with little deterioration.

The parasitic elements on prototypes have been made from silicon-bronze welding rod, aluminum rod, brass hobby tubing, and #10 or #12 AWG solid copper ground wire. So that you can solder to the driven element, use the welding rod, hobby tubing or copper wire. The driven element is folded at one end with its ends inserted through the boom.

Figure 15.31 shows the basic plan for the antenna and labels the dimensions that are given in the table for each band. All table dimensions are given in inches.

Figure 15.32 shows how the driven element is constructed for each antenna. Trim the free end of the driven element to tune it for minimum SWR at the desired frequency. **Figure 15.33** shows how to attach coaxial cable to the feed point. Sliding a quarter-wave sleeve along the coax had little effect, so there's not much RF on the outside of the coax. You may use a ferrite bead choke balun if you like, but these antennas are designed for minimum expense!

install an element, drill a hole through the boom and insert the element. A drop of cyanoacrylate "super glue," epoxy, or silicone adhesive is used to hold the elements in place. There is no boom-to-mast plate — drill holes in the boom and use a U-bolt to attach it to the mast! The life of the antenna

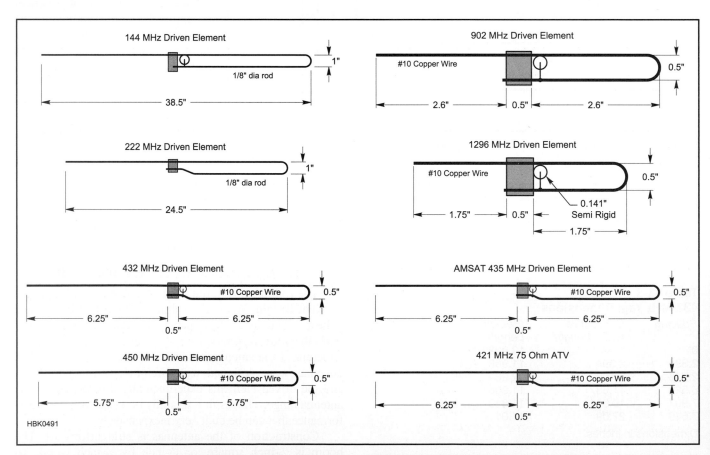

Figure 15.32 — Driven element dimensions for the Cheap Yagis. Attaching the coax shield to the center of the driven element is appropriate because that is the lowest impedance point of the element.

Table 15-4
WA5VJB 144 and 222 MHz Yagi Dimensions
144 MHz Yagi

		Ref	DE	D1	D2	D3	D4
3-element	Length	41.0	—	37.0			
	Spacing	0	8.5	20.0			
4-element	Length	41.0	—	37.5	33.0		
	Spacing	0	8.5	19.25	40.5		
6-element	Length	40.5	—	37.5	36.5	36.5	32.75
	Spacing	0	7.5	16.5	34.0	52.0	70.0

222 MHz Yagi

		Ref	DE	D1	D2	D3	D4
3-element	Length	26.0	—	23.75			
	Spacing	0	5.5	13.5			
4-element	Length	26.25	—	24.1	22.0		
	Spacing	0	5.0	11.75	23.5		
6-element	Length	26.25	—	24.1	23.5	23.5	21.0
	Spacing	0	5.0	10.75	22.0	33.75	45.5

Dimensions in inches.

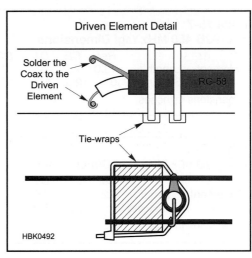

Figure 15.33 — Construction details and feed line attachment for the Cheap Yagi driven element.

Table 15-5
WA5VJB 432 MHz Yagi Dimensions

		Ref	DE	D1	D2	D3	D4	D5	D6	D7	D8	D9
6-element	Length	13.5	—	12.5	12.0	12.0	11.0					
	Spacing	0	2.5	5.5	11.25	17.5	24.0					
8-element	Length	13.5	—	12.5	12.0	12.0	12.0	12.0	11.25			
	Spacing	0	2.5	5.5	11.25	17.5	24.0	30.75	38.0			
11-element	Length	13.5	—	12.5	12.0	12.0	12.0	12.0	12.0	11.75	11.75	11.0
	Spacing	0	2.5	5.5	11.25	17.5	24.0	30.75	38.0	45.5	53.0	59.5

Dimensions in inches.

Table 15-6
WA5VJB 435 MHz Yagi Dimensions

		Ref	DE	D1	D2	D3	D4	D5	D6	D7	D8	D9
6-element	Length	13.4	—	12.4	12.0	12.0	11.0					
8-element	Length	13.4	—	12.4	12.0	12.0	12.0	12.0	11.1			
10-element	Length	13.4	—	12.4	12.0	12.0	12.0	12.0	11.75	11.75	11.1	
11-element	Length	13.4	—	12.4	12.0	12.0	12.0	12.0	11.75	11.75	11.75	11.1
	Spacing	0	2.5	5.5	11.25	17.5	24.0	30.5	37.75	45.0	52.0	59.5

Dimensions in inches.

144 MHz Yagi: While others have reported good luck with 16-element long-boom wood antennas, six elements was about the maximum for most rovers. The design is peaked at 144.2 MHz, but performance is still good at 146.5 MHz. All parasitic elements are made from 3/16-inch aluminum rod and the driven element is made from 1/8-inch rod. Lengths and spacings are given in **Table 15-4**.

222 MHz Yagi: This antenna is peaked at 222.1 MHz, but performance has barely changed at 223.5 MHz. You can drill the mounting holes to mount it with the elements horizontal or vertical. All parasitic elements are made from 3/16-inch aluminum rod and the driven element is made from 1/8-inch rod. Lengths and spacings are given in Table 15-4.

432 MHz Yagi: At this band the antenna is getting very practical and easy to build. All parasitic elements are made from 1/8-inch diameter rod and the driven element is made from #10 AWG solid copper wire. Lengths and spacings are given in **Table 15-5**.

435 MHz Yagi for AMSAT: Ed Krome, K9EK, provided help and motivation for these antennas. A high front-to-back ratio (F/B) was a major design consideration of all versions. The model predicts 30 dB F/B for the six-element and over 40 dB for the others. For gain, *NEC* predicts 11.2 dBi for the six-element, 12.6 dBi for the eight-element, and 13.5 dBi for the 10-element, and 13.8 dBi for the 11-element.

Using 3/4-inch square wood for the boom makes it easy to build two antennas on the same boom for cross-polarization.

Table 15-7
WA5VJB 450 MHz Yagi Dimensions

		Ref	DE	D1	D2	D3	D4
6-element	Length	13.0	—	12.1	11.75	11.75	10.75
	Spacing	0	2.5	5.5	11.0	18.0	28.5

Dimensions in inches.

Table 15-8
WA5VJB 902 MHz Yagi Dimensions

		Ref	DE	D1	D2	D3	D4	D5	D6	D7	D8
10-element	Length	6.2	—	5.6	5.5	5.5	5.4	5.3	5.2	5.1	5.1
	Spacing	0	2.4	3.9	5.8	9.0	12.4	17.4	22.4	27.6	33.0

Dimensions in inches.

Table 15-9
WA5VJB 1296 MHz Yagi Dimensions

		Ref	DE	D1	D2	D3	D4	D5	D6	D7	D8
10-element	Length	4.3	—	3.9	3.8	3.75	3.75	3.65	3.6	3.6	3.5
	Spacing	0	1.7	2.8	4.0	6.3	8.7	12.2	15.6	19.3	23.0

Dimensions in inches.

Table 15-10
WA5VJB 421.25 MHz 75-Ω Yagi Dimensions

		Ref	DE	D1	D2	D3	D4	D5	D6	D7	D8	D9
6-element	Length	14.0	—	12.5	12.25	12.25	11.0					
9-element	Length	14.0	—	12.5	12.25	12.25	12.0	12.0	11.25			
11-element	Length	14.0	—	12.5	12.25	12.25	12.0	12.0	12.0	11.75	11.75	11.5
	Spacing	0	3.0	6.5	12.25	17.75	24.5	30.5	36.0	43.0	50.25	57.25

Dimensions in inches.

Offset the two antennas 6-1/2 inch along the boom and feed them in-phase for circular polarization, or just use one for portable operations. All parasitic elements are made from ⅛-inch diameter rod and the driven element is made from #10 AWG solid copper wire. Lengths and spacings are given in **Table 15-6**. The same element spacing is used for all four versions of the antenna.

450 MHz Yagi for FM: this six-element Yagi is a good, cheap antenna to get a newcomer into a repeater or make a simplex-FM QSO during a contest. RadioShack ⅛-inch diameter aluminum ground wire was used in the prototype for all the elements except the driven element, which is made from #10 AWG solid copper wire. Other ⅛-inch diameter material could be used. Lengths and spacings are given in **Table 15-7**.

902 MHz Yagi: The 2.5-ft length has proven very practical. All parasitic elements are made from ⅛-inch-diameter rod and the driven element is made from #10 AWG solid copper wire. Lengths and spacings are given in **Table 15-8**.

1296 MHz Yagi: This antenna is the veteran of several "Grid-peditions" and has measured 13.5 dBi on the Central States VHF Society antenna range. Dimensions must be followed with great care. The driven element is small enough to allow 0.141-inch semi-rigid coax to be used. The prototype antennas use ⅛-inch silicon-bronze welding rod for the elements, but any ⅛-inch-diameter material can be used. The driven element is made from #10 AWG solid copper wire. Lengths and spacings are given in **Table 15-9**.

421.25 MHz 75-Ω Yagi for ATV: 421 MHz vestigial sideband video is popular in North Texas for receiving the FM video input repeaters. These antennas are made for 421 MHz use and the driven element is designed for 75 Ω. RG-59 or an F adapter to RG-6 can be directly connected to a cable-TV converter or cable-ready TV on channel 57. All parasitic elements are made from ⅛-inch diameter rod and the driven element is made from #10 AWG solid copper wire. Lengths and spacings are given in **Table 15-10**. The same spacing is used for all versions.

15.3.5 HIGH-PERFORMANCE YAGIS FOR 144, 222 AND 432 MHZ

This construction information is presented as an introduction to the three high-performance VHF/UHF Yagis that follow. All were designed and built by Steve Powlishen, K1FO. A Yagi designer from Europe, Gunter Hoch, DL6WU, has produced a family of alternative high-performance designs that can be found in the article referenced in the Bibliography.

At 144 MHz and above, most operators desire Yagi antennas two or more wavelengths in length. This length (2 λ) is where most classical designs start to fall apart in terms of gain per boom length, bandwidth and pattern quality. Extensive computer and antenna range analysis has proven that the best possible design is a Yagi that has both varying element spacings and varying element lengths.

This design approach starts with closely spaced directors. The director spacings gradually increase until a constant spacing of about 0.4 λ is reached. Conversely, the director lengths start out longest with the first director and decrease in length in a decreasing rate of change until they are virtually constant in length. This method of construction results in a wide gain bandwidth. A bandwidth of 7% of the center frequency at the −1 dB forward-gain points is typical for these Yagis even when they are longer than 10 λ. The log-taper design also reduces the rate of change in driven-element impedance vs frequency. This allows the use of simple dipole driven elements while still obtaining acceptable driven-element SWR over a wide frequency range. Another benefit

is that the resonant frequency of the Yagi changes very little as the boom length is increased.

The driven-element impedance also changes moderately with boom length. The tapered approach creates a Yagi with a very clean radiation pattern. Typically, first sidelobe levels of ~17 dB in the E plane, ~15 dB in the H plane, and all other lobes at ~20 dB or more are possible on designs from 2 λ to more than 14 λ.

The actual rate of change in element lengths is determined by the diameter of the elements (in wavelengths). The spacings can be optimized for an individual boom length or chosen as a best compromise for most boom lengths.

The gain of long Yagis has been the subject of much debate. Measurements and computer analysis by both amateurs and professionals indicates that given an optimum design, doubling a Yagi's boom length will result in a maximum theoretical gain increase of about 2.6 dB. In practice, the real gain increase may be less because of escalating resistive losses and the greater possibility of construction error. **Figure 15.34** shows the maximum possible gain per boom length expressed in decibels, referenced to an isotropic radiator. The actual number of directors does not play an important part in determining the gain vs boom length as long as a reasonable number of directors are used. The use of more directors per boom length will normally give a wider gain bandwidth, however, a point exists where too many directors will adversely affect all performance aspects.

While short antennas (< 1.5 λ) may show increased gain with the use of quad or loop elements, long Yagis (> 2 λ) will not exhibit measurably greater forward gain or pattern integrity with loop-type elements. Similarly, loops used as driven elements and reflectors will not significantly change the properties of a long log-taper Yagi. Multiple-dipole driven-element assemblies will also not result in any significant gain increase per given boom length when compared to single-dipole feeds.

Once a long-Yagi director string is properly tuned, the reflector becomes relatively non critical. Reflector spacings between 0.15 λ and 0.2 λ are preferred. The spacing can be chosen for best pattern and driven element impedance. Multiple-reflector arrangements will not significantly increase the forward gain of a Yagi which has its directors properly optimized for forward gain. Many multiple-reflector schemes such as tri-reflectors and corner reflectors have the disadvantage of lowering the driven element impedance compared to a single optimum-length reflector. The plane or grid reflector, shown in **Figure 15.35**, may however reduce the intensity of unwanted rear lobes. This can be used to reduce noise pickup on EME or satellite arrays. This type of reflector will usually increase the driven-element

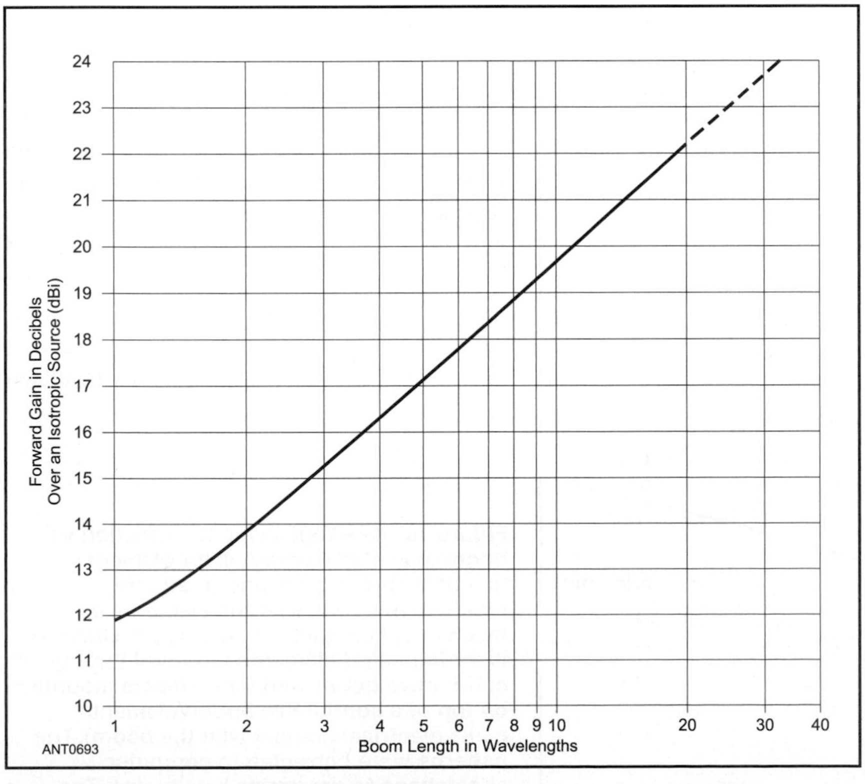

Figure 15.34 — This chart shows maximum gain per boom length for optimally designed long Yagi antennas.

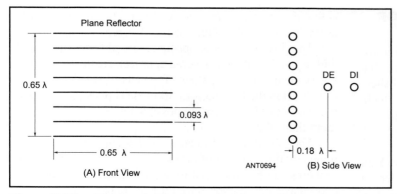

Figure 15.35 — Front and side views of a plane-reflector antenna.

impedance compared to a single reflector. This sometimes makes driven-element matching easier. Keep in mind that even for EME, a plane reflector will add considerable wind load and weight for only a few tenths of a decibel of receive signal-to-noise improvement.

Yagi Construction

Normally, aluminum tubing or rod is used for Yagi elements. Hard-drawn enamel-covered copper wire can also be used on Yagis above 420 MHz. Resistive losses are inversely proportional to the square of the element diameter and the square root of its conductivity.

Element diameters of less than ³⁄₁₆ inch or 4 mm should not be used on any band. The size should be chosen for reasonable strength. Half-inch diameter is suitable for 50 MHz, ³⁄₁₆ to ³⁄₈ inch for 144 MHz and ³⁄₁₆ inch is recommended for the higher bands. Steel, including stainless steel and unprotected brass or copper wire, should not be used for elements.

Boom material may be aluminum tubing, either square or round. High-strength aluminum alloys such as 6061-T6 or 6063-T651 offer the best strength-to-weight advantages. Fiberglass poles have been used (where available as surplus). Wood is a popular low-cost boom material. The wood should be well seasoned and free from knots. Clear pine, spruce and Douglas fir are often used. The wood should be well treated to avoid water absorption and warping.

Elements may be mounted insulated or uninsulated, above or through the boom. Mounting uninsulated elements through a metal boom is the least desirable method unless the elements are welded in place. The Yagi elements will oscillate, even in moderate winds. Over several years this element oscillation will work open the boom holes. This will allow the elements to move in the boom. This will create noise (in your receiver) when the wind blows, as the element contact changes. Eventually the element-to-boom junction will corrode (aluminum oxide is a good insulator). This loss of electrical contact between the boom and element will reduce the boom's effect and change the resonant frequency of the Yagi.

Noninsulated elements mounted above the boom will perform fine as long as a good mechanical connection is made. Insulating blocks mounted above the boom will also work, but they require additional fabrication. One of the most popular construction methods is to mount the elements through the boom using insulating shoulder washers. This method is lightweight and durable. Its main disadvantage is difficult disassembly, making this method of limited use for portable arrays.

If a conductive boom is used, element lengths must be corrected for the mounting method used. The amount of correction is dependent upon the boom diameter in wavelengths. See **Figure 15.36**. Elements mounted through the boom and not insulated require the greatest correction. Mounting on top of the boom or through the boom on insulated shoulder washers requires about half of the through-the-boom correction. Insulated

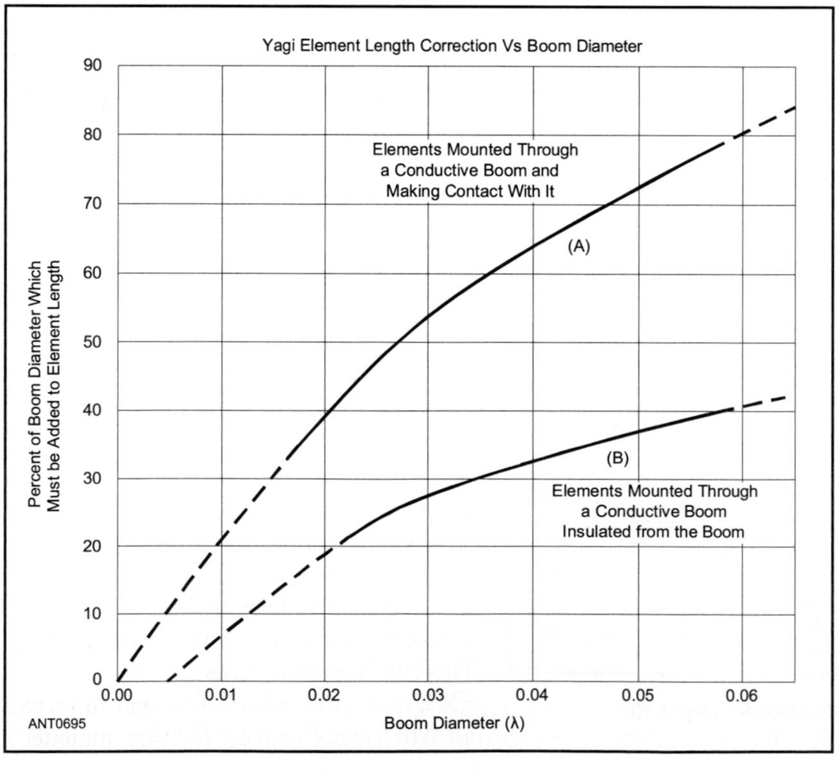

Figure 15.36 — Yagi element correction vs boom diameter. Curve A is for elements mounted through a round or square conductive boom, with the elements in mechanical contact with the boom. Curve B is for insulated elements mounted through a conductive boom, and for elements mounted on top of a conductive boom (elements make electrical contact with the boom). The patterns were corrected to computer simulations to determine Yagi tuning. The amount of element correction is not affected by element diameter.

Table 15-11
Specifications for the 144-MHz Yagi Family

No. of Ele.	Boom Length (λ)	Gain (dBd)	DE Impedance (Ω)	F/B Ratio (dB)	Beamwidth E/H (°)	Stacking E/H (°)
10	1.8	11.4	27	17	39/42	10.2/9.5
11	2.2	12.0	38	19	36/40	11.0/10.0
12	2.5	12.5	28	23	34/37	11.7/10.8
13	2.9	13.0	23	20	32/35	12.5/11.4
14	3.2	13.4	27	18	31/33	12.8/12.0
15	3.6	13.8	35	20	30/32	13.2/12.4
16	4.0	14.2	32	24	29/30	13.7/13.2
17	4.4	14.5	25	23	28/29	14.1/13.6
18	4.8	14.8	25	21	27/28.5	14.6/13.9
19	5.2	15.0	30	22	26/27.5	15.2/14.4

Table 15-12
Free-Space Dimensions for the 144-MHz Yagi Family

Element diameter is ¼ inch

Element No.	Element Position (mm from reflector)	Element Length
Refl.	0	1038
DE	312	955
D1	447	956
D2	699	932
D3	1050	916
D4	1482	906
D5	1986	897
D6	2553	891
D7	3168	887
D8	3831	883
D9	4527	879
D10	5259	875
D11	6015	870
D12	6786	865
D13	7566	861
D14	8352	857
D15	9144	853
D16	9942	849
D17	10744	845

elements mounted at least one element diameter above the boom require no correction over the free-space length.

The three following antennas have been optimized for typical boom lengths on each band.

A High-Performance 144 MHz Yagi

This 144-MHz Yagi design uses the latest log-tapered element spacings and lengths. It offers near theoretical gain per boom length, an extremely clean pattern and wide bandwidth. The design is based upon the spacings used in a 4.5-λ 432-MHz computer-developed design by Tom Kirby, W1EJ (SK). It is quite similar to the 432 MHz Yagi described elsewhere in this chapter. Refer to that project for additional construction diagrams and photographs.

Mathematical models do not always directly translate into real working examples. Although the computer design

provided a good starting point, the author, Steve Powlishen, K1FO, built several test models before the final working Yagi was obtained. This hands-on tuning included changing the element-taper rate in order to obtain the flexibility that allows the Yagi to be built with different boom lengths.

The design is suitable for use from 1.8 λ (10 elements) to 5.1 λ (19 elements). When elements are added to a Yagi, the center frequency, feed impedance and front-to-back ratio will range up and down. A modern tapered design will minimize this effect and allow the builder to select any desired boom length. This Yagi's design capabilities per boom length are listed in **Table 15-11**.

The gain of any Yagi built around this design will be within 0.1 to 0.2 dB of the maximum theoretical gain at the design frequency of 144.2 MHz. The design is intentionally peaked high in frequency (calculated gain peak is about 144.7 MHz). It has been found that by doing this, the SWR bandwidth and pattern at 144.0 to 144.3 MHz will be better, the Yagi will be less affected by weather and its performance in arrays will be more predictable. This design starts to drop off in performance if built with fewer than 10 elements. At less than 2 λ, more traditional designs perform well.

Table 15-12 gives free-space element lengths for ¼ inch-diameter elements. The use of metric notation allows for much easier dimensional changes during the design stage. Once you become familiar with the metric system, you'll probably find that construction is easier without the burden of cumbersome English fractional units. For ³⁄₁₆-inch diameter elements, lengthen all parasitic elements by 3 mm. If ³⁄₈-inch diameter elements are used, shorten all of the directors and the reflector by 6 mm. The driven element will have to be adjusted for the individual Yagi if the 12-element design is not adhered to.

For the 12-element Yagi, ¼-inch diameter elements were selected because smaller-diameter elements become rather flimsy at 2 meters. Other diameter elements can be used as described previously. The 2.5-λ boom was chosen because it has an excellent size and wind load versus gain and pattern trade-off. The size is also convenient; three 6-foot-long pieces of aluminum tubing can be used without any waste. The relatively large-diameter boom sizes (1¼ and 1³⁄₈ inches) were chosen, as they provide an extremely rugged Yagi that does not require a boom support. The 12-element 17-foot-long design has a calculated wind survival of close to 120 mph! The absence of a boom support also makes vertical polarization possible.

Longer versions could be made by telescoping smaller-size boom sections into the last section. Some sort of boom support will be required on versions longer than 22 feet. The elements are mounted on shoulder insulators and mounted through the boom. However, elements may be mounted,

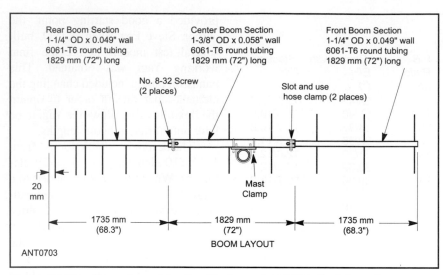

Figure 15.37 — Boom layout for the 12-element 144-MHz Yagi. Lengths are given in millimeters to allow precise duplication.

and T-match adjustments are made. Different driven-element dimensions are required if you change the boom length. The calculated natural driven-element impedance is given as a guideline. A balanced T-match was chosen because it's easy to adjust for best SWR and provides a balanced radiation pattern. A 4:1 half-wave coaxial balun is used, although impedance-transforming quarter-wave sleeve baluns could also be used. The calculated natural impedance will be useful in determining what impedance transformation will be required at the 200-Ω balanced feed point. Information on calculating folded-dipole and T-match driven-element parameters is available in the **Transmission Line Coupling and Impedance Matching** chapter. A balanced feed is important for best operation on this antenna. Gamma matches can severely distort the pattern balance. Other useful driven-element arrangements are the delta match and the folded dipole, if you're willing to sacrifice some flexibility. **Figure 15.38** details the driven-element dimensions.

A noninsulated driven element was chosen for mounting convenience. An insulated driven element may also be used. A grounded driven element may be less affected by static build-up. On the other hand, an insulated driven element allows the operator to easily check his feed lines for water or other contamination by the use of an ohmmeter from the shack.

Figure 15.39 shows computer-predicted E- and H-plane radiation patterns for the 12-element Yagi. The patterns are plotted on a 1-dB-per-division linear scale instead of the usual ARRL polar-plot graph. This expanded scale plot is used to show greater pattern detail. The pattern for the 12-element Yagi is so clean that a plot done in the standard ARRL format would be almost featureless, except for the main lobe and first sidelobes.

The excellent performance of the 12-element Yagi is demonstrated by the reception of Moon echoes from several of the larger 144 MHz EME stations with only one 12-element Yagi. Four of the 12-element Yagis will make an excellent starter EME array, capable of working many EME QSOs while being relatively small in size. The advanced antenna builder can use the information in Table 15-11 to design a dream array of virtually any size.

insulated or uninsulated, above or through the boom, as long as appropriate element length corrections are made. Proper tuning can be verified by checking the depth of the nulls between the main lobe and first sidelobes. The nulls should be 5 to 10 dB below the first side-lobe level at the primary operating frequency. The boom layout for the 12-element model is shown in **Figure 15.37**. The actual corrected element dimensions for the 12-element 2.5-λ Yagi are shown in **Table 15-13**.

The design may also be cut for use at 147 MHz. There is no need to change element spacings. The element lengths should be shortened by 17 mm for best operation between 146 and 148 MHz. Again, the driven element will have to be adjusted as required.

The driven-element size (½-inch diameter) was chosen to allow easy impedance matching. Any reasonably sized driven element could be used, as long as appropriate length

A High-Performance 222 MHz Yagi

Modern tapered Yagi designs are easily applied to 222 MHz. This design uses a spacing progression that is in between the 12-element 144-MHz design, and the 22-element 432-MHz design. The result is a design with maximum gain per boom length, a clean, symmetrical radiation pattern, and wide bandwidth. Although it was designed for weak-signal operation (tropospheric scatter and EME), the design is suited to all modes of 222-MHz operation, such as

Table 15-13
Dimensions for the 12-Element 2.5-λ Yagi

Element Number	Element Position (mm from reflector)	Element Length (mm)	Boom Diam (inches)
Refl.	0	1044	
DE	312	955	
D1	447	962	1¼
D2	699	938	
D3	1050	922	
D4	1482	912	
D5	1986	904	
D6	2553	898	1⅜
D7	3168	894	
D8	3831	889	
D9	4527	885	1¼
D10	5259	882	

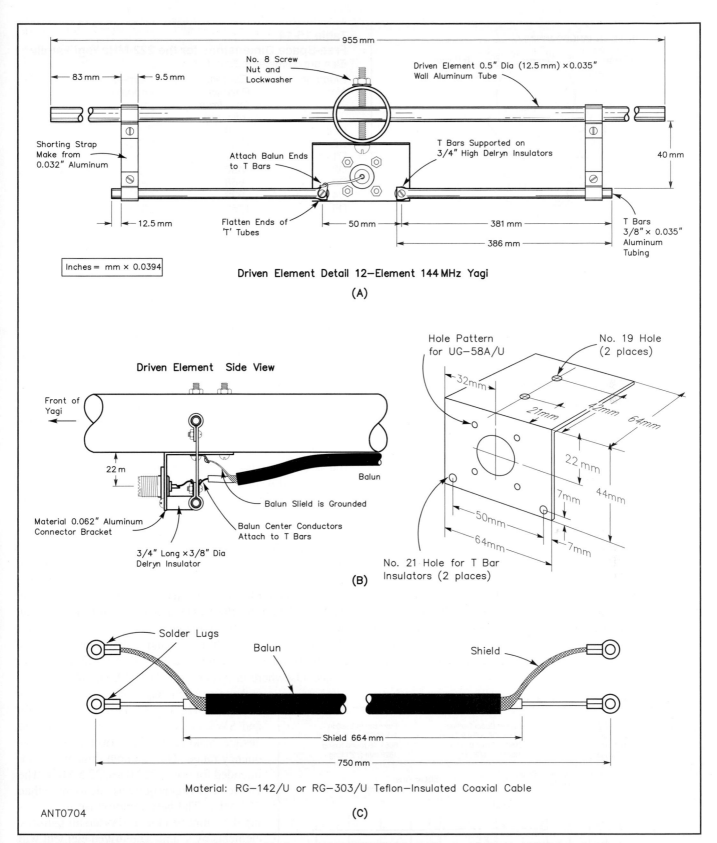

Figure 15.38 — Driven-element detail for the 12-element 144-MHz Yagi. Lengths are given in millimeters to allow precise duplication.

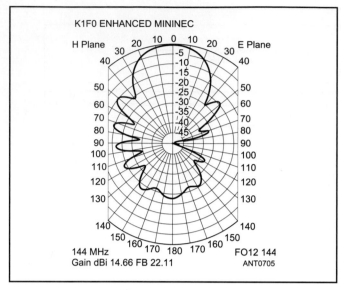

Figure 15.39 — H- and E-plane pattern for the 12-element 144-MHz Yagi.

Table 15-14
Free-Space Dimensions for the 222-MHz Yagi Family
Element diameter is 3/16-inch.

Element No.	Element Position (mm from reflector)	Element Length (mm)
Refl.	0	676
DE	204	647
D1	292	623
D2	450	608
D3	668	594
D4	938	587
D5	1251	581
D6	1602	576
D7	1985	573
D8	2395	569
D9	2829	565
D10	3283	562
D11	3755	558
D12	4243	556
D13	4745	554
D14	5259	553
D15	5783	552
D16	6315	551
D17	6853	550
D18	7395	549
D19	7939	548
D20	8483	547

packet radio, FM repeater operation and control links.

The spacings were chosen as the best compromise for a 3.9-λ 16-element Yagi. The 3.9-λ design was chosen, like the 12-element 144-MHz design, because it fits perfectly on a boom made from three 6-foot-long aluminum tubing sections. The design is quite extensible, and models from 12 elements (2.4 λ) to 22 elements (6.2 λ) can be built from the dimensions given in **Table 15-14**. Note that free-space lengths are given. They must be corrected for the element-mounting method. Specifications for various boom lengths are shown in **Table 15-15**.

Construction

Large-diameter (1¼ and 1⅜ inch diameter) boom construction is used, eliminating the need for boom supports. The Yagi can also be used vertically polarized. Three-sixteenths-inch-diameter aluminum elements are used. The exact alloy is not critical; 6061-T6 was used, but hard aluminum welding

rod is also suitable. Quarter-inch-diameter elements could also be used if all elements are shortened by 3 mm. Three-eighths-inch-diameter elements would require 10-mm shorter lengths. Elements smaller than ³⁄₁₆ inch-diameter are not recommended. The elements are insulated and run through the boom. Plastic shoulder washers and stainless steel retainers are used to hold the elements in place. The various pieces needed to build the Yagi may be obtained from Directive Systems (**www.directivesystems.com**). **Figure 15.40** details the boom layout for the 16-element Yagi. **Table 15-16** gives the dimensions for the 16-element Yagi as built. The driven element is fed with a T match and a 4:1 balun. See **Figure 15.41** for construction details. See the 432-MHz Yagi project elsewhere in this chapter for additional photographs and construction diagrams.

The Yagi has a relatively broad gain and SWR curve, as is typical of a tapered design, making it usable over a wide frequency range. The example dimensions are intended for use at 222.0 to 222.5 MHz. The 16-element Yagi is quite usable to more than 223 MHz. The best compromise for covering the entire band is to shorten all parasitic elements by 4 mm. The driven element will have to be adjusted in length for best match.

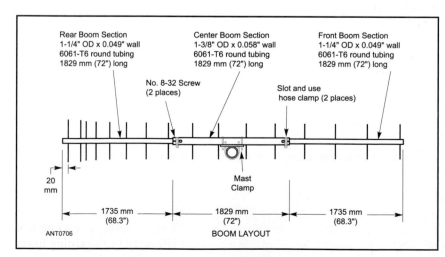

Figure 15.40 — Boom layout for the 16-element 222-MHz Yagi. Lengths are given in millimeters to allow precise duplication.

Table 15-15
Specifications for the 222-MHz Yagi Family

No of Ele.	Boom Length (λ)	Gain (dBd)	F/B Ratio (dB)	DE Impedance (Ω)	Beamwidth E/H (°)	Stacking E/H (feet)
12	2.4	12.3	22	23	37/39	7.1/6.7
13	2.8	12.8	19	28	33/36	7.8/7.2
14	3.1	13.2	20	34	32/34	8.1/7.6
15	3.5	13.6	24	30	30/33	8.6/7.8
16	3.9	14.0	23	23	29/31	8.9/8.3
17	4.3	14.35	20	24	28/30.5	9.3/8.5
18	4.6	14.7	20	29	27/29	9.6/8.9
19	5.0	15.0	22	33	26/28	9.9/9.3
20	5.4	15.3	24	29	25/27	10.3/9.6
21	5.8	15.55	23	24	24.5/26.5	10.5/9.8
22	6.2	15.8	21	23	24/26	10.7/10.2

Table 15-16
Dimensions for 16-Element 3.9-λ 222-MHz Yagi

Element Number	Element Position (mm from reflector)	Element Length (mm)	Boom Diam (inches)
Refl.	0	683	
DE	204	664	
D1	292	630	
D2	450	615	
D3	668	601	1¼
D4	938	594	
D5	1251	588	
D6	1602	583	
D7	1985	580	
D8	2395	576	
D9	2829	572	1⅜
D10	3283	569	
D11	3755	565	
D12	4243	563	
D13	4745	561	1¼
D14	5259	560	

The position of the T-wire shorting straps may also have to be moved.

The aluminum boom provides superior strength, is lightweight, and has a low wind-load cross section. Aluminum is doubly attractive, as it will long outlast wood and fiberglass. Using state-of-the-art designs, it is unlikely that significant performance increases will be achieved in the next few years. Therefore, it's in your best interest to build an antenna that will last many years. If suitable wood or fiberglass poles are readily available, they may be used without any performance degradation, at least when the wood is new and dry. Use the free-space element lengths given in Table 15-16 for insulated-boom construction.

The pattern of the 16-element Yagi is shown in **Figure 15.42**. Like the 144-MHz Yagi, a l-dB-per-division plot is used to detail the pattern accurately. This 16-element design makes a good building block for EME or tropo DX arrays. Old-style narrow-band Yagis often perform unpredictably when used in arrays. The theoretical 3.0-dB stacking gain is rarely observed. The 16-element Yagi (and other versions of the design) reliably provides stacking gains of nearly 3 dB. (The spacing dimensions listed in Table 15-15 show just over 2.9 dB stacking gain.) This has been found to be the best compromise between gain, pattern integrity and array size. Any phasing line losses will subtract from the possible stacking gain. Mechanical misalignment will also degrade the performance of an array.

A High-Performance 432 MHz Yagi

This 22-element, 6.1-λ, 432-MHz Yagi was originally designed for use in a 12-Yagi EME array built by K1FO. A lengthy evaluation and development process preceded its construction. Many designs were considered and then analyzed on the computer. Next, test models were constructed and evaluated on a homemade antenna range. The resulting design is based on the W1EJ (SK) computer-optimized spacings.

The attention paid to the design process has been worth the effort. The 22-element Yagi not only has exceptional forward gain (17.9 dBi), but has an unusually clean radiation pattern. The measured E-plane pattern is shown in **Figure 15.43**. Note that a 1-dB-per-division axis is used to show pattern detail. A complete description of the design process and construction methods appears in December 1987 and January 1988 QST. (See Bibliography.)

Like other log-taper Yagi designs, this one can easily be adapted to other boom lengths. Versions of this Yagi have been built by many amateurs. Boom lengths ranged between 5.3 λ (20 elements) and 12.2 λ (37 elements).

The size of the original Yagi (169 inches long, 6.1 λ) was chosen so the antenna could be built from small-diameter boom material (⅞-inch and 1-inch round 6061-T6 aluminum) and still survive high winds and ice loading. The 22-element Yagi weighs about 3.5 pounds and has a wind load of approximately 0.8 square feet. This allows a high-gain EME array to be built with manageable wind load and weight. This same low wind load and weight lets the tropo operator add a high-performance 432-MHz array to an existing tower

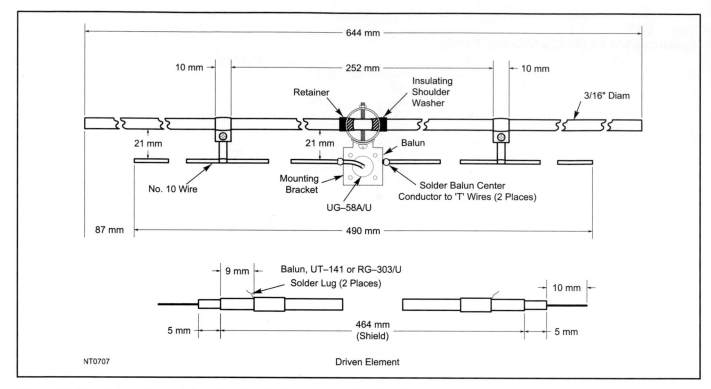

NT0707

Driven Element

Figure 15.41 — Driven-element detail for the 16-element 222-MHz Yagi. Lengths are given in millimeters to allow precise duplication.

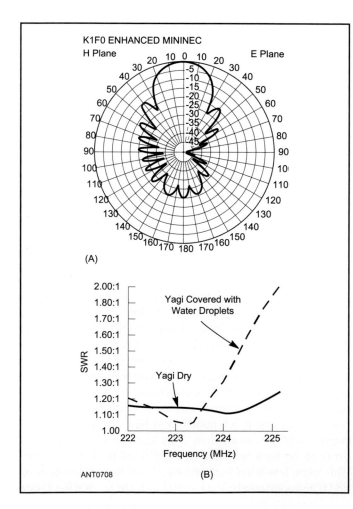

K1F0 ENHANCED MININEC

H Plane

E Plane

(A)

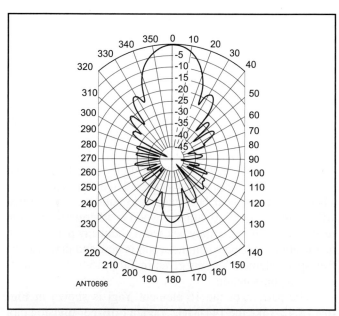

Yagi Covered with Water Droplets

Yagi Dry

ANT0708

(B)

ANT0696

Figure 15.42 — H- and E-plane patterns for the 16-element 222-MHz Yagi at A. The driven-element T-match dimensions were chosen for the best SWR compromise between wet and dry weather conditions. The SWR vs frequency curve shown at B demonstrates the broad frequency response of the Yagi design.

Figure 15.43 — Measured E-plane pattern for the 22-element Yagi. Note: This antenna pattern is drawn on a linear dB grid, rather than on the standard ARRL log-periodic grid, to emphasize low sidelobes.

Table 15-17
Specifications for 432-MHz Yagi Family

No. of Ele.	Boom Length (λ)	Gain (dBi)*	F/B Ratio (dB)	DE Impedance (Ω)	Beamwidth E/H (°)	Stacking E/H (inches)
15	3.4	15.67	21	23	30/32	53/49
16	3.8	16.05	19	23	29/31	55/51
17	4.2	16.45	20	27	28/30	56/53
18	4.6	16.8	25	32	27/29	58/55
19	4.9	17.1	25	30	26/28	61/57
20	5.3	17.4	21	24	25.5/27	62/59
21	5.7	17.65	20	22	25/26.5	63/60
22	6.1	17.9	22	25	24/26	65/62
23	6.5	18.15	27	30	23.5/25	67/64
24	6.9	18.35	29	29	23/24	69/66
25	7.3	18.55	23	25	22.5/23.5	71/68
26	7.7	18.8	22	22	22/23	73/70
27	8.1	19.0	22	21	21.5/22.5	75/72
28	8.5	19.20	25	25	21/22	77/75
29	8.9	19.4	25	25	20.5/21.5	79/77
30	9.3	19.55	26	27	20/21	80/78
31	9.7	19.7	24	25	19.6/20.5	81/79
32	10.2	19.8	23	22	19.3/20	82/80
33	10.6	19.9	23	23	19/19.5	83/81
34	11.0	20.05	25	22	18.8/19.2	84/82
35	11.4	20.2	27	25	18.5/19.0	85/83
36	11.8	20.3	27	26	18.3/18.8	86/84
37	12.2	20.4	26	26	18.1/18.6	87/85
38	12.7	20.5	25	25	18.9/18.4	88/86
39	13.1	20.6	25	23	18.7/18.2	89/87
40	13.5	20.8	26	21	17.5/18	90/88

*Gain is approximate real gain based on gain measurements made on six different-length Yagis.

without sacrificing antennas on other bands.

Table 15-17 lists the gain and stacking specifications for the various length Yagis. The basic Yagi dimensions are shown in **Table 15-18**. These are free-space element lengths for ³⁄₁₆-inch-diameter elements. Boom corrections for the element mounting method must be added

in. The element-length correction column gives the length that must be added to keep the Yagi's center frequency optimized for use at 432 MHz. This correction is required to use the same spacing pattern over a wide range of boom lengths. Although any length Yagi will work well, this design is at its best when made with 18 elements or more (4.6 λ). Element material of less than ³⁄₁₆-inch diameter is not recommended because resistive losses will reduce the gain by about 0.1 dB, and wet-weather performance will be worse.

Quarter-inch-diameter elements could be used if all elements are shortened by 3 mm. The element lengths are intended for use with a slight chamfer (0.5 mm) cut into the element ends. The gain peak of the array is centered at 437 MHz. This allows acceptable wet-weather performance, while reducing the gain at 432 MHz by only 0.05 dB.

The gain bandwidth of the 22-element Yagi is 31 MHz (at the –1 dB points). The SWR of the Yagi is less than 1.4:1 between 420 and 440 MHz. **Figure 15.44** is a network analyzer plot of the driven-element SWR vs frequency. These numbers indicate just how wide the frequency response of a log-taper Yagi can be, even with a simple dipole driven element. In fact, at one antenna gain contest, some ATV operators conducted gain vs frequency measurements from 420 to 440 MHz. The 22-element Yagi beat all entrants including those with so-called broadband feeds.

To peak the Yagi for use on 435 MHz (for satellite use), you may want to shorten all the elements by 2 mm. To peak it for use on 438 MHz (for ATV applications), shorten all elements by 4 mm. If you want to use the Yagi on FM between 440 MHz and 450 MHz, shorten all the elements by 10 mm. This will provide 17.6 dBi gain at 440 MHz, and 18.0 dBi gain at 450 MHz. The driven element may have to be adjusted if the element lengths are shortened.

Although this Yagi design is relatively broadband, it is suggested that close attention be paid to copying the design exactly as built. Metric dimensions are used because they are convenient for a Yagi sized for 432 MHz. Element holes should be drilled within ±2 mm. Element lengths should be kept within ±0.5 mm. Elements can be accurately constructed if they are first rough cut with a hack saw and then held in a vise and filed to the exact length.

The larger the array, the more attention you should pay to making all Yagis identical. Elements are mounted on shoulder insulators and run through the boom (see **Figure 15.45**). The element retainers are stainless-steel push nuts. These are made by several companies, including Industrial Retaining Ring Co (**www.truarc.com**) and Auveco Products (**www.auveco.**

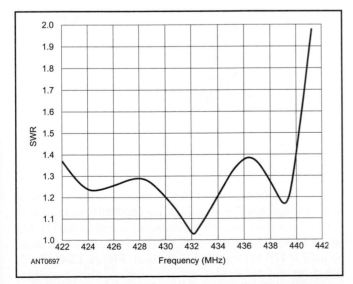

Figure 15.44 — SWR performance of the 22-element Yagi in dry weather.

Table 15-18
Free-Space Dimensions for 432-MHz Yagi Family
*Element correction is the amount to shorten or lengthen all elements when building a Yagi of that length.
Element lengths are for ³⁄₁₆-inch diameter material.

Ele. No.	Element Position (mm from reflector)	Element Length (mm)	Element Correction*
Refl	0	340	
DE	104	334	
D1	146	315	
D2	224	306	
D3	332	299	
D4	466	295	
D5	622	291	
D6	798	289	
D7	990	287	
D8	1196	285	
D9	1414	283	
D10	1642	281	−2
D11	1879	279	−2
D12	2122	278	−2
D13	2373	277	−2
D14	2629	276	−2
D15	2890	275	−1
D16	3154	274	−1
D17	3422	273	−1
D18	3693	272	0
D19	3967	271	0
D20	4242	270	0
D21	4520	269	0
D22	4798	269	0
D23	5079	268	0
D24	5360	268	+1
D25	5642	267	+1
D26	5925	267	+1
D27	6209	266	+1
D28	6494	266	+1
D29	6779	265	+2
D30	7064	265	+2
D31	7350	264	+2
D32	7636	264	+2
D33	7922	263	+2
D34	8209	263	+2
D35	8496	262	+2
D36	8783	262	+2
D37	9070	261	+3
D38	9359	261	+3

Figure 15.45 — Element-mounting detail. Elements are mounted through the boom using plastic insulators. Stainless steel push-nut retaining rings hold the element in place.

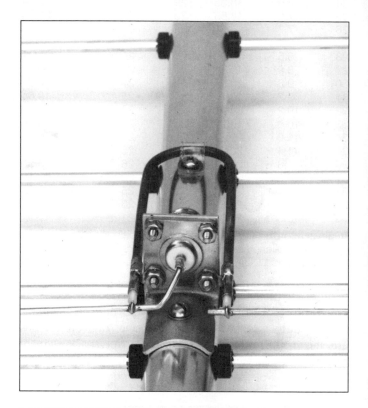

Figure 15.46 — Several views of the driven element and T match.

com). Local industrial hardware distributors can usually order them for you. The element insulators are not critical. Teflon or black polyethylene are probably the best materials. The Yagi in the photographs is made with black Delrin insulators. Suitable insulators and retainers ("keepers") are available from Directive Systems (**www.directive systems. com**).

The driven element uses a UG-58A/U connector mounted on a small bracket. The UG58A/U should be the type with the press-in center pin. UG-58s with center pins held in by "C"

clips will usually leak water. Some connectors use steel retaining clips, which will rust and leave a conductive stripe across the insulator. The T-match wires are supported by the UT-141 balun. RG-303/U or RG-142/U Teflon-insulated cable could be used if UT-141 cannot be obtained. **Figure 15.46** shows details of the driven-element construction. Driven element dimensions are given in **Figure 15.47**.

Dimensions for the 22-element Yagi are listed in

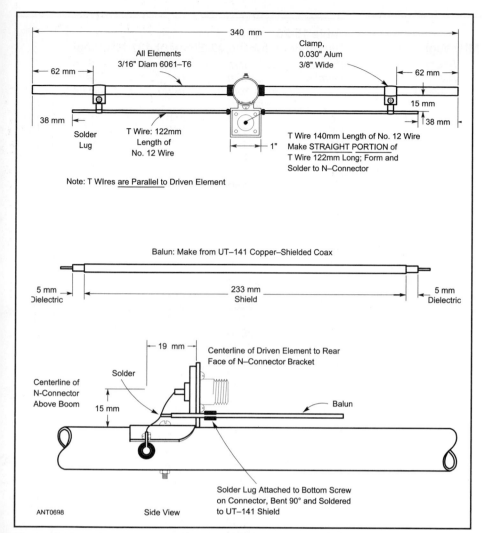

Figure 15.47 — Details of the driven element and T match for the 22-element Yagi. Lengths are given in millimeters to allow precise duplication of the antenna. See text.

Table 15-19. **Figure 15.48** details the Yagi's boom layout. Element material can be either $\frac{3}{16}$ inch 6061-T6 aluminum rod or hard aluminum welding rod.

A 24-foot-long, 10.6-λ, 33-element Yagi was also built. The construction method used were the same as for the 22-element Yagi. Telescoping round boom sections of 1, 1⅛, and 1¼ inches in diameter were used. A boom support is required to keep boom sag acceptable. At 432 MHz, if boom sag is much more than two or three inches, H-plane pattern distortion will occur. Greater amounts of boom sag will reduce the gain of a Yagi. **Table 15-20** lists the proper dimensions for the antenna when built with the previously given boom diameters. The boom layout is shown in **Figure 15.49**, and the driven element is described in **Figure 15.50**. The 33-element Yagi exhibits the same clean pattern traits as the 22-element Yagi (see **Figure 15.51**). Measured gain of the 33-element Yagi is 19.9 dBi at 432 MHz. A measured gain sweep of the 33-element Yagi gave a −1 dB gain bandwidth of 14 MHz with the −1 dB points at 424.5 MHz and 438.5 MHz.

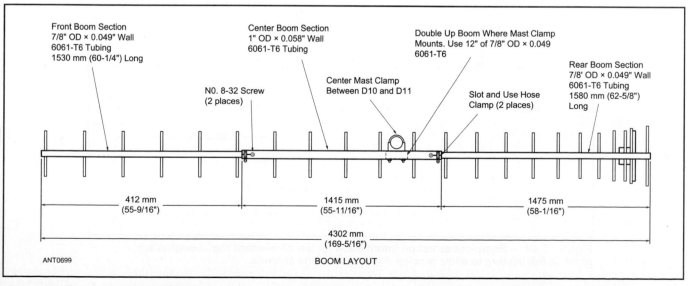

Figure 15.48 — Boom-construction information for the 22-element Yagi Lengths are given in millimeters to allow precise duplication of the antenna. See text.

Table 15-19
Dimensions for the 22-Element 432-MHz Yagi

Element Number	Element Position (mm from reflector)	Element Length (mm)	Boom Diam (inches)
Refl	30	346	
DE	134	340	
D1	176	321	
D2	254	311	7/8
D3	362	305	
D4	496	301	
D5	652	297	
D6	828	295	
D7	1020	293	
D8	1226	291	
D9	1444	289	
D10	1672	288	
D11	1909	286	
D12	2152	285	1
D13	2403	284	
D14	2659	283	
D15	2920	281	
D16	3184	280	
D17	3452	279	7/8
D18	3723	278	
D19	3997	277	
D20	4272	276	

Table 15-20
Dimensions for the 33-Element 432-MHz Yagi

Element Number	Element Position (mm from reflector)	Element Length (mm)	Boom Diam (inches)
Refl.	30	348	
DE	134	342	
D1	176	323	
D2	254	313	
D3	362	307	
D4	496	303	1
D5	652	299	
D6	828	297	
D7	1020	295	
D8	1226	293	
D9	1444	291	
D10	1672	290	
D11	1909	288	
D12	2152	287	1 1/8
D13	2403	286	
D14	2659	285	
D15	2920	284	
D16	3184	284	
D17	3452	283	
D18	3723	282	1 1/4
D19	3997	281	
D20	4272	280	
D21	4550	278	
D22	4828	278	
D23	5109	277	1 1/8
D24	5390	277	
D25	5672	276	
D26	5956	275	
D27	6239	274	
D28	6524	274	1
D29	6809	273	
D30	7094	273	
D31	7380	272	

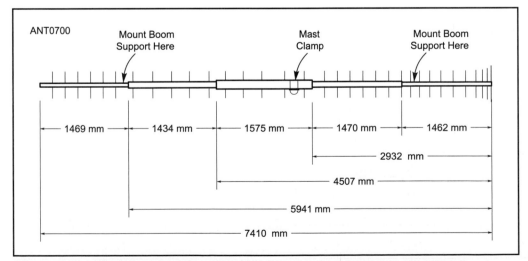

Figure 15.49 — Boom-construction information for the 33-element Yagi. Lengths are given in millimeters to allow precise duplication of the antenna.

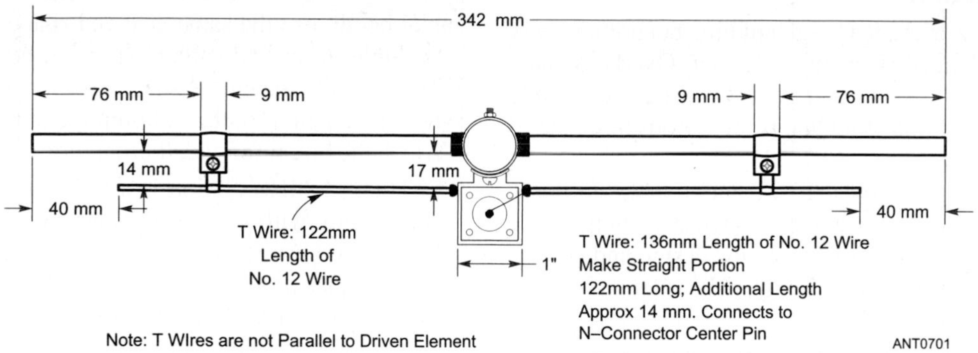

Figure 15.50 — Details of the driven element and T match for the 33-element Yagi. Lengths are given in millimeters to allow precise duplication of the antenna.

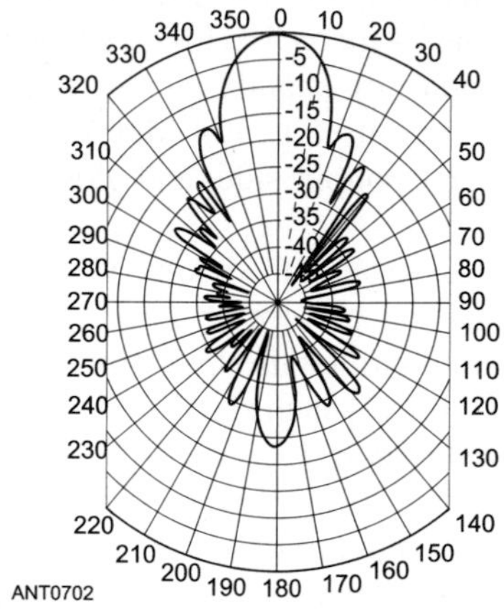

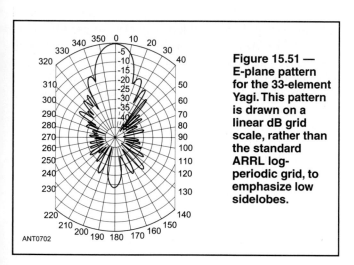

Figure 15.51 — E-plane pattern for the 33-element Yagi. This pattern is drawn on a linear dB grid scale, rather than the standard ARRL log-periodic grid, to emphasize low sidelobes.

15.3.6 QUAGI ANTENNAS

At higher frequencies, especially 420 MHz and above, Yagi arrays using dipole-driven elements can be difficult to feed and match, unless special care is taken to keep the feed point impedance relatively high by proper element spacing and tuning. The cubical quad described earlier overcomes the feed problems to some extent. When many parasitic elements are used, however, the loops are not nearly as convenient to assemble and tune as are straight cylindrical ones used in conventional Yagis. The *Quagi*, designed and popularized by Wayne Overbeck, N6NB, is an antenna having a full-wave loop driven element and reflector, and Yagi type straight rod directors. He first published information on this antenna in 1977. (See Bibliography.)

Table 15-21
Dimensions, Eight-Element Quagi

Element Lengths	*144.5 MHz*	*147 MHz*	*Frequency 222 MHz*	*432 MHz*	*446 MHz*
Reflector[1]	86⅝"	85"	56⅜"	28"	27⅛"
Driven[2]	82"	80"	53½"	26⅝"	25⅞"
Directors	35¹⁵⁄₁₆" to 35" in ³⁄₁₆" steps	35⁵⁄₁₆" to 34⅜" in ³⁄₁₆" steps	23⅜" to 23¾" in ⅛" steps	11¾" to 11⁷⁄₁₆" in ¹⁄₁₆" steps	11⅜" to 11¹⁄₁₆" in ¹⁄₁₆" steps
Spacing					
R-DE	21"	20½"	13⅝"	7"	6.8"
DE-D1	15¾"	15⅜"	10¼"	5¼"	5.1"
D1-D2	33"	32½"	21½"	11"	10.7"
D2-D3	17½"	17⅛"	11⅜"	5.85"	5.68"
D3-D4	26.1"	25⅝"	17"	8.73"	8.46"
D4-D5	26.1"	25⅝"	17"	8.73"	8.46"
D5-D6	26.1"	25⅝"	17"	8.73"	8.46"
Stacking Distance Between Bays					
	11'	10' 10"	7' 1½"	3'7"	3' 5 ⅝"

[1]All #12 AWG TW (electrical) wire, closed loops.
[2]All #12 AWG TW wire loops, fed at bottom.

Quagi Construction

There are a few tricks to Quagi building, but nothing very difficult or complicated is involved. In fact, Overbeck mass produced as many as 16 in one day. **Table 15-21** and **Table 15-22** give the dimensions for Quagis for various frequencies up to 446 MHz.

For the designs of Tables 15-21 and 15-22, the boom is *wood* or any other nonconductor (such as, fiberglass or Plexiglas). If a metal boom is used, a new design and new element lengths will be required. Many VHF antenna builders

---

Table 15-22
432-MHz, 15-Element, Long Boom Quagi Construction Data

Element Lengths (Inches)	Interelement Spacing (Inches)
R — 28	R-DE — 7
DE — 26⅝	DE-D1 — 5¼
D1 — 11¾	D1-D2 — 11
D2 — 11¹¹⁄₁₆	D2-D3 — 5⅞
D3 — 11⅝	D3-D4 — 8¾
D4 — 11⁹⁄₁₆	D4-D5 — 8¾
D5 — 11½	D5-D6 — 8¾
D6 — 11⁷⁄₁₆	D6-D7 — 12
D7 — 11⅜	D7-D8 — 12
D8 — 11⁵⁄₁₆	D8-D9 — 11¼
D9 — 11⁵⁄₁₆	D9-D10 — 11½
D10 — 11¼	D10-D11 — 9³⁄₁₆
D11 — 11³⁄₁₆	D11-D12 — 12⅜
D12 — 11⅛	D12-D13 — 13¾
D13 — 11¹⁄₁₆	

Boom: 1 × 2 inch × 12-ft Douglas fir, tapered to ⅝ inch at both ends.

Driven element: #12 AWG TW copper wire loop in square configuration, fed at bottom center with type N connector and 52-Ω coax.

Reflector: #12 AWG TW copper wire loop, closed at bottom.

Directors: ⅛ inch rod passing through boom.

Figure 15.52 — A close-up view of the feed method used on a 432-MHz Quagi. This arrangement produces a low SWR and gain in excess of 13 dBi with a 4-ft 10-inch boom! The same basic arrangement is used on lower frequencies, but wood may be substituted for the Plexiglas spreaders. The boom is ½-inch exterior plywood.

go wrong by failing to follow this rule: If the original uses a metal boom, use the same size and shape metal boom when you duplicate it. If it calls for a wood boom, use a nonconductor. Many amateurs dislike wood booms, but in a salt air environment they outlast aluminum (and surely cost less). Varnish the boom for added protection.

The 144-MHz version is usually built on a 14 foot, 1 × 3 inch boom, with the boom tapered to 1 inch at both ends. Clear pine is best because of its light weight, but construction grade Douglas fir works well. At 222 MHz the boom is under 10 feet long, and most builders use 1 × 2 or (preferably) ¾ × 1¼ inch pine molding stock. At 432 MHz, except for long-boom versions, the boom should be ½ inch thick or less. Most builders use strips of ½-inch exterior plywood for 432 MHz.

The quad elements are supported at the current maxima (the top and bottom, the latter beside the feed point) with Plexiglas or small strips of wood. See **Figure 15.52**. The quad elements are made of #12 AWG copper wire, commonly used in house wiring. Some builders may elect to use #10 AWG wire on 144 MHz and #14 AWG wire on 432 MHz, although this changes the resonant frequency slightly. Solder a type N connector (an SO-239 is often used at 144 MHz) at the midpoint of the driven element bottom side, and close the reflector loop.

The directors are mounted through the boom. They can be made of almost any metal rod or wire of about ⅛-inch diameter. Welding rod or aluminum clothesline wire works well if straight. (The designer uses ⅛-inch stainless-steel rod obtained from an aircraft surplus store.)

A TV type U bolt mounts the antenna on a mast. A single machine screw, washers and a nut are used to secure the spreaders to the boom so the antenna can be quickly "flattened" for travel. In permanent installations two screws are recommended.

Based on the experiences of Quagi builders, the following hints are offered. First, remember that at 432 MHz even a ⅛-inch measurement error results in performance deterioration. Cut the loops and elements as carefully as possible. No precision tools are needed, but accuracy is necessary. Also make sure to get the elements in the right order. The longest director goes closest to the driven element.

Finally, remember that a balanced antenna is being fed with an unbalanced line. Every balun the designer tried introduced more trouble in terms of losses than the feed imbalance caused. Some builders have tightly coiled several turns of the feed line near the feed point to limit line radiation. In any case, the feed line should be kept at right angles to the antenna. Run it from the driven element directly to the supporting mast and then up or down perpendicularly for best results.

A Quagi for 1296 MHz

This Quagi is designed for the 1296-MHz band, where good performance is extremely difficult to obtain from homemade conventional Yagis. **Figure 15.53** shows the construction and **Table 15-23** gives the design information for antennas with 10, 15 and 25 elements.

At 1296 MHz, even slight variations in design or building

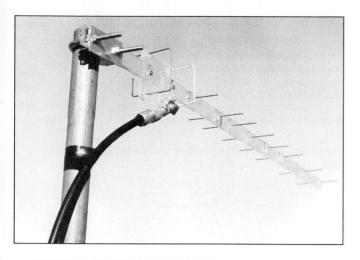

Figure 15.53 — A view of the 10-element version of the 1296-MHz Quagi. It is mounted on a 30-inch Plexiglas boom with a 3 × 3-inch square of Plexiglas to support the driven element and reflector. Note how the driven element is attached to a standard UG-290 BNC connector. The elements are held in place with silicone sealing compound.

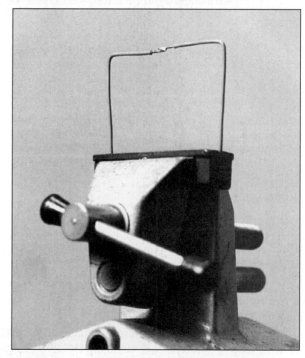

Figure 15.54 — These photos show the construction method used for the 1296-MHz quad type parasitic elements. The two ends of the #18 AWG bell wire are brought together with an overlap of ⅛ inch and soldered.

materials can cause substantial changes in performance. The 1296 MHz antennas described here work every time — but only if the same materials are used and the antennas are built *exactly* as described. This is not to discourage experimentation, but if modifications to these 1296-MHz antenna designs are contemplated, consider building one antenna as described here, so a reference is available against which variations can be compared.

The Quagis (and the cubical quad) are built on ¼-inch thick Plexiglas booms. The driven element and reflector (and also the directors in the case of the cubical quad) are made of insulated #18 AWG solid copper bell wire, available at hardware and electrical supply stores. Other types and sizes of wire work equally well, but the dimensions vary with the wire diameter. Even removing the insulation usually necessitates changing the loop lengths.

Quad loops are approximately square (**Figure 15.54**), although the shape is relatively uncritical. The element lengths,

Table 15-23
Dimensions, 1296-MHz Quagi Antennas

Note: All lengths are gross lengths. See text and photos for construction technique and recommended overlap at loop junctions. All loops are made of #18 AWG solid-covered copper bell wire. The Yagi type directors are $\frac{1}{16}$-inch brass brazing rod. See text for a discussion of director taper.

Feed: Direct with 52-Ω coaxial cable to UG-290 connector at driven element; run coax symmetrically to mast at rear of antenna.

Boom: 1¼-inch thick Plexiglas, 30 inches long for 10-element quad or Quagi and 48 inches long for 15-element Quagi; 84 inches. for 25-element Quagi.

10-Element Quagi for 1296 MHz

Element	Length (Inches)	Construction	Element	Interelement Spacing (inches)
Reflector	9.5625	Loop	R-DE	2.375
Driven	9.25	Loop	DE-D1	2.0
Director 1	3.91	Brass rod	D1-D2	3.67
Director 2	3.88	Brass rod	D2-D3	1.96
Director 3	3.86	Brass rod	D3-D4	2.92
Director 4	3.83	Brass rod	D4-D5	2.92
Director 5	3.80	Brass rod	D5-D6	2.92
Director 6	3.78	Brass rod	D6-D7	4.75
Director 7	3.75	Brass rod	D7-D8	3.94
Director 8	3.72	Brass rod		

15-Element Quagi for 1296 MHz

The first 10 elements are the same lengths as above, but the spacing from D6 to D7 is 4.0 inches; D7 to D8 is also 4.0 inches.

Director 9	3.70	D8-D9	3.75
Director 10	3.67	D9-D10	3.83
Director 11	3.64	D10-D11	3.06
Director 12	3.62	D11-D12	4.125
Director 13	3.59	D12-D13	4.58

25-Element Quagi for 1296 MHz

The first 15 elements use the same element lengths and spacings as the 15-element model. The additional directors are evenly spaced at 3.0-inch intervals and taper in length successively by 0.02 inch per element. Thus, D23 is 3.39 inches.

---

however, *are* critical. At 1296 MHz, variations of $\frac{1}{16}$ inch alter the performance measurably, and a $\frac{1}{8}$ inch departure can cost several decibels of gain. The loop lengths given are *gross* lengths. Cut the wire to these lengths and then solder the two ends together. There is a $\frac{1}{8}$-inch overlap where the two ends of the reflector (and director) loops are joined, as shown in Figure 15.54.

The driven element is the most important of all. The #18 AWG wire loop is soldered to a standard UG-290 chassis-mount BNC connector as shown in the photographs. This exact type of connector must be used to ensure uniformity in construction. Any substitution may alter the driven element electrical length. One end of the 9¼ inch driven loop is pushed as far as it can go into the center pin, and is soldered in that position. The loop is then shaped and threaded through small holes drilled in the Plexiglas support. Finally, the other end is fed into one of the four mounting holes on the BNC connector and soldered. In most cases, the best SWR is obtained if the end of the wire just passes through the hole so it is flush with the opposite side of the connector flange.

15.3.7 LOOP YAGIS

The loop Yagi fits into the quad family of antennas, as each element is a closed loop with a length of approximately 1 λ. Several versions are described, so the builder can choose the boom length and frequency coverage desired for the task at hand. Mike Walters, G3JVL, brought the original loop-Yagi design to the amateur community in the 1970s in the out-of-print RSGB *VHF/UHF Manual*. Since then, many versions have been developed with different loop and boom dimensions. G3JVL's *Loopquad* software is available online at **g3jvl.com/programPages/loopQuad.php** to design loop Yagis. Along with the 1296-MHz version described below construction articles for a 902-MHz and 2304-MHz are included on this book's CD-ROM.

A Loop Yagi for 1296 MHz

Described here are loop Yagis for the 1296-MHz band designed by Chip Angle, N6CA. Three sets of dimensions are given. Good performance can be expected if the dimensions are carefully followed. Check all dimensions before cutting or drilling anything. The 1296-MHz version is intended for weak-signal operation, while the 1270-MHz version is optimized for FM and mode L satellite operation. The 1283-MHz antenna provides acceptable performance from 1280 to 1300 MHz.

These antennas have been built on 6- and 12-foot booms. Results of gain tests at VHF conferences and by individuals around the country show the gain of the 6-foot model to be about 18 dBi, while the 12-foot version provides about 20.5 dBi. Swept measurements indicate that gain is about 2 dB down from maximum gain at ±30 MHz from the design frequency. The SWR, however, deteriorates within a few megahertz on the low side of the design center frequency.

The Boom

The dimensions given here apply only to a ¾-inch OD boom. If a different boom size is used, the dimensions must be scaled accordingly. Many hardware stores carry aluminum

tubing in 6- and 8-foot lengths, and that tubing is suitable for a short Yagi. If a 12-foot antenna is planned, find a piece of more rugged boom material, such as 6061-T6 grade aluminum. Do not use anodized tubing. The 12-foot antenna must have additional boom support to minimize boom sag. The 6-foot version can be rear mounted. For rear mounting, allow 4½ inches of boom behind the last reflector to eliminate SWR effects from the support.

The antenna is attached to the mast with a gusset plate. This plate mounts at the boom center. See **Figure 15.55**. Drill the plate mounting holes perpendicular to the element mounting holes (assuming the antenna polarization is to be horizontal).

Elements are mounted to the boom with no. 4-40 machine screws, so a series of no. 33 (0.113 inch) holes must be drilled along the center of the boom to accommodate this hardware. **Figure 15.56** shows the element spacings for different parts of the band. Dimensions should be followed as closely as possible.

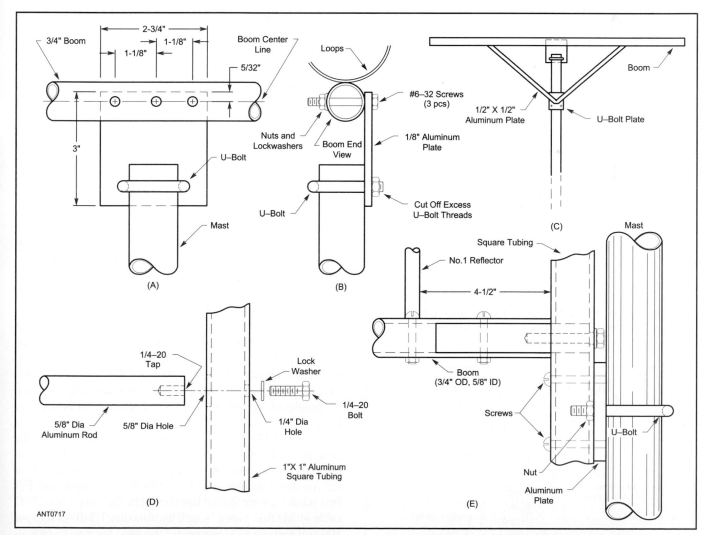

Figure 15.55 — Loop Yagi boom-to-mast plate details are given at A. At B, the mounting of the antenna to the mast is detailed. A boom support for long antennas is shown at C. The arrangement shown in D and E may be used to rear-mount antennas up to 6 or 7 ft long.

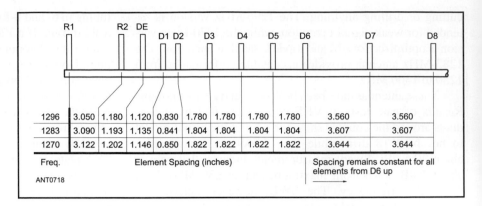

Figure 15.56 — Boom drilling dimensions. These dimensions must be carefully followed and the same materials used if performance is to be optimum. Element spacings are the same for all directors after D6 — use as many as necessary to fill the boom.

Freq.	R1–R2	R2–DE	DE–D1	D1–D2	D2–D3	D3–D4	D4–D5	D5–D6	D6–D7	D7–D8
1296	3.050	1.180	1.120	0.830	1.780	1.780	1.780	1.780	3.560	3.560
1283	3.090	1.193	1.135	0.841	1.804	1.804	1.804	1.804	3.607	3.607
1270	3.122	1.202	1.146	0.850	1.822	1.822	1.822	1.822	3.644	3.644

Freq. — Element Spacing (inches) — Spacing remains constant for all elements from D6 up

ANT0718

Parasitic Elements

The reflectors and directors are cut from 0.032-inch thick aluminum sheet and are ¼ inch wide. Figure 15.57 indicates the lengths for the various elements. These lengths apply only to elements cut from the specified material. For best results,

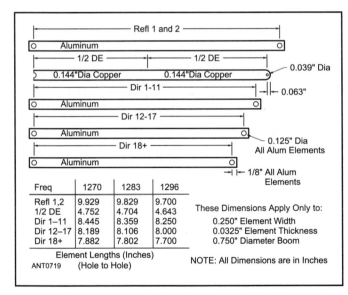

Freq	1270	1283	1296
Refl 1,2	9.929	9.829	9.700
1/2 DE	4.752	4.704	4.643
Dir 1–11	8.445	8.359	8.250
Dir 12–17	8.189	8.106	8.000
Dir 18+	7.882	7.802	7.700

Element Lengths (Inches)
(Hole to Hole)
ANT0719

These Dimensions Apply Only to:
0.250" Element Width
0.0325" Element Thickness
0.750" Diameter Boom

NOTE: All Dimensions are in Inches

Figure 15.57 — Parasitic elements for the loop Yagi are made from aluminum sheet, the driven element from copper sheet. The dimensions given are for ¼-inch wide by 0.0325-inch thick elements only. Lengths specified are hole to hole distances; the holes are located ⅛ inch from each element end.

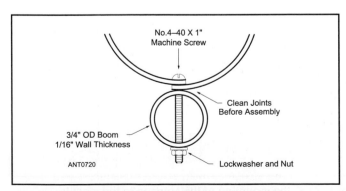

No.4–40 X 1" Machine Screw

Clean Joints Before Assembly

3/4" OD Boom 1/16" Wall Thickness

Lockwasher and Nut

ANT0720

Figure 15.58 — Element-to-boom mounting details.

the element strips should be cut with a shear. If the edges are left sharp, birds won't sit on the elements.

Drill the mounting holes as shown in Figure 15.57 after carefully marking their locations. After the holes are drilled, form each strap into a circle. This is easily done by wrapping the element around a round form. (A small juice can works well.)

Mount the loops to the boom with no. 4-40 × 1-inch machine screws, lock washers and nuts. See **Figure 15.58**. It is best to use only stainless steel or plated-brass hardware. Although the initial cost is higher than for ordinary plated-steel hardware, stainless or brass hardware will not rust and need replacement after a few years. Unless the antenna is painted, the hardware will definitely deteriorate.

Driven Element

The driven element is cut from 0.032-inch copper sheet and is ¼ inch wide. Drill three holes in the strap as detailed in Figure 15.56. Trim the ends as shown and form the strap into a loop similar to the other elements. This antenna is like a quad; if the loop is fed at the top or bottom, it is horizontally polarized.

Driven element mounting details are shown in **Figure 15.59**. A mounting fixture is made from a ¼-20 × 1¼ inch brass bolt. File the bolt head to a thickness of ⅛ inch. Bore a 0.144-inch (no. 27 drill) hole lengthwise through the center of the bolt. A piece of 0.141 inch semi-rigid hardline (UT-141 or equivalent) mounts through this hole and is soldered to the driven loop feed point. The point at which the UT-141 passes through the copper loop and brass mounting fixture should be left unsoldered at this time to allow for matching adjustments when the antenna is completed, although the range of adjustment is not very large.

The UT-141 can be any convenient length. Attach the connector of your choice (preferably type N). Use a short piece of low-loss RG-8 size cable (or ½-inch Hardline) for the run down the boom and mast to the main feed line. For best results, the main feed line should be the lowest loss 50-Ω cable obtainable. Good ⅞-inch hardline has 1.5 dB of loss per 100 feet and virtually eliminates the need for remote mounting of the transmit converter or amplifier.

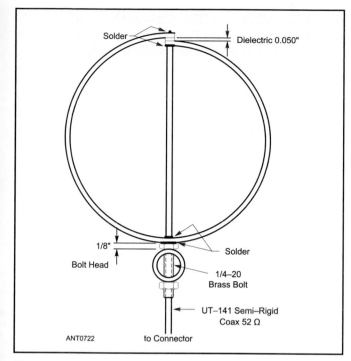

Figure 15.59 — Driven-element details. See Figure 15.57 and the text for additional information.

Tuning the Driven Element

If the antenna is built carefully to the dimensions given, the SWR should be close to 1:1. Just to be sure, check the SWR if you have access to test equipment. Be sure the signal source is clean, however; wattmeters respond to "dirty" signals and can give erroneous readings. If problems are encountered, recheck all dimensions. If they look good, a minor improvement may be realized by changing the shape of the driven element. Slight bending of reflector 2 may also improve the SWR. When the desired match has been obtained, solder the point where the UT-141 jacket passes through the loop and brass bolt.

15.3.8 QUADS FOR VHF

The quad antenna can be built with inexpensive materials, yet its performance is comparable to other arrays of its size. Adjustment for resonance and impedance matching can be accomplished readily.

Quads can be stacked horizontally and vertically to provide high gain, without sharply limiting frequency response. Quads can be mounted side by side or one above the other, or both, in the same general way as other beam antennas. Sets of driven elements can also be mounted in front of a screen reflector. The recommended spacing between adjacent element sides is ½ λ. Phasing and feed methods are similar to those employed with other antennas described in this chapter.

Parasitic elements ahead of the driven element work in a manner similar to those in a Yagi array. Closed loops can be used for directors by making them 5% shorter than the driven element. Spacings are similar to those for conventional Yagis. In an experimental model the reflector was spaced 0.25 λ and the director 0.15 λ. A square array using four 3-element bays worked extremely well.

Because of the small size of the quad at VHF and UHF, many of the mechanical issues associated with HF quads are no longer significant. PVC pipe, fiberglass rod, and wood are all acceptable materials for booms and spreaders.

Quad antennas are best suited for the 6 meter and 2 meter bands. They are very popular for portable and backpacking operation. A quad design for 144 MHz is presented below. See the **Portable Antennas** chapter for a 2-element, 6 meter quad design.

A 144-MHz 4-Element Quad

Element spacing for quad antennas found in the literature ranges from 0.14 λ to 0.25 λ. Factors such as the number of elements in the array and the parameters to be optimized (F/B ratio, forward gain, bandwidth, etc), determine the optimum element spacing within this range. The 4-element quad antenna described here was designed for portable use, so a compromise between these factors was chosen. This antenna, pictured in **Figure 15.60**, was designed and built by Philip D'Agostino, W1KSC.

Figure 15.60 — The 4-element 144-MHz portable quad, assembled and ready for operation. Sections of clothes closet poles joined with pine strips make up the mast. (W1MPO photo)

Based on several experimentally determined correction factors related to the frequency of operation and the wire size, optimum design dimensions were found to be as follows.

$$\text{Reflector length (ft)} = 1046.8/f_{MHz} \qquad \text{(Eq 1)}$$

$$\text{Driven element length (ft)} = 985.5/f_{MHz} \qquad \text{(Eq 2)}$$

$$\text{Directors (ft)} = 937.3/f_{MHz} \qquad \text{(Eq 3)}$$

Cutting the loops for 146 MHz provides satisfactory performance across the entire 144-MHz band.

Materials

The quad was designed for quick and easy assembly and disassembly, as illustrated in **Figure 15.61**. Wood (clear trim pine) was chosen as the principal building material because of its light weight, low cost and ready availability. Pine is used for the boom and element supporting arms. Round wood clothes closet poles comprise the mast material. Strips connecting the mast sections are made of heavier pine trim. Elements are made of #8 AWG aluminum wire. Plexiglas is used to support the feed point. **Table 15-24** lists the hardware and other parts needed to duplicate the quad.

Construction

The elements of the quad are assembled first. The mounting holes in the boom should be drilled to accommodate 1½ inch #8 hardware. Measure and mark the locations where the holes are to be drilled in the element spreaders, **Figure 15.62**. Drill the holes in the spreaders just large enough to accept the #8 AWG wire elements. It is important to drill all the holes straight so the elements line up when the antenna is assembled.

Construction of the wire elements is easiest if the directors are made first. A handy jig for bending the elements can be made from a piece of 2 × 3-inch wood cut to the side length of the directors. It is best to start with about 82 inches

of wire for each director. The excess can be cut off when the elements are completed. (The total length of each director is 77 inches.) Two bends should initially be made so the directors can be slipped into the spreaders before the remaining corners are bent. See **Figure 15.63**. Electrician's copper-wire clamps can be used to join the wires after the final bends are made, and they facilitate adjustment of element length. The reflector is made the same way as the directors, but the total length is 86 inches.

Table 15-24
Parts List for the 144 MHz 4-element Quad

Boom: ¾ × ¾ × 48-inch pine
Driven element support (spreader): ½ × ¾ × 21¼ inch pine
Driven element feed point strut: ½ × ¾ × 7½ inch pine
Reflector support (spreader): ½ × ¾ × 22½ inch pine
Director supports (spreaders): ½ × ¾ × 20¼ inch pine, 2 req'd
Mast brackets: ¾ × 1½ × 12 inch heavy pine trim, 4 req'd
Boom to mast bracket: ½ × 1⅝ × 5 inch pine
Element wire: Aluminum ground wire (Radio Shack no. 15-035)
Wire clamps: ¼ inch electrician's copper or zinc plated steel clamps, 3 req'd

Boom hardware:
 6 no. 8-32 × 1½ inch stainless steel machine screws
 6 no. 8-32 stainless steel wing nuts
 12 no. 8 stainless steel washers
Mast hardware:
 8 hex bolts, ¼-20 × 3½ inch
 8 hex nuts, ¼-20
 16 flat washers
Mast material: 1⁵⁄₁₆ inch × 6 ft wood clothes closet poles, 3 req'd
Feed point support plate: 3½ × 2½ inch Plexiglas sheet
Wood preparation materials: Sandpaper, clear polyurethane, wax
Feed line: 52-Ω RG-8 or RG-58 cable
Feed line terminals: Solder lugs for no. 8 or larger hardware, 2 req'd
Miscellaneous hardware: 4 small machine screws, nuts, washers; 2 flat-head wood screws

---

Figure 15.61 — **The complete portable quad, broken down for travel. Visible in the foreground is the driven element. The pine box in the background is a carrying case for equipment and accessories. A hole in the lid accepts the mast, so the box doubles as a base for a short mast during portable operation. (W1MPO photo)**

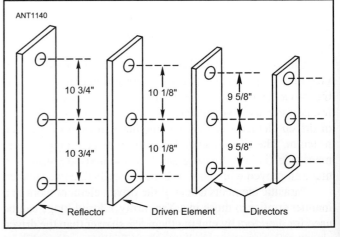

Figure 15.62 — Dimensions for the pine element spreaders for the 144-MHz 4-element quad.

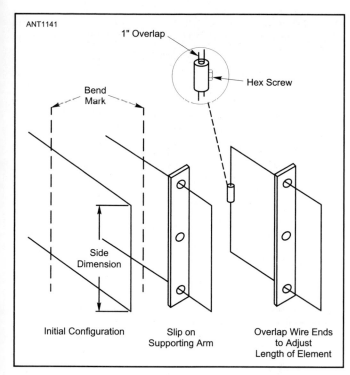

Figure 15.63 — Illustration showing how the aluminum element wires are bent. The adjustment clamp and its location are also shown.

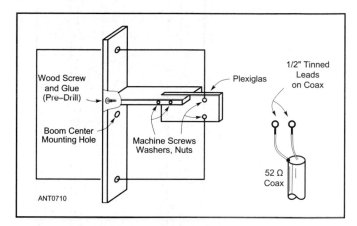

Figure 15.64 — Layout of the driven element of the 144-MHz quad. The leads of the coaxial cable should be stripped to ½ inch and solder lugs attached for easy connection and disconnection. See text regarding impedance at loop support points.

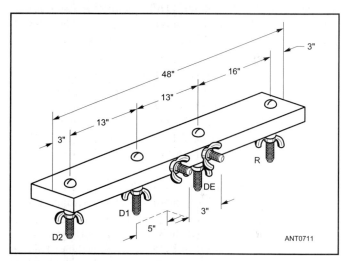

Figure 15.65 — Detail of the boom showing hole center locations and boom to mast connection points.

The driven element, total length 81 inches, requires special attention, as the feed attachment point needs to be adequately supported. An extra hole is drilled in the driven element spreader to support the feed point strut, as shown in **Figure 15.64**. A Plexiglas plate is used at the feed point to support the feed point hardware and the feed line. The feed point support strut should be epoxied to the spreader, and a wood screw used for extra mechanical strength.

For vertical polarization, locate the feed point in the center of one side of the driven element, as shown in Figure 15.64. Although this arrangement places the spreader supports at voltage maxima points on the four loop conductors, D'Agostino reports no adverse effects during operation. However, if the antenna is to be left exposed to the weather, the builder may wish to modify the design to provide support for the loops at current maxima points, such as shown in Figure 15.64. (The element of Figure 15.64 should be rotated 90° for horizontal polarization.)

Orient the driven element spreader so that it mounts properly on the boom when the antenna is assembled. Bend the driven element the same way as the reflector and directors, but do not leave any overlap at the feed point. The ends of the wires should be ¾ inch apart where they mount on the Plexiglas plate. Leave enough excess that small loops can be bent in the wire for attachment to the coaxial feed line with stainless steel hardware.

Drill the boom as shown in **Figure 15.65**. It is a good idea to use hardware with wing nuts to secure the element spreaders to the boom. After the boom is drilled, clean all the wood parts with denatured alcohol, sand them, and give them two coats of glossy polyurethane. After the polyurethane dries, wax all the wooden parts.

The boom to mast attachment is made next. Square the ends of a 6-foot section of clothes closet pole (a miter box is useful for this). Drill the center holes in both the boom attachment piece and one end of the mast section (**Figure 15.66**). Make certain that the mast hole is smaller than the flat-head screw to be used to ensure a snug fit. Accurately drill the holes for attachment to the boom as shown in Figure 15.66.

Countersink the hole for the flat-head screw to provide a smooth surface for attachment to the boom. Apply epoxy cement to the surfaces and screw the boom attachment piece securely to the mast section. One 6 foot mast is used for attachment to the other mast sections.

Two additional 6-foot mast sections are prepared next. This brings the total mast height to 18 feet. It is important to square the ends of each pole so the mast stands straight when assembled. Mast-section connectors are made of pine as shown in **Figure 15.67**. Using 3½ × ¼-inch hex bolts, washers and nuts, sections may be attached as needed, for a

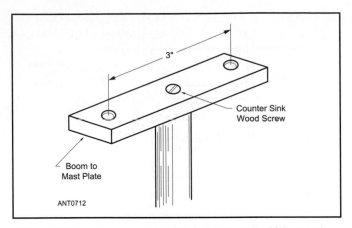

Figure 15.66 — Boom to mast plate for the 144-MHz quad. The screw hole in the center of the plate should be countersunk so the wood screw attaching it to the mast does not interfere with the fit of the boom.

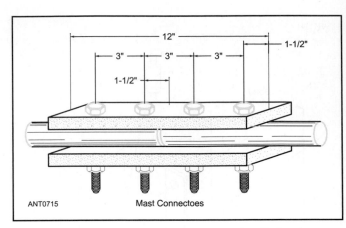

Figure 15.67 — Mast coupling connector details for the portable quad. The plates should be drilled two at a time to ensure the holes line up.

total height of 6, 12 or 18 feet. Drill the holes in two connectors at a time. This ensures good alignment of the holes. A drill press is ideal for this job, but with care a hand drill can be used if necessary.

Line up two mast sections end to end, being careful that they are perfectly straight. Use the predrilled connectors to maintain pole straightness, and drill through the poles, one at a time. If good alignment is maintained, a straight 18-foot mast section can be made. Label the connectors and poles immediately so they are always assembled in the same order.

When assembling the antenna, install all the elements on the boom before attaching the feed line. Connect the coax to the screw connections on the driven element support plate and run the cable along the strut to the boom. From there, the cable should be routed directly to the mast and down. Assemble the mast sections to the desired height. The antenna provides good performance, and has a reasonable SWR curve over the entire 144 MHz band (**Figure 15.68**).

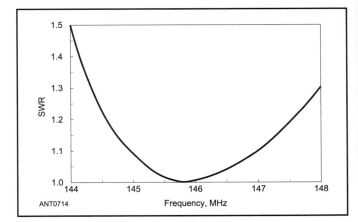

Figure 15.68 — Typical SWR curve for the 144-MHz portable quad. The large wire diameter and the quad design provide excellent bandwidth.

15.4. LOG-PERIODIC AND DISCONE ANTENNAS

Log-periodic antennas designed for use on single VHF or UHF bands have largely been displaced by Yagi designs that can be used across an entire band. The shorter wavelengths at VHF and above make "heavily filled" designs practical that can cover wide frequency ranges. (The design of log-periodic antennas was presented in the **Log-Periodic Dipole Arrays** chapter. See also the short article "V-Shaped Elements versus Straight Elements" by K4ERO on this book's CD-ROM.)

Operation on several bands with a single antenna makes the log-periodic antenna a popular choice for the amateur with limited antenna options. An example of such a design is the Tennadyne T-28 shown in **Figure 15.69**. This antenna covers 50 to 1300 MHz with a boom length of only 12 feet.

Figure 15.69 — The Tennadyne T-28 covers 50-1300 MHz with boom length of 12 feet.

Yes, That's a TV Antenna!

If you have noticed the similarities between TV-receive antennas and the log-periodic antennas that cover the amateur VHF and lower UHF bands, you are not alone! In an article included on this book's CD-ROM, John Stanley, K4ERO, shows how to modify a mid-sized log-periodic originally designed for receiving TV broadcasts into a stealthy, yet effective ham antenna covering 50 through 222 MHz. For hams limited to TV-antennas only, this might be a good solution to getting on at least a few of the ham bands and you can answer truthfully when asked about your new "TV antenna"!

In addition, the antenna looks very much like a TV-receive antenna, attracting much less attention than a stack of mono-band Yagis for the same frequency range!

Two VHF log-periodic designs are presented by reprints of *QST* articles included on this book's CD-ROM. The first is a single-band design covering 2 meters, "An LPDA for 2 Meter Plus," by L.B. Cebik, W4RNL (SK). The antenna, described in **Figure 15.70**, covers 130-170 MHz and can be used for listening to air band and public safety channels along with transmit and receive operation across 2 meters.

The second design is a three-band log-periodic covering the 144, 222, and 432 MHz bands, "A Three-Band Log-Periodic Antenna," by Robert Heslin, K7RTY, from

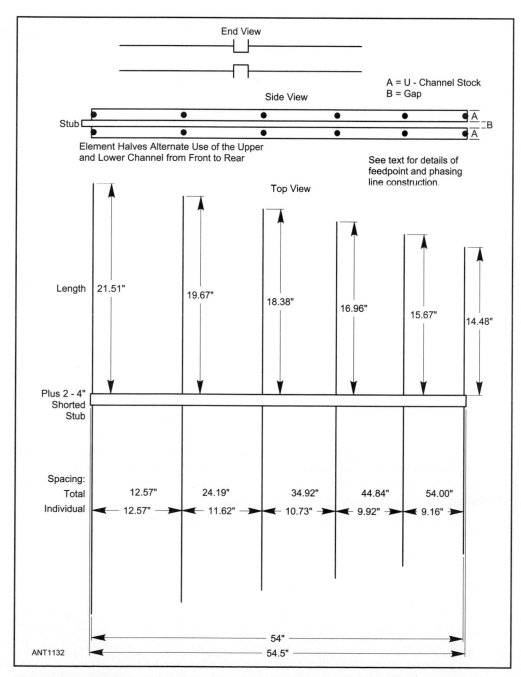

Figure 15.70 — Outline and sketch of the dimensions for the 2 meter Plus log-periodic antenna covering 130 to 170 MHz.

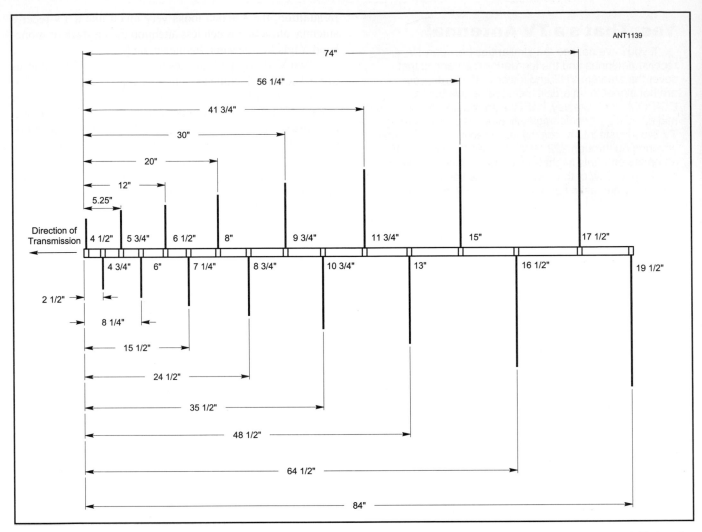

Figure 15.71 — Outline and sketch of the dimensions for the log-periodic antenna covering the 144, 222, and 432 MHz bands.

June 1963 *QST*. This antenna is shown in **Figure 15.71**. The design is based on the same principles used today and the antenna is similar to that of commercial models covering the same frequency range.

The wideband discone antenna is a very popular omnidirectional antenna for scanner use at VHF and above with numerous commercial models available. (Discone design is discussed in the **Multiband Antennas** chapter.) Discones for VHF and UHF coverage are fairly simple to build, such as the design shown in **Figure 15.72** from the May 2003 *QST* article, "A VHF/UHF Discone Antenna," by Bob Patterson, K5DZE. The antenna is constructed from wire-mesh hardware cloth but sheet metal or heavy screen can be used. As the author mentions in the article, even aluminum foil on cardboard worked fine as an indoor receive antenna!

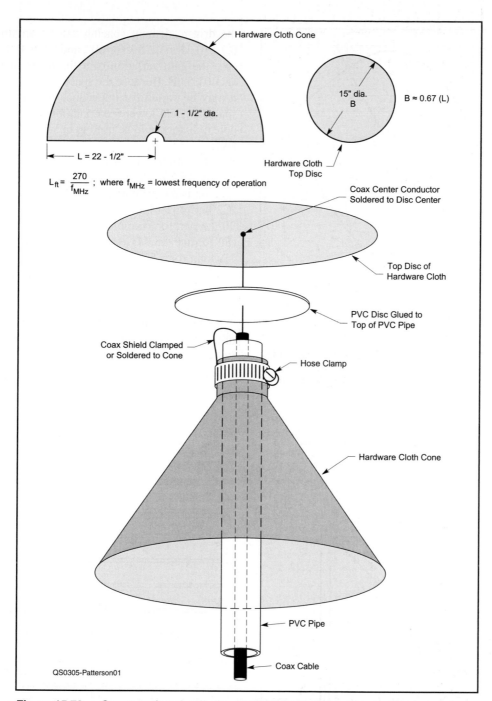

Figure 15.72 — Construction details for a VHF/UHF discone antenna. The largest dimension of the discone is determined by the lowest frequency of use.

Within the figure:

Hardware Cloth Cone

1 - 1/2" dia.

L = 22 - 1/2"

$L_{ft} = \dfrac{270}{f_{MHz}}$; where f_{MHz} = lowest frequency of operation

15" dia. B

$B \approx 0.67$ (L)

Hardware Cloth Top Disc

Coax Center Conductor Soldered to Disc Center

Top Disc of Hardware Cloth

PVC Disc Glued to Top of PVC Pipe

Coax Shield Clamped or Soldered to Cone

Hose Clamp

Hardware Cloth Cone

PVC Pipe

Coax Cable

QS0305-Patterson01

15.5 REFLECTOR ANTENNAS

When a single driven element is used, the reflector screen may be bent to form an angle, giving an improvement in the radiation pattern and gain. At 222 and 420 MHz its size assumes practical proportions, and at 902 MHz and higher, practical reflectors can approach ideal dimensions (very large in terms of wavelengths), resulting in more gain and sharper patterns. The corner can be used at 144 MHz, though usually at much less than optimum size. For a given aperture, the reflector does not equal a parabola in gain, but it is simple to construct, broadband, and offers gains from about 9 to 14 dBi, depending on the angle and size. This section was written by Paul M. Wilson, W4HHK (SK).

15.5.1 CORNER REFLECTORS

The corner angle can be 90, 60 or 45°, but the side length must be increased as the angle is narrowed. For a 90° corner,

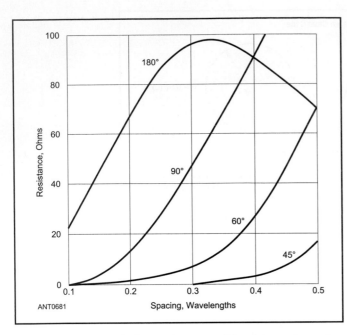

Figure 15.73 — Radiation resistance of the driven element in a corner reflector array for corner angles of 180° (flat sheet), 90°, 60° and 45° as a function of spacing D, as shown in Figure 15.74.

the driven element spacing can be anything from 0.25 to 0.7 λ, 0.35 to 0.75 λ for 60°, and 0.5 to 0.8 λ for 45°. In each case the gain variation over the range of spacings given is about 1.5 dB. Because the spacing is not very critical to gain, it may be varied for impedance-matching purposes. Closer spacings yield lower feed point impedances, but a folded dipole radiator could be used to raise this to a more convenient level.

Radiation resistance is shown as a function of spacing in **Figure 15.73**. The maximum gain obtained with minimum spacing is the primary mode (the one generally used at 144, 222 and 432 MHz to maintain reasonable side lengths). A 90° corner, for example, should have a minimum side length (S, **Figure 15.74**) equal to twice the dipole spacing, or 1 λ long for 0.5-λ spacing. A side length greater than 2 λ is ideal. Gain with a 60° or 90° corner reflector with 1-λ sides is about 10 dB. A 60° corner with 2-λ sides has about 13 dBi gain, and a 45° corner with 3-λ sides has about 14 dBi gain.

Reflector length (L, Figure 15.74) should be a minimum of 0.6 λ. Less than that spacing causes radiation to increase to the sides and rear, and decreases gain.

Spacing between reflector rods (G, Figure 15.74) should not exceed 0.06 λ for best results. A spacing of 0.06 λ results

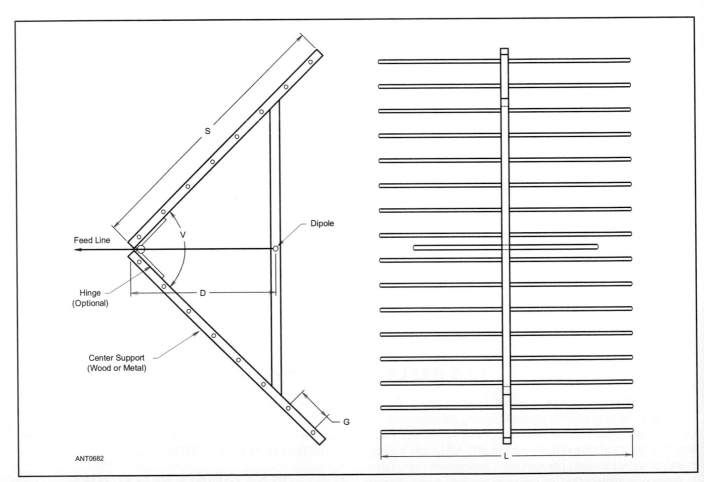

Figure 15.74 — Construction of a corner reflector array. The frame can be wood or metal. Reflector elements are stiff wire or tubing. Dimensions for several bands are given in Table 15-25. Reflector element spacing, G, is the maximum that should be used for the frequency; closer spacings are optional. The hinge permits folding for portable use.

Table 15-25
Dimensions of Corner Reflector Arrays for VHF and UHF

Freq (MHz)	Side Length, S (inches)	Dipole to Vertex, D (inches)	Reflector Length, L (inches)	Reflector Spacing, G (inches)	Corner Angle, Vo	Radiation Resistance (Ω)
144*	65	27½	48	7¾	90	70
144	80	40	48	4	90	150
222*	42	18	30	5	90	70
222	52	25	30	3	90	150
222	100	25	30	Screen	60	70
420	27	8¾	16¼	2⅝	90	70
420	54	13½	16¼	Screen	60	70
915	20	6½	25¾	0.65	90	70
915	51	16¾	25¾	Screen	60	65
915	78	25¾	25¾	Screen	45	70
1296	18	4½	27½	½	90	70
1296	48	11¾	27½	Screen	60	65
1296	72	18¼	27½	Screen	45	70
2304	15½	2½	20½	¼	90	70
2304	40	6¾	20½	Screen	60	65
2304	61	10¼	20½	Screen	45	70

*Side length and number of reflector elements somewhat below optimum — slight reduction in gain.

Notes:

915 MHz
Wavelength is 12.9 inches
Side length S is 3 × D, dipole
 to vertex distance
Reflector length L is 2.0 λ
Reflector spacing G is 0.05 λ

1296 MHz
Wavelength is 9.11 inches
Side length S is 4 × D, dipole
 to vertex distance
Reflector length L is 3.0 λ
Reflector spacing G is 0.05 λ

2304 MHz
Wavelength is 5.12 inches
Side length S is 6 × D, dipole
 to vertex distance
Reflector length L is 4.0 λ
Reflector spacing G is 0.05 λ

in a rear lobe that is about 6% of the forward lobe (down 12 dB). A small mesh screen or solid sheet is preferable at the higher frequencies to obtain maximum efficiency and highest F/B ratio, and to simplify construction. A spacing of 0.06 λ at 1296 MHz, for example, requires mounting reflector rods about every ½ inch along the sides. Rods or spines may be used to reduce wind loading. The support used for mounting the reflector rods may be of insulating or conductive material. Rods or mesh weave should be parallel to the radiator.

A suggested arrangement for a corner reflector is shown in Figure 15.74. The frame may be made of wood or metal, with a hinge at the corner to facilitate portable operation or assembly atop a tower. A hinged corner is also useful in experimenting with different angles. **Table 15-25** gives the

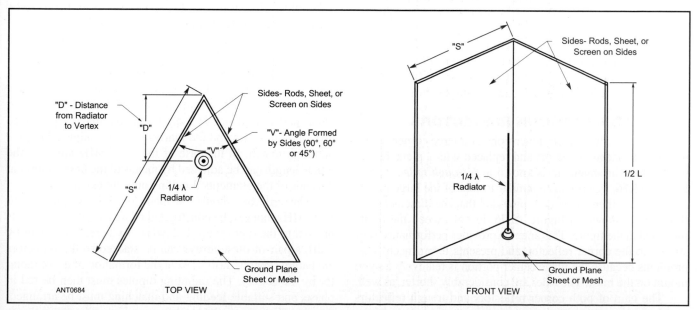

Figure 15.75 — A ground-plane corner reflector antenna for vertical polarization, such as FM communications or packet radio. The dimension ½ L in the front view refers to data in Table 15-25.

principal dimensions for corner reflector arrays for 144 to 2300 MHz. The arrays for 144, 222 and 420 MHz have side lengths of twice to four times the driven element spacing. The 915 MHz corner reflectors use side lengths of three times the element spacing, 1296 MHz corners use side lengths of four times the spacing, and 2304 MHz corners employ side lengths of six times the spacing. Reflector lengths of 2, 3, and 4 wavelengths are used on the 915, 1296 and 2304 MHz reflectors, respectively. A $4 \times 6\ \lambda$ reflector closely approximates a sheet of infinite dimensions.

A corner reflector may be used for several bands, or for UHF television reception, as well as amateur UHF operation. For operation on more than one frequency, side length and reflector length should be selected for the lowest frequency, and reflector spacing for the highest frequency. The type of driven element plays a part in determining bandwidth, as does the spacing to the corner. A fat cylindrical element (small λ/dia ratio) or triangular dipole (bow tie) gives more bandwidth than a thin driven element. Wider spacings between driven element and corner give greater bandwidths. A small increase in gain can be obtained for any corner reflector by mounting collinear elements in a reflector of sufficient size, but the simple feed of a dipole is lost if more than two elements are used.

A dipole radiator is usually employed with a corner reflector. This requires a balun between the coaxial line and the balanced feed point impedance of the antenna. Baluns are easily constructed of coaxial line on the lower VHF bands, but become more difficult at the higher frequencies. This problem may be overcome by using a ground-plane corner reflector, which can be used for vertical polarization. A ground-plane corner with monopole driven element is shown in **Figure 15.75**. The corner reflector and a ¼ λ radiator are mounted on the ground plane, permitting direct connection to a coaxial line if the proper spacing is used. The effective aperture is reduced, but at the higher frequencies, second- or third-mode radiator spacing and larger reflectors can be employed to obtain more gain and offset the loss in effective aperture. A J antenna could be used to maintain the aperture area and provide a match to a coaxial line.

For vertical polarization operation, four 90° corner reflectors built back-to-back (with common reflectors) could be used for scanning 360° of horizon with modest gain. Feed line switching could be used to select the desired sector.

15.5.2 TROUGH REFLECTORS

To reduce the overall dimensions of a large corner reflector the vertex can be cut off and replaced with a plane reflector. Such an arrangement is known as a *trough reflector*. See **Figure 15.76**. Performance similar to that of the large corner reflector can thereby be had, provided that the dimensions of S and T as shown in Figure 15.76 do not exceed the limits indicated in the figure. This antenna provides performance very similar to the corner reflector, and presents fewer mechanical problems because the plane center portion is relatively easy to mount on the mast. The sides are considerably shorter, as well.

The gain of both corner reflectors and trough reflectors may be increased by stacking two or more and arranging them to radiate in phase, or alternatively by adding further collinear

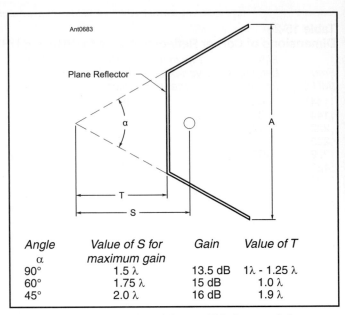

Angle α	Value of S for maximum gain	Gain	Value of T
90°	1.5 λ	13.5 dB	1λ - 1.25 λ
60°	1.75 λ	15 dB	1.0 λ
45°	2.0 λ	16 dB	1.9 λ

Figure 15.76 — The trough reflector. This is a useful modification of the corner reflector. The vertex has been cut off and replaced by a simple plane section. The tabulated data shows the gain obtainable for greater values of S than those covered in Table 15-25, assuming that the reflector is of adequate size.

dipoles (fed in phase) within a wider reflector. Not more than two or three radiating units should be used, because the great virtue of the simple feeder arrangement would then be lost.

Trough Reflectors for 432 and 1296 MHz

Dimensions are given in **Figure 15.77** for 432- and 1296-MHz trough reflectors. The gain to be expected is 16 dBi and 15 dBi, respectively. A very convenient arrangement, especially for portable operation, is to use a metal hinge at each angle of the reflector. This permits the reflector to be folded flat for transit. It also permits experiments to be carried out with different apex angles.

A housing is required at the dipole center to prevent the entry of moisture and, in the case of the 432-MHz antenna, to support the dipole elements. The dipole may be moved in and out of the reflector to get either minimum SWR or, if this cannot be measured, maximum gain. If a two-stub tuner or other matching device is used, the dipole may be placed to give optimum gain and the matching device adjusted to give optimum match. In the case of the 1296-MHz antenna, the dipole length can be adjusted by means of the brass screws at the ends of the elements. Locking nuts are essential.

The reflector should be made of sheet aluminum for 1296 MHz, but can be constructed of wire mesh (with twists parallel to the dipole) for 432 MHz. To increase the gain by 3 dB, a pair of these arrays can be stacked so the reflectors are barely separated (to prevent the formation of a slot radiator by the edges). The radiating dipoles must then be fed in phase, and suitable feeding and matching must be arranged. A two-stub tuner can be used for matching either a single- or double-reflector system.

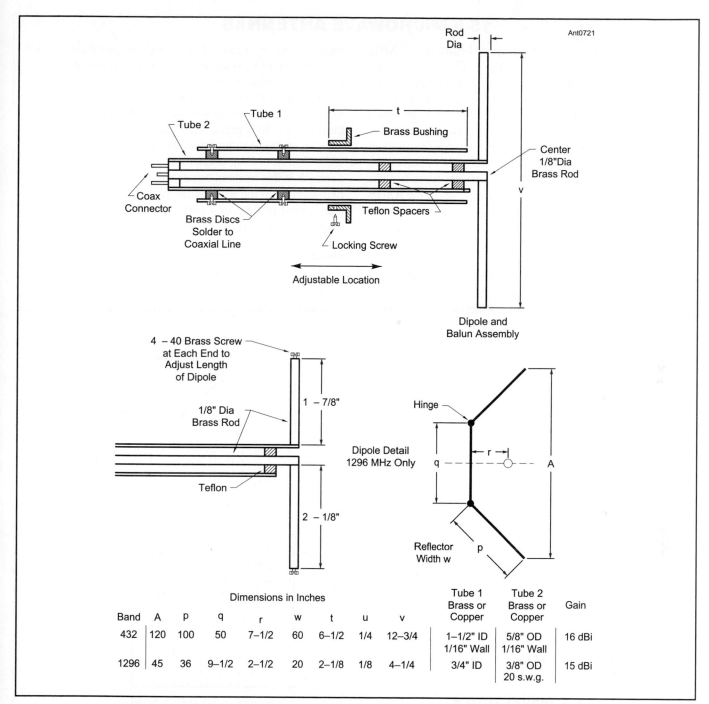

Dimensions in Inches

Band	A	p	q	r	w	t	u	v	Tube 1 Brass or Copper	Tube 2 Brass or Copper	Gain
432	120	100	50	7–1/2	60	6–1/2	1/4	12–3/4	1–1/2" ID 1/16" Wall	5/8" OD 1/16" Wall	16 dBi
1296	45	36	9–1/2	2–1/2	20	2–1/8	1/8	4–1/4	3/4" ID	3/8" OD 20 s.w.g.	15 dBi

Figure 15.77 — Practical construction information for trough reflector antennas for 432 and 1296 MHz.

15.6 MICROWAVE ANTENNAS

The domain of amateur microwaves begins at 902 MHz and includes all higher frequency bands. (The 10 GHz and higher bands are also referred to as mm-wave bands.) The short wavelength of microwaves enables a wide range of interesting designs quite different from the antennas based on discrete linear and loop elements popular at lower frequencies. At microwaves, surfaces and shapes are used in ways that are impractical at longer wavelengths. This section surveys several common microwave antenna types but the interested reader is encouraged to obtain copies of the RSGB texts listed in the Bibliography for a more complete treatment of amateur microwave antennas.

A caveat for the amateur interested in microwaves — many antenna construction practices that are common on lower frequencies cannot be used at microwave frequencies. This is the most important reason why all who venture to microwaves are not equally successful. When a proven antenna design is used, copy it exactly; don't change *anything*.

Do not allow the mast to pass through the elements, as is common on antennas for lower frequencies. Avoid any unnecessary metal around the antenna: ¼ λ at 1296 MHz is only a little over 2 inches. Cut all U-bolts and mounting hardware to the minimum length needed so that no resonant or near-resonant conductors are present to couple to the antenna's field.

After antenna performance, feed line loss is the next most important aspect of antenna system design. Mount the antennas to keep feed line losses to an absolute minimum. Antenna height is less important than keeping the line losses low.

Use the best feed line you can get. As an example of why this is important, here are some realistic measurements of common coaxial cables at 1296 MHz (loss per 100 feet):

RG-8, 213, 214 coaxial cable: 11 dB
½ inch foam/copper hardline: 4 dB
⅞ inch foam/copper hardline: 1.5 dB

Preamps should be mounted at the antenna wherever practical and only connectors designed for frequency of operation should be used.

15.6.1 WAVEGUIDES

Above 2 GHz, coaxial cable is a losing proposition for communications operation. Fortunately, at this frequency the wavelength is short enough to allow practical, efficient energy transfer by an entirely different means. A *waveguide* is a conducting tube through which energy is transmitted in the form of electromagnetic waves. The tube is not considered as carrying a current in the same sense that the wires of a two-conductor line do, but rather as a *boundary* that confines the waves in the enclosed space. Skin effect prevents any electromagnetic effects from being evident outside the guide. The energy is injected at one end, either through capacitive or inductive coupling or by radiation, and is removed from the other end in a like manner. Waveguide merely confines the energy of the fields, which are propagated through it to the receiving end by means of reflections against its inner walls.

Analysis of waveguide operation is based on the assumption that the guide material is a perfect conductor of electricity. Typical distributions of electric and magnetic fields in a rectangular guide are shown in **Figure 15.78**. The intensity of the electric field is greatest (as indicated by closer spacing of the lines of force) at the center along the X dimension (Figure 15.78C), diminishing to zero at the end walls. The fields must diminish in this manner, because the existence of any electric field parallel to the walls at the surface would cause an infinite current to flow in a perfect conductor. Waveguides, of course, cannot carry RF in this fashion.

Modes of Propagation

Figure 15.78 represents the most basic distribution of the electric and magnetic fields in a waveguide. There are an infinite number of ways in which the fields can arrange

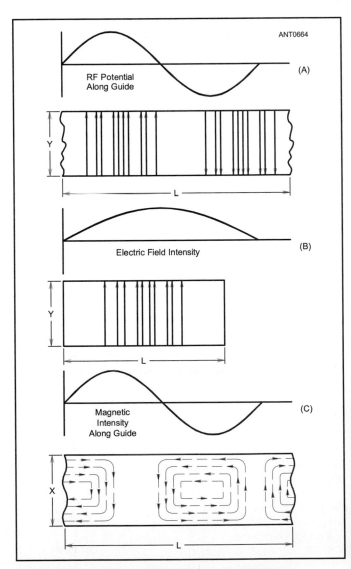

Figure 15.78 — Field distribution in a rectangular waveguide. The TE10 mode of propagation is depicted.

themselves in a waveguide (for frequencies above the low cutoff frequency of the guide in use). Each of these field configurations is called a *mode*.

The modes may be separated into two general groups. One group, designated *TM* (transverse magnetic), has the magnetic field entirely transverse to the direction of propagation, but has a component of the electric field in that direction. The other type, designated *TE* (transverse electric) has the electric field entirely transverse, but has a component of magnetic field in the direction of propagation. TM waves are sometimes called *E waves*, and TE waves are sometimes called *H waves*, but the TM and TE designations are preferred.

The mode of propagation is identified by the group letters followed by two subscript numerals. For example, TE_{10}, TM_{11}, etc. The number of possible modes increases with frequency for a given size of guide, and there is only one possible mode (called the *dominant mode*) for the lowest frequency that can be transmitted. The dominant mode is the one generally used in amateur operation.

Waveguide Dimensions

In a rectangular guide the critical dimension is X in Figure 15.78. This dimension must be more than $\frac{1}{2}\lambda$ at the lowest frequency to be transmitted. In practice, the Y dimension usually is made about equal to $\frac{1}{2}$ X to avoid the possibility of operation in other than the dominant mode.

Cross-sectional shapes other than a rectangle can be used, the most important being the circular pipe. Much the same considerations apply as in the rectangular case.

Wavelength dimensions for rectangular and circular guides are given in **Table 15-26**, where X is the width of a rectangular guide and r is the radius of a circular guide. All figures apply to the dominant mode.

Coupling to Waveguides

Energy may be introduced into or extracted from a waveguide or resonator by means of either the electric or magnetic field. The energy transfer frequently is through a coaxial line. Two methods for coupling to coaxial line are shown in **Figure 15.79**. The probe shown at A is simply a short extension of the inner conductor of the coaxial line, oriented so that it is parallel to the electric lines of force. The loop shown at B is arranged so that it encloses some of the magnetic lines of force. The point at which maximum coupling is obtained depends upon the mode of propagation in the guide or cavity.

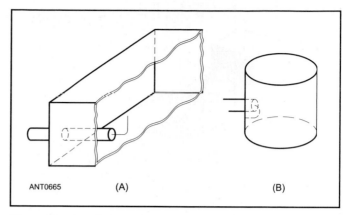

Figure 15.79 — Coupling coaxial line to waveguide and resonators.

Coupling is maximum when the coupling device is in the most intense field.

Coupling can be varied by turning the probe or loop through a 90° angle. When the probe is perpendicular to the electric lines the coupling is minimum. Similarly, when the plane of the loop is parallel to the magnetic lines the coupling is minimum.

If a waveguide is left open at one end it will radiate energy. This radiation can be greatly enhanced by flaring the waveguide to form a pyramidal horn antenna. The horn acts as a transition between the confines of the waveguide and free space. To effect the proper impedance transformation the horn must be at least $\frac{1}{2}\lambda$ on a side. A horn of this dimension (cutoff) has a unidirectional radiation pattern with a null toward the waveguide transition. The gain at the cutoff frequency is 3 dB, increasing 6 dB with each doubling of frequency. Horns are used extensively in microwave operation, both as primary radiators and as feed elements for more elaborate focusing systems. Details for constructing 10-GHz horn antennas are given later in this chapter.

Evolution of a Waveguide

Suppose an open-wire line is used to carry RF energy from a generator to a load. If the line has any appreciable length it must be mechanically supported. The line must be well insulated from the supports if high losses are to be avoided. Because high-quality insulators are difficult to construct at microwave frequencies, the logical alternative is to support the transmission line with $\frac{1}{4}\lambda$ stubs, shorted at the end opposite the feed line. The open end of such a stub presents an infinite impedance to the transmission line, provided the shorted stub is nonreactive. However, the shorting link has a finite length, and therefore some inductance. The effect of this inductance can be removed by making the RF current flow on the surface of a plate rather than a thin wire. If the plate is large enough, it will prevent the magnetic lines of force from encircling the RF current.

An infinite number of these $\frac{1}{4}\lambda$ stubs may be connected in parallel without affecting the standing waves of voltage

Table 15-26
Waveguide Dimensions

	Rectangular	Circular
Cutoff wavelength	2X	3.41r
Longest wavelength transmitted with little attenuation	1.6X	3.2r
Shortest wavelength before next mode becomes possible	1.1X	2.8r

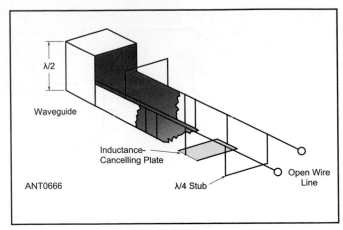

Figure 15.80 — At its cutoff frequency a rectangular waveguide can be thought of as a parallel two-conductor transmission line supported from top and bottom by an infinite number of ¼-λ stubs.

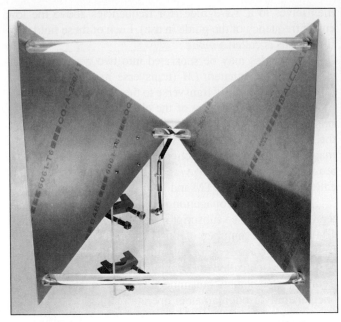

Figure 15.81 — An experimental two-sided pyramidal horn constructed in the ARRL laboratory. A pair of muffler clamps allow mounting the antenna on a mast. This model has sheet-aluminum sides, although window screen would work as well. Temporary elements could be made from cardboard covered with aluminum foil. The horizontal spreaders are Plexiglas rod. Oriented as shown here, the antenna radiates horizontally polarized waves.

and current. The transmission line may be supported from the top as well as the bottom, and when an infinite number of supports are added, they form the walls of a waveguide at its cutoff frequency. **Figure 15.80** illustrates how a rectangular waveguide evolves from a two-wire parallel transmission line as described. This simplified analysis also shows why the cutoff dimension is ½ λ.

While the operation of waveguides is usually described in terms of fields, current does flow on the inside walls, just as on the conductors of a two-wire transmission line. At the waveguide cutoff frequency, the current is concentrated in the center of the walls, and disperses toward the floor and ceiling as the frequency increases.

15.6.2 HORNS AND DISHES

Two forms of antenna that are only used at microwave frequencies are the horn antenna and the parabolic reflector or dish antenna.

Horn Antennas

Horn antennas were briefly introduced in the section on coupling energy into and out of waveguides. For amateur purposes, horns begin to show usable gain with practical dimensions in the 902 MHz band.

It isn't necessary to feed a horn with waveguide. If only two sides of a pyramidal horn are constructed, the antenna may be fed at the apex with a two-conductor transmission line. The impedance of this arrangement is on the order of 300 to 400 Ω. A 60° two-sided pyramidal horn with 18 inch sides is shown in **Figure 15.81**. This antenna has a theoretical gain of 15 dBi at 1296 MHz, although the feed system detailed in **Figure 15.82** probably degrades this value somewhat. A ¼λ, 150-Ω matching section made from two parallel lengths of twin-lead connects to a bazooka balun made from RG-58 cable and a brass tube. This matching system

Figure 15.82 — Matching system used to test the horn. Better performance would be realized with open wire line. See text.

was assembled strictly for the purpose of demonstrating the two-sided horn in a 50-Ω system. In a practical installation the horn would be fed with open-wire line and matched to 50 Ω at the station equipment.

Parabolic Reflector Antennas

When an antenna is located at the focus of a parabolic reflector (dish), it is possible to obtain considerable gain. Furthermore, the beamwidth of the radiated energy will be very narrow, provided all the energy from the driven element is directed toward the reflector. This section was written by Paul M. Wilson, W4HHK (SK).

Gain is a function of parabolic reflector diameter, surface accuracy and proper illumination of the reflector by the feed. Gain may be found from

$$G = 10 \log k \left(\frac{\pi D}{\lambda} \right)^2 \quad \text{(Eq 4)}$$

where

G = gain over an isotropic antenna, dBi (subtract 2.15 dB for gain over a dipole)
k = efficiency factor, usually about 55%
D = dish diameter in feet
λ = wavelength in feet

See **Table 15-27** for parabolic antenna gain for the bands 420 MHz through 10 GHz and diameters of 2 to 30 feet.

A close approximation of beamwidth may be found from

$$\psi = \frac{70\lambda}{D} \quad \text{(Eq 5)}$$

where

ψ = beamwidth in degrees at half-power points (3 dB down)
D = dish diameter in feet
λ = wavelength in feet

At 420 MHz and higher, the parabolic dish becomes a practical antenna. A simple, single feed point eliminates phasing harnesses and balun requirements. Gain is dependent on good surface accuracy, which is more difficult to achieve with increasing frequency. Surface errors should not exceed ⅛ λ in amateur operation. At 430 MHz ⅛ λ is 3.4 inches, but at 10 GHz it is 0.1476 inch! Mesh can be used for the reflector surface to reduce weight and wind loading, but hole size should be less than ¹⁄₁₂ λ. At 430 MHz the use of 2-inch hole diameter poultry netting (chicken wire) is acceptable. Fine mesh aluminum screening works well as high as 10 GHz.

A support form may be fashioned to provide the proper parabolic shape by plotting a curve (**Figure 15.83**) from

$$Y^2 = 4SX$$

as shown in the figure.

Optimum illumination occurs when power at the reflector edge is 10 dB less than that at the center. A circular waveguide feed of correct diameter and length for the frequency and correct beamwidth for the dish focal length to diameter (f/D) ratio provides optimum illumination at 902 MHz and higher. This, however, is impractical at 432 MHz, where a dipole and plane reflector are often used. An f/D ratio between 0.4 and 0.6 is considered ideal for maximum gain and simple feeds.

The focal length of a dish may be found from

$$f = \frac{D^2}{16d} \quad \text{(Eq 6)}$$

where

f = focal length
D = diameter
d = depth distance from plane at mouth of dish to vertex

Table 15-27
Gain, Parabolic Antennas*

	Dish Diameter (Feet)						
Frequency	2	4	6	10	15	20	30
420 MHz	6.0	12.0	15.5	20.0	23.5	26.0	29.5
902	12.5	18.5	22.0	26.5	30.0	32.5	36.0
1215	15.0	21.0	24.5	29.0	32.5	35.0	38.5
2300	20.5	26.5	30.0	34.5	38.0	40.5	44.0
3300	24.0	30.0	33.5	37.5	41.5	43.5	47.5
5650	28.5	34.5	38.0	42.5	46.0	48.5	52.0
10 GHz	33.5	39.5	43.0	47.5	51.0	53.5	57.0

*Gain over an isotropic antenna (subtract 2.1 dB for gain over a dipole antenna). Reflector efficiency of 55% assumed.

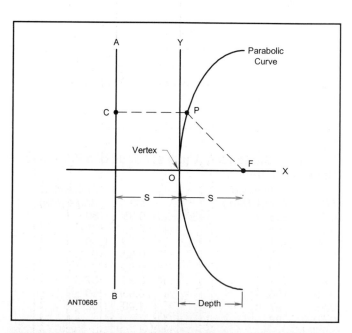

Figure 15.83 — Details of the parabolic curve, $Y^2 = 4SX$. This curve is the locus of points that are equidistant from a fixed point, the focus (F), and a fixed line (AB) that is called the *directrix*. Hence, FP = PC. The focus (F) is located at coordinates S,0.

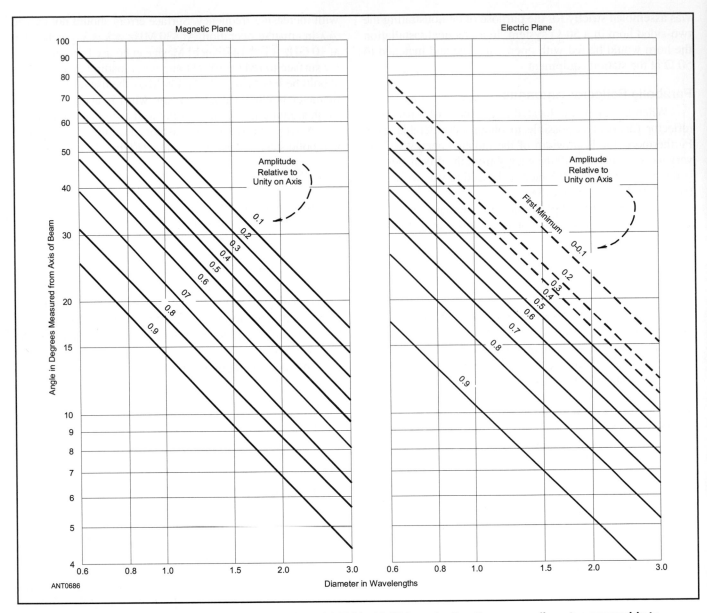

Figure 15.84 — This graph can be used in conjunction with Table 15-28 for selecting the proper diameter waveguide to illuminate a parabolic reflector.

Table 15-28
f/D Versus Subtended Angle at Focus of a Parabolic Reflector Antenna

f/D	Subtended Angle (Deg.)	f/D	Subtended Angle (Deg.)
0.20	203	0.65	80
0.25	181	0.70	75
0.30	161	0.75	69
0.35	145	0.80	64
0.40	130	0.85	60
0.45	117	0.90	57
0.50	106	0.95	55
0.55	97	1.00	52
0.60	88		

Taken from graph "f/D vs Subtended Angle at Focus," page 170 of the 1966 *Microwave Engineers' Handbook and Buyers Guide.* Graph courtesy of K. S. Kelleher, Aero Geo Astro Corp, Alexandria, Virginia

The units of focal length f are the same as those used to measure the depth and diameter. **Table 15-28** gives the subtended angle at focus for dish f/D ratios from 0.2 to 1.0. A dish, for example, with a typical f/D of 0.4 requires a 10-dB beamwidth of 130°. A circular waveguide feed with a diameter of approximately 0.7 λ provides nearly optimum illumination, but does not uniformly illuminate the reflector in both the magnetic (TM) and electric (TE) planes. **Figure 15.84** shows data for plotting radiation patterns from circular guides. The waveguide feed aperture can be modified to change the beamwidth.

One approach used successfully by some experimenters is the use of a disc at a short distance behind the aperture as shown in **Figure 15.85**. As the distance between the aperture and disc is changed, the TM plane patterns become alternately broader and narrower than with an unmodified aperture. A disc about 2 λ in diameter appears to be as effective as a

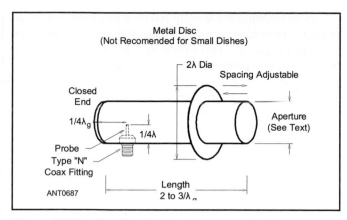

Figure 15.85 — Details of a circular waveguide feed.

Table 15-29
Circular Waveguide Dish Feeds

Freq. (MHz)	Inside Diameter Circular Waveguide Range (inches)
915	8.52-9.84
1296	6.02-6.94
2304	3.39-3.91
3400	2.29-2.65
5800	1.34-1.55
10,250	0.76-0.88

much larger one. Some experimenters have noted a 1 to 2 dB increase in dish gain with this modified feed. Rectangular waveguide feeds can also be used, but dish illumination is not as uniform as with round guide feeds.

The circular feed can be made of copper, brass, aluminum or even tin in the form of a coffee or juice can, but the latter must be painted on the outside to prevent rust or corrosion. The circular feed must be within a proper size (diameter) range for the frequency being used. This feed operates in the dominant circular waveguide mode known as the *mode*. The guide must be large enough to pass the mode with no attenuation, but smaller than the diameter that permits the next higher mode to propagate. To support the desirable mode in circular waveguide, the cutoff frequency, F_C, is given by

$$F_C (TE_{11}) = \frac{6917.26}{d \text{ (inches)}} \quad \text{(Eq 7)}$$

where
F_C = cutoff frequency in MHz for mode
d = waveguide inner diameter

Circular waveguide will support the mode having a cutoff frequency

$$F_C (TM_{01}) = \frac{9034.85}{d \text{ (inches)}} \quad \text{(Eq 8)}$$

The wavelength in a waveguide always exceeds the free-space wavelength and is called guide wavelength, λ_g. It is related to the cutoff frequency and operating frequency by the equation

$$\lambda_g = \frac{11802.85}{\sqrt{f_0^2 - f_C^2}} \quad \text{(Eq 9)}$$

where
λ_g = guide wavelength, inches
f_0 = operating frequency, MHz
f_C = waveguide cutoff frequency, MHz

An inside diameter range of about 0.66 to 0.76 λ is suggested. The lower frequency limit (longer dimension) is dictated by proximity to the cutoff frequency. The higher frequency limit (shorter dimension) is dictated by higher order

waves. See **Table 15-29** for recommended inside diameter dimensions for the 902- to 10,000-MHz amateur bands.

The probe that excites the waveguide and makes the transition from coaxial cable to waveguide is ¼ λ long and spaced from the closed end of the guide by ¼ guide wavelength. The length of the feed should be two to three guide wavelengths. The latter is preferred if a second probe is to be mounted for polarization change or for polaplexer operation where duplex communication (simultaneous transmission and reception) is possible because of the isolation between two properly located and oriented probes. The second probe for polarization switching or polaplexer operation should be spaced 3/4 guide wavelength from the closed end and mounted at right angles to the first probe. (A polaplexer is a polarization-based diplexer antenna, or antenna feed, which supports two simultaneous inputs or outputs that are independent and isolated from each other by use of orthogonal (at right angles) linear polarization. See the article by Munn listed in the Bibliography.)

The feed aperture is located at the focal point of the dish and aimed at the center of the reflector. The feed mounts should permit adjustment of the aperture either side of the focal point and should present a minimum of blockage to the reflector. Correct distance to the dish center places the focal point about 1 inch inside the feed aperture. The use of a non-metallic support minimizes blockage. PVC pipe, fiberglass and Plexiglas are commonly used materials. A simple test by placing a material in a microwave oven reveals if it is satisfactory up to 2450 MHz. PVC pipe has tested satisfactorily and appears to work well at 2300 MHz. A simple, clean looking mount for a 4-foot dish with 18 inches focal length, for example, can be made by mounting a length of 4-inch PVC pipe using a PVC flange at the center of the dish. At 2304 MHz the circular feed is approximately 4 inches ID, making a snug fit with the PVC pipe. Precautions should be taken to keep rain and small birds from entering the feed.

Never look into the open end of a waveguide when power is applied, or stand directly in front of a dish while transmitting. Tests and adjustments in these areas should be done while receiving or at extremely low levels of transmitter power (less than 0.1 watt). The US Government has set a limit of 10 mW/cm^2 averaged over a 6-minute period as the safe maximum. Other authorities believe even lower levels should be used. Destructive thermal heating of body tissue results from excessive exposure. This heating effect is especially dangerous to the eyes. The accepted safe level of 10 mW/cm² is reached in the near field of a parabolic antenna if the level at 2D²/λ is 0.242 mW/cm². The equation for power density at the far-field boundary is

$$\text{Power density} = \frac{137.8 \, P}{D^2} \, mW/cm^2 \qquad \text{(Eq 10)}$$

where
  P = average power in kilowatts
  D = antenna diameter in feet
  λ = wavelength in feet

New commercial dishes are expensive, but surplus ones can often be purchased at low cost. Some amateurs build theirs, while others modify UHF TV dishes or circular metal snow sleds for the amateur bands. **Figure 15.86** shows a dish using the homemade feed just described. Practical details for dish antennas are given in the **Antennas for Space Communications** chapter. A number of horn and dish designs, including conversion of surplus offset-feed satellite TV receive dishes are presented in the RSGB publication *Antennas for VHF and Above*. (See Bibliography.)

A Horn Antenna for 10 GHz

The horn antenna is the easiest antenna for the beginner on 10 GHz to construct. It can be made out of readily available flat sheet brass. Because it is inherently a broadband structure, minor constructional errors can be tolerated. The one drawback is that horn antennas become physically cumbersome at gains over about 25 dBi, but for most line-of-sight operation this much gain is rarely necessary. This antenna was designed by Bob Atkins, KA1GT, and appeared in *QST* for April and May 1987.

Figure 15.86 — Coffee-can 2304 MHz feed described in text and Figure 15.85 mounted on a 4-foot dish.

Horn antennas are usually fed by waveguide. When operating in its normal frequency range, waveguide propagation is in the TE₁₀ mode. This means that the electric (E) field is across the short dimension of the guide and the magnetic (H) field is across the wide dimension. This is the reason for the E-plane and H-plane terminology shown in **Figure 15.87**.

There are many varieties of horn antennas. If the waveguide is flared out only in the H-plane, the horn is called an H-plane sectoral horn. Similarly, if the flare is only in the E-plane, an E-plane sectoral horn results. If the flare is in both planes, the antenna is called a pyramidal horn.

For a horn of any given aperture, directivity (gain along the axis) is maximum when the field distribution across the aperture is uniform in magnitude and phase. When the fields are not uniform, sidelobes that reduce the directivity of the antenna are formed. To obtain a uniform distribution, the horn should be as long as possible with minimum flare angle. From a practical point of view, however, the horn should be as short as possible, so there is an obvious conflict between performance and convenience.

Figure 15.88 illustrates this problem. For a given flare

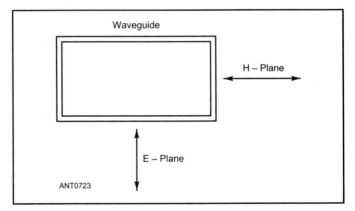

Figure 15.87 — 10-GHz antennas are usually fed with waveguide. See text for a discussion of waveguide propagation characteristics.

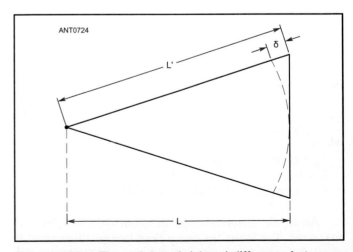

Figure 15.88 — The path-length (phase) difference between the center and edge of a horn antenna is δ.

angle and a given side length, there is a path-length difference from the apex of the horn to the center of the aperture (L), and from the apex of the horn to the edge of the aperture (L'). This causes a phase difference in the field across the aperture, which in turn causes formation of sidelobes, degrading directivity (gain along the axis) of the antenna. If L is large this difference is small, and the field is almost uniform. As L decreases however, the phase difference increases and directivity suffers. An optimum (shortest possible) horn is constructed so that this phase difference is the maximum allowable before sidelobes become excessive and axial gain markedly decreases.

The magnitude of this permissible phase difference is different for E-plane and H-plane horns. For the E-plane horn, the field intensity is quite constant across the aperture. For the H-plane horn, the field tapers to zero at the edge. Consequently, the phase difference at the edge of the aperture in the E-plane horn is more critical and should be held to less than 90° (¼ λ). In an H-plane horn, the allowable phase difference is 144° (0.4 λ). If the aperture of a pyramidal horn exceeds one wavelength in both planes, the E-plane and H-plane patterns are essentially independent and can be analyzed separately.

The usual direction for orienting the waveguide feed is with the broad face horizontal, giving vertical polarization. If this is the case, the H-plane sectoral horn has a narrow horizontal beamwidth and a very wide vertical beamwidth. This is not a very useful beam pattern for most amateur applications. The E-plane sectoral horn has a narrow vertical beamwidth and a wide horizontal beamwidth. Such a radiation pattern could be useful in a beacon system where wide coverage is desired.

The most useful form of the horn for general applications is the optimum pyramidal horn. In this configuration the two beamwidths are almost the same. The E-plane (vertical) beamwidth is slightly less than the H-plane (horizontal), and also has greater sidelobe intensity.

Building the Antenna

A 10-GHz pyramidal horn with 18.5 dBi gain is shown in **Figure 15.89**. The first design parameter is usually the required gain, or the maximum antenna size. These are of course related, and the relationships can be approximated by the following:

$$L = \text{H-plane length } (\lambda) = 0.0654 \times \text{gain} \qquad \text{(Eq 11)}$$

$$A = \text{H-plane aperture } (\lambda) = 0.0443 \times \text{gain} \qquad \text{(Eq 12)}$$

$$B = \text{E-plane aperture } (\lambda) = 0.81 \text{ A} \qquad \text{(Eq 13)}$$

where gain is expressed as a *ratio*; 20 dBi gain = 100, and L, A and B are dimensions shown in **Figure 15.90**.

From these equations, the dimensions for a 20-dBi gain horn for 10.368 GHz can be determined. One wavelength at 10.368 GHz is 1.138 inches. The length (L) of such a horn is 0.0654 × 100 = 6.54 λ. At 10.368 GHz, this is

Figure 15.89 — This pyramidal horn has 18.5 dBi gain at 10 GHz. Construction details are given in the text.

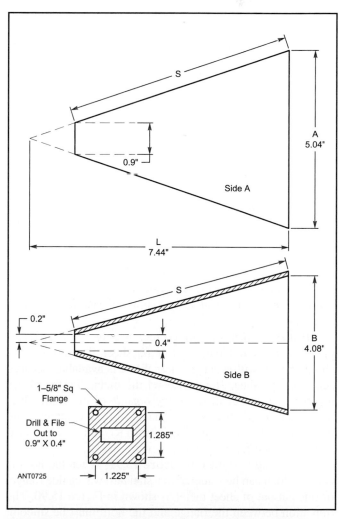

Figure 15.90 — Dimensions of the brass pieces used to make the 10-GHz horn antenna. Construction requires two of each of the triangular pieces (side A and side B).

7.44 inches. The corresponding H-plane aperture (A) is 4.43 λ (5.04 inches), and the E-plane aperture (B), 4.08 inches.

The easiest way to make such a horn is to cut pieces from brass sheet stock and solder them together. Figure 15.90 shows the dimensions of the triangular pieces for the sides and a square piece for the waveguide flange. (A standard commercial waveguide flange could also be used.) Because the E-plane and H-plane apertures are different, the horn opening is not square. Sheet thickness is unimportant; 0.02 to 0.03 inch works well. Brass sheet is often available from hardware or hobby shops.

Note that the triangular pieces are trimmed at the apex to fit the waveguide aperture (0.9 × 0.4 inch). This necessitates that the length, from base to apex, of the smaller triangle (side B) is shorter than that of the larger (side A). Note that the length, S, of the two different sides of the horn must be the same if the horn is to fit together! For such a simple looking object, getting the parts to fit together properly requires careful fabrication.

The dimensions of the sides can be calculated with simple geometry, but it is easier to draw out templates on a sheet of cardboard first. The templates can be used to build a mock antenna to make sure everything fits together properly before cutting the sheet brass.

First, mark out the larger triangle (side A) on cardboard. Determine at what point its width is 0.9 inch and draw a line parallel to the base as shown in Figure 15.90. Measure the length of the side S; this is also the length of the sides of the smaller (side B) pieces.

Mark out the shape of the smaller pieces by first drawing a line of length B and then constructing a second line of length S. One end of line S is an end of line B, and the other is 0.2 inch above a line perpendicular to the center of line B as shown in Figure 15.89. (This procedure is much more easily followed than described.) These smaller pieces are made slightly oversize (shaded area in Figure 15.90) so you can construct the horn with solder seams on the outside of the horn during assembly.

Cut out two cardboard pieces for side A and two for side B and tape them together in the shape of the horn. The aperture at the waveguide end should measure 0.9 × 0.4 inch and the aperture at the other end should measure 5.04 × 4.08 inches.

If these dimensions are correct, use the cardboard templates to mark out pieces of brass sheet. The brass sheet should be cut with a bench shear if one is available, because scissors type shears tend to bend the metal. Jig the pieces together and solder them on the *outside* of the seams. It is important to keep both solder and rosin from contaminating the inside of the horn; they can absorb RF and reduce gain at these frequencies.

Assembly is shown in **Figure 15.91**. When the horn is completed, it can be soldered to a standard waveguide flange, or one cut out of sheet metal as shown in Figure 15.90. The transition between the flange and the horn must be smooth. This antenna provides an excellent performance-to-cost ratio (about 20 dBi gain for about five dollars in parts).

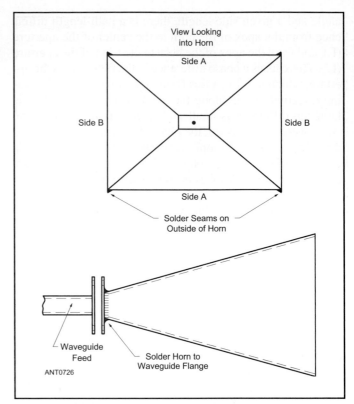

Figure 15.91 — Assembly of the 10-GHz horn antenna.

15.6.3 VIVALDI ANTENNAS

The following material is reprinted from the RSGB publication *Microwave Know-How*. (See Bibliography.) The Vivaldi antenna in **Figure 15.92** is an exponential antenna from the same family as V-beams and Rhombics (see the **Long-Wire and Traveling-Wave Antennas** chapter). They have exceptionally wide bandwidth. The lowest frequency is determined by the width of the opening.

The higher frequency of operation is determined by how accurately the slot is formed. As an example, the 75 mm PCB version has an excellent return loss from 5 GHz to 18 GHz and is usable from 2 GHz. (See **www.wa5vjb. com/pcb-pdfs/10-25GHzSweep.pdf** for additional construction information.)

All versions start with the template shown in Figure 15.92. Place the template on a photocopy machine and enlarge or reduce to the desired frequency range as shown in **Table 15-30**. Cut out the template and mark your material

Table 15-30
Scaling for the Vivaldi Antenna Template

Opening	Low End Frequency Response
40 mm	10 GHz
75 mm	5 GHz
150 mm	2 GHz
200 mm	1 GHz

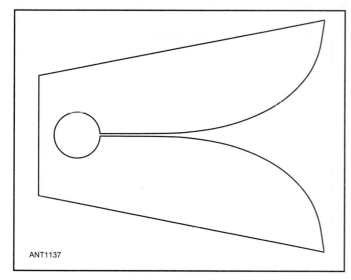

Figure 15.92 — The template for a Vivaldi antenna. Scale as shown in Table 15-30.

Figure 15.93 — Marking out a Vivaldi antenna using the template placed on your chosen material.

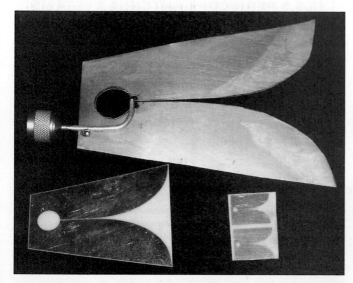

Figure 15.94 — A complete Vivaldi antenna.

as shown in **Figure 15.93**. Thin brass, tin plate, or PC board material have all been used.

Cut out the antenna using sharp scissors or a band saw. The feed line shield should be soldered to one side of the slot and the center conductor to the other side as close to the circle as possible. (See **Figure 15.94**.) Both semi-rigid and Teflon braided coax types can be used.

Vivaldi antenna make excellent test antennas for use with a test instruments or can be used as dish feeds over several bands. The phase center of the Vivaldi does move back and forth in the narrow region of the slot, but when the dish is focused at the highest frequency of planned use, the lower bands will be very close. Mount the narrow area of the slot at the focus of the dish.

15.6.4 PATCH ANTENNAS

The following material is adapted from the RSGB publication *Microwave Know-How.* (See Bibliography for additional articles by Kraus and Krug.) Patch antennas (also called *microstrip antennas*) are a good example of how an antenna's shape is used at microwave frequencies in ways not possible at 70 cm and longer wavelengths. Patch antennas become practical at and above the 902 MHz band and are very common in commercial microwave applications such as GPS reception, wireless telephony, and wireless data links. As more amateurs investigate operation at microwave frequencies, the patch antenna should receive more attention.

The patch, an example of which is shown in **Figure 15.95**, consists of a radiating surface mounted over a ground plane although there are many variations of the basic design. The patch is approximately $\lambda/2$ on a side for a square patch. Patch antenna gain is on the order of 7 to 9 dBi.

Some patches are constructed of double-sided PCB material with the patch etched on one side and the unetched side acting as the ground plane. The shape of the patch is such that when excited by a signal, the resulting currents form patterns that create a useful radiation pattern. It works the same as an arrangement of discrete elements. The closest electrical analogy is that the square patch acts similarly to a pair of slot antennas fed in phase and approximately $\lambda/2$ apart.

Figure 15.95 — Two patch antennas for the 23 cm band. The patch on the left is constructed from sheet metal and the one on the right from PCB material.

Since the impedance of the patch is high at the edges where current is low (just as in a linear element), the feed point is usually close to the center of the patch. Placement of the feed point determines the feed point impedance and also influences the pattern of current on the surface of the patch. An alternate method of feeding the patch is to create a 50-Ω microstrip or stripline transmission line from a location with a 50-Ω impedance to the edge of the structure where a feed line can be attached.

It is not necessary for the patch to be rectangular in shape and could conveniently be round or polygon shaped. A rectangular patch with its opposite corners cut off will produce circular polarization.

A Patch Antenna for 23 cm

This simple patch antenna for the middle range of the 23 cm band was designed by Kent Britain, WA5VJB. The antenna works for use as a dish feed as well as for point-to-point communication such as for D-STAR, ATV, or satellite contacts.

The antenna can be made from almost any sheet metal. The base can be made from sheet aluminum, brass, copper, or PCB material. It is probably easier to assemble if the patch is made from something that can be soldered. Figure 15.95 shows two patches. The one on the right is made from PCB material and the one on the left from galvanized sheet steel. **Figure 15.96** shows the dimensions for the 23 cm band patch.

Since the very center of the patch is electrically neutral, similar to the center of a dipole, you can use a metal screw to support the patch over the conductive plate or ground plane. This provides a dc ground for the antenna and dissipates any static charge. A #4 or #6 brass or similar screw can be used. The diameter of the screw is not important but the height at which it holds the patch above the ground plane is. Adjust the height of the patch above the ground plane for the best impedance match. If swept frequency measurements are not possible, adjustment at a single frequency is acceptable.

Coaxial feed line is attached to the patch 23 mm from the mounting screw as shown in Figure 15.96 and **Figure 15.97**. The orientation of the line from the feed point to the center of the patch determines the antenna's polarization. If the antenna is placed with the feed point below the center, the antenna will be vertically polarized.

An SMA connector is used for this design, but coax can be soldered directly to the patch. The center conductor attaches to the patch and the shield to the ground plane. Ground plane size is not critical and 150 mm × 150 mm or larger will work well.

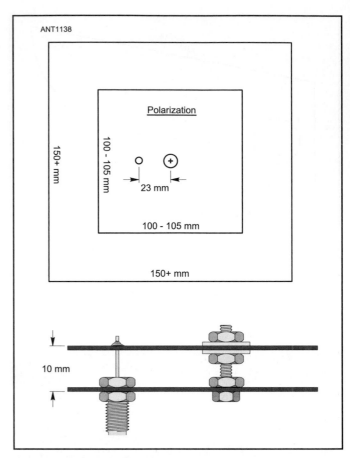

Figure 15.96 — Dimensions for the 23 cm patch antenna. The size of the patch determines the frequency range of the antenna (see text). The orientation of the feed point determines the antenna's polarization.

The typical patch will have a bandwidth of 50 MHz at this frequency. To use the 1240-1280 MHz portion of the band, increase the patch to 105 mm × 105 mm. For 1280-1325 MHz reduce the patch size to 100 mm × 100 mm.

15.6.5 PERISCOPE ANTENNA SYSTEMS

One problem common to all who use microwaves is that of mounting an antenna at the maximum possible height while trying to minimize feed line losses. The higher the frequency, the more severe this problem becomes, as feeder losses increase with frequency. Because parabolic dish reflectors are most often used on the higher bands, there is also the difficulty of waterproofing feeds (particularly waveguide feeds). Inaccessibility of the dish is also a problem when

Figure 15.97 — An illustration showing how the patch is mounted above the ground plane using the center screw and, in this case, the SMA connector.

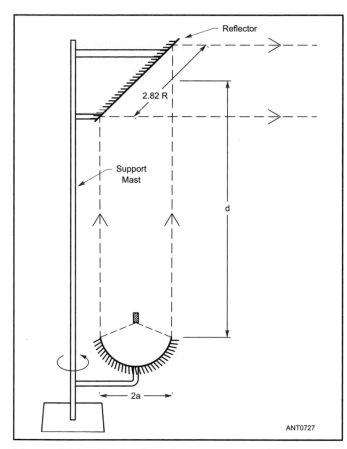

Figure 15.98 — The basic periscope antenna. This design makes it easy to adjust the feed antenna.

changing bands. Unless the tower is climbed every time and the feed changed, there must be a feed for each band mounted on the dish. One way around these problems is to use a periscope antenna system (sometimes called a "fly-swatter antenna").

The material in this section was prepared by Bob Atkins, KA1GT, and appeared in *QST* for January and February 1984. **Figure 15.98** shows a schematic representation of a periscope antenna system. A plane reflector is mounted at the top of a rotating tower at an angle of 45°. This reflector can be elliptical with a major to minor axis ratio of 1.41, or rectangular. At the base of the tower is mounted a dish or other type of antenna such as a Yagi, pointing straight up. The advantage of such a system is that the feed antenna can be changed and worked on easily. Additionally, with a correct choice of reflector size, dish size, and dish to reflector spacing, feed losses can be made small, increasing the effective system gain. In fact, for some particular system configurations, the gain of the overall system can be greater than that of the feed antenna alone.

Gain of a Periscope System

Figure 15.99 shows the relationship between the effective gain of the antenna system and the distance between the reflector and feed antenna for an elliptical reflector. At first sight, it is not at all obvious how the antenna system can have a higher gain than the feed alone. The reason lies in the fact that, depending on the feed to reflector spacing, the reflector may be in the near field (Fresnel) region of the antenna,

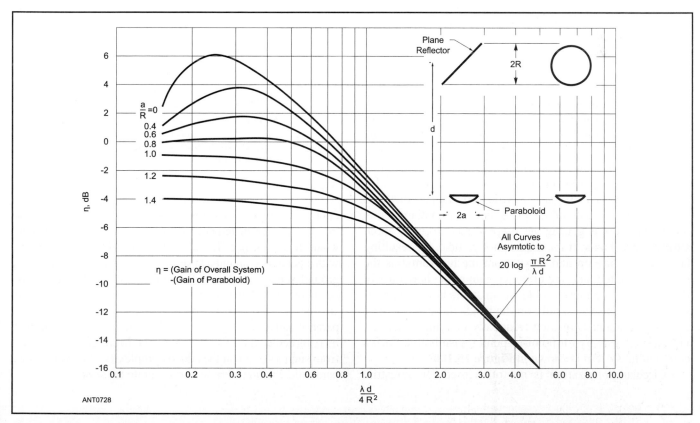

Figure 15.99 — Gain of a periscope antenna using a plane elliptical reflector (after Jasik — see Bibliography).

the far field (Fraunhöffer) region, or the transition region between the two.

In the far field region, the gain is proportional to the reflector area and inversely proportional to the distance between the feed and reflector. In the near field region, seemingly strange things can happen, such as decreasing gain with decreasing feed to reflector separation. The reason for this gain decrease is that, although the reflector is intercepting more of the energy radiated by the feed, it does not all contribute in phase at a distant point, and so the gain decreases.

In practice, rectangular reflectors are more common than elliptical. A rectangular reflector with sides equal in length to the major and minor axes of the ellipse will, in fact, normally give a slight gain increase. In the far field region, the gain will be proportional to the area of the reflector. To use Figure 15.99 with a rectangular reflector, R^2 may be replaced by A / π, where A is the projected area of the reflector. The antenna pattern depends in a complicated way on the system parameters (spacing and size of the elements), but **Table 15-31** gives an approximation of what to expect. R is the radius of the projected circular area of the elliptical reflector (equal to the minor axis radius), and b is the length of the side of the projected square area of the rectangular reflector (equal to the length of the short side of the rectangle).

For those wishing a rigorous mathematical analysis of this type of antenna system, several references are given in the Bibliography at the end of this chapter.

Mechanical Considerations

There are some problems with the physical construction of a periscope antenna system. Since the antenna gain of a microwave system is high and, hence, its beamwidth narrow, the reflector must be accurately aligned. If the reflector does not produce a beam that is horizontal, the useful gain of the system will be reduced. From the geometry of the system, an angular misalignment of the reflector of X degrees in the vertical plane will result in an angular misalignment of 2X degrees in the vertical alignment of the antenna system pattern. Thus, for a dish pointing straight up (the usual case), the reflector must be at an angle of 45° to the vertical and should not fluctuate from factors such as wind loading.

The reflector itself should be flat to better than $\frac{1}{10}$ λ for the frequency in use. It may be made of mesh, provided that the holes in the mesh are also less than $\frac{1}{10}$ λ in diameter. A second problem is getting the support mast to rotate about a truly vertical axis. If the mast is not vertical, the resulting beam will swing up and down from the horizontal as the system is rotated, and the effective gain at the horizon will fluctuate. Despite these problems, amateurs have used periscope antennas successfully on the bands through 10 GHz. Periscope antennas are used frequently in commercial service, though usually for point-to-point transmission. Such a commercial system is shown in **Figure 15.100**.

Circular polarization is not often used for terrestrial

Table 15-31
Radiation Patterns of Periscope Antenna Systems

	Elliptical Reflector	Rectangular Reflector
3-dB beamwidth, degrees	60 λ/2R	52 λ/b
6-dB beamwidth, degrees	82 λ/2R	68 λ/b
First minimum, degrees from axis	73 λ/2R	58 λ/b
First maximum, degrees from axis	95 λ/2R	84 λ/b
Second minimum, degrees from axis	130 λ/2R	116 λ/b
Second maximum, degrees from axis	156 λ/2R	142 λ/b
Third minimum, degrees from axis	185 λ/2R	174 λ/b

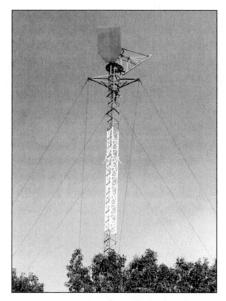

Figure 15.100 — Commercial periscope antennas, such as this one, are often used for point-to-point communication.

operation, but if it is used with a periscope system there is an important point to remember. The circularity sense changes when the signal is reflected. Thus, for right hand circularity with a periscope antenna system, the feed arrangement on the ground should produce left hand circularity. It should also be mentioned that it is possible (though more difficult for amateurs) to construct a periscope antenna system using a parabolically curved reflector. The antenna system can then be regarded as an offset fed parabola. More gain is available from such a system at the added complexity of constructing a parabolically curved reflector, accurate to $\frac{1}{10}$ λ.

15.7 BIBLIOGRAPHY

Source material and more extended discussion of topics covered in this chapter can be found in the references given below and in the textbooks listed at the end of the **Antenna Fundamentals** chapter.

RSGB Books

Antennas for VHF and Above, (Potters Bar: RSGB, 2008).
International Microwave Handbook (Potters Bar: RSGB, 2008).
Microwave Know-How for the Radio Amateur (Potters Bar: RSGB, 2010).
Radio Communication Handbook, 10th ed. (Potters Bar: RSGB, 2009).

Other Publications

B. Atkins, "Periscope Antenna Systems," The New Frontier, *QST*, Jan 1984, p 70 and Feb 1984, p 68.
B. Atkins, "Horn Antennas for 10 GHz," The New Frontier, *QST*, Apr 1987, p 80 and May 1987, p 63.
B. Atkins, "The New Frontier: Loop Yagi for 2304 MHz," *QST*, Sep 1981, p 76.
R. Bancroft, *Microstrip and Printed Antenna Design (2nd Edition)* (Raleigh, NC: SciTech Publishing, 2009)
J. Belrose, "Technical Correspondence: Gain of Vertical Collinear Antennas," *QST*, Oct 1982, pp 40-41.
L.B. Cebik, "A Short Boom, Wideband 3 Element Yagi for 6 Meters," *QST*, Aug 2007, pp 41-45.
L.B. Cebik, "2X3=6," *QST*, Feb 2000, p 34-36.
L.B. Cebik, "Building a Medium-Gain, Wide-Band, 2 Meter Yagi," *QST*, Dec 2004, pp 33-37.
L.B. Cebik, "Notes on the OWA Yagi," *QEX*, Jul/Aug 2002, pp 22-34.
L.B. Cebik, "An LPDA for 2 Meters Plus," *QST*, Oct 2001, pp 42-46.
J. Drexler, "An Experimental Study of a Microwave Periscope," *Proc. IRE*, Correspondence, Vol 42, Jun 1954, p 1022.
D. Evans and G. Jessop, *VHF-UHF Manual*, 3rd ed. (London: RSGB), 1976.
N. Foot, "WA9HUV 12 foot Dish for 432 and 1296 MHz," The World Above 50 Mc., *QST*, Jun 1971, pp 98-101, 107.
N. Foot, "Cylindrical Feed Horn for Parabolic Reflectors," *Ham Radio*, May 1976, pp 16-20.
G. Gobau, "Single-Conductor Surface-Wave Transmission Lines," *Proc. IRE*, Vol 39, Jun 1951, pp 619-624; also see *Journal of Applied Physics*, Vol 21 (1950), pp 1119-1128.

R. E. Greenquist and A. J. Orlando, "An Analysis of Passive Reflector Antenna Systems," *Proc. IRE*, Vol 42, Jul 1954, pp 1173-1178.
G. A. Hatherell, "Putting the G Line to Work," *QST*, Jun 1974, pp 11-15, 152, 154, 156.
R. Heslin, "Three-Band Log Periodic Antenna," *QST*, Jun 1963, pp 50-52.
D. L. Hilliard, "A 902 MHz Loop Yagi Antenna," *QST*, Nov 1985, pp 30-32.
G. Hoch, "Extremely Long Yagi antennas," *VHF Communications Magazine*, Mar 1982, pp 131-138.
G. Hoch, "More Gain from Yagi Antennas," *VHF Communications Magazine*, Apr 1997, pp 204-211.
W. C. Jakes, Jr., "A Theoretical Study of an Antenna-Reflector Problem," *Proc. IRE*, Vol 41, Feb 1953, pp 272-274.
H. Jasik, *Antenna Engineering Handbook*, 2nd ed. (New York: McGraw-Hill, 1984).
R. T. Knadle, "UHF Antenna Ratiometry," *QST*, Feb 1976, pp 22-25.
G. Kraus, "Modern Patch Antenna Design," *VHF Communications Magazine*, Jan 2001, pp 49-63.
F. Krug, "Micro-Stripline Antennas," *VHF Communications Magazine,* Apr 1985, pp 194-207.
Z. Lau, "RF: A Small 70-cm Yagi," *QEX*, Jul 2001, p 55.
T. Moreno, *Microwave Transmission Design Data* (New York: McGraw-Hill, 1948).
E. Munn, "The Polaplexer Revisited," **www.ham-radio. com/sbms/sd/ppxrdsgn.htm**.
W. Overbeck, "The VHF Quagi," *QST*, Apr 1977, pp 11-14.
W. Overbeck, "The Long-Boom Quagi," *QST*, Feb 1978, pp 20-21.
W. Overbeck, "Reproducible Quagi Antennas for 1296 MHz," *QST*, Aug 1981, pp 11-15.
J. Post, "The Copper Cactus," *73*, Feb 1992, p 9.
J. Reisert, "VHF/UHF World: Designing and Building Loop Yagis," *Ham Radio*, Sep 1985, pp 56-62.
G. Southworth, *Principles and Applications of Waveguide Transmission* (New York: D. Van Nostrand Co, 1950).
P. P. Viezbicke, "Yagi Antenna Design," *NBS Technical Note 688* (U. S. Dept. of Commerce/National Bureau of Standards, Boulder, CO), Dec 1976.
D. Vilardi, "Easily Constructed Antennas for 1296 MHz," *QST*, Jun 1969, pp 47-49.
D. Vilardi, "Simple and Efficient Feed for Parabolic Antennas," *QST*, Mar 1973, pp 42-44.

TABLE OF CONTENTS

Chapter 16

VHF and UHF Mobile Antennas

VHF/UHF mobile antennas can be very efficient, if installed properly. This section presents the popular types of mobile antennas for VHF and UHF and discusses issues regarding mounting style and installation technique. The material was revised and updated from previous editions by Alan Applegate, KØBG.

16.1 ANTENNAS FOR VHF-UHF FM

Antennas for Hand-held Transceivers

For frequencies above 30 MHz, most mobile installations permit the use of a full-size antenna but for hand-held radios smaller, loaded antennas are used. Antennas designed for use with VHF/UHF handheld FM transceivers can also be considered mobile antennas, even "rubber ducky" antennas consisting of a spiral winding of flexible wire in a flexible enclosure.

Pictured in **Figure 16.1** is a telescoping full-size quarter-wave antenna for 2 meters and beside it a flexible "rubber ducky" antenna for the same band. The rubber ducky antenna is a helically wound radiator made of stiff copper wire enclosed in a protective covering. The inductance of the helical windings provides electrical loading for the antenna. This avoids the problems of a lengthier, cumbersome antenna attached to a handheld radio while sacrificing some efficiency and bandwidth compared to the full-size antenna. The rubber ducky, being compact and flexible, withstands the normal rigors of portable use much better than would a full-size antenna. For these antennas, survivability over long use outweighs electrical efficiency.

The use of a full-size antenna will greatly improve the performance of hand-held transceivers. By using a coax adapter, the transceiver can be connected directly to the feed line of mobile antennas such as those described in the following sections. This allows much more effective use of a hand-held transceiver in a vehicle. A mobile antenna can also be installed on top of a metal appliance at home for improved operation. For example, a mag mount antenna on top of a refrigerator or file cabinet is a popular way of improving local coverage of a hand-held radio.

Mobile Antennas

At VHF and UHF, mobile antennas are often full-size whips (meaning ¼- to ½-wavelength long) and simple collinear arrays that provide extra gain on the higher frequency

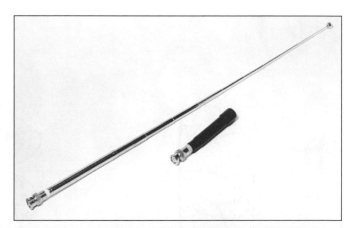

Figure 16.1 — A telescoping ¼-wavelength antenna and a "rubber ducky" antenna, both designed for use on 2 meters. The telescoping antenna is approximately 19 inches long when extended, while the rubber ducky antenna is only 3½ inches long. The rubber ducky is a helically wound radiator used because of its mechanical strength.

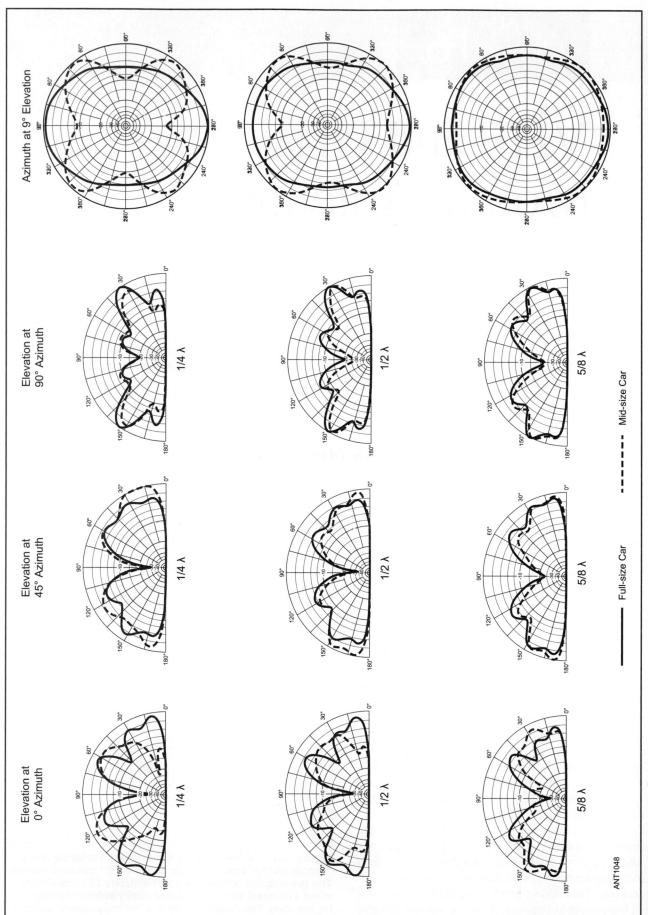

Figure 16.2 — Elevation and azimuth patterns showing the comparison for full and mid-sized cars for the three most popular VHF mobile antennas. (From "VHF Mobile Antenna Performance — The Other Half of the Story" by Dan Richardson, K6MHE.)

bands. There is always great debate about the best antenna for urban and/or suburban FM use. Which antenna to select depends on many factors — mounting style, mechanical characteristics, local terrain — and can't be based solely on advertised gain. Mobile antennas come in ¼-, ½-, ⅝-λ, and even in collinear styles where several elements are stacked atop one another.

It has been established that in general, ¼-λ vertical antennas for mobile repeater work are not as effective as ⅝-λ verticals. With a ⅝-λ antenna, more of the transmitted signal is directed at a low vertical angle, toward the horizon, offering a gain of about 1 dB over the ¼-λ vertical. However, in areas where the repeater is located nearby on a very high hill or a mountain top, the ¼-λ antenna will usually offer more reliable performance because it radiates more power at higher vertical angles.

Dan Richardson, K6MHE, has done extensive work on mobile VHF antennas, including modeling the various types, and how mounting location affects their radiation patterns. **Figure 16.2** shows representative azimuth patterns for roof mounted antennas. (The complete article is posted on his website **k6mhe.com/files/mobile_vhf_ant.pdf**.) The radiation patterns of antennas mounted on a trunk lid would be different from those depicted in the chart. Where — and how — the antenna is mounted would determine the actual pattern. Radiation pattern distortion aside, proper trunk lid mounting is a good alternative to roof mounting, especially when garage door clearance is an issue.

As can be seen from the patterns, there really isn't much difference between the radiation patterns of a ¼-, ½-, or ⅝-λ antenna. In fact, the vehicle in question and the antenna's mounting location affect the pattern more than the style! Since most mobile VHF and UHF operation is via FM repeaters, where the difference in height between the mobile and the repeater can be a major consideration, a ¼-λ antenna with more radiation at higher vertical angles can be a better choice.

Single-band whips are inexpensive and give excellent performance with proper mounting. If more gain and multiband use is required, the dual-band collinear that operates on both 2 meters and 70 cm is very popular. The Larsen NMO2/70BK shown in **Figure 16.3** is a typical example. Electrically it is a center-loaded ½-λ on 2 meters with gain identical to a ¼-λ ground-plane. On 70 cm it is a 2-element collinear with a few dB

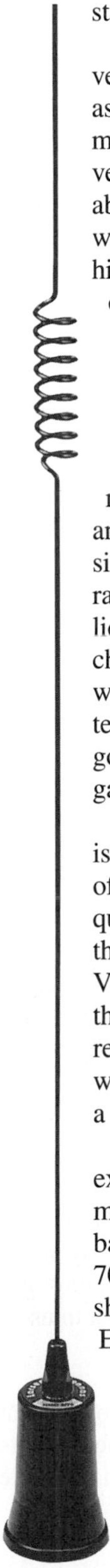

Figure 16.3 — A common style of dual-band VHF/UHF mobile whip antenna. (Larsen model NMO2/70BK)

Antenna Types for SSB and CW on VHF/UHF

Operating SSB and CW on 6 and 2 meters and 70 cm offers some exciting prospects for all license classes. While communications on the VHF bands are often considered line-of-site, propagation *beyond* line-of-site is common as discussed in the **Propagation of Radio Waves** chapter. This is especially true when using a "weak signal" mode such as SSB or CW, but there's a catch.

FM communications utilize vertically polarized antennas. Vertical polarization can be used for SSB but depending on the propagation path, signal strength via a vertically-polarized mobile antenna can have a 20+ dB disadvantage compared to a horizontally-polarized antenna.

Fortunately, horizontally-polarized antennas are of manageable size on the VHF bands, although they are not as simple to construct as vertically polarized whips. Dipoles and small beams present too much wind resistance to withstand the normal mobile environment. The usual solution is a loop antenna.

Figure 16.A shows an M² Antenna Systems (**www.m2inc.com**) horizontally polarized 6 meter loop called a *halo* (for circular versions) or *squalo* (if square as shown). Equivalent antennas for 2 meters and 70 cm are common. Although this particular design is square, they're still called loops and have a roughly omnidirectional pattern. The "Big Wheel" design is another option. Projects for both types of antennas are provided in the projects section.

Modern mobile SSB/CW transceivers usually output 100 W PEP on 6 meters and at least 50 W PEP on 2 meters and 70 cm. Under good band conditions, using horizontally-polarized antennas, *beyond* line-of-sight distances can exceed 200 miles even without any skywave or tropospheric scatter present!

Figure 16.A — A squalo (square halo) is a popular horizontally polarized VHF/UHF mobile antenna.

gain over a ¼-λ ground-plane. Other models are available which operate on three and even four bands. Antennas covering three or four bands are heavier and require sturdier mounting.

Six Meter FM Antennas

Technically, the 6 meter band is considered VHF but it often exhibits HF band properties while it also has an FM repeater sub band. Antennas for 6 meter FM operation look just like larger versions of those for 2 meters and they often use the same mounts. However, their ground plane requirements are more significant, similar to their HF cousins as discussed in the **Mobile and Maritime HF Antennas** chapter.

16.2 MOUNTS FOR WHIP ANTENNAS

VHF and UHF antennas are much smaller and lighter than HF antennas, making mounting quite a bit easier. Some permanent mounts require drilling holes in the vehicle, while others use a hood or trunk lid seam so screw holes don't show. Still others clamp around the outside of a trunk or door edge. For temporary installations, magnetic base mounts are available. For best performance, VHF and UHF antennas should be permanently affixed to the vehicle.

The roof of a vehicle is an inviting place to mount a VHF or UHF antenna as this maximizes performance, but a few precautions need to be followed. First, it is not uncommon for side air bags to be mounted within the headliner area with control wiring running through the roof support pillars. Further, the roof is supported by cross bracing to meet rollover standards. These braces must be avoided. A repair manual for the vehicle in question is a good resource in avoiding installation problems and finding the manufacturer's preferred routes for coaxial and control cables.

The type of mount is also a concern when roof mounting, as the mount must be securely waterproof. If you're unsure about drilling holes in your vehicle (see the sidebar "To Drill Or Not to Drill?"), use the services of a local two-way radio service or vehicle entertainment system installation company.

The center of the trunk lid is a second-best location but care must be taken to assure the antenna doesn't interfere with the opening of the trunk. With the trunk fully open, place the antenna at the desired mounting location to check clearance. Don't forget to include the height of the mount itself and account for vibration of the antenna and trunk lid. Whatever mount is used, care must be taken to assure clearance of the coax cable and control leads if present.

If the antenna's overall length is too great, overhead clearance becomes a problem. While lightly touching the garage door or carport top may be acceptable, if the antenna is long enough to drag the inner surface of the door or roof, you run the chance of catching the antenna between garage door panels or getting it stuck in a rafter. This will damage the antenna and often the vehicle. In these cases, you're much better off with a shorter ¼-λ antenna.

NMO — New Motorola Mount

The recommended antenna mount for VHF and UHF antennas is the NMO (from "New Motorola") as it is waterproof even when the antenna is removed. A permanent NMO mount (see **Figure 16.4**) usually requires a ¾-inch hole. Antennas with an NMO base have an integral O-ring or washer to seal the internal surfaces against water.

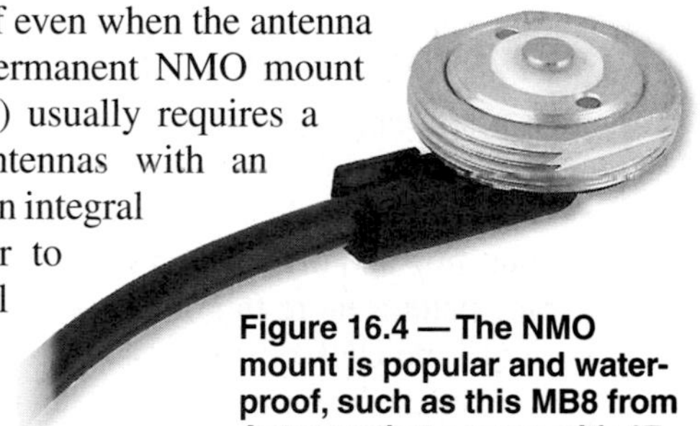

Figure 16.4 — The NMO mount is popular and waterproof, such as this MB8 from Antenex that comes with 17 feet of RG-58A coaxial cable.

SO-239 Mount

Some VHF antennas mounts have a modified SO-239 chassis coax connector with the mating PL-259 forming the base of the antenna. The standard connector type allows you to connect a coaxial cable to the antenna mount, if desired. Most SO-239 mounts *are not* waterproof, especially when the antenna is removed, and shouldn't be used for through-hole body mounting and should be capped when not in use.

Stud Mount

While popular at HF, the stud mount is less common at VHF and UHF. Larsen and other manufacturers offer mounts with a male ⁵⁄₁₆-24 stud. Detachable whips are then available for all VHF and UHF bands.

Angle Brackets

Angle brackets are generally attached by three or more sheet metal screws. Properly secured, they work well for

---

To Drill Or Not To Drill?

The decision to drill holes in sheet metal to mount antennas can be hotly debated. While no-hole mounts can be used satisfactorily, it is best to look at both sides of the issue.

One common reason given not to drill is if the vehicle in question is leased, but that doesn't preclude a drilled hole. If it did, there wouldn't be any leased commercial vehicles. What lease agreements specify is body damage such as from an accident or mistreatment. Properly installed NMO mounts, for example, are often acceptable.

Drilled holes and waterproof mounts also minimize common-mode current on the coaxial feed line that could interfere with or receive RFI from on-board computers and electrical devices. Aside from the hole itself, a permanent mount also minimizes damage to the finish.

Figure 16.5 — This angle bracket mounts to the vehicle body with three sheet metal screws and is drilled to accept a standard NMO mount.

lightweight antennas but routing coax through weather seals can be troublesome.

Angle brackets come in about a dozen different styles. The one shown in **Figure 16.5** is pre-drilled for an NMO mount. The brackets are often well-suited for installation along the hood and trunk seams.

Modern vehicles have very little clearance between the body structure and the various doors and hatches. Be sure to check clearance before you actually attach the bracket. Some vehicles may require specially bent or extended brackets as well.

Clip or Lip Mounts

There are a variety of mounts designed to clamp on the edge or "lip" of a trunk, hood, or hatch. Set screws are used to secure the mount to the lip and provide the requisite grounding of the mount. The set screws both secure the mount and make a connection to the sheet metal through the body paint. **Figure 16.6A** shows a typical "hatchback" style adjustable mount with an NMO base and **Figure 16.6B** is a close-up showing the set screws holding the mount to the vehicle body.

All modern vehicles are dipped in a zinc compound before final assembly and painting. When exposed to air, zinc rapidly oxidizes but in this case the oxidation is a good thing! When a piece of road debris nicks the paint down to the zinc layer, it quickly oxidizes, and protects the base metal underneath. Do not remove this zinc coating to bare metal! This removes the protective coating, allowing the underlying steel to rust and creates an intermittent connection.

Be aware that the coax must often be bent sharply around the lip of the trunk. Because clearance is minimal many lip mounts come preassembled with about 10 feet of RG-174 sized coax (0.110 inch OD). While the loss per foot isn't much of a concern at HF, it becomes critical at UHF where the feed line loss is just over 4 dB! If coax loss is important in your installation, use a mount with RG-58 cable.

All lip mounts bring the coax cable into the trunk or passenger cabin through the weather seal, potentially allowing water to enter. Running the cable under the seal as in Figure 16.6 is often an option. Take care to dress the cables and seals to direct water toward a drain hole or other exit.

Glass Mounts

"Through-glass" or "on-glass" mounts such as the Larsen KG2/70CXPL use adhesive to hold the base of the antenna and cable fitting to opposite sides of a window, relying on metal foil surfaces to create a capacitor and pass VHF/UHF signals. The mount must be clear of window heating strips and cannot be used on tinted (passivated) glass that contains colloidal-sized metallic particles to provide protection from harmful UVA and UVB rays. Antenna performance is somewhat of a compromise because of the lack of a ground-plane but allows a permanent mount without holes, clamps, or magnets.

(A)

(B)

Figure 16.6 — (A) shows an adjustable lip mount made by Diamond. (B) is a close-up of the mount showing the set screws that hold the mount to the vehicle and make an electrical connection to the vehicle.

The outside surface of the coaxial feed line also becomes part of an on-glass antenna because there is no ground-plane, creating a path for common mode current. This allows the coax to both radiate and pick up noise in the vehicle interior.

Luggage Rack Mounts

The biggest issue with using luggage racks as an antenna mount is excessive ground loss. Most luggage racks consist of plastics, composites, and insulated metal beams electrically isolated from the vehicle's metal body. As such, they rarely provide a good ground-plane for the antenna and routing the feed line through door or window weather seals can create leaks. Like on-glass antenna mounts, luggage rack mounting is a compromise for when a permanent mount is not possible

Magnet Mounts

Mag (magnet) mounts are very popular for VHF and UHF operation. They rely on capacitance to make their electrical connection to the vehicle ground plane, so common-mode current on the feed line shield can become a problem. Nevertheless, mag mounts do deliver acceptable performance at VHF and UHF.

Mag mounts are available with the antenna and feed line attached as in **Figure 16.7** or as the mount by itself. There are mag mounts for any of the popular antenna bases — NMO, stud mount, and SO-239. A spare dual-band mag mount, a set of VHF and UHF whips, and several coax connector adapters are a valuable addition to your emergency response capabilities.

Be wary of the fine grit that can work its way under the magnet and scratch the paint. If you do use a mag mount for long periods of time, remove it and clean the magnet surface occasionally. For temporary installations, a plastic sandwich

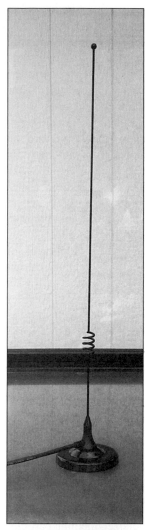

Figure 16.7 — A typical dual-band VHF/UHF mag mount with an integral antenna and feed line.

Figure 16.8 — The mirror-mount style of clamp-on bracket. This particular bracket is drilled for an SO-239 to ⅜-24 stud mount. The bracket can be mounted on vertical or horizontal struts.

bag around the magnet protects the finish against grit while still maintaining a solid attachment.

Specialty Brackets and Adapters

Because there are so many variations in vehicles there are many different types of brackets for mounting antennas. One of the most common is the three-way mirror mount in **Figure 16.8** that is sold by many companies. This particular version is drilled to pass the shoulder insulator of the SO-239 to ⅜-24 threaded stud-mount adapter shown in the foreground. You can find a wide variety of brackets at hamfest flea markets, from vendors of antenna accessories, online from manufacturers and distributors, and at truck stops and CB shops.

The performance of the antenna depends on the size of what the bracket is attached to. Most mirrors mounts are just barely big enough to act as a counterpoise at UHF but if they are securely mounted to a metal vehicle body, performance will be acceptable. The radiation pattern of the antenna will rarely be omnidirectional due to the off-center antenna placement.

Adapters are also available that convert mounts such as the NMO to other types of bases and connectors, such as the various stud mounts and SO-239 connector. This allows your antenna mount to accommodate other types of antennas but generally increases the length of the antenna by an inch or so, lowering the antenna's resonant frequency. A few mount adapters should be included in your mobile equipment kit.

16.3 PROJECT: MOBILE WHIPS FOR VHF AND UHF

16.3.1 ¼-WAVELENGTH WHIPS FOR VHF AND UHF

The ¼-wavelength vertical whip is simple to make and can be made for nearly any type of mount. The preferred stainless steel wire or rod is available from two-way radio shops and CB antenna dealers. Cut the whip to length using a grinding wheel or score it with a file and break it — use eye protection! Any type of wire can be used in a pinch. Coat hangers, copper wire from home wiring cable, galvanized fence wire — all have been successfully used to replace broken or missing whips. Being able to repair or substitute for a broken antenna is a skill any amateur can learn for flexibility and resiliency during emergency situations.

Table 16-1 shows the approximate lengths for ¼-λ whips in the VHF and UHF amateur bands based on a ³⁄₃₂-inch diameter whip. Thinner whips will be slightly longer and thicker whips slightly shorter. Be sure to include the antenna base in the total length of the antenna. If the base holds the whip with a set screw, cut the whip approximately 5% long and adjust for best SWR before making a final trim to length.

Table 16-1
¼-Wavelength Whip Lengths

Frequency (MHz)	Length (inches)
53	53
146	19³⁄₁₆
222	12⁵⁄₈
440	6
902	2⁷⁄₁₆

16.3.2 ⅝-WAVELENGTH WHIP FOR 2 METERS

As compared to a ¼-λ whip, the ⅝-λ whip has 1 dB of gain. This antenna is suitable for mobile or fixed-station use because it is small, omnidirectional, and can be used with radials or a solid-plane ground (such as a car body). If radials are used, they need be only ¼-λ long. The whip can be any tempered rod or wire that will spring easily.

Construction

The antenna shown here is made from low-cost materials. **Figure 16.9** shows the base coil and aluminum mounting plate. The coil form is a piece of low-loss solid rod, such as plexiglass or phenolic. The dimensions for this and other parts of the antenna are given in **Figure 16.10**. A length of brazing rod is used as the whip section.

The whip should be 47 inches long. However, brazing rod comes in standard 36-inch lengths, so if used, it is necessary to solder an 11-inch extension to the top of the whip. A piece of #10 AWG copper wire will suffice. Alternatively, a stainless-steel rod can be purchased to make a 47-inch whip. Shops that sell CB antennas should have such rods for replacement purposes on base-loaded antennas. The limitation one can expect with brazing rod is the relative fragility of the material, especially when the threads are cut for screwing the rod into the base coil form. Excessive stress can cause the rod to break where it enters the form. The problem is complicated

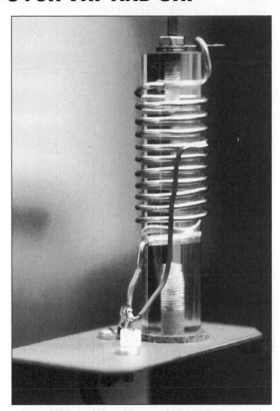

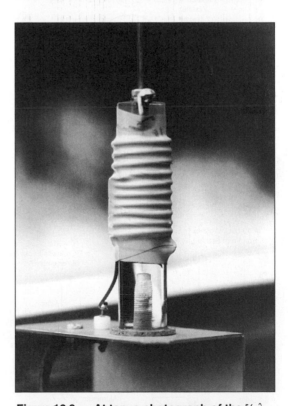

Figure 16.9 — At top, a photograph of the ⅝-λ vertical base section. The matching coil is affixed to an aluminum bracket that screws onto the inner lip of the car trunk. Below is the completed assembly. The coil has been wrapped with electrical tape to keep out dirt and moisture.

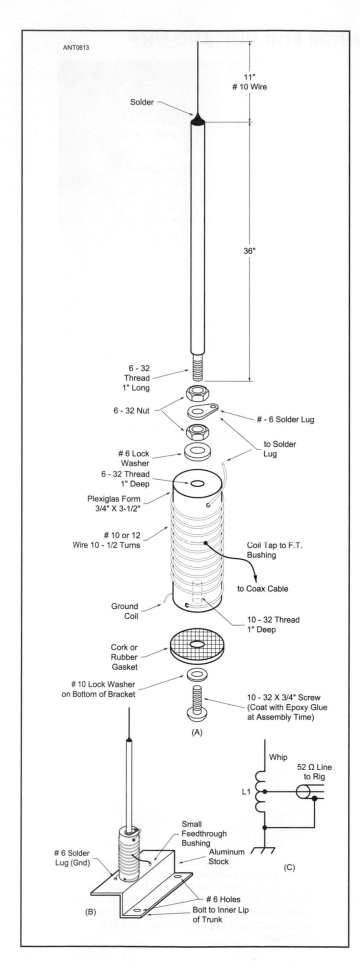

ANT0613

11"
10 Wire

Solder

36"

6 - 32
Thread
1" Long

6 - 32 Nut

- 6 Solder Lug

6 Lock
Washer

to Solder
Lug

6 - 32 Thread
1" Deep

Plexiglas Form
3/4" X 3-1/2"

10 or 12
Wire 10 - 1/2 Turns

Coil Tap to F.T.
Bushing

to Coax Cable

Ground
Coil

10 - 32 Thread
1" Deep

Cork or
Rubber
Gasket

10 Lock Washer
on Bottom of Bracket

10 - 32 X 3/4" Screw
(Coat with Epoxy Glue
at Assembly Time)

(A)

Whip

52 Ω Line
to Rig

L1

(C)

Small
Feedthrough
Bushing

6 Solder
Lug (Gnd)

Aluminum
Stock

6 Holes
Bolt to Inner Lip
of Trunk

(B)

Figure 16.10 — Structural details for the 2 meter ⅝-λ antenna are provided at A. The mounting bracket is shown at B and the equivalent circuit is given at C.

somewhat in this design because a spring is not used at the antenna mounting point. Builders of this antenna can find all kinds of solutions to the problems just outlined by changing the physical design and using different materials when constructing the antenna. The main purpose of this description is to provide dimensions and tune-up information.

The aluminum mounting bracket must be shaped to fit the car with which it will be used. The bracket can be used to create a no-holes mount with respect to the exterior portion of the car body. The inner lip of the vehicle trunk (or hood) can be the point where the bracket is attached by means of #6 or #8 sheet-metal screws. The remainder of the bracket is bent so that when the trunk lid or car hood is raised and lowered, there is no contact between the bracket and the moving part. Details of the mounting unit are given in Fig 16.10B. For rigidity, 14-gauge metal (or thicker) is recommended.

Wind 10½ turns of #10 or #12 AWG copper wire on the ¾-inch diameter coil form. The tap on L1 is placed approximately four turns below the whip end. A secure solder joint is imperative.

Tune-Up

After the antenna has been mounted on the vehicle, connect an SWR bridge in the 50-Ω feed line. (An antenna analyzer could also be used without the requirement of transmitting a signal during antenna adjustment.) Key the 144-MHz transmitter and experiment with the coil tap placement. If the whip section is 47 inches long, an SWR of 1:1 can be obtained when the tap is at the right location. As an alternative method of adjustment, place the tap at four turns from the top of L1, make the whip 50 inches long, and trim the whip length until an SWR of 1:1 occurs. Keep the antenna well away from other objects during tune-up, as they may detune the antenna and yield false adjustments for a match.

16.3.3 ⅝-WAVELENGTH MOBILE WHIP FOR 222 MHZ

The antenna shown in **Figures 16.11** and **16.12** is similar to the 2 meter version discussed in the previous section. The base insulator portion is made of ½-inch plexiglass rod. A few minutes' work on a lathe is sufficient to shape and drill the rod. (The innovative builder can use an electric drill and a file for the lathe work.) The bottom ½-inch of the rod is turned down to a diameter of ⅜-inch. This portion will now fit into a PL-259 UHF connector. A ⅛-inch diameter hole is drilled through the center of the rod. This hole will hold the wires that make the connections between the center conductor of the connector and the coil tap. The connection between the whip and the top of the coil is also run through this opening. A stud is force-fitted into the top of the plexiglass rod. This

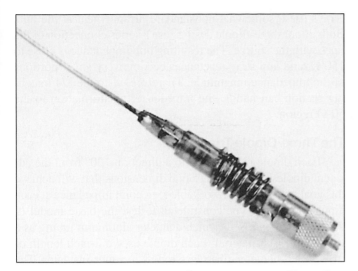

Figure 16.11 — The 222-MHz ⅜-λ mobile antenna. The coil turns are spaced over a distance of 1 inch and the bottom end of the coil is soldered to the coax connector.

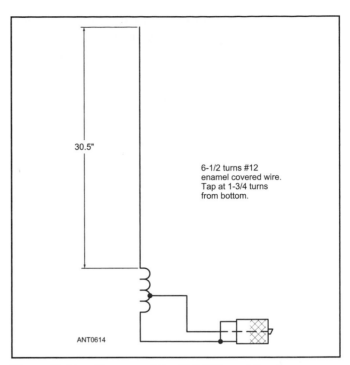

30.5"

6-1/2 turns #12 enamel covered wire. Tap at 1-3/4 turns from bottom.

ANT0614

Figure 16.12 — Diagram of the 222-MHz mobile antenna.

allows for removal of the whip from the insulator.

The coil should be initially wound on a form slightly smaller than the base insulator. When the coil is transferred to the plexiglass rod, it will keep its shape and will not readily move. After the tap point has been determined, a longitudinal hole is drilled into the center of the rod. A #22 AWG wire can then be inserted through the center of the insulator into the connector. This method is also used to attach the whip to the top of the coil. After the whip has been fully assembled,

a coating of epoxy cement is applied. This seals the entire assembly and provides some additional strength. During a full winter's use there was no sign of cracking or other mechanical failure. The adjustment procedure is the same as for the 144-MHz version described above.

16.4 PROJECT: BIG WHEEL FOR TWO METERS

The following section is an overview of the construction project, "A New Spin on the Big Wheel" by L. B. Cebik, W4RNL (SK), and Bob Cerreto, WA1FXT, in the March 2008 issue of *QST*. The complete article detailing the design's history, evolution, and critical elements is available on this book's CD-ROM with all construction details and drawings.

Most attempts to develop a horizontally polarized omnidirectional (HPOD) 2 meter antenna have sought to minimize the antenna's size. Shapes such as circles (halos), squares and

rectangles usually result in the need for either hypercritical dimensions or difficult matching conditions — or both. By turning to more conventional full size structures using three dipoles, we can reduce the number of critical parameters and ease the process of replicating the antennas in a home workshop. In fact, we shall describe two versions of the same basic antenna. One is a triangle of three dipoles that folds into a flat package, suitable for easy transport to a hilltop. The other is a circle of three dipoles suitable for mobile operation that

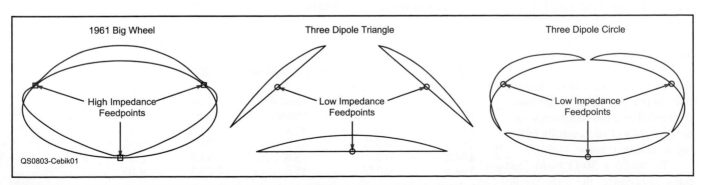

1961 Big Wheel

High Impedance Feedpoints

Three Dipole Triangle

Low Impedance Feedpoints

Three Dipole Circle

Low Impedance Feedpoints

QS0803-Cebik01

Figure 16.13 — Relative current magnitudes on three different three element HPOD antennas.

requires somewhat less space but needs greater precision in construction. Both antennas share a common feed system and display broadband characteristics that ease the builder's task.

The Three Dipole Design

The center and right outlines in **Figure 16.13** show the basic triangular and circular forms that emerged from the original design at left. Note that the current magnitude curves place the feed points of the dipoles at high current, relatively low impedance positions.

Both forms are very broadband in virtually every operating parameter once the builder gets the dimensions correct. The triangle, with a wider separation between the dipole end tips, is less critical with respect to dimensions, but requires more space. The circular version, with tighter coupling between dipole tips, requires more careful construction, but results in a more compact structure. In fact, for the same performance, the circular three-dipole antenna is smaller than the original big wheel.

The far-field performance of the three-dipole HPODs and the big wheel are virtually identical. Therefore, the data in **Figure 16.14** applies equally to all three designs. At a height of 20 feet above average ground, the three elements in all of the designs provide an average gain in the lowest lobe of about 7.2 dBi. The azimuth pattern is as close to circular as is possible with fewer than four elements. The gain variation for the worst case was less than 0.3 dB.

The modeled SWR curve applies to both of the three-dipole models. Because the dipoles of the final designs present feed point impedance close to 50 Ω, we may use standard coaxial cable of virtually any length to reach the hub without changing the impedance significantly. Matched to a 50-Ω main feed point at the hub junction, the SWR curve is very flat and in the model shown in the graph, the SWR is acceptable (well under 2:1) for at least 8 MHz in the 2 meter range. Moreover, the circularity of the pattern and the gain are virtually constant across the entire 2 meter band. Even though the antenna is likely to see service only in the first MHz of the band, the broadband characteristics ease the difficulty of successfully building a version at home.

To obtain a 50-Ω main feed point impedance, the three-dipole

arrays use a somewhat nonstandard arrangement at the hub. Both of our three-dipole designs use a series connection of the lines with the source. The resulting hub impedance is close to 150 Ω, and any stray reactances become very small portions of the impedance magnitude. Therefore, a simple λ/4 matching section can handle the impedance transformation to the 50-Ω region.

The Three-Dipole Triangle

Each dipole is broadside to a direction 120° from the adjacent dipoles. The goal is to find dimensions that will achieve this goal plus provide a workable feed point impedance at each dipole. The prototype constructed to test the basic model of this arrangement used ½-inch diameter aluminum tubing as a light but sturdy material. Each dipole used a 2-inch length of 0.375-inch diameter fiberglass rod as a center insulator. The dipole halves are held in place with #6 stainless steel sheet metal screws. The gap should be as small as is feasible, ⅛ to ¼ inch. These same screws fasten the ends of the coax cable to the element with a stainless steel washer to prevent electrolysis between the aluminum element and the copper wires. For ease

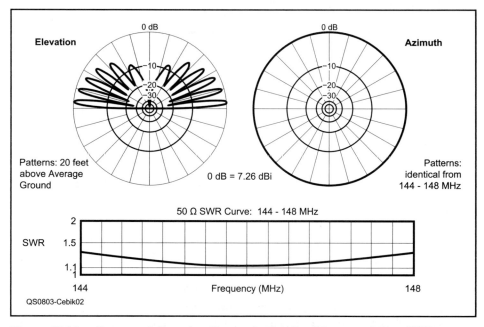

Figure 16.14 — Representative elevation and azimuth patterns and 50-Ω SWR curve for a three-dipole HPOD antenna using either a triangular or a circular shape at 20 feet above average ground. The patterns of the original big wheel are virtually identical in shape and strength.

Table 16-2
Dimensions for a Three-Dipole 2 Meter Triangle

Design Frequency (MHz)	Element Diameter (inches)	Radius to Feed Point (inches)	Dipole Length (inches)	Tip-to-tip Spacing (inches)
146	0.5	15.4	34.3	9.5
146	0.375	15.3	34.7	9.15
144.5	0.5	15.6	34.7	9.6
144.5	0.375	15.5	35.1	9.25

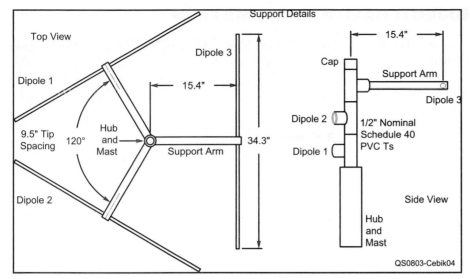

Figure 16.15 — Some details of the support structure used for the three-dipole 2 meter triangle.

than an independent dipole composed of the same material. The resonant impedance (50 Ω) is lower than the usual value for a standard dipole of about 70 Ω. The three dipoles in the triangle do interact by virtue of both the proximity of their feed points and the closeness of their tips. The dimensions of the triangle are therefore quite critical to successful operation of the array as designed. However, in the triangular form, they are not finicky, and cutting errors of ⅛ to ¼ inch will not materially affect performance.

In fact, the relatively relaxed conditions for the triangle prompted the particular design that emerged. The prototype may be useful for field or hilltop service, since the support structure and the elements and their cable come apart and store in a flat package for transport. **Figure 16.15** provides a few of the support structure details and **Figure 16.16** shows the antenna disassembled for transport.

For a permanent installation or for mobile use, you may prefer a circle of three dipoles as shown in **Figure 16.17**. The circle has no loose dipole ends and is more compact than the triangle. Indeed, it is aesthetically more pleasing. However, such pleasure comes at a cost. The construction and adjustment of the elements are somewhat more critical, although completely manageable.

of disassembly in portable operation, the prototype used lugs under the screws.

Table 16-2 lists some dimensions for both 0.5- and 0.375-inch aluminum tubing, perhaps the two most likely materials for this project. For the triangle, 146 MHz was used as the design frequency because the performance and the SWR do not significantly change across the band. This center-design frequency also provided a good view of the antenna's broadband properties. However, the table also lists dimensions that are usable if the builder wishes to place the performance center of the antenna at 144.5 MHz. The prototype used the half-inch-diameter material and the 146 MHz dimensions for that material.

Note the length of the dipole. It is about 3.3 inches shorter

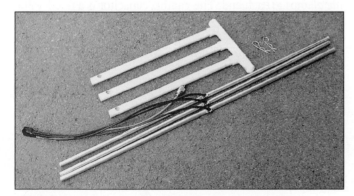

Figure 16.16 — The triangle HPOD disassembled for transport.

Figure 16.17 — The circular HPOD suitable for mobile use.

16.5 PROJECT: HALO FOR SIX METERS

The following section is based on the construction project, "A 6 Meter Halo" by Paul Danzer, N1II, in the September 2004 issue of *QST*. The complete article is available on this book's CD-ROM with all construction details and drawings. This inexpensive halo — the basic design was originally published in the 1975 *ARRL Handbook* — satisfies several key elements for an inexpensive 6 meter antenna: omnidirectional, horizontal polarization, no exotic components or materials, easy to adjust. With care, the construction should be robust enough for mobile use.

The halo is basically a half-wave dipole bent into a circle and fed with a gamma match. **Figure 16.18** shows the basic design and list of typical dimensions. The resonant frequency is quite sensitive to tip-to-tip spacing at the ends of the dipole but should initially be in the range of 50 to 52 MHz without requiring critical measurements or assembly.

Figure 16.19 is a photograph of the finished antenna, built from 20 feet of copper tubing and ¾-inch schedule 40 PVC pipe and fittings. The vertical support mast and horizontal supports are also PVC pipe. As the author notes, make sure the PVC fittings are aligned properly after the cement is applied as bonding takes place almost instantly and they can't be realigned.

Copper tubing can be formed into a circle by hand. The open ends of the halo and the gamma match are attached with ⅜-inch #8 or #10 sheet metal screws to PVC pipe stubs mounted in a PVC T fitting on the horizontal support. (See **Figure 16.20.**) The ends of the tubing are flattened with a vise or hammer and drilled for the screws. Tune the antenna first before permanently attaching the tubing ends to the support. Use short screws to avoid adding significant surface area after tuning is completed.

At the mounting point on the vertical mast, the center of the halo can be attached with a pair of copper tubing clamps as shown in **Figure 16.21** or the tubing simply flattened and

Figure 16.19 — The halo from the rear. A copper strap connects the matching section to the halo on the left.

Figure 16.20 — The ends of the tubing are flattened and attached to the PVC pipe stubs with sheet metal screws.

attached with a sheet metal screw. (The latter technique may not be strong enough to withstand highway speed mobile use.)

The gamma shorting bar is made from a short piece of strap, braid, or heavy wire attached to a pair of copper tubing clamps at each end. The gamma capacitor is a fixed-value

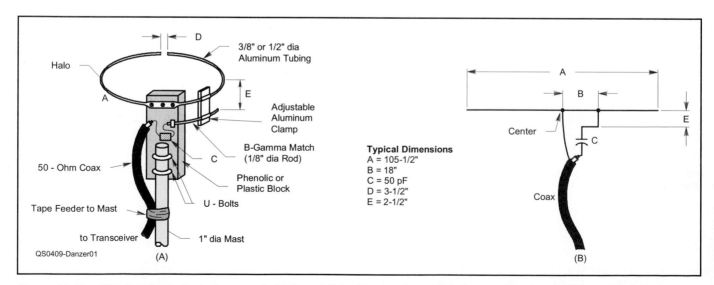

Typical Dimensions
A = 105-1/2"
B = 18"
C = 50 pF
D = 3-1/2"
E = 2-1/2"

QS0409-Danzer01

Figure 16.18 — The 6 meter halo design as originally published in the 1975 *ARRL Handbook*. The author substituted copper tubing in his version.

Figure 16.21 — Details of the feed connection. The main element could be mounted using the flattened tube approach instead of with clamps as shown.

capacitor as shown in the photograph. To connect the feed line, the author used an SO-239 connector mounted on a bracket attached to the vertical support mast. (See Figure 16.21.) Solid wire, strap, or tinned braid may be used for the connection between the SO-239 and the main element of the antenna.

Use an anti-oxidation compound such as Noalox or Penetrox for all unsoldered metal-to-metal connections to avoid corrosion.

Tuning the Halo

Tuning of the halo's resonant frequency can be done by changing the size of the gap between the dipole ends. Use electrical tape to temporarily attach the tubing ends to the PVC pipe stubs. Once you are satisfied with results, mark and drill the PVC fitting, then attach the tubing with the sheet metal screws.

To adjust the gamma match for lowest SWR at the resonant frequency, a 50-100 pF variable capacitor can be used. Once the proper setting has been obtained, measure the variable capacitor's value and replace it permanently with a fixed value capacitor. The author used two capacitors in series for the final value of less than 20 pF. The antenna then presented an SWR of less than 2:1 over the range of 50.0 to 50.4 MHz. Be sure to use capacitors rated for at least 100 V for use at 100 W and higher voltages if higher power is used.

Waterproof the electrical connections at the SO-239 and gamma capacitor connections with silicone sealant.

Other Halo Designs

Construction of halos and squalos is a popular antenna-building activity. You may also enjoy reading two additional construction articles included on this book's CD-ROM; "Six Meters from your Easy Chair," by Dick Stroud, W9SR in the January 2002 issue of *QST* and one of the original halo articles, "A Two-Band Halo for V.H.F. Mobile," by Ed Tilton, W1HDQ, in the September 1958 issue of *QST*.

TABLE OF CONTENTS

Chapter 17

Antennas for Space Communications

When we consider amateur space communications, we usually think about two basic modes: satellite and Earth-Moon-Earth (EME — also referred to as *moonbounce*). At their essence, both modes communicate using one of the Earth's satellites — our natural satellite (the Moon) or one of a variety of man-made satellites. (Antennas for meteor scatter modes are covered in the **VHF and UHF Antenna Systems** chapter.) The distances involved and the motion of the targets place special requirements on antennas for both types of communications as discussed in this chapter.

Because of technological advances, particularly regarding new digital modes that allow communications with extremely weak signals, the traditional distinction between antenna systems for satellite communications and for EME communications has become blurred. Thus, this chapter has been rearranged by antenna type and then specific requirements for each type of operation are discussed.

Material in this chapter has been contributed by several authors. Dick Jansson, KD1K, developed satellite-related topics while the EME material is largely the work of Dave Hallidy, K2DH and Joe Taylor, K1JT. References to KD1K also include material contributed with the call sign WD4FAB, Jansson's previous call sign. Wherever possible, designs referenced or illustrated in the text are also listed in the Bibliography. For additional information on constructing antennas, feeds and equipment techniques for use at microwave frequencies, see the ARRL and RSGB books listed in the Bibliography. All of these books provide a wealth of information for the experimenter.

17.1 SPACE COMMUNICATION ANTENNA SYSTEMS

There are two main differences between the Moon and man-made satellites in orbits closer to the Earth. The first is one of distance. The Moon is about 250,000 miles from Earth, while man-made satellites in highly elliptical orbits can be as far as 52,000 miles away. This 5:1 difference in distance makes a huge difference in the signals that arrive at the satellite, since transmission loss varies as the square of the distance. In other words, the signal arriving at the Moon is 20 dB weaker than that arriving at a geosynchronous satellite 25,000 miles high, due to distance alone.

The second difference between the Moon and a man-made satellite is that the Moon is a *passive reflector* — and not a very good one at that, since it has a craggy and rather irregular surface, at least when compared to a flat mirror-like surface that would make an ideal reflector. Signals scattered by the Moon's irregular surface are thus weaker than those for better reflecting surfaces. By comparison, a man-made satellite is an *active* system, where the satellite receives the signal coming from Earth, amplifies it and then retransmits the signal (usually at a different frequency) using a high-gain antenna. Think of a satellite as an ideal reflector, with gain.

The net result of these differences between a man-made satellite and the Earth's natural satellite is that moonbounce (EME) operation challenges the station builder considerably more than satellite operation, particularly in the area of antennas. Successful EME requires higher transmitting power and receiver sensitivity, along with sophisticated computer software for digital modes or an excellent operator capable of pulling weak analog signals out of the noise.

There are areas of commonality between satellite and EME antenna requirements, of course. Both require consideration of the effects of polarization and elevation angle, along with the azimuth directions of transmitted and received signals. High-performance Yagi arrays or helical antenna systems designed for satellite operation will likely suffice to make EME contacts using digital modes such as those of the *WSJT* software suite (**www.physics.princeton. edu/pulsar/K1JT**). Dish antennas, such as those converted from commercial C-band (4-8 GHz range) TVRO (television, receive only) service will certainly suffice for both types of communication.

This chapter will first explore antennas suitable for satellite operations and then describe the antennas needed for EME work.

17.1.1 ANTENNA SYSTEMS FOR SATELLITES

Amateur satellites provide links from 2 meters and up and these provide opportunities to use antennas of many types — from the very simple to the pretty complex. Antenna design and construction requirements for use with amateur satellites vary from low-gain antennas for low-Earth-orbit (LEO) satellites to higher-gain antennas for the high-altitude elliptical-orbit satellites (HEO). The AMSAT website (**www. amsat.org**) is a good general resource for antenna and transceiver design, operating information and satellite parameters.

Contacts can be made via FM LEO satellites with a basic dual-band VHF/UHF FM transceiver. Some amateurs manage to work the FM birds with hand-held radios and a multielement directional antenna such as the popular Arrow Antenna shown in **Figure 17.1A**. Of course, this means they must aim their antennas at the satellites, even as they cross overhead. Other operators have even had success using an FM hand-held radio with the stock "rubber duck" antenna although the extended flexible antenna as shown in Figure 17.1B provides for a better signal.

High-quality omnidirectional antennas for LEO service come in quite a number of forms and shapes. M^2 Enterprises EB-144 and EB-432 Eggbeater antennas have proven to be very useful and do not require any rotators for control. See **Figure 17.2**. The turnstile-over-reflector antenna has been around for a long time, as shown in **Figure 17.3**.

For even better performance, at the modest cost of a single, simple TV antenna rotator, check out the fixed-elevation *Texas Potato Masher* antenna by Gerald Brown, K5OE shown in **Figure 17.4.** This antenna provides a dual-band solution for medium-gain directional antennas for LEO satellites. This is a considerable improvement over omnidirectional antennas and does not require an elevation rotator for good performance.

There was still one early LEO satellite operating on the 10 meter band as of early 2011; the 1974 AO-7 spontaneously

(A)

(B)

Figure 17.1 — At A, Keith Baker, KB1SF/VA3KSF, uses a Kenwood TH-78A dual-band handheld and a lightweight Arrow Antenna to make a contact through AO-51 from the shores of Lake Huron in Michigan. When used with a full-duplex handheld in an open location free of foliage, such as a beach or field, the antenna provides enough uplink and downlink gain to successfully work the FM birds, even on passes close to the horizon. (KB1OGF/VA3OGF photo) At B, Kate Baker, KB1OGF/VA3OGF, makes a contact through AO-51 satellite on the shores of Lake Huron in Michigan with her Kenwood TH-78A dual-band HT. The extended flexible antenna (MFJ Model 1717 from MFJ Enterprises) and about 5 W of uplink power provides just enough gain on the uplink and downlink to briefly work the satellite on near overhead passes. (KB1SF/VA3KSF photo)

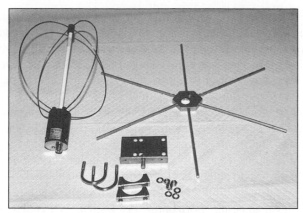

Figure 17.2 — Eggbeater antennas are popular for base station LEO satellite operations. This M² EB-432 eggbeater antenna for 70 cm is small enough to put in an attic. Antenna gain pattern is helped with the radials placed below the antenna.

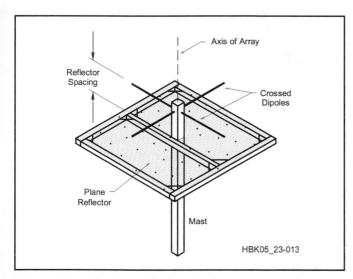

Figure 17.3 — The Turnstile Over Reflector antenna has served well for LEO satellite service for a number of years.

Figure 17.4 — Jerry Brown, K5OE, uses his Texas Potato Masher antennas to work LEO satellites.

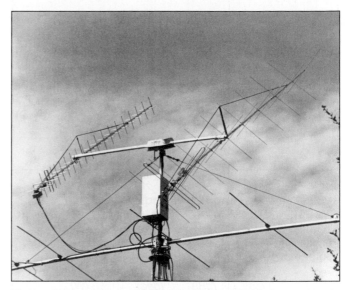

Figure 17.5 — Dick Jansson, KD1K, used these 2 meter and 70 cm crossed Yagis for HEO operations. The satellite antennas are shown mounted above a 6 meter long-boom Yagi.

recovered from a battery failure and can be used whenever its solar panels are illuminated. Its 10 meter downlink covers 29.3 to 29.5 MHz. Low-gain antennas for 10 meters, such as dipoles or long-wire antennas, are used to receive the signal from this satellite.

High-altitude Phase 3 satellites such as the now defunct AO-10 and AO-13 were deployed in the 1980s and another similar satellite is under development by AMSAT-DL). Ultimately there may be geostationary satellites for amateur use and the same requirements would apply as well to them. The greater distances to these satellites mean that more transmitted power is needed to access them and weaker signals are received on the ground. Successful stations usually require ground-station antennas with significant gain (12 dBi or more), such as a set of high-gain Yagi antennas. See **Figure 17.5**.

Satellite S-band (2.4 GHz) downlinks have become very popular for HEO operations for a variety of reasons:
- Good performance with physically small downlink antennas.
- Availability of good quality downconverters.
- Availability of preamps at reasonable prices.

A number of people advocate S-band operation, including Bill McCaa, KØRZ, who led the team that designed and built the AO-13 S-band transponder and James Miller, G3RUH, who operated one of the AO-40 command stations. Ed Krome, K9EK, and James Miller have published a number of articles detailing construction of preamps, downconverters and antennas for S band. (See **Table 17-1** for a list of the satellite band designations used throughout this chapter.)

Table 17-1
Amateur Satellite Band Designations
10 meters (29 MHz): H
2 meters (145 MHz): V
70 cm (435 MHz): U
23 cm (1260 MHz): L
13 cm (2.4 GHz): S
5 cm (5.6 GHz): C
3 cm (10 GHz): X

17.1.2 ANTENNA SYSTEMS FOR EARTH-MOON-EARTH (EME)

The antenna is arguably the most important element in determining an EME station's capability. It is not accidental that the baseline station requirements outlined in **Table 17-2** use Yagi arrays on the VHF bands and parabolic dishes at 1296 MHz and above. One of these two antenna types is almost always the best choice for EME.

Table 17-2
Typical Antenna and Power Requirements for CW EME

For use with JT65 or other encoded digital modes, subtract approximately 10 dB of gain or power.

Freq (MHz)	Ant Type[1]	G (dBi)	HPBW (deg)	TxPwr (W)
50	4×12 m	19.7	18.8	1200
144	4×6 m	21.0	15.4	500
432	4×6 m	25.0	10.5	250
1296	3 m	29.5	5.5	160
2304	3 m	34.5	3.1	60
3456	2 m	34.8	3.0	120
5760	2 m	39.2	1.8	60
10368	2 m	44.3	1.0	25

[1]Example antennas for 50, 144 and 432 MHz are Yagi arrays with stated lengths; those for 1296 MHz and higher are parabolic dishes of specified diameter.

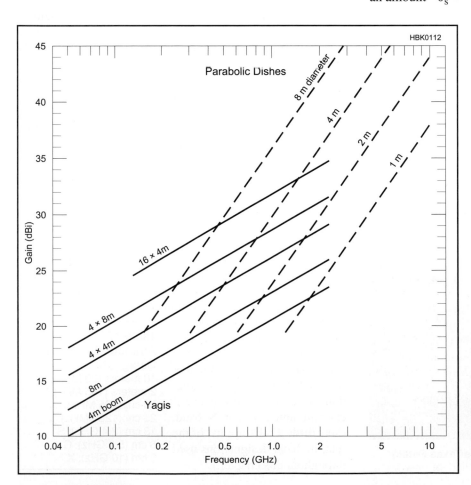

The gains of some nominal antennas of each type are illustrated graphically in **Figure 17.6**, which helps to show why Yagis are nearly always the best choice for EME on the VHF bands. They are light, easy to build and have relatively low wind resistance. Stacks of four Yagis are small enough that they can be mounted on towers for sky coverage free of nearby obstructions. Larger arrays of 8, 16 or even more Yagis are possible, although the complexity and losses in phasing lines and power dividers then become important considerations, especially at higher frequencies. Long Yagis are narrowband antennas, usable on just a single band.

We usually think of the linear polarization of a transmitted signal as being "horizontal" or "vertical." Of course, on the spherical Earth these concepts have meaning only locally. As seen from the Moon, widely separated horizontal antennas may have very different orientations (see **Figure 17.7**). Therefore, in the absence of Faraday rotation an EME signal transmitted with horizontal polarization by station A will have its linear polarization misaligned at stations B and C by angles known as the spatial polarization offset. (Faraday rotation is a rotation of the polarization of radio waves when the waves travel through the ionosphere, in the presence of the Earth's magnetic field.) In Figure 17.7 the signal from A arrives with vertical polarization at B and at 45° to the horizon at C. Suppose C is trying to work A and $\theta_s = 45°$ is the spatial polarization offset from A to C. The return signal from C to A will be offset in the opposite direction, that is, by an amount $-\theta_s = -45°$. The Faraday rotation angle θ_F, on the other hand, has the same sign for transmission in both directions. Thus the net polarization shift from A to C is $\theta_F + \theta_s$, while that from C to A is $\theta_F - \theta_s$. If θ_F is close to any of the values ±45°, ±135°, ±225°, ..., then one of the net polarization shifts is nearly 90° while the other is close to 0°. The result for stations with fixed linear polarization will be apparent one-way propagation: for example, A can copy C, but C cannot copy A.

Obviously no two-way contact can be made under these conditions, so the operators must wait for more favorable circumstances or else implement some form of polarization control or polarization diversity. One cost-effective solution is to mount two full sets of Yagi elements at right angles on the same boom. Arrays of such cross-polarized or "Xpol" Yagis make especially attractive EME antennas

Figure 17.6 — Representative gains of practical Yagi antennas, arrays of Yagis and parabolic dishes as a function of frequency. Yagi arrays make the most cost-effective and convenient antennas for EME on the VHF bands, while parabolic dishes are generally the best choice above 1 GHz.

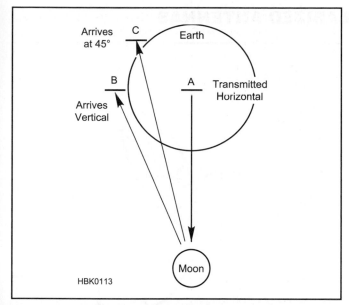

Figure 17.7 — The spherical Earth creates spatial polarization offsets for well-separated stations with horizon-oriented linear polarization. Here, a signal transmitted horizontally at A arrived with vertical polarization at B and midway between horizontal and vertical at C. When combined with Faraday rotation, offsets close to 45° can lead to apparent one-way propagation. See text for details.

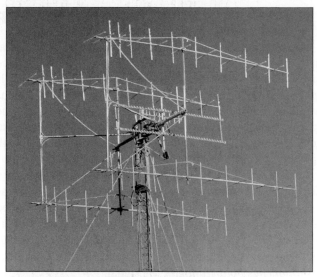

Figure 17.8 — Array of four 10-element, dual-polarization 144-MHz Yagis at KL7UW. Alaskan frost makes the horizontal and vertical elements stand out clearly. A pair of loop Yagis for 1296 MHz can be seen inside the 2 meter array.

on the VHF and lower UHF bands because they offer a flexible solution to the linear polarization misalignment problem. As an example, **Figure 17.8** shows the 4 × 10 element, dual-polarization EME array at KL7UW. This antenna and a 160-W solid-state amplifier have accounted for hundreds of EME contacts with the state of Alaska on 2 meters.

At 1296 MHz and above, gains of 30 dBi and more can be achieved with parabolic dishes of modest size. As a result, these antennas are almost always the best choice on these bands. Their structure does not depend on any radio frequency resonances, so in many ways dishes are less critical to build than Yagis. Element lengths in high-gain Yagis must be accurate to better than 0.005 λ, while the reflecting surface of a dish need be accurate only to about 0.1 λ.

A parabolic antenna has a single feed point, so there are no losses in phasing lines or power splitters. You can use a dish on several bands by swapping feeds, and with suitable feed designs you can produce either linear or circular polarization, including dual polarizations. A very attractive and convenient option is to transmit in one sense of circular polarization and receive in the opposite sense. Transmitting in right-hand circular and receiving in left-hand circular has become the standard for EME at 1296 and 2304 MHz, and will probably become the standard on higher bands as well. More information about circular polarization is presented later in this chapter.

As made clear in Figure 17.6, the 432 MHz band lies in a transition region where both Yagis and parabolic dishes have attractive features. Either four long Yagis or a 6 meter dish can produce enough gain (about 25 dBi) to let you work many other EME stations on this band. Many linear-polarization systems

are already in use — for good reason, since most amateur use of this band is for terrestrial communication — so converting everyone to circular polarization is impractical. Therefore, schemes have been devised to physically rotate dish feeds and even whole Yagi arrays to cope with the resulting polarization alignment problems. Another scheme is to use a dual-polarization dish feed or dual-polarization Yagis, as described above and increasingly used on 144 MHz. This approach has not yet gained wide popularity on 432 MHz, however.

Antenna Pattern

A clean pattern with good suppression of side and rear lobes is important for all EME antennas — especially at 432 MHz and above, where excessive noise pickup through sidelobes can significantly increase the system noise temperature, T_s. For Yagi arrays you should use modern, computer optimized designs that maximize G/T_s, the ratio of forward gain to system noise temperature. Be sure to pay attention to maintaining a clean pattern when stacking multiple antennas. First sidelobes within 10-15° of the main beam may not be a major problem, because their solid angle is small and they will look mostly at cold sky when EME conditions are favorable. Side and rear lobes farther from the main beam should be suppressed as much as possible, however. Remember that even close-in sidelobes will degrade your receiving performance at low elevations.

For parabolic dishes, G/T_s is optimized by using a feed with somewhat larger taper in illumination at the edge of the dish than would yield the highest forward gain. Best forward gain is generally obtained with edge taper around −10 dB, while best G/T_s occurs around −15 dB. Edge taper of −12 dB is usually a good compromise. Some good reproducible designs for dish feeds are described or referenced later in this chapter.

17.2 CIRCULARLY POLARIZED ANTENNAS

Linearly polarized antennas are horizontal or vertical in terms of the antenna's position relative to the surface of the Earth, a reference that loses its meaning in space. If spacecraft antennas used linear polarization, ground stations would not be able to maintain polarization alignment with the spacecraft because of its changing orientation. Thus the ideal antenna for random satellite signal polarization is one with *circular polarization* or *CP*.

Circular polarization is simply linear polarization with a direction that continually rotates as it travels through space as in **Figure 17.9**. The direction of polarization can be imagined as the second hand of a watch that is moving forward with the wave such that the second hand makes one complete revolution per wavelength traveled. The second hand represents the *instantaneous polarization* of the signal.

Figure 17.5 shows a pair of Yagi antennas mounted on each boom to provide circular polarization. (See the **Antenna Fundamentals** chapter for additional background on polarization.) There are several commonly used antennas with circular polarization described in the following sections.

Polarization Sense

Polarization *sense* is a critical factor, especially in EME and satellite work. The IEEE standard uses the term "clockwise circular polarization" for a *receding* wave (one traveling away from the observer). Amateur technology follows the IEEE standard, calling clockwise polarization for a receding wave as *right-hand circular polarization* or *RHCP*. This means that the second hand of the watch traveling with the receding wave is revolving clockwise. A wave for which polarization rotates in the opposition direction is *left-hand circular polarization* or *LHCP*.

When making satellite contacts using a circularly polarized antenna, it is often convenient to have the capability of switching polarization sense. This is because the sense of the received signal from some of the LEO satellites reverses when the satellite passes its nearest point to you. If the received signal has right-hand circular polarization as the satellite approaches, it may have left-hand circular polarization as the satellite recedes. A sense reversal occurs in EME communications as well, because of the phase reversal of the signal as it is reflected from the lunar surface. A signal transmitted with RHCP will be returned to the Earth with LHCP. Similarly, the polarization is reversed as it is reflected from a dish antenna so that to transmit an RHCP signal, the feed antenna for the dish needs to be LHCP.

17.2.1 CROSSED LINEAR ELEMENTS

Dipoles radiate linearly polarized signals and the polarization direction depends on the orientation of the antenna. If two dipoles are arranged as horizontal and vertical dipoles, and the two outputs are combined with the correct phase difference (90°), a circularly polarized wave results. Because the electric fields are identical in magnitude, the power from the transmitter will be divided equally between the two fields.

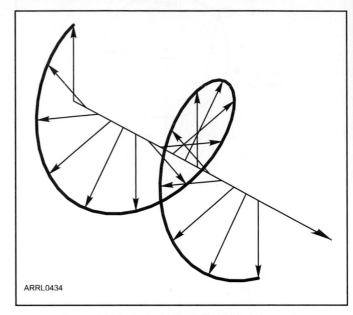

ARRL0434

Figure 17.9 — The polarization of a circularly polarized wavefront rotates around its central axis, either clockwise (right-hand or RHCP) or counterclockwise (left-hand or LHCP).

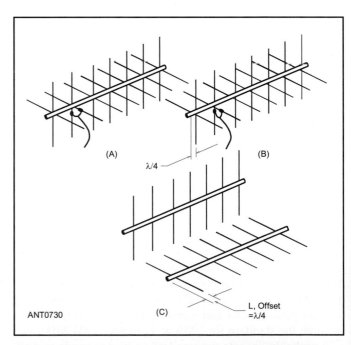

ANT0730

Figure 17.10 — Evolution of the circularly polarized Yagi. The simplest form of crossed Yagi, A, is made to radiate circularly by feeding the two driven elements 90° out of phase. Antenna B has the driven elements fed in phase, but has the elements of one bay mounted ¼ λ forward from those of the other. Antenna C offers elliptical (circular) polarization using separate booms. The elements in one set are perpendicular to those of the other and are ¼ λ forward from those of the other.

Figure 17.11 — This VHF crossed Yagi design by KH6IJ (Jan 1973 *QST*) illustrates the co-planar, fixed-circularity Yagi.

lines to a *coplanar pair* of crossed-Yagi antennas in which the elements lie approximately in the same plane, as shown in **Figure 17.10A**. One feed line section is ¼ λ longer than the other, as shown in Figure 17.10. These separate feed lines are then connected in parallel with a common transmission line to the transmitter or receiver. An example is shown in **Figure 17.11** and **Figure 17.12**. Assuming negligible coupling between the crossed antennas, the impedance presented to the common transmission line by the parallel combination is one half that of either section alone. (This is not true when there is mutual coupling between the antennas, as in phased arrays.)

This creates some difficulties for the antenna builder. With this phasing-line method, any mismatch at one antenna will be magnified by the extra ¼ λ of transmission line. This upsets the current balance between the two antennas, resulting in a loss of polarization circularity. Another factor to consider is the attenuation of the cables used in the harness, along with the connectors. Good low-loss coaxial line should be used with Type N or BNC connectors. A practical construction method for implementing a RHCP/LHCP coplanar switched system is shown in **Figure 17.13**.

Another method to obtain circular polarization is to use equal-length feed lines and place one antenna ¼ λ ahead of the other. This offset pair of Yagi-crossed antennas is shown in Figure 17.10B. The advantage of equal-length feed lines is that identical load impedances will be presented to the common feeder, as shown in **Figure 17.14**, which shows a fixed circularity-sense feed. To obtain a switchable-sense feed with the offset Yagi pair, you can use a configuration as in **Figure 17.15**, although you must compensate for the extra phase shift added by the relay and connectors.

Figure 17.10C diagrams a popular method of mounting

Another way of looking at this is to consider the power as being divided between the two antennas — hence the gain of each is decreased by 3 dB when taken alone in the plane of its orientation.

A 90° phase shift must exist between the two antennas and the simplest way to obtain this shift is to use two feed

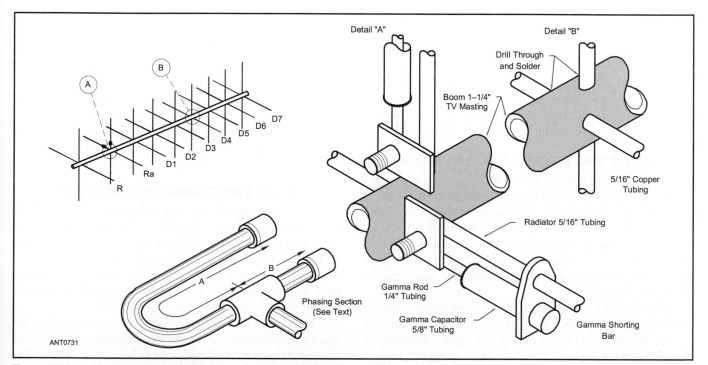

Figure 17.12 — Construction details of a co-planar crossed-Yagi antenna.

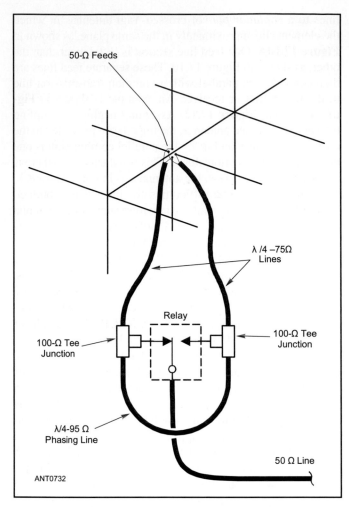

Figure 17.13 — Co-planar crossed Yagi, circularly polarized antenna with switchable polarization phasing harness.

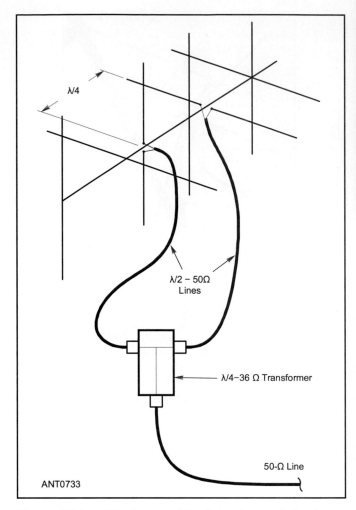

Figure 17.14 — Offset crossed-Yagi circularly polarized antenna-phasing harness with fixed polarization.

two separate off-the-shelf Yagis at right angles to each other. The two Yagis may be physically offset by ¼ λ and fed in parallel, as shown in Figure 17.10C, or they may be mounted with no offset and fed 90° out of phase. Neither of these arrangements on two separate booms produces true circular polarization. Instead, *elliptical* polarization results from such a system, an example of which is shown in **Figure 17.16**.

17.2.2 THE EGGBEATER ANTENNA

The eggbeater antenna shown in Figure 17.2 is a popular design named after the old-fashioned kitchen utensil it resembles. The antenna is composed of two full-wave loops of rigid wire or metal tubing. Each of the two loops has an impedance of 100 Ω, and when coupled in parallel they offer an ideal 50-Ω impedance for coaxial feed lines. The loops are fed 90° out of phase with each other and this creates a circularly polarized pattern.

An eggbeater may also use one or more parasitic reflector elements beneath the loops to focus more of the radiation pattern upward. This effect makes it a "gain" antenna, but that gain is at the expense of low-elevation reception. Toward the horizon an eggbeater is actually horizontally polarized.

As the pattern rises in elevation, it becomes more and more right-hand circularly polarized. Experience has shown that eggbeaters seem to perform best when reflector elements are installed just below the loops.

Eggbeaters can be built relatively easily, but commercial models such as the one shown in Figure 17.2 are available. The spherical shape of the eggbeater creates a fairly compact antenna when space is an issue, which is another reason why it is an attractive design. (See this book's CD-ROM.)

17.2.3 THE TURNSTILE ANTENNA

The basic turnstile antenna in Figure 17.3 consists of two horizontal half-wave dipoles mounted at right angles to each other (arranged like the letter "X") in the same horizontal plane with a reflector screen beneath. When these two antennas are excited with equal currents 90° out of phase, their typical figure-eight patterns merge to produce a nearly circular pattern. (See this book's CD-ROM.)

To get the radiation pattern in the upward direction for space communications, the turnstile antenna needs a reflector underneath. For a broad pattern it is best to maintain a distance of ⅜ λ at the operating frequency between the reflector

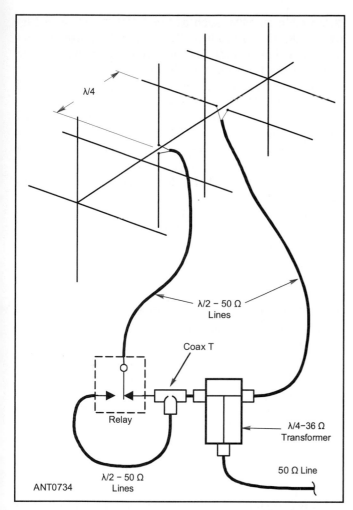

Figure 17.15 — Offset crossed-Yagi circularly polarized antenna-phasing harness with switchable polarization.

and the turnstile. Homemade turnstile reflectors often use metal window-screen material that you can pick up at many hardware stores. (Make sure it is a metal, not plastic, screen material.)

Like their cousins the eggbeaters, turnstiles are relatively easy to build. In fact, building one may be your only choice since turnstiles are rarely available off the shelf.

17.2.4 THE LINDENBLAD ANTENNA

The Lindenblad antenna shown in **Figure 17.17A** is constructed from linear elements, is circularly polarized, and has an omnidirectional radiation pattern. With most of its gain at low elevation angles as shown in Figure 17.17B,

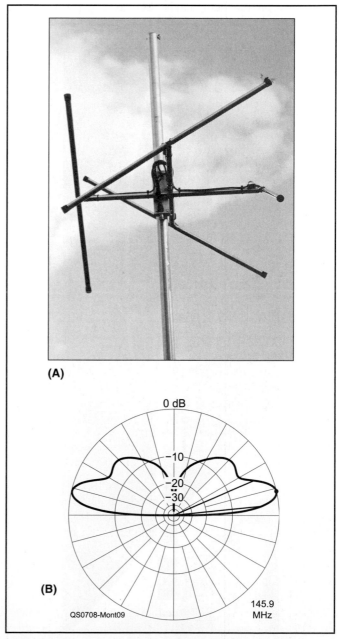

Figure 17.17 — The Lindenblad antenna in A has circular polarization and an omnidirectional azimuthal pattern as shown in B. (AA2TX photo)

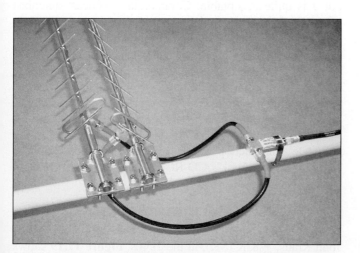

Figure 17.16 — An example of offset crossed-Yagi circularly polarized antennas with fixed polarization. This example is a pair of M2 23CMM22EZA antennas for 1296 MHz, mounted on an elevation boom.

it is ideal for accessing Low-Earth-Orbit (LEO) satellites. Because it is omnidirectional, it does not need to be pointed at a satellite, eliminating the need for an azimuth/elevation (az/el) rotator system. This makes the Lindenblad especially useful for portable or temporary satellite operations. It is also a good general purpose antenna for a home station because its circular polarization is compatible with the linearly polarized antennas used for FM/repeater and SSB/CW operation. Two complete construction articles for Lindenblad antennas are included on this book's CD-ROM.

17.2.5 THE QUADRIFILAR HELIX (QFH)

Designed for spacecraft use in the early days of space exploration, the *quadrifilar helix* (QFH) antenna (also called the quadrifilar helicoidal antenna) has not gained much popularity on the ham bands. Yet, as a general-purpose

Figure 17.18 — W6NBC's Quadrifilar Helix base station antenna (W6NBC photo)

base-station antenna, such as the 2 meter version in **Figure 17.18**, it's hard to beat. The pattern is almost omnidirectional in both planes, like the mythical *isotropic* radiator, receiving nearly to the horizon. No matter what direction signals come from, or whether the polarization is vertical or horizontal, the QFH receives them. It's good for overhead satellites, such as the International Space Station, for horizontally polarized 2 meter SSB simplex stations on the horizon, and also for vertically polarized mobile and repeater stations. It isn't a gain antenna — no true omni can be. The primary benefit of a QFH is the coverage afforded by its pattern.

The QFH is often used by hams for receiving weather satellite pictures from the 137 MHz NOAA automatic picture transmitting (APT) satellites in low polar orbit. Its omnidirectional and circular polarization characteristics accommodate the constantly changing direction and polarization of the APT satellite signals. Several have been built for this service. Three of these weather birds still fly by every day — NOAA 15, 17, 18 and 19. (Pictures of these satellites are available at **w6nbc.com**.)

The QFH can be envisioned as follows: Take two vertical full wavelength rectangular loops with open feed points *at the top*. Now place them on the same vertical axis, but with one loop rotated 90° horizontally so that they are in quadrature. Also, you need to make one loop slightly larger than the other. This creates a phase shift at the feed point to compensate for the physical rotation of the loops. Next, twist both loops horizontally a quarter turn into helices. Finally connect the feed points in parallel to create a quadrifilar helix antenna.

The curious eggbeater-like configuration of the QFH has useful characteristics — an almost perfectly spherical radiation pattern as well as circular polarization throughout the pattern. This version is right-handed. For left, twist the loops in the opposite direction. For the general purpose 2 meter base station antenna, the twist direction does not matter. And yes, there is a small loss working linear polarized signals (vertical or horizontal) with a circularly polarized antenna, but it is quite acceptable. Commercial broadcast antennas often use this very technique to accommodate both mobile (vertical) as well as home antennas (horizontal).

After experimenting ham style with square loops and tall versus thin rectangular ones, and the small size difference between the two loops as well as the amount of twist, it has been concluded that the QFH is a dimensionally tolerant design. The performance changed little with all these variations.

The antenna shown in Figure 17.18 is described in the complete construction article by John Portune, W6NBC, included on this book's CD-ROM along with another QFH construction article by Eugene Ruperto, W3KH.

17.2.6 HELICAL ANTENNAS

The axial-mode helical antenna was introduced by Dr John Kraus, W8JK (SK), in the 1940s. **Figure 17.19** shows examples of S-band (2400-MHz), V-band (145-MHz), and U-band (435-MHz) helical antennas, all constructed by KD1K for satellite service.

(A)

(B)

Figure 17.19 — At top, a 16-turn S-band helical antenna. This is about the maximum length of any practical helix. Note the SSB UEK2000 downconverter mounted behind the reflector of the antenna. At bottom, a pair of helical antennas for service on 2 meters and 70 cm. The 2 meter helical antenna is not small! (KD1K photos.)

This antenna has two characteristics that make it especially interesting and useful in many applications. First, the helix is circularly polarized with a fixed polarization sense determined by its configuration. The polarization rotates about the axis of the antenna.

The second interesting property of the helical antenna is its predictable pattern, gain and impedance characteristics over a wide frequency range. This is one of the few antennas with both broad bandwidth and high gain. The benefit of this property is that, when used for narrowband applications, the helical antenna is very forgiving of mechanical inaccuracies.

Probably the most common amateur use of the helical antenna is in satellite communications, where the spinning of the satellite antenna system (relative to the Earth) and the effects of *Faraday rotation* cause the polarization of the satellite signal to be unpredictable. Using a linearly polarized antenna in this situation can result in deep fading, but with the helical antenna (which responds equally to linearly polarized signals), fading is essentially eliminated.

This same characteristic makes helical antennas useful in polarization-diversity systems. The advantages of circular polarization have been demonstrated on VHF voice schedules over non-optical paths, in cases where linearly polarized beams did not perform satisfactorily.

Another use for the helical antenna is the transmission of color ATV signals. Many beam antennas (when adjusted for maximum gain) have far less bandwidth than the required 6 MHz, or lack uniform gain over this frequency range. The result is significant distortion of the transmitted and received signals, affecting color reproduction and other features. This problem becomes more aggravated over non-optical paths. The helix exhibits maximum gain (within 1 dB) across a range of more than 20 MHz anywhere above 420 MHz.

The helical antenna can be used to advantage with multimode rigs, especially above 420 MHz. Not only does the helix give high gain over an entire amateur band, but it also allows operation on FM, SSB and CW without the need for separate vertically and horizontally polarized antennas.

Helical Antenna Basics

The helical antenna is an unusual specimen in the antenna world, in that its physical configuration gives a hint to its electrical performance. A helix looks like a large air-wound coil with one of its ends fed against a ground plane, as shown in **Figure 17.20**. The ground plane is a screen of 0.8 to 1.1 λ diameter (or on a side for a square ground plane). The circumference (C_λ) of the coil form must be between 0.75 and 1.33 λ for the antenna to radiate in the axial mode. The

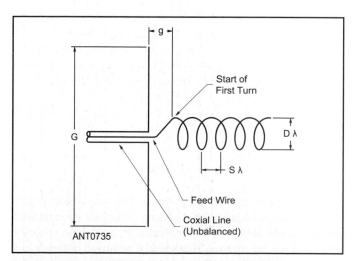

Figure 17.20 — The basic helical antenna and design parameters.

coil should have at least three turns to radiate in this mode. The ratio of the spacing between turns (in wavelengths), S_λ to C_λ, should be in the range of 0.2126 to 0.2867. This ratio range results from the requirement that the pitch angle, α, of the helix be between 12° and 16°, where:

$$\alpha - \arctan \frac{S_\lambda}{C_\lambda} \qquad \text{(Eq 1)}$$

These constraints result in a single main lobe along the axis of the coil. This is easily visualized from Figure 17.19. The winding of the helix comes away from the reflector with a clockwise winding direction for RHCP. (The winding can also be counterclockwise — this results in a LHCP polarization sense.)

A helix with a C_λ of 1 λ has a wave propagating from one end of the coil (at the ground plane), corresponding to an instantaneous dipole "across" the helix. The electrical rotation of this dipole produces circularly polarized radiation. Because the wave is moving along the helix conductor at nearly the speed of light, the rotation of the electrical dipole is at a very high rate, and true circular polarization results.

The IEEE definition, in simple terms, is that when viewing the antenna from the feed point end, a clockwise wind results in right-hand circular polarization (RHCP), and a counterclockwise wind results in left-hand circular polarization (LHCP). This is important, because when two stations use helical antennas over a nonreflective path, both must use antennas with the same polarization sense. If antennas of opposite sense are used, a signal loss of at least 20 dB results from the cross-polarization alone.

As mentioned previously, circularly polarized antennas can be used in communication with any linearly polarized antenna (horizontal or vertical), because circularly polarized antennas respond equally to all linearly polarized signals. The gain of a helix appears 3 dB less than the theoretical gain in this case, because the linearly polarized antenna does not respond to linearly polarized signal components orthogonal to it.

The response of a helix to all polarizations is indicated by a term called *axial ratio*, also known as *circularity*. Axial ratio is the ratio of amplitude of the polarization that gives maximum response to the amplitude of the polarization that gives minimum response. An ideal circularly polarized antenna has an axial ratio of 1.0. A well-designed practical helix exhibits an axial ratio of 1.0 to 1.1. The axial ratio of a helix is:

$$AR = \frac{2n+1}{2n} \qquad \text{(Eq 2)}$$

where
    AR = axial ratio
    n = the number of turns in the helix

Axial ratio can be measured in two ways. The first is to excite the helix and use a linearly polarized antenna with an amplitude detector to measure the axial ratio directly. This is done by rotating the linearly polarized antenna in a plane perpendicular to the axis of the helix and comparing the maximum and minimum amplitude values. The ratio of

maximum to minimum is the axial ratio.

The impedance of the helix is easily predicted. The terminal impedance of a helix is unbalanced, and is defined by:

$$Z = 140 \times C_\lambda \qquad \text{(Eq 3)}$$

where Z is the impedance of the helix in ohms.

The gain of a helical antenna is determined by its physical characteristics. Gain can be calculated from:

$$\text{Gain (dBi)} = 11.8 + 10 \log (C_\lambda^2 n S_\lambda) \qquad \text{(Eq 4)}$$

In practice, helical antennas do not deliver the gain in Eq 4 for antennas with turns count greater than about twelve. This will be discussed further regarding practical antennas.

The beamwidth of the helical antenna (in degrees) at the half-power points is:

$$BW = \frac{52}{C_\lambda \sqrt{n S_\lambda}} \qquad \text{(Eq 5)}$$

The diameter of the helical antenna conductor should be between 0.006 and 0.05 λ but smaller diameters have been used successfully at 144 MHz. The previously noted diameter of the ground plane (0.8 to 1.1 λ) should not be exceeded if you desire a clean radiation pattern. As the ground plane size is increased, the sidelobe levels also increase. The ground plane need not be solid; it can be in the form of a spoked wheel or a frame covered with hardware cloth or screen. Cupped ground planes have also been used according to Kraus. (See the Bibliography.)

50-Ω Helix Feed

Joe Cadwallader, K6ZMW, presented this feed method in June 1981 *QST*. Terminate the helix in an N connector mounted on the ground screen at the periphery of the helix. See **Figure 17.21**. Connect the helix conductor to the N connector as close to the ground screen as possible (**Figure 17.22**). Then adjust the first quarter turn of the helix to a close spacing from the reflector.

This modification goes a long way toward curing a deficiency of the helix — the 140-Ω nominal feed point

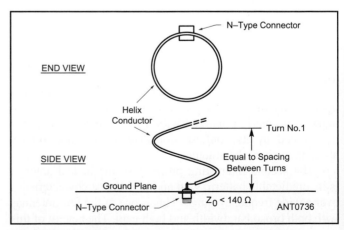

Figure 17.21 — End view and side view of peripherally fed helix.

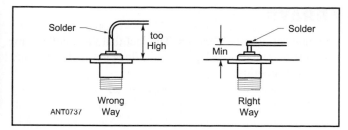

Figure 17.22 — Wrong and right ways to attach a helix to a type N connector for 50-Ω feed.

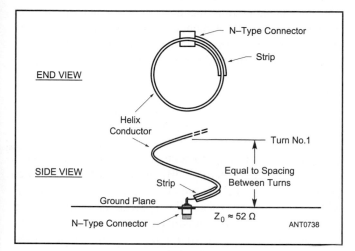

Figure 17.23 — End view and side view of peripherally fed helix with metal strip added to improve transformer action.

impedance. The traditional λ/4 matching section has proved difficult to fabricate and maintain. But if the helix is fed at the periphery, the first quarter turn of the helix conductor (leaving the N connector) acts much like a transmission line — a single conductor over a perfectly conducting ground plane. The impedance of such a transmission line is:

$$Z_0 = 138 \log \frac{4h}{d}$$
(Eq 6)

where

   Z_0 = line impedance in ohms
   h = height of the center of the conductor above the
       ground plane
   d = conductor diameter (in the same units as h).

The impedance of the helix is 140 Ω a turn or two away from the feed point. But as the helix conductor curves down toward the feed connector (and the ground plane), h gets smaller, so the impedance decreases. The 140-Ω nominal impedance of the helix is transformed to a lower value. For any particular conductor diameter, an optimum height can be found that will produce a feed point impedance equal to 50 Ω. The height should be kept very small, and the diameter should be large. Apply power to the helix and measure the SWR at the operating frequency. Adjust the height for an optimum match.

Typically, the conductor diameter may not be large enough to yield a 50-Ω match at practical (small) values of h.

In this case, a strip of thin brass shim stock or flashing copper can be soldered to the first quarter turn of the helix conductor (**Figure 17.23**). This effectively increases the conductor diameter, causing the impedance to decrease further yet. The edges of this strip can be slit every ½ inch or so, and the strip bent up or down (toward or away from the ground plane) to tune the line for an optimum match.

This approach yields a perfect match to nearly any coax. The usually wide bandwidth of the helix (70% for less than 2:1 SWR) will be reduced slightly (to about 40%) for the same conditions. This reduction is not enough to be of any consequence for most amateur work. The improvements in performance, ease of assembly and adjustment are well worth the effort in making the helix more practical to build and tune.

Portable Helix for 435 MHz

Helical antennas for 435 MHz are excellent uplinks for U-band satellite communications. The true circular polarization afforded by the helix minimizes signal *spin fading* that is so common in these applications. The antenna shown in **Figure 17.24** fills the need for an effective portable uplink antenna for OSCAR operation. Speedy assembly and disassembly and light weight are among the benefits of this array. This antenna was designed by Jim McKim, WØCY.

Although the helix is about the most tolerant of any antenna in terms of dimensions, the dimensions given here should be followed as closely as possible. Most of the materials specified are available in any well supplied do-it-yourself hardware or building supply store.

The portable helix consists of eight turns of ¼-inch soft-copper tubing spaced around a 1-inch fiberglass tube or maple dowel rod 4 feet, 7 inches long. Surplus solid aluminum shield hardline can be used instead of the copper tubing if necessary. The turns of the helix are supported by 5-inch lengths of ¼-inch maple dowel mounted through the 1-inch rod in the center of the antenna. For further details, a complete parts list and construction information see the CD-ROM included with this book.

Figure 17.24 — The portable 435-MHz helix assembled and ready for operation. (WØCY photo)

17.3 YAGI ARRAYS

The Yagis in this section are typical of the high-performance designs used for terrestrial communications. For satellite or EME operation, they are often combined into arrays of 2, 4, 8 or even more antennas with both azimuth and elevation position control. Designs of such Yagis can be found in the **VHF and UHF Antenna Systems** chapter or commercial models are available.

17.3.1 ARRAYS FOR SATELLITES

It is not necessary to use a high-gain Yagi array to access an LEO satellite except possibly when it is very near the horizon. Reliable operation via the HEO satellites, however, requires more gain and Yagi arrays are very popular from VHF through 1.2 and 2.4 GHz.

Figure 17.25 shows the satellite antennas at KD1K. The Yagi antennas are used for the U- and L-band uplinks and the V-band downlink, while the S-band dish antenna is for downlink. These satellite antennas are tower mounted at 63 feet (19 meters) to avoid pointing into the many nearby trees and suffering from the resulting "green attenuation." Of course, satellite antennas do not always need to be mounted high on a tower if dense foliage is not a problem. If satellite antennas are mounted lower, feed line length and losses can reduced.

Another benefit, however, to tower mounting of satellite antennas is that they can be used for terrestrial ham

Figure 17.25 — Details of KD1K's tower cluster of satellite antennas including a home-brew elevation rotator. Top to bottom: M2 436-CP30, a CP U-band antenna; two M2 23CM22EZA antennas in a CP array for L band; "FABStar" dish antenna with helix feed for S band; M2 2M-CP22, a CP V-band antenna (only partially shown.) To left of dish antenna is a NEMA 4 weatherproof equipment box with an internal 40-W L-band amplifier, and also hosts externally mounted preamplifiers. (KD1K photo)

communications and contests. The fact that the antennas are set up for circular polarization (CP) does not really degrade these other operating activities.

Experience has clearly shown the advantages of using RHCP antennas for both the uplink and downlink communications. The antennas shown in Figure 17.25 are a single-boom RHCP Yagi antenna for U band, a pair of closely spaced Yagi antennas phased for RHCP for L band (see Figure 17.16), and a helix-fed offset dish antenna for S band described below. The antenna gain requirements for U band can easily be met with the gain of a 30-element crossed Yagi. Antennas of this size have boom lengths of 4 to 4.5 wavelengths. The enterprising amateur can build a Yagi antenna from one of several references but most of us prefer to purchase well-tested antennas from commercial sources. In the past, KLM (now out of business) had offered a 40-element CP Yagi for U-band satellite service, and many of these are still in satisfactory use today.

U-band uplink requirements have clearly demonstrated the need for gain of 16 to 17 dBic RHCP, with an RF power of less than 50 W PEP at the antenna (≈ 2500 WPEP EIRP with a RHCP antenna) depending upon the *squint angle*. (The squint angle is the angle at which the main axis of the satellite is pointed away from your antenna on the ground. If the squint angle is less than half of the half-power beamwidth, the ground station will be within the spacecraft antenna's nominal beamwidth. dBic means the gain of a circularly polarized antenna with respect to that of an isotropic antenna with the same polarization characteristic.)

A gain of 16 to 17 (dB iscotropic-circular) RHCP can be obtained from a 30-element crossed Yagi — good news, considering that the satellite may be over 60,000 km (37,000 miles) from your station. Success on U-band uplinks is easier than those for L band at squint angles wider than 20°. At squint angles less than 10°, U-band uplink operation can even be done with 1-5 W power outputs to a RHCP antenna (≈ 200 W PEP EIRP with RHCP). These lower levels mean that smaller antennas can be used. In practice, these uplinks will produce downlink signals that are 10 to 15 dB above the noise floor, or S7 signals over an S3 noise floor. The beacon will give a downlink S9 signal for these same conditions.

Experience with L-band uplinks has demonstrated that 40 W PEP delivered to an antenna with a gain of ≈ 19 dBic (3000 W PEP EIRP with RHCP) is needed for operations at the highest altitudes and with squint angles ≈ 15°. The compact L-band antenna arrangement with two 22-element antennas in a RHCP array shown in Figure 17.16 is an example of such an antenna system.

Using the L-band uplink for HEO operations instead of the U-band uplink allows the use of Yagi antennas that are more manageable since their size for a given gain is only one third of those for U-band. With L band there is a narrower difference between using a dish antenna and a Yagi, since a 21- to 22-dBic dish antenna would be only about 1.2 meters (4 feet) in diameter. However, some of us may not have such

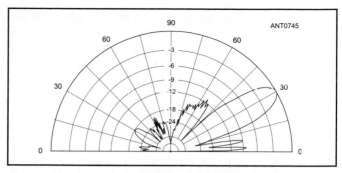

Figure 17.27 — **EZNEC Pro** elevation pattern for four 14-element 2 meter Yagis (3.6-λ boom lengths) at an elevation angle of 30° above the horizon. The computed system gain is 21.5 dBi, suitable for 2 meter EME. This assumes that the phasing system is made of open-wire transmission lines so that feed line losses can be kept below 0.25 dB.

Figure 17.26 — Domenico, I8CVS, has this cluster of satellite antennas. Left to right: array of 4 × 23-element Yagi horizontally polarized for L band; 1.2-meter dish with 3-turn helix feed for S band; 15-turn RHCP helical antenna for U band; 60-cm dish for X band. All microwave preamplifiers and power amplifiers are homebrew and are mounted on this antenna cluster. (I8CVS photo)

Figure 17.28 — K5GW's huge 48-Yagi 2 meter EME array. (Photo courtesy K5GW)

"real estate" available on our towers and may seek the lower wind-loading solution offered by Yagis. Long-boom rod-element Yagi, or loop-Yagi antennas are commercially offered by M² and DEM, although this band is about the highest for practical Yagis. The example shown in Figure 17.16 is a pair of rod-element Yagi antennas from M² in a CP arrangement with a gain of 18 to 19 dBic.

Other amateurs have successful HEO experience with different arrangements. **Figure 17.26** shows I8CVS's 4 × 23 element linear array for a 1270 MHz, a 1.2 meter solid dish for 2400 MHz, a 15 turn helical antenna for 435 MHz, and a 60 cm dish for 10,451 MHz This arrangement clearly shows the advantage and accessibility of having a roof-mounted antenna.

17.3.2 ARRAYS FOR EME

Several types of antennas for 2 meters and 70 cm are popular among EME enthusiasts. Perhaps the most popular antenna for 144-MHz operation is an array of either 4 or 8 long-boom (14 to 15 dBi gain) Yagis. The 4-Yagi

array provides approximately 20 dB gain, and an 8-Yagi array gives an approximate 3 dB increase over the 4-antenna array. **Figure 17.27** shows the computed response at a 30° tilt above the horizon for a stack of four 14-element 2-meter Yagis, each with a boom length of 3.1 λ (22 feet). At 432 MHz, EME enthusiasts often use 8 or 16 long-boom Yagis in an array as seen in Figure 17.8 previously. For an idea of what a truly large array looks like, the monster 48-Yagi 2 meter array of Gerald Williamson, K5GW, is shown in **Figure 17.28.**

The main disadvantage of Yagi arrays is that the polarization plane of the individual Yagis cannot be conveniently changed. One way around this is to use cross-polarized Yagis and a relay switching system to select the desired polarization, as described in the previous section. This represents a considerable increase in system complexity to select the desired polarization. Some amateurs have gone so far as to build complicated mechanical systems to allow constant polarization adjustment of all the Yagis in a large array.

Polarization shift of EME signals at 144 MHz is fairly

rapid, and the added complexity of a relay-controlled cross-polarized antenna system or a mechanical polarization adjustment scheme is probably not worth the effort. At 432 MHz, however, where the polarization shifts at a much slower rate, an adjustable polarization system does offer a definite advantage over a fixed one.

Although not as popular as Yagis, *Quagi* antennas (made from both quad and Yagi elements) are sometimes used for EME work. Slightly more gain per unit boom length is possible as compared to the conventional Yagi, at the expense of some robustness. Additional information on the Quagi is presented in the **VHF and UHF Antenna Systems** chapter.

The collinear array is an older type of antenna for EME work. A 40-element collinear array has approximately the same frontal area as an array of four Yagis, but produces approximately 1 to 2 dB less gain. One attraction to a collinear array is that the depth dimension is considerably less than the long-boom Yagis. An 80-element collinear is marginal for EME communications, providing approximately 19 dB gain. As with Yagi and Quagi antennas, the collinear cannot be adjusted easily for polarity changes. From a construction standpoint, there is little difference in complexity and material costs between the collinear and Yagi arrays.

17.4 PARABOLIC REFLECTOR (DISH) ANTENNAS

Very few antennas evoke as much interest among UHF amateurs as the parabolic dish, and for good reason. First, the parabola and its cousins — Cassegrain, hog horn and Gregorian — are probably the ultimate in high-gain antennas. One of the highest-gain antennas in the world (148 dB) is a parabola. This is the 200-inch Mt. Palomar telescope. (The very short wavelength of light rays causes such a high gain to be realizable.)

Second, the efficiency of the parabola does not change as size increases. With Yagis and collinear arrays, the losses in the phasing harness increase as the array size increases. The corresponding component of the parabola is lossless air between the feed horn and the reflecting surface. If there are a few surface errors, the efficiency of the system stays constant regardless of antenna size.

The major problems associated with parabolic dish antennas are mechanical ones. For example, a dish of about 16 feet in diameter is the minimum size required for successful analog EME operation on 432 MHz. With wind and ice loading, structures of this size place a real strain on the mounting and positioning system. Extremely rugged mounts are required for large dish antennas, especially when used in windy locations. **Figure 17.29** shows the impressive 7-meter

diameter dish built by David Wardley, ZL1BJQ. A smaller dish used for 1296 MHz operation is shown in **Figure 17.30**.

Several aspects of parabolic dish antennas make the extra mechanical problems worth the trouble, however. For example, the dish antenna is inherently broadband, and may be used on several different amateur bands by simply changing the feed. An antenna that is suitable for 432 MHz work will most likely be usable on several of the higher amateur bands too. Increased gain is available as the frequency of operation is increased.

Figure 17.30 — This 3-meter TVRO dish with aluminum frame and mesh surface was outfitted for 1296 MHz EME as a joint effort by VA7MM and VE7CNF. The dual circular polarization feed is a VE4MA/W2IMU design.

Figure 17.29 — ZL1BJQ's homemade 7-meter (23-foot) parabolic dish, just prior to adding ½-inch wire mesh. (Photo courtesy ZL1BJQ)

Another advantage of a dish is the flexibility of the feed system. The polarization of the feed, and therefore the polarization of the antenna, can be changed with little difficulty. It is a relatively easy matter to devise a system to rotate the feed remotely from the shack to change polarization. Because polarization changes can account for as much as 30 dB of signal attenuation, the rotatable feed can make the difference between consistent communications and no communications at all.

A great deal of useful information on microwave antennas, particularly dishes, is online at *The W1GHZ Online Microwave Antenna Book* at **www.w1ghz.org/antbook/contents.htm**. There are several chapters that are of particular interest to satellite and EME operators.

17.4.1 DISH ANTENNA BASICS

The *parabolic reflector* or dish antenna must have a feed source looking into the surface of the dish. Some dishes are designed so that the feed source is mounted directly in front of the dish. This is referred to as a *center-fed dish*. Other dishes are designed so that the feed source is off to one side, referred to as an *off-center-fed dish*, or just offset-fed dish, as shown in **Figure 17.31**. The offset-fed dish may be considered a side section of a center-fed dish. The center-fed dish experiences some signal degradation due to blockage of the feed system, but this is usually an insignificantly small amount. The offset-fed dish is initially more difficult to aim, since the direction of reception is not the center axis, as it is for center-fed dishes but signal blockage caused by the feed system is essentially eliminated.

The dish's parabola can be designed so the focus point is closer to the surface of the dish, referred to a *short-focal-length* dish, or further away from the dish's surface, referred to as a *long-focal-length* dish. To determine the exact focal length, measure the diameter of the dish and the depth of the dish.

$$f = \frac{D^2}{16d} \qquad \text{(Eq 7)}$$

The focal length divided by the diameter of the dish gives the *focal ratio*, commonly shown as f/D. Center-fed dishes usually have short focal ratios in the range of f/D = 0.3 to

0.45. Offset-fed dishes usually have longer focal lengths, with f/D = 0.45 to 0.80. If you attach two small mirrors to the outer front surface of a dish and then point the dish at the Sun, you can easily find the focus point of the dish. Put the reflector of the patch or helix feed just beyond this point of focus.

An alternate method for finding a dish's focal length is suggested by W1GHZ (ex-N1BWT), who provides a computer program called *HDL_ANT*, available at **www.w1ghz.org/10g/10g_home.htm**. The method literally measures a solid-surface dish by the dimensions of the bowl of water that it will form when properly positioned. (See **www.w1ghz.org/antbook/chap5.pdf**.) KD1K used this method on the dish of Figure 17.31, carefully leveling the bowl, plugging bolt holes, and filling it with water to measure the data needed by the W1GHZ calculation.

17.4.2 DISH ANTENNA CONSTRUCTION

There are three parts to the dish antenna — the parabolic reflector, the boom and the feed. There are as many ways to construct this as there are builders so this is an excellent opportunity for experimentation and adaptation of existing designs.

As an example, **Figure 17.32** is a detail drawing of TJ Moss, G3RUH's S-band dish antenna. (See the Bibliography for the complete article.) You need not slavishly replicate every nuance of the design. The only critical dimensions occur in the feed system. After construction, you will have a 60-cm diameter S-band RHCP dish antenna with a gain of about

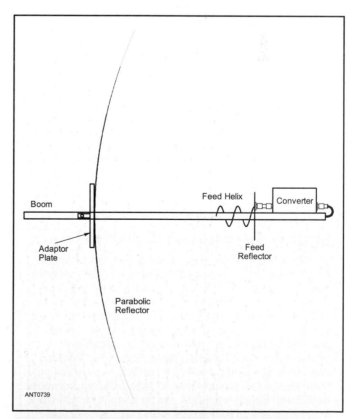

Figure 17.32 — Detail of 60-cm S-band dish antenna with feed.

Figure 17.31 — PrimeStar offset-fed dish with KD1K's helix-feed antenna. NØNSV was so pleased with the modification that he renamed the dish "FABStar," and made a new label! (NØNSV photo)

Build a Dish Kit

You can also build a dish antenna from a kit, available in 1.2-meter and 1.8-meter diameters. One ingenious design by KG6IAL is available from **www.teksharp.com**. Figure 17.43 shows one of KG6IAL's cleverly designed 1.2-meter dishes with an f/D of 0.30 as constructed by KD1K. The 1.2-meter dish is fed with a dual-band patch feed for L and S bands. The 1.8-meter dish is designed for up to three bands using a tri-band patch feed for the U, L and S bands. This dish will permit U-band operation. A Central States VHF Society (**www.csvhfs.org**) measurement on a similarly sized dish (by WØLMD) with a patch feed showed a gain of about 17.1 dBic (actual measurement was 12.0 dBd linearly fed). This performance along with a small V-band (145 MHz) Yagi would permit a very modest satellite antenna assembly for all of the VHF/UHF LEO and HEO satellites.

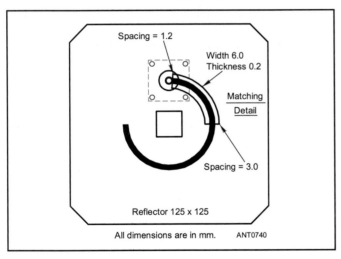

Figure 17.33 — Details of helix feed for S-band dish antennas. The type-N connector is fixed with three screws and is mounted on a 1.6-mm spacer to bring the Teflon molding flush with the reflector. An easier mounting can be using a smaller TNC connector. Reflectors should be 95 to 100 mm in diameter.

Using Surplus Grill Dishes

While many of us enjoy building our own antennas, surplus-market availability of these small dish antennas makes their construction unproductive. Many HEO operators have followed the practices of earlier operators using a surplus MMDS linear-screen parabolic reflector antenna as in Figure 17.45 and Figure 17.46. These grid-dish antennas are often called *barbeque-grill dishes*. K5OE and K5GNA have shown how to greatly improve these linearly polarized reflectors by adapting them for the CP service desired (see **wb5rmg.somenet.net/k5oe**). Simple methods can be used to circularize a linear dish and to further add to its gain using simple methods to increase the dish area and feed efficiency.

20 dBi and a 3-dB beamwidth of 18°. Coupled with the proper downconverter, performance will be more than adequate for S-band downlink reception.

The parabolic reflector used for the original antenna was intended to be a lampshade. Several of these aluminum reflectors were located in department store surplus. The dish is 585 mm in diameter and 110 mm deep, corresponding to an f/D ratio of 585/110/16 = 0.33 and a focal length of 0.33 × 585 = 194 mm. The f/D of 0.33 is a bit too concave for a simple feed to give optimal performance but the price was right, and the under-illumination keeps ground noise pickup to a minimum. The reflector already had a 40-mm hole in the center with three 4-mm holes around it in a 25-mm radius circle.

A small helix is used for the S-band antenna feed as shown in **Figure 17.33**. The reflector for the helix is made from a 125-mm square piece of 1.6-mm thick aluminum. The center of the reflector has a 13-mm hole to accommodate the square center boom described above. The type-N connector is mounted to the reflector about 21.25 mm from the middle. This distance from the middle is, of course, the radius of a helical antenna for S-band. Mount the N connector with spacers so that the back of the connector is flush with the reflector surface.

Surfacing Materials

The choice of surface materials is a compromise between RF reflecting properties and wind loading. Aluminum screening, with its very fine mesh (and weight of 4.3 pounds per 100 square feet) is useful beyond 10 GHz because of its very close spacing. This screening is easy to roll up and is therefore ideal for a portable dish. This close spacing causes the screen to be a 34% filled aperture, bringing the wind force at 60 mph to more than 400 *pounds* on this 12-foot dish. Those considering a permanent installation of this dish should investigate other surfacing materials.

Mesh surfaces are attractive at frequencies up to at least 5 GHz, because of their light weight and lower wind resistance. Openings in the mesh can be as large as 0.05 λ without allowing much ground noise to feed through the surface.

Hexagonal 1-inch poultry netting (chicken wire), which is an 8% filled aperture, is nearly ideal for 432-MHz operation. It weighs 10 pounds per 100 square feet, and exhibits only 81 pounds of force with 60 mph winds. Measurement on a large piece reveals 6 dB of feedthrough at 1296 MHz, however. Therefore, on 1296 MHz, one fourth of the power will feed through the surface material. This will cause a loss of only 1.3 dB of forward gain. Since the low-wind loading material will provide a 30-dBi gain potential, it is still a very good tradeoff.

Poultry netting is very poor material for 2300 MHz and above, because the hole dimensions approach ½ λ. As with all surfacing materials, minimum feedthrough occurs when the E-field polarization is parallel to the longest dimension of the surfacing holes.

Hardware cloth with ½-inch mesh weighs 20 pounds per 100 square feet and has a wind loading characteristic of

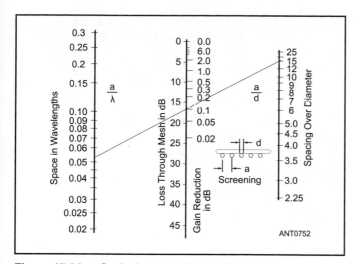

Figure 17.34 — Surfacing material quality.

162 pounds with 60 mph winds. The filled aperture is 16%, and this material is useful to 2300 MHz.

There are some general considerations to be made in selecting surface materials:

1) Joints of screening do not have to make electrical contact. The horizontal wires reflect the horizontal wave. Skew polarizations are merely a combination of horizontal and vertical components which are thus reflected by the corresponding wires of the screening. To a horizontally polarized wave, the spacing and diameter of only the horizontal wires determine the reflection coefficient (see **Figure 17.34**). Many amateurs have the mistaken impression that screening materials that do not make electrical contact at their junctions are poor reflectors.

2) By measuring wire diameter and spacings between the wires, a calculation of percentage of aperture that is filled can be made. This will be one of the major determining factors of wind pressure when the surfacing material is dry.

Effects of Surface Errors

How accurate must a parabolic surface be? This is a frequently asked question. According to the Rayleigh limit for telescopes, little gain increase is realized by making the mirror accuracy greater than $\pm\frac{1}{8}\lambda$ peak error. John Ruze of the MIT Lincoln Laboratory, among others, has derived an equation for parabolic antennas and built models to verify it. The tests show that the tolerance loss can be predicted within a fraction of a decibel, and less than 1 dB of gain is sacrificed with a surface error of $\pm\frac{1}{8}\lambda$. ($\frac{1}{8}\lambda$ is 3.4 inches at 432 MHz, 1.1 inches at 1296 MHz and 0.64 inch at 2300 MHz.)

Some confusion about requirements of greater than $\frac{1}{8}$-λ accuracy may be the result of technical literature describing

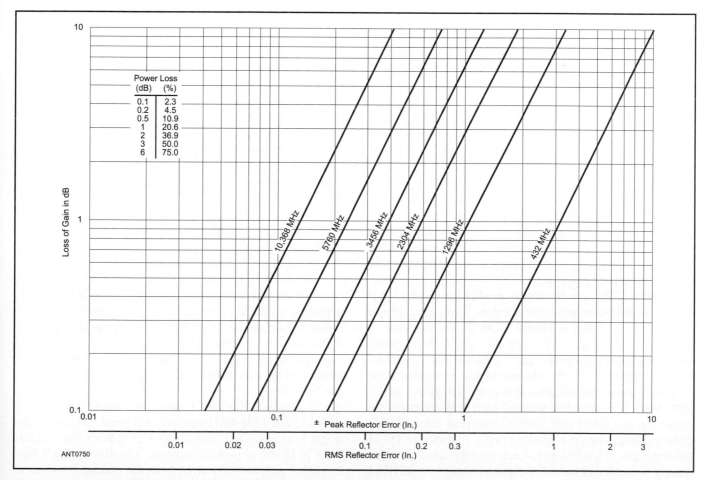

Figure 17.35 — Gain deterioration versus reflector error. By Richard Knadle, K2RIW.

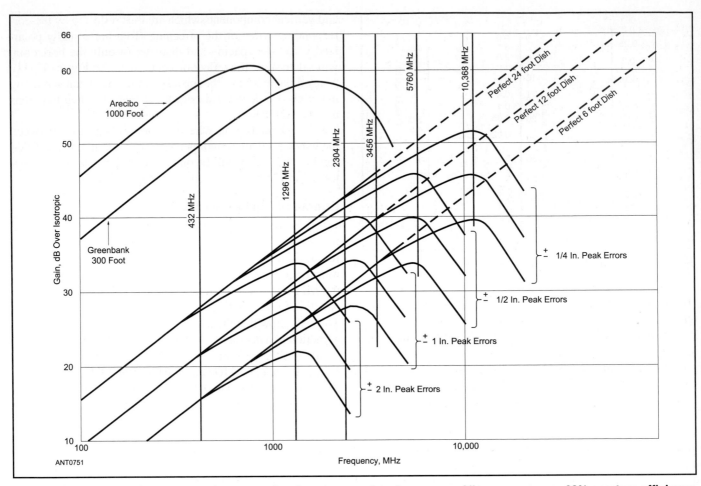

Figure 17.36 — Parabolic-antenna gain versus size, frequency and surface errors. All curves assume 60% aperture efficiency and 10-dB power taper. Graph by K2RIW for amateur bands, using display technique of J. Ruze, British IEE.

highly accurate surfaces. Low sidelobe levels are the primary interest in such designs. Forward gain is a much greater concern than low sidelobe levels in amateur work; therefore, these stringent requirements do not apply.

When a template is held up against a surface, positive and negative (±) peak errors can be measured. The graphs of dish accuracy requirements are frequently plotted in terms of RMS error, which is a mathematically derived function much smaller than ± peak error (typically ⅓). These small RMS accuracy requirements have discouraged many builders who confuse them with ± peak errors.

Figure 17.35 may be used to predict the resultant gain of various dish sizes with typical errors. There are a couple of surprises, as shown in **Figure 17.36**. As the frequency is increased for a given dish, the gain increases 6 dB per octave until the tolerance errors become significant. Gain deterioration then increases rapidly. Maximum gain is realized at the frequency where the tolerance loss is 4.3 dB. Notice that at 2304 MHz, a 24-foot dish with ±2-inch peak errors has the same gain as a 6-foot dish with ±1-inch peak errors. This is quite startling, when it is realized that a 24-foot dish has 16 times the area of a 6-foot dish. Each time the diameter or frequency is doubled or halved, the gain changes by 6 dB. Each time all the errors are halved, the frequency of maximum gain

is doubled. With this information, the gain of other dish sizes with other tolerances can be predicted.

These curves are adequate for predicting gain, assuming a high-efficiency feed horn is used (as described earlier), which realizes 60% aperture efficiency. At frequencies below 1296 MHz where the horn is large and causes considerable blockage, the curves are somewhat optimistic. A properly built dipole and "splashplate" feed (a round disc reflector) will have about 1.5 dB less gain when used with a 0.6 f/D dish than the dual-mode feed system described.

The worst kind of surface distortion is where the surface curve in the radial direction is not parabolic but gradually departs in a smooth manner from a perfect parabola. The decrease in gain can be severe, because a large area is involved. If the surface is checked with a template, and if reasonable construction techniques are employed, deviations are controlled and the curves represent an upper limit to the gain that can be realized.

If a 24-foot dish with ±2-inch peak errors is being used with 432 and 1296-MHz multiple feed horns, the constructor might be discouraged from trying a 2300-MHz feed because there is 15 dB of gain degradation. The dish will still have 29 dBi of gain on 2300 MHz, however, making it worthy of consideration.

The near-field range of a 12-foot stressed dish is 703 feet at 2300 MHz. By using the Sun as a noise source and observing receiver noise power, it was found that the antenna had two main lobes about 4° apart. The template showed a surface error (insufficient spoke bending at ¾ radius), and a correction was made. A re-check showed one main lobe, and the solar noise was almost 3 dB stronger.

SHF EME Challenges for Dishes

The challenges met when successfully building a station for EME at 900 MHz to 5.7 GHz only become more significant on the SHF bands at 10 GHz and above. Absolute attention to detail is the primary requirement, and this extends to every aspect of the EME antenna system. The dish surface is probably the most difficult problem to solve. As was discussed earlier, shape and accuracy of the reflector contribute directly to the overall gain of the antenna.

But where slight errors in construction can be tolerated at the lower frequencies, the same cannot be said at millimeter wavelengths. Those who have attempted EME on 10 and 24 GHz have discovered that the weight of the dish reflector itself will distort its shape enough to lower the gain to the point where echoes are degraded. Stiffening structures at the back of such dishes are often found necessary.

Pointing accuracy is also paramount. A 16-foot dish at 10 GHz has a beamwidth about equal to the diameter of the Moon — 0.5°. This means that the echo degradation due to the Moon's movement away from where the dish is pointed is almost immediate, and autotracking systems become more of a necessity than a luxury. At these frequencies, most amateurs actually peak their antennas on Moon noise — the black-body radiation from the Moon that becomes the dominant source of noise in space.

At these frequencies, the elevation of the Moon above the horizon also plays a role in the ability to communicate since tropospheric absorption due to water vapor is greatest at low elevation angles (the signal must pass through a greater portion of the troposphere than when the Moon is highly elevated). It is beyond the abilities of most amateurs to construct their own dishes for these frequencies, so surplus dishes for Ku-band (12 GHz) satellite TV (typically 3 meters in diameter) are usually employed, as are high-performance dishes designed for millimeter-wave radar and point-to-point communications at 23 and 38 GHz.

17.4.3 DISH FEEDS

Dr Robert Suding, WØLMD, has described the two major factors of feeding a dish that determine the efficiency: the feed source should evenly illuminate the entire dish and none of the feed energy should spill over outside the dish's reflecting surface. No feed system is perfect in illuminating a dish. Losses affect the gain from either under-illuminating or over-illuminating the dish (spillover losses). Typical dish efficiency is 50%. That's 3 dB of lost gain. A great feed system for one dish can be a real lemon on another. A patch feed system is very wide angle, but a helix feed system is narrow angle.

WØLMD has also experimented with helical feeds

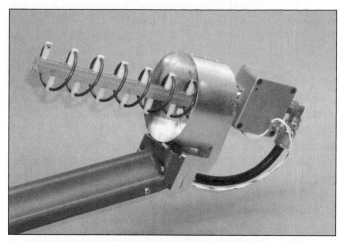

Figure 17.37 — A seven-turn LHCP S-band dish feed for a long f/D offset dish antenna. This helical antenna uses a cupped reflector and has a preamplifier mounted directly to the antenna feed point. (KD1K photo)

for low f/D antennas ("deep" dishes) and has shown that circularly polarized (CP) patch antennas are the preferred feed system. When used with high f/D offset-fed dishes, a patch-type feed system will result in a considerable spillover, or over-illumination loss, with an increased sensitivity to off-axis QRM, due to the f/D of this dish. Offset-fed dishes do much better when fed with a helix antenna, as shown in **Figure 17.37**.

A Helix Feed for an Offset-Dish Antenna

This section describes KD1K's surplus PrimeStar offset-fed dish antenna with a 7-turn helical feed antenna shown in Figure 17.31. This S-band antenna can receive Sun noise 5 dB above sky noise. (Don't try to receive Sun noise with the antenna looking near the horizon, since terrestrial noise will likely be greater than 5 dB in most urban and suburban environments.)

The dish's reflector is a bit out of the ordinary, with the shape of a horizontal ellipse. It is still a single paraboloid, illuminated with an unusual feed horn. At 2401 MHz (S band) we can choose to under-illuminate the sides of the dish while properly feeding the central section, or over-illuminate the center while properly feeding the sides. KD1K chose to under-illuminate. The W1GHZ water-bowl measurements showed this to be a dish with a focal point of 500.6 mm and requiring a feed for an f/D = 0.79. The total illumination angle of the feed is 69.8°. At 50% efficiency this antenna was calculated to provide a gain of 21.9 dBi. A 7-turn helical feed antenna was estimated to provide the needed characteristics for this dish and is shown in Figure 17.33.

The helix is basically constructed as described previously for the G3RUH parabolic dish. A matching section for the first ¼ turn of the helix is spaced from the reflector at 2 mm at the start and 8 mm at the end of that fractional turn. Modifications of the G3RUH design include the addition of a cup reflector, a design feature used by the originator of the helical antenna, John Kraus, W8JK (SK). For the reflector, a

2-mm thick circular plate is cut for a 94 mm (0.75 λ) diameter with a thin aluminum sheet metal cup, formed with a depth of 47 mm. Employment of the cup enhances the performance of the reflector for a dish feed, as shown by K5OE. (See the K5OE material on the CD-ROM accompanying this book.)

The important information for this 7-turn helical antenna is:

- Boom: 12.7-mm square tube or "C" channel.
- Element: ⅛-inch diameter copper wire or tubing.

Close wind the element on a circular 1.50-inch tube or rod; the finished winding is 40 mm in diameter and spaced to a helical angle of 12.3°, or 28 mm spacing. These dimensions work out for an element circumference of 1.0 λ about the center of the wire.

KD1K chose to use PTFE (Teflon) support posts every ½ turn. This closer spacing of posts permitted a careful control of the helix-winding diameter and spacing and also made the antenna very robust. He set up a fixture on the drill press to uniformly pre-drill the holes for the element spacers and boom. Attachment of the reflector is through three very small aluminum angle brackets on the element side of the boom.

The W1GHZ data for this focal point is 500.6 mm from the bottom edge of the dish and 744.4 mm from the top edge. A two-string measurement of this point can confirm the focal point, as shown by W1GHZ in his writings. When mounting this feed antenna the builder must be cautious to aim the feed at the beam-center of the dish. Taking the illumination angle information noted above, the helical feed antenna should be aimed 5.5° down from the geometric center of the dish.

As illustrated in Figure 17.37, a preamp was directly mounted to the feed helix, using a TNC female connector on the helix, chosen for this case since N connectors are quite large for this antenna. A male chassis connector should be mounted on the preamp so that the preamp can be directly connected to the antenna without any adaptors.

Exposed connectors must be protected from precipitation. KD1K chose to make a rain cover instead from a 2-liter soft-drink bottle. (See **Figure 17.38**) Cutting off the top of the bottle allows it to be slid over the helix reflector cup and secured with a large hose clamp. You must provide

UV protection for the plastic bottle and that was done with a wrapping of aluminum foil pressure-sensitive adhesive tape.

Patch Feeds for Dish Antennas

Feeds made from patch antennas are almost as simple as helix feeds. (See the **VHF and UHF Antenna Systems** chapter for a discussion of patch and Vivaldi antennas.) A patch can be practically summarized as building a shape that resonates at the desired frequency, compensated in size by the capacitive inductance between itself and the reflector. A patch can be practically any shape since it basically acts like a parallel-plate transmission line. Current in the patch flows from the feed point to the outer edge(s), where all the radiation occurs. (See the Bibliography for a tutorial on patch antennas provided by Orban Microwave.)

A patch antenna typically is constructed as an N connector on a flat reflector plate with a tuned flat-metal plate soldered to the center terminal. Sometimes the flat plate is square; sometimes it is rectangular; sometimes it is round. It could have two feed points, 90° out of phase for circular polarization. Some patches are rectangular with truncated corners to create a circular radiation pattern.

On 2401 MHz, the radiator plate is 57 mm square and spaced 3 mm away from the reflector. The RF feed point is about halfway between the center and the edge. A round patch for 2401 MHz is about 66 mm in diameter. These patches work well on the shorter focal length center-fed MMDS and TVRO dishes. (MMDS means Multichannel Multipoint Distribution Service, also known as wireless cable TV.)

W0LMD has done a considerable amount of experimenting with patch feeds for his larger TVRO dish antennas. One tri-band feed is shown in **Figure 17.39**. These are circular patches that have CP properties through the arrangement of the feed point and a small piston-variable capacitor that is

Figure 17.38 — Rain cover for preamp using a two-liter soft-drink bottle with aluminum foil tape for protection from Sun damage. (KD1K photo)

Figure 17.39 — A triband (U, L and S bands) patch-CP feed for large dish antennas for HEO service. (W0LMD photo)

offset from the feed point.

Some recent satellites have L-band (23-cm) receivers on 1268-1269 MHz. The reasons for using L band can be varied, but there is no arguing the benefits in reduced antenna size and AGC suppression. The types of L-band antennas are varied as well. Many use helices. Others use beams and arrays of beams. Still others use dishes, small and large.

K5OE has done a lot of experimenting with dishes in the range of 1.2 to 1.5 meters as to what feed schemes work for both S-band and L-band. This led him to experiment for months with different configurations, leading ultimately to a design with:

- Good performance on both S-band receive and L-band uplink.
- An easy-to-produce model using common hardware and simple hand tools.

Patch antennas turn out to be better than helices as dish feeds as illustrated by the radiation pattern for the G3RUH patch feed (see **www.jrmiller.demon.co.uk/products/ patch.html**). When K5OE modeled that pattern and entered it into the W1GHZ feed pattern program, it produced an amazing 72% efficiency. The best helix he ever modeled has about 60% efficiency. I8CVS recently ran his own antenna range tests of a design similar to the G3RUH patch and produced a similarly impressive pattern.

The *truncated corners* square patch design popularized by K3TZ is attributed to 7N1JVW, JF6BCC and JG1IIK. There are references in the literature going back over a decade for this now-common commercial design. The first model K5OE built outperformed his best helix-in-cup design by a full S unit of signal-to-noise ratio. Compared to a helix, the patch simply has better illumination efficiency with less spillover from sidelobes.

The reputed, but often disputed, circularity of the truncated corner patch is accomplished by effectively designing two antennas into the patch element (of two different diagonal lengths) and feeding them 90° out of phase. The full details of K5OE's work are available at **home.swbell.net/k5oe/dual- patch/dual_patch.htm**.

Figure 17.40 shows KD1K's version of K5OE's dual-band patch antenna while **Figure 17.41** shows the mounting of the K5GNA S-band converter and **Figure 17.42** shows the weatherproofing of the feed assembly.

One final design issue deals with the first harmonic of the L-band antenna. You must significantly reduce the potentially destructive effect from the 1269-MHz signal's second harmonic. Severe desense could result and potentially even overload and damage the first active device in your receive system. Sensitive preamps and downconverters without a pre-RF-amplifier filter will need an external filter. K5OE has used a G3WDG stub filter rated at 100-dB rejection with good success ahead of his preamp. His current setup, however, uses the K5GNA supplied AIDC-3731AA downconverter with its internal comb-line filter providing adequate filtering. Using the downconverter directly at the feed point has a noise figure (NF) of 1.0 dB, compared to the cumulative NF of 1.6 dB

Figure 17.40 — Dual L-band and S-band patch feed assembly. (KD1K photo)

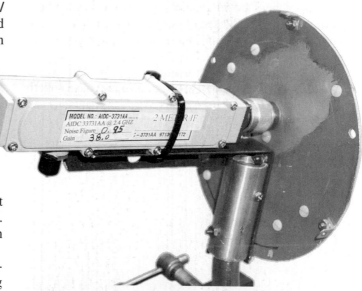

Figure 17.41 — The K5GNA S-band downconverter assembled to the rear of the patch feed assembly. The L-band connector is hidden in this view. (KD1K photo)

Figure 17.42 — The dual-band feed radome cover from the Martha Stewart Collection! (KD1K photo)

using a filter and a preamp.

Construction of the feed begins with selection of material for both the electrical parts (the antennas) and the mechanical parts (the support structure). The L-band antenna is constructed using a 6×6-inch double-sided circuit board for the reflector and a piece of 26-gauge copper sheet for the driven element (patch). A flanged female type-N connector is used for the feed connection. The S-band antenna is constructed of two pieces of 26-gauge copper sheeting and the feed connection is made with a short piece of UT-141 (0.141-inch copper-clad semi-rigid coax) terminated in a male SMA fitting. Figure 17.37 illustrates the assembly of the L-band reflector with the nylon-center support bolt, the L-band N connector, and the S-band semi-rigid coax terminated onto an SMA-to-N adapter through the circuit board. (See the Bibliography for more on patch feeds.)

17.4.4 DISH ANTENNAS FOR SATELLITES

Dish antennas are not required for satellite operation except in the case of HEO satellites operating with microwave up or down-links. At lower frequencies, Yagi arrays are the more practical choice.

A 1.2-meter L-band dish antenna and 40 W of RF power (6100 W PEP EIRP with RHCP) can also provide a superb uplink for squint angles even up to 25°. A dish antenna can have a practical gain of about 21 to 22 dBic. These uplinks will provide the user a downlink that is 10 to 18 dB above the transponder noise floor. In more practical terms, these are S7 to 8 signals over an S3 transponder noise floor, making for very comfortable "armchair" copy.

KD1K shows in **Figure 17.43** what can be done with a 1.2 meter dish antenna kit for HEO operations. **Figure 17.44** shows a WØLMD 8-foot TVRO dish with patch feed, az/cl mount, a U-band Yagi, and an L-band helical antenna.

Other hams have also taken advantage of surplus dishes. **Figure 17.45** shows modified MMDS dishes, by K5GNA, and **Figure 17.46**, by K5OE, both using helix feeds.

One very popular spun-aluminum dish antenna in HEO

Figure 17.44 — WØLMD created this 8-foot dish with patch feed for S band for working HEO satellites. On the left is a helical antenna for L band and on the right is a 2 × 9-element offset-feed Yagi for U band. A homebrew az/el mount is provided. (WØLMD photo)

Figure 17.43 — KD1K's completed HEO antenna system mounted to the tower and ready to go. The 40 W, 23 cm amplifier is in the box below the KG6IAL 1.2 meter dish. (KD1K photo)

Figure 17.45 — K5GNA's "circularized" mesh modification of an MMDS dish antenna with a helix-CP feed and preamp. The dish modification reduces the spillover loss by making the antenna fully circular. (K5OE photo)

use has been the G3RUH-ON6UG 60-cm unit with its S-band patch feed shown in **Figure 17.47**. With a gain of 21 dBic it provides a 2.5 dB Sun noise signal. Surplus dishes have not been the only source of antennas for HEO operations — even cardboard boxes lined with aluminum foil will work as shown in **Figure 17.48**! (This interesting antenna was the subject of the March 2003 *QST* article "Work OSCAR 40 with Cardboard-Box Antennas!" by AA2TX which is included on this book's CD-ROM.)

Figure 17.46 — Mesh modification of an MMDS dish antenna by K5OE, with a helix-CP feed and preamplifier by Down-East Microwave mounted directly to the helix feed point. (K5OE photo)

Figure 17.47 — G3RUH's 60-cm spun-aluminum dish with CP-patch feed is available as a kit. This antenna has been popular with HEO operators all over the world.

Figure 17.48 — The completed high-performance corner-reflector uplink antenna for U band. Note how the box corners hold the reflectors and dipole feed in place. The rear legs set the antenna elevation to 20° — this gives good coverage at the design latitude but will need modification for other stations.

17.4.5 C-BAND TVRO DISHES

Since the 1990s, there has been a significant change in the systems people use to watch satellite TV broadcasts. Formerly, C band satellite receivers were used, along with parabolic dish antennas in the 3- to 5-meter diameter range. Now, Ku-band (12 GHz) receivers are the norm, with their associated small (usually 18-inch) dish antennas. This has provided a large body of surplus C-band dishes, which can be used for EME — certainly on the bands at 33 cm and above, and for the larger dishes (5 meters), even at 70 cm. Many times, these dishes and their mounts can be had for the asking so they truly become an inexpensive way to build a multiband EME antenna.

As an example of how these dishes can be converted to amateur use, the following sections summarize an article first presented by David Hallidy, K2DH (ex-KD5RO) in the *ARRL UHF/Microwave Projects Manual* describing the use of a 3-meter (10-foot) TVRO antenna for EME. Additional photos of other TVRO dish installations are available on this book's CD-ROM.

Background

Calculations show that a 3-meter dish will have about 30 dBi gain at 1296 MHz. With a state-of-the-art LNA (Low-Noise Amplifier or preamp) at the feed, an efficient feed horn illuminating the dish surface, and 200 W at 1296 MHz, lunar echoes should be easily detected and many stations can be worked. The biggest challenges to such a system are assembling the dish to its mount and steering it to track the Moon. As much as possible, the KISS ("Keep It Simple, Stupid") principle was used to accomplish this task.

In 1987, WA5TNY, KD5RO, KA5JPD and W7CNK proved that such an EME system could work, even as high as 3.4 and 5.7 GHz, to provide the first EME contacts on those bands. An additional advantage to this (or any) small dish is its ability to be mounted to a trailer and taken out on EME expeditions. It can also be easily disassembled and stored, if necessary.

As can be seen from **Figure 17.49**, the entire setup is very simple, using a standard amateur tower as the main support for the dish.

Azimuth Drive

In azimuth, direct drive of the main rotating shaft was selected, and a small prop-pitch motor was used. These motors, while not as plentiful as they were some years ago, still turn up with some regularity at flea markets for very little money. The beauty of the prop-pitch motor is that it turns slowly, is reversible, provides very high torque, and requires no braking system (the gear reduction, on the order of 4000:1, provides the necessary braking). Prop-pitch motors are dc motors, and were designed to vary the pitch of propeller blades of older large airplanes at start-up, take-off and landing. Thus, they can be run at different speeds merely by varying the dc voltage to the motor, and can be reversed by reversing the polarity of the dc voltage. By mounting a thrust bearing of the appropriate size at the top of the tower, and mounting the motor directly below it at the end of the rotating shaft that turns the antenna, a simple direct-drive system can be constructed.

The dc power supply and control relays are located in a weatherproof box on the side of the tower, next to the motor. This system requires only 9 V dc at about 5 A to adequately start, turn and stop the prop-pitch motor, and this voltage turns the antenna through 360° of rotation in about 2½ minutes.

Azimuth position sensing is also a simple task. See **Figure 17.50**. A linear multiturn potentiometer is driven by the rotating shaft, using a simple friction drive. A strip of rubber is attached to the rotating shaft and a wheel is connected to the shaft of the pot. The pot is then mounted so that it presses against the rubber strip, and as the shaft turns so does the pot. If a 10-turn pot is used, and the system is aligned such that the pot is at the center of its rotation when the antenna is pointed approximately south, the pot will not rotate past the end at either extreme of the antenna's rotation (clockwise/counterclockwise north), and absolute alignment is a simple task of calibrating the change in resistance (change in voltage, when the pot is fed from a constant voltage source) with degrees of rotation (see the discussion on Position Display for details).

Elevation Drive

The elevation drive is also very simple. Most (nearly all) TVRO setups have a means of moving the dish across the sky to align it with various satellites. To do this, most companies

Figure 17.49 — View of K2DH's (ex-KD5RO) complete TVRO antenna installation. (K2DH photo)

Figure 17.50 — Azimuth rotation systems, showing prop-pitch motor and position sensor.

use a device called a *linear actuator*. This is a dc motor to which is attached a long lead screw that pulls (or pushes) the outer shell of the actuator in or out to make it longer or shorter. The movable end of the actuator is attached to the dish and the motor end is fixed to the mount. The dish rests on pivots, which allow it to move as the actuator extends/retracts. To convert this type of mount (called a *polar mount*) to an az/el mount is usually very simple.

Figure 17.51 shows how this can be done. Simply breaking the welds that held the mount in a polar fashion allows the mount to be turned on its side and used to pivot the dish vertically with the linear actuator. Another feature of linear actuators is that they also have some means of feeding their relative position to the satellite receiver. This is usually just a multiturn potentiometer geared to the lead screw. All we

Figure 17.51 — Elevation system, showing modified TVRO mount.

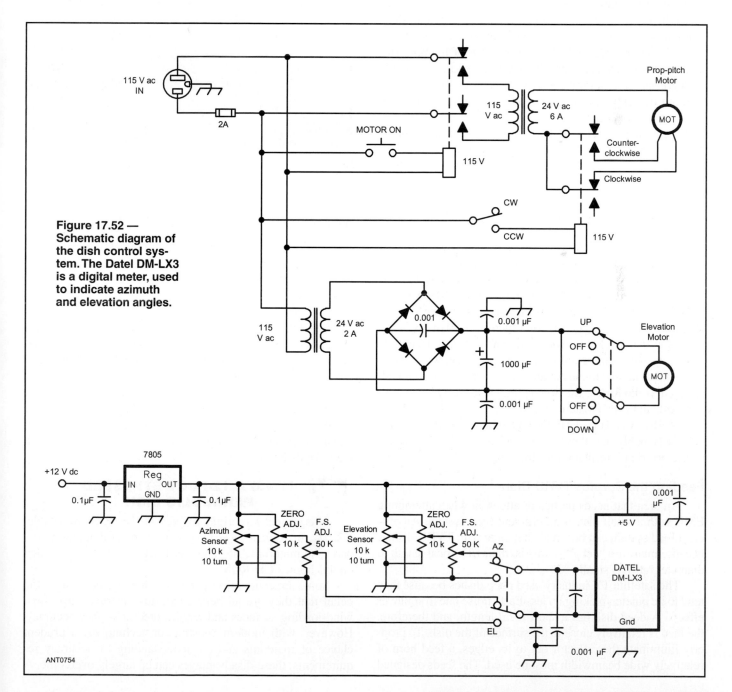

Figure 17.52 — Schematic diagram of the dish control system. The Datel DM-LX3 is a digital meter, used to indicate azimuth and elevation angles.

ANT0754

have to do is connect this pot to a readout system, and we can calibrate the lift of the actuator in degrees. We thus have a simple means of rotating the dish and elevating it — but how do we know that it's pointed at the Moon?

Position Display

Displaying the position of the antenna, in both azimuth and elevation is also a relatively simple task. On the surplus market there are available digital voltmeters (DVMs) using LED or LCD displays that can do this job nicely, and that have more precision than is probably necessary for a dish (or Yagi array) of small size. As mentioned earlier, a multiturn potentiometer on the elevation-drive mechanism can be used to readout elevation, and the same technique can be used for azimuth readout — a potentiometer coupled to the main rotating shaft that turns the antenna.

When using a pot for readout, the most important thing to know is how many degrees of antenna position change occur (in azimuth or elevation) for each turn of the pot. This then can be used to calibrate a voltmeter to read volts directly as degrees — for example, 3.60 V could correspond to 360° azimuth (Clockwise North), and 9.0 V could correspond to 90° elevation (straight up).

A resistance bridge circuit is best used in this application, since it is less sensitive to changes in the supply voltage. The only thing to be careful about is that the DVM must have both the positive (high) and negative (low) inputs isolated from ground (assuming the power supply used to power the DVM is grounded). You could also use a pair of small, inexpensive digital multimeters (DMMs). Because they are battery powered, the isolation issue just discussed is eliminated.

Figure 17.52 is a complete schematic of the azimuth, elevation and readout electronics for this antenna-drive system. Also note that while this discussion is geared toward the use of a small dish, the same positioning and readout systems could be used in a Yagi array for 2 meters or 70 cm.

Now that we know where the dish is pointed, how do we know where the Moon is? There are several software programs available to the Amateur for tracking celestial bodies such as the Moon, the Sun, certain stars (usable as noise sources), and even amateur satellites. Programs by W2MRO (ex W9IP), VK3UM, F1EHN and others can be obtained very reasonably and these work well to provide highly accurate position information for tracking.

Feeding the Surplus TVRO Dish

An area that needs particular attention when attempting EME with a small dish is an efficient feed system. An efficient feed system can be a real challenge with TVRO dishes, because many are "deep" — that is, their f/D (focal length to diameter ratio) is small.

The satellite TV industry used deep dishes because they tend to be quieter, picking up less Earth noise due to spillover effects. A deep dish has a short focal length, and therefore, the feed is relatively close to the surface of the dish. To properly illuminate the reflector out to its edges, a feed horn of relatively wide beamwidth must be used. The feeds designed

Figure 17.53 — View of feed, showing coffee-can feed horn and hybrid coupler.

several years ago by Barry Malowanchuk, VE4MA, are intended for use with just such dishes, and have the advantage of being adjustable to optimize their pattern to the dish in use.

The feed that was used with this dish was modeled after VE4MA's 1296-MHz feed, and a version was even scaled for use at 2304 MHz that worked as well as the original. See **Figure 17.53** and the Bibliography at the end of this chapter. (Also see the earlier section of this chapter describing patch feeds for dishes.)

17.4.6 A 12-FOOT STRESSED PARABOLIC DISH

This project was originally presented by Richard Knadle, K2RIW, in August 1972 *QST* and the full article, including parts and materials lists, and construction details is included on this book's CD-ROM.

Some amateurs reject parabolic antennas because of the belief that they are all heavy, hard-to-construct, have large wind-loading surfaces and require precise surface accuracy. However, with modern construction techniques, a prudent choice of materials and an understanding of accuracy requirements, these disadvantages can be largely overcome. A

Figure 17.54 — A 12-foot stressed parabolic dish set up for satellite signal near 2280 MHz. A preamplifier is shown taped below the feed horn. The dish was designed by K2RIW, standing at the right. The complete *QST* construction article is available on this book's CD-ROM.

parabola may be constructed with a 0.6 f/D (focal length/ diameter) ratio, producing a rather flat dish, which makes it easy to surface and allows the use of recent advances in high-efficiency feed horns. This results in greater gain for a given dish size over conventional designs.

Such an antenna is shown in **Figure 17.54**. This parabolic dish is lightweight, portable, easy to build, and can be used for 432 and 1296 MHz mountaintopping, as well as on 2304, 3456 and 5760 MHz. Disassembled, it fits into the trunk of a car and can be assembled in 45 minutes.

The usually heavy structure that supports the surface of most parabolic dish antennas has been replaced in this design by aluminum spokes bent into a near parabolic shape by strings. These strings serve the triple function of guying the focal point, bending the spokes and reducing the error at the dish perimeter (as well as at the center) to nearly zero. By contrast, in conventional designs, the dish perimeter (which has a greater surface area than the center) is farthest from the supporting center hub. For these reasons, it often has the greatest error. This error becomes more severe when the wind blows.

Here, each of the spokes is basically a cantilevered beam with end loading. The equations of beam bending predict a near-perfect parabolic curve for extremely small deflections. Unfortunately the deflections in this dish are not that small and the loading is not perpendicular. For these reasons, mathematical prediction of the resultant curve is quite difficult. A much better solution is to measure the surface error with a template and make the necessary correction by bending each of the spokes to fit. This procedure is discussed later.

The uncorrected surface is accurate enough for 432 and 1296-MHz use. Trophies taken by this parabola in antenna-gain contests were won using a completely natural surface with no error correction. By placing the transmission line inside the central pipe that supports the feed horn, the area of the shadows or blockages on the reflector surface is much smaller than in other feeding and supporting systems, thus increasing gain. For 1296 MHz, a backfire feed horn may be constructed to take full advantage of this feature. At 432 MHz, a dipole and reflector assembly produces 1.5 dB additional gain over a corner-reflector feed system. Because the preamplifier is located right at the horn on 2300 MHz, a conventional feed horn may be used. The texts listed in the Bibliography have more information on horn antennas.

17.5 WEATHERPROOFING RELAYS AND PREAMPLIFIERS

For stations using crossed Yagi antennas for CP operation, one feature that has been quite helpful for communicating through most of the LEO satellites is the ability to switch polarization from RHCP to LHCP. In some satellite operation this switchable CP ability has been essential. For those using helical antennas or helical-fed dish antennas, we just would not have the choice to switch CP unless an entirely new antenna is added to the cluster for that purpose. Not many of us have the luxury of that kind of space available on our towers.

For stations with switchable-polarization Yagi antennas, experience with exposed switching relays and preamplifiers mounted on antennas have shown that they are prone to failure caused by a mechanism known as *diurnal pumping*. Often these relays are covered with a plastic case, and the seam between the case and PC board is sealed with a silicone sealant. Preamps may also have a gasket seal for the cover, while the connectors can easily leak air. None of these methods create a true hermetic seal and as a result the day/night temperature swings pump air and moisture in and out of the relay or preamp case. Under the right conditions of temperature and humidity, moisture from the air will condense inside the case when the outside air cools down. Condensed water builds up inside the case, promoting extensive corrosion and unwanted electrical conduction, seriously degrading component performance in a short time.

A solution for those antennas with "sealed" plastic relays, such as the KLM CX series, is to avoid problems by making the modifications shown in **Figure 17.55**. Relocate the 4:1 balun as shown and place a clear polystyrene plastic refrigerator container over the relay. Notch the container edges for the driven element and the boom so the container will sit down over the relay, sheltering it from the elements.

Figure 17.55 — KLM 2M-22C antenna CP switching relay with relocated balun. The protective cover is needed for rain protection, be sure to use a polystyrene kitchen box, see text. (KD1K photo)

Bond the container in place with a few dabs of silicone adhesive. (Be sure to use sealers that do not release acetic acid during curing — see the **Antenna Materials and Construction** chapter.) Position the antenna in an "X" orientation, so neither set of elements is parallel to the ground. The switcher board should now be canted at an angle, and one side of the relay case should be lower than the other. An example for the protective cover for an S-band preamp can be seen in the discussion on feeds for parabolic antennas.

For both the relay and preamp cases, carefully drill a ³⁄₃₂-inch hole through the low side of the case to provide the needed vent. The added cover keeps rainwater off the relay and preamp, and the holes will prevent any buildup of

Figure 17.56 — A NEMA 4 box is used to shelter the L-band electronics and power supply. The box flanges are convenient for mounting preamplifiers. The box is shown inverted since it is on a tilt-over tower. (KD1K photo)

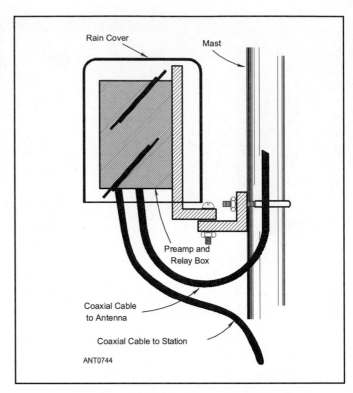

Figure 17.57 — Protection for tower-mounted equipment need not be elaborate. Be sure to dress the cables as shown so that water drips off the cable jacket before it reaches the enclosure. One hazard for such open-bottom enclosures is that of animals gnawing on the cable insulation. Flying insects also like to build their houses in these enclosures.

condensation inside the relay case. Relays and preamplifiers so treated have remained clean and operational over periods of years without problems.

Another example for the protection of remotely, tower-mounted equipment is shown in Figure 17.25, illustrating the equipment box and mast-mounted preamplifiers at the top of KD1K's tower. The commercial NEMA 4 equipment box, detailed in **Figure 17.56** (shown inverted), is used to protect the 23 cm power amplifier and its power supply, as well as a multitude of electrical connections. This steel box is very weather resistant, with an exceptionally good epoxy finish, but it is not sealed and so it will not trap moisture to be condensed with temperature changes. Be sure to use a box with at least a NEMA 3 rating for rainwater and dust protection. The NEMA 4 rating provides a little better protection than the NEMA 3 rating. Using a weather-rated equipment enclosure is very well worth the expense. As you can see, the box also provides some pretty good flanges to mount the mast-mounted preamplifiers for three bands. This box is an elegant solution for the simple need of rain shelter for your equipment. See **Figure 17.57**.

17.6 ANTENNA POSITION CONTROL

EME and satellite antennas have high gain and narrow main beams that must be properly aimed in two coordinates. Although polar mounts (one axis parallel to the Earth's axis) have sometimes been used, by far the most popular mounting scheme today is the elevation-over-azimuth or az/el mount. Readily available computer software can provide azimuth and elevation coordinates for the Moon, and a small computer can also control antenna positioning motors to automate the whole pointing system.

For mechanical reasons it is desirable to place the antenna's center of gravity close to the intersection of the vertical (azimuth) and horizontal (elevation) axes. On the other hand, the mounting structure must not interfere with critical active regions of the antenna. Stacked Yagis are generally mounted so that metallic supporting members are perpendicular to the radiating elements or located at midpoints where the effective apertures of separate Yagis meet. Feed lines and conducting support members must not lie in the active planes containing Yagi elements, unless they run wholly along the boom. For dual-polarization Yagis, feed lines should be routed toward the rear of each Yagi and any mid-boom support members must be nonconducting. For space communications there is nothing magical about using horizontal and vertical for the two orthogonal polarizations, and there are some advantages to mounting cross-Yagis with elements in the "X" rather than "+" orientation.

Parabolic dishes are usually mounted from behind, with counterweights extending rearward to relieve torque imbalance on the elevation axis. Jack-screw actuators designed for positioning TVRO dishes can be readily adapted for elevation control. Standard heavy-duty antenna rotators can be used for azimuth positioning of dishes up to about 3 meters in size. Larger dishes may require heavier, one-of-a-kind designs for pointing control.

17.6.1 POSITION CONTROLLERS

Operators through the years have employed many methods for the control of their antenna positions, ranging from true *arm-strong* manual positioning, to manual operation of the powered antenna azimuth and elevation rotators, to fully automated computer control of the rotators. While computer control of the rotators is not essential, operation is greatly eased with their use.

For many years, one of the key control units for rotators has been the *Kansas City Tracker* (KCT) board installed in your computer. This device is no longer available new but many are in use or available used. Information on the KCT is available from AMSAT (**www.amsat.org**).

A recent trend for amateur antenna control has been evolving in the form of a standalone controller that translates computer antenna-position information into controller commands with an understanding of antenna-position limits. AMSAT-NA has developed the LVB Tracker by G6LVB (**www.g6lvb.com**) shown in **Figure 17.58** that can be obtained in several different forms of kits or completely

Figure 17.58 — AMSAT-NA LVB Tracker Box assembly.

assembled from AMSAT. This tracker uses an internal PIC microcontroller that uses a 10-bit ADC encoder for rotator position feedback, resulting in sub-degree precision for both elevation and azimuth. Yaesu (**www.yaesu.com**) also sells the GS-232 computer control interface that can be used for tracking with their G-5500 az/el rotator system. AlfaSpid (**www.alfaradio.ca**) also manufactures an az/el rotator.

Other position readout and control options are available. For many years ham operators have employed synchros, or *selsyns*, for their position readouts. These are specialized transformers, using principles developed over sixty years ago and employed in such devices as surplus "radio compass" steering systems for aircraft. While the position readout of these devices can be quite precise, in general they only provide a visual position indication, one that is not easily adapted to computer control. I8CVS employs such a system at his station and he uses a weighted arm on the elevation synchro to provide a constant reference to the Earth's gravity vector.

The more up-to-date, computer-friendly position readout methods used these days are usually based on precision potentiometers or digital position encoders. **Figure 17.59** shows a variety of digital encoders employed by WØLMD. He notes that such systems, while providing a very high precision of

Figure 17.59 — WØLMD has experimented with highly precise optical encoders for his antenna position systems. See text. (WØLMD photo)

angular position, they are not absolute systems and that once calibrated, they must be continually powered so they do not lose their calibration. Precision potentiometers, on the other hand, provide an absolute position reference, but with a precision that is limited to the quality of the potentiometer, typically 0.5% (0.45° in elevation and 1.80° in azimuth) to 1.0%. So the choices have their individual limits, unless a lot of money is spent for very precise commercial systems.

17.6.2 ELEVATION CONTROL

Satellite antennas need to have elevation control to point up to the sky. This is the "el" part of az/el control of satellite antennas. Generally, elevation booms for CP satellite antennas need to be nonconducting so that the boom does not affect the radiation pattern of the antenna. In the example shown next, the elevation boom center section is a piece of extra-heavy-wall 1½-inch pipe (for greater strength) with a tubular fiberglass-epoxy boom extension for the 70 cm antenna and a long home-brew extension for the 2 meter antenna. The boom uses large PVC pipe reinforced with four braces of Phillystran nonmetallic guy cable. (PVC pipe is notoriously flexible, but the Phillystran cables make a quite stiff and strong boom of the PVC pipe.) For smaller installations, a continuous piece of fiberglass-epoxy boom can be placed directly through the elevation rotator.

Elevation boom motion needs to be powered and one solution by KD1K, shown in **Figure 17.60**, uses a surplus jackscrew drive mechanism. I8CVS has also built his own robust elevation mechanism. (See **Figure 17.61.**) Note in each of these applications the methods used to provide bearings for the elevation mechanism. In KD1K's case, the elevation axis is a piece of heavy-duty 1½-inch pipe, (1¹⁵⁄₁₆-inch OD) and large 2 inch journal bearings are used for the motion. I8CVS uses a very large hinge to allow his motion.

Robust commercial solutions for az/el rotators have given operators good service over the years. See **Figure 17.62**. Manufacturers such as Yaesu and M² are among these suppliers. One operator, VE5FP, found a solution for his az/el rotator needs by using two low-cost, lightweight TV rotators as shown in Figure 17.62.

Figure 17.60 — KD1K's homebrew elevation rotator drive using a surplus-store drive screw mechanism. Note also the large journal bearing supporting the elevation axis pipe shaft. (KD1K photo)

Figure 17.61 — I8CVS's homebrew elevation mechanism using a very large, industrial hinge as the pivot and a jackscrew drive. (I8CVS photo)

Figure 17.62 — At left, Yaesu az/el antenna-rotator mounting system is shown. Note that antenna loads must be more carefully balanced on this rotator than in the previously shown systems. At right, VE5FP has a solution for his az/el rotators by bolting two of them together as described in "An Inexpensive Az-El Rotator System" published in December 1998 *QST*.

17.7 BIBLIOGRAPHY

ARRL and RSGB Books

ARRL UHF/Microwave Projects CD, ARRL
(**www.arrl.org**).
ARRL UHF/Microwave Experimenter's Manual, ARRL
(**www.arrl.org**), out of print.
International Microwave Handbook — 2nd Edition, RSGB
(**www.rsgb.org**).
Microwave Know How, RSGB (**www.rsgb.org**).
Microwave Projects, Vol. 1 and Vol. 2, RSGB
(**www.rsgb.org**).

Other Publications

G. Brown, "A Helix Feed for Surplus MMDS, Antennas,"
Proceedings of the 2001AMSAT-NA Symposium,
Oct 2001, pp 89-94; (also see **members.aol.com/k5oe**).
G. Brown, "A K-Band Receiver for AO-40," *Proceedings of
the 2002 AMSAT-NA Space Symposium*, Oct 2002.
G. Brown, "Build This No-Tune Dual-Band Feed for Mode
L/S," *The AMSAT Journal*, Vol 26, No 1, Jan/Feb 2003.

G. Brown, "Dual-Band Dish Feeds for 13/23 cm,"
Proceedings of the 2002AMSAT-NA Symposium,
Oct 2002, pp 123-131.
G. Brown, "MMDS Dishes," available from **members.aol.com/k5oe**.
G. Brown, "Patch Feeds," available from **members.aol.com/k5oe**.
G. Brown, "The Texas Potato Masher: A Medium-Gain
Directional Satellite Antenna For LEOs," *The AMSAT
Journal*, Vol 22, No. 1, Jan/Feb 1999.
D. DeMaw, "The Basic Helical Beam," *QST*, Nov 1965,
pp 20-25, 170.
N. Foot, "Cylindrical Feed horn for Parabolic Reflectors,"
Ham Radio, May 1976, pp 16-20.
D. Hallidy, "Microwave EME Using a Ten-Foot TVRO
Antenna," *The ARRL UHF/Microwave Projects Manual*,
Vol 2 (Newington: ARRL, 1997) pp 10-9 to 10-13.
Available on the *ARRL UHF/Microwave Projects CD*.
D. Jansson, "Product Review: M² 23CM22EZA 1.2 GHz
Antenna," *QST*, Sep 2002, pp 59-61.

H. Jasik, *Antenna Engineering Handbook*, 1st ed. (New York: McGraw-Hill, 1961).

M. Kingery, "Setting Up for AO-40 L-Band Uplink," *The AMSAT Journal*, May/Jun 2002, pp 14-16, also: **web.infoave.net/~mkmk518**.

R. Knadle, "A Twelve-Foot Stressed Parabolic Dish," *QST*, Aug 1972, pp 16-22.

J. Koehler, "An Inexpensive Az-El Rotator System", *QST*, Dec 1998, pp 42-46.

J. Kraus, *Antennas* (New York: McGraw-Hill Book Company, 1988). See "The Helical Antenna," Chapter 7.

J. Kraus, *Antennas* (New York: McGraw-Hill Book Company, 1988). See "Patch or Microstrip Antennas," pp 745-749.

J. D. Kraus, "A 50-Ohm Input Impedance for Helical Beam Antenna," *IEEE Transactions on Antennas and Propagation*, Nov 1977, p 913.

E. Krome, "Development of a Portable Mode S Ground Station." *The AMSAT Journal*, Vol 16, No. 6, Nov/Dec 1993, pp 25-28.

E. Krome, "S band Reception: Building the DEM Converter and Preamp Kits," *The AMSAT Journal*, Vol 16, No. 2, Mar/Apr 1993, pp 4-6.

E. Krome, *Mode S: The Book*, pp 96, 109. Available from AMSAT (**www.amsat.org**).

E. Krome, "Mode S: Plug and Play!," *The AMSAT Journal*, Vol 14, No. 1, Jan 1991, pp 21-23, 25.

H. Long, "My Shack Configuration — Spring 2002" (see **www.g6lvb.com/g6lvb_shack_spring_2002.htm**).

W. McCaa, "Hints on Using the AMSAT-OSCAR 13 Mode S Transponder," *The AMSAT Journal*, Vol 13, No. 1, Mar 1990, pp 21-22.

A. MacAllister, "Field Day 2002," *73 Amateur Radio Today*, Sep 2002, pp 48-52.

B. Malowanchuk, "Use of Small TVRO Dishes for EME," *Proceedings of the 21st Conference of The Central States VHF Society, 1987*, pp 68-77.

B. Malowanchuk, "Selection of An Optimum Dish Feed," *Proceedings of the 23rd Conference of The Central States VHF Society, 1989*, pp 35-43.

J. Miller, "Mode S — Tomorrow's Downlink?," *The AMSAT Journal*, Vol 15, No. 4, Sep/Oct 1992, pp 14-15.

J. Miller, "'Patch' Feed For S-Band Dish Antennas"(see **www.jrmiller.demon.co.uk/products/patch.html**).

J. Miller, "A 60-cm S-Band Dish Antenna," *The AMSAT Journal*, Vol 16 No. 2, Mar/Apr 1993, pp 7-9.

J. Miller, "Small is Best," *The AMSAT Journal*, Vol 16, No. 4, Jul/Aug 1993, p 12.

A. Monteiro, "Work OSCAR 40 with Cardboard-box Antennas!," *QST*, Mar 2003, pp 57-62.

A. Monteiro, "An EZ-Lindenblad Antenna for 2 Meters," *QST*, Aug 2007, pp 37-40.

A. Monteiro, "A Parasitic Lindenblad Antenna for 70 cm," *QST*, Feb 2010, p 46.

Orban Microwave, "The Basics of Patch Antennas," (see **www.orbanmicrowave.com/antenna_application_notes.htm**).

J. Portune, "The Quadrifilar Helix as a 2 Meter Base Station Antenna," *QST*, Oct 2009, pp 30-32.

E. Ruperto, "The W3KH Quadrifilar Helix Antenna," *QST*, Aug 1996, pp 30-34. See also "Feedback", Jun 1999 *QST*, p 78 and Sep 1999 *QST*, p 80.

M. Seguin, "OSCAR 40 on 24 GHz", *QST*, Dec 2002, pp 55-56.

R. Seydler, "Modifications of the AIDC 3731 Downconverters," (see **members.aol.com/k5gna/AIDC3731modifications.doc**).

G. Suckling, "K-Band Results From AO-40," (see **www.g3wdg.free-online.co.uk/kband.htm**).

G. Suckling, "Notch Filters for AO-40 Mode L/S," (see **www.g3wdg.free-online.co.uk.notch.htm**).

D. Thiel and S. Smith, *Switched Parasitic Antennas for Cellular Communications*, (Artech House, 2002). See Chapter 3, "Patch Antennas," pp 79-96.

G. Tillitson, "The Polarization Diplexer — A Polaplexer," *Ham Radio*, Mar 1977, pp 40-43.

D. Thornburg and L. Kramer, "The Two-Meter Eggbeater," *QST*, April 1971, pp 44-46.

D. Vilardi, "Simple and Efficient Feed for Parabolic Antennas," *QST*, Mar 1973, pp 42-44.

P. Wade, *Online Microwave Antenna Handbook*, 1998-2004. See "Chapter 4, Parabolic Dish Antennas," **www.w1ghz.org/antbook/contents.htm**.

T. Zibrat, "2.4 GHz Patch Design," (see **www.qsl.net/k3tz**).

TABLE OF CONTENTS

Chapter 18

Repeater Antenna Systems

Antenna systems for VHF and UHF repeater systems are discussed in this chapter. Most repeater antennas are fairly simple, being based on dipoles and vertical monopoles — no exotic theory is required. Because repeaters must simultaneously transmit and receive, however, special care and techniques are required for filtering and system construction.

Obtaining the data necessary for repeater frequency coordination is also discussed. Material on duplexers and other topics was originally prepared by Domenic Mallozzi, N1DM. The chapter has been reviewed and updated for this edition by Ed Karl, KØKL, trustee for the KOØA and WBØHSI repeater systems.

18.1 BASIC REPEATER CONCEPTS

The antenna is a vital part of any repeater installation. Because the function of a repeater is to extend the range of communications between mobile and portable stations, the repeater antenna should be installed in the best possible location to provide the desired coverage. This usually means getting the antenna as high above the average local terrain as possible. In some instances, a repeater may need to have coverage only in a limited area or direction. When this is the case, antenna installation requirements will be completely different, with certain limits being set on height, gain and power.

18.1.1 HORIZONTAL AND VERTICAL POLARIZATION

Until the upsurge in FM repeater activity in the 1970s, most amateur VHF antennas were horizontally polarized. These days, very few repeater groups use horizontal polarization. The vast majority of VHF and UHF repeaters use vertically polarized antennas and all the antennas discussed in this chapter are of that type. (Horizontal polarization is sometimes used to allow separate repeaters to share the same input and/or output frequencies with closer-than-normal

geographical spacing by using cross-polarization to provide additional rejection of the unwanted signals.)

18.1.2 TRANSMISSION LINES

Transmission lines used at VHF and above become very important antenna system components because feed line losses increase with frequency. The characteristics of feed lines commonly used at VHF and above are discussed in the chapter **Transmission Lines**. Although information is provided there for small-diameter RG-58 and RG-59 coaxes, these should not be used except for very short feed lines (25 feet or less) and interconnecting cables. These cable types are very lossy at VHF. In addition, the losses can be much higher if fittings and connections are not carefully installed.

The differences in loss between solid-polyethylene dielectric types (RG-8 and RG-11) and those using foamed polyethylene are significant at VHF and UHF. Hardline has the lowest loss and is often available as surplus. Buy the line with the lowest loss you can afford. Feed line losses should be included in designing your repeater antenna system and must be included when calculating *effective radiated power (ERP)* as shown later in this chapter.

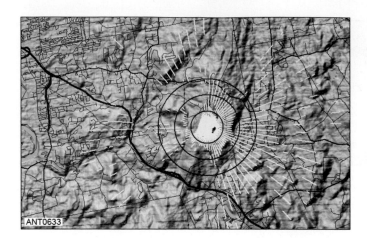

Figure 18.1 — *MicroDEM* topographic map, showing the coverage for a repeater placed on a 30-meter high tower in Glastonbury, CT. The white radial lines indicate the coverage in 5° increments of azimuth around the tower. The range circles are 1000 meters apart.

If you must bury coaxial cable, check with the cable manufacturer before doing so. Many popular varieties of coaxial cable should not be buried since the dielectric can become contaminated from moisture and soil chemicals. Some coaxial cables are labeled as "direct burial." Such a rating is the best way to be sure your cable can be buried without damage.

18.1.3 MATCHING

Losses are lowest in transmission lines that are matched to their characteristic impedances. If there is a mismatch at the end of the line, the losses increase. The *only way* to reduce the SWR on a transmission line is by matching the line *at the antenna*. Changing the length of a transmission line does not reduce the SWR except through loss, which is detrimental to system performance. The SWR is established by the impedance of the line and the impedance of the antenna, so matching must be done at the antenna end of the line.

The importance of matching, so far as feed line losses are concerned, is sometimes overstressed. But under some conditions, it is necessary to minimize feed line losses related to SWR if repeater performance is to be consistent. It is important to keep in mind that most VHF/UHF equipment is designed to operate into a 50-Ω load. The output circuitry will not be loaded properly if connected to a mismatched line. This leads to a reduction in output power, and in extreme cases, damage to the transmitter.

18.2 REPEATER ANTENNA SYSTEM DESIGN

Choosing a repeater or remote-base antenna system is as close as most amateurs come to designing a commercial-grade antenna system. The term *system* is used because most repeaters utilize not only an antenna and a transmission line, but also include duplexers, cavity filters, circulators or isolators in some configuration. Assembling the proper combination of these items in constructing a reliable system is both an art and a science. In this section, the functions of each component in a repeater antenna system and their successful integration are discussed. While every possible complication in constructing a repeater cannot be foreseen at the outset, this discussion should serve to steer you along the right lines in solving any problems encountered.

18.2.1 DETERMINING REPEATER COVERAGE AREA

Modern computer programs can show the coverage of a repeater using readily available topographic data from the Internet. In the chapter **HF Antenna System Design**, we described the *MicroDEM* program supplied on the CD-ROM accompanying this book. Dr Peter Guth, the author of *MicroDEM*, built into it the ability to generate terrain profiles that can be used with ARRL's *HFTA* (HF Terrain Assessment) program (also included on the CD-ROM).

MicroDEM has a wide range of capabilities beyond simply making terrain profiles. It can do *LOS* (line of sight) computations, based on visual or radio-horizon considerations.

Figure 18.1 shows a *MicroDEM* map for the area around Glastonbury, Connecticut. This is somewhat hilly terrain, and as a result the coverage for a repeater placed here on a 30-meter (100-foot) high tower would be somewhat spotty. Figure 18.1 shows a "Viewshed" on the map, in the form of the white terrain profile strokes in 5° increments around the tower.

Figure 18.2 shows the LOS for an azimuth of 80°, from a 30-meter high tower out to a distance of 8000 meters. The light-shaded areas on the profile are those that are illuminated directly by the antenna on the tower, while the dark portions of the profile are those that cannot be seen directly from the tower. This profile assumes that the mobile station is 2 meters high — the height of a 6-foot tall person with a handheld radio.

The terrain at an 80° azimuth allows direct radio view from the top of the tower out to about 1.8 km. From here, the downslope prevents direct view until about 2.5 km, where the terrain is briefly visible again from several hundred meters, disappearing from radio view until about 2.8 km, after which it becomes visible until about 3.6 km. Note that other than putting the repeater antenna on a higher tower, there is nothing that can be done to improve repeater coverage over this hilly terrain, although knife-edge diffraction off the hill tops will help fill in coverage gaps.

Repeater coverage can also be estimated by using the program *Radio Mobile for Windows* by Roger Coudé, VE2DBE (**www.cplus.org/rmw/english1.html**). The software is free

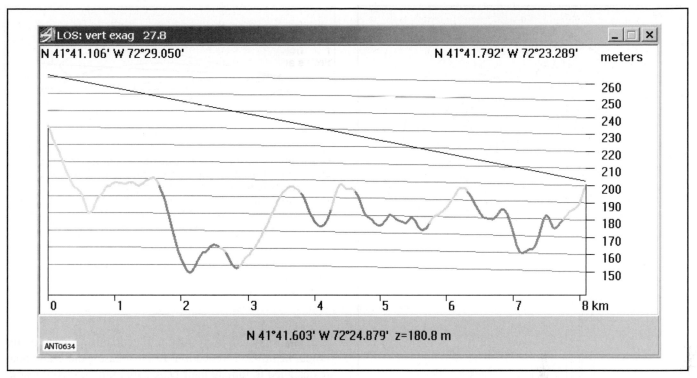

LOS: vert exag 27.8

N 41°41.106' W 72°29.050'   N 41°41.792' W 72°23.289'   meters

260
250
240
230
220
210
200
190
180
170
160
150

0   1   2   3   4   5   6   7   8 km

N 41°41.603' W 72°24.879' z=180.8 m

ANT0634

Figure 18.2 — An "LOS" (line of sight) profile at an azimuth of 80° from the tower in Figure 18.1. The light-gray portions of the terrain profile are visible from the top of the tower, while the dark portions are blocked by the terrain.

for amateur and other non-commercial uses. It produces coverage maps based on selectable environmental models and digitized terrain data. It does not produce output files that can be used by *HFTA* or other programs that automate the process of determining a repeater antenna's *height above average terrain (HAAT)*, a figure often required for frequency coordination applications.

18.2.2 THE REPEATER ANTENNA PATTERN

The most important part of the system is the antenna itself. As with any antenna, it must radiate and collect RF energy as efficiently as possible. Many repeaters use omnidirectional collinear antennas (see the Bibliography entries for Belrose and Collis at the end of this chapter) or groundplanes. These antennas are simple, mechanically robust, and are the most common type of antennas for both amateur and commercial repeaters.

An omnidirectional antenna is not always the best choice. For example, suppose a group wishes to set up a repeater to cover towns A and B and the interconnecting state highway shown in **Figure 18.3**. The available repeater site is marked on the map. No coverage is required to the west or south, or over the ocean. If an omnidirectional antenna is used in this case, a significant amount of the radiated signal goes in undesired directions. By using an antenna with a cardioid pattern, as shown in Figure 18.3, the coverage is concentrated in the desired directions. The repeater will be more effective in these locations, and signals from low-power portables and mobiles will be more reliable.

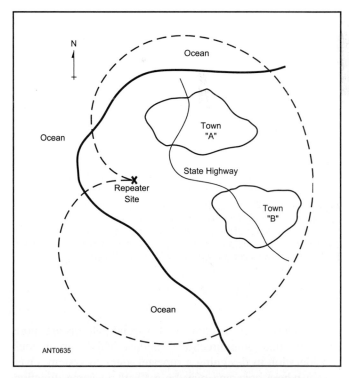

Figure 18.3 — There are many situations where equal repeater coverage is not desired in all directions from the "machine." One such situation is shown here, where the repeater is needed to cover only towns A and B and the interconnecting highway. An omnidirectional antenna would provide coverage in undesired directions, such as over the ocean. The broken line shows the radiation pattern of an antenna that is better suited to this circumstance.

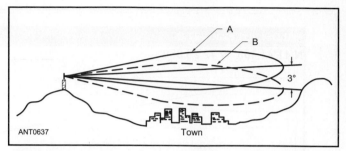

Figure 18.5 — Vertical-beam downtilt is another form of radiation-pattern distortion useful for improving repeater coverage. This technique can be employed in situations where the repeater station is at a greater elevation than the desired coverage area, when a high-gain omnidirectional antenna is used. Pattern A shows the normal vertical-plane radiation pattern of a high-gain omnidirectional antenna with respect to the desired coverage area (the town). Pattern B shows the pattern tilted down, and the coverage improvement is evident.

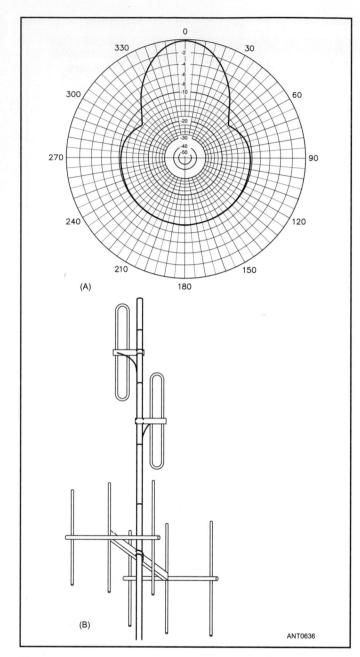

Figure 18.4 — The "keyhole" horizontal radiation pattern at A is generated by the combination of phased Yagis and vertical elements shown at B. Such a pattern is useful in overcoming coverage blockages resulting from local terrain features. (*Based on a design by Decibel Products*)

In many cases, antennas with special patterns are more expensive than omnidirectional models. This is an obvious consideration in designing a repeater antenna system. Over terrain where coverage may be difficult in some direction from the repeater site, it may be desirable to skew the antenna pattern in that direction. This can be accomplished by using a phased-vertical array or a combination of a Yagi and a phased vertical to produce a "keyhole" pattern. See **Figure 18.4**.

Repeaters are common on 440 MHz and above, and many groups invest in high-gain omnidirectional antennas.

Obtaining high gain from an omnidirectional antenna requires vertical beamwidth reduction. In most cases, these antennas are designed to radiate their peak gain at the horizon, resulting in optimum coverage when the antenna is located at a moderate height over normal terrain. Unfortunately, in cases where the antenna is located at a very high site (overlooking the coverage area) this may not be the most desirable pattern. The vertical pattern of the antenna can be tilted downward, however, to facilitate coverage of the desired area. This is called *vertical-beam downtilt*.

An example of such a situation is shown in **Figure 18.5**. The repeater site overlooks a town in a valley. A 450-MHz repeater is needed to serve low-power portable and mobile stations. Constraints on the repeater dictate the use of an antenna with a gain of 11 dBi. (An omnidirectional antenna with this gain has a vertical beamwidth of approximately 6°.) If the repeater antenna has its peak gain at the horizon, a major portion of the transmitted signal is directed *above* the town, which becomes the best area from which to access the repeater. By tilting the pattern down 3°, the peak radiation will occur in the town.

Vertical-beam downtilt is generally produced by feeding the elements of a collinear vertical array slightly out of phase with each other. Lee Barrett, K7NM, showed such an array in *Ham Radio* magazine. (See the Bibliography at the end of this chapter.) Barrett gives the geometry and design of a four-pole array with progressive phase delay, and a computer program to model it. The technique is shown in **Figure 18.6**, with a free-space elevation plot showing downtilt in **Figure 18.7**.

Commercial antennas are sometimes available (at extra cost) with built-in downtilt characteristics. Before ordering such a commercial antenna, make sure that you really require it — they generally are special-order items and are not returnable.

There are disadvantages to improving coverage by means of vertical-beam downtilt. When compared to a standard collinear array, an antenna using vertical-beam downtilt will have somewhat greater minor lobes in the vertical pattern, resulting

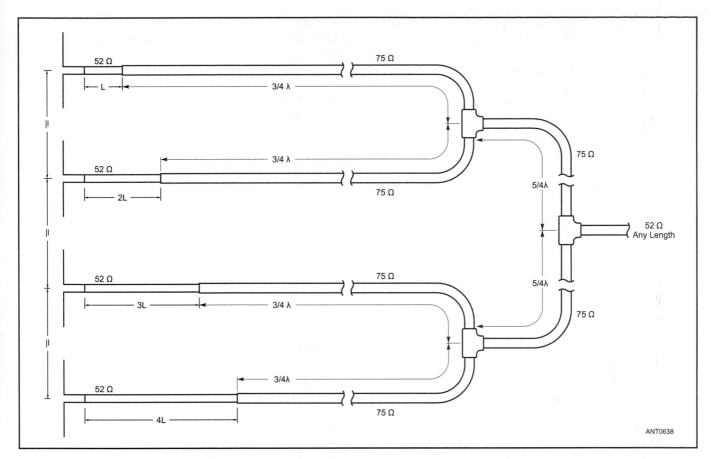

Figure 18.6 — Vertical-beam downtilt can be facilitated by inserting 52-Ω delay lines in series with the 75-Ω feed lines to the collinear elements of an omnidirectional antenna. The delay lines to each element are progressively longer so the phase shift between elements is uniform. Odd ¼-λ coaxial transformers are used in the main (75-Ω) feed system to match the dipole impedances to the driving point. Tilting the vertical beam in this way often produces minor lobes in the vertical pattern that do not exist when the elements are fed in phase.

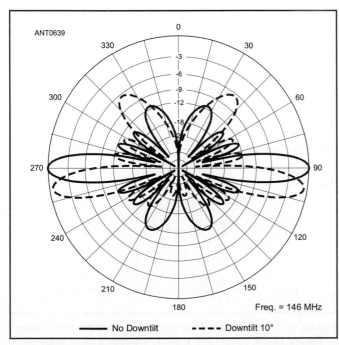

Figure 18.7 — Free-space elevation-plane patterns showing downtilting that results from progressive phase shifts for the feed currents for the dipole in Figure 18.6.

in reduced gain (usually less than 1 dB). Bandwidth is also slightly reduced. The reduction in gain, when combined with the downtilt characteristic, results in a reduction in total coverage area. These trade-offs, as well as the increased cost of a commercial antenna with downtilt, must be compared to the improvement in total performance in a situation where vertical-beam downtilt is contemplated.

If the antenna is located at the outer edge of desired coverage, *mechanical beamtilt* can also be used. The antenna is physically tilted several degrees to lower the main lobe in the favored direction. (It is raised in the unfavored direction.) For example, in the above cited installation a cardioid pattern gets the energy in the desired direction, tilting the antenna ensures the energy is directed into the desired geography.

An alternative to using special techniques to produce downtilt is to use an antenna with significant radiation at high elevation angles and invert it. Using such a low gain antenna mounted upside down results in all the energy being directed below the antenna. Consider the pattern of a ¼-wavelength ground-plane antenna. Most of the energy is radiated at angles between the horizon and the top of the radiator.

By inverting the ground plane antenna, you obtain solid coverage from the base of the antenna's mounting structure to the horizon. The tradeoff is losing some gain advantage in favor of good nearby coverage and elimination of the pattern nulls created when using electrical beamtilt.

Top Mounting and Side Mounting

Amateur repeaters often share towers with commercial and public service users. In many of these cases, other antennas are at the top of the tower, so the amateur antenna must be side mounted. A consequence of this arrangement is that the free-space pattern of the repeater antenna is distorted by the tower. This effect is especially noticeable when an omnidirectional antenna is side mounted on a structure.

The effects of supporting structures are most pronounced at close antenna spacings to the tower and with large support dimensions. The result is a measurable increase in gain in one direction and a partial null in the other direction (sometimes 15 dB deep). The shape of the supporting structure also influences pattern distortion. Many antenna manufacturers publish radiation patterns showing the effect of side mounting antennas in their catalogs.

Side mounting is not always a disadvantage. In cases where more (or less) coverage is desired in one direction, the supporting structure can be used to advantage. If pattern distortion is not acceptable, a solution is to mount antennas around the perimeter of the structure and feed them with the proper phasing to synthesize an omnidirectional pattern. Many manufacturers make antennas to accommodate such situations.

The effects of different mounting locations and arrangements can be illustrated with an array of exposed dipoles, **Figure 18.8**. Such an array is a very versatile antenna because, with simple rearrangement of the elements, it can develop either an omnidirectional pattern or an offset pattern. Figure 18.8A shows a basic collinear array of four vertical ½-λ elements. The vertical spacing between adjacent elements is 1 λ. All elements are fed in phase. If this array is placed in the clear and supported by a nonconducting mast, the calculated radiation resistance of each dipole element is on the order of 63 Ω. If the feed line is completely decoupled, the resulting azimuth pattern is omnidirectional. The vertical-plane pattern is shown in **Figure 18.9**.

Figure 18.8B shows the same array in a side-mounting arrangement, at a spacing of ¼ λ from a conducting mast. In this mounting arrangement, the mast takes on the role of a reflector, producing an F/B on the order of 5.7 dB. The azimuth pattern is shown in **Figure 18.10**. The vertical pattern is not significantly different from that of Figure 18.9, except the four small minor lobes (two on either side of the vertical axis) tend to become distorted. They are not as "clean," tending to merge into one minor lobe at some mast heights. This apparently is a function of currents in the supporting mast. The proximity of the mast also alters the feed-point impedance. For elements that are resonant in the configuration of Figure 18.8A, the calculated impedance in the arrangement of Figure 18.8B is in the order of $72 + j\,10\,\Omega$.

If side mounting is the only possibility and an omnidirectional pattern is required, the arrangement of Figure 18.8C may be used. The calculated azimuth pattern takes on a slight cloverleaf shape, but is within 1.5 dB of being circular. However, gain performance suffers, and the idealized vertical pattern of Figure 18.9 is not achieved. See **Figure 18.11**. Spacings other than ¼-λ from the mast were not investigated.

Effects of Other Conductors

Feed line proximity and tower-access ladders or cages

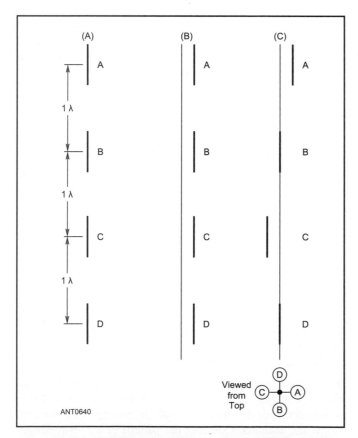

Figure 18.8 — Various arrangements of exposed dipole elements. At A is the basic collinear array of four elements. B shows the same elements mounted on the side of a mast, and C shows the elements in a side-mounted arrangement around the mast for omnidirectional coverage. See text and Figures 18.9 through 18.11 for radiation-pattern information.

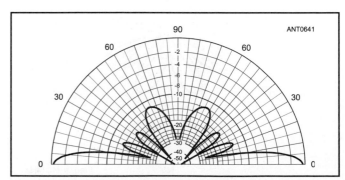

Figure 18.9 — Calculated vertical-plane pattern of the array of Figure 18.8A, assuming a nonconducting mast support and complete decoupling of the feeder. In azimuth the array is omnidirectional. The calculated gain of the array is 8.6 dBi at 0° elevation; the −3 dB point is at 6.5°.

also have an effect on the radiation patterns of side-mounted antennas. This subject was studied by Connolly and Blevins, and their findings are given in *IEEE Conference Proceedings* (see the Bibliography). Those considering mounting antennas on air-conditioning evaporators or maintenance penthouses on commercial buildings should consult this article. It gives considerable information on the effects of these structures on both unidirectional and omnidirectional antennas.

Metallic guy wires also affect antenna radiation patterns. Yang and Willis studied this and reported the results in *IRE Transactions on Vehicular Communications*. As expected, the closer the antenna is to the guy wires, the greater the effect on the radiation patterns. If the antennas are near the point where the guy wires meet the tower, the effect of the guy wires can be minimized by breaking them up with insulators every 0.75 λ for a distance of 2.25 λ to 3.0 λ from the antenna.

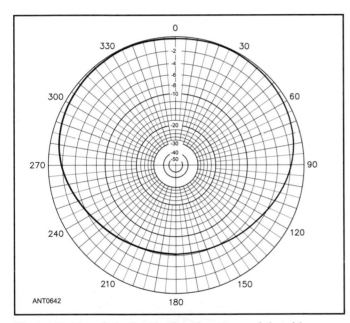

Figure 18.10 — Calculated azimuth pattern of the side-mounted array of Figure 18.8B, assuming ¼-λ spacing from a 4-inch mast. The calculated gain in the favored direction, away from the mast and through the elements, is 10.6 dBi.

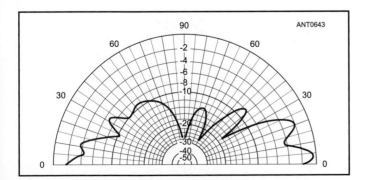

Figure 18.11 — Calculated vertical pattern of the array of Figure 18.8C, assuming ¼-λ element spacing from a 4-inch mast. The azimuth pattern is circular within 1.5 dB, and the calculated gain is 4.4 dBi.

Mechanical Construction Issues

Repeater antennas are usually installed in locations that are exposed to far more extreme weather conditions than ground-mounted antennas. Because they are installed on mountaintops, tall buildings, and tall towers, high winds, extreme temperatures, icing, and other hostile conditions are often encountered. For this reason, most garden variety amateur antennas are not suitable for repeater use even though they may meet electrical specifications for gain and frequency coverage. Unless you are skilled at the construction of mechanically-rugged antennas, it is recommended that a commercial antenna is used, particularly if the antenna is not easily accessed for repair and testing.

Mechanical integrity of the mount is also of great importance. An antenna hanging by the feed line and banging against the tower provides far from optimum performance and reliability. Use a mount that is appropriately secured to the tower and the antenna. Also use high-quality mounting hardware, preferably stainless steel (or bronze). If your local hardware store does not carry stainless steel hardware, try a marine supply store.

Be certain that the feed line connectors are properly waterproofed and that the feed line is properly supported along its length. Long lengths of cable are subject to contraction and expansion with temperature from season to season, so it is important that the cable not be so tight that contraction causes it to stress the connection at the antenna. This can cause the connection to become intermittent (and noisy) or, at worst, an open circuit. This is far from a pleasant situation if the antenna connection is 300 feet up a tower, and it happens to be the middle of the winter!

18.2.3 ISOLATION REQUIREMENTS

Because repeaters generally operate in full *duplex* (the transmitter and receiver operate simultaneously), the antenna system must act as a filter to keep the transmitter from blocking the receiver. The degree to which the transmitter and receiver must be isolated is a complex problem. It is quite dependent on the equipment used and the difference in transmitter and receiver frequencies (offset). Instead of going into great detail, a simplified example can be used for illustration.

Consider the design of a 144-MHz repeater with a 600-kHz offset. The transmitter has an RF output power of 10 W, and the receiver has a squelch sensitivity of 0.1 μV. This means there must be at least 1.9×10^{-16} W at the 52-Ω receiver-antenna terminals to detect a signal. If both the transmitter and receiver were on the same frequency, the isolation (attenuation) required between the transmitter and receiver antenna jacks to keep the transmitter from activating the receiver would be

$$\text{Isolation} = 10 \log \frac{10 \text{ W}}{1.9 \times 10^{-16} \text{ W}} = 167 \text{ dB}$$

Obviously there is no need for this much attenuation, because the repeater does not transmit and receive on the same frequency.

If the 10-W transmitter has noise 600 kHz away from the carrier frequency that is 45 dB below the carrier power, that 45 dB can be subtracted from the isolation requirement. Similarly, if the receiver can detect a 0.1 μV on-frequency signal in the presence of a signal 600 kHz away that is 40 dB greater than 0.1 μV, this 40 dB can also be subtracted from the isolation requirement. Therefore, the isolation requirement is

167 dB – 45 dB – 40 dB = 82 dB

Other factors enter into the isolation requirements as well. For example, if the transmitter power is increased by 10 dB (from 10 to 100 W), this 10 dB must be added to the isolation requirement. Typical requirements for 144- and 440-MHz repeaters are shown in **Figure 18.12**.

Obtaining the required isolation is the first problem to be considered in constructing a repeater antenna system. There are three common ways to obtain this isolation:

1) Physically separate the receiving and transmitting antennas so the combination of path loss for the spacing and the antenna radiation patterns results in the required isolation.

2) Use a combination of separate antennas and high-Q filters to develop the required isolation. (The high-Q filters serve to reduce the physical distance required between antennas.)

3) Use a combination filter and combiner system to allow the transmitter and receiver to share one antenna. Such a filter and combiner is called a *duplexer*.

Repeaters operating on 28 and 50 MHz generally use separate antennas to obtain the required isolation. This is largely because duplexers in this frequency range are both large and very expensive. It is generally less expensive to buy two antennas and link the sites by a committed phone line or an RF link than to purchase a duplexer. At 144 MHz and higher, duplexers are more commonly used. Duplexers are discussed in greater detail in a later section.

18.2.4 ISOLATION BY SEPARATE ANTENNAS

Receiver *desensing or de-sense* (gain reduction caused by the presence of a strong off-frequency signal) can be reduced and often eliminated by separation of the transmitting and receiving antennas. Obtaining the full 55 to 90 dB of isolation required for a repeater requires the separate antennas to be spaced a considerable distance apart (in wavelengths). (Separate antennas are not a solution for wide-band noise generated in the transmitter on the receive frequency. That noise must be removed with filters.)

Figure 18.13 shows the distances required to obtain specific values of isolation for vertical dipoles having horizontal separation (at A) and vertical separation (at B). The isolation gained by using separate antennas is subtracted from the total isolation requirement of the system. For example, if the transmitter and receiver antennas for a 450-MHz repeater are separated horizontally by 400 feet, the total isolation requirement in the system is reduced by about 64 dB.

Note from Figure 18.13B that a vertical separation of only about 25 feet also provides 64 dB of isolation. Vertical separation yields much more isolation than horizontal separation. Vertical separation is also more practical than horizontal, since only a single support is required.

An explanation of the significant difference between the two graphs is in order. The vertical spacing requirement for

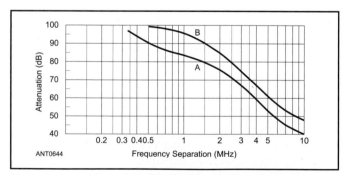

Figure 18.12 — Typical isolation requirements for repeater transmitters and receivers operating in the 132-174 MHz band (Curve A), and the 400-512 MHz band (Curve B). Required isolation in dB is plotted against frequency separation in MHz. These curves were developed for a 100-W transmitter. For other power levels, the isolation requirements will differ by the change in decibels relative to 100 W. Isolation requirements will vary with receiver sensitivity. (The values plotted were calculated for transmitter-carrier and receiver-noise suppression necessary to prevent more than 1 dB degradation in receiver 12-dB SINAD sensitivity.)

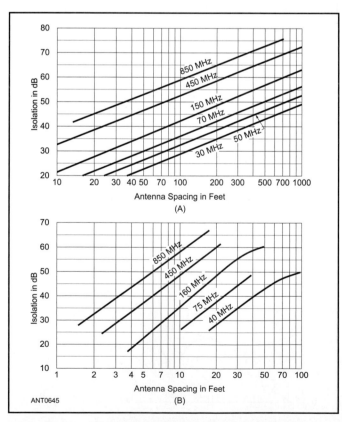

Figure 18.13 — At A, the amount of attenuation (isolation) provided by horizontal separation of vertical dipole antennas. At B, isolation afforded by vertical separation of vertical dipoles.

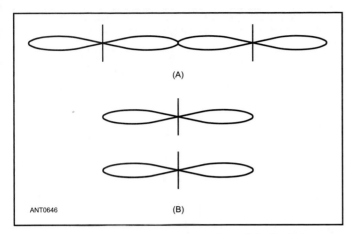

Figure 18.14 — A relative representation of the isolation advantage afforded by separating antennas horizontally (A) and vertically (B) is shown. A great deal of isolation is provided by vertical separation, but horizontal separation requires two supports and much greater distance to be as effective. Separate-site repeaters (those with transmitter and receiver at different locations) benefit much more from horizontal separation than do single-site installations.

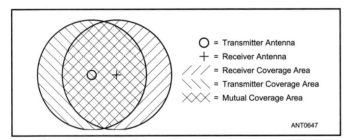

Figure 18.15 — Coverage disparity is a major problem for separate-site repeater antennas. The transmitter and receiver coverage areas overlap, but are not entirely mutually inclusive. Solving this problem requires a great deal of experimentation, as many factors are involved. Among these factors are terrain features and distortion of the antenna radiation patterns from supports.

60 dB attenuation (isolation) at 150 MHz is about 43 feet. The horizontal spacing for the same isolation level is on the order of 700 feet. **Figure 18.14** shows why this difference exists. The radiation patterns of the antennas at A overlap; each antenna has gain in the direction of the other. The path loss between the antennas is given by

$$\text{Path loss (dB)} = 20 \ \log \left(\frac{4 \ \pi \ d}{\lambda} \right)$$

where
  d = distance between antennas
  λ = wavelength, in the same units as d.

The isolation between the antennas in Figure 18.14A is the path loss less the antenna gains. Conversely, the antennas at B share pattern nulls, so the isolation is the path loss added to the depth of these nulls. This significantly reduces the spacing requirement for vertical separation. Because the depth of

Figure 18.16 — A coaxial cavity filter of the type used in many amateur and commercial repeater installations. Center-conductor length (and thus resonant frequency) is varied by adjustment of the knob (top).

the pattern nulls is not infinite, some spacing is required. Combined horizontal and vertical spacing is much more difficult to quantify because the results are dependent on both radiation patterns and the positions of the antennas relative to each other.

Separate antennas have one major disadvantage: They create disparity in transmitter and receiver coverage. For example, say a 50-MHz repeater is installed over average terrain with the transmitter and repeater separated by 2 miles. If both antennas had perfect omnidirectional coverage, the situation depicted in **Figure 18.15** would exist. In this case, stations able to hear the repeater may not be able to access it, and vice versa. In practice, the situation can be considerably worse. This is especially true if the patterns of both antennas are not omnidirectional. If this disparity in coverage cannot be tolerated, the solution involves skewing the patterns of the antennas until their coverage areas are essentially the same.

18.2.5 ISOLATION BY CAVITY RESONATORS

As just discussed, receiver desensing can be reduced by separating the transmitter and receiver antennas. But the amount of transmitted energy that reaches the receiver input must often be decreased even farther. Other nearby transmitters can cause desensing as well. A *cavity resonator* (cavity filter) can be helpful in solving these problems. When properly designed and constructed, this type of resonator has very high Q. A commercially made cavity is shown in **Figure 18.16**.

A cavity resonator placed in series with a transmission line acts as a band-pass filter. For a resonator to operate in series, it must have input and output coupling loops (or probes). A cavity resonator can also be connected across (in parallel with) a transmission line. The cavity then acts as a band-reject (notch) filter, greatly attenuating energy at the frequency to which it is tuned. Only one coupling loop or probe is required for this method of filtering. This type of cavity could be used in the receiver line to "notch" the transmitter signal. Several cavities can be connected in series or parallel to increase the attenuation in a given configuration. The graphs of **Figure 18.17** show the attenuation of a single cavity (A) and a pair of cavities (B).

The only situation in which cavity filters would not help is the case where the off-frequency noise of the transmitter was right on the receiver frequency. With cavity resonators, an important point to remember is that addition of a cavity

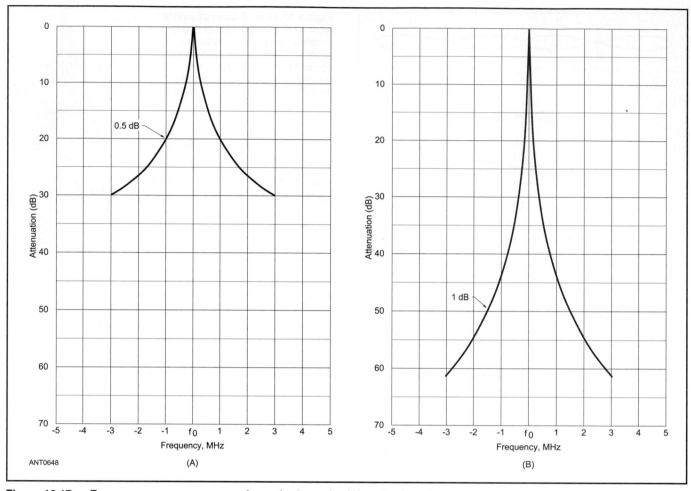

Figure 18.17 — Frequency response curves for a single cavity (A) and two cavities cascaded (B). These curves are for cavities with coupling loops, each having an insertion loss of 0.5 dB. (The total insertion loss is indicated in the body of each graph.) Selectivity will be greater if lighter coupling (greater insertion loss) can be tolerated.

across a transmission line may change the impedance of the system. This change can be compensated by adding tuning stubs along the transmission line.

18.2.6 ISOLATION BY DUPLEXERS

Most amateur repeaters in the 144-, 222- and 440-MHz bands use duplexers to obtain the necessary transmitter to receiver isolation. (Duplexers for 50 MHz systems are quite large and impractical at lower frequencies.) Duplexers have been commonly used in commercial repeaters for many years. The duplexer consists of two high-Q filters. One filter is used in the feed line from the transmitter to the antenna, and another between the antenna and the receiver. These filters must have low loss at the frequency to which they are tuned while having very high attenuation at the surrounding frequencies. To meet the high attenuation requirements at frequencies within as little as 0.4% of the frequency to which they are tuned, the filters usually take the form of cascaded transmission-line cavity filters. These are either band-pass filters, or band-pass filters with a rejection notch. (The rejection notch is tuned to the center frequency of the other filter.) The number of cascaded filter sections is determined

Duplexer or Diplexer?

Hams use these terms casually, often not realizing they refer to different functions. From the Amateur Radio perspective, a *duplexer* allows a transmitter and receiver operating on the same band to share a common antenna. Repeaters use duplexers. A *diplexer* allows multiple radios operating on different bands to share a common antenna. A diplexer would be used to allow a VHF and a UHF radio to share the same multiband antenna.

by the frequency separation and the ultimate attenuation requirements.

Duplexers for the amateur bands represent a significant technical challenge, because in most cases amateur repeaters operate with significantly less frequency separation than their commercial counterparts. Many manufacturers market high-quality duplexers for the amateur frequencies.

Experience with modern receivers and transmitters used in commercial two-way service enables the successful use of four-cavity duplexers. Four-cavity duplexers should be capable of isolation in the high 70 dB range. Today's commercial transceivers are very low in spurious products. Receiving sections are quite insensitive to off frequency signals. This results in repeater performance only dreamt of in the early days. Ease of alignment and low cost greatly ease the process of modern repeater installation.

Duplexers consist of very high-Q cavities whose resonant frequencies are determined by mechanical components, in particular the tuning rod. **Figure 18.18** shows the cutaway view of a typical duplexer cavity. A construction project for 144 MHz duplexer cavities is included on the CD-ROM included with this book.

The rod is usually made of a material that has a limited thermal expansion coefficient (such as Invar). Detuning of the cavity by environmental changes introduces unwanted losses in the antenna system. An article by Arnold in *Mobile Radio Technology* considered the causes of drift in the cavity (see the Bibliography). These can be divided into four major categories.

1) Ambient temperature variation (which leads to mechanical variations related to the thermal expansion coefficients of the materials used in the cavity).

2) Humidity (dielectric constant) variation.

3) Localized heating from the power dissipated in the cavity (resulting from its insertion loss).

4) Mechanical variations resulting from other factors (vibration, etc).

In addition, because of the high-Q nature of these cavities, the insertion loss of the duplexer increases when the signal is not at the peak of the filter response. This means, in practical terms, that less power is radiated for a given transmitter output power. Also, the drift in cavities in the receiver line results in increased system noise figure, reducing the sensitivity of the repeater.

As the frequency separation between the receiver and the transmitter decreases, the insertion loss of the duplexer reaches certain practical limits. At 144 MHz, the minimum insertion loss for 600 kHz spacing is 1.5 dB per filter.

Testing and using duplexers requires some special considerations (especially as frequency increases). Because duplexers are very high-Q devices, they are very sensitive to the termination impedances at their ports. A high SWR on any port is a serious problem because the apparent insertion loss of the duplexer will increase and the isolation may appear to decrease. Some have found that when duplexers are used at the limits of their isolation capabilities, a small change in antenna SWR is enough to cause receiver desensitization. This occurs most often under ice-loading conditions on antennas with open-wire phasing sections.

The choice of connectors in the duplexer system is important. BNC connectors are good for use below 300 MHz. Above 300 MHz their use is discouraged because even though many types of BNC connectors work well up to 1 GHz, older style standard BNC connectors are inadequate at UHF and above. Type N connectors should be used above 300 MHz. It is false economy to use marginal quality connectors. Some commercial users have reported deteriorated isolation in commercial UHF repeaters when using such connectors. Determining the location of a bad connector in a system is a complicated and frustrating process. Despite all these considerations, the duplexer is still the best method for obtaining isolation in the 144- to 925-MHz range.

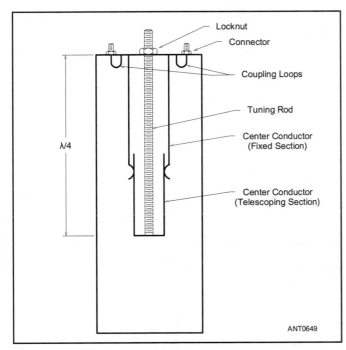

Figure 18.18 — Cutaway view of a typical cavity. Note the relative locations of the coupling loops to each other and to the center conductor of the cavity. A locknut is used to prevent movement of the tuning rod after adjustment.

18.3 ADVANCED TECHNIQUES

As the number of available antenna sites decreases and the cost of various peripheral items (such as coaxial cable) increases, amateur repeater groups are required to devise advanced techniques if repeaters are to remain effective. Some of the techniques discussed here have been applied in commercial services for many years, but until recently have not been economically justified for amateur use.

18.3.1 COUPLERS

One technique worth consideration is the use of *cross-band couplers*. To illustrate a situation where a cross-band coupler would be useful, consider the following example. A repeater group plans to install 144- and 902-MHz repeaters on the same tower. The group intends to erect both antennas on a horizontal cross arm at the 325-foot level. A 325-foot run of ⅞-inch Heliax costs several thousand dollars. If both antennas are to be mounted at the top of the tower, the logical approach would require two separate feed lines. A better solution involves the use of a single feed line for both repeaters, along with a cross-band coupler at each end of the line.

The use of the cross-band coupler is shown in **Figure 18.19.** As the term implies, the coupler allows two signals on different bands to share a common transmission line. Such couplers cost approximately $300 each. In our hypothetical example, this represents a significant saving over the cost of using separate feed lines. But, as with all compromises, there are disadvantages. Cross-band couplers have a loss of about 0.5 dB per unit. Therefore, the pair required represents a loss of 1.0 dB in *each* transmission path. If this loss can be tolerated, the cross-band coupler is a good solution.

Cross-band couplers do not allow two repeaters *on the same band* to share a single antenna and feed line. As repeater sites and tower space become scarcer, it may be desirable to have two repeaters on the same band share the same antenna. The solution to this problem is the use of a *transmitter multicoupler*. The multicoupler is related to the duplexers discussed earlier. It is a cavity filter and combiner that allows multiple transmitters and receivers to share the same antenna. This is a common commercial practice. A block diagram of a multicoupler system is shown in **Figure 18.20**.

The multicoupler, however, is a very expensive device, and has the disadvantage of even greater loss per transmission path than the standard duplexer. For example, a well-designed duplexer for 600 kHz spacing at 146 MHz has a loss per transmission path of approximately 1.5 dB. A four-channel multicoupler (the requirement for two repeaters) has an insertion loss per transmission path on the order of 2.5 dB or more. Another constraint of such a system is that the antenna must present a good match to the transmission line at all frequencies on which it will be used (both transmitting and receiving). This becomes difficult for the system with two repeaters operating at opposite ends of a band.

If you elect to purchase a commercial base-station

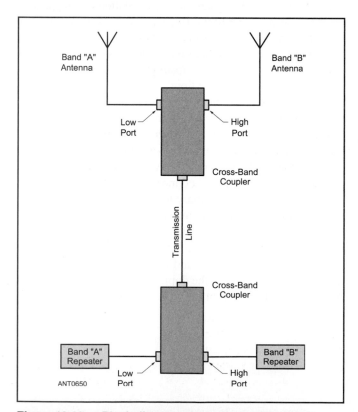

Figure 18.19 — Block diagram of a system using cross-band couplers to allow the use of a single feed line for two repeaters. If the feeder to the antenna location is long (more than 200 feet or so), cross-band couplers may provide a significant saving over separate feed lines, especially at the higher amateur repeater frequencies. Cross-band couplers cannot be used with two repeaters on the same band.

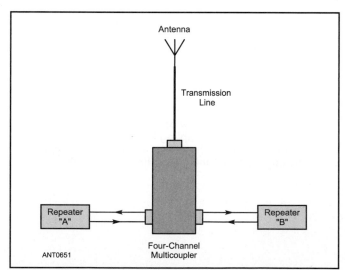

Figure 18.20 — Block diagram of a system using a transmitter multicoupler to allow a single feed line and antenna to be used by two repeaters on one band. The antenna must be designed to operate at all frequencies that the repeaters utilize. More than two repeaters can be operated this way by using a multicoupler with the appropriate number of input ports.

antenna that requires you to specify a frequency to which the antenna must be tuned, be sure to indicate to the manufacturer the intended use of the antenna and the frequency extremes. In some cases, the only way the manufacturer can accommodate your request is to provide an antenna with some vertical-beam uptilt at one end of the band and some downtilt at the other end of the band. In the case of antennas with very high gain, this in itself may become a serious problem. Careful analysis of the situation is necessary before assembling such a system.

18.3.2 DIVERSITY TECHNIQUES FOR REPEATERS

Mobile flutter, "dead spots" and similar problems are a real problem for the mobile operator. The popularity of hand-held transceivers using low power and mediocre antennas causes similar problems. A solution to these difficulties is the use of some form of *diversity reception*. Diversity reception works because signals do not fade at the same rate when received by antennas at different locations (space diversity) or of different polarizations (polarization diversity).

Repeaters with large transmitter coverage areas often have difficulty "hearing" low power stations in peripheral areas or in dead spots. Space diversity is especially useful in such a situation. Space diversity utilizes separate receivers at different locations that are linked to the repeater. The repeater uses a circuit called a *voter* that determines which receiver has the best signal, and then selects the appropriate receiver from which to feed the repeater transmitter. This technique is helpful in urban areas where shadowing from large buildings and bridges causes problems. Space-diversity receiving,

when properly executed, can give excellent results. But with the improvement come some disadvantages: added initial cost, maintenance costs, and the possibility of failure created by the extra equipment required. If installed and maintained carefully, problems are generally minimal.

A second improvement technique is the use of *circularly polarized* repeater antennas. This technique has been used in the FM broadcast field for many years, and has been considered for use in the mobile telephone service as well. Some experiments by amateurs have proved very promising, as discussed by Pasternak and Morris (see the Bibliography).

The improvement afforded by circular polarization is primarily a reduction in *mobile flutter*. The flutter on a mobile signal is caused by reflections from large buildings (in urban settings) or other terrain features. These reflections cause measurable polarization shifts, sometimes to the point where a vertically polarized signal at the transmitting site may appear to be primarily horizontally polarized after reflection.

A similar situation results from *multipath propagation*, where one or more reflected signals combine with the direct signal at the repeater to create varying effects on the signal. The multipath signal is subjected to large amplitude and phase variations at a relatively rapid rate.

In both of the situations described here, circular polarization can offer considerable improvement. This is because circularly polarized antennas respond equally to all linearly polarized signals, regardless of the plane of polarization. At this writing, there are no known sources of commercial circularly polarized omnidirectional antennas for the amateur bands. Pasternak and Morris describe a circularly polarized antenna made by modifying two commercial four-pole arrays.

18.4 DETERMINING EFFECTIVE ISOTROPIC RADIATED POWER (EIRP)

It is useful to know effective isotropic radiated power (EIRP) in calculating the coverage area of a repeater. The FCC formerly required EIRP to be entered in the log of every amateur repeater station. Although logging EIRP is no longer required, it is still useful to have this information on hand for repeater-coordination purposes and so system performance can be monitored periodically.

Calculation of EIRP is straightforward. The PEP output of the transmitter is simply multiplied by the gains and losses in the transmitting antenna system. (These gains and losses are best added or subtracted in decibels and then converted to a multiplying factor.) The following worksheet and example illustrate the calculations.

Transmitter power output (TPO)   _____W (PEP)

Feed line loss	_____ dB
Misc connecting cable loss	_____ dB
Duplexer loss	_____ dB
Isolator loss	_____ dB
Cross-band coupler loss	_____ dB
Cavity filter loss	_____ dB
Other loss	_____ dB

Total Losses (L)   _____ dB

G (dB) = antenna gain (dBi) – Total Losses (L)

where G = antenna system gain. (If antenna gain is specified in dBd, add 2.14 dB to obtain the gain in dBi.)

$M = 10^{G/10}$

where M = multiplying factor

EIRP (watts) = transmitter output (TPO) × M

Example

A repeater transmitter has a power output of 50 W PEP (50 W FM transmitter). The transmission line has a total loss of 1.8 dB. The duplexer used has a loss of 1.5 dB, and a circulator on the transmitter port has a loss of 0.3 dB. There are no cavity filters or cross-band couplers in the system. Antenna gain is 5.6 dBi.

Feed line loss	1.8 dB
Duplexer loss	1.5 dB
Isolator loss	0.3 dB
Cross-band coupler loss	0 dB
Cavity filter loss	0 dB
	———
Total Losses (L)	3.6 dB

Antenna system gain in dB = G = antenna gain (dBi) – L

G = 5.6 dBi – 3.6 dB = 2 dB

Multiplying factor = $M = 10^{G/10}$

$M = 10^{2/10} = 1.585$

EIRP (watts) = transmitter output (TPO) × M

EIRP = 50 W × 1.585 = 79.25 W

If the antenna system is lossier than this example, G may be *negative*, resulting in a multiplying factor less than one. The result is an EIRP that is less than the transmitter output power. This situation can occur in practice, but for obvious reasons is not desirable.

18.5 ASSEMBLING A REPEATER ANTENNA SYSTEM

This section will aid you in planning and assembling your repeater antenna system. First, a repeater antenna selection checklist such as this will help you in evaluating the antenna system for your needs.

Gain needed _____ dBi
Pattern required _____ Omnidirectional
_____ Offset
_____ Cardioid
_____ Bidirectional
_____ Special pattern
(specify)
Mounting _____ Top of tower
_____ Side of tower

(Determine effects of tower on pattern. Is the result consistent with the pattern required?)

Is downtilt required? _____ Yes
_____ No
Type of RF connector _____ UHF
_____ N
_____ BNC
_____ Other (specify)
Size (length) _____
Weight _____
Maximum cost $_____

Commercial components are available for repeater and remote-base antenna systems from companies such as Celwave/RFS, Decibel Products (Andrew Corp), Sinclair Radio Laboratories Inc, TX/RX Systems Inc and Telewave Systems. Even though almost any antenna can be used for a repeater, heavy-duty antennas built to commercial standards are recommended for repeater service. Some companies offer their antennas with special features for repeater service (such as vertical-beam downtilt). It is best to review the print or online catalogs of current products from the manufacturers, both for general information and to determine which special options are available on their products. See the Resources for Repeater Builders section later in this chapter.

18.5.1 FREQUENCY COORDINATION

In order for a repeater system to be accepted by the regional frequency coordinator, the precise location of the repeater antenna system and its power output must be supplied. A typical list of data follows:

1) Latitude and longitude using the NAD27 continental US database

2) Antenna structure FAA registration number, if any

3) Antenna structure ground elevation

4) Antenna height above ground (the center of the radiating portion of the antenna)

5) Height Above Average Terrain (HAAT — see below)

6) Effective Isotropic Radiated Power (EIRP — see above)

7) Mounting and pattern of the antenna — omnidirectional, cardioid, elliptical, or bidirectional

8) Whether the antenna is top or side mounted and the favored and shadowed directions

9) Antenna beamwidth and front-to-back ratio, if applicable

10) Antenna polarization: vertical, horizontal, or circular/elliptical

Most of this information is easily obtained from the equipment specifications and antenna mounting plans.

Height Above Average Terrain or HAAT can be determined manually from topographic maps as explained on most frequency coordination websites. However, with online databases HAAT can be determined automatically. You will need the precise latitude and longitude of your antenna from a GPS receiver or from an online website such as **itouchmap.com/latlong.html** and the elevation of the site, also available online such as from **itouchmap.com/?r=googleearth**. The online FCC HAAT calculator is located at **www.fcc.gov/mb/audio/bickel/haat_calculator.html**.

Enter your site data and the calculator will then report your HAAT. (RCAMSL is the sum of the antenna mounting structure's base elevation and the height to the radiating center of the antenna.) It can also produce a file that provides the required data from each of your specified radials. The following example is the calculator's output text for a repeater antenna located in St Charles, MO with a base at 180 meters of elevation and a supporting tower 50 meters high. HAAT was given as 85 meters and the following table reports average elevation along eight equally-spaced radials as required by most coordinators.

| 38 | 46 | 56.00 | N | 90 | 30 | 22.00 | W |
| FCC/NGDC Continental USA |
0.0	98.2
45.0	99.3
90.0	81.5
135.0	66.7
180.0	88.4
225.0	72.7
270.0	77.6
315.0	97.3

18.5.2 RESOURCES FOR REPEATER BUILDERS

Repeater building is a very popular activity and there are significant online resources for the repeater builder. For example, the Repeater Builder website (**www.repeater-builder.com**) has extensive archives of material on everything from the power supply to the antenna. An associated email reflector list is available at **groups.yahoo.com/group/Repeater-Builder**.

You can locate your state or regional frequency coordinator through the ARRL's website at **www.arrl.org/nfcc-coordinators**. Most of the local and regional frequency coordinators also maintain their own websites that offer support to repeater operators. For example, the Area Repeater Coordination Council for Eastern Pennsylvania and Southern New Jersey (**www.arcc-inc.org**) supplies worksheets and other resources for determining repeater performance information.

18.6 BIBLIOGRAPHY

Source material and more extended discussions of the topics covered in this chapter can be found in the references below.

P. Arnold, "Controlling Cavity Drift in Low-Loss Combiners," *Mobile Radio Technology*, Apr 1986, pp 36-44.

L. Barrett, "Repeater Antenna Beam Tilting," *Ham Radio*, May 1983, pp 29-35. (See correction, *Ham Radio*, Jul 1983, p 80.)

J. Belrose, "Gain of Vertical Collinear Antennas," *QST*, Oct 1982, pp 40-41.

W. F. Biggerstaff, "Operation of Close Spaced Antennas in Radio Relay Systems," *IRE Transactions on Vehicular Communications*, Sep 1959, pp 11-15.

J. J. Bilodeau, "A Homemade Duplexer for 2-Meter Repeaters," *QST*, Jul 1972, pp 22-26, 47.

W. B. Bryson, "Design of High Isolation Duplexers and a New Antenna for Duplex Systems," *IEEE Transactions on Vehicular Communications*, Mar 1965, pp 134-140.

M. Collis, "Omni-Gain Vertical Collinear for VHF and UHF," *73*, Aug 1990.

K. Connolly and P. Blevins, "A Comparison of Horizontal Patterns of Skeletal and Complete Support Structures," *IEEE 1986 Vehicular Technology Conference Proceedings*, pp 1-7.

S. Kozono, T. Tsuruhara and M. Sakamoto, "Base Station Polarization Diversity Reception for Mobile Radio," *IEEE Transactions on Vehicular Technology*, Nov 1984, pp 301-306.

J. Kraus, *Antennas*, 2nd ed. (New York: McGraw-Hill Book Co., 1988).

W. Pasternak and M. Morris, *The Practical Handbook of Amateur Radio FM & Repeaters*, (Blue Ridge Summit, PA: Tab Books Inc., 1980), pp 355-363.

M. W. Scheldorf, "Antenna-To-Mast Coupling in Communications," *IRE Transactions on Vehicular Communications*, Apr 1959, pp 5-12.

R. D. Shriner, "A Low Cost PC Board Duplexer," *QST*, Apr 1979, pp 11-14.

W. V. Tilston, "Simultaneous Transmission and Reception with a Common Antenna," *IRE Transactions on Vehicular Communications*, Aug 1962, pp 56-64.

E. P. Tilton, "A Trap-Filter Duplexer for 2-Meter Repeaters," *QST*, Mar 1970, pp 42-46.

R. Wheeler, "Fred's Advice solves Receiver Desense Problem," *Mobile Radio Technology*, Feb 1986, pp 42-44.

R. Yang and F. Willis, "Effects of Tower and Guys on Performance of Side Mounted Vertical Antennas," *IRE Transactions on Vehicular Communications*, Dec 1960, pp 24-31.

TABLE OF CONTENTS

Chapter 19

Portable Antennas

Portable operation is usually taken to mean a temporary operating site away from a fixed station location. Field Day is probably the best-known such example and so a casual search through the literature will find literally dozens of "Field Day Special" antennas intended to provide coast-to-coast coverage on the HF bands and some directivity on the VHF/ UHF bands. Rover-style operation is also very popular on the VHF/UHF bands during contests and "hilltopping" has always been fun whenever the bands are open. You will also find stations operating portable while camping or RVing or hiking and special event stations are often using temporary antennas as well. Emergency communications or "emcomm" operation during local and regional communications emergencies also requires portable antennas.

With portable operation becoming increasingly popular, antennas for temporary operation are receiving a lot of interest. As of early 2011, a count on the **www.eham.net** review forum — Antennas: HF Portable (not mobile) — shows 83 different portable antennas! They must be designed to be easily packed and stored, transported, unpacked and erected — usually by a single person. They should be able to radiate and receive effectively in a variety of installation environments and they should be robust enough to be used again and

again. With such a wide range of operating needs, it should not be a surprise that antennas designated as "portable" come in a wide variety of sizes and shapes for use on any amateur frequency. Similarly, "transport" can mean anything from a backpack to a truck.

Bearing this range of uses in mind, this chapter describes antennas that are designed for portability. However, many of these antennas can also be used in more permanent installations, particularly where a "low profile" antenna is needed as discussed in the **Stealth and Limited Space Antennas** chapter. The antennas in the **Mobile and Maritime HF Antennas** chapter can often be employed as portable antennas, too, so there is overlap between the three applications. Often, the only meaningful difference is the mounting of the antenna or how it is supported! As you read these chapters, envision how each antenna might be adapted to other uses. The goal of this chapter is not necessarily for you to reproduce a design exactly but to give you examples of how other amateurs have satisfied their operating needs in ways you might find useful as well.

The complete construction articles for all antenna designs in this chapter are provided on the CD-ROM included with this book. Additional articles are listed in the Bibliography.

19.1 HORIZONTAL ANTENNAS

The most common horizontal wire antenna used for portable operation is the λ/2 dipole or inverted-V, followed by an end-fed dipole or Zepp. These typically require some kind of support several meters high — such as a tree or one of the portable masts described later in this chapter. If trees are used, some means of getting the support lines over a branch is also required.

Some types of operation such as backpacking place a premium on minimizing weight of the entire antenna system — antenna, feed line, antenna tuner and supporting lines. For this type of antenna system, some extra loss or operation on a single band is an acceptable tradeoff.

Another solution often used when the operation will be of short duration or if frequent stops along a route will be made is to use a pair of loaded mobile whips in a dipole configuration. These antennas can be mounted on a short mast and tripod. Setting up and taking down these antennas is quick and is completely independent of any other support.

19.1.1 ZIP-CORD ANTENNAS AND FEED LINES

Previous editions of this book included a section on the use of common zip cord (used for ac power cords) for antennas and feed lines. That information was based on a March 1979 *QST* article by Jerry Hall, K1TD and it has been updated for this edition according to the March 2009 *QST* article by William Parmley, KR8L. (see Bibliography)

A lighter weight style of zip cord (#22 AWG speaker wire, Radioshack part number 278-1385) was used compared to the heavier ac power zip cord in the original article. **Tables 19-1** and **19-2** give the measured values for velocity factor and loss in dB/100 feet. The characteristic impedance was estimated to be 150 Ω, somewhat higher than the 105 Ω for ac power cord. Performance of the lighter zip cord appears to be intermediate between the miniature RG-174 coaxial cable (light, but lossy) and RG-58 (less lossy, but heavy). This may be a good trade-off for your application. The author notes that some samples of light speaker cord were measured to be more lossy and suggests that loss be measured before committing to a particular type of line.

Antennas are made using the electrician's knot shown in **Figure 19.1** — a handy knot to use whenever zip cord is used. The dipole length is calculated as described in the **Dipoles and Ground-Planes** chapter. At the end of the dipole, extra wire folded back on itself to make a loop for attachment to a support line.

If a low SWR at the transmitter is important, the feed line length can be cut to some multiple of λ/2 using the measured velocity factor. This causes the dipole's feed point impedance to be replicated at the opposite end of the feed line, regardless of the line's characteristic impedance. (See the **Transmission Lines** chapter for an explanation.)

At the transmitter end of the feed line, unzip the wire a couple of inches and attach a banana plug to one side and an alligator clip to the other. The banana plug fits perfectly in the center conductor of a transceiver's SO-239 coax connector, while the alligator clip makes a convenient way to attach to the transceiver's ground connection (as shown in **Figure 19.2**). At low power or QRP levels, the unbalanced connection did not present any problems.

After building antennas and feed lines for 30, 20 and

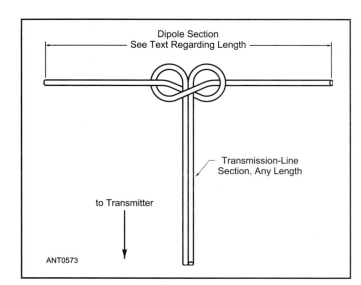

Figure 19.1 — The electrician's knot, often used inside lamp bases and appliances in lieu of a plastic grip, can also serve to prevent the feed line section of a zip-cord antenna from unzipping itself under the tension of dipole suspension. To tie the knot, first use the right-hand conductor to form a loop, passing the wire behind the un-separated zip cord and off to the left. Then pass the left-hand wire of the pair behind the wire extending off to the left, in front of the un-separated pair, and thread it through the loop already formed. Adjust the knot for symmetry while pulling on the two dipole wires.

Table 19-1
Measured Velocity Factor

Frequency (MHz)	Velocity Factor (VF)
3.31	0.68
6.75	0.69
13.67	0.70
27.77	0.71

Table 19-2
Calculated Attenuation of Zip Cord Compared to Small Coax, dB/100 feet

Frequency (MHz)	RS 278-1385	RG-174	RG-58
3.31	0.97	2.7	0.8
6.75	1.48	3.3	1.2
13.67	2.39	4.0	1.6
27.77	3.41	5.3	2.4

Figure 19.2 — Rear of radio showing banana plug and clip lead connections.

17 meters, the antennas were installed in an inverted-V configuration with the apex at about 20 feet. This was done using either a telescoping fishing pole, or by tossing a line over a tree branch and pulling the dipole up with that. The ends of the dipole were brought down to 6 to 8 feet off the ground and tied off with nylon line that was then tied to tent stakes.

The dipole was pruned to resonance by changing the fold point at the end. The extra wire was left in place and was not trimmed off. The 20 meter and 17 meter antennas were also tested as indoor dipoles by attaching the apex to a ceiling lamp and taping the ends to the walls with masking tape. In this configuration they were easily tuned to resonance.

Once the antenna was tuned to resonance it was possible to adjust and optimize the feed point impedance by changing both the horizontal and vertical angles between the two legs. For the author's outdoor installation the best match was obtained with the dipole legs arranged at a horizontal (azimuthal) angle of between 90 and 120°. For indoor applications the feed point impedance was found to be adjustable by changing the amount of droop in the legs, proximity to walls or floors, and the angle between the legs.

As should always be done with parallel-wire feeders, keep the feed line clear of other objects and equidistant from both legs of the dipole to the maximum extent practical.

19.1.2 TWINLEAD FOLDED DIPOLE

A lightweight folded dipole developed by Jay Rusgrove, W1VD, and Jerry Hall, K1TD, is made from TV twinlead. The characteristic impedance of this type of dipole is near 300 Ω, but this can easily be transformed to a 50-Ω impedance by placing a lumped capacitive reactance at a strategic distance from the input end of the line. **Figure 19.3** illustrates the construction method and gives important dimensions for the twinlead dipole.

A silver-mica capacitor is shown for the reactive element,

Table 19-3
Twinlead Dipole Dimensions and Capacitor Values

Frequency	Length A	Length C	C_s	Stub Length
3.75 MHz	124' 9½"	13' 0"	289 pF	37' 4"
7.15	65' 5½"	6' 10"	151 pF	19' 7"
10.125	46' 2½"	4' 10"	107 pF	13' 10"
14.175	33' 0"	3' 5½"	76 pF	9' 10½"
18.118	25' 10"	2' 8½"	60 pF	7' 9"
21.225	22' ½"	2' 3½"	51 pF	6' 7"
24.94	18' 9"	1' 11½"	43 pF	5' 7½"
28.5	16' 5"	1' 8½"	38 pF	4' 11"

but an open-end stub of twinlead can serve as well, provided it is dressed at right angles to the transmission line for some distance. The stub method has the advantage of easy adjustment of the system resonant frequency.

The dimensions and capacitor values for twinlead dipoles for the HF bands are given in **Table 19-3**. To preserve the balance of the feeder, a 1:1 balun must be used at the end of the feed line. (See the **Transmission Line Coupling and Impedance Matching** chapter.) In most backpack QRP applications the balance is not critical, and the twinlead can be connected directly to a coaxial output jack as shown in Figure 19.2.

Because of the transmission-line effect of the shorted-radiator sections, a folded dipole exhibits a wider bandwidth than a single-conductor type. The antennas described here are not as broad as a standard folded dipole because the impedance-transformation mechanism is frequency selective. However, the bandwidth should be adequate. An antenna cut for 14.175 MHz, for example, will present an SWR of less than 2:1 over the entire 14-MHz band.

19.1.3 PORTABLE INVERTED V ANTENNA

The antenna shown in **Figure 19.4** is a strong, lightweight, rotatable portable system that is constructed of inexpensive and readily available materials. (See the Bibliography entry for Joseph Littlepage, WE5Y.) The apex of the antenna can be raised or lowered to any convenient height. The antenna is light enough for limited backpacking and can be used for emergency communications and Field Day. Since it is easy to raise and lower, it might also be a good choice for a stealth antenna where permanent antennas may not be used.

A telescoping pushup pole is used as a support mast. A

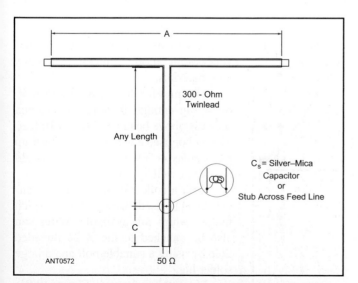

Figure 19.3 — A twinlead folded dipole makes an excellent portable antenna that is easily matched to 50-Ω equipment. See text and Table 19-3 for details.

Table 19-4
Wire Half-Element Lengths

Band (Meters)	Design Frequency (MHz)	Length
20	14.175	16' 6½"
17	18.1	12' 11½"
15	21.175	11' ⅝"
12	24.94	9' 4⅝"
10	28.4	8' 2⅞"

Figure 19.4 — The portable inverted-V antenna is built using a lightweight fiberglass support mast and two fishing poles. No additional supports are required and the antenna can be moved and rotated by hand.

portable antenna tripod is used to support the pushup pole. The basic construction of the antenna is described in **Figure 19.5**. The feed line and wire elements are brought together at an angle of at least 90°. Two 10-foot telescoping fishing poles are used as spreaders. A ¾-inch PVC cross sliding on the central support mast is used to mount the fishing poles (see the full article on CD-ROM for construction details).

Lengths for the elements on the 20 through 10 meter bands are given in **Table 19-4**. Final measurement and adjustment can be made with an antenna analyzer or SWR bridge.

To set up the antenna, attach the antenna feed point to the top of the mast. The author found the top section of his mast too weak to support the antenna and leaves it telescoped into the next section for additional strength. The mast is then raised section by section and the feed line secured to the mast as it rises.

19.1.4 PORTABLE WHIP DIPOLES

Figure 19.6 shows an antenna that is typical of the style that uses a pair of mobile whip antennas to create a loaded dipole. The design was originally published in the May 2003 issue of *QST* by Ron Herring, W7HD. This style of antenna can be adapted to any band for which mobile whips are available. The low height of the dipole makes this antenna useful for NVIS operation in support of emergency communications, as described in the January 2005 *QST* article by Robert Hollister, N7INK. (See the Bibliography for both articles.)

A bracket for mounting the mobile whips can be homemade as described in the article and shown in **Figure 19.7**. Any whip antenna that uses ⅜-24 threads can be used. Similar brackets are available from commercial vendors of mobile antenna supplies and materials.

The mast for the antenna needs only be strong enough to hold the antenna securely above head height, 8 to 10 feet. The author used a wooden pole. Push-up paint poles or TV mast sections would also work well.

With a collection of whips, the antenna can be used on any band for which mobile whips are available. Wires can also be attached to the ⅜-24 threaded hole by using a suitable bolt and a large solder lug.

The antenna shown in **Figure 19.8** is similar to the dipole made from mobile whips but uses telescoping whip sections

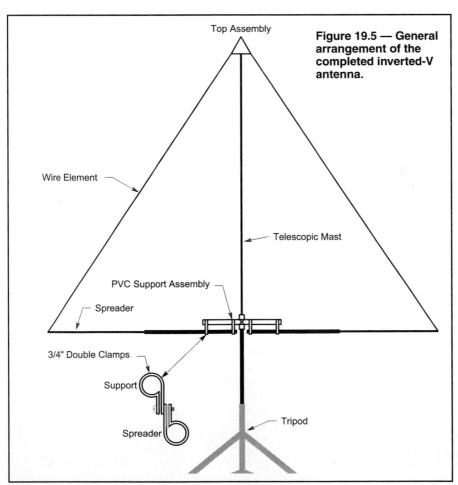

Top Assembly

Figure 19.5 — General arrangement of the completed inverted-V antenna.

Wire Element

Telescopic Mast

PVC Support Assembly

Spreader

3/4" Double Clamps

Support

Spreader

Tripod

Figure 19.6 — A portable dipole made from a pair of mobile whip antennas. The mounting bracket can be homemade as in the article or purchased from a vendor of mobile antenna materials. Any suitable mast can be used.

Figure 19.8 — This portable dipole uses a fixed center section and extendable telescoping whips to adjust the resonant frequency.

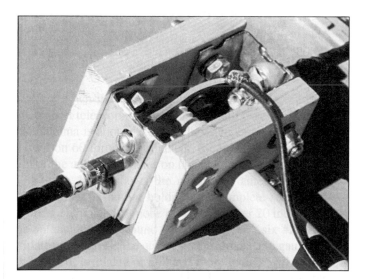

Figure 19.7 — The homemade dipole center support showing the wooden mast, the antenna mounts and the connected transmission line.

Figure 19.9 — One side of the antenna with the telescoped whip attached.

attached to a fixed-length center section. The center section is made from copper and PVC plumbing parts. A small loading coil connects the center section to the whip on the lower bands. The design was originally published by Clarke Cooper, K8BP in the May 2007 issue of *QST* (see Bibliography).

The telescoping whips (MFJ Enterprises MFJ-1954) are 10 feet long when fully extended. (see **Figure 19.9**) A table of lengths for each band allows the operator to quickly adjust the antenna for the desired frequency. The antenna has been tested on 20 through 10 meters and should be useable on 6 meters with a shorter whip. By using loading coils with more turns, operation on 30 and 40 meters may be possible, as well.

As with the previous antenna, the support mast is not a critical part of the assembly, only needing to be high enough to hold the antenna above head level. The author uses a folding portable flood light base to hold the mast.

TABLE OF CONTENTS

Chapter 20

Stealth and Limited Space Antennas

The biggest challenge facing many hams today is putting up an effective antenna. Many homes come with severe restrictions or even prohibitions on external antennas of any sort. Apartment and condominium dwellers have even more limiting circumstances. The traveling ham faces a new set of challenges at every stop. Yet many persevere and have rewarding experiences in Amateur Radio without big towers and high wires. The secret? According to Steve Ford, WB8IMY, author of the ARRL's *Small Antennas for Small Spaces*, it's "using the best antenna possible for a given circumstance." That may be a wire in an attic or dangling from a high-rise window but you can get on the air and make lots of contacts. In fact, Joe Gregory, W7QN, moved to an apartment building several years ago and has been making thousands of contacts with nothing more than a mobile antenna clamped to his balcony railing. Enjoyable hamming — even DXing — is very achievable without the traditional "aluminum farm" and that is the focus of this chapter.

Much of the material in this chapter is collected from WB8IMY's book mentioned above and Steve Nichols, GØKYA's RSGB book *Stealth Antennas*. In addition, several projects from the pages of *QST* and other sources are provided. It is not expected that you will be able to exactly duplicate these designs. Use them as a starting point for adaptation to your particular circumstances and learn to adjust and work with the resources available. You may also find the **Portable Antennas** chapter interesting reading.

The goal of presenting this collection of antenna designs is to inspire imagination and innovation on the part of the reader. As you review these antennas, think about how you might apply the same styles and approaches to your station. Perhaps these antennas will answer the question, "Would antenna X work in my situation?" Give your imagination free reign!

Once you have selected a design, be prepared to experiment and adjust. The *antenna analyzer* described in the **Antenna and Transmission Line Measurement** chapter is an invaluable tool for this type of antenna building.

20.1 INSTALLATION SAFETY

Why start with a discussion of safety? Because your antennas will likely be a lot closer to power wiring and power lines than the traditional dipole in the trees. In addition, you and your family and possibly your neighbors will be a lot closer to the antenna than if it is installed outside and well above the ground. The *ARRL Handbook* contains additional information on electrical and RF safety and grounding.

20.1.1 ELECTRICAL SAFETY

Before installing or even designing an antenna, check the area around your home and property for power lines, including the household voltage "service drops" to your house. Don't mistake a power line for a cable TV or telephone line. Working on building roofs or lowering wires and cables over the edge of a building or out a window can place you or a wire or cable in contact with hazardous, even lethal, voltages. Here are some rules to live by:

- Keep all objects — including masts, poles, ladders, tools, and antennas far away from power lines at all times. If in doubt — stop. You can be electrocuted if you are touching anything even a little bit conductive that comes in contact with a power line. High voltage electricity does not need much conductivity to create hazardous currents.

■ Antennas and masts should never be closer than 10 feet to a power line or your electrical service wiring.

■ If you are moving an antenna or taking one down, look for new power lines that may have been installed or rerouted since the antenna was first put in place.

■ Never assume that any power line is insulated — any contact may be lethal.

■ Don't rely on fiberglass or wooden poles to act as insulators.

■ Know first aid for electrical shock and don't work alone if possible.

Installing indoor and otherwise stealthy antennas invariably means drilling holes through and driving fasteners into walls and ceilings. Before drilling or hammering or driving, be sure that you are not about to come in contact with an electrical wire or a water or gas pipe. If you are in doubt, stop and get professional help. The cost and small delay are minor compared to that of a fire or leak. Remember that detectors designed to find metal piping or conduits will not find plastic pipe.

20.1.2 PERSONAL SAFETY

You may have seen comedy sketches where someone puts a foot through the ceiling but it isn't very funny when it's your or your friend's ceiling! Take steps to be sure that you are working safely and not placing yourself in a risky position. When working in unusual spaces in, around, or on top of your home, someone else should be at home in case you become stuck or fall.

When working in an attic or crawl space, make sure you have adequate lighting. If you plan on working in these areas frequently, consider installing permanent lighting. At any rate, an ac "trouble light" with a florescent or CFL bulb will provide plenty of light. (Incandescent bulbs have a habit of breaking the filament when a trouble light is dropped or bumped

into something.) Carry a strong flashlight with fresh batteries since it is inevitable that you'll be working in the shadows at some point. A head-mounted LED lamp works well.

Do not attempt to walk on attic joists as they make poor footing, leading to the aforementioned ceiling damage and possible injury. Use boards placed across the joists to support your weight. Again, if you expect to be working in the attic regularly, permanently install boards or plywood sheets.

Glass wool insulation is an irritant as the fibers break off and can stick in skin or be inhaled. Wear gloves, long-sleeve shirts and pants when working around insulation. If the insulation is loose (not in batts or rolls) wear a face mask. A face mask is also a good idea in crawl spaces to avoid inhaling rodent or insect droppings, dust or mold spores.

If you are working on a pitched roof, consider using a safety harness sturdily anchored to a tie point or chimney. Review basic climbing safety techniques and equipment in the chapter **Building Antenna Systems and Towers**.

20.1.3 RF SAFETY

It is a good assumption that the antennas in this chapter will be installed fairly close to people. As such, you should consider the potential effects of your transmitted signal and are required to evaluate your station for RF exposure.

The evaluation procedure — required of all FCC-licensed amateurs — isn't as involved as you might think. No test equipment is required and no paperwork must be submitted to the FCC although you need to log your evaluation results and keep them at your station. An RF safety evaluation amounts to entering some values into an online calculator to determine whether your station is in compliance — it's that simple.

Figure 20.1 shows the RF Power Density calculator created by Paul Evans, VP9KF at **hintlink.com/power_density. htm**. For many of the antennas in this chapter, you can assume the gain is 0 dB. If you use a directional antenna, be sure to use the maximum gain figure and be aware of where the antenna is likely to be pointed.

The calculator mentions *controlled* and *uncontrolled* environments. These terms refer to whether people know RF is present and can take steps to control their exposure. (The **Antenna Fundamentals** chapter defines these terms and includes a large section on RF exposure and RF safety and the ARRL publishes the book *RF Exposure and You* for more information.) Assuming other people live in your home and nearby, the uncontrolled environment should be used. Even so, you will probably find that in most cases your station is in full compliance when transmitting with 100 W or less and for separations of approximately 10 feet. You will find that you must be running a fair amount of power at VHF or UHF and be fairly close to the antenna to exceed the RF level for compliance. As you use the calculator, print the screen images to create your evaluation record.

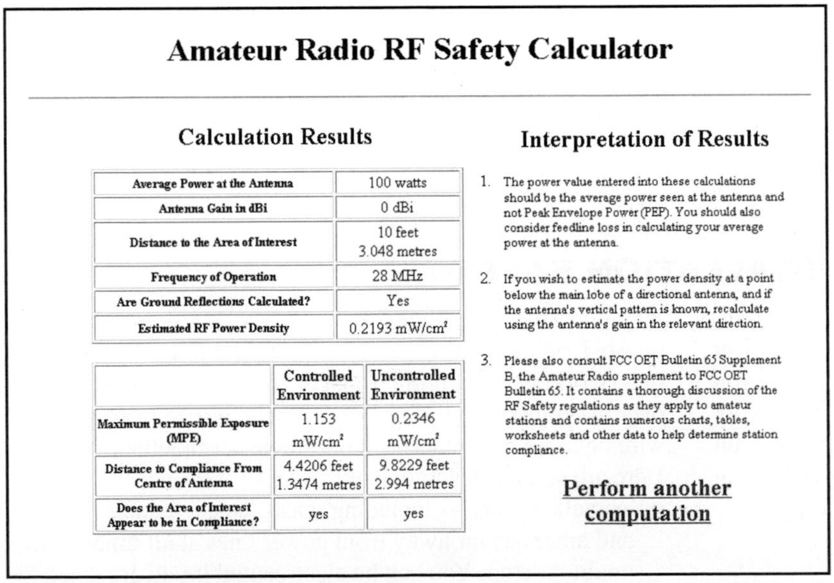

Amateur Radio RF Safety Calculator

Calculation Results

Average Power at the Antenna	100 watts
Antenna Gain in dBi	0 dBi
Distance to the Area of Interest	10 feet 3.048 metres
Frequency of Operation	28 MHz
Are Ground Reflections Calculated?	Yes
Estimated RF Power Density	0.2193 mW/cm²

	Controlled Environment	Uncontrolled Environment
Maximum Permissible Exposure (MPE)	1.153 mW/cm²	0.2346 mW/cm²
Distance to Compliance From Centre of Antenna	4.4206 feet 1.3474 metres	9.8229 feet 2.994 metres
Does the Area of Interest Appear to be in Compliance?	yes	yes

Interpretation of Results

1. The power value entered into these calculations should be the average power seen at the antenna and not Peak Envelope Power (PEP). You should also consider feedline loss in calculating your average power at the antenna.

2. If you wish to estimate the power density at a point below the main lobe of a directional antenna, and if the antenna's vertical pattern is known, recalculate using the antenna's gain in the relevant direction.

3. Please also consult FCC OET Bulletin 65 Supplement B, the Amateur Radio supplement to FCC OET Bulletin 65. It contains a thorough discussion of the RF Safety regulations as they apply to amateur stations and contains numerous charts, tables, worksheets and other data to help determine station compliance.

Perform another computation

Figure 20.1 — The RF Power Density calculator created by Paul Evans, VP9KF, at hintlink.com/power_density.htm.

20.2 LOCATIONS FOR ANTENNAS

If you live in an apartment or condominium, do you have an attic space overhead? If so, find the access door. It is often hidden away in a closet or utility room. With a ladder or step-stool, grab a flashlight, open the hatch and take a look around. If you can easily (and safely) climb into the attic, go ahead and take some measurements. How much height is available? How much horizontal length? What does the insulation look like? Is it blown-in material or paper-backed batts or do you see sections of insulation with reflective metallic backing? Metallic-backed insulation acts as a shield and rules out such spaces for antennas. The same concern applies to metal buildings or buildings with metal siding or roofing.

As a test, take a portable radio into the space and try to receive signals. If you have a "world-band" shortwave radio, this is a great use for it. Start outside the space by tuning in a signal near a frequency at which you will want to operate. Then enter the space with the radio operating. If the signals stay the same level or get louder, an antenna will probably work well in the space. If the signal levels drop, the space will probably not work well for whatever reason. For VHF/UHF operation, a hand-held radio can be used in the same way.

If you don't have an attic, check out the inside of the apartment. Are there any rooms that might accommodate an antenna secured to the ceiling? If so, how much space is available? If you are considering VHF/UHF antennas, don't neglect the windows, especially if you live above the ground floor or have multiple floor levels. If the windows have metal screens, can they be removed? It is quite possible to be successful in pointing directional VHF/UHF antennas through windows.

Even apartment and condominium dwellers should examine the property for nearby trees. Depending on how restrictive the landlord or condo association might be, trees provide excellent opportunities for discreet long-wire antennas.

If you live in a house, your antenna location options expand considerably. Take a walk around the yard and make some measurements. Look for convenient supports such as trees and note their distances from each other and your house. Make a simple map from your measurements for planning.

Don't neglect the roof of your home. A chimney can support small VHF antennas but is not designed to handle the stresses of larger antennas. You may wish to consider a roof tripod such as are available for large TV antennas. (See the **Building Antenna Systems and Towers** chapter for examples.)

It cannot be over-emphasized that you will likely need to be inventive to a degree not required of the traditional outdoor antenna builder. Browse websites, read magazine articles and books, and ask other club members about their experiences. The more information you have, the more likely it is that you'll be able to find an acceptable solution for your particular situation with a little experimentation.

20.3 RF INTERFERENCE

Because your antenna is likely to be close to your living quarters, it will also be close to the many electronic devices in use today, including appliances and security systems. Realistically, you should expect some interference when operating at (or above) the 100-W level. You will probably also experience interference *from* these devices and systems. *The ARRL RFI Book* is an excellent resource to help you deal with interference as is *The ARRL Handbook*.

Nevertheless, many interference issues are quite manageable. Perhaps you can operate with low power. Keep the antennas as far as possible from your electronics and those of your neighbors. Learn how the radiation patterns of your antennas might be used to direct your strongest signal away from them. Study how to apply ferrite chokes to keep your signal out of electronics and vice versa — Jim Brown, K9YC has written an on-line tutorial (see Bibliography) about the use of ferrites to fight RFI.

Be especially aware that indoor antennas often couple very strongly to nearby or adjacent power wiring, telephone and network cables, security system wiring, etc. The best solution is to avoid placing antennas in close proximity to other wiring. If that is not possible, be prepared to mitigate interference with chokes and other measures such as the "Resonant Breaker" described in "Better Results with Indoor Antennas" by Fred Brown, W6HPH, on this book's CD-ROM.

Another option is to use modes that concentrate your power into narrow bandwidths, allowing you to communicate with a minimum amount of power. For example, Morse (CW) and the various PSK modes pack the entire signal into a bandwidth of less than 100 Hz. In addition, PSK is a *constant-power* mode and does not cause clicks and thumps and garbled voice in equipment receiving the signal unintentionally. In fact, PSK31 is used by many hams with antenna restrictions to make contacts around the world at powers of just a few watts.

20.4 INDOOR ANTENNAS

20.4.1 INDOOR HF WIRE ANTENNAS

The basic antennas presented in the chapters **Dipoles and Monopoles** and **Loop Antennas** can be adapted to many styles of installation. Most of them are quite forgiving of being bent and folded although you will have to make adjustments from the full-size antenna to achieve resonance at the frequency you want. Remember that the more an antenna is folded or coiled, the less efficient it becomes because the radiation from the different parts of the antenna tend to cancel out. Keep as much of the antenna in a straight line as you can.

The common λ/2 dipole in **Figure 20.2** is a very tolerant antenna. At 14 MHz, it is approximately 33 feet long and can be bent to fit many different rooms, under a roof line or eaves, in a hallway, etc. Very thin wire can be used at low power such as #30 AWG solid wire-wrap wire that comes in a number of colors to blend in with the surrounding material. You can use adhesive tape or hooks to hold it against the wall or ceiling. **Figure 20.3** shows a multiband antenna fed with ladder line. You can also use the clear 300-Ω twinlead sold for use with FM radio antennas.

Loop antennas can also be used as long as they are not too much smaller than one wavelength. (Very small transmitting loops are covered later in this chapter.) **Figure 20.4** shows how a loop extended around a ceiling can be fed with low-loss ladder line or twin-lead on multiple bands. Making the loop as large as possible allows it to be effective on the lowest possible frequencies. A loop can also be installed in an attic as described in the section below.

Attics and upper-story bedrooms under peaked roofs can make a good home for inverted-V style antennas. Support the feed point at or near the peak of the roof and run the legs down the roof joists or to the floor joists. A dual-band inverted-V can be installed with the pairs of legs connected in parallel and run at right angles to each other. Inverted-V wire Yagi antennas for 20 meters and higher frequency bands can also be made if the attic has a desirable orientation.

If you are working in an attic-type space, the simplest way to hold wire against wooden trusses and joists is a plastic coaxial cable clip of the sort used for cable TV wiring. Avoid attaching bare or enameled wire directly against wood. PVC-insulated wire can be carefully stapled directly to wood supports.

To get the feed line from the attic to your transmitter, you may be able to find the cap for an internal wall and drill a hole in it for the feed line to drop down between wall studs. You can then install an "old work" electrical box and an appropriate plastic cover plate for a professional-quality installation. Do not run feed line through the same hole as ac wiring or in conduit carrying ac wiring as that is an unsafe practice as well as increasing the probability of RF interference.

An Indoor Stealth Loop

Ted Phelps, W8TP, wrote an article in *The ARRL Antenna Compendium, Vol 7* describing his attic-mounted wire loop

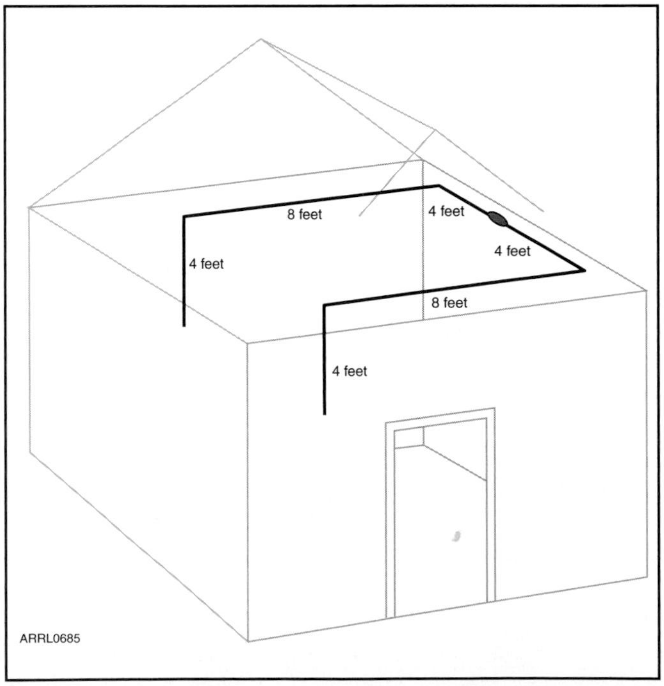

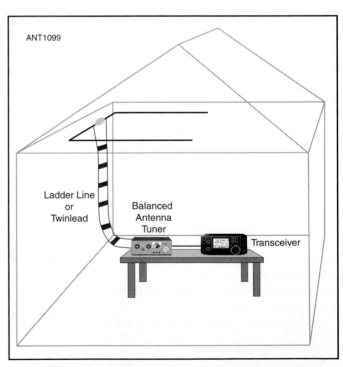

Figure 20.2 — A dipole antenna for the 20 meter band can fit into a small room with a bit of folding.

Figure 20.3 — A multiband ceiling dipole fed with ladder line or twinlead. Unlike a tuned dipole, the length isn't critical. As a rule of thumb, make each leg of the dipole as long as the space allows and make sure both legs are of equal length.

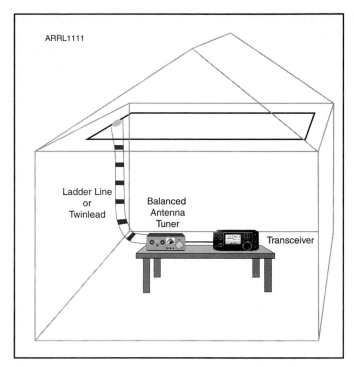

Figure 20.4 — A loop installed around the ceiling of a room and fed with balanced feed line and a tuner for multiband operation.

antenna, fed with an automatic antenna tuner. Here is a shortened version of that article.

If you drive down my street in Whitechapel Village in Newark, Delaware, trying to find my ham location by looking for my antenna, you wouldn't find it. Even if you pulled up in front of my condo, you wouldn't notice any telltale signs, because my multiband antenna is completely hidden. It's in the attic of my two-bedroom condominium in a small retirement community completed in 1999.

Before the move, I had given considerable thought to what type of antenna I might use, if any. I already knew that permanent outdoor types were out of the question, due

to restrictive real estate and condo association rules. So I planned a clause for any sales contract I might sign, specifically mentioning Amateur Radio and my desire to set up a station in my new living quarters. I decided I would not move where my lifelong hobby would be severely restricted or prohibited.

That meant that to be reasonably sure I could continue enjoying Amateur Radio as before, I would have to install an indoor antenna that could perform as well as a typical outdoor system. What kind? In Ohio, I had tried a horizontally polarized attic dipole made with #14 AWG wire. It didn't work very well — it was just too low to the ground.

I learned about a high-tech method of remote antenna tuning using an antenna coupler that contains a microprocessor. I found this kind of automatic tuner available from two American manufacturers and within a reasonable price range. Although our move was still a few months ahead, I purchased a model SG-230 antenna coupler made by SGC Inc, for use in Delaware.

Figure 20.5 shows the final dimensions of my hidden loop, which is a single-turn rectangular loop, erected in a north-south vertical plane and made from nearly 78 feet of #6 AWG stranded, aircraft primary wire in a PVC jacket, held taut at the lower corners and supported by a pulley and guy rope at each upper corner. Because it's vertically polarized, it supports low-angle radiation reasonably well. By the way, if you're wondering why I used such a relatively large-gauge wire as #6 AWG for the loop antenna, it was readily available from my son-in-law!

Figure 20.6 shows my completed condo unit. Note the doghouse dormer on the roof about 12 feet above ground at the attic floor. This is the level of my hidden loop's base leg.

In constructing my system I had to overcome RFI problems on my own premises. Each condo unit has its own electronic security panel on an upper shelf in a closet. As soon as I applied moderate power to my radio and loop, the fire alarm sounded and firefighters came to my door! The burglar/intrusion signal was triggered a couple of times, too. Working with a security installation technician, I found that *there was no ground wire connected to my security panel.*

The Slinky Antenna

If folding an antenna reduces its effectiveness, what about coiling it? This is just what happens when a Slinky™ toy is used as the antenna element! The Slinky Antenna was first described in an Oct 1974 *QST* article by W7ZCB (see Bibliography and this book's CD-ROM). As you might imagine, the antenna is nothing more than a dipole made out of two metal Slinky toys and stretched out until resonance is reached. W7ZCB was able to use his version on 80, 40, and 20 meters. It has been reported that the standard Slinky's quarter-wave resonance occurs on 40 meters when stretched to about 7.5 feet, so a full half-wave dipole would be about 15 feet long. This is well within the space available in a good-sized room. If you try this antenna, be sure to get a metal version as there are plastic models, as well.

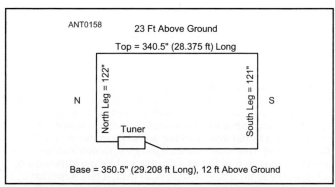

Figure 20.5 — Diagram showing layout of W8TP's indoor hidden loop antenna.

Figure 20.6 — The indoor loop is hidden inside at about the level of the dormer at right.

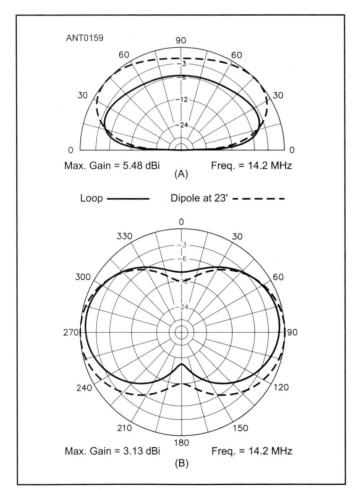

Figure 20.7 — At A, computed elevation pattern at 14.2 MHz for W8TP's hidden loop (solid line), compared to a 20 meter dipole (dashed line) at a height of 23 feet. At B, a comparison of the azimuth patterns at a 20° elevation angle for W8TP's loop (solid line) and the same 20 meter dipole (dashed line). The loop has a slightly asymmetrical response because it is fed at a corner, but its performance is competitive to an outdoor dipole. In fact, it has superior low-angle performance, typical of a vertically polarized antenna compared to a low horizontal antenna.

"We don't bother with that," said the tech, and then, reacting to my surprise, connected a #14 AWG ground between the security panel and the house water-pipe ground. I then installed a ferrite bead on each lead entering the security panel. I also placed ferrite beads on keyer-paddle leads, GFCI electrical outlets, etc. Those measures seem to have eliminated my RFI problems.

When we moved into our condo, I took the obvious precaution of not using a linear amplifier. I took extra care to establish a single-point ground for my station equipment by connecting all equipment grounds to the cover plate of the dedicated metallic outlet box behind the operating position, and thence to a separate ground rod in our front yard. I use a 1-kW RL Drake low-pass filter in the transceiver-antenna feed line.

Is this indoor antenna system safe? I believe so. In the attic it is not at all close to our living space. It is fixed firmly in place and unlike most amateur antennas it is *out of the weather*! I therefore do not use a quick-grounding system for times when a thunderstorm approaches.

Figure 20.7 shows the computed elevation and azimuth patterns on 20 meters. The tuner is able to hold the SWR down low enough so that my JRC-245 transceiver can operate through its internal antenna tuner.

20.4.2 MOBILE HF ANTENNAS INDOORS

Another popular option for indoor HF use is antennas intended for mobile operation. After all, mobiling is certainly another example of a limited-space application! (See the chapter **Mobile and Maritime HF Antennas** for more information about the mobile antennas described in this section.)

The same general concerns for mobile antennas mounted on vehicles apply to mobile antennas used indoors regarding the importance of how the antennas are mounted and having a large conductive surface to act as a ground plane. A mobile whip can be used quite effectively when mounted on a sufficiently large metal surface. For example, a windowsill (see **Figure 20.8**) or balcony railing will suffice. If those metal structures are also tied into a building's steel frame, the antenna will be very effective.

When using a mobile antenna in this way, if the metal item to which the antenna is clamped is not sufficiently large, a counterpoise wire should be added to the system. The counterpoise should be approximately λ/4 long at the frequency of operation and acts as the "missing half" of the antenna in lieu of a full ground plane. The counterpoise in this case is actually a radiating element and should be kept away from the operator and any electronics. If above the ground floor, the counterpoise can be allowed to hang down alongside the building. There may be significant RF voltage present at the end of the counterpoise so place it where it cannot be touched or arc to another surface.

The popular "screwdriver" mobile antenna can also make an effective and tunable HF antenna in an attic or unused room. **Figure 20.9** shows the screwdriver mounted on a ground plane that in turn rests on the ceiling joists. Shorter models are small enough to fit comfortably under a peaked

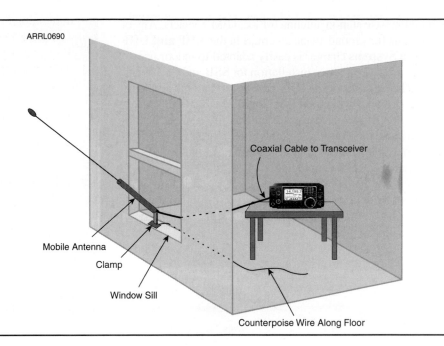

ARRL0690

Figure 20.8 — A mobile antenna can be clamped to a windowsill or balcony railing. A counterpoise wire approximately λ/4 long at the operating frequency provides an additional radiating element for the RF "return" current. For multiband operation, a counterpoise cut for each band should be used. If the frame or railing is tied into the building's metal structure, the counterpoise may not be necessary.

Coaxial Cable to Transceiver

Mobile Antenna

Clamp

Window Sill

Counterpoise Wire Along Floor

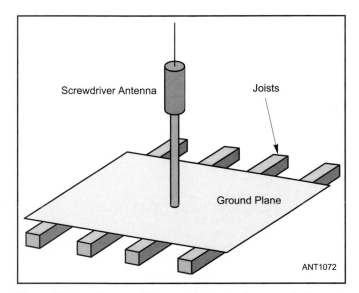

Screwdriver Antenna

Joists

Ground Plane

ANT1072

Figure 20.9 — A screwdriver antenna can be mounted on a ground plane for an effective, tunable attic antenna.

roof. Along with sheet metal any mesh will do for the ground plane, such as hardware cloth or chicken wire. Even aluminum foil could be used. The more extensive the ground plane, the more effective the antenna will be. Screwdriver antennas also have the advantage of being tunable with a remote controller for use on all HF bands.

It is also possible to use mobile whips configured to form a dipole as in **Figure 20.10**. Many antenna parts dealers sell brackets with an SO-239 coax connector and tapped fittings for the popular 3/8-24 threaded antenna base. A pair of mobile whips can be attached as in the figure and supported on a camera tripod or other suitable base. This makes an excellent portable antenna, too.

20.4.3 INDOOR VHF AND UHF ANTENNAS

Operating with indoor antennas for VHF and UHF operation is much less difficult than creating an effective HF antenna indoors. For example, placing a simple mag mount whip on top of a refrigerator or filing cabinet makes a

Figure 20.10 — This pair of CB mobile antennas were trimmed slightly to resonate on 10 meters then attached to a mounting bracket. This created an effective apartment-sized antenna.

reasonable base station antenna for local FM contacts. Any of the designs for ground-plane antennas in the **VHF and UHF Antenna Systems** chapter is easily adapted to indoor use.

Creating an effective installation for SSB and CW operation — the so-called *weak signal* modes — is more challenging. Horizontal polarization is required for sustained success but it is not always necessary to have multi-element beams. On 6 meters, for example, relatively omnidirectional antennas such as a horizontal "halo" (**Figure 20.11**) or dipole can make many contacts, including with distant stations when sporadic E propagation is occurring. (See the **Radio Wave Propagation** chapter.) The Lindenblad and turnstile antennas described in the **Antennas for Space Communications** chapter will also work.

Figure 20.12 — The 2 meter PortaQuad by National RF isn't intended for permanent outdoor use, but it would be a fine directional antenna inside a room or attic.

Figure 20.11 — A typical 6 meter horizontal full-wave loop antenna can be used either indoors or outdoors. The radiation pattern is omnidirectional with horizontal polarization.

Nevertheless, if you can manage an antenna with some directivity, it will help. Quad beams for VHF and UHF are fairly small antennas, even on 6 meters where quad elements are only 5 feet on a side. A 2-element quad for 6 meters can fit many attic spaces or be suspended from a ceiling mount. The 2-element Moxon design for 6 meters described by Allen Baker, KG4JJH (see Bibliography) measures 84 × 31 inches and being flat, is a natural candidate for ceiling mounting.

Quads and small beams for 2 meters and higher frequencies are even smaller as **Figure 20.12** shows. A light-duty TV rotator can turn any of these antennas. A note of caution — the higher the frequency of operation, the higher the attenuation from building materials as well as rain and snow on roofs, especially at UHF and microwaves.

20.5 OUTDOOR ANTENNAS

This book contains plenty of candidates for outdoor antenna designs in spaces of limited size. The antennas in the chapter **Portable Antennas** address similar limited-space needs as the amateur with a limited fixed space. The builder should start with a good idea of the available supports or ground area, decide on a horizontal or vertical antenna, and begin reviewing the antenna books and articles.

The main challenge addressed in this chapter, however, is how to put up such an antenna in the face of restrictions against them or when esthetics just don't permit the usual construction techniques. There are two basic approaches to putting up such a stealth antenna; invisibility and disguise.

20.5.1 INVISIBLE ANTENNAS

An invisible antenna is one that is constructed so as to be difficult to see. Many amateurs have been able to operate for long periods using invisible antennas without being detected. The secret to making an antenna invisible is to think small and thin. Thin wire, small coax, placing the antenna in trees or other foliage — all of these are time-tested techniques for making an antenna "disappear."

Thin wire can be used up to surprisingly high power before its resistance becomes an issue. Assuming you'll be using power levels of 100 W or less, you can use wire as small as #30 AWG. For sizes below #24 AWG, however, the challenge

Making Radials Disappear

How do you create an effective ground screen of the recommended 32 or more radial wires without an unsightly mess covering your lawn? The answer is to let the lawn do the work for you!

Get a large pizza cutter — it will be ruined for kitchen use so don't use the family's prize pie divider. You'll also need a spool of thin stiff iron wire - rebar tie wire will do fine. Cut at least a half-dozen 6-inch lengths of wire for each radial you plan on installing and bend them in half to form a narrow U — these are radial pins. Your radial wire can be any convenient type although a dark insulation or enamel coating will help with the disappearing act. Bare wire is fine, too.

Start by mowing the grass as short as you reasonably can. Attach a radial to the base of the antenna and cut a narrow slot in the grass into which you lay your radial wire. As you move away from the antenna, hold the radial down with the radial pins every few feet. The cost of each pin is quite low so use as many as you need.

Once all of the radials are in, water the grass well. A little fertilizer won't hurt. In a matter of days, the grass will have grown high enough to completely hide the radial wires — you won't be able to see them even if you know they are there! Over time, the grass (and the worms) will conspire to pull the wires deeper toward and even below the surface of the ground. The radial pins will also quickly rust away and disappear if you used iron wire. The only thing sticking up out of the yard will be the ends of the radials at the antenna.

of keeping it up due to breakage becomes the bigger issue. Use stranded wire for better flexibility and be careful not to tension the wire too heavily — it will stretch, then break.

Think "small," too. Insulators, feed points, supporting lines, and coaxial feed line all need to be small so as not to attract the eye. Insulators and feed points can be homebrewed from scrap plastic or fishing supplies. Woven fishing line is usually tough, UV-resistant, and very hard to see against the sky or foliage (just ask the fish!). If possible, use colors that blend in to the surroundings.

Small diameter coax such as RG-174 can be dismayingly lossy (see the table of coaxial cable parameters in the **Transmission Lines** chapter) and should only be used for very short runs. RG-58, RG-59, and RG-6 can be used for longer runs and have the added benefit of looking very much like the cable TV service drop. Parallel-wire lines have much lower loss and are lighter than coax but are much harder to conceal. If you get a good deal on a long length of subminiature Teflon-insulated cable such as RG-393 or similar, it makes a very good miniature feed line.

20.5.2 DISGUISED ANTENNAS

A disguised antenna is an antenna that is easy to see but the viewer doesn't recognize it as an antenna! The classic example of the disguised antenna is a flagpole antenna such as that described by Geoff Haines, N1GY in the December 2010 issue of *QST*. To the non-ham, it's a basic flagpole. To the ham, it's a 23-foot ground-plane vertical with an automatic tuner at the base. Albert Parker, N4AQ took a different tack by hiding a Hustler 4-BTV 4-band trap vertical inside a flagpole made of PVC pipe (see Bibliography).

Another long-time favorite method is hiding the antenna near an approved structure such as a drain pipe or gutter. Hams have even used metal gutters and downspouts as antennas with a variety of results but it can be difficult to maintain good connections at joints. With plastic guttering so common, why not put a wire antenna directly into the gutter? With horizontal gutters, pooling water can be a problem but most vertical gutters are immune. Put your antenna in the gutter itself!

(A)

(B)

Figure 20.13 — Martin, G8JNJ, converted a scrap laundry drying rack into a stealthy HF vertical. At A is the complete antenna showing the top and bottom counterpoise and capacity hat, respectively. B shows the upper capacity hat. (Photos courtesy of the RSGB and Martin Ehrenfried, G8JNJ)

The challenge will be to get the feed line to the antenna and keep water out of the feed line.

Take a look around and see what metal objects are outside in your yard or around your home. Almost anything can be made into an antenna as the photo in **Figure 20.13** shows. Martin Ehrenfried, G8JNJ (**www.g8jnj.webs.com**) converted an outdoor drying rack into a vertical dipole with end loading. Lawn chairs, garden tools, sports equipment — any

metal object can be made to radiate. The Ventenna (**www.ventanna.com**) is a roof-mounted antenna for VHF or UHF that looks just like an ordinary drain pipe.

Don't forget about "re-purposing" an approved antenna such as for TV broadcasts. The CD-ROM folder for the chapter **VHF and UHF Antenna Systems** contains an article describing the conversion of a regular VHF TV antenna to one that can be used on the VHF amateur bands!

20.6 SMALL TRANSMITTING LOOPS

The theory of these small loops is presented in the **Loop Antennas** chapter. The following material was adapted and updated by Domenic Mallozzi, N1DM, from content provided by Robert T. (Ted) Hart, W5QJR.

Small receiving loops are common but are not efficient enough to handle transmit power levels. There are serious challenges to designing a loop that is small and also efficient enough to be useful. This section addresses some of those challenges in the context of two designs. Construction details for both of these designs are provided on this book's CD-ROM.

20.6.1 PRACTICAL SMALL TRANSMITTING LOOPS

The ideal small transmitting antenna would have performance equal to a large antenna. A small loop antenna can approach that performance except for a reduction in bandwidth, but that effect can be overcome by retuning.

As pointed out above, small antennas are characterized by low radiation resistance. For a typical small antenna, such as a short dipole, loading coils are often added to achieve resonance. However, the loss inherent in the coils can result in an antenna with low efficiency. If instead of coils a large, low-loss capacitor is added to a low-loss conductor to achieve resonance, and if the antenna conductor is bent to connect the ends to the capacitor, a loop is formed.

Based on this concept, the small loop is capable of relatively high efficiency, compared to its coil-loaded cousin. In addition, the small loop, when mounted vertically, can radiate efficiently over the wide range of elevation angles required on the lower frequency bands. This is because it has both high-angle and low-angle response. See **Figure 20.14**, which shows the elevation response for a compact transmitting loop only 16.2 inches wide at 14.2 MHz. This loop is vertically polarized and its bottom is 8 feet above average ground, which has a conductivity of 5 mS/m and a dielectric constant of 13. For comparison, Figure 20.14 also shows the responses of three other reference antennas — the same small loop flipped sideways at a height of 30 feet to produce horizontal radiation, a full-sized ¼-λ ground plane antenna mounted 8 feet above average ground using two tuned radials, and finally a simple ½ λ flattop dipole mounted 30 feet above flat ground. The considerably smaller transmitting loop comes to within 3 dB of the larger ¼-λ vertical at a 10° elevation angle, and

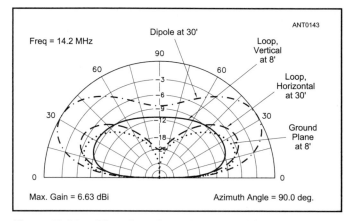

Figure 20.14 — Elevation-plane plot at 14.2 MHz, showing response of an 8.5-foot circumference octagonal copper loop (width of 16.2 inches), compared to a full-sized λ/4 ground-plane vertical with two elevated λ/4 radials, the same small loop flipped horizontally at a height of 30 feet, and lastly, a λ/2 flattop dipole also at a height of 30 feet. Both the λ/4 ground-plane vertical and the vertically polarized loop are elevated 8 feet above typical ground, with σ = 5 mS/m and ε = 13. The low vertically polarized loop is surprisingly competitive, only down about 2.5 dB compared to the far larger ground plane at low elevation angles. Note that the vertical loop has both high-angle as well as low-angle radiation, and hence would be better at working close-in local stations than the ground-plane vertical, with its deep nulls at higher angles. The simple flattop dipole, however, is better than either vertical because of the poor ground reflection for a vertically polarized compared to a horizontally polarized signal.

it is far stronger for high elevation angles because it does not have the null at high elevation angles that the ground plane has. Of course, this characteristic does make it more susceptible to strong signals received at high elevation angles. Incidentally, just in case you were wondering, adding more radials to the λ/4 ground plane doesn't materially improve its performance when mounted at an 8-foot height on 20 meters.

The simple horizontal dipole in Figure 20.14 would be the clear winner in any shootout because its horizontally polarized radiation does not suffer as much attenuation at reflection from ground as does a vertically polarized wave. The case is not quite so clear-cut, however, for the small loop mounted horizontally at 30 feet. While it does have increased gain at medium elevation angles, it may not be worth the effort needed to mount it on a mast, considering the slight loss at low angles compared to its twin mounted vertically only 8 feet above ground.

A physically small antenna like the 16.2-inch-wide vertically polarized loop does put out an impressive signal compared to far larger competing antennas. Though somewhat ungainly, it is a substantially better performer than most mobile whips, for example. The main deficiency in a compact transmitting loop is its narrow bandwidth — it must be accurately tuned to the operating frequency. The use of a remote motor drive allows the loop to be tuned over a wide frequency range.

For example, for fixed-station use, two loops could be constructed to provide continuous frequency coverage from 3.5 to 30 MHz. A loop with an 8.5-foot circumference, 16 inches wide, could cover 10 through 30 MHz and a loop with a 20-foot circumference, 72 inches wide, could cover 3.5 to 10.1 MHz.

Through computer analysis, the optimum size conductor was determined to be ¾-inch rigid copper water pipe, considering both performance and cost. Performance will be compromised, but only slightly, if ⅝-inch flexible copper tubing is used. This tubing can easily be bent to any desired shape, even a circle. The rigid ¾-inch copper pipe is best used with 45° elbows to make an octagon.

The loop circumference should be between ¼ and ⅛ λ at the operating frequency. It will become self-resonant above ¼ λ, and efficiency drops rapidly below ⅛ λ. In the frequency ranges shown in **Table 20-1**, the high frequency is tuned with a minimum capacitance of about 29 pF — including stray capacitance.

Controlling Losses

Contrary to earlier reports, adding quarter-wave ground radials underneath a vertically polarized transmitting loop doesn't materially increase loop efficiency. The size of the conductor used for a transmitting loop, however, does directly affect several interrelated aspects of loop performance.

Note that the efficiency is higher and the Q is lower for loops having a circumference near ¼ λ. Larger pipe size will reduce the loss resistance, but the Q increases. Therefore the bandwidth decreases, and the voltage across the tuning capacitor increases. Rigid ¾-inch copper water pipe is a good electrical compromise and can also help make a small-diameter loop mechanically sturdy.

The equivalent electrical circuit for the loop is a parallel resonant circuit with a very high Q, and therefore a narrow bandwidth. The efficiency is a function of radiation resistance divided by the sum of the radiation plus loss resistances. The radiation resistance is much less than 1 Ω, so it is necessary to minimize the loss resistance, which is largely the skin-effect loss of the conductor, assuming that

Table 20-1
Design Data for Loops

Loop Circumference = 8.5' (Width = 32.4"), Vertically Polarized

Frequency, MHz	10.1	14.2	21.2	29.0
Max Gain, dBi	−4.47	−1.42	+1.34	+2.97
Max Elevation Angle	40°	30°	22°	90°
Gain, dBi @10°	−8.40	−4.61	−0.87	+0.40
Total Capacitance, pF	145	70	29	13
Peak Capacitor kV	23	27	30	30

Loop Circumference = 8.5' (Width = 32.4"), Horizontally Polarized, @30'

Frequency, MHz	10.1	14.2	21.2	29.0
Max Gain, dBi	−3.06	+1.71	+5.43	+6.60
Max Elevation Angle	34°	28°	20°	16°
Gain, dBi @10°	−9.25	−3.11	+2.61	+5.34
Total Capacitance, pF	145	70	29	13
Peak Capacitor kV	23	27	30	30

Loop Circumference = 20' (Width = 6'), Vertically Polarized

Frequency, MHz	3.5	4.0	7.2	10.1
Max Gain, dBi	−7.40	−6.07	−1.69	−0.34
Max Elevation Angle	68°	60°	38°	30°
Gain, dBi @10°	−11.46	−10.12	−5.27	−3.33
Capacitance, pF	379	286	85	38
Peak Capacitor kV	22	24	26	30

Loop Circumference = 20' (Width = 6'), Horizontally Polarized, @30'

Frequency, MHz	3.5	4.0	7.2	10.1
Max Gain, dBi	−13.32	−10.60	−0.20	+3.20
Max Elevation Angle	42°	42°	38°	34°
Gain, dBi @10°	−21.62	−18.79	−7.51	−3.22
Capacitance, pF	379	286	85	38
Peak Capacitor kV	22	24	26	30

Loop Circumference = 38' (Width = 11.5'), Vertically Polarized

Frequency, MHz	3.5	4.0	7.2
Max Gain, dBi	−2.93	−2.20	−0.05
Max Elevation Angle	46°	42°	28°
Gain, dBi @10°	−6.48	−5.69	−2.80
Capacitance, pF	165	123	29
Peak Capacitor kV	26	27	33

Notes: These loops are octagonal in shape, constructed with ¾-inch copper water pipe and soldered 45° copper elbows. The gain figures assume a capacitor unloaded Qc = 5000, typical for vacuum-variable type of tuning capacitor. The bottom of the loop is assumed to be 8 feet high for safety and the ground constants are "typical" at conductivity = 5 mS/m and dielectric constant = 13. Transmitter power is 1500 W. The voltage across the tuning capacitor for lower powers goes down with a multiplier of

$$\sqrt{P / 1500}$$

For example, at 100 W using the 38-foot-circumference loop at 7.2 MHz, the peak voltage would be

$$33 \text{ kV} \times \sqrt{100 / 1500} = 8.5 \text{ kV}$$

the tuning capacitor has very low loss. Poor construction techniques must be avoided. All joints in the loop must be brazed or soldered. Do not use clamps or screws.

However, if the system loss is too low, for example by using even larger diameter tubing, the Q may become excessive and the bandwidth may become too narrow for practical use. These reasons dictate the need for a complete analysis to be performed before proceeding with the construction of a loop.

There is another source of additional loss in a completed loop antenna besides the conductor and capacitor losses. If the loop is mounted near lossy metallic conductors, the large magnetic field produced will induce currents into those conductors and be reflected as losses in the loop. Therefore the loop should be as far from other conductors as possible. If you use the loop inside a building constructed with large amounts of iron or near ferrous materials, you will simply have to live with the loss if the loop cannot otherwise be relocated.

The Tuning Capacitor

Figure 20.15 demonstrates the selection of loop size versus tuning capacitance for any desired operating frequency range for the HF amateur bands. This is for octagonal-shaped loops using ¾-inch copper water pipe with 45° copper elbows. For example, a capacitor that varies from 5 to 50 pF, used with a loop 10 feet in circumference, tunes from 13 to 27 MHz (represented by the left dark vertical bar). A 25 to 150-pF capacitor with a 13.5-foot loop circumference covers the 7 to 14.4-MHz range, represented by the right vertical bar.

Air Variable Capacitors

Special care must be taken with the tuning capacitor if

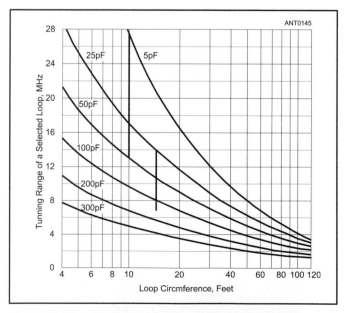

Figure 20.15 — Frequency tuning range of an octagon-shaped loop using ¾-inch copper water pipe, for various values of tuning capacitance and loop circumference.

an air-variable type is used. The use of a split-stator capacitor eliminates the resistance of wiper contacts, resistance that is inherent in a single-section capacitor. The ends of the loop are connected to the stators, and the rotor forms the variable coupling path between the stators. With this arrangement the value of capacitance is divided by two, but the voltage rating is doubled.

You must carefully select a variable capacitor for transmitting-loop application — that is, all contacts must be welded, and no mechanical wiping contacts are allowed. For example, if the spacers between plates are not welded to the plates, there will be loss at each joint, and thus degraded loop efficiency. (Earlier transmitting loops exhibited poor efficiency because capacitors with wiping contacts were used.)

There are several suitable types of capacitors for this application. A vacuum variable is an excellent choice, provided one is selected with an adequate voltage rating. Unfortunately, those capacitors are very expensive.

W5QJR used a specially modified air-variable capacitor in his designs. This had up to 340 pF maximum per section, with ¼-inch spacing, resulting in 170 pF when both sections were in series as a butterfly capacitor. Another alternative is to obtain a large air variable, remove the aluminum plates, and replace them with copper or double-sided PC board material to reduce losses. Connect all plates together on the rotor and on the stators. Solder copper straps to the capacitor for soldering to the loop itself.

The spacing between plates in an air-variable capacitor determines the voltage-handling capability, rated at 75,000 V per inch. For other power ratings, multiply the spacing (and voltage) by the square root of the ratio of your power to 1000 W. For example, for 100 W, the ratio would be = 0.316.

Short articles describing two other methods of constructing tuning capacitors ("A Teflon-Insulated Trombone Variable Capacitor" and "A Cookie-Sheet and Picture-Frame-Glass Variable Capacitor") are provided on this book's CD-ROM. This issue is discussed further by Brian Cake, KF2YN in the book *Antenna Designer's Notebook* (see Bibliography) along with another loop design.

20.6.2 TYPICAL TRANSMITTING LOOP CONSTRUCTION

After you select the electrical design for your loop application, you must consider how to mount it and how to feed it. If you wish to cover only the upper HF bands of 20 through 10 meters, you will probably choose a loop that has a circumference of about 8.5 feet. You can make a reasonably sturdy loop using 1-inch diameter PVC pipe and ⅝-inch flexible copper tubing bent into the shape of a circle. Robert Capon, WA3ULH, did this for a QRP-level transmitting loop described in May 1994 *QST*. **Figure 20.16** shows a picture of his loop, with PVC H-frame stand. (The complete construction article is provided on the CD-ROM accompanying this book.)

This loop design used a 20-inch long coupling loop made

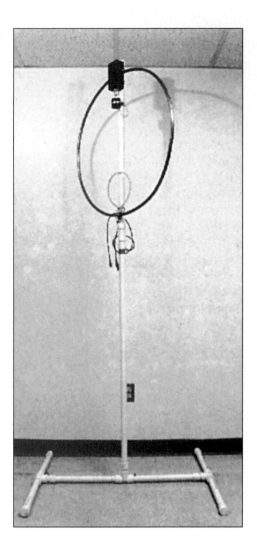

Figure 20.16 — Photo of compact transmitting loop designed by Robert Capon, WA3ULH. This uses a 1-inch PVC H-frame to support the loop made of flexible ⅝-inch copper tubing. The small coupling loop made of RG-8 coax braid couples the loop to the coax feed line. The tuning capacitor and drive motor are at the top of the loop, shown here in the ARRL Laboratory during testing.

of RG-8 coax to magnetically couple into the transmitting loop rather than the gamma-match arrangement used by W5QJR in his loop designs. The coupling loop was fastened to the PVC pipe frame using 2-inch long #8 bolts that also held the main loop to the mast.

A more rugged loop can be constructed using rigid ¾-inch copper water pipe, as shown in the W5QJR design in **Figure 20.17**. (See Bibliography and this book's CD-ROM.) While a round loop is theoretically a bit more efficient, an octagonal shape is much easier to construct.

If there is metal near any small transmitting loop, the additional loss will reduce the Q and therefore the impedance of the loop. In those cases it will be necessary to increase the length of the matching line and tap higher up on the loop to obtain a 50-Ω match.

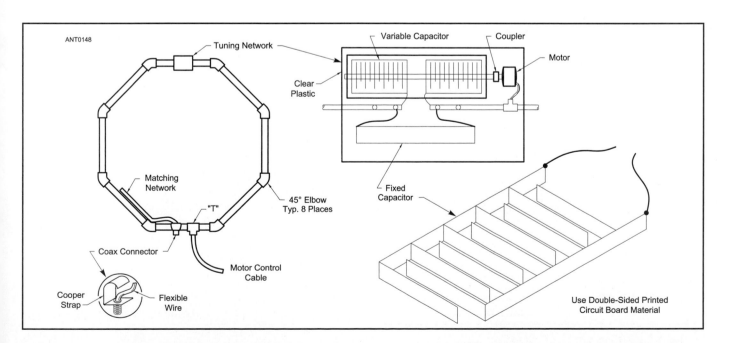

Figure 20.17 — Octagonal loop construction details. See the full article on this book's CD-ROM for more construction information and dimensions for different HF bands.

20.7 BIBLIOGRAPHY

A. Baker, "A 6-Meter Moxon Antenna," *QST*, Apr 2004, pp 65-69.

J. Belrose, "An Update on Compact Transmitting Loops," *QST*, Nov 1993, pp 37-40.

F. Brown, "Better Results with Indoor Antennas," *QST*, Oct 1979, pp 18-21.

J. Brown, "RFI, Ferrites, and Common Mode Chokes For Hams," **www.audiosystemsgroup.com/publish.htm**.

B. Cake, *Antenna Designer's Notebook* (Newington: ARRL, 2010).

S. Ford, *Small Antennas for Small Spaces* (Newington: ARRL, 2011).

M. Gruber, Ed., *The ARRL RFI Book*, 3rd Edition (Newington: ARRL, 2010).

G. Haines, "Constructing a Flagpole Antenna," *QST*, Dec 2010, pp 30-32.

E. Hare, *RF Exposure and You* (Newington: ARRL, 1998).

T. Hart, "Small, High-Efficiency Loop Antennas," *QST*, Jun 1986, pp 33-36.

T. Hart, *Small High Efficiency Antennas Alias The Loop* (Melbourne, FL: W5QJR Antenna Products, 1985).

J. Malone, "Can a 7 foot 40m Antenna Work?." *73*, Mar 1975, pp 33-38.

R. Marris, "An In-Room 80-Meter Transmitting Multiturn Loop Antenna," *QST*, Feb 1996, pp 43-45. Also see Feedback, *QST*, May 1996, p 48.

L. McCoy, "The Army Loop in Ham Communications," *QST*, Mar 1968, pp 17, 18, 150, 152. (See also Technical Correspondence, *QST*, May 1968, pp 49-51 and Nov 1968, pp 46-47.)

S. Nichols, *Stealth Antennas* (Potters Bar: RSGB, 2010).

A. Parker, "A Disguised Flagpole Antenna," *QST*, May 1993, p 65.

K. Patterson, "Down-To-Earth Army Antenna," *Electronics*, Aug 21, 1967, pp 111-114.

A. Peterson, "Apartment Dwellers' Slinky Jr Antenna," *QST*, Oct 1974, pp 22-23.

T. Phelps, "A Hidden Loop Antenna," *The ARRL Antenna Compendium*, *Vol 7* (Newington: ARRL, 2002), pp 160-162.

W. Silver, Ed., *The ARRL Handbook* (Newington: ARRL, 2011).

TABLE OF CONTENTS

Chapter 21

Mobile and Maritime HF Antennas

Mobile antennas are designed for use while in motion. At the mention of mobile antennas, most amateurs think of a whip antenna mounted on an automobile or other vehicle. While it is true that most mobile antennas are vertical whips, mobile antennas can also be found in other places. For example, antennas intended for use aboard a boat or ship are usually called *marine* or *maritime antennas*. Whip antennas are common in maritime service, but wire antennas installed on masts are also common.

Few amateurs construct their own antennas for HF mobile and maritime use, since safety requirements dictate very sound mechanical construction. Even if commercially made antennas are installed, most require some adjustment to optimize the particular installation and type of operation desired. The information in this chapter will provide a better understanding of the requirements for designing and choosing HF mobile antennas and using them effectively.

The chapter begins with a discussion of mobile antenna fundamentals at HF, updated from previous editions by Alan Applegate, KØBG. The following sections explain the more important attributes of the most popular designs and how to get the best from them. This will include mounting, impedance matching, and other important issues to all types of mobile antennas. Several examples of mobile antenna installation are provided. Information on constructing a capacitive hat-loaded whip and an adjustable "screwdriver" HF mobile antenna is included on the CD-ROM accompanying this book.

The second half of the chapter covers maritime HF antennas for sail and power boats and was updated by Rudy Severns, N6LF for this edition. The text discusses important issues regarding placement and safety of the maritime HF system. Several examples of common installation practices are given, based on antenna designs presented elsewhere in this book.

21.1 HF MOBILE ANTENNA FUNDAMENTALS

High frequency mobile antennas come in every imaginable configuration of efficiency, overall length, quality, design, sturdiness, ease of mounting, and selling price. The design, mounting method employed, and most importantly where the antenna is mounted, all have an effect on maximum efficiency — the holy grail of HF mobile operation. The right combination of strengths and weaknesses depends on how you expect to use the antenna.

Propagation conditions and ignition noise are usually the limiting factors for mobile operation on 10 through 28 MHz. Antenna size restrictions affect operation somewhat on 7 MHz and much more on 3.5 and 1.8 MHz. From this perspective, perhaps the optimum band for HF-mobile operation is 7 MHz. The popularity of regional mobile nets on 7 MHz is perhaps the best indication of how effective mobile communication can be on that band.

If you intend to chase DX, 20 meters and above are perhaps the best choices as antennas for those bands offer the best efficiency for a given physical size. For local communication, 28 MHz is also useful as a full-size whip without

Fig 21.1 — A simple HF mobile whip can be mounted on almost any vehicle. (*NØAX photo*)

efficiency. Bruce Brown, W6TWW, first presented this approach in *The ARRL Antenna Compendium Volume 1*. (See the Bibliography following the sections on mobile antennas.)

21.1.1 THE EQUIVALENT CIRCUIT OF A TYPICAL MOBILE ANTENNA

It is customary in solving problems involving electric and magnetic fields (such as antenna systems) to try to find an equivalent network with which to replace the antenna for analysis reasons. In many cases, the network may be an accurate representation over only a limited frequency range. However, this is often a valuable method in matching the antenna to the transmission line.

Antenna resonance is defined as the frequency at which the input impedance at the antenna terminals is purely resistive. The shortest length at which this occurs for a vertical antenna over a ground plane is when the antenna is an electrical quarter-wavelength at the operating frequency; the impedance value for this length (neglecting losses) is about 36 Ω. The idea of resonance can be extended to antennas shorter (or longer) than a quarter-wave and means only that the input impedance is purely resistive.

When the frequency of operation is lowered below the antenna's resonant frequency, the antenna looks like a series RC circuit, as shown in **Figure 21.2**. For the average 8-foot whip, the capacitive reactance may range from about –150 Ω at 21 MHz to as high as –8000 Ω at 1.8 MHz, while the radiation resistance R_R, varies from about 15 Ω at 21 MHz to as low as 0.1 Ω at 1.8 MHz.

For an antenna less than 0.1 λ long, the approximate radiation resistance may be determined from the following:

$$R_R = 273 \times (\ell\, f)^2 \times 10^{-8} \qquad (1)$$

where ℓ is the length of the whip in inches and f is the frequency in MHz.

Since the radiation resistance is low, considerable current must flow in the circuit if any appreciable power is to be

loading coils is not too large for convenient use and is easy to build. In fact, a slightly shortened CB whip works very well.

On the HF bands, the physical size of full-size whips becomes a problem and some form of electrical loading is usually employed to shorten the antenna. Commonly used loading techniques consist of placing a coil at the base of the whip (base loading), or at the center of the whip (center loading). **Figure 21.1** shows a typical mobile whip installation. These and other techniques for reducing the physical size of antennas are discussed in this chapter.

For typical antenna lengths used in mobile operation, the difficulty in constructing suitable loading coils increases as the frequency of operation is lowered. Radiation resistance of the antenna decreases as the antenna becomes electrically shorter, which is the same as lowering the frequency of operation for a fixed-length antenna. In addition, the required inductance to resonate the antenna gets larger. The result is that the fraction of the applied power lost as heating in ohmic losses increases and the antenna becomes less efficient.

Designing short HF mobile antennas requires a careful balance of loading coil Q, loading coil position in the antenna, ground loss resistance, and length-to-diameter ratio of the antenna. The optimum balance of these parameters can be realized only through a thorough understanding of how they interact. This section presents a mathematical approach to designing mobile antennas for maximum radiation

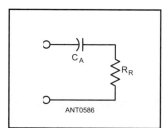

Fig 21.2 — At frequencies below resonance, the whip antenna will show capacitive reactance as well as resistance. R_R is the radiation resistance, and C_A represents the antenna capacitance.

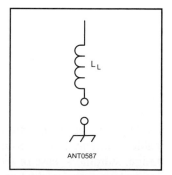

Fig 21.3 — The capacitive reactance at frequencies below the resonant frequency of the whip can be canceled by adding an equivalent inductive reactance in the form of a loading coil in series with the antenna.

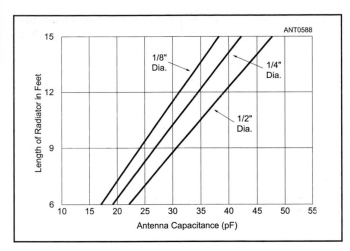

Fig 21.4 — Graph showing the approximate capacitance of short vertical antennas for various diameters and lengths. These values should be approximately halved for a center-loaded antenna.

dissipated in the form of radiation in R_R. Yet it is apparent that little current can be made to flow in the circuit as long as the comparatively high series reactance remains.

Antenna Capacitance

Capacitive reactance can be canceled by connecting an equivalent inductive reactance (coil) in series, as shown in **Figure 21.3**, thus tuning the system to resonance.

The capacitance of a vertical antenna shorter than one-quarter wavelength is given by:

$$C_A = \frac{17\ell}{\left[\left(\ln\frac{24\ell}{D}\right)-1\right]\left[1-\left(\frac{f\ell}{234}\right)^2\right]} \qquad (2)$$

where
C_A = capacitance of antenna in pF
ℓ = antenna height in feet
D = diameter of radiator in inches
f = operating frequency in MHz

Figure 21.4 shows the approximate capacitance of whip antennas of various average diameters and lengths. For 1.8, 4 and 7 MHz, the loading coil inductance required (when the loading coil is at the base) would be approximately the inductance required to resonate in the desired band (with the whip capacitance taken from the graph). For 10 through 21 MHz, this rough calculation will give more than the required inductance, but it will serve as a starting point for the final experimental adjustment that must always be made.

21.1.2 LOADING A SHORT MOBILE ANTENNA

To minimize loading coil loss, the coil should have a high ratio of reactance-to-resistance (that is, a high unloaded Q). A loading coil for use at 4 MHz, wound with small wire

on a small-diameter solid form of poor quality and enclosed in a metal protector, may have a Q as low as 50, with a loss resistance of 50 Ω or more. High-Q coils require a large conductor, air-wound construction, large spacing between turns, and the best insulating material available. A diameter not less than half the length of the coil (not always mechanically feasible) and a minimum of metal in the field of the coil are also necessities for optimum efficiency. Such a coil may show a Q of 300 or more at 4 MHz, with a resistance of 12 Ω or less.

The coil could then be placed at the base of the antenna in series with the feed line and the antenna to tune out the unwanted capacitive reactance, as shown in Figure 21.3. Such a method is often referred to as *base-loading*, and many practical mobile antenna systems have been built using this scheme.

Over the years, the question has come up as to whether more efficient designs than simple base loading are possible. While many ideas have been tried with varying degrees of success, only a few have been generally accepted and incorporated into actual antenna systems. These are *center loading*, *continuous loading*, and combinations of the latter with more conventional antennas.

Base Loading and Center Loading

If a whip antenna is short compared to a wavelength and the current is uniform along the length ℓ, the electric field strength E, at a distance d, away from the antenna is approximately:

$$E = \frac{120\,\pi\,I\,\ell}{d\,\lambda} \qquad (3)$$

where
I = the antenna current in amperes
λ = the wavelength in the same units as d and ℓ.

A uniform current flowing along the length of the whip is an idealized situation, however, since the current is greatest at the base of the antenna and goes to a minimum at the top. In practice, the field strength will be less than that given by the above equation, because it is a function of the current distribution on the whip.

The reason that the current is not uniform on a whip antenna can be seen from the circuit approximation shown in **Figure 21.5**. A whip antenna over a ground plane is similar in many respects to a tapered coaxial cable where the center conductor remains the same diameter along its length, but with an increasing diameter outer conductor. The inductance per unit length of such a cable would increase along the line, while the capacitance per unit length would decrease. In Figure 21.5 the antenna is represented by a series of LC circuits in which C1 is greater than C2, which is greater than C3, and so on. L1 is less than L2, which is less than succeeding inductances. The net result is that most of the antenna current returns to ground near the base of the antenna, and very little near the top.

Two things can be done to improve this distribution and

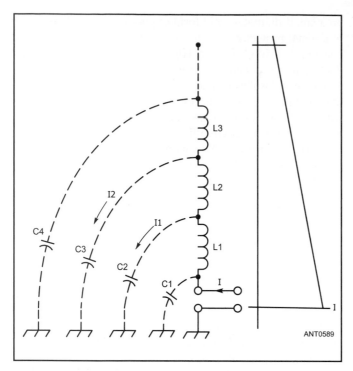

Fig 21.5 — A circuit approximation of a simple whip over a perfectly conducting ground plane. The shunt capacitance per unit length gets smaller as the height increases, and the series inductance per unit length gets larger. Consequently, most of the antenna current returns to the ground plane near the base of the antenna, giving the current distribution shown at the right.

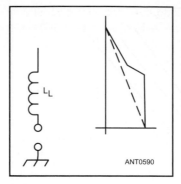

Fig 21.6 — Improved current distribution resulting from center loading.

make the current more uniform in order to increase field strength. One would be to increase the capacitance of the top of the antenna to ground through the use of *top loading* or a *capacitance hat*, as discussed in the chapter on **Single Band MF and HF Antennas**. Unfortunately, the wind resistance of the hat makes it somewhat unwieldy for mobile use. The other method is to place the loading coil farther up the whip, as shown in **Figure 21.6**, rather than at the base. If the coil is resonant (or nearly so) at the frequency of operation with the capacitance to ground of the section above the coil, the current distribution is improved as also shown in Figure 21.6. The result with either top loading and center loading is that the radiation resistance is increased, offsetting the effect of losses and making matching easier.

Table 21-1 shows the approximate loading coil inductance for the various amateur bands. Also shown in the table are approximate values of radiation resistance to be expected with an 8-foot whip, and the resistances of loading coils — one group having a Q of 50, the other a Q of 300. A comparison of radiation and coil resistances will show the importance

Table 21-1
Approximate Values for 8-foot Mobile Whip

f(MHz)	Loading L (μH)	R_C(Q50) (Ω)	R_C(Q300) (Ω)	R_R (Ω)	Feed R* (Ω)	Matching L (μH)
Base Loading						
1.8	345	77	13	0.1	23	3
3.8	77	37	6.1	0.35	16	1.2
7.2	20	18	3	1.35	15	0.6
10.1	9.5	12	2	2.8	12	0.4
14.2	4.5	7.7	1.3	5.7	12	0.28
18.1	3.0	5.0	1.0	10.0	14	0.28
21.25	1.25	3.4	0.5	14.8	16	0.28
24.9	0.9	2.6	—	20.0	22	0.25
29.0	—	—	—	—	36	0.23
Center Loading						
1.8	700	158	23	0.2	34	3.7
3.8	150	72	12	0.8	22	1.4
7.2	40	36	6	3.0	19	0.7
10.1	20	22	4.2	5.8	18	0.5
14.2	8.6	15	2.5	11.0	19	0.35
18.1	4.4	9.2	1.5	19.0	22	0.31
21.25	2.5	6.6	1.1	27.0	29	0.29

R_C = loading coil resistance; R_R = radiation resistance.
*Assuming loading coil Q = 300, and including estimated ground-loss resistance.

Table 21-2
Suggested Loading Coil Dimensions

Req'd L (μH)	Turns	Wire Size	Dia. (Inches)	Length (Inches)
700	190	22	3	10
345	135	18	3	10
150	100	16	2.5	10
77	75	14	2.5	10
77	29	12	5	4.25
40	28	16	2.5	2
40	34	12	2.5	4.25
20	17	16	2.5	1.25
20	22	12	2.5	2.75
8.6	16	14	2	2
8.6	15	12	2.5	3
4.5	10	14	2	1.25
4.5	12	12	2.5	4
2.5	8	12	2	2
2.5	8	6	2.375	4.5
1.25	6	12	1.75	2
1.25	6	6	2.375	4.5

of reducing the coil resistance to a minimum, especially on the three lower frequency bands. **Table 21-2** shows suggested loading-coil dimensions for the inductance values given in Table 21-1.

21.1.3 RADIATION RESISTANCE OF A SHORT MOBILE ANTENNA

The determination of radiation efficiency requires the knowledge of resistive power losses and radiation losses. Radiation loss — the power radiated by the antenna as electromagnetic energy — is expressed in terms of radiation resistance. Radiation resistance is defined as the resistance that would dissipate the same amount of power as is radiated by the antenna. The variables used in the equations that follow are defined once in the text and are summarized in **Table 21-3**. Radiation resistance of vertical antennas shorter than 45 electrical degrees (⅛ wavelength) is approximately:

$$R_R = h^2/312 \qquad (4)$$

where

R_R = radiation resistance in Ω
h = antenna length in electrical degrees.

Antenna height in electrical degrees is expressed by:

$$II = \frac{\ell}{984} \times f(MHz) \times 360 \qquad (5)$$

where

ℓ = antenna length in feet
f (MHz) = operating frequency in MHz.

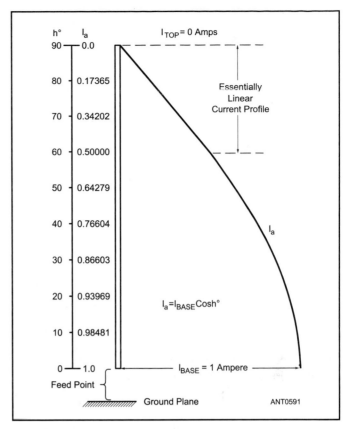

Fig 21.7 — Relative current distribution on a vertical antenna of height h = 90 electrical degrees.

End effect is purposely omitted to ensure that an antenna is electrically long. This is so that resonance at the design frequency can be obtained easily by removing a turn or two from the loading coil.

Eq 4 is valid only for antennas having a sinusoidal current distribution and no reactive loading. However, it can be used as a starting point for deriving an equation that is useful for shortened antennas with other than sinusoidal current distributions.

Refer to **Figure 21.7**. The current distribution on an antenna 90° long electrically (¼ wavelength) varies with the cosine of the length in electrical degrees. The current distribution over the top 30° of the antenna is essentially linear. It is this linearity that allows for derivation of a simpler, more useful equation for radiation resistance.

The radiation resistance of an electrically-short, base-loaded vertical antenna can be conveniently defined in terms of a geometric figure, a triangle, as shown in **Figure 21.8**. The radiation resistance is given by:

$$R_R = KA^2 \qquad (6)$$

where

K = a constant (to be derived shortly)
A = area of the triangular current distribution in degree-amperes.

Degree-ampere area is a product of current and electrical

Table 21-3
Variables used in Eqs 4 through 20

A = area in degree-amperes
a = antenna radius in English or metric units
dB = signal loss in decibels
E = efficiency in percent
f (MHz) = frequency in megahertz
H = height in English or metric units
h = height in electrical degrees
h_1 = height of base section in electrical degrees
h_2 = height of top section in electrical degrees
I = I_{base} = 1 ampere base current
k = 0.0128
k_m = mean characteristic impedance
k_{m1} = mean characteristic impedance of base section
k_{m2} = mean characteristic impedance of top section
L = length or height of the antenna in feet
P_I = power fed to the antenna
P_R = power radiated
Q = coil figure of merit
R_C = coil loss resistance in Ω
R_G = ground loss resistance in Ω
R_R = radiation resistance in Ω
X_L = loading-coil inductive reactance

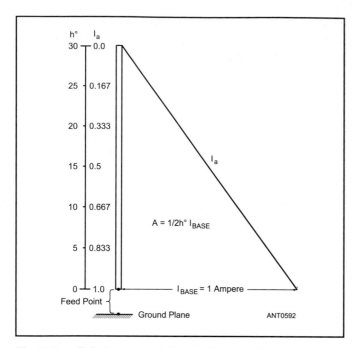

Fig 21.8 — Relative current distribution on a base-loaded vertical antenna of height H = 30 electrical degrees (linearized). The base loading coil is not shown here.

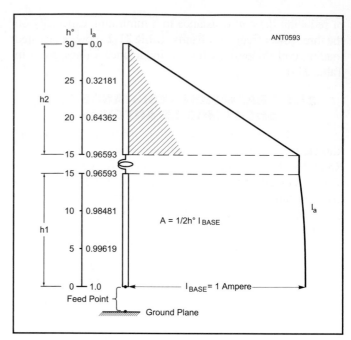

Fig 21.9 — Relative current distribution on a center-loaded antenna with base and top sections each equal to 15 electrical degrees in length. The cross-hatched area shows the current distribution that would exist in the top 15° of a 90°-high vertical fed with 1 ampere at the base.

length, calculated for a triangular current distribution as

$$A = \frac{1}{2} h \times I_{BASE} \qquad (7)$$

It is referred to as "area" because it is the area between a plot of current and the electrical length axis, as shown in Figures 21.7 and 21.8. More current flowing over a longer electrical distance in degrees results in a higher degree-ampere area and more power being radiated.

By combining Eqs 4 and 6 and solving for K, we get

$$K = \frac{h^2}{312 \times A^2} \qquad (8)$$

By substituting the values from Figure 21.8 into Eq 8 we get

$$K = \frac{30^2}{312 \times (0.5 \times 30 \times 1)^2} = 0.0128$$

and by substituting the derived value of K into Eq 6 we get

$$R_R = 0.0128 \times A^2 \qquad (9)$$

Eq 9 is useful for determining the radiation resistance of coil-loaded vertical antennas less than 30° in length. The derived constant differs slightly from that presented by Laport (see Bibliography) as he used a different equation for radiation resistance than Eq 4.

21.1.4 OPTIMUM LOADING COIL INDUCTANCE AND PLACEMENT

The optimum location for a loading coil in an antenna can be found experimentally, but it requires many hours of designing and constructing models and making measurements to ensure the validity of the design. A faster and more reliable way of determining optimum coil location is through the use of a personal computer. This approach allows the variation of any single variable, while observing the cumulative effects on the system. When plotted graphically, the data reveals that the placement of the loading coil is critical if maximum radiation efficiency is to be realized. (See the program *MOBILE.EXE*, which may be downloaded from **www.arrl.org/antenna-book**.)

When the loading coil is moved up the antenna (away from the feed point), the current distribution is modified as shown in **Figure 21.9**. The current varies with the cosine of the height in electrical degrees at any point in the base section. Therefore, the current flowing into the bottom of the loading coil is less than the current flowing at the base of the antenna.

But what about the current in the top section of the antenna? Because the loading coil is a lumped constant, disregarding losses and radiation from the coil, it maintains the same current flow throughout. As a result, the current at the top of a high-Q coil is essentially the same as that at the bottom. This is easily verified by measuring RF current immediately above and below the loading coil in a test antenna. Thus, the coil "forces" much more current into the top section than would flow in the equivalent section of an antenna that is a full 90° long. This occurs as a result of the extremely high voltage that appears at the top of the loading coil. This higher current flow results in more radiation than would

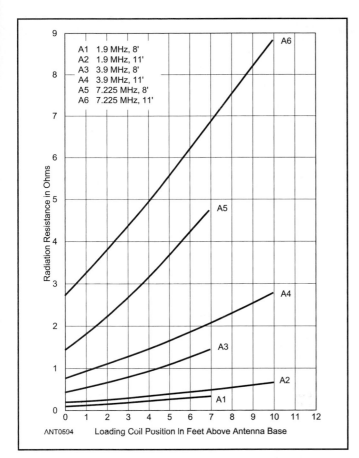

A1 1.9 MHz, 8'
A2 1.9 MHz, 11'
A3 3.9 MHz, 8'
A4 3.9 MHz, 11'
A5 7.225 MHz, 8'
A6 7.225 MHz, 11'

ANT0504 Loading Coil Position In Feet Above Antenna Base

Fig 21.10 — Radiation resistance plotted as a function of loading coil position.

occur from the equivalent section of a quarter-wave antenna. (This is true for conventional coils. However, radiation from long thin coils allows coil current to decrease, as in helically wound antennas.)

The cross-hatched area in Figure 21.9 shows the current that would flow in the equivalent part of a 90° high antenna, and reveals that the degree-ampere area of the whip section of the short antenna is greatly increased as a result of the modified current distribution. The current flow in the top section decreases almost linearly to zero at the top. This can be seen in Figure 21.9.

The degree-ampere area of Figure 21.9 is the sum of the triangular area represented by the current distribution in the top section, and the nearly trapezoidal current distribution in the base section. Radiation from the coil is not included in the degree-ampere area because it is small and difficult to define. Any radiation from the coil can be considered a bonus.

The degree-ampere area is expressed by:

$$A = \tfrac{1}{2} [h_1(1 + \cos h_1) + h_2 (\cos h_1)] \tag{10}$$

where
   h_1 = electrical length in degrees of the base section
   h_2 = electrical height in degrees of the top section.

The degree-ampere area (calculated by substituting Eq 10 into Eq 9) can be used to determine radiation resistance

when the loading coil is at any position other than the base of the antenna. Radiation resistance has been calculated with these equations and plotted against loading coil position at three different frequencies for 8- and 11-foot antennas in **Figure 21.10**. Eight feet is a typical length for commercial antennas, and 11-foot antennas are about the maximum practical length that can be installed on a vehicle.

In Figure 21.10 the curves reveal that the radiation resistance increases almost linearly as the loading coil is moved up the antenna. They also show that the radiation resistance rises rapidly as the frequency is increased. If the analysis were stopped at this point, one might conclude that the loading coil should be placed at the top of the antenna. This is not so, and the reason will become apparent shortly.

Required Loading Coil Inductance

Calculation of the loading coil inductance needed to resonate a short antenna can be done easily and accurately by using the antenna transmission-line analog described by Boyer in *Ham Radio*. For a base-loaded antenna as in Figure 21.8, the loading coil reactance required to resonate the antenna is given by

$$X_L = -j\,K_m \cot h \tag{11}$$

where
   X_L = inductive reactance required
   K_m = mean characteristic impedance (defined in Eq 12).

The $-j$ term indicates that the antenna presents capacitive reactance at the feed point. A loading coil must cancel this reactance.

The mean characteristic impedance of an antenna is expressed by

$$K_m = 60\,[\,(\,\ln\,(2H/a) - 1\,] \tag{12}$$

where
   H = physical antenna height (excluding the length of the loading coil)
   a = radius of the antenna in the same units as H.

From Eq 12 you can see that decreasing the height-to-diameter ratio of an antenna by increasing the radius results in a decrease in K_m. With reference to Eq 11, a decrease in K_m decreases the inductive reactance required to resonate an antenna. As will be shown later, this will increase radiation efficiency. In mobile applications, we quickly run into wind-loading problems if we attempt to use an antenna that is physically large in diameter.

If the loading coil is moved away from the base of the antenna, the antenna is divided into a base and top section, as depicted in Figure 21.9. The loading coil reactance required to resonate the antenna when the coil is away from the base is given by

$$X_L = j\,K_{m2}\,(\cot h_2) - j\,K_{m1}\,(\tan h_1) \tag{13}$$

In mobile-antenna design and construction, the top section is usually a whip with a much smaller diameter than the base section. Because of this, it is necessary to compute separate values of K_m for the top and base sections. K_{m1} and K_{m2} are the mean characteristic impedances of the base and top sections, respectively.

Loading coil reactance curves for the 3.8-MHz antennas of Figure 21.10 have been calculated and plotted in **Figure 21.11**. These curves show the influence of the loading coil position on the reactance required for resonance. The curves in Figure 21.11 show that the required reactance decreases with longer antennas. The curves also reveal that the required loading coil reactance grows at an increasingly rapid rate after the coil passes the center of the antenna. Because the highest possible loading coil Q is needed, and because optimum Q is attained when the loading coil diameter is twice the loading coil length, the coil would grow very quickly to an impractical size above the center of the antenna. It is for this reason that the highest loading coil position is limited to one foot from the top of the antenna in all computations.

Loading Coil Resistance

Loading coil resistance constitutes one of the losses consuming power that could otherwise be radiated by the antenna. Heat loss in the loading coil is not of any benefit, so it should be minimized by using the highest possible loading coil Q. Loading coil loss resistance is a function of the coil Q and is given by

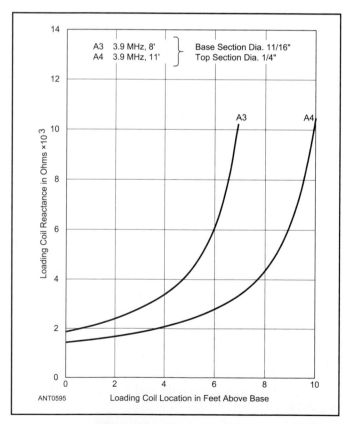

14
A3   3.9 MHz, 8'   Base Section Dia. 11/16"
A4   3.9 MHz, 11'   Top Section Dia. 1/4"

Loading Coil Reactance in Ohms ×10³

Loading Coil Location in Feet Above Base
ANT0595

Fig 21.11 — Loading coil reactance required for resonance, plotted as a function of coil height above the antenna base. The resonant frequency is 3.9 MHz.

$$R_C = \frac{X_L}{Q} \qquad (14)$$

where

R_C = loading coil loss resistance in Ω
X_L = loading coil reactance
Q = coil figure of merit

Inspection of Eq 14 reveals that, for a given value of inductive reactance, loss resistance will be lower for higher Q coils. Measurements made with a Q meter show that typical, commercially manufactured coil stock produces a Q between 150 and 160 at 3.8 MHz.

Higher Q values can be obtained by using larger diameter coils having a diameter-to-length ratio of two, by using larger diameter wire, by using more spacing between turns, and by using low-loss polystyrene supporting and enclosure materials. In theory, loading coil turns should not be shorted for tuning purposes because shorted turns somewhat degrade Q. Pruning to resonance should be done by removing turns from the coil.

In fairness, it should be pointed out that many practical mobile antennas use large-diameter loading coils with shorted turns to achieve resonance. The popular "Texas Bug Catcher" coils come to mind here. (See the section "HF Mobile Antenna Types.") Despite general proscriptions against shorting turns, these systems are often more efficient than antennas with small, relatively low-Q, fixed loading coils.

21.1.5 RADIATION EFFICIENCY

The ratio of power radiated to power fed to an antenna determines the radiation efficiency. It is given by:

$$E = \frac{P_R}{P_I} \times 100\% \qquad (15)$$

where

E = radiation efficiency in percent
P_R = power radiated
P_I = power fed to the antenna at the feed point.

In a short, coil-loaded mobile antenna, a large portion of the power fed to the antenna is dissipated in ground and coil resistances. A relatively insignificant amount of power is also dissipated in the antenna conductor resistance and in the leakage resistance of the base insulator. Because these last two losses are both very small and difficult to estimate, they are here neglected in calculating radiation efficiency.

Another loss worth noting is matching network loss. Because we are concerned only with power fed to the antenna in the determination of radiation efficiency, matching network loss is not considered in any of the equations. Suffice it to say that matching networks should be designed for minimum loss in order to maximize the transmitter power available at the antenna.

The radiation efficiency equation may be rewritten and expanded as follows:

$$E = \frac{I^2 R_R \times 100}{I^2 R_R + I^2 R_G + \left(I \cos h_1\right)^2 R_C} \quad (16)$$

where

I = antenna base current in amperes
R_G = ground loss resistance in Ω
R_C = coil loss resistance in Ω
R_R = radiation resistance in Ω

Each term of Eq 16 represents the power dissipated in its associated resistance. All the current terms cancel, simplifying this equation to

$$E = \frac{R_R \times 100}{R_R + R_G + R_C \cos^2 h_1} \quad (17)$$

For base-loaded antennas the term $\cos^2$ drops to unity and may be omitted.

Ground Loss

Eq 14 shows that the total resistive losses in the antenna system are:

$$R_T = R_R + R_G + R_C (\cos^2 h_1) \quad (18)$$

where R_T is the total resistive loss. Ground loss resistance can be determined by rearranging Eq 18 as follows:

$$R_G = R_T - R_R - R_C \cos^2 h_1 \quad (19)$$

R_T may be measured in a test antenna installation on a vehicle using an R-X noise bridge or an SWR analyzer. You can then calculate R_R and R_C.

Ground loss is a function of vehicle size, placement of the antenna on the vehicle, and conductivity of the ground over which the vehicle is traveling. It is only feasible to control the first two variables. Larger vehicles provide better ground planes than smaller ones. The vehicle ground plane is only partial, so the result is considerable RF current flow (and ground loss) in the ground around and under the vehicle.

By raising the antenna base as high as possible on the vehicle, ground losses are decreased. This results from a decrease in antenna capacitance to ground that also increases the capacitive reactance to ground. This, in turn, reduces ground currents and ground losses.

This effect has been verified by installing the same antenna at three different locations on two different vehicles, and by determining the ground loss from Eq 19. In the first test, the antenna was mounted 6 inches below the top of a large station wagon, just behind the left rear window. This placed the antenna base 4 feet 2 inches above the ground, and resulted in a measured ground loss resistance of 2.5 Ω. The second test used the same antenna mounted on the left rear fender of a mid-sized sedan, just to the left of the trunk lid. In this test, the measured ground loss resistance was 4 Ω. The third test used the same mid-sized car, but the antenna was mounted on the rear bumper. In this last test, the measured ground loss resistance was 6 Ω.

The same antenna therefore sees three different ground

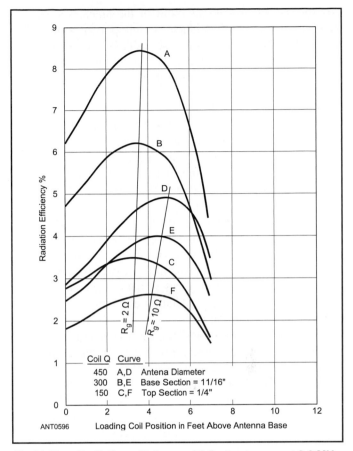

Fig 21.12 — Radiation efficiency of 8-foot antennas at 3.9 MHz.

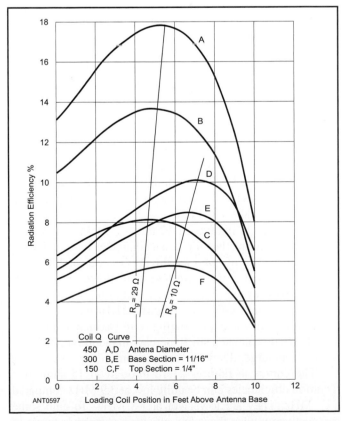

Fig 21.13 — Radiation efficiency of 11-foot antennas at 3.9 MHz.

loss resistances as a direct result of the antenna mounting location and size of the vehicle. It is important to note that the measured ground loss increases as the antenna base nears the ground. The importance of minimizing ground losses in mobile antenna installations cannot be overemphasized.

Efficiency Curves

With the equations defined previously, a computer was used to calculate the radiation efficiency curves depicted in **Figures 21.12** through **21.15**. These curves were calculated for 80 and 40 meter antennas of 8- and 11-foot lengths. Several values of loading coil Q were used, for both 2 and 10 Ω of ground loss resistance. For the calculations, the base section is ½-inch diameter electrical EMT which has an outside diameter of ¹¹⁄₁₆ inch. The top section is fiberglass bicycle-whip material covered with Belden braid. These are readily available materials, which can be used by the average amateur to construct an inexpensive but rugged antenna.

Upon inspection, these radiation-efficiency curves reveal some significant information:

1) higher coil Q produces higher radiation efficiencies,
2) longer antennas produce higher radiation efficiencies,
3) radiation efficiency increases at high frequencies,
4) lower ground loss resistances produce higher radiation efficiencies,
5) higher ground loss resistances force the loading coil above the antenna center to reach a peak in the radiation-efficiency curve, and
6) higher coil Q sharpens the radiation-efficiency curves, resulting in the coil position being more critical for optimum radiation efficiency.

Note that the radiation efficiency curves reach a peak and then begin to decline as the loading coil is raised farther up the antenna. This is because of the rapid increase in loading coil reactance required above the antenna center. Refer to Figure 21.11. The rapid increase in coil size required for resonance results in the coil loss resistance increasing much more rapidly than the radiation resistance. This results in decreased radiation efficiency, as shown in Figure 21.10.

A slight reverse curvature exists in the curves between the base-loaded position and the one-foot coil-height position. This is caused by a shift in the curve that resulted from insertion of a base section of larger diameter than the whip when the coil is above the base.

The curves in Figures 21.12 through 21.15 were calculated with constant (but not equal) diameter base and whip sections. Because of wind loading, it is not desirable to increase the diameter of the whip section. However, the base-section diameter can be increased within reason to further improve radiation efficiency. **Figure 21.16** was calculated for base-section diameters ranging from ¹¹⁄₁₆ inch to 3 inches. The curves reveal that a small increase in radiation efficiency results from larger diameter base sections.

The curves in Figures 21.12 through 21.15 show that radiation efficiencies can be quite low at 3.9 MHz compared to 7 MHz. They are lower yet at 1.8 MHz. To gain some perspective on what these low efficiencies mean in terms of

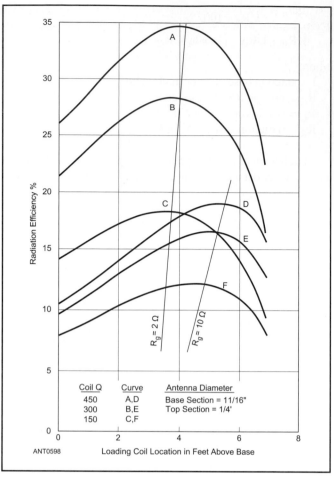

Fig 21.14 — Radiation efficiency of 8-foot antennas at 7.225 MHz.

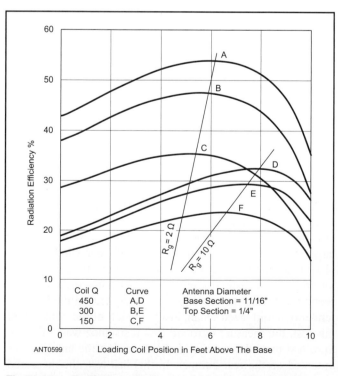

Fig 21.15 — Radiation efficiency of 11-foot antennas at 7.225 MHz.

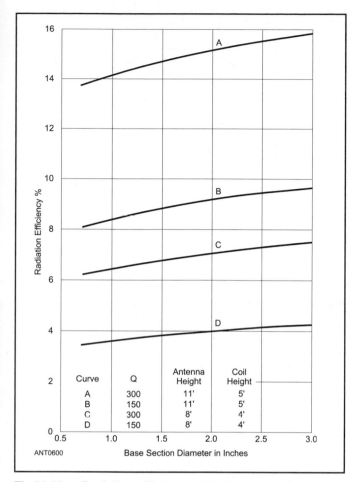

Fig 21.16 — Radiation efficiency plotted as a function of base section diameter. Frequency = 3.9 MHz, ground loss resistance = 2 Ω, and whip section = 1/4-inch diameter.

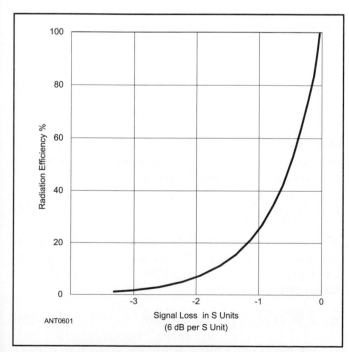

Fig 21.17 — Mobile antenna signal loss as a function of radiation efficiency, compared to a quarter-wave vertical antenna over perfect ground.

signal strength, **Figure 21.17** was calculated using the following equation:

$$dB = \log \frac{100}{E} \qquad (20)$$

where

dB = signal loss in decibels

E = efficiency in percent.

The curve in Figure 21.17 reveals that an antenna having 25% efficiency has a signal loss of 6 dB (approximately one S unit) below a quarter-wave vertical antenna over perfect ground. An antenna efficiency in the neighborhood of 6% will produce a signal strength on the order of two S units or about 12 dB below the same quarter-wave reference vertical. By careful optimization of mobile-antenna design, signal strengths from mobiles can be made fairly competitive with those from fixed stations using comparable power. Additional improvement can be obtained by operating in an open area and over or near good ground, such as wetlands and fresh or saltwater.

21.1.6 IMPEDANCE MATCHING

The input impedance of short, high-Q coil-loaded antennas is quite low. For example, an 8-foot antenna optimized for 3.9 MHz with an unloaded coil Q of 300 and a ground-loss resistance of 2 Ω has a base input impedance of about 13 Ω. This low impedance value causes a standing wave ratio of 4:1 in 50-Ω coax at resonance. This high SWR is not compatible with the requirements of solid-state transmitters. Also, the bandwidth of shortened vertical antennas is very narrow. This severely limits the capability to maintain transmitter loading over even a small frequency range.

Impedance matching can be accomplished by means of L networks or impedance-matching transformers, but the narrow bandwidth limitation remains. A more elegant solution to the impedance matching and narrow band- width problem is to install an automatic tuner at the antenna base. Such a device matches the antenna and feed line automatically, and permits operation over a wide frequency range.

The tools are now available to tailor a mobile antenna design to produce maximum radiation efficiency. Mathematical modeling with a personal computer reveals that loading coil Q factor and ground loss resistance greatly influence the optimum loading coil position in a short vertical antenna. It also shows that longer antennas, higher coil Q, and higher operating frequencies produce higher radiation efficiencies.

End effect has not been included in any of the equations to assure that the loading coil will be slightly larger than necessary. Pruning the antenna to resonance should be done by removing coil turns, rather than by shorting turns or shortening the whip section excessively. Shortening the whip reduces radiation efficiency, by both shortening the antenna and moving the optimum coil position. Shorting turns in the loading coil degrades the Q of the coil.

Matching to the Transmitter

Most modern transmitters require a 50-Ω load and because the feed point impedance of a mobile whip is quite low, a matching network is usually necessary. Although calculations are helpful in the initial design, considerable experimenting is often necessary in final tune-up. This is particularly true for the lower bands, where the antenna is electrically short compared with a quarter-wave whip. The reason is that the loading coil is required to tune out a very large capacitive reactance, and even small changes in component values result in large reactance variations. Since the feed point resistance is low to begin with, the problem is even more aggravated.

You can transform the low resistance of the whip to a value suitable for a 50-Ω system with an RF transformer or with a shunt-feed arrangement, such as an L network. The latter may only require a shunt coil or shunt capacitor at the base of the whip since the net series capacitive or inductive reactance of the antenna and its loading coil may be used as part of the network. The following example illustrates the calculations involved.

Assume that a center-loaded whip antenna, 8.5 feet in overall length, is to be used on 7.2 MHz. From Table 21-1 earlier in this chapter we see that the feed point resistance of the antenna will be approximately 19 Ω and from Figure 21.4 that the capacitance of the whip, as seen at its base, is approximately 24 pF. Since the antenna is to be center loaded, the capacitance value of the section above the coil will be cut approximately in half, to 12 pF. From this, it may be calculated that a center-loading inductor of 40.7 μH is required to resonate the antenna by canceling out the capacitive reactance. (This figure agrees with the approximate value of 40 μH shown in Table 21-1. The resulting feed point impedance would then be $19 + j\,0\ \Omega$.)

Solution: The antenna can be matched to a 52-Ω line such as RG-8 by tuning it either above or below resonance and then canceling out the undesired component with an appropriate shunt element, capacitive or inductive. The way in which the impedance is transformed up can be seen by plotting the admittance of the series RLC circuit made up of the loading coil, antenna capacitance, and feed point resistance. Such a plot is shown in **Figure 21.18** for a constant feed point resistance of 19 Ω. There are two points of interest, P1 and P2, where the input conductance is 19.2 millisiemens, corresponding to 52 Ω. The undesired susceptance is shown as $1/X_P$ and $-1/X_P$, which must be canceled with a shunt element of the opposite sign but with the same magnitude. The value of the canceling shunt reactance, X_P, may be found from the formula:

$$X_P = \frac{R_f Z_0}{\sqrt{R_f(Z_0 - R_f)}} \tag{21}$$

where X_P is the reactance in Ω, R_f is the feed point resistance, and Z_0 is the feed line impedance. For $Z_0 = 52\ \Omega$ and $R_f = 19\ \Omega$, $X_P = \pm 39.5\ \Omega$. A coil or good quality mica capacitor may be used as the shunt element. With the tune-up procedure described later, the value is not critical and a fixed-value component may be used.

To arrive at point P1, the value of the center loading-coil inductance would be less than that required for resonance. The feed point impedance would then appear capacitive, and

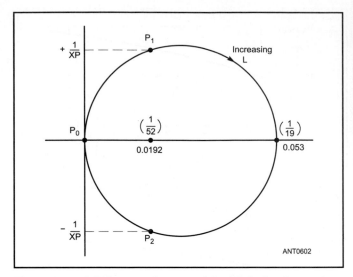

Fig 21.18 — **Admittance diagram of the RLC circuit consisting of the whip capacitance, radiation resistance and loading coil discussed in text. The horizontal axis represents conductance, and the vertical axis susceptance. The point P_0 is the input admittance with no whip loading inductance. Points P_1 and P_2 are described in the text. The conductance equals the reciprocal of the resistance, if no reactive components are present. For a series RX circuit, the conductance is given by**

$$G = \frac{R}{R^2 + X^2}$$

and the susceptance is given by

$$B = \frac{-X}{R^2 + X^2}$$

Consequently, a parallel equivalent G-B circuit to the series RX circuit can be found that makes computations easier. This is because conductances and susceptances add in parallel the same way resistances and reactances add in series.

an inductive shunt matching element would then be required. To arrive at point P2, the center loading coil should be more inductive than required for resonance, and the shunt element would need to be capacitive. The value of the center loading coil required for the shunt-matched and resonated condition may be determined from the equation:

$$L = \frac{10^6}{4\pi^2 f^2 C} \pm \frac{X_S}{2\pi f} \tag{22}$$

where addition is performed if a capacitive shunt is to be used and subtraction performed if the shunt is inductive, and where L is in μH, f is the frequency in MHz, C is the capacitance of the antenna section being matched in pF, and

$$X_S = \sqrt{R_f(Z_0 - R_f)} \tag{23}$$

For the example given, where $Z_0 = 52\ \Omega$, $R_f = 19\ \Omega$, f = 7.2 MHz, and C = 12 pF, X_S is found to be 25.0 Ω. The required antenna loading inductance is either 40.2 μH or

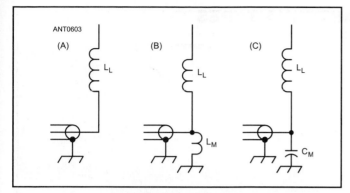

Fig 21.19 — At A, a whip antenna that is resonated with a center loading coil. At B and C, the value of the loading coil has been altered slightly to make the feed point impedance appear reactive, and a matching component is added in shunt to cancel the reactance. This provides an impedance transformation to match the Z_0 of the feed line. An equally acceptable procedure, rather than altering the loading coil inductance, is to adjust the length of the top section above the loading coil for the best match, as described in the tune-up section of the text.

41.3 µH, depending on the type of shunt. Various matching possibilities for this example are shown in **Figure 21.19**. At A, the antenna is shown as tuned to resonance with L_L, a 40.7 µH coil, but with no provisions included for matching the resulting 19-Ω impedance to the 52-Ω line. At B, L_L has been reduced to 40.2 µH to make the antenna appear net capacitive, and L_M, having a reactance of 39.5 Ω, is added in shunt to cancel the capacitive reactance and transform the feed point impedance to 50 Ω. The arrangement at C is similar to that at B except that L_L has been increased to 41.3 µH, and C_M (a shunt capacitor having a negative reactance of 39.5 Ω) is added, which also results in a 52-Ω nonreactive termination for the feed line.

The values determined for the loading coil in the above example point out an important consideration concerning the matching of short antennas — relatively small changes in values of the loading components will have a greatly magnified effect on the matching requirements. A change of less than 3% in the loading coil inductance value necessitates a completely different matching network! Likewise, calculations show that a 3% change in antenna capacitance will give similar results, and the value of the precautions mentioned earlier becomes clear. The sensitivity of the circuit with regard to

Shunt Coil Matching

The use of a shunt coil is the preferred matching methodology for two reasons. First, it provides a dc ground for the antenna which helps control static buildup. Second, once adjusted, no further adjustment is needed to cover all of the HF bands between 80 and 10 meters. Thus it is an ideal matching scenario for remotely-controlled (tuned) antennas. Capacitive matching, on the other hand, requires changing capacitance for every band, and sometimes within a band. It should be noted that any HF mobile antenna for bands at frequencies below 20 MHz that do not require matching to obtain a low SWR are less than optimal performers.

frequency variations is also quite critical, and an excursion around practically the entire circle in Figure 21.18 may represent only 600 kHz, centered around 7.2 MHz, for the above example. This is why tuning up a mobile antenna can be very frustrating unless a systematic procedure is followed.

Tune-Up

Assume that inductive shunt matching is to be used with the antenna in the previous example, Figure 21.19B, where 39.5 Ω is needed for L_M. This means that at 7.2 MHz, a coil of 0.87 µH will be needed across the whip feed point terminal to ground. With a 40-µH loading coil in place, the adjustable whip section above the loading coil should be set for minimum height. Signals in the receiver will sound weak and the whip should be lengthened a bit at a time until signals start to peak. Turn the transmitter on and check the SWR at a few frequencies to find where a minimum occurs. If it is below the desired frequency, shorten the whip slightly and check again. It should be moved approximately ¼ inch at a time until the SWR reaches a minimum at the center of the desired range. If the frequency where the minimum SWR occurs is above the desired frequency, repeat the procedure above, but lengthen the whip only slightly.

If a shunt capacitance is to be used, as in Figure 21.19C, a value of 560 pF would correspond to the required –39.5 Ω of reactance at 7.2 MHz. With a capacitive shunt, start with the whip in its longest position and shorten it until signals peak up.

21.2 HF MOBILE ANTENNA TYPES

21.2.1 THE SCREWDRIVER ANTENNA

No doubt the biggest change in HF mobile operation has been brought about by the screwdriver antenna. Originally conceived by Don Johnson, W6AAQ (SK), the basic design has become ubiquitous, available from many different manufacturers. They consist of a large, hollow lower mast, an extendable coil assembly, and a whip, typically 60 to 96 inches long.

The unused portion of the coil is stored in the mast of the antenna. Finger stock at the top of the mast makes contact with the coil. A dc motor, controlled remotely, drives a screw arrangement that extends or retracts the coil to tune lower or higher in frequency, respectively. That tuning can be done while in motion is an attractive feature, hence their popularity.

A decent quality, high-Q, screwdriver antenna is not inexpensive and can cost upward of $1000, although most are about half this amount. They're relatively heavy and require both a feed line (coax), and a motor control lead. Some varieties also use a reed switch to count the turns of the screw (see the "Mobile Antenna Controllers and Tuners" section).

Shortened versions of the screwdriver are available from several manufacturers and have become very popular. Their light weight, short length, and ease of mounting, account for their popularity. However, because of their short overall length and low-Q coils, they take a big hit in performance over their full-sized cousins, especially when mounted on lip mounts. They also require some special considerations when coupled to automatic antenna controllers, as covered later.

It should be noted that not all models use the same mounting scheme. Some use standard ⅜-24 bolts, and at least one uses a ¾-inch bolt. Some form of base insulator is also required in most cases.

If you wish to build your own screwdriver antenna, plans for doing so are included on the CD-ROM supplied with this *Antenna Book*.

21.2.2 MONOBAND ANTENNAS

There are several types of monoband antennas, including the "bug catcher", linear-loaded varieties, and the ever-popular Hustler series.

The bug catcher shown in **Figure 21.20** can be the most efficient of all of the mobile antenna types, if mounted correctly. (The name derives from the tendency of the coil to "catch bugs" while driving.) However, it has several drawbacks, not the least of which is wind-loading, especially when equipped with a capacitive top-hat, which is discussed later.

Bug catcher antennas, in which a large air-wound loading coil is used for center loading, are monoband by nature but can be made multiband. The usual practice is to make the coil large enough in reactance to resonant the antenna on 80 meters. Then a jumper wire is used to short coil turns to resonate the antenna on the higher bands. However, shorting turns reduces coil Q and lowers efficiency.

They tend to be heavier than other monoband antennas,

Fig 21.20 — A "bug catcher" style antenna showing the large, air-wound center-loading coil.

requiring heavy-duty mounting and base springs — even guys to keep them stable at highway speeds.

Helical-Wound Antennas

These lightweight antennas are commonly referred to as "ham-sticks," but the name Ham Stick is actually a registered trademark of the Lakewood Company (**www.hamstick.com**). They are quite popular due to their low cost and reasonable performance. They look similar to the continuously loaded antennas covered below except they use a single, fixed-value loading coil.

The antenna itself is basically a fiberglass tube or rod with a small-gauge wire wound around it. Toward the top of the tube, the wire is close-wound in a loading coil and the antenna is topped off with a short, adjustable-length whip, commonly referred to as a *stinger*.

Due to their light weight, a mag-mount, angle, or trunk lip mount may be used with surprisingly good results considering their low Q, and relatively short length (≈7 feet). Changing bands requires changing the complete antenna, but most models have quick disconnects available making the task quicker and easier. As a general rule, they don't require impedance matching, as their overall losses bring the input impedance very close to 50 Ω.

Continuously-Loaded Antennas

There are several manufacturers of both monoband and multiband antennas that could be described as continuously-loaded. (Sometimes referred to as "linear-loaded," this is

Extending Bandwidth

Monoband antennas have a finite bandwidth. Depending on the band and installation parameters, the 2:1 bandwidth may be as little as 12 kHz on 80 meters to as much as 1 MHz or more on 10 meters. Since modern solid state transceivers start to reduce on their output at SWR above 2:1, it would be convenient to extend the bandwidth.

One way to do this is to use an internal (or external) auto-coupler (antenna tuner or ATU for short). The technique works well, as long as we don't try to match an antenna on a band it is not resonant on as this greatly increases the overall losses. However, few if any made-for-mobile transceivers have built in ATUs. Using an external unit will certainly suffice if you're willing to put up with the added complexity.

As we learned in the "HF Mobile Antenna Fundamentals" section, we can use a shunt element to match the antenna's input impedance to 50-Ω feed line. If we substitute a ¼-wave shorted coaxial stub for the fixed-value shunt element, we can effectively increase the bandwidth in the process. This is possible because the shorted stub's reactance swing is opposite that of the antenna's as we change frequencies — the ¼-wave stub's reactance will become more capacitive above resonance as the antenna's feed point reactance becomes more inductive.

Typically, the useable SWR bandwidth will increase from 30% to as much as 50%, again based on the frequency and installation parameters. The drawback is that we have to use a different stub for each band of operation.

---

not the linear-loading technique used to shorten dipoles and beam antennas.) For these antennas, loading is done using multiple fixed-value inductors spaced over the length of the antenna or winding a continuous coil with a large pitch (ratio of turn length to turn diameter) along the antenna.

The multiband versions use what is commonly called a "flying lead" connected at the base, which in turn connects to taps along the coil making up the body of the antenna to select the band.

Proponents incorrectly argue that the large length-to-diameter, up to 25 to 1, allows the coil to radiate, thus increasing efficiency. However, what little advantage this form of loading has, it is more than offset by the low coil Q, and short overall length (4 to 7 feet).

These antennas typically do not require matching but a few models exhibit input impedances of greater than 100 Ω and thus need to be matched.

Shortened Dipoles

A few amateurs opt to purchase two identical mobile antennas, and mount them in a V configuration. Knowing that ground loss is the dominate factor in determining antenna efficiency, they reason that replacing the ground loss with a second antenna is a viable solution. While they're correct that

it increases radiation resistance as well as the feed point input impedance, efficiency remains largely the same because ground loss has been replaced with the second antenna's loss of about the same magnitude. Gain claims are often exaggerated, as well. A full-size, lossless dipole in free space has a maximum theoretical gain of 2.15 dBi — higher values assume the presence of ground reflections and antenna heights of ½ wavelength or more which are impractical at best for a mobile station.

Stainless Steel Whips

Almost without exception, most whips referred to as "CB whips" are made from 17-7 stainless steel wire. Their overall length is 102 inches but at one time 108- and 120-inch versions were available. They are made from wire about 0.220 to 0.250 inch in diameter that is straightened and ground down to an OD of 0.200 inch. Beginning at about 60 inches above the base, they're tapered down to 0.100 inch OD at the tip. The whip is finished off with a swaged-on ⅜-24 threaded brass base fitting and a small corona ball added at the tip.

Stainless steel isn't the best of RF conductors, especially on the lower HF bands. When compared to an aluminum conductor of the same size, the additional resistive losses may reduce the ERP (effective radiated power) by ≈3 dB on 160 meters, depending on the overall length of the whip in use.

The unfortunate truth is, there is no viable alternative with the strength and flexibility of 17-7 stainless steel! Whips can be copper plated (a costly step) but the improvement is minimal. Covering the whip with silver-plated copper braid is easy to do, but again, the ERP improvement versus the additional wind loading might not be worth the effort.

Corona Balls

The small corona balls supplied atop standard CB whips provide a slight amount of eye protection but their effect on reducing corona is questionable. What is corona and how does a corona ball prevent it?

As we learned in the **HF Mobile Antenna Fundamentals** section, the highest RF voltage occurs at the very top of the whip. Under the right weather conditions, it is possible to see the corona discharge from the end of a pointed whip even when running modest power levels. *Corona discharge* is caused by the small radius of the whip's tip creating large differences in voltage that exceed the breakdown voltage of air across small distances. This causes the air to ionize and conduct. The discharge then extends away from the antenna as "streamers" until voltage is reduced below the level of ionization. Static discharges from the pointed tip can also become a problem on receive.

The solution is to replace the pointed end with a smoother, larger surface. The corona ball's smooth, round surface creates reduces voltage changes with distance that cause corona discharge. The corona ball must be large enough to be effective — at least 0.5 inch in diameter and preferably 1 inch — and are available from several *QST* advertisers. Above 1 inch, wind loading becomes a problem.

Capacitance hats, or cap-hats or top-hats for short, are a method of increasing the efficiency of HF mobile antennas at the expense of complexity and higher wind loading. They increase efficiency by adding capacitance to that portion of the antenna above the loading coil, effectively increasing the overall electrical length.

They may consist of a single stiff wire, two or more wires, a disc made up of several more wires like the spokes of a wheel, a set of loops, or wire arranged as the spokes of a wheel as shown in **Figure 21.21**. The larger the hat (physically), the greater the capacitance and the greater the effective increase in electrical length. Since less inductance is then required to resonate the electrically longer antenna, coil Q losses will also decrease.

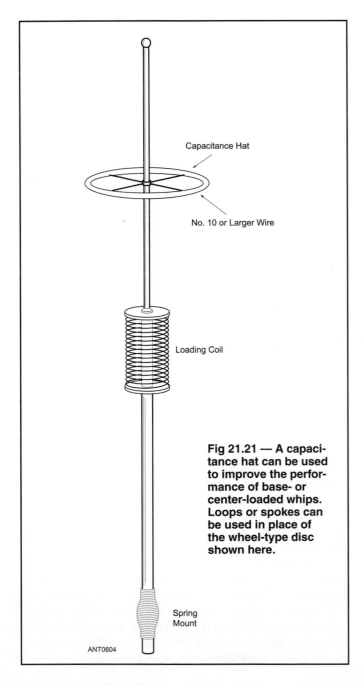

Fig 21.21 — A capacitance hat can be used to improve the performance of base- or center-loaded whips. Loops or spokes can be used in place of the wheel-type disc shown here.

Capacitance Hat

No. 10 or Larger Wire

Loading Coil

Spring Mount

ANT0604

No matter where the hat is located, the added capacitance will be the same. However, if placed too close to the coil, the added capacitance will decrease efficiency rather than improve it. The most effective position is at the very top of the antenna. At a minimum, hats should be placed at least half their diameter above the coil (Figure 21.21 shows the hat in the center of the whip) and as far away from vehicle sheet metal as possible. These facts require robust antenna construction and mounting techniques but the increase in performance is worth the effort.

Plans for a capacitive hat hub designed and made by Ken Muggli, KØHL are provided on the included CD-ROM including where to buy materials. The supporting whip in this case is a 102-inch CB whip that has been cut down to 60 inches.

As described and when mounted atop a Scorpion 680 screwdriver antenna, 80 through 17 meter operation is possible. Measured field strength improvement over an unloaded 102-inch whip is between 3 dB, and 6 dB, depending on the band.

21.2.3 ANTENNA MOUNTING

Antenna mounts come in so many different styles that it is difficult to decide which is best for any specific installation. Ball mounts, clip mounts, bracket mounts, stake pocket mounts, trailer hitch mounts, and even "mag" (magnet) mounts are popular. Which mount you pick and where you install it depends on many factors. Among them are weight, overall length, frequency of operation, the vehicle in question, and personal preferences.

Weight may be a few ounces for a UHF antenna to as much as 20 pounds for a full-sized, high Q, "bug catcher" antenna. The length may be a few inches for a UHF antenna, to as much as 13 feet or more for an HF one.

Some vehicles lend themselves to antenna mounting and some don't. In general, pickup trucks make better antenna platforms than vans and SUVs. No doubt the biggest decision for many hams is whether or not to drill holes in body sheet metal.

Another often-overlooked requirement is deciding on which side of the vehicle the antenna should be mounted. For rear-mounted antennas, the driver's side of the vehicle is preferred. This can be very important if you live in an area with low bridges and overhanging trees as there is typically more clearance toward the center of the street. Further, it is easier to see the antenna in the side mirrors if they are on the driver's side. If you've chosen front mounting, common when pulling a trailer or RV, then it should be mounted to the right in order to avoid distraction or obstruction of your vision.

Whatever method you choose for mounting your antenna, it must be sturdy enough to hold the weight and withstand the wind loading imposed by the antenna without too much flexing. It should be attached in such a way to maximize what little ground plane a vehicle represents. The key phrase for mounting the antenna is: *It is the metal mass directly under the antenna, not what's alongside, that counts the most!* Keep in mind, no matter what the antenna, permanent and secure mounting maximizes performance and safety.

HF Mobile Antenna Mounts

Figure 21.22 shows a typical center-loaded, remote-controlled, 80 through 10 meter screwdriver antenna, a Scorpion Antennas SA-680. This homebrew mount was made by Joe McEneaney, KG6PCI. The 18-pound antenna is supported by a steel mast welded to a frame extension. There is a stainless steel plate at the top of the mast, bolted to the top of the bed rail, that secures the antenna and reduces ground losses. A quick disconnect at the base of the antenna facilitates removal when desired.

Because of the difficulty in designing and finding someone to weld a special mount, most mobile operators opt for a commercial trailer hitch mount from one of the many *QST* advertisers. While secure, trailer hitch mounting schemes increase ground losses, and should be avoided if possible.

If you drive a pickup truck, mounts in the top of the bed rail or in the bed offer more efficient operation. A stake pocket mount like the Breedlove model shown in **Figure 21.23** is a good, no-holes choice. Its offset design allows it to extend from beneath most bed covers.

3/8-Inch Threaded Mounts

Most monoband, a few screwdriver types, and some VHF antennas mount via a male or female ⅜-24 threaded stud. Ball mounts, clip and lip mounts, and mag mounts are frequently supplied with this type of threaded base. Mounts so equipped often require base insulators to isolate the antenna from the mounting hardware. Feed line connections may be simple wire lugs, an SO-239 connector, or a coaxial cable pigtail with or without a female RF connector installed.

The studs themselves are often stainless steel, but some are mild steel or brass. If the antenna in question is a heavy bug-catcher, a strong stud is in order. A replacement stud can be easily made from a 2-inch, class-8 bolt by cutting off and redressing the threaded portion. The resulting stud has over twice the tensile strength of the stainless steel version.

Ball Mounts

Ball mounts like the one shown in **Figure 21.24** aren't used much anymore as late-model automotive sheet metal isn't as strong as it once was or has been replaced by plastic or composite materials. Further, most hams don't have the necessary tools to fabricate heavy-duty insulators and large backing plates to overcome the thin sheet metal problem for the larger, heavier antennas. However, for ham-sticks and shortened CB whips, ball mounts are more than adequate, even on lighter sheet metal.

Clip or Lip Mounts

Clip mounts are a mixed bag of tricks. Most are quite adaptable to any surface angle including those offered by trunk lids, rear hatches, and even side doors. For light-duty VHF and UHF antennas, they offer a convenient mounting method. If you're careful in closing the door or hatch they're attached to, they work quite well. Clearance between the mount and the vehicle body structure should be checked before purchase, however.

Typical clip mounts are secured by setscrews. The

Figure 21.22 — A Scorpion 680 screwdriver antenna mounted on the truck of KG6PCI. *(Photo courtesy of Alan Applegate, KØBG and Ron Douglass, NI7J)*

Fig 21.23 — Stake-pocket mounts are designed to fit into the square holes in the walls of a pickup truck's bed. An offset mount as shown in the photo will also clear most bed covers.

Fig 21.24 — A ball mount is attached to a vertical or nearly-vertical vehicle panel and can be adjusted so that the antenna is vertical. The spring shown in this photo may or may not be included with the mount. The length of the spring must be included in the antenna's total length.

folded-over sheet metal of the car body to which the set screws make contact is often jagged and thus offers a less than secure electrical connection. Even modest and lightweight antennas tend to stress the connection. When the connection loosens, intermittent SWR and RFI problems are often the result. Therefore, as a general rule, clip mounts should be restricted to antennas weighing less than 2 pounds. (Larger antennas can be used if guyed or otherwise stabilized above the mount.)

All modern vehicles are dipped in a zinc compound before final assembly and painting. When exposed to air, zinc rapidly oxidizes but in this case the oxidation is a good thing! When a piece of road debris nicks the paint down to the zinc layer, it quickly oxidizes, and protects the base metal underneath. Do not remove this zinc coating to bare metal! This removes the protective coating, allowing the underlying steel to rust and creates an intermittent connection.

All lip mounts bring the coax cable into the trunk or passenger cabin through the weather seal potentially allowing water to enter. The problem is often exacerbated by the larger control cable most screwdriver antennas require. Take care to dress the cables and seals to direct water toward a drain hole or other exit.

Angle Brackets

Angle brackets come in a variety of sizes, shapes, angles, hole size, attachment style, strength, and colors. They're great for lightweight antennas like ham-sticks and VHF antennas, but shouldn't be used for heavier ones. There are special hood seam versions for some models of trucks and other vehicles. They require holes for attachment screws. Some mounts can be clamped on mirror arms or other tubes and struts.

Magnet "Mag" Mounts

Lots of folks use mag mounts with good success for both HF and VHF antennas. Models are available that can secure just about any size antenna. In fact, some VHF antennas come preassembled with mag mounts. Although they're meant for temporary mounting, it is common for them to be used as permanent mounts as a way to avoid drilling holes. Mag mounts have several drawbacks that tend to limit them to temporary installation.

Coax routing is always a problem if for no other reason than weather sealing. The magnet tends to collect road debris, primarily metallic brake dust that eventually gets under the magnet and rusts or scratches the vehicle's finish.

Regardless of the number or size of the magnets, the ultimate holding power relies on the metal surface. For example, some newer vehicles use steel-reinforced composite materials and although the magnets stick to the surface, the force with which they do so is less than on an all-steel surface. In these cases, mag mounts *should not* be used.

For larger antennas mounts are available with from three to five large magnets. These mounts tend to be very heavy and are difficult to install and remove. When used with large antennas, even large mag mounts should be securely tethered and/or guyed to keep them in place for very obvious reasons.

High ground loss and common-mode currents on the coax shield can be a problem when using mag mounts, as they rely on capacitive coupling to the vehicle body for RF return current. Installing a ground strap to the nearest chassis hard point is often recommended but does little to solve these problems.

21.2.4 MOBILE ANTENNA CONTROLLERS AND TUNERS

Screwdriver antennas have become very popular in part because their operating frequency can be changed while in motion. Most manufacturers offer some form of manual control box as an option. However, manual controllers require the operator to watch either an internal or external SWR indicator during tuning, which isn't safe while in motion. Fortunately, there is a solution — the automatic antenna controller.

There are two basic types with several variations, SWR sensing and turn counters. Both types require special attention with respect to RF on the antenna's control leads and we'll cover that issue, as well. Most have a built-in *park* feature which retracts the coil all the way into the mast. If you have garage or carport clearance issues, this is a nice feature.

SWR Sensing Controllers

The BetterRF 7000 screwdriver controller shown in **Figure 21.25** is a typical example. It reads SWR as data directly from a mating ICOM IC-7000 via the CI-V data port. Other types read SWR with a separate sensing unit by activating a TUNE function on a transceiver after a basic setup routine is completed. Afterward, all that is needed to QSY is to change bands on your transceiver, push the radio's TUNE button, and let the controller do all of the work.

One clear advantage of most SWR sensing controllers is

Fig 21.25 — An SWR-sensing controller adjusts the length of the screwdriver coil for minimum SWR automatically.

that they store the previous operating frequency. Therefore, when you change frequency, the controller always moves the antenna in the correct direction, saving wear and tear on the motor assembly.

Turn Counter Controllers

Most screwdriver antennas come equipped with a turns counter, usually in the form of a magnet attached to the drive assembly that closes a magnetic reed switch. As the motor turns, the switch opens and closes once or twice every 360°. The controller counts the closures and moves the antenna to a *predetermined* resonance point. **Figure 21.26**, an Ameritron SDC-102, is an example of this type of turns-counting controller. "Jog" buttons are included to touch up the SWR once the predetermined point is reached.

Like some SWR type controllers, turn counters are prone to RF currents on their control leads, so proper RF choking is essential.

Common-Mode Current Problems

In an ideal world, RF flows down the outer surface of the center conductor of coaxial cable and returns on the inner surface of the coax shield. In the real world, RF current will flow on the *outside* of the coax shield, completely independently of the currents inside. The skin effect electrically separates the inside and outside of the shield. This creates a "third wire" — the outside of the shield — that is often connected directly to one side of an antenna. For mobile antennas, the outside of the shield is usually connected to the vehicle body. In addition, if the coax is not itself shielded from the antenna's radiated field, the outside of the shield will pick up RF energy radiated by the antenna. This unbalanced RF current is called "common-mode current" as opposed to the balanced differential-mode currents inside the coax. The common-mode RF current can radiate a signal of its own, just like from any antenna carrying RF, and it can also cause RFI to your radio and to the vehicle's electronic systems.

In the case of HF mobile antennas, the magnitude of common-mode current on feed lines and other cables increases as ground impedance increases which also increases ground losses. As a result the coax and control cables running to clamp or lip-mount and mag-mount antennas will

typically carry more common-mode current than body-mounted antennas.

Because of the potential for RFI from common-mode currents, it is prudent to add RF chokes to reduce common-mode currents in a mobile installation, even though there may be no direct indication of a problem. The best place to install a common-mode RF choke is near the base of the antenna where the feed line is connected and not inside the vehicle.

The most convenient way to create an RF choke is to use the "split bead" or "split core" ferrite cores. A mix 31, ¾-inch ID split bead may be utilized with great effect. Depending on the coax size, between five and seven turns of either RG-58 or RG-8X can be wound through that size bead as shown in **Figure 21.27A**. The impedance will be somewhat greater than 1.8 kΩ at 10 MHz which is adequate in most cases. If not, a second split bead can be used effectively doubling the impedance. Take care not to bend the coaxial cable too sharply in making the choke, particularly for foam-insulation cables, as the center conductor can be forced through the insulation over time, creating a short circuit. For more information on ferrite common-mode chokes, see the **Transmission Line Coupling and Impedance Matching** chapter.

Control Lead RF Chokes

All screwdriver antennas have one thing in common: Their control motor and any reed switches are housed inside the antenna. Therefore, the control leads will be "hot" with RF during transmissions. This RF must be prevented from reaching the controller or erratic operation may result. This is especially important when utilizing short antennas on clip mounts with their inherent ground losses.

Figure 21.27B shows a motor lead choke utilizing a ¾-inch ID, mix 31 split bead. These specific split beads are available from a variety of *QST* advertisers. The one shown is

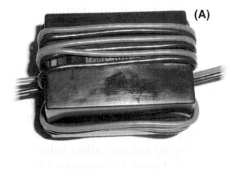
(A)

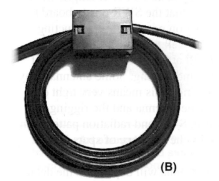
(B)

Fig 21.27 — At A, dc power leads are wound around a split ferrite bead to form an RF choke. B shows how coaxial cable can be wound on a split ferrite bead to form an RF choke on the outside of the cable shield. Wind coax loosely to avoid forcing the center conductor through the center insulation.

Fig 21.26 — A turns-counting controller keeps track of coil position by counting switch closures from a reed switch mounted on the antenna.

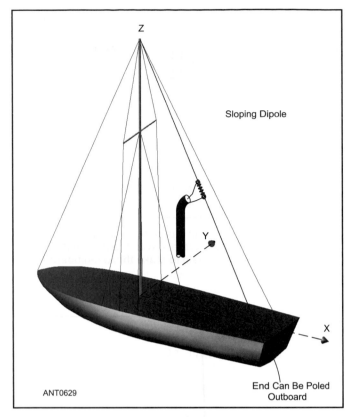

Fig 21.37 — One end of dipole can be attached to the main halyard and pulled up to the masthead. The bottom end of the dipole should be pulled out away from the rigging as much as possible to reduce the impact of the rigging on the impedance.

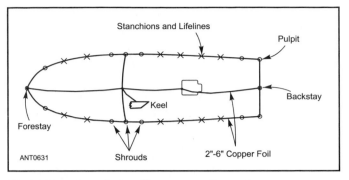

Fig 21.38 — A typical sailboat grounding scheme.

impedance grounding but that material may not always be readily available. It turns out that a pair of parallel wires (say #12) spaced a few inches apart will have an impedance similar to a wide copper strap and may be easier to install.

The question arises: "What about electrolysis between the keel and propeller if you bond them together?" This has to be dealt with on a case-by-case basis. If your protective zincs are depleting more rapidly after you install a grounding system, change it by disconnecting something — the engine-shaft-propeller, for example.

Grounding will vary in every installation and has to be customized to each vessel. However, just as on shore, the better the ground system, the better the performance of the vertical!

21.4.7 ANTENNAS FOR POWER BOATS

Power boaters are not usually faced with the problems and opportunities created by the mast and rigging on a sailboat. A powerboat may have a small mast, but usually not on the same scale as a sailboat. Antennas for power boats have much more in common with automotive mobile operation, but with some important exceptions:

1) In an automobile, the body is usually metal and it provides a ground plane for a whip antenna. Most modern powerboats, however, have fiberglass hulls. These are basically insulators and will not work as a counterpoise. (On the other hand, metal-hulled power boats can provide nearly ideal grounding!)

2) A height restriction on automotive mobile whips is imposed by clearance limits on highway overpasses and also by the need to sustain wind speeds of up to 80+ miles per hour on the highway. Hopefully your vessel will not experience these wind speeds!

3) In general, powerboats can have much taller antennas that can be lowered for the occasional low bridge.

4) The motion on a powerboat, especially in rough seas, can be quite severe. This places additional mechanical strain on the antennas.

5) On both powerboats and sailboats, operation in a saltwater marine environment is common. This means that a careful choice of materials must be made for the antennas to reduce corrosion and premature failure.

The problem of a ground plane for vertical antennas can be handled in much the same manner as shown in Figure 21.38 for sailboats. Since there will most likely not be a large keel structure to connect to and provide a large surface area, additional copper foil can be added inside the hull to increase the counterpoise area. Because of the small area of the propeller, it may be better not to connect to the engine, but to rely instead on increasing the area of the counterpoise and operate it as a true counterpoise — that is, isolated from ground.

Sometimes a number of radial wires are used for a vertical, much like that for a ground-plane antenna. This is not a very good idea unless the "wires" are actually wide copper-foil strips that can lower the Q substantially. The problem is the high voltage present at the ends of normal ground-plane antenna radials. For a boat these radials are likely to be in close proximity to the cabin, which in turn contains both people and electronic equipment. The high potential at the ends of the radials is both a safety hazard and can result in RF coupling back into the equipment, including ham gear, navigational instruments and entertainment devices. The cook is not likely to be happy if he or she gets an RF burn after touching the galley stove! Decoupling the counterpoise from the transmission line, as discussed in the chapter **Effects of Ground**, can be very helpful to keep RF out of other equipment.

One way to avoid many of the problems associated with

grounding is to use a rigid dipole antenna as suggested in Figure 21.31. For short-range communication, a low dipole over saltwater can be effective. However, if long-range communication is needed, then a well-designed vertical, operating over seawater, will work much better. For these to work, of course, you must have the ground system associated with a vertical. It is not uncommon for large powerboats to have a two or three-element multiband Yagi installed on a short mast. While these can be effective, if they are not mounted high (> λ/2) they may be disappointing for longer-range communication. Over saltwater, vertical polarization is very effective for longer distances. A simpler, but well-designed, vertical system on a boat may outperform a low Yagi.

21.5 BIBLIOGRAPHY FOR HF MARITIME ANTENNAS

Source material and more extended discussions of topics covered in this chapter can be found in the references given below, in the references listed at the end of the mobile antennas material, and in the textbooks listed at the end of the **Antenna Fundamentals** chapter.

1. *EZNEC* by Roy Lewallen, W7EL, **www.eznec.com**, see also the free version of *EZNEC-ARRL* supplied on the CD-ROM included with this book
2. *4NEC2* by Ari Voors, **home.ict.nl/~arivoors**
3. *EZNEC-Pro/4*, Version 5.0 (see reference 1)
4. SteppIR Antennas, **www.steppir.com**
5. Joel Hallas, W1ZR, *The ARRL Guide to Antenna Tuners* (Newington: ARRL, 2010).

TABLE OF CONTENTS

Chapter 22

Receiving and Direction-Finding Antennas

22.1 RECEIVING ANTENNAS

The following introduction is excerpted from the section "Introduction to Receiving Antennas" written by Robye Lahlum, W1MK, in *ON4UN's Low-Band DXing*.

Separate antennas are necessary because optimum receiving and transmitting have different requirements. For a transmit antenna, we want maximum possible field strength in a given direction (or directions) at the most useful elevation (wave) angles. We cannot tolerate unnecessary power loss in a transmit antenna, because any amount of transmitting loss decreases signal-to-noise ratio at the distant receiver.

A receiving antenna on the other hand has a different design priority. The goal is obtaining a signal that can be read comfortably, which means having the greatest possible signal-to-noise (S/N) and signal-to-QRM ratio. Receiving antennas providing the best performance can and will be different under different circumstances, even at the same or similar locations. There is no such thing as a universal "best low-band receiving antenna."

Typical low band receiving antennas like the Beverage require more space that most hams have available. In recent years, computer modeling has enabled the development of small loops and arrays that provide meaningful improvements in receiving ability without requiring large areas or overly specialized construction techniques.

22.1.1 THE BEVERAGE ANTENNA

Perhaps the best known type of wave antenna is the *Beverage*. Many 160 meter enthusiasts have used Beverage antennas to enhance the signal-to-noise ratio while attempting to extract weak signals from the often high levels of atmospheric noise and interference on the low bands. Alternative antenna systems have been developed and used over the years, such as loops and long spans of unterminated wire on or slightly above the ground, but the Beverage antenna seems to be the best for 160 meter weak-signal reception. The information in this section was prepared originally by Rus Healy, K2UA.

A Beverage is simply a directional wire antenna, at least one wavelength long, supported along its length at a fairly low height and terminated at the far end in its characteristic impedance. This antenna is shown in **Figure 22.1A**. It takes its name from its inventor, Harold Beverage, W2BML.

Many amateurs choose to use a single-wire Beverage because they are easy to install and they work well. The drawback is that Beverages are physically long and they do require that you have the necessary amount of real estate to install them. Sometimes, a neighbor will allow you to put up a temporary Beverage for a particular contest or DXpedition on his land, particularly during the winter months.

Beverage antennas can be useful into the HF range, but they are most effective at lower frequencies, mainly on 160 through 40 meters. The antenna is responsive mostly to low-angle incoming waves that maintain a constant (vertical) polarization. These conditions are nearly always satisfied on 160 meters, and most of the time on 80 meters. As the frequency is increased, however, the polarization and arrival angles are less and less constant and favorable, making Beverages less effective at these frequencies. Many amateurs have, however, reported excellent performance from Beverage antennas at frequencies as high as 14 MHz, especially when rain or snow (precipitation) static prevents good reception on the Yagi or dipole transmitting antennas used on the higher frequencies.

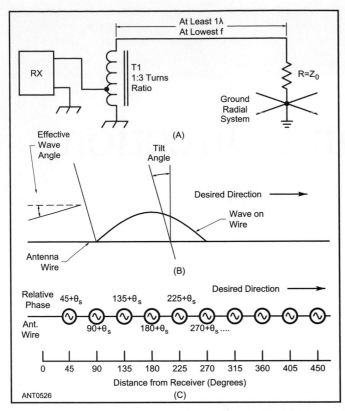

Figure 22.1 — At A, a simple one-wire Beverage antenna with a variable termination impedance and a matching 9:1 autotransformer for the receiver impedance. At B, a portion of a wave from the desired direction is shown traveling down the antenna wire. Its tilt angle and effective takeoff angle are also shown. At C, a situation analogous to the action of a Beverage on an incoming wave is shown. See text for discussion.

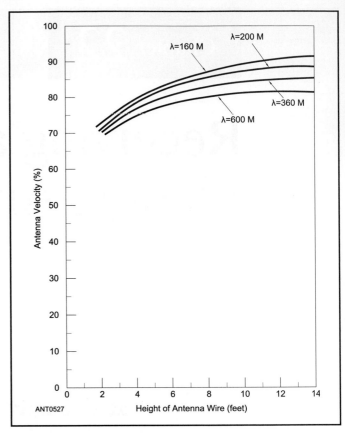

Figure 22.2 — Signal velocity on a Beverage increases with height above ground, and reaches a practical maximum at about 10 feet. Improvement is minimal above this height. (100% represents the velocity of light.)

Beverage Theory

The Beverage antenna acts like a long transmission line with one lossy conductor (the ground), and one good conductor (the wire). Beverages have excellent directivity if erected properly, but they are quite inefficient because they are mounted close to the ground. This is in contrast with the terminated long-wire antennas described earlier, which are typically mounted high off the ground. Beverage antennas are not suitable for use as transmitting antennas.

Because the Beverage is a traveling wave, terminated antenna, it has no standing waves resulting from radio signals. As a wave strikes the end of the Beverage from the desired direction, the wave induces voltages along the antenna and continues traveling in space as well. Figure 22.1B shows part of a wave on the antenna resulting from a desired signal. This diagram also shows the tilt of the wave. The signal induces equal voltages in both directions. The resulting currents are equal and travel in both directions. The component traveling toward the termination end moves against the wave and thus builds down to a very low level at the termination end. Any residual signal resulting from this direction of current flow will be absorbed in the termination (if the termination is equal to the antenna impedance). The component of the

signal flowing in the other direction, as we will see, becomes a key part of the received signal.

As the wave travels along the wire, the wave in space travels at approximately the same velocity. (There is some phase delay in the wire, as we shall see.) At any given point in time, the wave traveling along in space induces a voltage in the wire in addition to the wave already traveling on the wire (voltages already induced by the wave). Because these two waves are nearly in phase, the voltages add and build toward a maximum at the receiver end of the antenna.

This process can be likened to a series of signal generators lined up on the wire, with phase differences corresponding to their respective spacings on the wire (Figure 22.1C). At the receiver end, a maximum voltage is produced by these voltages adding in phase. For example, the wave component induced at the receiver end of the antenna will be in phase (at the receiver end) with a component of the same wave induced, say, 270° (or any other distance) down the antenna, after it travels to the receiver end.

In practice, there is some phase shift of the wave on the wire with respect to the wave in space. This phase shift results from the velocity factor of the antenna. (As with any transmission line, the signal velocity on the Beverage is somewhat less than in free space.) Velocity of propagation

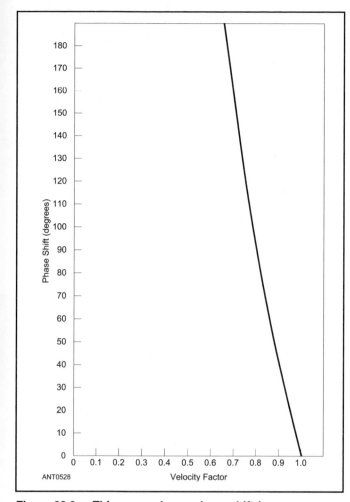

Figure 22.3 — This curve shows phase shift (per wavelength) as a function of velocity factor on a Beverage antenna. Once the phase shift for the antenna goes beyond 90°, the gain drops off from its peak value, and any increase in antenna length will decrease gain.

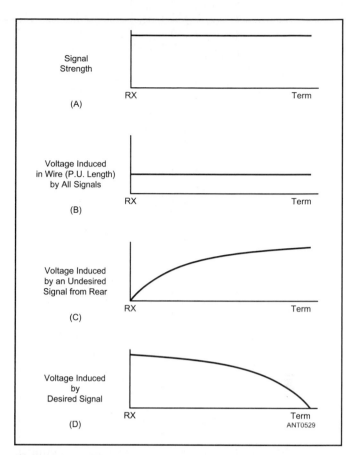

Figure 22.4 — These curves show the voltages that appear in a Beverage antenna over a period of several cycles of the wave. Signal strength (at A) is constant over the length of the antenna during this period, as is voltage induced per unit length in the wire (at B). (The voltage induced in any section of the antenna is the same as the voltage induced in any other section of the same size, over the same period of time.) At C, the voltages induced by an undesired signal from the rearward direction add in phase and build to a maximum at the termination end, where they are dissipated in the termination (if $Z_{term} = Z_0$). The voltages resulting from a desired signal are shown at D. The wave on the wire travels closely with the wave in space, and the voltages resulting add in phase to a maximum at the receiver end of the antenna.

on a Beverage is typically between 85 and 98% of that in free space. As antenna height is increased to a certain optimum height (which is about 10 feet for 160 meters), the velocity factor increases. Beyond this height, only minimal improvement is afforded, as shown in **Figure 22.2**. These curves are the result of experimental work done in 1922 by RCA, and reported in a *QST* article (November 1922) entitled "The Wave Antenna for 200-Meter Reception," by H. H. Beverage. The curve for 160 meters was extrapolated from the other curves.

Phase shift (per wavelength) is shown as a function of velocity factor in **Figure 22.3**, and is given by:

$$\theta = 360 \left(\frac{100}{k} - 1 \right) \qquad \text{(Eq 1)}$$

where k = velocity factor of the antenna in percent.

The signals present on and around a Beverage antenna are shown graphically in A through D of **Figure 22.4**. These curves show relative voltage levels over a number of periods of the wave in space and their relative effects in terms of the total signal at the receiver end of the antenna.

Performance in Other Directions

The performance of a Beverage antenna in directions other than the favored one is quite different than previously discussed. Take, for instance, the case of a signal arriving perpendicular to the wire (90° either side of the favored direction). In this case, the wave induces voltages along the wire that are essentially *in phase*, so that they arrive at the receiver end more or less out of phase, and thus cancel. (This can be likened to a series of signal generators lined up along the antenna as before, but having no progressive phase differences.)

As a result of this cancellation, Beverages exhibit deep nulls off the sides. Some minor sidelobes will exist, as with other long-wire antennas, and will increase in number with the length of the antenna.

In the case of a signal arriving from the rear of the

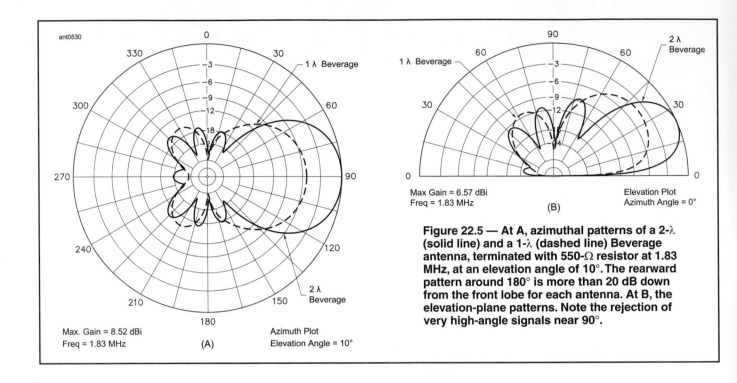

Figure 22.5 — At A, azimuthal patterns of a 2-λ (solid line) and a 1-λ (dashed line) Beverage antenna, terminated with 550-Ω resistor at 1.83 MHz, at an elevation angle of 10°. The rearward pattern around 180° is more than 20 dB down from the front lobe for each antenna. At B, the elevation-plane patterns. Note the rejection of very high-angle signals near 90°.

antenna, the behavior of the antenna is very similar to its performance in the favored direction. The major difference is that the signal from the rear adds in phase at the termination end and is absorbed by the termination impedance. **Figure 22.5** compares the azimuth and elevation patterns for a 2-λ (1062 foot) and a 1-λ (531 foot) Beverage at 1.83 MHz. The wire is mounted 8 feet above flat ground (to keep it above deer antlers and away from humans too) and is terminated with a 500-Ω resistor in each case, although the exact value of the terminating resistance is not very critical. The ground constants assumed in this computer model are conductivity of 5 mS/m and a dielectric constant of 13. Beverage dielectric performance tends to decrease as the ground becomes better. Beverages operated over saltwater do not work as well as they do over poor ground.

For most effective operation, the Beverage should be terminated in an impedance equal to the characteristic impedance Z_{ANT} of the antenna. For maximum signal transfer to the receiver you should also match the receiver's input impedance to the antenna. If the termination impedance is not equal to the characteristic impedance of the antenna, some part of the signal from the rear will be reflected back toward the receiver end of the antenna.

If the termination impedance is merely an open circuit (no terminating resistor), total reflection will result and the antenna will exhibit a bidirectional pattern (still with very deep nulls off the sides). An unterminated Beverage will not have the same response to signals in the rearward direction as it exhibits to signals in the forward direction because of attenuation and re-radiation of part of the reflected wave as it travels back toward the receiver end. **Figure 22.6** compares the response from two 2-λ Beverages, one terminated and the other unterminated. Just like a terminated long-wire

transmitting antenna (which is mounted higher off the ground than a Beverage, which is meant only for receiving), the terminated Beverage has a reduced forward lobe compared to its unterminated sibling. The unterminated Beverage exhibits about a 5 dB front-to-back ratio for this length because of the radiation and wire and ground losses that occur before the forward wave gets to the end of the wire.

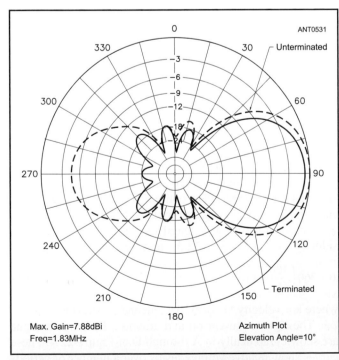

Figure 22.6 — Comparing the azimuthal patterns for a 2-λ Beverage, terminated (solid line) and unterminated (dashed line).

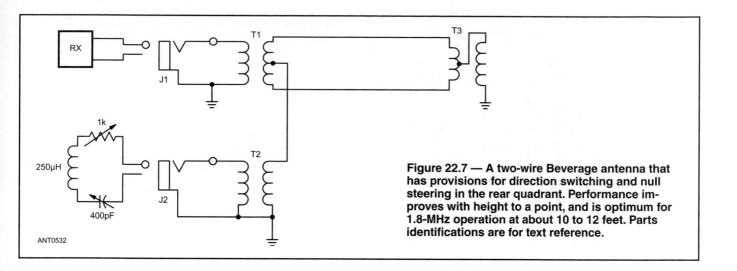

Figure 22.7 — A two-wire Beverage antenna that has provisions for direction switching and null steering in the rear quadrant. Performance improves with height to a point, and is optimum for 1.8-MHz operation at about 10 to 12 feet. Parts identifications are for text reference.

If the termination is between the extremes (open circuit and perfect termination in Z_{ANT}), the peak direction and intensity of signals off the rear of the Beverage will change. As a result, an adjustable reactive termination can be employed to *steer* the nulls to the rear of the antenna (see **Figure 22.7**). This can be of great help in eliminating a local interfering signal from a rearward direction (typically 30° to 40° either side of the back direction). Such a scheme doesn't help much for interfering skywave signals because of variations encountered in the ionosphere that constantly shift polarity, amplitude, phase and incoming elevation angles.

To determine the appropriate value for a terminating resistor, you need to know the characteristic impedance (surge impedance), Z_{ANT}, of the Beverage. It is interesting to note that Z_{ANT} is not a function of the length, just like a transmission line.

$$Z_{ANT} = 138 \times \log\left(\frac{4h}{d}\right) \qquad \text{(Eq 2)}$$

where
    Z_{ANT} = characteristic impedance of the Beverage =
        terminating resistance needed
    h = wire height above ground
    d = wire diameter (in the same units as h)

Another aspect of terminating the Beverage is the quality of the RF ground used for the termination. For most types of soil a ground rod is sufficient, since the optimum value for the termination resistance is in the range of 400 to 600 Ω for typical Beverages and the ground-loss resistance is in series with this. Even if the ground-loss resistance at the termination point is as high as 40 or 50 Ω, it still is not an appreciable fraction of the overall terminating resistance. For soil with very poor conductivity, however, (such as sand or rock) you can achieve a better ground termination by laying radial wires on the ground at both the receiver and termination ends. These wires need not be resonant quarter-wave in length, since the ground detunes them anyway. Like the ground counterpoise for a vertical antenna, a number of short radials is better than a few long ones. Some amateurs use chicken-wire ground

screens for their ground terminations.

As with many other antennas, improved directivity and gain can be achieved by lengthening the antenna and by arranging several antennas into an array. One item that must be kept in mind is that by virtue of the velocity factor of the antenna, there is some phase shift of the wave on the antenna with respect to the wave in space. Because of this phase shift, although the directivity will continue to sharpen with increased length, there will be some optimum length at which the gain of the antenna will peak. Beyond this length, the current increments arriving at the receiver end of the antenna will no longer be in phase, and will not add to produce a maximum signal at the receiver end. This optimum length is a function of velocity factor and frequency, and is given by:

$$L = \frac{\lambda}{4\left(\dfrac{100}{k} - 1\right)} \qquad \text{(Eq 3)}$$

where
    L = maximum effective length
    λ = signal wavelength in free space (same units as L)
    k = velocity factor of the antenna in percent

Because velocity factor increases with height (to a point, as mentioned earlier), optimum length is somewhat longer if the antenna height is increased. The maximum effective length also increases with the number of wires in the antenna system. For example, for a two-wire Beverage like the bidirectional version shown in Figure 22.7, the maximum effective length is about 20% longer than the single-wire version. A typical length for a single-wire 1.8-MHz Beverage (made of #16 AWG wire and erected 10 feet above ground) is about 1200 feet.

Feed Point Transformers for Single-Wire Beverages

Matching transformer T1 in Figure 22.1 is easily constructed. Small toroidal ferrite cores are best for this application, with those of high permeability (μ_i = 125 to 5000) being the easiest to wind (requiring fewest turns) and having the

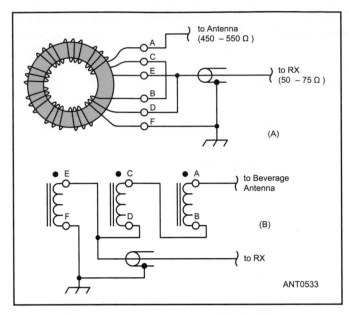

Figure 22.8 — Constructing the feed point transformer for a single-wire Beverage. See text for details.

best high-frequency response (because few turns are used). Trifilar-wound autotransformers are most convenient.

Most users are not concerned with a small amount of SWR on the transmission line feeding their Beverages. For example, let us assume that the Z_{ANT} of a particular Beverage is 525 Ω and the terminating resistance is made equal to that value. If a standard 3:1 turns-ratio autotransformer is used at the input end of the antenna, the nominal impedance transformation 50 Ω × 3^2 = 450 Ω. This leads to the terminology often used for this transformer as a *9:1 transformer*, referring to its impedance transformation. The resulting SWR on the feed line going back to the receiver would be 525/450 = 1.27:1, not enough to be concerned about. For a Z_{ANT} of 600 Ω, the SWR is 600/450 = 1.33:1, again not a matter of concern.

Hence, most Beverage users use standard 9:1 (450:50 Ω) autotransformers. You can make a matching transformer suitable for use from 160 to 40 meters using eight trifilar turns of #24 AWG enameled wire wound over a stack of two Amidon FT-50-75 or two MN8-CX cores. See **Figure 22.8**.

Make your own trifilar cable bundle by placing three 3-foot lengths of the #24 AWG wire side-by-side and twisting them in a hand drill so that there is a uniform twist about one twist-per-inch. This holds the three wires together in a bundle that can be passed through the two stacked cores, rather like threading a needle. Remember that each time you put the bundle through the center of the cores counts as one turn.

After you finish winding, cut the individual wires to leave about ¾-inch leads, sand off the enamel insulation and tin the wires with a soldering iron. Identify the individual wires with an ohmmeter and then connect them together following Figure 22.8. Coat the transformer with Q-dope (liquid polystyrene) to finalize the transformer. White glue will work also. See the chapter **Transmission Line Coupling**

and Impedance Matching for more information. *The ARRL Handbook* and the chapter **Receiving Antennas** of *ON4UN's Low-Band DXing* book are also good sources of more information on winding toroidal transformers

Practical Considerations

Even though Beverage antennas have excellent directive patterns if terminated properly, gain never exceeds about –3 dBi in most practical installations. However, the directivity that the Beverage provides results in a much higher signal-to-noise ratio for signals in the desired direction than almost any other real-world antenna used at low frequencies.

A typical situation might be a station located in the US Northeast (W1), trying to receive Top Band signals from Europe to the northeast, while thunderstorms behind him in the US Southeast (W4) are creating huge static crashes. Instead of listening to an S7 signal with 10-dB over S9 noise and interference on a vertical, the directivity of a Beverage will typically allow you to copy the same signal at perhaps S5 with only S3 (or lower) noise and interference. This is certainly a worthwhile improvement. However, if you are in the middle of a thunderstorm, or if there is a thunderstorm in the direction from which you are trying to receive a signal, no Beverage is going to help you!

There are a few basic principles that must be kept in mind when erecting Beverage antennas if optimum performance is to be realized.

1) Plan the installation thoroughly, including choosing an antenna length consistent with the optimum length values discussed earlier.

2) Keep the antenna as straight and as nearly level as possible over its entire run. Avoid following the terrain under the antenna too closely — keep the antenna level with the average terrain.

3) Minimize the lengths of vertical downleads at the ends of the antenna. Their effect is detrimental to the directive pattern of the antenna. It is best to slope the antenna wire from ground level to its final height (over a distance of 50 feet or so) at the feed point end. Similar action should be taken at the termination end. Be sure to seal the transformers against weather.

4) Use a noninductive resistor for terminating a single-wire Beverage. If you live in an area where lightning storms are common, use 2-W terminating resistors, which can survive surges due to nearby lightning strikes.

5) Use high-quality insulators for the Beverage wire where it comes into contact with the supports. Plastic insulators designed for electric fences are inexpensive and effective.

6) Keep the Beverage away from parallel conductors such as electric power and telephone lines for a distance of at least 200 feet. Perpendicular conductors, even other Beverages, may be crossed with relatively little interaction, but do not cross any conductors that may pose a safety hazard.

7) Run the coaxial feed line to the Beverage so that it is not directly under the span of the wire. This prevents common-mode currents from appearing on the shield of the coax. It may be necessary to use a ferrite-bead choke on the

feed line if you find that the feed line itself picks up signals when it is temporarily disconnected from the Beverage.

8) If you use elevated radials in your transmitting antenna system, keep your Beverage feed lines well away from them to avoid stray pickup that will ruin the Beverage's directivity.

The Two-Wire Beverage

The two-wire antenna shown in Figure 22.7 has the major advantage of having signals from both directions available at the receiver at the flip of a switch between J1 and J2. Also, because there are two wires in the system (equal amounts of signal voltage are induced in both wires), greater signal voltages will be produced. (The April 2006 *QST* article "A Cool Beverage Four Pack" by Ward Silver, NØAX, describes a four-directional array created from a pair of two-wire Beverages at right angles.)

A signal from the left direction in Figure 22.7 induces equal voltages in both wires, and equal in-phase currents flow as a result. The *reflection transformer* (T3 at the right-hand end of the antenna) then inverts the phase of these signals and reflects them back down the antenna toward the receiver, using the antenna wires as a balanced open-wire transmission line. This signal is then transformed by T1 down to the input impedance of the receiver (50 Ω) at J1.

Signals traveling from right to left also induce equal voltages in each wire, and they travel in phase toward the receiver end, through T1, and into T2. Signals from this direction are available at J2.

T1 and T2 are standard 9:1 wideband transformers capable of operating from 1.8 to at least 10 MHz. Like any two parallel wires making up a transmission line, the two-wire Beverage has a certain characteristic impedance — we'll call it Z_1 here — depending on the spacing between the two wires and the insulation between them. T3 transforms the terminating resistance needed at the end of the line to Z_1. Keep in mind that this terminating resistance is equal to the characteristic impedance Z_{ANT} of the Beverage — that is, the impedance of the parallel wires over their images in the ground below. For example, if Z_1 of the Beverage wire is 300 Ω (that is, you used TV twin-lead for the two Beverage wires), T3 must transform the balanced 300 Ω to the unbalanced 500 Ω Z_{ANT} impedance used to terminate the Beverage.

The design and construction of the reflection transformer used in a two-wire Beverage is more demanding than that for the straightforward matching transformer T1 because the exact value of terminating impedance is more critical for good F/B. See the **Receiving Antennas** chapter in *ON4UN's Low-Band DXing* for details on winding the reflection transformers for a two-wire Beverage.

Another convenient feature of the two-wire Beverage is the ability to steer the nulls off either end of the antenna while receiving in the opposite direction. For instance, if the series RLC network shown at J2 is adjusted while the receiver is connected to J1, signals can be received from the left direction while interference coming from the right can be partially or completely nulled. The nulls can be steered over a 60° (or more) area off the right-hand end of the antenna. The same

null-steering capability exists in the opposite direction with the receiver connected at J2 and the termination connected at J1.

The two-wire Beverage is typically erected at the same height as a single-wire version. The two wires are at the same height and are spaced uniformly — typically 12 to 18 inches apart for discrete wires. Some amateurs construct two-wire Beverages using "window" ladder-line, twisting the line about three twists per foot for mechanical and electrical stability in the wind.

The characteristic impedance Z_{ANT} of a Beverage made using two discrete wires with air insulation between them depends on the wire size, spacing and height and is given by:

$$Z_{ANT} = \frac{69}{\sqrt{\varepsilon}} \times \log\left[\frac{4h}{d}\sqrt{1 + \left(\frac{2h}{S}\right)^2}\right] \qquad \text{(Eq 4)}$$

where

Z_{ANT} = Beverage impedance = desired terminating resistance
S = wire spacing
h = height above ground
d = wire diameter (in same units as S and h)
ε = 2.71828

Beverages in Echelon

The pattern of a Beverage receiving antenna is dependent on the terminating resistance used for a particular antenna, as was demonstrated at the extremes by Figure 22.6. This compared the patterns for a terminated and an unterminated Beverage. The pattern of even a poorly terminated Beverage can be significantly improved by the addition of a second Beverage. The additional Beverage is installed so that it is operated *in echelon*, a word deriving from the fact that the two wires look like the parallel rungs on a ladder. For a practical 160 and 80 meter setup the second Beverage wire is parallel to the first Beverage, spaced from it by about 5 meters, and also staggered 30 meters ahead. See **Figure 22.9**.

The forward Beverage is fed with a phase difference of +125° such that the total phase, including that due to the forward staggering, is 180°. This forms the equivalent of an end-fire array fed out-of-phase, but it takes advantage of the natural directivity of each Beverage. **Figure 22.10** compares the pattern of a single 1-λ 160 meter Beverage that is sloppily terminated with two Beverages fed in echelon. The Beverages in echelon gives a modest additional gain of almost 2 dB. But where the two Beverages in echelon really shine is how they clean up the rearward pattern — from an average about 15 dB for the single Beverage to more than 25 dB for the two Beverages.

Even at a spacing of 5 meters, there is very little mutual coupling between the two Beverage wires because of their inherently small radiation resistance when they are mounted low above lossy ground. If you adjust for a low SWR (using proper transformers to match the feed line coaxes), the phase difference will depend solely on the difference in length of the

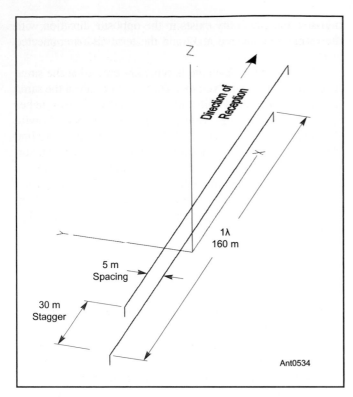

Figure 22.9 — Layout of two 160 meter 1-λ long Beverages in echelon, spaced 5 meters apart, with 30 meter forward stagger. The upper antenna has a 125° phase shift in its feed system.

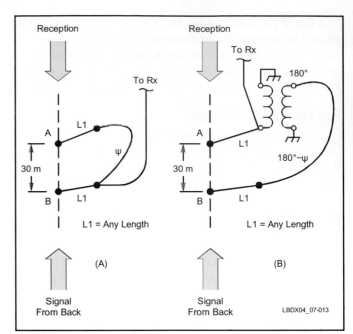

Figure 22.11 — Two ways of feeding the two-Beverage echelon array in Figure 22.9. On the left, a feed system good for one frequency; on the right, a "cross-fire" feed system good for 1.8 and 3.6 MHz. For this system we want a phase shift due to the coax length of +116° at the back Beverage A. The angle φ is thus 180° − 116° = 64° long on 160 meters. In the system on the right, a 64° length on 160 meters becomes 128° long on 80 meters. So with the phase-inverting transformer the net phase shift becomes 53° on 80 meters, a reasonable compromise. (*Courtesy W8JI and ON4UN*)

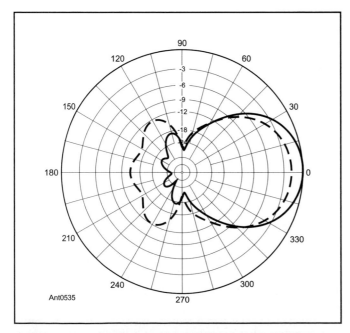

Figure 22.10 — Azimuth pattern at 10° takeoff angle for single Beverage (dashed line) and two Beverages in an echelon end-fire array. The rearward pattern is considerably cleaner on the echelon. Thus, two closely spaced, short Beverages can give considerable improvement over a single short Beverage.

two coaxes feeding the Beverage wires. **Figure 22.11** shows a wideband feed system designed by Tom Rauch, W8JI, as a "cross-fire" feed system. The 180° wideband phase-inverting transformer allows the system to work on two bands, say 160 and 80 meters. See the **Receiving Antennas** chapter in *ON4UN's Low-Band DXing* book for transformer details.

22.1.2 K6STI LOOP

The K6STI Loop (see Bibliography and this book's CD-ROM) in **Figure 22.12** is a horizontal loop that combines rejection of vertically polarized ground wave signals with a null in the vertical radiation pattern to reject high-angle local and regional noise. The sky wave response to lower-angle signals is approximately omnidirectional.

The 80 meter version of the antenna measures 25 feet on a side, is mounted horizontally 10 feet above ground, and made of #14 AWG wire. It's fed at opposite corners with phasing lines made of #14 AWG wire spaced 1.5 inches apart. A small ferrite transformer at the junction of the phasing lines matches the antenna to 50-Ω coax feed line and also functions as a balun. The trimmer capacitor (about 40 pF required) in series with the antenna-side winding resonates the loop at 3.5 MHz.

The loop can be constructed as small as 10 feet on a side and still provide noise-rejecting benefits. The loop must be resonated with a variable capacitor and requires a

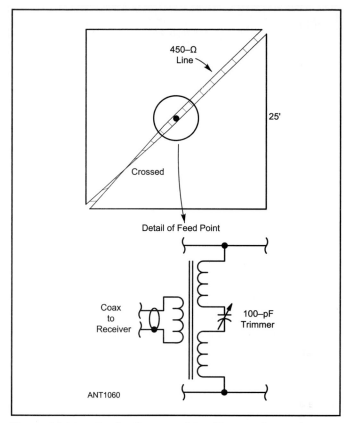

Figure 22.12 — Basic diagram of the 80 meter low-noise loop antenna showing detail of the feed point arrangement.

preamplifier in most cases. (See the section on ferrite-loop antennas later in this chapter for a suitable design.) The design can be scaled to higher and lower bands by multiplying lengths, transformer turns, and capacitance values by $3.5 / f_{MHz}$.

22.1.3 EWE ANTENNA

The EWE antenna invented by Floyd Koontz, WA2WVL, combines two short vertical wires and one horizontal wire as shown in **Figure 22.13**. (See the Bibliography.) Although the EWE looks similar to a Beverage antenna as described previously, the EWE is essentially a two-element driven array. The antenna receives best in the plane of the array in the direction opposite the termination. The pattern is a broad cardioid with

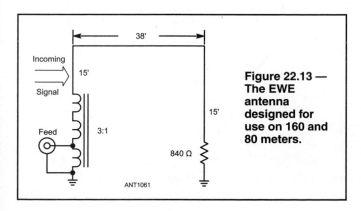

Figure 22.13 — The EWE antenna designed for use on 160 and 80 meters.

a null in the direction of the terminated "rear" element. The horizontal gain of the antenna is about 20 dB lower than the vertical gain and is directed at a high angle off the side.

The version in Figure 22.13 is designed to operate from 1.8 to 4.0 MHz with a front-to-back ratio of greater than 25 dB without adjustment. The EWE can be bottom fed as shown in the figure or at the top of the front vertical element. If separate feed lines and transformers are used for each of the vertical elements, the termination can be switched between elements, creating a reversible pattern. Arrays can also be created as described in the referenced articles, creating a steerable pattern.

22.1.4 K9AY LOOP

Described here by its inventor, Gary Breed, K9AY, the loop achieves modest, but useful directivity in a small area, making it a popular choice for hams wanting to improve their receiving ability. (See the Bibliography.) The loop is a hybrid that combines two antenna types. Referring to **Figure 22.14**, if the termination resistor is zero — a short circuit — the antenna becomes a classic "small loop" (usually defined as less than 0.1λ diameter). The near-field response of small loops is predominantly to the magnetic field (H-field) component of an electromagnetic wave. Next, with an infinite resistor — an open circuit — the antenna becomes a short, bent monopole. Short monopole antennas respond most strongly to the electric field (E-field) component of an electromagnetic wave.

In the K9AY Loop, the terminating resistor serves to balance the ratio of the small loop and monopole responses, with energy from the two modes summed at the feed point. When the value of the resistor is adjusted to the optimum

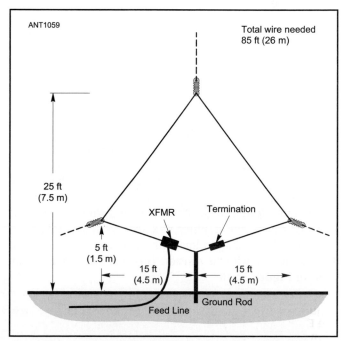

Figure 22.14 — Configuration of the K9AY Loop at the maximum size that allows coverage of both 160 and 80 meter ham bands with a resistive termination.

value (typically near 400 Ω), there is cancellation of arriving signals in one of the directions in line with the plane of the loop. This cancellation occurs because of the rotational "sense" of the H-field. While the E-field is one-dimensional (amplitude only), the H-field obeys the "right hand rule" that can be visualized as spiral rotation as a wave travels through space. Waves arriving from opposite directions will thus have opposite rotation. From one direction, the E- and H-field contributions are summed at the feed point. But for signals from the opposite direction, the antenna output is the difference of these contributions.

This same type of behavior is present in two other devices familiar to hams; a directional coupler such as those used in the familiar Bird wattmeter, and the direction-finding (DF) loop with sense antenna described in many (mostly older) antenna reference books.

The tradeoff for obtaining a directional pattern with small size is low efficiency. With the dimensions given above, the K9AY Loop has a gain of approximately –26 dBi. For comparison, a ¼-wave vertical has a gain near 0 dBi, and a typical one-wavelength Beverage antenna has a gain about –11 dBi. The loop should be used with a good high dynamic range preamplifier for best results. It is not suitable for transmitting, since most of the RF energy will be absorbed by the resistor.

Computer Modeling

One of the challenges of designing the K9AY Loop was developing an accurate computer model, since *NEC*-based modeling programs will give inconsistent results for an antenna connected directly to lossy ground. K9AY's approach was to first create a free-space model of the loop, doubled in size with its mirror-image — just like making a ¼-wave vertical into a ½-wave dipole. This model is repeatable and shows the actual gain and pattern shape, including the location of the rearward null.

K9AY then returned to the as-built dimensions, installed over ground. The final model uses the *MININEC* ground option, which assumes perfect ground when calculating impedance. Ground losses are simulated by placing a resistor in the ground connection. A little trial-and-error determined that a resistor of approximately 150 Ω results in a pattern that matched the free-space model (and on-air behavior, as best as it can be determined). **Figure 22.15** is a diagram showing the modeling dimensions and parameters. This model has proven accurate for modeling loops of different sizes and shapes, and for arrays of loops.

For the chosen shape of the loop, and with the influence of lossy ground, the resulting null appears at an angle about 45° above horizontal, in line with the plane of the loop and toward the side with the resistor. This is shown in the pattern plots of **Figure 22.16**.

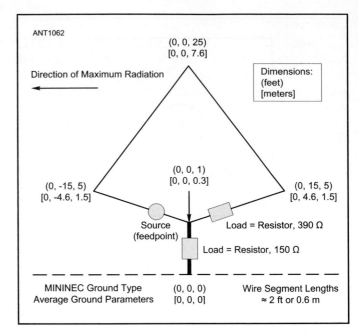

Figure 22.15 — Diagram of the K9AY Loop with dimensions and parameters for computer modeling.

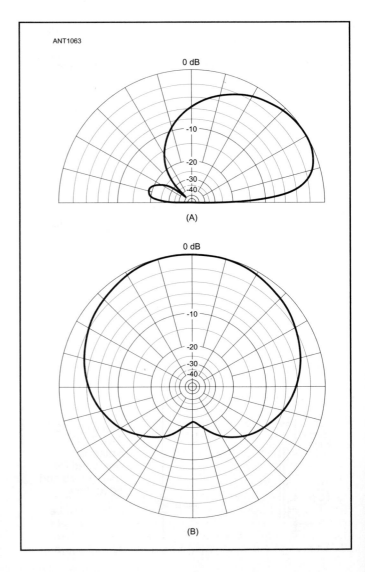

Figure 22.16 — Vertical (A) and horizontal (B) radiation patterns for the K9AY Loop at 1.825 MHz.

Construction

Construction of the K9AY Loop is shown in Figure 22.14. Approximately 85 feet of wire is arranged into a four-sided shape that is almost triangular. This shape was chosen primarily for its mechanical arrangement — it has a single center support approximately 25 feet high, and it can share that support with a second loop installed at right angles (see **Figure 22.17**).

Connections are made at the bottom. One end of the loop wire goes to the high impedance side of a 9:1 matching transformer; the other end to a resistor with an optimum value that is typically about 400 Ω. Because the connections to each end are at a central point, it is a simple matter to include a relay at this point to reverse the connections, which reverses the directional pattern of the loop. As noted above, a second loop can be installed. Since its connections are also located in the same place, a switching system with four directions is easily implemented. The ability to switch the pattern to several directions is the primary advantage of the K9AY Loop over other small receiving antenna designs. A schematic diagram of four-direction relay switching is shown in **Figure 22.18**.

Installation and Operating Notes

Location — Because the K9AY Loop will often be installed where there is limited space, there may be interaction with nearby objects. Other antennas, house wiring, metal siding and gutters, overhead utilities, metal fences and other conductors can distort the pattern and reduce the depth of the null. The key test for proper operation is good front-to-back ratio. If F/B is poor, you will need to identify the problem. It is usually easiest to change the loop location compared to changing the surroundings!

Transmitting Antennas — Proximity to transmitting antennas may result in high RF levels on the loop, sent into the shack on the feed line. Your receiver should be protected! Protective devices are available from ham radio dealers, or you can make a simple relay box that disconnects the feed

line when transmitting. It's best to open both the center conductor and shield connections.

Ground Connection — Experience has shown that locations with almost any type of "real dirt" soil only require a single ground rod for proper operation. However, some installations may experience seasonal changes in soil moisture. Desert and salt water installations will change the behavior, too. It sometimes helps to install additional ground radials to maintain consistent performance. Four or eight short radials are sufficient. Make them the same length, and place the first four directly under the loop wires. Note that the optimum

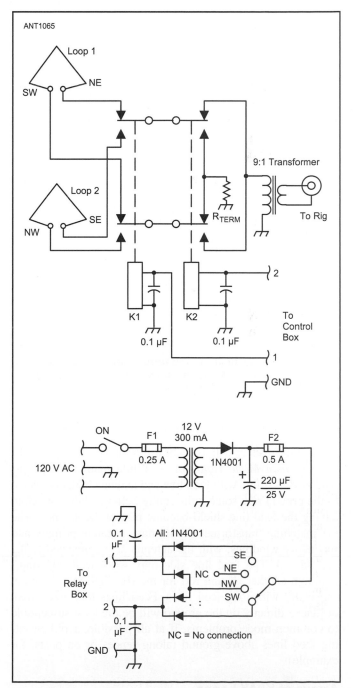

Figure 22.18 — Outdoor antenna switching (top) and indoor control (bottom) circuits for a four-direction, two-loop system.

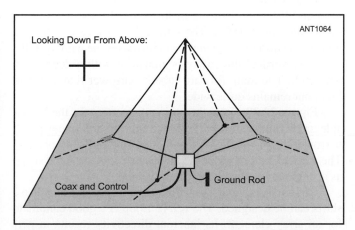

Figure 22.17 — Two loops can be installed with the same central support, creating a two-loop system that can be switched to cover four different directions. In a typical installation for 160 and 80 meter operation, the loops are 25 feet high and ±15 feet from the center (30 feet across).

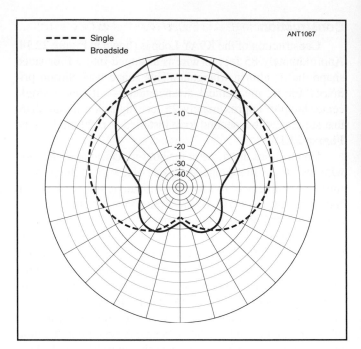

Figure 22.20 — Horizontal pattern for two K9AY Loops, spaced ½ λ, fed as a broadside array with 0° phasing. Frequency is 1.825 MHz.

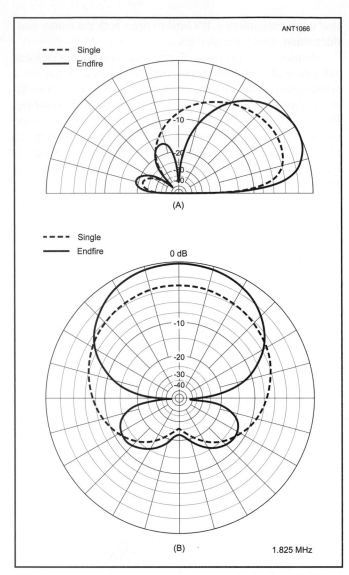

Figure 22.19 — Vertical (A) and horizontal (B) radiation patterns for two K9AY Loops, spaced ½ λ, fed in end-fire mode with 180° phasing. Frequency is 1.825 MHz

value of the resistor will likely be different when using radials.

Common Mode Isolation — While many installations will work just fine with feed line and antenna both connected to the ground rod, some will require better isolation to avoid having the feed line shield become part of the antenna. The 9:1 matching transformer should have separate primary and secondary windings, with the antenna side connected to the ground rod. The feed line side may work well "floating," although another ground rod for the feed line may be wise, especially with long feed lines. Feed lines that are buried, or placed directly on the ground will be the least susceptible to common mode problems. If at all possible, avoid elevating feed lines above ground (along fences or on posts, for example).

Arrays of K9AY Loops

Although the K9AY Loop has useful directivity, its

pattern is modest compared to a one-wavelength or longer Beverage. One way to improve performance, while keeping most of the antenna's limited-space appeal, is to combine two or more of them in an array. One of the simplest arrays is to install two crossed-loop sets with a spacing of ½-wavelength (140 feet on 80 meters, 270 feet on 160 meters). For simplicity, a phase shift of 0° for broadside operation and 180° for end-fire operation can be used to avoid the need for additional phase shift circuitry — phasing can be accomplished by simply reversing the windings of one matching transformer when the array is in the end-fire mode.

Figure 22.19 compares the radiation patterns of a single loop and the two-elements in line with the loops (end-fire mode, phasing = 180°). The array adds two very deep side nulls to the horizontal pattern, and increases the gain by 3 dB. Also, the vertical directivity is enhanced with a deep overhead null. The main forward lobe is narrower than a single loop, but remains quite wide.

Figure 22.20 shows the horizontal pattern for the broadside mode (phase shift = 0°). The main forward lobe is much narrower than a single loop, and good side nulls are present. The vertical pattern is not shown because it is the same shape as a single loop, plus the 3 dB array gain.

Of course, other arrays with different spacings and phase shifts can be designed. The K9AY Loop is a good candidate for an array element. Its inherent directivity results in performance that is better than the same array using omnidirectional elements such as verticals. The loops also have a low VSWR on the feed line, which simplifies the design of a phasing network.

22.1.5 FLAG AND PENNANT ANTENNAS

Jose Mata, EA3VY, and Earl Cunningham, K6SE (SK), developed the pennant and flag receiving antennas in **Figure 22.21** which have become popular for the low band DXer. The antennas were developed to eliminate the need for a good ground for predictable low noise directional reception. Their small size makes them practical for those DXers without the room to construct a Beverage or Four Square. Configured as either a rectangle, triangle or diamond in the vertical plane, the 160 and 80 meter version is about 29 feet long and 14 feet high and mounted about 6 feet above the ground. The reader is referred to the Bibliography for more information along with the original article on this book's CD-ROM.

Pennant and flag antennas have a feed point impedance in the range of 945 Ω (the termination opposite the feed point is also 945 Ω). The flag version shows about 5.5 dB higher "gain" than the pennant version. Their directivity is toward the feed point direction and appears cardioidal. The front-to-back ratio is in excess of 35 dB. A simple 16 to 1 toroidal or balun transformer can be used to couple to low impedance coax lines.

Mark Connelly, WA1ION, (**www.qsl.net/wa1ion**) has come up with a modification to allow a flag antenna to be electrically reversed in direction and also to allow remote optimization of the termination. In his version 16:1 transformers are put at both the termination and feed point locations and a coax cable is brought from the low impedance winding of both of these into the shack. The user can then attach one of these to the receiver and the other to a noninductive potentiometer and adjust the potentiometer so that it is in the range of 55 to 70 Ω to see an impedance at the antenna in the 880 to 1120 Ω range (when the transformer ratio is taken into effect). This allows an in-shack switching box to be constructed to allow these receiver and termination connections to be reversed to allow the null to be moved in the opposite direction.

22.1.6 A RECEIVING LOOP FOR 1.8 MHz

You can use a small balanced loop antenna to improve reception under certain conditions, especially at the lower amateur frequencies. (The theory of this antenna is presented in the chapter **Loop Antennas**.) This is particularly true when high levels of man-made noise are prevalent, when the second-harmonic energy from a nearby broadcast station falls in the 160 meter band, or when interference exists from some other amateur station in the immediate area. A properly constructed and tuned small loop will exhibit approximately 30 dB of front-to-side response, the minimum response being at right angles to the plane of the loop. Therefore, noise and interference can be reduced significantly or completely nulled out, by rotating the loop so that it is sideways to the interference-causing source.

Generally speaking, small balanced loops are far less

Figure 22.22 — The 160 meter shielded loop uses bamboo cross arms to support the antenna.

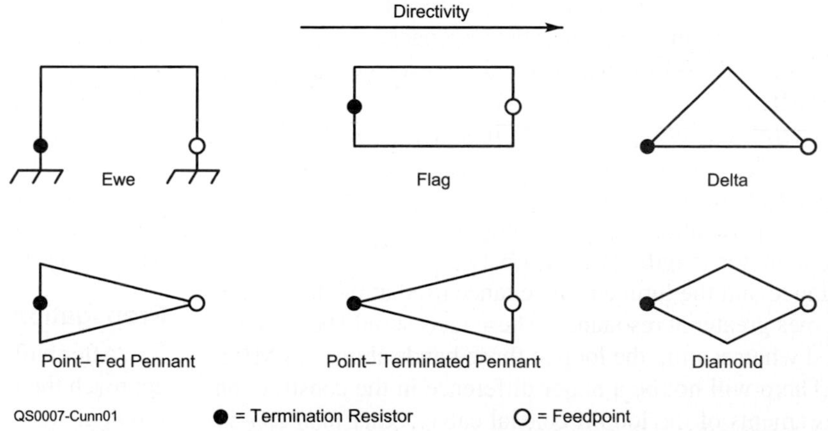

Figure 22.21 — Configurations of the flag and pennant antennas. The dimensions of the Flag, both Pennants, and the Diamond (a modification of the Flag) are 29 feet by 14 feet. The Delta (a type of half-Diamond) is 17 feet high and 28 feet long. The ground-independent antennas are 6 feet above ground.

Directivity

Ewe

Flag

Delta

Point– Fed Pennant

Point– Terminated Pennant

Diamond

QS0007-Cunn01   ● = Termination Resistor   ○ = Feedpoint

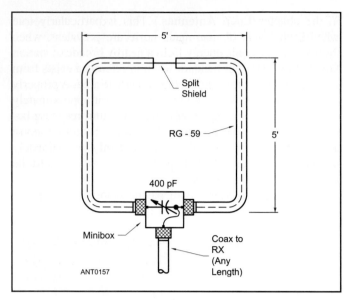

Figure 22.23 — Schematic diagram of the loop antenna. The dimensions are not critical provided overall length of the loop element does not exceed approximately 0.1 λ. Small loops which are one half or less the size of this one will prove useful where limited space is a consideration.

responsive to man-made noise than are the larger antennas used for transmitting and receiving. But a trade-off in performance must be accepted when using the loop, for the strength of received signals will be 10 or 15 dB less than when using a full-size resonant antenna. This condition is not a handicap on 1.8 or 3.5 MHz, provided the station receiver has normal sensitivity and overall gain. Because a front-to-side ratio of 30 dB may be expected, a small loop can be used to eliminate a variety of receiving problems if made rotatable, as shown in **Figure 22.22**.

To obtain the sharp bidirectional pattern of a small loop, the overall length of the conductor must not exceed 0.1 λ. The loop of **Figure 22.23** has a conductor length of 20 feet. At 1.81 MHz, 20 feet is 0.037 λ. With this style of loop, 0.037 λ is about the maximum practical dimension if you want to tune the element to resonance. This limitation results from the distributed capacitance between the shield and inner conductor of the loop. RG-59 was used for the loop element in this example. The capacitance per foot for this cable is 21 pF, resulting in a total distributed capacitance of 420 pF. An additional 100 pF was needed to resonate the loop at 1.810 MHz.

Therefore, the approximate inductance of the loop is 15 μH. The effect of the capacitance becomes less pronounced at the higher end of the HF spectrum, provided the same percentage of a wavelength is used in computing the conductor length. The ratio between the distributed capacitance and the lumped capacitance used at the feed point becomes greater at resonance. These facts should be contemplated when scaling the loop to those bands above 1.8 MHz.

There will not be a major difference in the construction requirements of the loop if coaxial cables other than RG-59

are used. The line impedance is not significant with respect to the loop element. Various types of coaxial line exhibit different amounts of capacitance per foot, however, thereby requiring more or less capacitance across the feed point to establish resonance.

Balanced loops are not affected noticeably by nearby objects, and therefore they can be installed indoors or out after being tuned to resonance. Moving them from one place to another does not significantly affect the tuning.

In the version shown in Figure 22.22, a supporting structure was fashioned from bamboo poles. The X frame is held together at the center with two U bolts. The loop element is taped to the cross-arms to form a square. You could likely use metal cross arms without seriously degrading the antenna performance. Alternatively, wood can be used for the supporting frame.

A Minibox was used at the feed point of the loop to hold the resonating variable capacitor. In this model a 50 to 400-pF compression trimmer was used to establish resonance. You must weatherproof the box for outdoor installations.

Remove the shield braid of the loop coax for one inch directly opposite the feed point. You should treat the exposed areas with a sealing compound once this is done.

In operation this receiving loop has proven very effective for nulling out second-harmonic energy from local broadcast stations. During DX and contest operations on 160 meters it helped prevent receiver overloading from strong nearby stations. The marked reduction in response to noise has made the loop a valuable station accessory when receiving weak signals. It is not used all of the time, but is available when needed by connecting it to the receiver through an antenna selector switch. Reception of European stations with the loop has been possible from New England at times when other antennas were totally ineffective because of noise.

It was also discovered that the effects of approaching storms (with attendant atmospheric noise) could be nullified considerably by rotating the loop away from the storm front. It should be said that the loop does not exhibit meaningful directivity when receiving sky-wave signals. The directivity characteristics relate primarily to ground-wave signals. This is a bonus feature in disguise, for when nulling out local noise or interference, one is still able to copy sky-wave signals from all compass points!

For receiving applications it is not necessary to match the feed line to the loop, though doing so may enhance the performance somewhat. If no attempt is made to obtain an SWR of 1, the builder can use 50- or 75-Ω coax for a feeder, and no difference in performance will be observed. The Q of this loop is sufficiently low to allow the operator to peak it for resonance at 1.9 MHz and use it across the entire 160 meter band. The degradation in performance at 1.8 and 2 MHz will be so slight that it will be difficult to discern.

Propagation Effects on Null Depth

After building a balanced loop you may find it does not approach the theoretical performance in the null depth. This problem may result from propagation effects. Tilting the loop away from a vertical plane may improve performance under some propagation conditions, to account for the vertical angle of arrival. Basically, the loop performs as described above only when the signal is arriving perpendicular to the axis of rotation of the loop. At incidence angles other than perpendicular, the position and depth of the nulls deteriorate. Bond explained this issue in his book on direction finding in 1944 along with the math to calculate the performance.

The problem can be even further influenced by the fact that if the loop is situated over less than perfectly conductive ground, the wave front will appear to tilt or bend. (This bending is not always detrimental; in the case of Beverage antennas, sites are chosen to take advantage of this effect.)

Another cause of apparent poor performance in the null depth can be from polarization error. If the polarization of the signal is not completely linear, the nulls will not be sharp. In fact, for circularly polarized signals, the loop might appear to have almost no nulls. Propagation effects are discussed further in the sections on direction finding.

Siting Effects on the Loop

The location of the loop has an influence on its performance that at times may become quite noticeable. For ideal performance the loop should be located outdoors and clear of any large conductors, such as metallic downspouts and towers. A VLF loop, when mounted this way, will show good sharp nulls spaced 180° apart if the loop is well balanced. This is because the major propagation mode at VLF is by ground wave. At frequencies in the HF region, a significant portion of the signal is propagated by sky wave, and nulls are often only partial.

Most hams locate their loop antennas near their operating position. If you choose to locate a small loop indoors, its performance may show nulls of less than the expected depth, and some skewing of the pattern. For precision direction finding there may be some errors associated with wiring, plumbing, and other metallic construction members in the building. Also, a strong local signal may be reradiated from the surrounding conductors so that it cannot be nulled with any positioning of the loop. There appears to be no known method of curing this type of problem. All this should not discourage you from locating a loop indoors; this information is presented here only to give you an idea of some pitfalls. Many hams have reported excellent results with indoor mounted loops, in spite of some of the problems.

Locating a receiving loop in the field of a transmitting antenna may cause a large voltage to appear at the receiver antenna terminals. This may be sufficient to destroy sensitive RF amplifier transistors or front-end protection diodes. This can be solved by disconnecting your loop from the receiver during transmit periods. This can obviously be done automatically with a relay that opens when the transmitter is activated.

22.1.7 ACTIVE ANTENNAS

The following material is based on the Sep 2001 *QST* article, "The AMRAD Active LF Antenna," by Frank Gentges, KØBRA. (This article is also included on this book's CD-ROM.) An active antenna is an electrically and physically small antenna combined with an active electronic circuit, such as an amplifier. An active antenna uses a small whip — one that is a fraction of a wavelength long at the desired frequency — connected to an active impedance-conversion circuit. Active antennas are used at HF and lower frequencies through VLF. A commercially available model, the DX Engineering DXE-ARAV3-1P (**www.dxengineering.com**), can be used from 100 kHz through 30 MHz and can be combined with other units into highly directional arrays.

An electrically short whip has a high output impedance. For example, a 1 meter whip at 100 kHz has an input impedance higher than 100 kΩ, mostly capacitive reactance. If such a whip were connected directly to a 50-Ω load, signals would be attenuated more than 80 dB than those from a 50-Ω antenna! Thus, some kind of active impedance-conversion is required, usually a high-input-impedance FET-based amplifier. The major challenges to the circuit are non-linearity and the resulting intermodulation distortion products (IMD). This is a particularly difficult issue close to transmitting antennas. A detailed treatment of the active circuit's performance was presented by Dr Ulrich Rhode, N1UL, in *RF Design*. (See the Bibliography.)

22.1.8 RECEIVING ANTENNAS BIBLIOGRAPHY

Source material and more extended discussion of topics covered in this chapter can be found in the references given below and in the textbooks listed at the end of the **Antenna Fundamentals** chapter.

Beverage Antennas

A. Bailey, S. W. Dean and W. T. Wintringham, "The Receiving System for Long-Wave Transatlantic Radio Telephony," *The Bell System Technical Journal*, Apr 1929.

J. S. Belrose, "Beverage Antennas for Amateur Communications," Technical Correspondence, *QST*, Sep 1981, p 51.

H. H. Beverage, "Antennas," *RCA Review*, Jul 1939.

H. H. Beverage and D. DeMaw, "The Classic Beverage Antenna Revisited," *QST*, Jan 1982, pp 11-17.

B. Boothe, "Weak-Signal Reception on 160 — Some Antenna Notes," *QST*, Jun 1977, pp 35-39.

M. F. DeMaw, *Ferromagnetic-Core Design and Application Handbook* (Englewood Cliffs, NJ: Prentice-Hall Inc, 1981).

J. Devoldere, *ON4UN's Low-Band DXing, Fifth Edition* (Newington: ARRL, 2010). See in particular the chapter "Receiving Antennas," for many practical details on Beverage antennas.

V. A. Misek, *The Beverage Antenna Handbook* (Wason Rd., Hudson, NH: W1WCR, 1977).

W. Silver, "A Cool Beverage Four Pack," *QST*, Apr 2006, pp 33-36.

Active Antennas

F. Gentges, "The AMRAD Active LF Antenna," *QST*, Sep 2001, pp 31-37.

P. Bertini, "Active Antenna Covers 0.5-30 MHz," *Ham Radio*, May 1985, pp 37-43.

R. Burhans, "Active Antenna Preamplifiers," *Ham Radio*, May 1986, pp 47-54.

R. Fisk, "Voltage-Probe Receiving Antenna," *Ham Radio*, Oct 1970, pp 20-21.

U. Rohde, "Active Antennas," *RF Design*, May/Jun 1981, pp 38-42.

Loops, Flags, and Pennants

B. Beezley, "A Receiving Antenna that Rejects Local Noise," *QST*, Sep 1995, pp 33-36.

D. Bond, *Radio Direction Finders*, 1st ed. (New York: McGraw-Hill Book Co, 1944).

G. Bramslev, "Loop Aerial Reception," *Wireless World*, Nov 1952, pp 469-472.

G. Breed, "The K9AY Terminated Loop — A Compact, Directional Receiving Antenna," *QST*, Sep 1997, pp 43-46.

G. Breed, K9AY, "Hum Problems When Switching the K9AY Loops," Technical Correspondence, *QST*, May 1998, p 73.

G. Breed, Various notes on the K9AY Loop are available at **www.aytechnologies.com** under the "Tech Notes" tab.

R. Burhans, "Experimental Loop Antennas for 60 kHz to 200 kHz," *Technical Memorandum (NASA) 71*, (Athens, OH: Ohio Univ, Dept of Electrical Engr), Dec 1979.

R. Burhans, "Loop Antennas for VLF-LF," *Radio-Electronics*, Jun 1983, pp 83-87.

M. Connelly, "New Termination Control Method for Flag, Pennant and Similar Antennas," International Radio Club of America reprint A162, Nov 2002.

M. Connelly, "Pennant Antenna with Remote Termination Control," **home.comcast.net/~markwa1ion/exaol2/pennant.htm**.

E. Cunningham, "Flag, Pennants and Other Ground-Independent Low-Band Receiving Antennas," *QST*, Jul 2000, pp 34-37.

R. Devore and P. Bohley, "The Electrically Small Magnetically Loaded Multiturn Loop Antenna," *IEEE Trans on Ant and Prop*, Jul 1977, pp 496-505.

R. J. Edmunds, Ed. "An FET Loop Amplifier with Coaxial Output," *N.R.C. Antenna Reference Manual, Vol 2*, 1st ed. (Cambridge, WI: National Radio Club, Oct 1982), pp 17-20.

S. Goldman, "A Shielded Loop for Low Noise Broadcast Reception," *Electronics*, Oct 1938, pp 20-22.

J. V. Hagan, "A Large Aperture Ferrite Core Loop Antenna for Long and Medium Wave Reception," *Loop Antennas Design and Theory*, M.G. Knitter, Ed. (Cambridge, WI: National Radio Club, 1983), pp 37-49.

F. M. Howes and F. M. Wood, "Note on the Bearing Error and Sensitivity of a Loop Antenna in an Abnormally Polarized Field," *Proc IRE*, Apr 1944, pp 231-233.

F. Koontz, "Is this EWE for You?," *QST*, Feb 1995, pp 31-33. See also Feedback, Apr 1995 *QST*, p 75.

F. Koontz, "More EWEs for You," *QST*, Jan 1996, pp 32-34.

F. Koontz, "The Horizontal EWE Antenna," *QST*, Dec 2006, pp 37-38.

G. Levy, "Loop Antennas for Aircraft," *Proc IRE*, Feb 1943, pp 56-66. Also see correction, *Proc IRE*, Jul 1943, p 384.

R. C. Pettengill, H. T. Garland and J. D. Meindl, "Receiving Antenna Design for Miniature Receivers," *IEEE Trans on Ant and Prop*, Jul 1977, pp 528-530.

W. J. Polydoroff, *High Frequency Magnetic Materials — Their Characteristics and Principal Applications* (New York: John Wiley and Sons, Inc, 1960).

E. Robberson, "QRM? Get Looped," *Radio and Television News*, Aug 1955, pp 52-54, 126.

D. Sinclair, "Flag and Pennant Antenna Compendium," **www.angelfire.com/md/k3ky**.

G. S. Smith, "Radiation Efficiency of Electrically Small Multiturn Loop Antennas," *IEEE Trans on Ant and Prop*, Sep 1972, pp 656-657.

E. C. Snelling, *Soft Ferrites — Properties and Applications* (Cleveland, OH: CRC Press, 1969).

C. R. Sullivan, "Optimal Choice for the Number of Strands in a Litz-Wire Transformer Winding," *IEEE Trans on Power Electronics*, Vol. 14 No. 2, Mar 1999, pp 283-291 (also available on line at **www.thayer.dartmouth.edu/inductor/papers/litzj.pdf**).

G. Thomas, "The Hot Rod — An Inexpensive Ferrite Booster Antenna," *Loop Antennas Theory and Design*, M. G. Knitter, Ed. (Cambridge, WI: National Radio Club, 1983), pp 57-62.

22.2 DIRECTION-FINDING ANTENNAS

The use of radio for direction finding purposes (RDF) is almost as old as its application for communications. Radio amateurs have learned RDF techniques and found much satisfaction by participating in hidden-transmitter hunts. Other hams have discovered RDF through an interest in boating or aviation, where radio direction finding is used for navigation and emergency location systems. (Amateur RDF which finds a transmitter from its transmitted signal, should be distinguished from aviation's radio direction-finding, which finds a direction based on a signal transmitted from a known location.)

In many countries of the world, the hunting of hidden amateur transmitters takes on the atmosphere of a sport, as participants wearing jogging togs or track suits dash toward the area where they believe the transmitter is located. The sport is variously known as *fox hunting*, *bunny hunting*, ARDF (Amateur Radio direction finding) or simply transmitter hunting. In North America, most hunting of hidden transmitters is conducted from automobiles, although hunts on foot are gaining popularity. Most ARDF activity uses 80 meter or 2 meter transmitters.

There are less pleasant RDF applications as well, such as tracking down noise sources or illegal operators from unidentified stations. Jammers of repeaters, traffic nets and other amateur operations can be located with RDF equipment. Or sometimes a stolen amateur rig will be operated by a person who is not familiar with Amateur Radio and by being lured into making repeated transmissions, the operator unsuspectingly permits their location to be determined with RDF equipment. The ability of certain RDF antennas to reject signals from selected directions has also been used to advantage in reducing noise and interference. Through APRS (Amateur Packet Reporting System), radio navigation is becoming a popular application of RDF. The locating of downed aircraft is another, and one in which amateurs often lend their skills. Indeed, there are many useful applications for RDF.

Although sophisticated and complex equipment pushing the state of the art has been developed for use by governments and commercial enterprises, relatively simple equipment can be built at home to offer the radio amateur an opportunity to RDF. This section deals with antennas suitable for that purpose.

The major types of RDF antennas used by amateurs are covered here, with a project or referenced article included for each. In ARDF events, it's very common to use integrated receiver/antenna combinations to reduce the amount of gear the competitor has to carry. Examples of this type of gear can be found through the Homing In website maintained by Joe Moell, KØOV (**www.homingin.com**). In ARDF, both magnetic loop and ferrite rod antennas are popular with magnetic loops being the more popular. On VHF, three-element Yagis are by far the most popular

How accurate should an RDF antenna be? In mobile and portable use, accuracy to a few degrees is fine. While the uncertainty of a few degrees sounds large, as the distance to the transmitter is reduced and more bearings are taken for triangulation, the amount of error also shrinks. If the antenna is fixed, such as for taking sky-wave bearings, precision is more important since distance to the transmitter does not change. In competitive events where the most common technique is to move toward peak signal on a relatively continuous basis, it is more important to be able to take a reading quickly and consistently.

22.2.1 RDF BY TRIANGULATION

It is impossible, using amateur techniques, to pinpoint the whereabouts of a transmitter from a single receiving location. With a directional antenna you can determine the direction of a signal source, but not how far away it is. To find the distance, you can then travel in the determined direction until you discover the transmitter location. However, that technique can be time consuming and often does not work very well.

A preferred technique is to take at least one additional direction measurement from a second receiving location. Then use a map of the area and plot the bearing or direction measurements as straight lines from points on the map representing the two locations. The approximate location of the transmitter will be indicated by the point where the two bearing lines cross. Even better results can be obtained by taking direction measurements from three locations and using the mapping technique just described. Because absolutely precise bearing measurements are difficult to obtain in practice, the three lines will almost always cross to form a triangle on the map, rather than at a single point. The transmitter will usually be located inside the area represented by the triangle. Additional information on the technique of triangulation and much more on RDF techniques may be found at the Homing In website mentioned above.

It is important to note that the directions determined by a DF receiver can be affected by skew paths (HF) and reflections (VHF). In addition, signals arriving by sky wave can appear to be coming from different azimuths than by ground wave. Knowing about and avoiding these errors are part of successful RDF.

22.2.2 DIRECTION-FINDING ANTENNAS

Required for any RDF system are a directive antenna and a device for detecting the radio signal. In amateur applications the signal detector is usually a transceiver and for convenience it will usually have a meter to indicate signal strength. Unmodified, commercially available portable or mobile receivers are generally quite satisfactory for signal detectors. At very close ranges a simple diode detector and dc microammeter may suffice for the detector.

On the other hand, antennas used for RDF techniques are not generally the types used for normal two-way communications. Directivity is a prime requirement, and here the word *directivity* takes on a somewhat different meaning than is commonly applied to other amateur antennas. Normally we associate directivity with gain, and we think of the ideal antenna pattern as one having a long, thin main lobe. Such a pattern may be of value for coarse measurements in RDF work, but precise bearing measurements are not possible. There is always a spread of a few (or perhaps many) degrees on the *nose* of the lobe, where a shift of antenna bearing produces no detectable change in signal strength. In RDF measurements, it is desirable to correlate an exact bearing or compass direction with the position of the antenna. In order to do this as accurately as possible, an antenna exhibiting a *null* in its pattern is used. A null can be very sharp in directivity, to within a half degree or less.

Loop Antennas

A simple antenna for HF RDF work is a small loop tuned to resonance with a capacitor. (Resonant loops are too small for VHF DFing and other antennas must be used.) Several factors must be considered in the design of an RDF loop. The loop must be small in circumference compared with the wavelength. In a single-turn loop, the conductor should be less than 0.08 λ long. For 28 MHz, this represents a length of less than 34 inches (a diameter of approximately 10 inches). Maximum response from the loop antenna is in the plane of the loop, with nulls exhibited at right angles to that plane. (A more detailed treatment is presented in the **Loop Antennas** chapter.)

To obtain the most accurate bearings, the loop must be balanced electrostatically with respect to ground. Otherwise, the loop will exhibit two modes of operation. One is the mode of a true loop, while the other is that of an essentially non-directional vertical antenna of small dimensions. This second mode is called the *antenna effect*. The voltages introduced by the two modes are seldom in phase and may add or subtract, depending upon the direction from which the wave is coming.

The theoretical true loop pattern is illustrated in **Figure 22.24A**. When properly balanced, the loop exhibits two nulls that are 180° apart. Thus, a single null reading with a small loop antenna will not indicate the exact direction toward the transmitter — only the line along which the transmitter lies. Ways to overcome this ambiguity are discussed later.

When the antenna effect is appreciable and the loop is tuned to resonance, the loop may exhibit little directivity, as shown in Figure 22.24B. However, by detuning the loop to shift the phasing, a pattern similar to Figure 22.24C may be obtained. Although this pattern is not symmetrical, it does exhibit a null. Even so, the null may not be as sharp as that obtained with a loop that is well balanced, and it may not be at exact right angles to the plane of the loop, making determining a bearing more difficult.

By suitable detuning, the unidirectional cardioid pattern of Figure 22.24D may be approached. This adjustment is sometimes used in RDF work to obtain a unidirectional bearing, although there is no complete null in the pattern. A cardioid pattern can also be obtained with a small loop antenna by adding a *sensing element*. Sensing elements are discussed in a later section of this chapter.

An electrostatic balance can be obtained by shielding the loop, as **Figure 22.25** shows. The shield is represented by the broken lines in the drawing, and eliminates the antenna effect. The response of a well-constructed shielded loop is quite close to the ideal pattern of Figure 22.24A.

For the low-frequency amateur bands, single-turn loops of convenient physical size for portability are generally found to be too large for RDF work. Therefore, multi-turn loops are generally used instead. Such a loop is shown in **Figure 22.26**. This loop may also be shielded, and if the total conductor length remains below 0.08 λ, the directional pattern is that of Figure 22.24A. A sensing element may also be used with a multi-turn loop.

Loop Circuits and Criteria

No single word describes a direction-finding loop of high

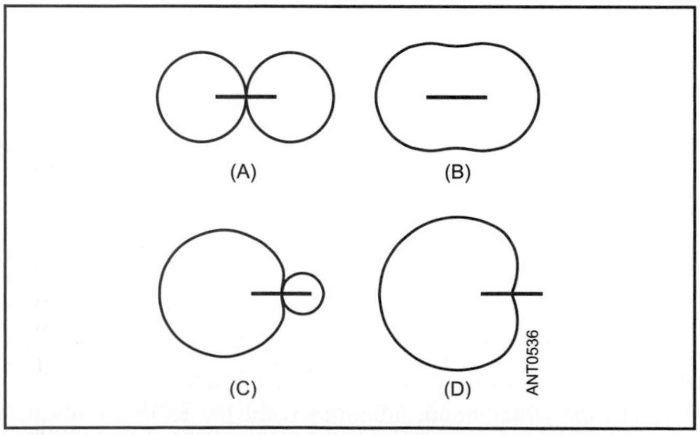

Figure 22.24 — Small-loop field patterns with varying amounts of antenna effect — the undesired response of the loop acting merely as a mass of metal connected to the receiver antenna terminals. The straight lines show the plane of the loop.

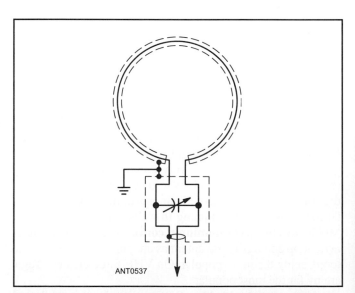

Figure 22.25 — Shielded loop for direction finding. The ends of the shielding turn are not connected, to prevent shielding the loop from magnetic fields. The shield is effective in balancing the loop's response to electric fields.

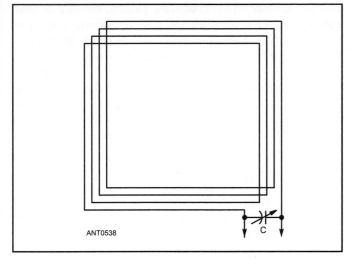

Figure 22.26 — Small loop consisting of several turns of wire. The total conductor length is very much less than a wavelength. Maximum response is in the plane of the loop.

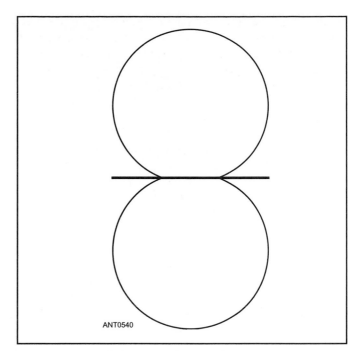

Figure 22.27 — Field pattern for a ferrite rod antenna. The dark bar represents the rod on which the loop turns are wound.

performance better than *symmetry*. To obtain an undistorted response pattern from this type of antenna, you must build it in the most symmetrical manner possible. The next key word is *balance*. The better the electrical balance, the deeper the loop null and the sharper the maxima.

The physical size of the loop for 7 MHz and below is not of major consequence. A 4-foot diameter loop will exhibit the same electrical characteristics as one which is only an inch or two in diameter. The smaller the loop, however, the lower its efficiency. This is because its aperture samples a smaller section of the wave front. Thus, if you use loops that are very small in terms of a wavelength, you will need preamplifiers to compensate for the reduced efficiency.

An important point to keep in mind about a small loop antenna oriented in a vertical plane is that it is vertically polarized. It should be fed at the bottom for the best null response. Feeding it at one side, rather than at the bottom, will not alter the polarization and will only degrade performance. To obtain horizontal polarization from a small loop, it must be oriented in a horizontal plane, parallel to the earth. In this position the loop response is essentially omnidirectional.

The earliest loop antennas were of the *frame antenna* variety. These were unshielded antennas built on a wooden frame in a rectangular format. The loop conductor could be a single turn of wire (on the larger units) or several turns if the frame was small. Later, shielded versions of the frame antenna became popular, providing electrostatic shielding — an aid to noise reduction from such sources as precipitation static.

Ferrite Rod Antennas

With advances in technology, magnetic-core loop antennas came into use. Their advantage was reduced size, and this appealed especially to the designers of aircraft and portable radios. Most of these antennas contain ferrite bars or cylinders, which provide high inductance and Q with a relatively small number of coil turns. Because of their reduced-size advantage, ferrite-rod *loopstick* antennas are used almost exclusively for portable work at frequencies below 150 MHz. Design of ferrite-core loop antennas is described in the **Loop Antennas** chapter and loopstick antennas for construction are described later in this chapter.

Maximum response of the loopstick antenna is broadside to the axis of the rod as shown in **Figure 22.27**, whereas maximum response of the ordinary loop is in a direction at right angles to the plane of the loop. Otherwise, the performances of the ferrite-rod antenna and of the ordinary loop are similar. The loopstick may also be shielded to eliminate the antenna effect, such as with a U-shaped or C-shaped channel of aluminum or other type of metal. The length of the shield should equal or slightly exceed the length of the rod.

Sensing Antennas

Because there are two nulls that are 180° apart in the directional pattern of a loop or a loopstick, an ambiguity exists as to which one indicates the true direction of the station being tracked. For example, assume you take a bearing measurement and the result indicates the transmitter is somewhere on a line running approximately east and west from your position. With this single reading, you have no way of knowing for sure if the transmitter is east of you or west of you.

If more than one receiving station takes bearings on a single transmitter, or if a single receiving station takes bearings on the transmitter from more than one position, the ambiguity may be worked out by triangulation, as described earlier. However, it is sometimes desirable to have a pattern

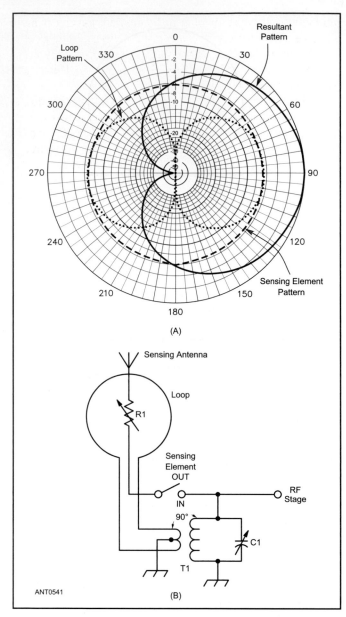

Figure 22.28 — At A, the directivity pattern of a loop antenna with sensing element. At B is a circuit for combining the signals from the two elements. C1 is adjusted for resonance with T1 at the operating frequency.

For the best null in the composite pattern, the signals from the loop and the sensing antenna must be of equal amplitude, so R1 is adjusted experimentally during setup. In practice, the null of the cardioid is not as sharp as that of the loop, so the usual measurement procedure is to first use the loop alone to obtain a precise bearing reading, and then to add the sensing antenna and take another reading to resolve the ambiguity. (The null of the cardioid is 90° away from the nulls of the loop.) For this reason, provisions are usually made for switching the sensing element in an out of operation.

22.2.3 DIRECTION-FINDING ARRAYS

Phased arrays are also used in amateur RDF work. Two general classifications of phased arrays are end-fire and broadside configurations. Depending on the spacing and phasing of the elements, end-fire patterns may exhibit a null in one direction along the axis of the elements. At the same time, the response is maximum off the other end of the axis, in the opposite direction from the null. A familiar arrangement is two elements spaced ¼ λ apart and fed 90° out of phase. The resultant pattern is a *cardioid*, with the null in the direction of the leading element. Other arrangements of spacing and phasing for an end-fire array are also suitable for RDF work. One of the best known is the *Adcock array*, discussed in the next section.

Broadside arrays are inherently bidirectional, which means there are always at least two nulls in the pattern. Ambiguity therefore exists in the true direction of the transmitter, but depending on the application, this may be no handicap. Broadside arrays are seldom used for amateur RDF applications however.

The Adcock Antenna

Loops are adequate in RDF applications where only the ground wave is present. The performance of an RDF system for sky-wave reception can be improved by the use of an Adcock antenna, one of the most popular types of end-fire phased arrays. A basic version is shown in **Figure 22.29**.

This system was invented by F. Adcock and patented in

with only one null, so there is no question about whether the transmitter in the above example would be east or west from your position.

A loop or loopstick antenna may be made to have a single null if a second antenna element is added. The element is called a *sensing antenna*, because it gives an added sense of direction to the loop pattern. The second element must be omnidirectional, such as a short vertical. When the signals from the loop and the vertical element are combined with a 90° phase shift between the two, a cardioid pattern results. The development of the pattern is shown in **Figure 22.28A**.

Figure 22.28B shows a circuit for adding a sensing antenna to a loop or loopstick. R1 is an internal adjustment and is used to set the level of the signal from the sensing antenna.

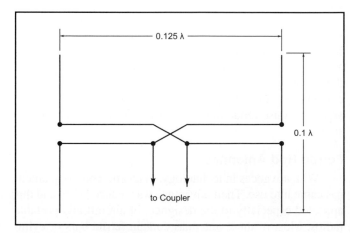

Figure 22.29 — A simple Adcock antenna.

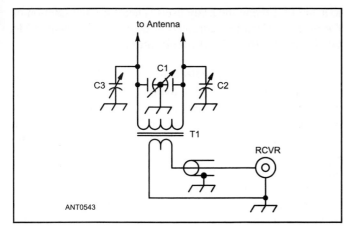

Figure 22.30 — A suitable coupler for use with the Adcock antenna.

1919. The array consists of two vertical elements fed 180° apart, and mounted so the system may be rotated. Element spacing is not critical, and may be in the range from 0.1 to 0.75 λ. The two elements must be of identical lengths, but need not be self-resonant. Elements that are shorter than resonant are commonly used. Because neither the element spacing nor the length is critical in terms of wavelengths, an Adcock array may be operated over more than one amateur band.

The response of the Adcock array to vertically polarized waves is similar to a conventional loop and the directive pattern is essentially the same. Response of the array to a horizontally polarized wave is considerably different from that of a loop, however. The currents induced in the horizontal members tend to balance out regardless of the orientation of the antenna, preserving the null. This effect has been verified in practice, where good nulls were obtained with an experimental Adcock under sky-wave conditions with rapidly varying polarization that produced poor nulls in small loops (both conventional and ferrite-loop models).

Generally speaking, the Adcock antenna has attractive properties for amateur RDF applications. Unfortunately, its portability leaves something to be desired, making it more suitable to fixed or semi-portable applications. While a metal support for the mast and boom could be used, wood, PVC or fiberglass are preferable because they are nonconductors and would therefore cause less pattern distortion.

Since the array is balanced, an antenna tuner is required to match the unbalanced input of a typical receiver. **Figure 22.30** shows a suitable link-coupled network. C2 and C3 are null-balancing capacitors. A low-power signal source is placed some distance from the Adcock antenna and broadside to it. C2 and C3 are then adjusted until the deepest null is obtained. The tuner can be placed below the wiring-harness junction on the boom. Connection can be made by means of a short length of 300-Ω twinlead.

The radiation pattern of the Adcock is shown in **Figure 22.31A**. The nulls are in directions broadside to the array, and become sharper with greater element spacings. However, with an element spacing greater than 0.75 λ, the pattern begins to take on additional nulls in the directions off the ends of the array axis. At a spacing of 1 λ the pattern is that of Figure 22.31B, and the array is unsuitable for RDF applications.

Short vertical monopoles over a ground plane are often used in what is sometimes called the *U-Adcock*, so named because the elements with their feeders take on the shape of the letter U. In this arrangement the elements are worked against the earth as a ground or counterpoise. (Replace the bottom half of the elements and feeders in Figure 22.29 with a ground plane.) If the array is used only for reception, earth losses are of no great consequence. Short, elevated vertical dipoles are also used in what is sometimes called the *H-Adcock*.

The Adcock array, with two nulls in its pattern, has the same ambiguity as the loop and the loopstick. Adding a sensing element to the Adcock array has not met with great success. Difficulties arise from mutual coupling between the array elements and the sensing element, among other things. Because Adcock arrays are used primarily for fixed-station applications, the ambiguity presents no serious problem. The fixed station is usually one of a group of stations in an RDF network.

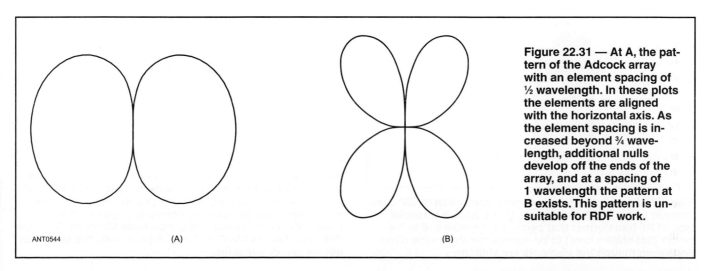

Figure 22.31 — At A, the pattern of the Adcock array with an element spacing of ½ wavelength. In these plots the elements are aligned with the horizontal axis. As the element spacing is increased beyond ¾ wavelength, additional nulls develop off the ends of the array, and at a spacing of 1 wavelength the pattern at B exists. This pattern is unsuitable for RDF work.

(A) (B)

Loops Versus Phased Arrays

Although loops can be made smaller than suitable phased arrays for the same frequency of operation, the phased arrays are preferred by some for a variety of reasons. In general, sharper nulls can be obtained with phased arrays, but this is also a function of the care used in constructing and feeding the individual antennas, as well as of the size of the phased array in terms of wavelengths. The primary constructional consideration is the shielding and balancing of the feed line against unwanted signal pickup, and the balancing of the antenna for a symmetrical pattern.

Loops are not as useful for skywave RDF work because of random polarization of the received signal. Phased arrays are somewhat less sensitive to propagation effects, probably because they are larger for the same frequency of operation and therefore offer some space diversity. In general, loops and loopsticks are used for mobile and portable operation, while phased arrays are used for fixed-station operation. However, phased arrays are used successfully above 144 MHz for portable and mobile RDF work. Practical examples of both types of antennas are presented later in this chapter.

The Goniometer

An early-day device that permits finding directions without moving the elements is called a *radiogoniometer*, or simply a *goniometer*. Various types of goniometers are still used today in many installations, and offer the amateur some possibilities.

The early style of goniometer is a special form of RF transformer, as shown in **Figure 22.32**. It consists of two fixed coils mounted at right angles to one another. Inside the fixed coils is a movable coil, not shown in Figure 22.32 to avoid cluttering the diagram. The pairs of connections marked A and B are connected respectively to two elements in an array, and the output to the detector or receiver is taken from the movable coil. As the inner coil is rotated, the coupling to one fixed coil increases while that to the other decreases. Both the amplitude and the phase of the signal coupled into the pickup winding are altered with rotation in a way that corresponds to actually rotating the array itself. Therefore, the rotation of the inner coil can be calibrated in degrees to correspond to bearing angles from the station location.

Electronic Antenna Rotation

With an array of many fixed elements, beam formation and rotation can be performed electronically by sampling and combining signals from various individual elements in the array. Contingent upon the total number of elements in the system and their physical arrangement, almost any desired antenna pattern can be formed by summing the sampled signals in appropriate amplitude and phase relationships. Delay networks are used for some of the elements before the summation is performed. In addition, attenuators may be used for some elements to develop patterns such as from an array with binomial current distribution.

One system using these techniques is the *Wullenweber* antenna, employed primarily in government and military installations. The Wullenweber consists of a very large number of elements arranged in a circle, usually outside of (or in front of) a circular reflecting screen. Delay lines and electronic switches create a beam-forming network that can be steered in any direction and with a wide variety of patterns.

For the moment, consider just two elements of a Wullenweber antenna, shown as A and B in **Figure 22.33**. Also shown is the wavefront of a radio signal arriving from a distant transmitter. As drawn, the wavefront strikes element A first, and must travel somewhat farther before it strikes element B. There is a finite time delay before the wavefront reaches element B.

The propagation delay may be measured by delaying the signal received at element A before summing it with that from element B. If the two signals are combined directly, the amplitude of the resultant signal will be maximum when the delay for element A exactly equals the propagation delay. This results in an in-phase condition at the summation point. Or if one of the signals is inverted and the two are summed, a null will exist when the element-A delay equals the propagation delay; the signals will combine in a 180° out-of-phase

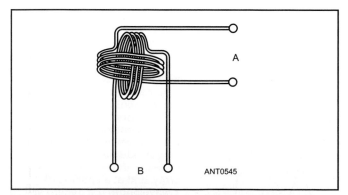

Figure 22.32 — An early type of goniometer that is still used today in some RDF applications. This device is a special type of RF transformer that permits a movable coil in the center (not shown here) to be rotated and determine directions even though the elements are stationary.

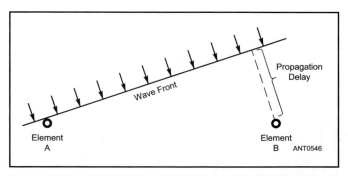

Figure 22.33 — This diagram illustrates one technique used in electronic beam forming. By delaying the signal from element A by an amount equal to the propagation delay, the two signals may be summed precisely in phase, even though the signal is not in the broadside direction. Because this time delay is identical for all frequencies, the system is not frequency sensitive.

relationship. Either way, once the time delay is known, it may be converted to distance. Then the direction from which the wave is arriving may be determined by trigonometry.

By altering the delay in small increments, the peak of the antenna lobe (or the null) can be steered in azimuth. This is true without regard to the frequency of the incoming wave. Thus, as long as the delay is less than the period of one RF cycle, the system is not frequency sensitive, other than for the frequency range that may be covered satisfactorily by the array elements themselves. Surface acoustic wave (SAW) devices or lumped-constant networks can be used for delay lines in such systems if the system is used only for receiving. Rolls of coaxial cable of various lengths are used in installations for transmitting. In this case, the lines are considered for the time delay they provide, rather than as simple phasing lines. The difference is that a phasing line is ordinarily designed for a single frequency (or for an amateur band), while a delay line offers essentially the same time delay at all frequencies.

A four-element, electronically-rotating RDF antenna system for amateur RDF was described in an article by Malcolm C. Mallette, WA9BVS, in November 1995 *QST* and included on this book's CD-ROM. The system is designed to be used while mobile and is based on *time-difference-of-arrival* techniques.

22.2.4 RDF SYSTEM CALIBRATION AND USE

Once an RDF system is initially assembled, it should be calibrated or checked out before actually being put into use. Of primary concern is the balance or symmetry of the antenna pattern. A lop-sided figure-8 pattern with a loop, for example, is undesirable; the nulls are not 180° apart, nor are they at exact right angles to the plane of the loop. If you didn't know this fact in actual RDF work, measurement accuracy would suffer.

It is also common to add a regular magnetic compass to an RDF antenna. This provides numeric bearings for events that combine orienteering or if reporting numeric bearings is important.

Initial checkout can be performed with a low-powered transmitter at a distance of a few hundred feet. It should be within visual range and if transmitting on HF must be operating into a vertical antenna. (A quarter-wave vertical or a loaded whip is quite suitable. Omni-directional horizontally polarized antennas work fine on VHF.) The site must be reasonably clear of obstructions, especially steel and concrete or brick buildings, large metal objects, nearby power lines, and so on. If the system operates above 30 MHz, you should also avoid trees and large bushes. An open field makes an excellent site.

The procedure is to find the transmitter with the RDF equipment as if its position were not known, and compare the RDF null indication with the visual path to the transmitter. For antennas having more than one null, each null should be checked.

If imbalance is found in the antenna system, there are two options available. One is to correct the imbalance. Toward this end, pay particular attention to the feed line. Using a coaxial feeder for a balanced antenna invites an asymmetrical pattern, unless an effective balun is used. A balun is not necessary if the loop is shielded, but an asymmetrical pattern can result with misplacement of the break in the shield itself. The builder may also find that the presence of a sensing antenna upsets the balance slightly, due to mutual coupling. Experiment with its position with respect to the main antenna to correct the error. You will also note that the position of the null shifts by 90° as the sensing element is switched in and out, and the null is not as deep. This is of little concern, however, as the intent of the sensing antenna is only to resolve ambiguities. The sensing element should be switched out when accuracy is desired.

The second option is to accept the imbalance of the antenna and use some kind of indicator to show the true directions of the nulls. Small pointers, painted marks on the mast, or an optical sighting system might be used. Sometimes the end result of the calibration procedure will be a compromise between these two options, as a perfect electrical balance may be difficult or impossible to attain.

Because of nearby obstructions or reflecting objects, the null in the pattern may not appear to indicate the precise direction of the transmitter. Do not confuse this with imbalance in the RDF array. Check for imbalance by rotating the array 180° and comparing readings.

The discussion above is oriented toward calibrating portable RDF systems such as would be used for competitive ARDF events and general-purpose fox hunting. The same general suggestions apply if the RDF array is fixed, such as an Adcock. However, it won't be possible to move it to an open field. Instead, the array must be calibrated in its intended operating position through the use of a portable or mobile transmitter and a table of bearing errors compiled that can be used during actual operation. Fixed DF antennas are rare in amateur service however.

22.2.5 A FRAME LOOP

It was mentioned earlier that the earliest style of receiving loops was the frame antenna. If carefully constructed, such an antenna performs well and can be built at low cost. **Figure 22.34** illustrates the details of a practical frame type of loop antenna. This antenna was designed by Doug DeMaw, W1FB (SK), and described in *QST* for July 1977. (See the Bibliography at the end of this chapter.) The circuit in Figure 22.34A is a 5-turn system tuned to resonance by C1. If the layout is symmetrical, good balance should be obtained. L2 helps to achieve this objective by eliminating the need for direct coupling to the feed terminals of L1. If the loop feed were attached in parallel with C1, a common practice, the chance for imbalance would be considerable.

L2 can be situated just inside or slightly outside of L1; a 1-inch separation works nicely. The receiver or preamplifier can be connected to terminals A and B of L2, as shown in Figure 22.34B. C2 controls the amount of coupling between the loop and the preamplifier. The lighter the coupling, the higher is the loop Q, the narrower is the frequency response,

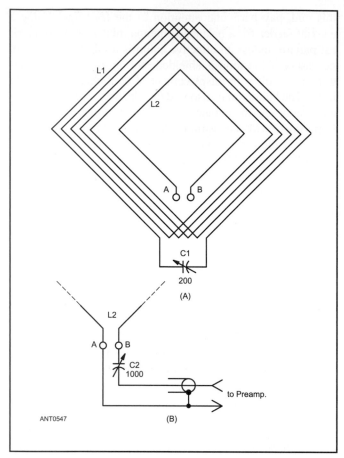

(A)

ANT0547

(B)

Figure 22.34 — A multiturn frame antenna is shown at A. L2 is the coupling loop. The drawing at B shows how L2 is connected to a preamplifier.

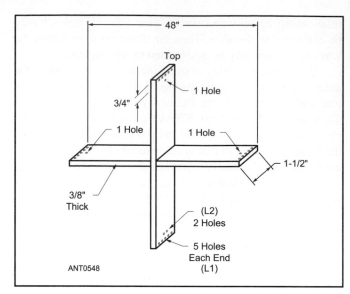

Figure 22.35 — A wooden frame can be used to contain the wire of the loop shown in Figure 12.

Figure 22.36 — An assembled table-top version of the electrostatically shielded loop. RG-58 cable is used in its construction.

and the greater is the gain requirement from the preamplifier. It should be noted that no attempt is being made to match the extremely low loop impedance to the preamplifier.

A supporting frame for the loop of Figure 22.34 can be constructed of wood, as shown in **Figure 22.35**. The dimensions given are for a 1.8-MHz frame antenna. For use on 75 or 40 meters, L1 of Figure 22.34A will require fewer turns, or the size of the wooden frame should be made somewhat smaller than that of Figure 22.35.

If electrostatic shielding is desired, the format shown in **Figure 22.36** and **Figure 22.37** can be adopted. In this example, the loop conductor and the single-turn coupling loop are made from RG-58 coaxial cable. The number of loop turns should be sufficient to resonate with the tuning capacitor at the operating frequency. Antenna resonance can be checked by first connecting C1 (Figure 22.34A) and setting it at midrange. Then connect a small 3-turn coil to the loop feed terminals, and couple to it with a dip meter. Just remember that the pickup coil will act to lower the frequency slightly from actual resonance.

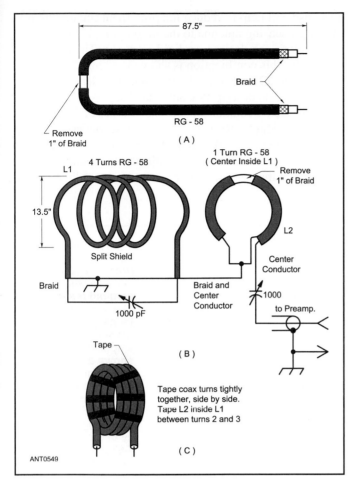

Figure 22.37 — Components and assembly details of the shielded loop shown in Figure 22.36. The dimensions and values given are for 1.8 MHz operation.

22.2.6 A FERRITE-CORE LOOP FOR 160 METERS

Figure 22.38 contains a diagram for a rod loop (loopstick antenna). This antenna was also designed by Doug DeMaw, W1FB (SK), and described in *QST* for July 1977. The winding (L1) has the appropriate number of turns to permit resonance with C1 at the operating frequency. L1 should be spread over approximately ⅓ of the core center. Litz wire will yield the best Q but enameled magnet wire can be used if desired. A layer of electrical tape is recommended as a covering for the core before adding the wire since ferrite is somewhat abrasive.

L2 functions as a coupling link over the exact center of L1. C1 is a dual-section variable capacitor, although a differential capacitor might be better toward obtaining optimum balance. The loop Q is controlled by means of C2, which is a mica-compression trimmer.

Electrostatic shielding of rod loops can be effected by centering the rod in a U-shaped aluminum, brass or copper channel, extending slightly beyond the ends of the rod loop (1 inch is suitable). The open side (top) of the channel can't be closed, as that would constitute a shorted turn and render the antenna useless. This can be proved by shorting across the

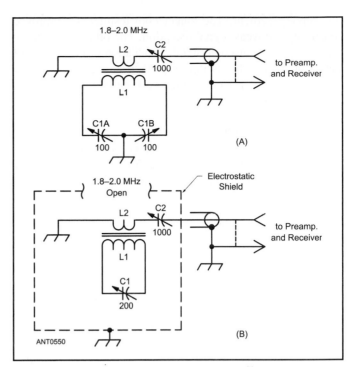

Figure 22.38 — At A, the diagram of a ferrite loop. C1 is a dual-section air-variable capacitor. The circuit at B shows a rod loop contained in an electrostatic shield channel (see text). A suitable low-noise preamplifier is shown in Figure 22.41.

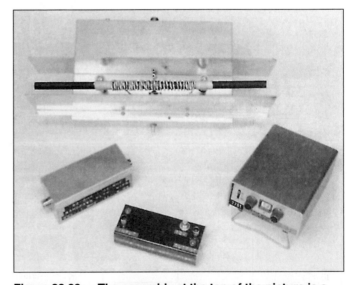

Figure 22.39 — The assembly at the top of the picture is a shielded ferrite-rod loop for 160 meters. Two rods have been glued end to end (see text). The other units in the picture are a low-pass filter (lower left), broadband preamplifier (lower center) and a Tektronix step attenuator (lower right). These were part of the test setup used when the antenna was evaluated.

center of the channel with a screwdriver blade when the loop is tuned to an incoming signal. The shield-braid gap in the co-axial loop of Figure 22.37 is maintained for the same reason.

Figure 22.39 shows the shielded rod loop assembly. This antenna was developed experimentally for 160 meters and uses two 7-inch ferrite rods, glued together end-to-end with epoxy cement. The longer core resulted in improved sensitivity for weak-signal reception. The other items in the photograph were used during the evaluation tests and are not pertinent to this discussion. This loop and the frame loop discussed in the previous section have bidirectional nulls, as shown in Figure 22.24A.

Obtaining a Cardioid Pattern

Although the bidirectional pattern of loop antennas can be used effectively in tracking down signal sources by means of triangulation, an essentially unidirectional loop response will help to reduce the time spent finding the fox. Adding a sensing antenna to the loop is simple to do, and it will provide the desired cardioid response. The theoretical pattern for this combination is shown in Figure 22.24D.

Figure 22.40 shows how a sensing element can be added to a loop or loopstick antenna. The link from the loop is connected by coaxial cable to the primary of T1, which is a tuned toroidal transformer with a split secondary winding. C3 is adjusted for peak signal response at the frequency of interest (as is C4), then R1 is adjusted for minimum back response of the loop. It will be necessary to readjust C3 and

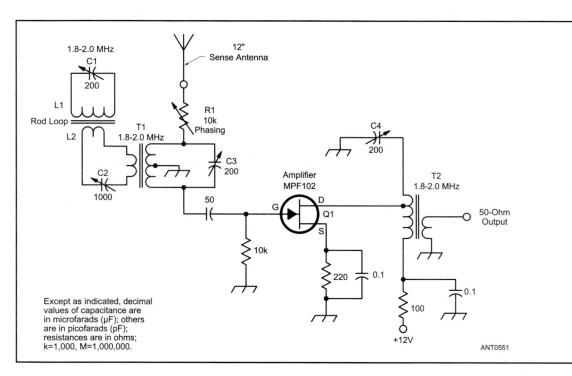

Figure 22.40 — Schematic diagram of a rod-loop antenna with a cardioid response. The sensing antenna, phasing network and a pre-amplifier are shown also. The secondary of T1 and the primary of T2 are tuned to resonance at the operating frequency of the loop. T-68-2 to T-68-6 Amidon toroid cores are suitable for both transformers. Amidon also sells ferrite rods for this type of antenna.

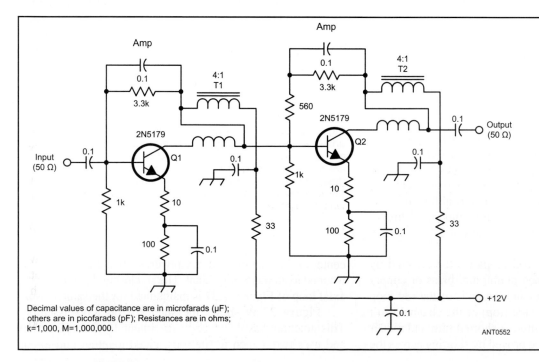

Figure 22.41 — Schematic diagram of a two-stage broadband amplifier patterned after a design by Wes Hayward, W7ZOI. T1 and T2 have a 4:1 impedance ratio and are wound on FT-50-61 toroid cores (Amidon) which have a μ_i of 125. They contain 12 turns of #24 AWG enamel wire, bifilar wound. The capacitors are disc ceramic. This amplifier should be built on double-sided circuit board for best stability.

R1 several times to compensate for the interaction of these controls. The adjustments are repeated until no further null depth can be obtained. Tests at ARRL Headquarters showed that null depths as great as 40 dB could be obtained with the circuit of Figure 22.40 on 80 meters. A near-field weak-signal source was used during the tests.

The greater the null depth, the lower the signal output from the system, so plan to include a preamplifier with 25 to 40 dB of gain. Q1 shown in Figure 22.40 will deliver approximately 15 dB of gain. In the interest of maintaining a good noise figure, even at 1.8 MHz, Q1 should be a low-noise device. A 2N4416, an MPF102, or a 3N201 MOSFET would be satisfactory. The circuit of **Figure 22.41** can be used following T2 to obtain an additional 24 dB of gain. The sensing antenna can be mounted from a few mm to 6 inches from the loop. The vertical whip need not be more than 12 inches long. Some experimenting may be necessary in order to obtain the best results. Optimization will also change with the operating frequency of the antenna.

22.2.7 A SIMPLE DIRECTION-FINDING SYSTEM FOR 80 METERS

This section gives an overview of the article by the same name in September 2005 *QST* by Dale Hunt, WB6BYU. (The full article is included on this book's CD-ROM.) The antenna (a multi-turn loop) and receiver are combined into a single package as shown in **Figure 22.42**. The receiver was designed to hear a 1-W signal from up to 3 miles away, to have low battery drain and to be lightweight and rugged for competitive RDF use.

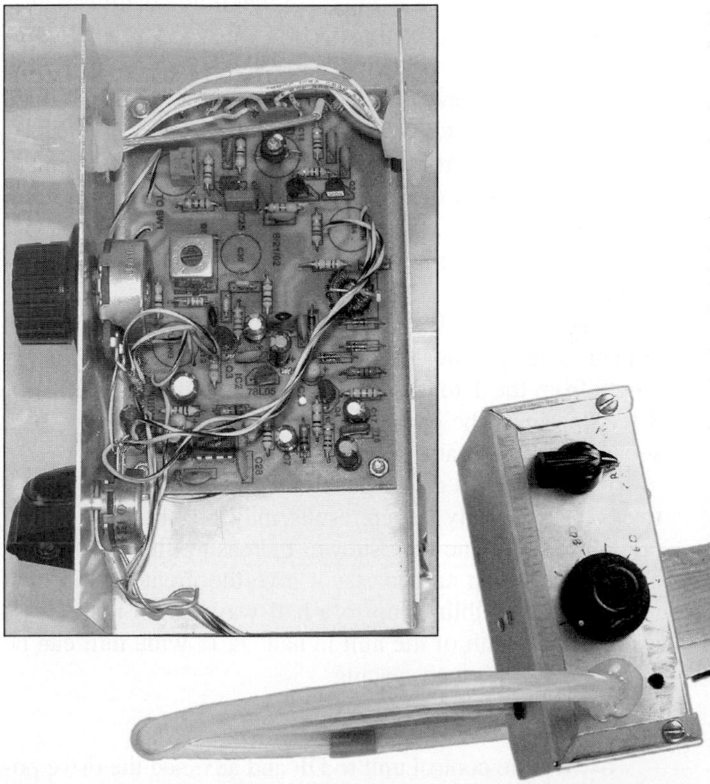

The four-turn loop is tuned to resonance to provide RF selectivity. Without the sense antenna, the loop alone is bidirectional. With the sense antenna switched in, a cardioid pattern is obtained. A shielded coupling loop of RG-174 coaxial cable is used to transfer the signal to the receiver which is described in detail in the article.

Operation is straightforward — plug in the headphones and turn on the radio. Adjust the RF gain to max and tune in the desired signal. Rotate the receiver to find the null in the pattern that is perpendicular to the loop. If the signal is too loud, reduce RF gain and try again. To resolve the direction of the transmitter (the loop's natural pattern is bidirectional) rotate the receiver 90° in either direction, switch in the sense antenna, and check signal strength. Then rotate the loop 180° and compare — one direction should be stronger than the other.

22.2.8 THE DOUBLE-DUCKY VHF DIRECTION FINDER

For direction finding, most amateurs use antennas having pronounced directional effects, either a null or a peak in signal strength. FM receivers are designed to eliminate the effects of amplitude variations, and so they are difficult to use for direction finding without looking at an S meter. Most modern HT transceivers do not have S meters.

This classic "Double-Ducky" direction finder (DDDF) was designed by David Geiser, WA2ANU, and was described in *QST* for July 1981. It works on the principle of switching between two nondirectional antennas, as shown in **Figure 22.43**. This creates phase modulation on the incoming signal that is heard easily on the FM receiver. When the two antennas are exactly the same distance (phase) from the transmitter, as in **Figure 22.44**, the tone disappears. (This technique is also known in the RDF literature as *Time-Difference-of-Arrival*, or TDOA, since signals arrive at each antenna at slightly different times, and hence at slightly different phases, from any direction except on a line perpendicular to and halfway in-between the two antennas. Another general term for this kind of two-antenna RDF technique is *interferometer. — Ed.*)

In theory the antennas may be very close to each other, but in practice the amount of phase modulation increases directly with the spacing, up to spacings of a half wavelength. While ½ λ separation on 2 meters (40 inches) is pretty large for a mobile array, ¼ λ gives entirely satisfactory results, and even ⅛ λ (10 inches) is acceptable.

Think in terms of two antenna elements with fixed spacing. Mount them on a ground plane and rotate that ground plane. The ground plane held above the hiker's head or car roof reduces the needed height of the array and the directional-distorting effects of the searcher's body or other conducting objects.

Figure 22.42 — The integrated antenna, handle, and receiver are built into a RadioShack aluminum box. The controls are made to be operated with one hand while using the antenna.

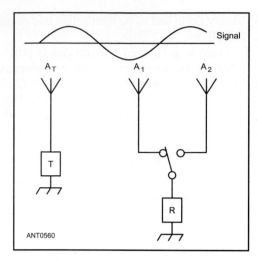

Figure 22.43 — At the left, A$_T$ represents the antenna of the hidden transmitter, T. At the right, rapid switching between antennas A$_1$ and A$_2$ at the receiver samples the phase at each antenna, creating a pseudo-Doppler effect. An FM detector detects this as phase modulation.

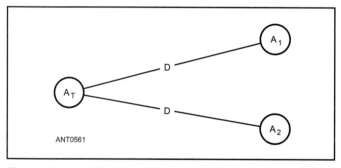

Figure 22.44 — If both receiving antennas are an equal distance (D) from the transmitting antenna, there will be no difference in the phase angles of the signals in the receiving antennas. Therefore, the detector will not detect any phase modulation, and the audio tone will disappear from the output of the detector.

The DDDF is bidirectional and, as described, its tone null points both toward and away from the signal origin. An L-shaped search path would be needed to resolve the ambiguity. Use the techniques of triangulation described earlier in this chapter.

Specific Design

It is not possible to find a long-life mechanical switch operable at a fairly high audio rate, such as 1000 Hz. Yet we want an audible tone, and the 400- to 1000-Hz range is perhaps most suitable considering audio amplifiers and average hearing. Also, if we wish to use the transmit function of a transceiver, we need a switch that will carry perhaps 10 W without much problem.

A solid-state switch, the PIN diode is used. The intrinsic region of this type of diode is ordinarily free of current carriers

and, with a bit of reverse bias, looks like a low-capacitance open space. A bit of forward bias (20 to 50 mA) will load the intrinsic region with current carriers that are happy to dance back and forth at a 148-MHz rate, looking like a resistance of an ohm or so. In a 10-W circuit, the diodes do not dissipate enough power to damage them.

Because only two antennas are used, the obvious approach is to connect one diode *forward* to one antenna, to connect the other *reverse* to the second antenna and to drive the pair with square-wave audio-frequency ac. **Figure 22.45** shows the necessary circuitry. RF chokes (Ohmite Z144, J. W. Miller RFC-144 or similar VHF units) are used to let the audio through to bias the diodes while blocking RF. Of course, the reverse bias on one diode is only equal to the forward bias on the other, but in practice this seems sufficient.

A number of PIN diodes were tried in the particular setup built. These were the Hewlett-Packard HP5082-3077, the Alpha LE-5407-4, the KSW KS-3542 and the Microwave Associates M/A-COM 47120. All worked well, but the HP diodes were used because they provided a slightly lower SWR (about 3:1).

A type 567 IC is used as the square-wave generator. The output does have a dc bias that is removed with a nonpolarized coupling capacitor. This minor inconvenience is more than rewarded by the ability of the IC to work well with between 7 and 15 V (a nominal 9-V minimum is recommended).

The nonpolarized capacitor is also used for dc blocking when the function switch is set to XMIT. D3, a light-emitting diode (LED), is wired in series with the transmit bias to indicate selection of the XMIT mode. In that mode there is a high battery current drain (20 mA or so). S1 should be a center-off locking type toggle switch. An ordinary center-off switch may be used, but beware. If the switch is left on XMIT you will soon have dead batteries.

Cables going from the antenna to the coaxial T connector were cut to an electrical ½ λ to help the open circuit, represented by the reverse-biased diode, look open at the coaxial T. (The length of the line within the T was included in the calculation.)

The length of the line from the T to the control unit is not particularly critical. If possible, keep the total of the cable length from the T to the control unit to the transceiver under 8 feet, because the capacitance of the cable does shunt the square-wave generator output.

Ground-plane dimensions are not critical. See **Figure 22.46**. Slightly better results may be obtained with a larger ground plane than shown. Increasing the spacing between the pickup antennas will give the greatest improvement. Every doubling (up to a half wavelength maximum) will cut the width of the null in half. A 1° wide null can be obtained with 20-inch spacing.

DDDF Operation

Switch the control unit to DF and advance the drive potentiometer until a tone is heard on the desired signal. Do not advance the drive high enough to distort or "hash up" the voice. Rotate the antenna for a null in the fundamental tone.

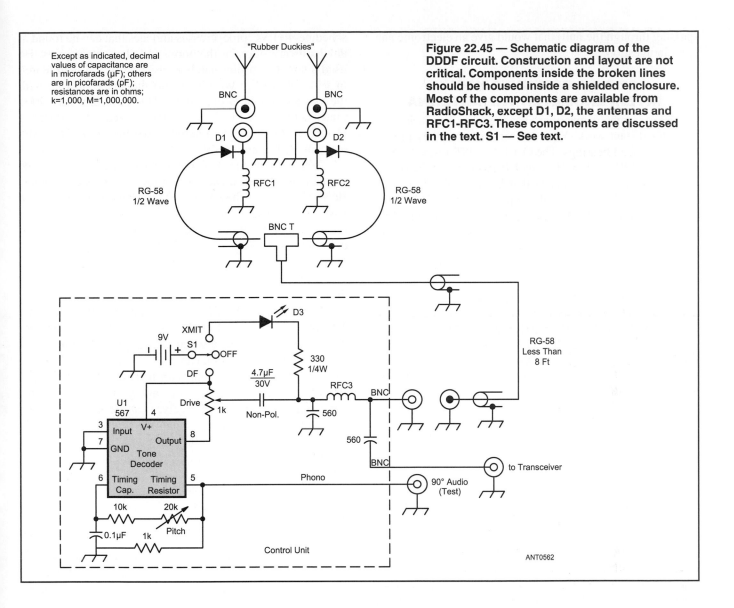

Figure 22.45 — Schematic diagram of the DDDF circuit. Construction and layout are not critical. Components inside the broken lines should be housed inside a shielded enclosure. Most of the components are available from RadioShack, except D1, D2, the antennas and RFC1-RFC3. These components are discussed in the text. S1 — See text.

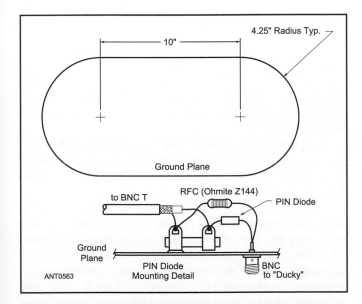

Figure 22.46 — Ground-plane layout and detail of parts at the antenna connectors.

Note that a tone an octave higher may appear.

If the incoming signal is quite out of the receiver linear region (10 kHz or so off frequency), the off-null antenna aim may present a fairly symmetrical AF output to one side. It may also show instability at a sharp null position. Aimed to the other side of a null, it will give a greatly increased AF output. This is caused by the different parts of the receiver FM detector curve used. The sudden tone change is the tip-off that the antenna null position is being passed.

The user should practice with the DDDF to become acquainted with how it behaves under known situations of signal direction, power and frequency. Even in difficult nulling situations where a lot of second-harmonic AF exists, rotating the antenna through the null position causes a very distinctive tone change. With the same frequencies and amplitudes present, the quality of the tone (timbre) changes. It is as if a note were first played by a violin, and then the same note played by a trumpet. (A good part of this is the change of phase of the fundamental and odd harmonics with respect to the even harmonics.) The listener can recognize differences (passing through the null) that would give an electronic analyzer indigestion.

22.2.9 A COMBINED YAGI — INTERFEROMETER VHF ANTENNA

Interferometers give sharp bearings, but they lack sensitivity for distant work. Yagis are sensitive, but they provide relatively broad bearings. The Oct 1998 *QST* article by R. F. Gillette, W9PE, "A Fox-Hunting DF Twin 'Tenna" describes a three-element Yagi antenna that blends both on a single boom to cover both ends of the hunt. (The article is included on this book's CD-ROM.) Being rigid, the elements of the antenna described in the article make it somewhat impractical for competitive DFing in brushy or wooded areas, but the design provides a starting point for experimentation and modification.

This antenna uses slide switches to configure it as either a Yagi or a single-channel interferometer. When used as an interferometer, a GaAs RF microcircuit switches the FM receiver between two matched dipoles at an audio frequency. To make the antenna compact W9PE used hinged, telescopic whips as the elements; they collapse and fold parallel to the boom for storage.

To form the interferometer, the two end elements are converted to dipoles and the center element is disabled. The feed line to the receiver is switched from the center element to the RF switch output, and the end elements are connected via feed lines to the RF switch inputs.

Now if both interferometer coax cables are of equal length (between the antennas and switch) and the two antennas are the same distance from the transmitter (broadside to it), the signals from both antennas will be in phase. Switching from one antenna to the other will have no effect on the received signal. If one antenna is a little closer to the transmitter than the other, however, there will be a phase shift when we switch antennas. When the antenna switch is at an audio rate, say 700 Hz, the repeated phase shifts result in a set of 700 Hz sidebands that can be heard by the operator as in the preceding DDDF design.

22.2.10 A TAPE-MEASURE ELEMENT YAGI FOR 2 METERS

Joe Leggio, WB2HOL, designed this antenna while searching for a beam with a really great front-to-back ratio to use in hidden transmitter hunts. It exhibits a very clean pattern and is perfect for RDF use. You can construct this beam using only simple hand tools, and it has been duplicated many times.

WB2HOL's first design requirement was to be able to get in and out of his car easily when hunting for a hidden transmitter. He accomplished this by using steel "tape-measure" elements, which fold easily when putting the antenna into a car and yet are self supporting. They also hold up well while crashing through the underbrush on a fox hunt. (This antenna isn't designed for mobile use — *Ed.*)

WB2HOL decided to use three elements to keep the boom from getting too long. He used inexpensive schedule-40 PVC pipe, crosses and tees that can be found at any hardware store for the boom and element supports. He used a simple hairpin match, consisting of a 5-inch length of #14 AWG solid wire bent into the shape of a U, with the two legs about ¾ inch apart. This gave in a very good match across the 2 meter band after he tweaked the distance (1-inch on his prototype) between the halves of the driven element for minimum SWR.

You can cut the 1-inch wide tape-measure elements with a pair of shears, chamfering the ends of the elements. Be very careful — the edges are very sharp and will inflict a nasty cut if you are careless. Use some sandpaper to remove the sharp edges and burrs and put some vinyl electrical tape or conformal coating such as Plasti-Dip on the ends of the elements to protect yourself from getting cut. Wear safety glasses while cutting the elements. See **Figure 22.47** for dimensions.

Ken Harker, WM5R recommends using wider tape measures to provide stiffer elements or stacking thinner elements. He also notes that when taking apart a tape measure, the internal spring tension can cause the pieces to fly apart. Covering the entire element with heat shrink provides additional stiffness and comes in a variety of colors. Ken also notes that a handheld-size receiver can be mounted to the boom of a beam to further integrate the package. Plastic brackets or hook-and-loop fasteners both work well.

Make sure you scrape or sand the paint off the tape-measure elements where the feed line is attached. Most tape measures have a very durable paint finish designed to stand up to heavy use. You do not want the paint to insulate your feed line connection!

If you are careful, you can solder the feed line to the element halves, but take care since the steel tape measure does not solder easily and the PVC supports can be easily melted. Tin the tape-measure elements before mounting them to the PVC cross if you decide to connect the feed line in this fashion.

If you decide not to solder to the tape-measure elements, you can use two other methods to attach the feed line. One method employs ring terminals on the end of the coax. The ring terminals are then secured under self-tapping screws or with 6-32 bolts and nuts into holes drilled in the driven-element halves. However, with this method you cannot fine-tune the antenna by moving the halves of the driven element in and out.

The simplest method is simply to slide the ends of the feed line under the driven element hose clamps and tighten the clamps to hold the ends of the coax. This is low-tech but it works just fine.

WB2HOL used 1½-inch stainless-steel hose clamps to attach each driven-element half to the PVC cross that acts as its support. This allowed him to fine-tune his antenna for lowest SWR simply by loosening the hose clamps and sliding the halves of the driven element in or out to lengthen or shorten the element. He achieved a 1:1 SWR at 146.565 MHz (the local fox-hunt frequency) when the two elements were spaced about 1 inch apart. **Figure 22.48** shows the

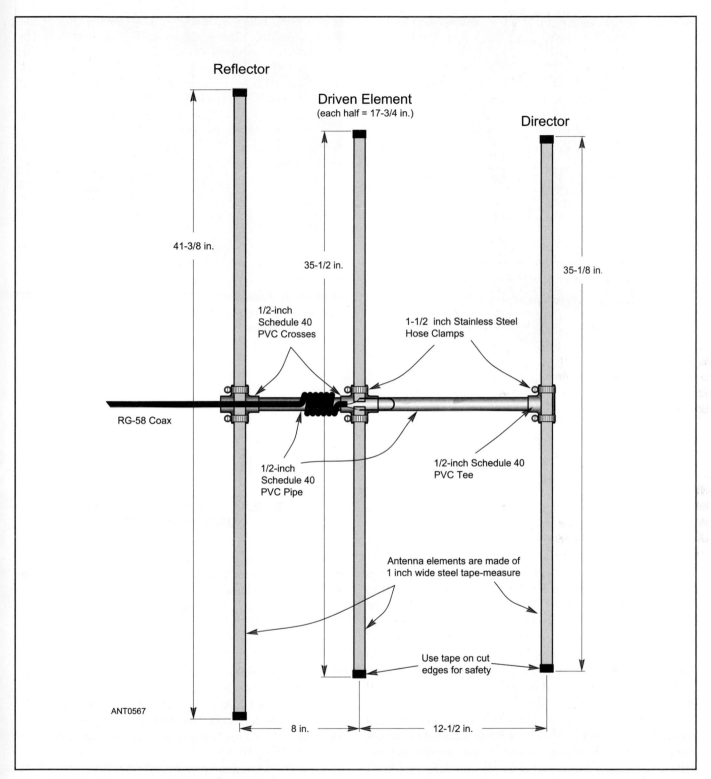

Reflector

Driven Element
(each half = 17-3/4 in.)

Director

41-3/8 in.

35-1/2 in.

35-1/8 in.

1/2-inch
Schedule 40
PVC Crosses

1-1/2 inch Stainless Steel
Hose Clamps

RG-58 Coax

1/2-inch Schedule 40
PVC Tee

1/2-inch
Schedule 40
PVC Pipe

Antenna elements are made of
1 inch wide steel tape-measure

Use tape on cut
edges for safety

ANT0567

8 in.

12-1/2 in.

Figure 22.47 — Tape-measure beam dimensions.

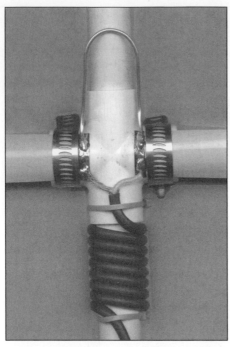

Figure 22.48 — Photo of driven-element mounted to PVC tee using hose clamps. The hairpin match wires are shown here soldered to the tape-measure elements, along with the RG-58 feed line.

Figure 22.49 — Photo of complete tape-measure beam, ready to hunt foxes!

hose-clamp method for attaching the driven element to the PVC cross, along with the hairpin wire and feed line coax. **Figure 22.49** shows the completed antenna.

Some builders have used rubber faucet washers between the tape-measure elements and the PVC-cross fittings on the director and reflector. These allow for the tape to fit the contour of the PVC fitting better and will make the antenna look nicer. It is normal for the reflector and director elements to buckle a bit as they are tightened to the PVC tee and cross if you don't use faucet washers. You can also eliminate the buckling if you use self-tapping screws to attach these elements instead of hose clamps. The beam will not be as rugged, however, as when you use hose clamps.

The RG-58 coax feed line is wound into an 8-turn coil along the boom to form the choke balun required to prevent feed line interaction from distorting the antenna pattern. (RG-174 is much lighter and does not introduce significant loss in the short length used here — *Ed.*) The coil is covered with electrical tape or tennis racket grip tape to secure it to the boom.

This beam has been used on fox hunts, on mountain tops, at local public-service events, outdoors, indoors in attics — just about everywhere. The SWR is typically very close to 1:1 once adjusted. Front-to-back performance is exactly as predicted. The null in the rear of the pattern is perfect for transmitter hunts.

22.2.11 DIRECTION FINDING BIBLIOGRAPHY

Source material and more extended discussion of topics covered in this chapter can be found in the references given below and in the textbooks listed at the end of the **Antenna Fundamentals** chapter.

W. U. Amfahr, "Unidirectional Loops for Transmitter Hunting," *QST*, Mar 1955, pp 28-29.

G. Bonaguide, "HF DF — A Technique for Volunteer Monitoring," *QST*, Mar 1984, pp 34-36.

D. S. Bond, *Radio Direction Finders*, 1st edition (New York: McGraw-Hill Book Co).

R. E. Cowan and T. A. Beery, "Direction Finding with the Interferometer," *QST*, Nov 1985, pp 33-37.

D. DeMaw, "Beat the Noise with a Scoop Loop," *QST*, Jul 1977, pp 30-34.

D. DeMaw, "Maverick Trackdown," *QST*, Jul 1980, pp 22-25.

T. Dorbuck, "Radio Direction-Finding Techniques," *QST*, Aug 1975, pp 30-36.

D. T. Geiser, "Double-Ducky Direction Finder," *QST*, Jul 1981, pp 11-14.

D. T. Geiser, "The Simple Seeker," *The ARRL Antenna Compendium, Vol 3*, p 126.

G. Gercke, "Radio Direction/Range Finder," *73*, Dec 1971, pp 29-30.

N. K. Holter, "Radio Foxhunting in Europe," Parts 1 and 2, *QST*, Aug 1976, pp 53-57 and Nov 1976, pp 43-46.

J. Isaacs, "Transmitter Hunting on 75 Meters," *QST*, Jun 1958, pp 38-41.

H. Jasik, *Antenna Engineering Handbook*, 1st edition (New York: McGraw-Hill, 1961).

R. Keen, *Wireless Direction Finding*, 3rd edition (London: Wireless World).

J. Kraus, *Antennas*, 2nd edition (New York: McGraw-Hill Book Co, 1988).

J. Kraus, *Electromagnetics*, 4th edition (New York: McGraw-Hill Book Co, 1992).

C. M. Maer, Jr., "The Snoop-Loop," *QST*, Feb 1957, pp 11-14.

M. C. Mallette, "The Four-Way DFer," *QST*, Nov 1995, pp 29-35.

L. R. Norberg, "Transmitter Hunting with the DF Loop," *QST*, Apr 1954, pp 32-33.

P. O'Dell, "Simple Antenna and S-Meter Modification for 2-Meter FM Direction Finding," Basic Amateur Radio, *QST*, Mar 1981, pp 43-47.

Ramo and Whinnery, *Fields and Waves in Modern Radio* (New York: John Wiley & Sons, 1944).

F. Terman, *Electronic and Radio Engineering* (New York: McGraw-Hill Book Co, 1955).

For more information on direction finding, see *Radio Orienteering-The ARDF Handbook* by Bob Titterington, G3ORY, David Williams, M3WDD and David Deane, G3ZOI and *Transmitter Hunting: Radio Direction Finding Simplified*, by Joe Moell, KØOV, and Thomas Curlee, WB6UZZ. These books are available from your local dealer or can be ordered directly from ARRL(**www.arrl.org/shop**).

TABLE OF CONTENTS

Chapter 23

Transmission Lines

23.1 BASIC THEORY OF TRANSMISSION LINES

The desirability of installing an antenna in a clear space, not too near buildings or power and telephone lines, cannot be stressed too strongly. On the other hand, the transmitter that generates the RF power for driving the antenna is usually, as a matter of necessity, located some distance from the antenna terminals. The connecting link between the two is the RF *transmission line*, feeder or feed line. Its sole purpose is to carry RF power from one place to another, and to do it as efficiently as possible. That is, the ratio of the power *transferred* by the line to the power *lost* in it should be as large as the circumstances permit.

At radio frequencies, every conductor that has appreciable length compared with the wavelength in use *radiates* power — every conductor is an antenna. Special care must be used, therefore, to minimize radiation from the conductors used in RF transmission lines. Without such care, the power radiated by the line may be much larger than that which is lost in the resistance of conductors and dielectrics (insulating materials). Power loss in resistance is inescapable, at least to a degree, but loss by radiation is largely avoidable.

Radiation loss from transmission lines can be prevented by using two conductors arranged and operated so the electromagnetic field from one is balanced everywhere by an equal and opposite field from the other. In such a case, the resultant field is zero everywhere in space — there is no radiation from the line.

For example, **Figure 23.1A** shows two parallel conductors having currents I1 and I2 flowing in opposite directions. If the current I1 at point Y on the upper conductor has the same amplitude as the current I2 at the corresponding point X on the lower conductor, the fields set up by the two currents are equal in magnitude. Because the two currents are flowing in opposite directions, the field from I1 at Y is 180° out of phase with the field from I2 at X. However, it takes a measurable interval of time for the field from X to travel to Y. If I1 and I2 are alternating currents, the phase of the field from I1 at Y changes in such a time interval, so at the instant the field from X reaches Y, the two fields at Y are not exactly 180° out of phase. The two fields are exactly 180° out of phase at every point in space only when the two conductors occupy the same space — an obviously impossible condition if they are to remain separate conductors.

The best that can be done is to make the two fields cancel each other as completely as possible. This can be achieved by keeping the distance d between the two conductors small enough so the time interval during which the field from X is moving to Y is a very small part of a cycle. When this is the case, the phase difference between the two fields at any given point is so close to 180° that cancellation is nearly complete.

Practical values of d (the separation between the two conductors) are determined by the physical limitations of line construction. A separation that meets the condition of being "very small" at one frequency may be quite large at another. For example, if d is 6 inches, the phase difference between the two fields at Y is only a fraction of a degree if the frequency is 3.5 MHz. This is because a distance of 6 inches is such a small fraction of a wavelength (1 λ = 281 feet) at 3.5 MHz.

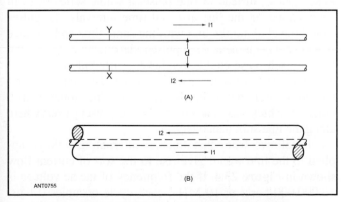

ANT0755

Figure 23.1 — Two basic types of transmission lines.

But at 144 MHz, the phase difference is 26°, and at 420 MHz, it is 77°. In neither of these cases could the two fields be considered to "cancel" each other. Conductor separation must be very small in comparison with the wavelength used; it should never exceed 1% of the wavelength, and smaller separations are desirable. Transmission lines consisting of two parallel conductors as in Figure 23.1A are called *open- or parallel-wire lines*, *parallel-conductor lines* or *two-wire lines*.

A second general type of line construction is shown in Figure 23.1B. In this case, one of the conductors is tube-shaped and encloses the other conductor. This is called a *coaxial line* (coax, pronounced "KOH-ax") or concentric line. The current flowing on the inner conductor is balanced by an equal current flowing in the opposite direction on the inside surface of the outer conductor. Because of skin effect, the current on the inner surface of the outer conductor does not penetrate far enough to appear on the outside surface. In fact, the total electromagnetic field outside the coaxial line (as a result of currents flowing on the conductors inside) is always zero, because the outer conductor acts as a shield at radio frequencies. The separation between the inner conductor and the outer conductor is therefore unimportant from the standpoint of reducing radiation.

A third general type of transmission line is the *waveguide*. Waveguides are discussed in the chapter **VHF and UHF Antenna Systems**.

23.1.1 CURRENT FLOW IN LONG LINES

In **Figure 23.2**, imagine that the connection between the battery and the two wires is made instantaneously and then broken. During the time the wires are in contact with the battery terminals, electrons in wire 1 will be attracted to the positive battery terminal and an equal number of electrons in wire 2 will be repelled from the negative terminal. This happens only near the battery terminals at first, because electromagnetic waves do not travel at infinite speed. Some time does elapse before the currents flow at the more extreme parts of the wires. By ordinary standards, the elapsed time is very short. Because the speed of wave travel along the wires may approach the speed of light at 300,000,000 meters per second, it becomes necessary to measure time in millionths of a second (microseconds, μs).

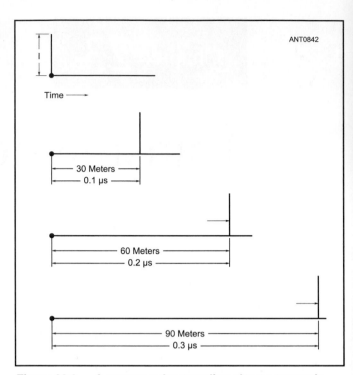

Figure 23.3 — A current pulse traveling along a transmission line at the speed of light would reach the successive positions shown at intervals of 0.1 μs.

For example, suppose that the contact with the battery is so short that it can be measured in a very small fraction of a microsecond. Then the "pulse" of current that flows at the battery terminals during this time can be represented by the vertical line in **Figure 23.3**. At the speed of light this pulse travels 30 meters along the line in 0.1 μs, 60 meters in 0.2 μs, 90 meters in 0.3 μs, and so on, as far as the line reaches.

The current does not exist all along the wires; it is only present at the point that the pulse has reached in its travel. At this point it is present in both wires, with the electrons moving in one direction in one wire and in the other direction in the other wire. If the line is infinitely long and has no resistance (or other cause of energy loss), the pulse will travel undiminished forever.

By extending the example of Figure 23.3, it is not hard to see that if, instead of one pulse, a whole series of them were started on the line at equal time intervals, the pulses would travel along the line with the same time and distance spacing between them, each pulse independent of the others. In fact, each pulse could even have a different amplitude if the battery voltage were varied between pulses. Furthermore, the pulses could be so closely spaced that they touched each other, in which case current would be present everywhere along the line simultaneously.

It follows from this that an alternating voltage applied to the line would give rise to the sort of current flow shown in **Figure 23.4**. If the frequency of the ac voltage is 10,000,000 hertz or 10 MHz, each cycle occupies 0.1 μs, so a complete cycle of current will be present along each

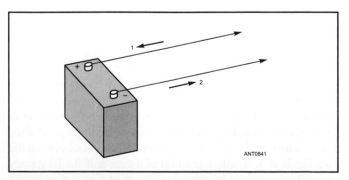

Figure 23.2 — A representation of current flow on a long transmission line.

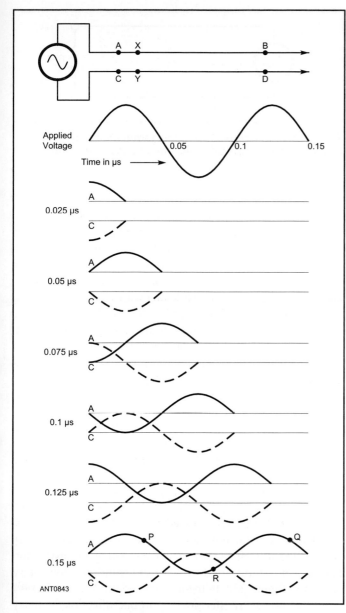

Figure 23.4 — Instantaneous current along a transmission line at successive time intervals. The frequency is 10 MHz; the time for each complete cycle is 0.1 µs.

30 meters of line. This is a distance of one wavelength. Any currents at points B and D on the two conductors occur one cycle later in time than the currents at A and C. Put another way, the currents initiated at A and C do not appear at B and D, one wavelength away, until the applied voltage has gone through a complete cycle.

Because the applied voltage is always changing, the currents at A and C change in proportion. The current a short distance away from A and C — for instance, at X and Y — is not the same as the current at A and C. This is because the current at X and Y was caused by a value of voltage that occurred slightly earlier in the cycle. This situation holds true all along the line; at any instant the current anywhere along the line from A to B and C to D is different from the current at any other point on that section of the line.

The remaining series of drawings in Figure 23.4 shows how the instantaneous currents might be distributed if we could take snapshots of them at intervals of ¼ cycle. The current travels out from the input end of the line in waves. At any given point on the line, the current goes through its complete range of ac values in one cycle, just as it does at the input end. Therefore (if there are no losses) an ammeter inserted in either conductor reads exactly the same current at any point along the line, because the ammeter averages the current over a whole cycle. (The phases of the currents at any two separate points are different, but the ammeter cannot show phase.)

23.1.2 VELOCITY OF PROPAGATION

In the example above it was assumed that energy travels along the line at the velocity of light. The actual velocity is very close to that of light only in lines in which the insulation between conductors is air. The presence of dielectrics other than air reduces the velocity.

Current flows at the speed of light only in a vacuum, although the speed in air is close to that in a vacuum. Therefore, the time required for a signal of a given frequency to travel down a length of practical transmission line is *longer* than the time required for the same signal to travel the same distance in free space. Because of this propagation delay, 360° of a given wave exists in a physically shorter distance on a given transmission line than in free space. The exact delay for a given transmission line is a function of the properties of the line, mainly the dielectric constant of the insulating material between the conductors. This delay is expressed in terms of the speed of light (either as a percentage or a decimal fraction), and is referred to as velocity factor (VF). The velocity factor is related to the dielectric constant (ε) by

$$VF = \frac{1}{\sqrt{\varepsilon}} \qquad \text{(Eq 1)}$$

The wavelength in a practical line is always shorter than the wavelength in free space, which has a dielectric constant $\varepsilon = 1.0$. Whenever reference is made to a line as being a half wavelength or quarter wavelength long ($\lambda/2$ or $\lambda/4$), it is understood that what is meant by this is the *electrical* length of the line. The physical length corresponding to an electrical wavelength on a given line is given by

$$\lambda \text{ (feet)} = \frac{983.6}{f} \times VF \qquad \text{(Eq 2)}$$

where
  f = frequency in MHz
  VF = velocity factor

Values of VF for several common types of lines are given later in this chapter. The actual VF of a given cable varies slightly from one production run or manufacturer to another, even though the cables may have exactly the same specifications.

As we shall see later, a quarter-wavelength line is frequently used as an impedance transformer, and so it is convenient to calculate the length of a quarter-wave line directly by

$$\lambda / 4 = \frac{245.9}{f} \times VF \qquad \text{(Eq 2A)}$$

It is important to note that Equation 1 is based on some simplifying assumptions about the cable and the frequency of use. At frequencies below 100 kHz, these assumptions become progressively less valid and VF drops dramatically. This is generally not an issue at amateur frequencies but could become significant when coaxial or twisted-pair transmission lines are used for software-defined radio applications. This is discussed more in the paper "Transmission Lines at Audio Frequencies, and a Bit of History" by Jim Brown, K9YC listed in the Bibliography.

23.1.3 CHARACTERISTIC IMPEDANCE

If the line could be *perfect* — having no resistive losses — a question might arise: What is the amplitude of the current in a pulse applied to this line? Will a larger voltage result in a larger current, or is the current theoretically infinite for an applied voltage, as we would expect from applying Ohm's Law to a circuit without resistance? The answer is that the current does depend directly on the voltage, just as though resistance were present.

The reason for this is that the current flowing in the line is something like the charging current that flows when a battery is connected to a capacitor. That is, the line has capacitance. However, it also has inductance. Both of these are "distributed" properties. We may think of the line as being composed of a whole series of small inductors and capacitors, connected as in **Figure 23.5**, where each coil is the inductance of an extremely small section of wire, and the capacitance is that existing between the same two sections. Each series inductor acts to limit the rate at which current can charge the following shunt capacitor, and in so doing establishes a very important property of a transmission line: its *surge impedance*, more commonly known as its *characteristic impedance*. This is abbreviated by convention as Z_0. While relatively constant at RF, Z_0 increases below 100 kHz, becoming much higher at and below audio frequencies as described in the previously noted Bibliography entry for Brown.

23.1.4 TERMINATED LINES

The value of the characteristic impedance is equal to $\sqrt{L / C}$ in a perfect line — that is, one in which the conductors

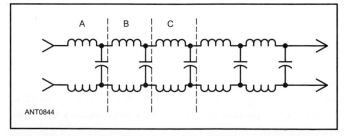

Figure 23.5 — Equivalent of an ideal (lossless) transmission line in terms of ordinary circuit elements (lumped constants). The values of inductance and capacitance depend on the line construction.

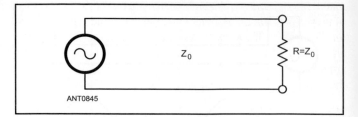

Figure 23.6 — A transmission line terminated in a resistive load equal to the characteristic impedance of the line.

have no resistance and there is no leakage between them — where L and C are the inductance and capacitance, respectively, per unit length of line. The inductance decreases with increasing conductor diameter, and the capacitance decreases with increasing spacing between the conductors. Hence a line with closely spaced large conductors has relatively low characteristic impedance, while one with widely spaced thin conductors has high impedance. Practical values of Z_0 for parallel-conductor lines range from about 200 to 800 Ω. Typical coaxial lines have characteristic impedances from 30 to 100 Ω. Physical constraints on practical wire diameters and spacings limit Z_0 values to these ranges.

In the earlier discussion of current traveling along a transmission line, we assumed that the line was infinitely long. Practical lines have a definite length, and they are terminated in a load at the output or load end (the end to which the power is delivered). In **Figure 23.6**, if the load is a pure resistance of a value equal to the characteristic impedance of a perfect, lossless line, the current traveling along the line to the load finds that the load simply "looks like" more transmission line of the same characteristic impedance.

The reason for this can be more easily understood by considering it from another viewpoint. Along a transmission line, power is transferred successively from one elementary section in Figure 23.5 to the next. When the line is infinitely long, this power transfer goes on in one direction — away from the source of power.

From the standpoint of Section B, Figure 23.5, for instance, the power transferred to section C has simply disappeared in C. As far as section B is concerned, it makes no difference whether C has absorbed the power itself or has transferred it along to more transmission line. Consequently, if we substitute a load for section C that has the same electrical characteristics as the transmission line, section B will transfer power into it just as if it were more transmission line. A pure resistance equal to the characteristic impedance of C, which is also the characteristic impedance of the line, meets this condition. It absorbs all the power just as the infinitely long line absorbs all the power transferred by section B.

Matched Lines

A line terminated in a load equal to the complex characteristic line impedance is said to be *matched*. In a matched transmission line, power is transferred outward along the line from the source until it reaches the load, where it is completely absorbed. Thus with either the infinitely long line or its matched counterpart, the impedance presented to the source of power (the line-input impedance) is the same *regardless of the line length*. It is simply equal to the characteristic impedance of the line. The current in such a line is equal to the applied voltage divided by the characteristic impedance, and the power put into it is E^2/Z_0 or I^2Z_0, by Ohm's Law.

Mismatched Lines

Now take the case where the terminating load is *not* equal to Z_0, as in **Figure 23.7**. The load no longer looks like more line to the section of line immediately adjacent. Such a line is said to be *mismatched*. The more the load impedance differs from Z_0, the greater the mismatch. The power reaching the load is not totally absorbed, as it was when the load was equal to Z_0, because the load requires a voltage to current ratio that is different from the one traveling along the line. The result is that the load absorbs only part of the power reaching it (the *incident* power); the remainder acts as though it had bounced off a wall and starts back along the line toward the source. This is known as *reflected power*, and the greater the mismatch, the larger the percentage of the incident power that is reflected. In the extreme case where the load is zero (a short circuit) or infinity (an open circuit), *all* of the power reaching the end of the line is reflected back toward the source.

Whenever there is a mismatch, power is transferred in both directions along the line. The voltage to current ratio is the same for the reflected power as for the incident power, because this ratio is determined by the Z_0 of the line. The voltage and current travel along the line in both directions in the same wave motion shown in Figure 23.4. If the source of power is an ac generator, the incident (outgoing) voltage and the reflected (returning) voltage are simultaneously present all along the line. The actual voltage at any point along the line is the vector sum of the two components, taking into

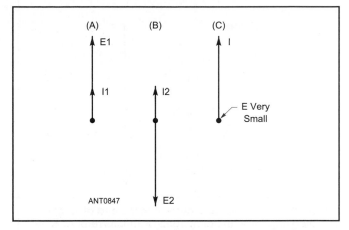

Figure 23.8 — Voltage and current at the short circuit on a short-circuited line. These vectors show how the incident voltage and current (A) combine with the reflected voltage and current (B) to result in high current and very low voltage in the short circuit (C).

account the *phases* of each component. The same is true of the current.

The effect of the incident and reflected components on the behavior of the line can be understood more readily by considering first the two limiting cases — the short-circuited line and the open-circuited line. If the line is short-circuited as in Figure 23.7B, the voltage at the end must be zero. Thus the incident voltage must disappear suddenly at the short. It can do this only if the reflected voltage is opposite in phase and of the same amplitude. This is shown by the vectors in **Figure 23.8**. The current, however, does not disappear in the short circuit. In fact, the incident current flows through the short and in addition, there is the reflected component in phase of the same amplitude as the incident current.

The reflected voltage and current must have the same amplitudes as the incident voltage and current, because no power is dissipated in the short circuit; all the power starts back toward the source. Reversing the phase of *either* the current or voltage (but not both) reverses the direction of power flow. In the short-circuited case the phase of the voltage is reversed on reflection, but the phase of the current is not.

If the line is open-circuited (Figure 23.7C) the current must be zero at the end of the line. In this case the reflected current is 180° out of phase with the incident current and has the same amplitude. By reasoning similar to that used in the short-circuited case, the reflected voltage must be in phase with the incident voltage, and must have the same amplitude. Vectors for the open-circuited case are shown in **Figure 23.9**.

Where there is a finite value of resistance (or a combination of resistance and reactance) at the end of the line, as in Figure 23.7A, only part of the power reaching the end of the line is reflected. That is, the reflected voltage and current are smaller than the incident voltage and current. If R is less than Z_0, the reflected and incident voltage are 180° out of phase, just as in the case of the short-circuited line, but the amplitudes are not equal because all of the voltage does not disappear at R. Similarly, if R is greater than Z_0, the reflected

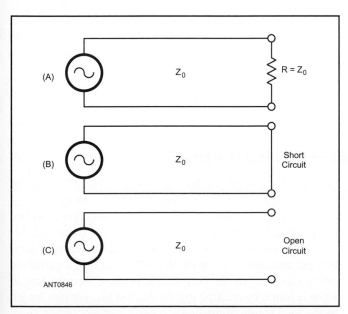

Figure 23.7 — Mismatched lines; extreme cases. At A, termination not equal to Z_0; at B, short-circuited line; At C, open-circuited line.

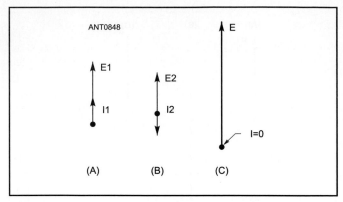

Figure 23.9 — Voltage and current at the end of an open-circuited line. At A, incident voltage and current; At B, reflected voltage and current; At C, resulting voltage and current.

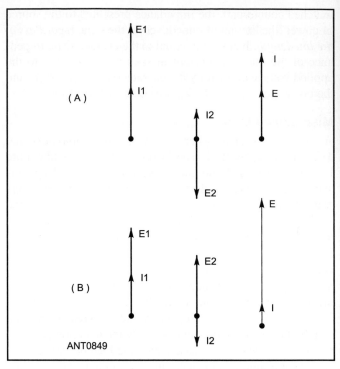

Figure 23.10 — Incident and reflected components of voltage and current when the line is terminated in a pure resistance R not equal to Z_0. In the case shown, the reflected components have half the amplitude of the incident components. At A, R less than Z_0; at B, R greater than Z_0.

and incident currents are 180° out of phase (as they were in the open-circuited line), but all of the current does not appear in R. The amplitudes of the two components are therefore not equal. These two cases are shown in **Figure 23.10**. Note that the resultant current and voltage are in phase in R, because R is a pure resistance.

Non-resistive Terminations

In most of the preceding discussions, we considered loads containing only resistance. Furthermore, our transmission line was considered to be lossless. Such a resistive load will consume some, if not all, of the power that has been transferred along the line. However, a nonresistive load such as a pure reactance can also terminate a length of line. Such terminations, of course, will consume no power, but will reflect all of the energy arriving at the end of the line. In this case the theoretical SWR (covered later) in the line will be infinite, but in practice, losses in the line will limit the SWR to some finite value at line positions back toward the source.

At first you might think there is little or no point in terminating a line with a nonresistive load. In a later section we shall examine this in more detail, but the value of input impedance depends on the value of the load impedance, on the length of the line, the losses in a practical line, and on the characteristic impedance of the line. There are times when a line terminated in a nonresistive load can be used to advantage, such as in phasing or matching applications. Remote switching of reactive terminations on sections of line can be used to reverse the beam heading of an antenna array, for example. The point of this brief discussion is that a line need not always be terminated in a load that will consume power.

23.2 PRACTICAL TRANSMISSION LINES

23.2.1 ATTENUATION

Every practical line will have some inherent loss, partly because of the resistance of the conductors, partly because power is consumed in the dielectric used for insulating the conductors, and partly because in many cases a small amount of power escapes from the line by radiation. We shall consider here in detail the losses associated with conductor and dielectric losses.

Matched-Line Losses

Power lost in a transmission line is not directly propor-

tional to the line length, but varies logarithmically with the length. That is, if 10% of the input power is lost in a section of line of certain length, 10% of the remaining power will be lost in the next section of the same length, and so on. For this reason it is customary to express line losses in terms of decibels per unit length, since the decibel is a unit of logarithmic ratios. Calculations are very simple because the total loss in a line is found by multiplying the decibel loss per unit length by the total length of the line.

The power lost in a matched line (that is, where the load is equal to the characteristic impedance of the line) is called *matched-line loss.* Matched-line loss is usually expressed in decibels per 100 feet. It is necessary to specify the frequency for which the loss applies, because the loss does vary with frequency.

Conductor and dielectric loss both increase as the operating frequency is increased, but not in the same way. This, together with the fact that the relative amount of each type of loss depends on the actual construction of the line, makes it impossible to give a specific relationship between loss and frequency that will apply to all types of lines.

One relationship that does apply is that for lines made of the same materials (for example, copper and solid polyethylene) higher impedance lines will have lower losses. This is because the current is lower in a higher impedance line, reducing resistive (I^2R) losses.

In practice, when selecting a feed line, each type of line must be considered individually. Actual loss values for practical lines are given in a later section of this chapter along with a discussion of how to select a feed line.

One effect of matched-line loss in a real transmission line is that the characteristic impedance, Z_0, becomes complex, with a non-zero reactive component X_0. Thus,

$$Z_0 = R_0 - jX_0 \qquad \text{(Eq 3)}$$

$$X_0 = -R_0 \frac{\alpha}{\beta} \qquad \text{(Eq 4)}$$

where

$$\alpha = \frac{\text{Attenuation (dB / 100feet)} \times 0.1151 \text{ (nepers / dB)}}{100 \text{ feet}},$$

the matched-line attenuation, in nepers per unit length (Nepers are a unitless non-logarithmic radio and 1 neper = 8.686 dB.)

$\beta = \dfrac{2\pi}{\lambda}$, the phase constant in radians/unit length.

The reactive portion of the complex characteristic impedance is always capacitive (that is, its sign is negative) and the value of X_0 is usually small compared to the resistive portion R_0.

23.2.2 REFLECTION COEFFICIENT

The ratio of the reflected voltage at a given point on a transmission line to the incident voltage is called the *voltage reflection coefficient*. The voltage reflection coefficient is also equal to the ratio of the incident and reflected currents. Thus

$$\rho = \frac{E_r}{E_f} = \frac{I_r}{I_f} \qquad \text{(Eq 5)}$$

where
  ρ = reflection coefficient
  E_r = reflected voltage
  E_f = forward (incident) voltage
  I_r = reflected current
  I_f = forward (incident) current

The reflection coefficient is determined by the relationship between the line Z_0 and the actual load at the terminated end of the line. In most cases, the actual load is not entirely resistive — that is, the load is a complex impedance, consisting of a resistance in series with a reactance, as is the complex characteristic impedance of the transmission line.

The reflection coefficient is thus a complex quantity, having both amplitude and phase, and is generally designated by the Greek letter ρ (rho), or sometimes as Γ (Gamma). The relationship between R_a (the load resistance), X_a (the load reactance), Z_0 (the complex line characteristic impedance, whose real part is R_0 and whose reactive part is X_0) and the complex reflection coefficient ρ is

$$\rho = \frac{Z_a - Z_0}{Z_a + Z_0} = \frac{(R_a \pm jX_a) - (R_0 \pm jX_0)}{(R_a \pm jX_a) + (R_0 \pm jX_0)} \qquad \text{(Eq 6)}$$

For high-quality, low-loss transmission lines at low frequencies, the characteristic impedance Z_0 is almost completely resistive, meaning that $Z_0 \cong R_0$ and $X_0 \cong 0$. The magnitude of the complex reflection coefficient in Eq 6 then simplifies to:

$$|\rho| = \sqrt{\frac{(R_a - R_0)^2 + X_a{}^2}{(R_a + R_0)^2 + X_a{}^2}} \qquad \text{(Eq 7)}$$

For example, if the characteristic impedance of a coaxial line at a low operating frequency is 50 Ω and the load impedance is 120 Ω in series with a capacitive reactance of –90 Ω, the magnitude of the reflection coefficient is

$$|\rho| = \sqrt{\frac{(120 - 50)^2 + (-90)^2}{(120 + 50)^2 + (-90)^2}} = 0.593$$

Note that the vertical bars on each side of ρ mean the *magnitude* of rho. If R_a in Eq 7 is equal to R_0 and if X_a is 0, the reflection coefficient, ρ, also is 0. This represents a *matched condition*, where all the energy in the incident wave is transferred to the load. On the other hand, if R_a is 0, meaning that the load has no real resistive part, the reflection coefficient is 1.0, regardless of the value of R_0. This means that all the forward power is reflected, since the load is completely reactive. As we shall see later on, the concept of reflection coefficient is a very useful one to evaluate the impedance seen looking into the input of a mismatched transmission line.

Another representation of the reflection coefficient concept is the *return loss*, which is the reflection coefficient expressed in dB.

$$RL = -20 \log |\rho| \text{ dB} \qquad \text{(Eq 8)}$$

For example, a reflection coefficient of 0.593 is a return loss of –20 log (0.593) = 4.5 dB. (Note that some texts express return loss as negative numbers, but most define it as positive.)

23.2.3 STANDING WAVES

As might be expected, reflection cannot occur at the load without some effect on the voltages and currents all along the line. To keep things simple for a while longer, let us continue to consider only resistive loads, without any reactance. The conclusions we shall reach are valid for transmission lines terminated in complex impedances as well.

The effects are most simply shown by vector diagrams. **Figure 23.11** is an example where the terminating resistance R is less than Z_0. The voltage and current vectors at R are shown in the reference position; they correspond with the vectors in Figure 23.10A, turned 90°. Back along the line from R toward the power source, the incident vectors, E1 and I1, lead the vectors at the load according to their position along the line measured in electrical degrees. (The corresponding distances in fractions of a wavelength are also shown.) The vectors representing reflected voltage and current, E2 and I2, successively lag the same vectors at the load.

This lag is the natural consequence of the direction in which the incident and reflected components are traveling, together with the fact that it takes time for power to be transferred along the line. The resultant voltage E and current I at each of these positions is shown as a dotted arrow. Although the incident and reflected components maintain their respective amplitudes (the reflected component is shown at half the incident-component amplitude in this drawing), their phase relationships vary with position along the line. The phase shift causes both the amplitude and phase of the *resultants* to vary with position on the line.

If the amplitude variations (disregarding phase) of the resultant voltage and current are plotted against position along the line, graphs like those of **Figure 23.12A** will result. If we could go along the line with a voltmeter and ammeter measuring the current and voltage at each point, plotting the collected data would give curves like these. In contrast, if the load matched the Z_0 of the line, similar measurements along the line would show that the voltage is the same everywhere (and similarly for the current). The mismatch between load and line is responsible for the variations in amplitude which, because of their stationary, wave-like appearance, are called *standing waves*.

Some general conclusions can be drawn from inspection

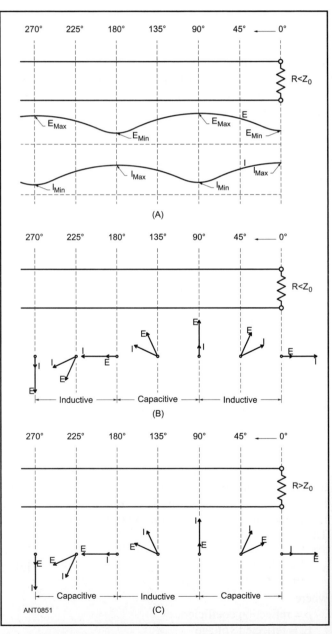

Figure 23.12 — Standing waves of current and voltage along the line for R less than Z_0. At A, resultant voltages and currents along a mismatched line are shown at B and C. At B, R less than Z_0; At C, R greater than Z_0.

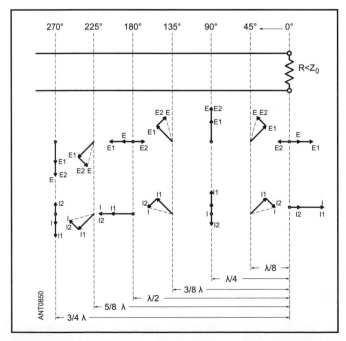

Figure 23.11 — Incident and reflected components at various positions along the transmission line, together with resultant voltages and currents at the same positions. The case shown is for R less than Z_0.

of the standing-wave curves: At a position 180° ($\lambda/2$) from the load, the voltage and current have the same values they do at the load. At a position 90° from the load, the voltage and current are "inverted." That is, if the voltage is lowest and current highest at the load (when R is less than Z_0), then 90° from the load the voltage reaches its highest value. The current reaches its lowest value at the same point. In the case where R is greater than Z_0, so the voltage is highest and the current lowest at the load, the voltage is lowest and the current is highest 90° from the load.

Note that the conditions at the 90° point also exist at the 270° point ($3\lambda/4$). If the graph were continued on toward the source of power it would be found that this duplication occurs at every point that is an odd multiple of 90° (odd multiple of $\lambda/4$) from the load. Similarly, the voltage and current are the same at every point that is a multiple of 180° (any multiple of $\lambda/2$) away from the load.

Standing-Wave Ratio

The ratio of the maximum voltage (resulting from the interaction of incident and reflected voltages along the line) to the minimum voltage — that is, the ratio of E_{max} to E_{min} in Figure 23.12A, is defined as the *voltage standing-wave ratio* (VSWR) or simply *standing-wave ratio* (SWR).

$$SWR = \frac{E_{max}}{E_{min}} = \frac{I_{max}}{I_{min}} \qquad \text{(Eq 9)}$$

The ratio of the maximum current to the minimum current is the same as the VSWR, so either current or voltage can be measured to determine the standing-wave ratio. The standing-wave ratio is an index of many of the properties of a mismatched line. It can be measured with fairly simple equipment, so it is a convenient quantity to use in making calculations on line performance.

The SWR is related to the magnitude of the complex reflection coefficient by

$$SWR = \frac{1+|\rho|}{1-|\rho|} \qquad \text{(Eq 10)}$$

and conversely the reflection coefficient magnitude may be defined from a measurement of SWR as

$$|\rho| = \frac{SWR-1}{SWR+1} \qquad \text{(Eq 11)}$$

We may also express the reflection coefficient in terms of forward and reflected power, quantities which can be easily measured using a directional RF wattmeter. The reflection coefficient may be computed as

$$\rho = \sqrt{\frac{P_r}{P_f}} \qquad \text{(Eq 12)}$$

where
P_r = power in the reflected wave
P_f = power in the forward wave.

From Eq 11, SWR is related to the forward and reflected power by

$$SWR = \frac{1+|\rho|}{1-|\rho|} = \frac{1+\sqrt{P_r/P_f}}{1-\sqrt{P_r/P_f}} \qquad \text{(Eq 13)}$$

Figure 23.13 converts Eq 13 into a convenient

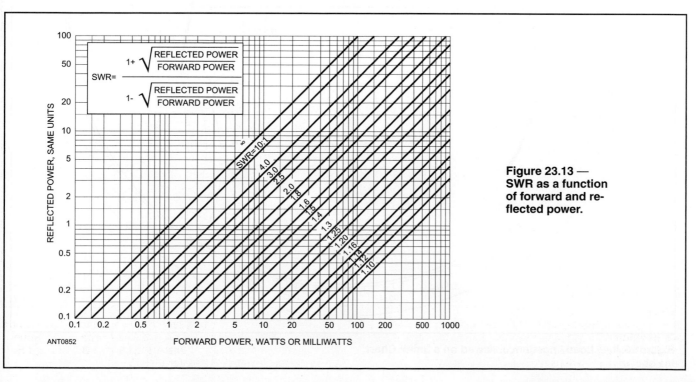

Figure 23.13 — SWR as a function of forward and reflected power.

SWR and Resonance

It is a common misunderstanding that for a transmission line connected to an antenna, minimum SWR occurs when the antenna is resonant. In a general sense, this is not true — minimum SWR occurs when the magnitude of the load's reflection coefficient, $|\rho|$, is at a minimum (see Eq 7). Viewing the load impedance on a Smith Chart as in **Figure 23.A**, the value of $|\rho|$ is represented by the distance from the origin (center) to the point representing the load impedance. (The Smith Chart is explored in the PDF supplement, "The Smith Chart" on this book's CD-ROM.)

As the frequency changes, the impedance of an antenna changes. The example in Figure 23.A shows points A, B and C — three plausible load impedances for an antenna at different frequencies. Point O is the origin. The antenna is resonant at both A and C since the points are on the X=0 line through the middle of the chart. At point A the impedance is 0.2 + j0 or 10 Ω in a 50-Ω system and C represents 4.0 + j0 Ω or 200 Ω. The magnitude of ρ at A is 0.67 and the SWR = 5:1. The magnitude of ρ at C is 0.6 and the SWR = 4:1. Point B represents the normalized load impedance 0.8 + j0.8, which is 40 + j40 Ω in a 50-Ω system. The magnitude of ρ at B is 0.062 and the SWR = 1.13. Even though the load impedance at B is reactive (nonresonant) the SWR is lower than at either of the two resonant points at A and C.

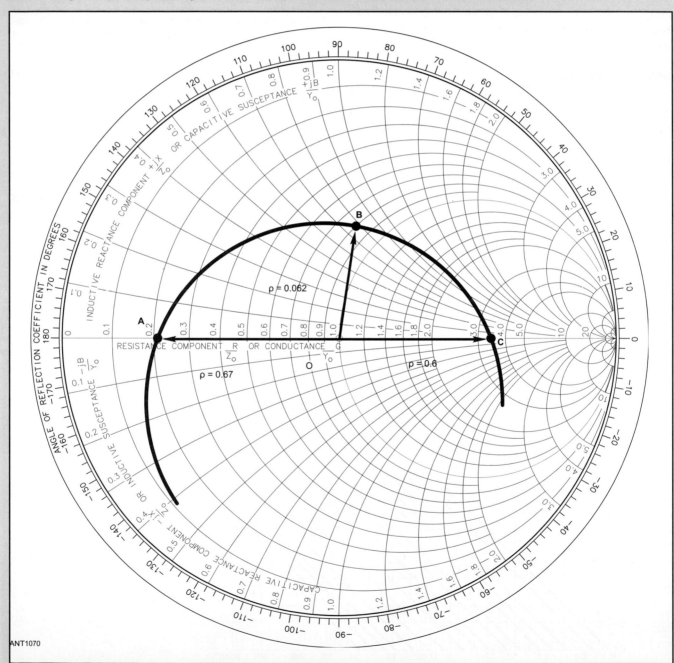

Figure 23.A — Load impedance viewed on a Smith Chart.

nomograph. In the simple case where the load contains no reactance, the SWR is numerically equal to the ratio between the load resistance R and the characteristic impedance of the line. When R is greater than Z_0,

$$SWR = \frac{R}{Z_0} \qquad \text{(Eq 14)}$$

When R is less than Z_0,

$$SWR = \frac{Z_0}{R} \qquad \text{(Eq 15)}$$

(The smaller quantity is always used in the denominator of the fraction so the ratio will be a number greater than 1).

It is important to note that in a lossless transmission line, SWR does not change with length of the line or along the line. While the values of voltage and current do change along the line, the ratio of their maximum and minimum values does not. The value of SWR shown by typical amateur SWR measuring instruments may change with line length but that can result from a number of causes; inaccuracy of the voltage or current sensing circuits, common-mode current on the outside of a coaxial feed line shield, and signals from a nearby transmitter upsetting the voltage or current measurement being the most common reasons.

Flat Lines

As discussed earlier, all the power that is transferred along a transmission line is absorbed in the load if that load is a resistance value equal to the Z_0 of the line. In this case, the line is said to be *perfectly matched*. None of the power is reflected back toward the source. As a result, no standing waves of current or voltage will be developed along the line. For a line operating in this condition, the waveforms drawn in Figure 23.12A become straight lines, representing the voltage and current delivered by the source. The voltage along the line is constant, so the minimum value is the same as the maximum value. The voltage standing-wave ratio is therefore 1:1. Because a plot of the voltage standing wave is a straight line, the matched line is also said to be *flat*.

23.2.4 ADDITIONAL POWER LOSS DUE TO SWR

The power lost in a given line is least when the line is terminated in a resistance equal to its characteristic impedance, and as stated previously, that is called the *matched-line loss*. There is however an *additional loss* that increases with an increase in the SWR. This is because the effective values of both current and voltage become greater on lines with standing waves. The increase in effective current raises the ohmic losses (I^2R) in the conductors, and the increase in effective voltage increases the losses in the dielectric (E^2/R).

The increased loss caused by an SWR greater than 1:1 may or may not be serious. If the SWR at the load is not greater than 2:1, the additional loss caused by the standing waves, as compared with the loss when the line is perfectly matched, does not amount to more than about ½ dB, even on very long lines. One-half dB is an undetectable change in signal strength. Therefore, it can be said that, from a practical standpoint in the HF bands, an SWR of 2:1 or less is every bit as good as a perfect match, so far as additional losses due to SWR are concerned.

However, above 30 MHz, in the VHF and especially the UHF range, where low receiver noise figures are essential for effective weak-signal work, matched-line losses for commonly available types of coax can be relatively high. This means that even a slight mismatch may become a concern regarding overall transmission line losses. At UHF one-half dB of additional loss may be considered intolerable!

The total loss in a line, including matched-line and the additional loss due to standing waves may be calculated from Eq 16 below for moderate levels of SWR (less than 20:1).

$$\text{Total Loss (dB)} = 10 \log \left(\frac{a^2 - |\rho|^2}{a\,(1 - |\rho|^2)} \right) \qquad \text{(Eq 16)}$$

where

$a = 10^{0.1\,ML}$ = matched-line loss ratio

ML = the matched-line loss in dB for the particular length of line

$|\rho|$ = the reflection coefficient at the load, calculated as in Eq 7

and reflected power is assumed to be re-reflected at the source.

Thus, the additional loss caused by the standing waves is calculated from:

Additional Loss (dB) = Total Loss – ML $\qquad$ (Eq 17)

For example, RG-213 coax at 14.2 MHz is rated at 0.795 dB of matched-line loss per 100 feet. A 150-foot length of RG-213 would have an overall matched-line loss of

$$(0.795/100) \times 150 = 1.193 \text{ dB}$$

Thus, if the SWR at the load end of the RG-213 is 4:1,

$$\alpha = 10^{1.193/10} = 1.316$$

$$|\rho| = \frac{4-1}{4+1} = 0.600$$

and the total line loss

$$= 10 \log \left(\frac{1.316^2 - 0.600^2}{1.316\,(1 - 0.600^2)} \right) = 2.12 \text{ dB}$$

The additional loss due to the SWR of 4:1 is 2.12 – 1.19 = 0.93 dB. **Figure 23.14A** is a graph of additional loss versus SWR. Figure 23.14B is a nomograph equivalent to Figure 23.14A. Figure 23.14C is an alternative graph that shows the fraction of input power actually delivered to the load for a given source SWR and line Matched Loss (ML).

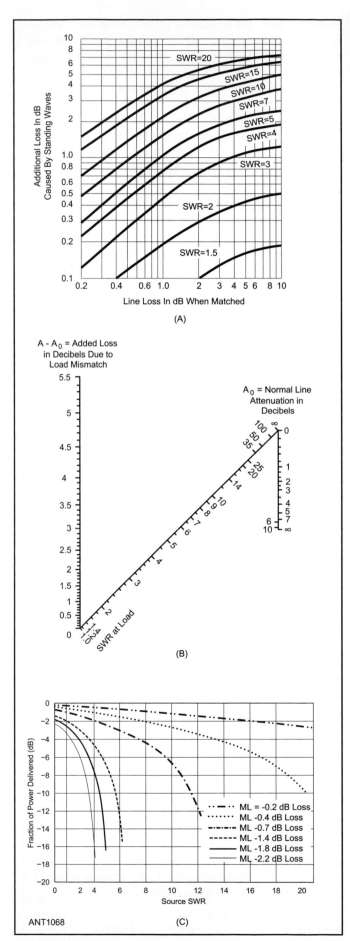

Figure 23.14 — (A) Additional line loss due to standing waves (SWR, measured at the load). See Figure 23.24 for matched-line loss. To determine the total loss in dB, add the matched-line loss to the value from this graph. **(B)** Nomograph showing Added Loss in dB due to mismatch (SWR at Load) with a known line attenuation. Place a straightedge along the points representing load SWR and line attenuation. Read additional loss on the left-hand scale. **(C)** Fractional amount of the input power delivered to the load given source or input SWR and line attenuation. (Graph provided courtesy of Refined Audiometrics Laboratory, LLC by David McLain, N7AIG.)

23.2.5 LINE VOLTAGES AND CURRENTS

It is often desirable to know the maximum voltages and currents that are developed in a line operating with standing waves. (We'll cover the determination of the exact voltages and currents along a transmission line later.) The voltage maximum may be calculated from Eq 18 below, and the other values determined from the result.

$$E_{max} = \sqrt{P \times Z_0 \times SWR} \qquad (Eq\ 18)$$

where

E_{max} = voltage maximum along the line in the presence of standing waves

P = power delivered by the source to the line input in watts

Z_0 = characteristic impedance of the line in ohms

SWR = SWR at the load

If 100 W of power is applied to a 600-Ω line with an SWR at the load of 10:1,

$$E_{max} = \sqrt{100 \times 600 \times 10} = 774.6\ V$$

Based on Eq 8, E_{min}, the minimum voltage along the line equals E_{max}/SWR = 774.6/10 = 77.5 V. The maximum current may be found by using Ohm's Law. I_{max} = E_{max}/Z_0 =774.6/600 = 1.29 A. The minimum current equals I_{max}/SWR = 1.29/10 = 0.129 A.

The voltage determined from Eq 17 is the RMS value — that is, the voltage that would be measured with an ordinary RF voltmeter. If voltage breakdown is a consideration, the value from Eq 18 should be converted to an *instantaneous peak voltage*. Do this by multiplying times $\sqrt{2}$ (assuming the RF waveform is a sine wave). Thus, the maximum instantaneous peak voltage in the above example is 774.6 × $\sqrt{2}$ = 1095.4 V.

Strictly speaking, the values obtained as above apply only near the load in the case of lines with appreciable losses. However, the resultant values are the maximum possible that can exist along the line, whether there are line losses or not. For this reason they are useful as a rule-of-thumb in determining whether or not a particular line can operate safely with a given SWR. Voltage ratings for various cable types are given in a later section.

Figure 23.15 shows the ratio of current or voltage at a loop, in the presence of standing waves, to the current or

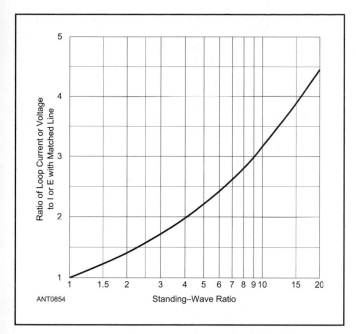

Figure 23.15 — Increase in maximum value of current or voltage on a line with standing waves, as referred to the current or voltage on a perfectly matched line, for the same power delivered to the load. Voltage and current at minimum points are given by the reciprocals of the values along the vertical axis. The curve is plotted from the relationship, current (or voltage) ratio = the square root of SWR.

voltage that would exist with the same power in a perfectly matched line. As with Eq 18 and related calculations, the curve literally applies only near the load.

23.2.6 INPUT IMPEDANCE

The effects of incident and reflected voltage and current along a mismatched transmission line can be difficult to envision, particularly when the load at the end of the transmission line is not purely resistive, and when the line is not perfectly lossless.

If we can put aside for a moment all the complexities of reflections, SWR and line losses, a transmission line can simply be considered to be an *impedance transformer*. A certain value of load impedance, consisting of a resistance and reactance, at the end of a particular transmission line is transformed into another value of impedance at the input of the line. The amount of transformation is determined by the electrical length of the line, its characteristic impedance, and by the losses inherent in the line. The input impedance of a real, lossy transmission line is computed using the following equation, called the *Transmission Line Equation*, which uses the hyperbolic cosine and sine functions.

$$Z_{in} = Z_0 \frac{Z_L \cosh(\gamma\ell) + Z_0 \sinh(\gamma\ell)}{Z_L \sinh(\gamma\ell) + Z_0 \cosh(\gamma\ell)} \qquad \text{(Eq 19)}$$

where

Z_{in} = complex impedance at input of line
Z_L = complex load impedance at end of line = $R_a \pm j X_a$
Z_0 = characteristic impedance of line = $R_0 - j X_0$

ℓ = physical length of line
γ = complex loss coefficient = $\alpha + j\beta$
α = matched-line loss attenuation constant, in nepers/unit length (1 neper = 8.686 dB; cables are rated in dB/100 ft)
β = phase constant of line in radians/unit length (related to physical length of line ℓ by the fact that 2π radians = one wavelength, and by Eq 2)

$$\beta = \frac{2\pi}{VF \times 983.6 / f(MHz)} \quad \text{for } \ell \text{ in feet}$$

VF = velocity factor

For example, assume that a half-wave dipole terminates a 50-foot long piece of RG-213 coax. This dipole is assumed to have an impedance of 43 + j 30 Ω at 7.15 MHz, and its velocity factor is 0.66. The matched-line loss at 7.15 MHz is 0.54 dB/100 feet, and the characteristic impedance Z_0 for this type of cable at this frequency is 50 − j 0.45 Ω. Using Eq 19, we compute the impedance at the input of the line as 65.8 + j 32.0 Ω.

Solving this equation manually is quite tedious, but it may be solved using a traditional paper Smith Chart or a computer program. (The PDF file "The Smith Chart" explains how to use the chart and is available on this book's CD-ROM.) *SimSmith* by AE6TY (**www.ae6ty.com/Smith_Charts.html**) is available for free download and there are several on-line calculators available if you search for "smith chart calculator" on the Internet. *TLW* (Transmission Line for Windows) is another ARRL program that performs this transformation, but without Smith Chart graphics. *TLW* is also on this book's CD-ROM.

One caution should be noted when using any of these computational tools to calculate the impedance at the input of a mismatched transmission line — the velocity factor of practical transmission lines can vary significantly between manufacturing runs of the same type of cable. For highest accuracy, you should measure the velocity factor of a particular length of cable before using it to compute the impedance at the end of the cable. See the chapter **Antenna and Transmission Line Measurements** for details on measurements of line characteristics.

Input SWR and Line Loss

If the line is not perfectly matched to the load the loss in the line reduces the amount of reflected power that returns to the source end of the line. This makes SWR appear lower at the source (transmitter) end of the line than it is at the load (antenna) end of the line. The longer the line or the higher the loss, the more power is dissipated as heat and the lower the input SWR. In fact, a long (many wavelengths) lossy transmission line can be used as a dummy load at VHF and higher frequencies.

A nomograph is given in **Figure 23.16** that relates load SWR, line attenuation, and load SWR. If you know any two of those three parameters, place a ruler between those two points and read the third from the intersection of the ruler with the scale for the unknown parameter.

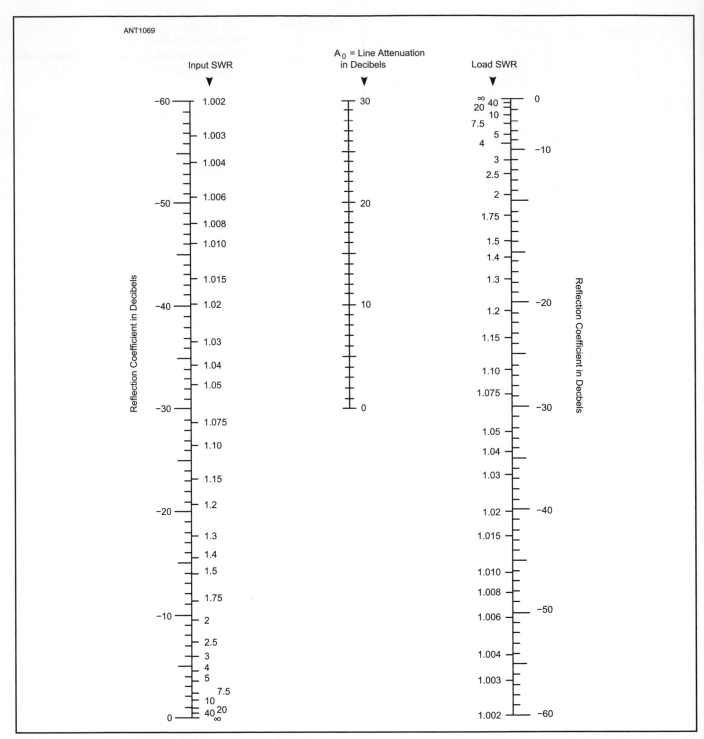

Figure 23.16 — Nomograph showing that load SWR, line attenuation or input SWR can be determined if two of the values are known. Place a straightedge between the two known values and read the value of the third where the straightedge crosses the scale for the third parameter.

Series and Parallel Equivalent Circuits

Once the series-form impedance $R_S \pm j\, X_S$ at the input of a particular line has been determined, either by measurement or by computation, you may wish to determine the equivalent parallel circuit $R_P \parallel \pm j\, X_P$, which is equivalent to the series form only at a single frequency. The equivalent parallel circuit is often useful when designing a matching circuit (such as an antenna tuner, for example) to transform the impedance at the input of the cable to another impedance. The following equations are used to make the transformation from series to parallel and from parallel to series. See **Figure 23.17**.

$$R_p = \frac{R_s^{\,2} + X_s^{\,2}}{R_s} \qquad\qquad \text{(Eq 20A)}$$

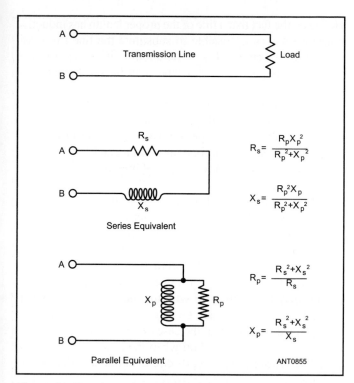

Figure 23.17 — Input impedance of a line terminated in a resistance. This impedance can be represented by either a resistance and reactance in series, or a resistance and reactance in parallel, at a single frequency. The relationships between the R and X values in the series and parallel equivalents are given by the equations shown. X may be either inductive or capacitive, depending on the line length, Z_0 and the load impedance, which need not be purely resistive.

$$X_p = \frac{R_s^2 + X_s^2}{X_s} \qquad \text{(Eq 20B)}$$

and

$$R_s = \frac{R_p X_p^2}{R_p^2 + X_p^2} \qquad \text{(Eq 21A)}$$

$$X_s = \frac{R_p^2 X_p}{R_p^2 + X_p^2} \qquad \text{(Eq 21B)}$$

The individual values in the parallel circuit are not the same as those in the series circuit (although the overall result is the same, but only at one frequency), but are related to the series-circuit values by these equations. For example, let us continue the example in the section above, where the impedance at the input of the 50 feet of RG-213 at 7.15 MHz is $65.8 + j\,32.0\ \Omega$. The equivalent parallel circuit at 7.15 MHz is

$$R_p = \frac{65.8^2 + 32.1^2}{65.8} = 81.46\ \Omega$$

$$X_p = \frac{65.8^2 + 31.2^2}{31.2} = 169.97\ \Omega$$

If we were to put 100 W of power into this parallel equivalent circuit, the voltage across the parallel components would be

$$P = \frac{E^2}{R}, \quad E = \sqrt{P \times R} = \sqrt{100 \times 81.46} = 90.26\ V$$

Thus, the current through the inductive part of the parallel circuit would be

$$I = \frac{E}{X_p} = \frac{90.26}{169.97} = 0.53\ A$$

Highly Reactive Loads

When highly reactive loads are used with practical transmission lines, especially coax lines, the overall loss can reach staggering levels. For example, a popular multiband antenna is a 100-foot long center-fed dipole located some 50 feet over average ground. At 1.83 MHz, such an antenna will exhibit a feed-point impedance of $4.5 - j\,1673\ \Omega$, according to the analysis program *EZNEC-ARRL*. The high value of capacitive reactance indicates that the antenna is extremely short electrically — after all, a half-wave dipole at 1.83 MHz is almost 270 feet long, compared to this 100 foot long antenna. If an amateur attempts to feed such a multiband antenna directly with 100 feet of RG-213 50-Ω coaxial cable, the SWR at the antenna terminals would be (using the *TLW* program) 1740:1. An SWR of more than 1700 to one is a very high level of SWR indeed! At 1.83 MHz the *matched-line loss* of 100 feet of the RG-213 coax by itself is only 0.26 dB. However, the *total line loss* due to this extreme level of SWR is 26 dB.

This means that if 100 W is fed into the input of this line, the amount of power at the antenna is reduced to only 0.25 W. Admittedly this is an extreme case. It is more likely that an amateur would feed such a multiband antenna with open-wire *ladder* or *window* line than coaxial cable. The matched-line loss characteristics for 450-Ω window open-wire line are far better than coax, but the SWR at the end of this line is still 793:1, resulting in an overall loss of 8.9 dB. Even for low-loss open-wire line, the total loss is significant because of the extreme SWR.

This means that only about 13% of the power from the transmitter is getting to the antenna, and although this is not very desirable, it is a lot better than the losses in coax cable feeding the same antenna. However, at a transmitter power level of 1500 W, the maximum voltage in a typical antenna tuner used to match this line impedance is almost 9200V with the open-wire line, a level which will certainly cause arcing or burning inside. (As a small compensation for all the loss in coax under this extreme condition, so much power is lost that the voltages present in the antenna tuner are not excessive.) Keep in mind also that an antenna tuner can lose significant power in internal losses for very high impedance levels, even if it has sufficient range to match such impedances in the first place.

Clearly, it would be far better to use a longer antenna at this 160 meter frequency. Another alternative would be to resonate a short antenna with loading coils (at the antenna). Either strategy would help avoid excessive feed line loss, even with low-loss line.

23.2.7 SPECIAL CASES

Beside the primary purpose of transporting power from one point to another, transmission lines have properties that are useful in a variety of ways. One such special case is a line an exact multiple of λ/4 (90°) long. As shown earlier, such a line will have a purely resistive input impedance when the termination is a pure resistance. Also, short-circuited or open-circuited lines can be used in place of conventional inductors and capacitors since such lines have an input impedance that is substantially a pure reactance when the line losses are low.

The Half-Wavelength Line

When the line length is a multiple of 180° (that is, a multiple of λ/2), the input resistance is equal to the load resistance, regardless of the line Z_0. As a matter of fact, a line an exact multiple of λ/2 in length (disregarding line losses) simply repeats, at its input or sending end, whatever impedance exists at its output or receiving end. It does not matter whether the impedance at the receiving end is resistive, reactive, or a combination of both. Sections of line having such length can be added or removed without changing any of the operating conditions, at least when the losses in the line itself are negligible.

Impedance Transformation with Quarter-Wave Lines

The input impedance of a line an odd multiple of λ/4 long is

$$Z_i = \frac{Z_0^{\,2}}{Z_L} \tag{Eq 22}$$

where Z_i is the input impedance and Z_L is the load impedance. If Z_L is a pure resistance, Z_i will also be a pure resistance. Rearranging this equation gives

$$Z_0 = \sqrt{Z_i Z_L} \tag{Eq 23}$$

This means that if we have two values of impedance that we wish to "match," we can do so if we connect them together by a λ/4 transmission line having a characteristic impedance equal to the square root of their product.

A λ/4 line is, in effect, a transformer, and in fact is often referred to as a *quarter-wave transformer*. It is frequently used as such in antenna work when it is desired, for example, to transform the impedance of an antenna to a new value that will match a given transmission line. This subject is considered in greater detail in a later chapter.

Lines as Circuit Elements

Two types of non-resistive line terminations are quite useful — short and open circuits. The impedance of the short-circuit termination is $0 + j\,0$, and the impedance of the open-circuit termination is infinite. Such terminations are used in *stub matching* as described in the **Transmission Line Coupling and Impedance Matching** chapter. An open- or short-circuited line does not deliver any power to a load, and for that reason is not, strictly speaking a "transmission" line.

However, the fact that a line of the proper length has inductive reactance makes it possible to substitute the line for a coil in an ordinary circuit. Likewise, another line of appropriate length having capacitive reactance can be substituted for a capacitor.

Sections of lines used as circuit elements are usually λ/4 or less long. The desired type of reactance (inductive or capacitive) or the desired type of resonance (series or parallel) is obtained by shorting or opening the far end of the line. The circuit equivalents of various types of line sections are shown in **Figure 23.18**.

When a line section is used as a reactance, the amount of reactance is determined by the characteristic impedance and the electrical length of the line. The type of reactance exhibited at the input terminals of a line of given length depends on whether it is open- or short-circuited at the far end.

The equivalent *lumped* value for any inductor or capacitor may be determined with the aid of the Smith Chart or Eq 19. Line losses may be taken into account if desired, as explained for Eq 19. In the case of a line having no losses, and to a close approximation when the losses are small, the inductive reactance of a short- circuited line less than λ/4 in length is

$$X_L \text{ in } \Omega = Z_0 \tan \ell \tag{Eq 24}$$

where ℓ is the length of the line in electrical degrees and Z_0 is the characteristic impedance of the line.

The capacitive reactance of an open-circuited line less than λ/4 in length is

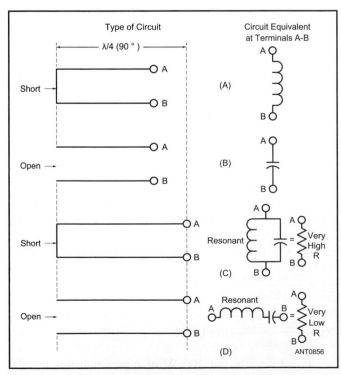

Figure 23.18 — Lumped-constant circuit equivalents of open- and short-circuited transmission lines.

$$X_C \text{ in } \Omega = Z_0 \cot \ell \qquad \text{(Eq 25)}$$

Lengths of line that are exact multiples of $\lambda/4$ have the properties of resonant circuits. With an open-circuit termination, the input impedance of the line acts like a series-resonant circuit. With a short-circuit termination, the line input simulates a parallel-resonant circuit. The effective Q of such linear resonant circuits is very high if the line losses, both in resistance and by radiation, are kept down. This can be done without much difficulty, particularly in coaxial lines, if air insulation is used between the conductors. Air-insulated open-wire lines are likewise very good at frequencies for which the conductor spacing is very small in terms of wavelength.

Applications of line sections as circuit elements in connection with antenna and transmission-line systems are discussed in later chapters.

23.2.8 VOLTAGE AND CURRENT ALONG A LINE

The voltage and current along a transmission line will vary in a predictable manner, whether that line is matched or mismatched at its load end. (The voltage and current along a matched line vary because of loss in the line.) Eq 26 below describes the voltage at point ℓ, while Eq 27 describes the current at point ℓ, each as a function of the voltage at the input of the line.

$$E_x = E_{in} \left(\cosh \gamma\ell - \frac{Z_0}{Z_{in}} \sinh \gamma\ell \right) \text{volts} \qquad \text{(Eq 26)}$$

$$I_x = \frac{E_{in}}{Z_{in}} \left(\cosh \gamma\ell - \frac{Z_{in}}{Z_0} \sinh \gamma\ell \right) \text{amperes} \qquad \text{(Eq 27)}$$

where γ = complex loss coefficient used in Eq 19, and cosh and sinh are the hyperbolic cosine and sine functions. The load end of the transmission line is, by definition, at a length of ℓ.

The power at the input and the output of a transmission line may be calculated using Eq 28 and Eq 29 below.

$$P_{in} = \left| E_{in} \right|^2 G_{in} \text{ watts} \qquad \text{(Eq 28)}$$

$$P_{load} = \left| E_{load} \right|^2 G_{load} \text{ watts} \qquad \text{(Eq 29)}$$

where G_{in} and G_{load} are the admittance at the input (the real part of $1/Z_{in}$) and the admittance at the load (the real part of $1/Z_{load}$) ends respectively of the line. Z_{in} is calculated using Eq 19 for a length of ℓ.

The power loss in the transmission line in dB is:

$$P_{loss} = 10 \log \left(\frac{P_{in}}{P_{load}} \right) \text{dB} \qquad \text{(Eq 30)}$$

23.3 FEED LINE CONSTRUCTION AND OPERATING CHARACTERISTICS

The two basic types of transmission lines, parallel conductor and coaxial, can be constructed in a variety of forms. Both types can be divided into two classes, (1) those in which the majority of the insulation between the conductors is air, where only the minimum of solid dielectric necessary for mechanical support is used, and (2) those in which the conductors are embedded in and separated by a solid dielectric. The first variety (air-insulated) has the lowest loss per unit length, because there is no power loss in dry air if the voltage between conductors is below the level at which corona forms. At the maximum power permitted in amateur transmitters, it is seldom necessary to consider corona unless the SWR on the line is very high.

23.3.1 AIR-INSULATED LINES

A typical construction technique used for parallel conductor or "two-wire" air-insulated transmission lines is shown in **Figure 23.19**. The two wires are supported a fixed distance apart by means of insulating rods called spacers. Spacers may be made from material such as Teflon, Plexiglas, phenolic, polystyrene, plastic clothespins or plastic hair curlers. Materials commonly used in high-quality spacers are isolantite or Steatite, Lucite and polystyrene. (Teflon is generally not used because of its higher cost.) The spacer length varies from 2 to 6 inches. Smaller spacings are desirable at higher

frequencies (28 MHz and above) so radiation from the transmission line is minimized.

Spacers must be used at small enough intervals along the line to keep the two wires from moving appreciably with respect to each other. For amateur purposes, lines using this

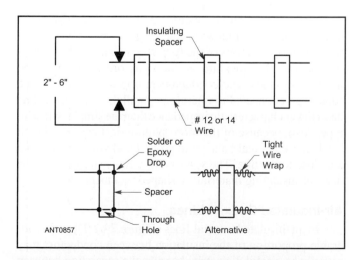

Figure 23.19 — Typical open-wire line construction. The spacers may be held in place by beads of solder or epoxy cement. Wire wraps can also be used, as shown.

construction ordinarily have #12 AWG or #14 AWG conductors, and the characteristic impedance is between 500 to 600 Ω. Although once used nearly exclusively, such homemade lines are enjoying a renaissance of sorts because of their high efficiency and low cost.

Where an air-insulated line with still lower characteristic impedance is needed, metal tubing from ¼ to ½-inch diameter is frequently used. With the larger conductor diameter and relatively close spacing, it is possible to build a line having a characteristic impedance as low as about 200 Ω. This construction technique is principally used for λ/4 matching transformers at the higher frequencies.

The characteristic impedance of an air-insulated parallel conductor line, neglecting the effect of the spacers, is given by

$$Z_0 = 120 \ \cosh^{-1}\left(\frac{S}{d}\right) = 276 \log\left[\frac{S}{d} + \sqrt{\left(\frac{D}{d}\right)^2 - 1}\right] \quad \text{(Eq 31A)}$$

where

    Z_0 = characteristic impedance in ohms
    S = center-to-center distance between conductors
    d = outer diameter of conductor (in the same units as S)

An approximation that can be used when S >> d is:

$$Z_0 = 276 \log\left(\frac{2S}{d}\right) \quad \text{(Eq 31B)}$$

The error of the approximation becomes significant for S/d < 3. A useful identity for working with the cosh⁻¹ or acosh function encountered in transmission line calculations is:

$$\cosh^{-1}(x) = \ln\left(x + \sqrt{x^2 - 1}\right)$$

The inverse hyperbolic cosine (cosh) is sometimes accessed on calculators by using the INV (inverse) key before COSH. Impedances for common sizes of conductors over a range of spacings are given in **Figure 23.20**.

Four-Wire Lines

Another parallel conductor line that is useful in some applications is the four-wire line (**Figure 23.21C**). In cross section, the conductors of the four-wire line are at the corners of a square. Spacings are on the same order as those used in two-wire lines. The conductors at opposite corners of the square are connected to operate in parallel. This type of line has a lower characteristic impedance than the simple two-wire type. Also, because of the more symmetrical construction, it has better electrical balance to ground and other objects that are close to the line. The spacers for a four-wire line may be discs of insulating material, X-shaped members, etc.

Air-Insulated Coaxial Lines

In air-insulated coaxial lines (Figure 23.21D), a considerable proportion of the insulation between conductors may actually be a solid dielectric, because the separation between the inner and outer conductors must be constant. This is particularly likely to be true in small diameter lines. The

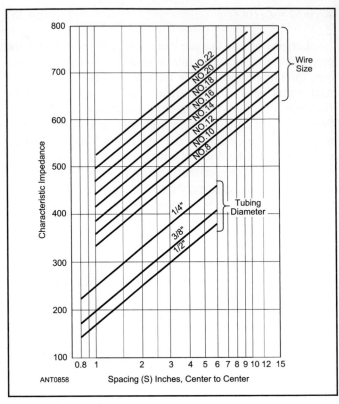

Figure 23.20 — **Characteristic impedance as a function of conductor spacing and size for parallel conductor lines.**

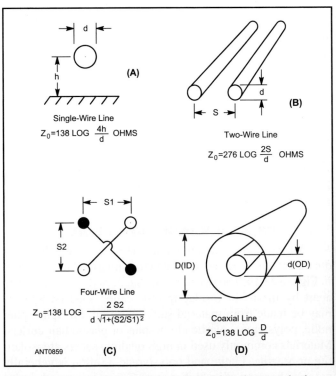

Figure 23.21 — **Construction of air-insulated transmission lines.**

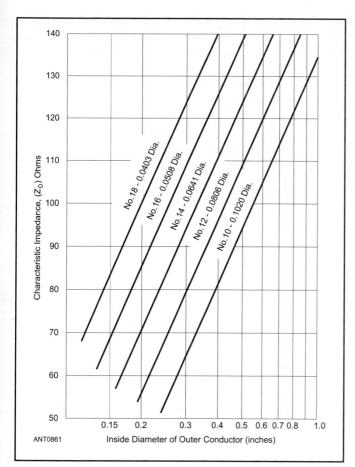

Figure 23.22 — Characteristic impedance of typical air insulated coaxial lines.

Z_0 = characteristic impedance in ohms
D = inside diameter of outer conductor
d = outside diameter of inner conductor
    (in same units as D)

Values for typical conductor sizes are graphed in **Figure 23.22**. The equation and the graph for coaxial lines are approximately correct for lines in which bead spacers are used, provided the beads are not too closely spaced.

23.3.2 FLEXIBLE LINES

Transmission lines in which the conductors are separated by a flexible dielectric have a number of advantages over the air-insulated type. They are less bulky, weigh less in comparable types and maintain more uniform spacing between conductors. They are also generally easier to install, and are neater in appearance. Both parallel conductor and coaxial lines are available with flexible insulation.

The chief disadvantage of such lines is that the power loss per unit length is greater than in air-insulated lines. Power is lost in heating of the dielectric, and if the heating is great enough (as it may be with high power and a high SWR) the line may break down mechanically and electrically.

Parallel-Conductor Lines

The construction of a number of types of flexible line is shown in **Figure 23.23**. In the most common 300-Ω type (twin-lead), the conductors are stranded wire equivalent to #20 AWG in cross-sectional area, and are molded in the edges of a polyethylene ribbon about ½-inch wide that keeps the wires spaced a constant amount away from each other. The effective dielectric is partly solid and partly air, and the presence of the solid dielectric lowers the characteristic impedance of the line as compared with the same conductors in air. The resulting impedance is approximately 300 Ω.

Because part of the field between the conductors exists outside the solid dielectric, dirt and moisture on the surface of the ribbon tend to change the characteristic impedance of the line. The operation of the line is therefore affected by weather conditions. The effect will not be very serious in a line terminated in its characteristic impedance, but if there is a considerable mismatch, a small change in Z_0 may cause wide fluctuations of the input impedance. Weather effects can be minimized by cleaning the line occasionally and giving it a thin coating of a water repellent material such as silicone grease or car wax.

To overcome the effects of weather on the characteristic impedance and attenuation of ribbon type line, another type of twin-lead is made using an oval polyethylene tube with an air core or a foamed dielectric core. The conductors are molded diametrically opposite each other in the walls. This increases the leakage path across the dielectric surface. Also, much of the electric field between the conductors is in the hollow (or foam-filled) center of the tube. This type of line is fairly impervious to weather effects. Care should be used when installing it, however, so any moisture that condenses on the inside with changes in temperature and humidity can

inner conductor, usually a solid copper wire, is supported at the center of the copper tubing outer conductor by insulating beads or a helically wound strip of insulating material. The beads are usually are isolantite or Steatite, and the wire is generally crimped on each side of each bead to prevent the beads from sliding. The material of which the beads are made, and the number of beads per unit length of line, will affect the characteristic impedance of the line. The greater the number of beads in a given length, the lower the characteristic impedance compared with the value obtained with air insulation only. Teflon is ordinarily used as a helically wound support for the center conductor. A tighter helical winding lowers the characteristic impedance.

The presence of the solid dielectric also increases the losses in the line. On the whole, however, a coaxial line of this type tends to have lower actual loss, at frequencies up to about 100 MHz, than any other line construction, provided the air inside the line can be kept dry. This usually means that air-tight seals must be used at the ends of the line and at every joint. The characteristic impedance of an air-insulated coaxial line is given by

$$Z_0 = 138 \log \frac{D}{d} \qquad \text{(Eq 32)}$$

where

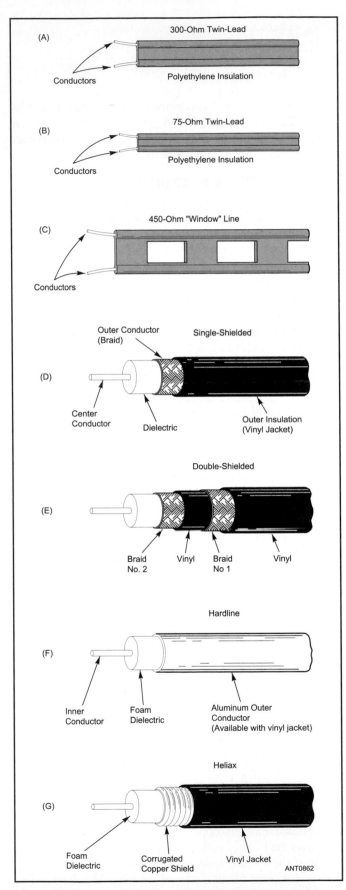

Figure 23.23 — Construction of flexible parallel conductor and coaxial lines with solid dielectric. A common variation of the double shielded design at E has the braids in continuous electrical contact.

drain out at the bottom end of the tube and not be trapped in one section. This type of line is made in two conductor sizes (with different tube diameters), one for receiving applications and the other for transmitting.

Transmitting type 75-Ω twin lead uses stranded conductors nearly equivalent to solid #12 AWG wire, with quite close spacing between conductors. Because of the close spacing, most of the field is confined to the solid dielectric, with very little existing in the surrounding air. This makes the 75-Ω line much less susceptible to weather effects than the 300-Ω ribbon type. The 75 Ω twinlead is becoming increasingly uncommon.

A third type of commercial parallel-line is so-called *window line*, illustrated in Figure 23.23C. This is a variation of twin-lead construction, except that *windows* are cut in the polyethylene insulation at regular intervals. This holds down on the weight of the line, and also breaks up the amount of surface area where dirt, dust and moisture can accumulate. Such window line is commonly available with a nominal characteristic impedance of 450 Ω, although 300-Ω line can be found also. A conductor spacing of about 1 inch is used in the 450-Ω line and ½ inch in the 300-Ω line. The conductor size is usually about #18 AWG. The impedances of such lines are somewhat lower than given by Figure 23.20 for the same conductor size and spacing, because of the effect of the dielectric constant of the spacer material used. The attenuation is quite low and lines of this type are entirely satisfactory for transmitting applications at amateur power levels.

23.3.3 COAXIAL CABLES

Coaxial cable is available in flexible and semi-flexible varieties. The fundamental design is the same in all types, as shown in Figure 23.23. The outer diameter varies from 0.06 inch to over 5 inches. Power handling capability and cable size are directly proportional, as larger dielectric thickness and larger conductor sizes can handle higher voltages and currents. Generally, losses decrease as cable diameter increases. The extent to which this is true is dependent on the properties of the insulating material.

Some coaxial cables have stranded wire center conductors while others use a solid copper conductor. Similarly, the outer conductor (shield) may be a single layer of copper braid, a double layer of braid (more effective shielding), solid aluminum (hardline and Heliax), aluminum foil or aluminized mylar, or a combination of these.

Voltage, Power and Loss Specifications

Selection of the correct coaxial cable for a particular application is not a casual matter. Not only is the attenuation loss of significance, but breakdown and heating (voltage and power) also need to be considered. If a cable were lossless, the power handling capability would be limited only by the breakdown voltage. There are two types of power ratings: *peak power* and *average power*. The peak power rating is limited by a voltage breakdown between the inner and outer conductors and is independent of frequency. The average power rating is governed by the safe long-term operating

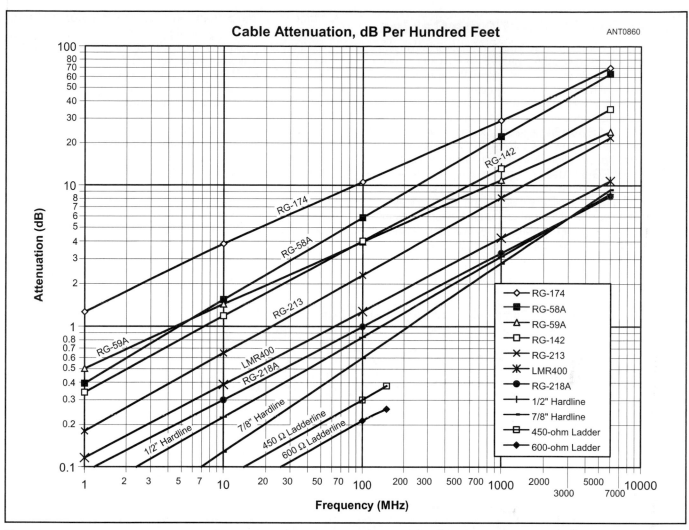

Figure 23.24 — Nominal matched-line attenuation in decibels per 100 feet of various common transmission lines. Total attenuation is directly proportional to length. Attenuation will vary somewhat in actual cable samples, and generally increases with age in coaxial cables having a type 1 jacket. Cables grouped together in the above chart have approximately the same attenuation. Types having foam polyethylene dielectric have slightly lower loss than equivalent solid types, when not specifically shown above.

temperature of the dielectric material and decreases as the frequency increases.

The power handling capability and loss characteristics of coaxial cable depend largely on the dielectric material between the conductors and the size of the conductors. The commonly used cables and many of their properties are listed in **Table 23-1**. The pertinent characteristics of unmarked coaxial cables can be determined from the equations in **Table 23-2**. The most common impedance values are 50, 75 and 95 Ω. However, impedances from 25 to 125 Ω are available in special types of manufactured line. The 25-Ω cable (miniature) is used extensively in magnetic-core broadband transformers.

In practical coaxial cables the copper and dielectric losses, rather than breakdown voltage, limit the maximum power than can be accommodated. If 1000 W is applied to a cable having a loss of 3 dB, only 500 W is delivered to the load. The remaining 500 W must be dissipated in the cable. The dielectric and outer jacket are good thermal insulators,

which prevent the conductors from efficiently transferring the heat to free air. As a result the cable can heat up, softening the plastic insulation and allowing the geometry of the conductors and the characteristic impedance to change or even short-circuit. Many amateur transmitter duty cycles are so low that substantial overload is permissible on current peaks so long as the SWR is relatively low, such as less than 2:1. **Figure 23.24** is a graph of the matched-line attenuation characteristics versus frequency for the most popular lines

A cable with a solid dielectric will handle higher power than a cable with a foam dielectric. RG-8/U with a solid dielectric will handle 5000 V maximum while the same cable with foam dielectric only has a 600 V rating. In addition, heating of the center conductor from cable loss can soften the center insulation. If the cable is heated while bent or wound into a coil, the center conductor can migrate through the insulation and change the cable's characteristic impedance or short to the outer shield. This is a particular problem for cables with foam insulation. When winding cables into a

RG-8, RG-213 and Type Cables

The most common coax used for amateur applications is RG-8/U — a 50-Ω cable approximately 0.4 inch in diameter, with solid or foamed polyethylene center insulation, and capable of handling full legal power. A close second to RG-8/U is RG-213/U, also a 50-Ω cable and nearly identical. The two cable types are almost identical as seen in Table 23-1, but RG-213/U is slightly lossier than RG-8.

Many amateurs are unaware that RG-8/U is an obsolete military specification designation, meaning that the part number RG-8/U does not confer any particular level of quality or performance on the cable. RG-213/U, on the other hand, is a current military designation that can only be used for cables manufactured to the military specification for that cable, both for materials as well as manufacturing processes. This results in a more consistent product.

It is also common for manufacturers to add "type" after a military specification label, such as "RG-8 Type" or "RG-213 Type". This means that the cable has much the same performance characteristics as the "non-type" cable but is not guaranteed to meet that higher level of performance.

Should you decide to use RG-8/U or a "type" cable, read the specifications carefully. The *shield coverage* (the percentage of the center insulator covered by the copper braid shield) should be from 95 to 97% for a high-quality cable. You should not be able to easily see the center insulation through holes in the shield.

Another advantage of RG-213/U is that the jacket is made from non-contaminating PVC and many types of RG-213/U are rated for direct burial.

Table 23.1

Nominal Characteristics of Commonly Used Transmission Lines

RG or Type	Part Number	Nom. Z_0 Ω	VF %	Cap. pF/ft	Cent. Cond. AWG	Diel. Type	Shield Type	Jacket Matl	OD inches	Max V (RMS)	1 MHz	10	100	1000
RG-6	Belden 1694A	75	82	16.2	#18 Solid BC	FPE	FC	P1	0.275	300	0.3	.7	1.8	5.9
RG-6	Belden 8215	75	66	20.5	#21 Solid CCS	PE	D	PE	0.332	2700	0.4	0.8	2.7	9.8
RG-8	Belden 7810A	50	86	23.0	#10 Solid BC	FPE	FC	PE	0.405	300	0.1	0.4	1.2	4.0
RG-8	TMS LMR400	50	85	23.9	#10 Solid CCA	FPE	FC	PE	0.405	600	0.1	0.4	1.3	4.1
RG-8	Belden 9913	50	84	24.6	#10 Solid BC	ASPE	FC	P1	0.405	300	0.1	0.4	1.3	4.5
RG-8	CXP1318FX	50	84	24.0	#10 Flex BC	FPE	FC	P2N	0.405	600	0.1	0.4	1.3	4.5
RG-8	Belden 9913F	50	83	24.6	#11 Flex BC	FPE	FC	P1	0.405	300	0.2	0.6	1.5	4.8
RG-8	Belden 9914	50	82	24.8	#10 Solid BC	FPE	FC	P1	0.405	300	0.2	0.5	1.5	4.8
RG-8	TMS LMR400UF	50	85	23.9	#10 Flex BC	FPE	FC	PE	0.405	600	0.1	0.4	1.4	4.9
RG-8	DRF-BF	50	84	24.5	#9.5 Flex BC	FPE	FC	PE	0.405	600	0.1	0.5	1.6	5.2
RG-8	WM CQ106	50	84	24.5	#9.5 Flex BC	FPE	FC	P2N	0.405	600	0.2	0.6	1.8	5.3
RG-8	CXP008	50	78	26.0	#13 Flex BC	FPE	S	P1	0.405	600	0.1	0.5	1.8	7.1
RG-8	Belden 8237	52	66	29.5	#13 Flex BC	PE	S	P1	0.405	3700	0.2	0.6	1.9	7.4
RG-8X	Belden 7808A	50	86	23.5	#15 Solid BC	FPE	FC	PE	0.240	300	0.2	0.7	2.3	7.4
RG-8X	TMS LMR240	50	84	24.2	#15 Solid BC	FPE	FC	PE	0.242	300	0.2	0.8	2.5	8.0
RG-8X	WM CQ118	50	82	25.0	#16 Flex BC	FPE	FC	P2N	0.242	300	0.3	0.9	2.8	8.4
RG-8X	TMS LMR240UF	50	84	24.2	#15 Flex BC	FPE	FC	PE	0.242	300	0.2	0.8	2.8	9.6
RG-8X	Belden 9258	50	82	24.8	#16 Flex BC	FPE	S	P1	0.242	300	0.3	0.9	3.2	11.2
RG-8X	CXP08XB	50	80	25.3	#16 Flex BC	FPE	S	P1	0.242	300	0.3	1.0	3.1	14.0
RG-9	Belden 8242	51	66	30.0	#13 Flex SPC	PE	SCBC	P2N	0.420	5000	0.2	0.6	2.1	8.2
RG-11	Belden 8213	75	84	16.1	#14 Solid BC	FPE	S	PE	0.405	300	0.1	0.4	1.3	5.2
RG-11	Belden 8238	75	66	20.5	#18 Flex TC	PE	S	P1	0.405	300	0.2	0.7	2.0	7.1
RG-58	Belden 7807A	50	85	23.7	#18 Solid BC	FPE	FC	PE	0.195	300	0.3	1.0	3.0	9.7
RG-58	TMS LMR200	50	83	24.5	#17 Solid BC	FPE	FC	PE	0.195	300	0.3	1.0	3.2	10.5
RG-58	WM CQ124	52	66	28.5	#20 Solid BC	PE	S	PE	0.195	1400	0.4	1.3	4.3	14.3
RG-58	Belden 8240	52	66	29.9	#20 Solid BC	PE	S	P1	0.193	1400	0.3	1.1	3.8	14.5
RG-58A	Belden 8219	53	73	26.5	#20 Flex TC	FPE	S	P1	0.195	300	0.4	1.3	4.5	18.1
RG-58C	Belden 8262	50	66	30.8	#20 Flex TC	PE	S	P2N	0.195	1400	0.4	1.4	4.9	21.5
RG-58A	Belden 8259	50	66	30.8	#20 Flex TC	PE	S	P1	0.192	1400	0.5	1.5	5.4	22.8
RG-59	Belden 1426A	75	83	16.3	#20 Solid BC	FPE	S	P1	0.242	300	0.3	0.9	2.6	8.5
RG-59	CXP 0815	75	82	16.2	#20 Solid BC	FPE	S	P1	0.232	300	0.5	0.9	2.2	9.1
RG-59	Belden 8212	75	78	17.3	#20 Solid CCS	FPE	S	P1	0.242	300	0.2	1.0	3.0	10.9
RG-59	Belden 8241	75	66	20.4	#23 Solid CCS	PE	S	P1	0.242	1700	0.6	1.1	3.4	12.0
RG-62A	Belden 9269	93	84	13.5	#22 Solid CCS	ASPE	S	P1	0.240	750	0.3	0.9	2.7	8.7
RG-62B	Belden 8255	93	84	13.5	#24 Flex CCS	ASPE	S	P2N	0.242	750	0.3	0.9	2.9	11.0
RG-63B	Belden 9857	125	84	9.7	#22 Solid CCS	ASPE	S	P2N	0.405	750	0.2	0.5	1.5	5.8
RG-142	CXP 183242	50	69.5	29.4	#19 Solid SCCS	TFE	D	FEP	0.195	1900	0.3	1.1	3.8	12.8
RG-142B	Belden 83242	50	69.5	29.0	#19 Solid SCCS	TFE	D	TFE	0.195	1400	0.3	1.1	3.9	13.5
RG-174	Belden 7805R	50	73.5	26.2	#25 Solid BC	FPE	FC	P1	0.110	300	0.6	2.0	6.5	21.3
RG-174	Belden 8216	50	66	30.8	#26 Flex CCS	PE	S	P1	0.110	1100	0.8	2.5	8.6	33.7
RG-213	Belden 8267	50	66	30.8	#13 Flex BC	PE	S	P2N	0.405	3700	0.2	0.6	2.1	8.0
RG-213	CXP213	50	66	30.8	#13 Flex BC	PE	S	P2N	0.405	600	0.2	0.6	2.0	8.2
RG-214	Belden 8268	50	66	30.8	#13 Flex SPC	PE	D	P2N	0.425	3700	0.2	0.7	2.2	8.0
RG-216	Belden 9850	75	66	20.5	#18 Flex TC	PE	D	P2N	0.425	3700	0.2	0.7	2.0	7.1
RG-217	WM CQ217F	50	66	30.8	#10 Flex BC	PE	D	PE	0.545	7000	0.1	0.4	1.4	5.2
RG-217	M17/78-RG217	50	66	30.8	#10 Solid BC	PE	D	P2N	0.545	7000	0.1	0.4	1.4	5.2
RG-218	M17/79-RG218	50	66	29.5	#4.5 Solid BC	PE	S	P2N	0.870	11000	0.1	0.2	0.8	3.4
RG-223	Belden 9273	50	66	30.8	#19 Solid SPC	PE	D	P2N	0.212	1400	0.4	1.2	4.1	14.5
RG-303	Belden 84303	50	69.5	29.0	#18 Solid SCCS	TFE	S	TFE	0.170	1400	0.3	1.1	3.9	13.5
RG-316	CXP TJ1316	50	69.5	29.4	#26 Flex BC	TFE	S	FEP	0.098	1200	1.2	2.7	8.0	26.1
RG-316	Belden 84316	50	69.5	29.0	#26 Flex SCCS	TFE	S	FEP	0.096	900	0.8	2.5	8.3	26.0
RG-393	M17/127-RG393	50	69.5	29.4	#12 Flex SPC	TFE	D	FEP	0.390	5000	0.2	0.5	1.7	6.1
RG-400	M17/128-RG400	50	69.5	29.4	#20 Flex SPC	TFE	D	FEP	0.195	1400	0.4	1.3	4.3	15.0

coil or bending them around corners, be sure that the bending radius is larger than the *minimum bending radius* specified for the cable.

As the operating frequency increases, the power-handling capability of a cable decreases because of increasing conductor loss (skin effect) and dielectric loss. RG-58 with foam dielectric has a breakdown rating of only 300 V, yet it can handle substantially more power than its ordinary solid dielectric counterpart because of the lower losses. Normally, the loss is inconsequential (except as it affects power handling capability) below 10 MHz in amateur applications. This is true unless extremely long runs of cable are used.

In general, full legal amateur power can be safely applied to inexpensive RG-58 coax in the bands below 10 MHz. RG-8 and similar cables can withstand full amateur power

through the VHF spectrum, but connectors must be carefully chosen in these applications. Connector choice is discussed in a later section.

Excessive RF operating voltage in a coaxial cable can cause noise generation, dielectric damage and eventual breakdown between the conductors.

Deterioration

Deterioration of coaxial cable is most commonly caused by water or moisture infiltration which causes corrosion of the shield, dramatically increasing its losses. This usually occurs at the ends of cables where connectors are installed or the cable is separated into two conductors for attachment to an antenna.

Exposure of the inner insulating material to moisture

RG or Type	Part Number	Nom. Z_0 Ω	VF %	Cap. pF/ft	Cent. Cond. AWG	Diel. Type	Shield Type	Jacket Matl	OD inches	Max V (RMS)	Matched Loss (dB/100') 1 MHz	10	100	1000
LMR500	TMS LMR500UF	50	85	23.9	#7 Flex BC	FPE	FC	PE	0.500	2500	0.1	0.4	1.2	4.0
LMR500	TMS LMR500	50	85	23.9	#7 Solid CCA	FPE	FC	PE	0.500	2500	0.1	0.3	0.9	3.3
LMR600	TMS LMR600	50	86	23.4	#5.5 Solid CCA	FPE	FC	PE	0.590	4000	0.1	0.2	0.8	2.7
LMR600	TMS LMR600UF	50	86	23.4	#5.5 Flex BC	FPE	FC	PE	0.590	4000	0.1	0.2	0.8	2.7
LMR1200	TMS LMR1200	50	88	23.1	#0 Copper Tube	FPE	FC	PE	1.200	4500	0.04	0.1	0.4	1.3
Hardline														
1/2"	CATV Hardline	50	81	25.0	#5.5 BC	FPE	SM	none	0.500	2500	0.05	0.2	0.8	3.2
1/2"	CATV Hardline	75	81	16.7	#11.5 BC	FPE	SM	none	0.500	2500	0.1	0.2	0.8	3.2
7/8"	CATV Hardline	50	81	25.0	#1 BC	FPE	SM	none	0.875	4000	0.03	0.1	0.6	2.9
7/8"	CATV Hardline	75	81	16.7	#5.5 BC	FPE	SM	none	0.875	4000	0.03	0.1	0.6	2.9
LDF4-50A	Heliax – 1/2"	50	88	25.9	#5 Solid BC	FPE	CC	PE	0.630	1400	0.02	0.2	0.6	2.4
LDF5-50A	Heliax – 7/8"	50	88	25.9	0.355" BC	FPE	CC	PE	1.090	2100	0.03	0.10	0.4	1.3
LDF6-50A	Heliax – 1¼"	50	88	25.9	0.516" BC	FPE	CC	PE	1.550	3200	0.02	0.08	0.3	1.1
Parallel Lines														
TV Twinlead (Belden 9085)		300	80	4.5	#22 Flex CCS	PE	none	P1	0.400	**	0.1	0.3	1.4	5.9
Twinlead (Belden 8225)		300	80	4.4	#20 Flex BC	PE	none	P1	0.400	8000	0.1	0.2	1.1	4.8
Generic Window Line		450	91	2.5	#18 Solid CCS	PE	none	P1	1.000	10000	0.02	0.08	0.3	1.1
WM CQ 554		440	91	2.7	#14 Flex CCS	PE	none	P1	1.000	10000	0.04	0.01	0.6	3.0
WM CQ 552		440	91	2.5	#16 Flex CCS	PE	none	P1	1.000	10000	0.05	0.2	0.6	2.6
WM CQ 553		450	91	2.5	#18 Flex CCS	PE	none	P1	1.000	10000	0.06	0.2	0.7	2.9
WM CQ 551		450	91	2.5	#18 Solid CCS	PE	none	P1	1.000	10000	0.05	0.02	0.6	2.8
Open-Wire Line		600	0.95-99***	1.7	#12 BC	none	none	none	**	12000	0.02	0.06	0.2	—

Approximate Power Handling Capability (1:1 SWR, 40°C Ambient):

	1.8 MHz	7	14	30	50	150	220	450	1 GHz
RG-58 Style	1350	700	500	350	250	150	120	100	50
RG-59 Style	2300	1100	800	550	400	250	200	130	90
RG-8X Style	1830	840	560	360	270	145	115	80	50
RG-8/213 Style	5900	3000	2000	1500	1000	600	500	350	250
RG-217 Style	20000	9200	6100	3900	2900	1500	1200	800	500
LDF4-50A	38000	18000	13000	8200	6200	3400	2800	1900	1200
LDF5-50A	67000	32000	22000	14000	11000	5900	4800	3200	2100
LMR500	18000	9200	6500	4400	3400	1900	1600	1100	700
LMR1200	52000	26000	19000	13000	10000	5500	4500	3000	2000

Legend:

**	Not Available or varies	N	Non-Contaminating
***	Varies with spacer material and spacing	P1	PVC, Class 1
ASPE	Air Spaced Polyethylene	P2	PVC, Class 2
BC	Bare Copper	PE	Polyethylene
CC	Corrugated Copper	S	Single Braided Shield
CCA	Copper Cover Aluminum	SC	Silver Coated Braid
CCS	Copper Covered Steel	SCCS	Silver Plated Copper Coated Steel
CXP	Cable X-Perts, Inc.	SM	Smooth Aluminum
D	Double Copper Braids	SPC	Silver Plated Copper
DRF	Davis RF	TC	Tinned Copper
FC	Foil + Tinned Copper Braid	TFE	Teflon®
FEP	Teflon® Type IX	TMS	Times Microwave Systems
Flex	Flexible Stranded Wire	UF	Ultra Flex
FPE	Foamed Polyethylene	WM	Wireman
Heliax	Andrew Corp Heliax		

Table 23-2
Coaxial Cable Equations

$$C \text{ (pF/foot)} = \frac{7.26\varepsilon}{\log(D/d)} \qquad \text{(Eq A)}$$

$$L \text{ (μH/foot)} = 0.14 \log \frac{D}{d} \qquad \text{(Eq B)}$$

$$Z_0 \text{ (ohms)} = \sqrt{\frac{L}{C}} = \left(\frac{138}{\sqrt{\varepsilon}}\right)\left(\log\frac{D}{d}\right) \qquad \text{(Eq C)}$$

$$VF\% \text{ (velocity factor, ref. speed of light)} = \frac{100}{\sqrt{\varepsilon}} \qquad \text{(Eq D)}$$

$$\text{Time delay (ns/foot)} = 1.016\sqrt{\varepsilon} \qquad \text{(Eq E)}$$

$$f \text{ (cutoff/GHz)} = \frac{7.50}{\sqrt{\varepsilon}\,(D+d)} \qquad \text{(Eq F)}$$

$$\text{Reflection Coefficient} = |\rho| = \frac{Z_L - Z_0}{Z_L + Z_0} = \frac{SWR - 1}{SWR + 1} \qquad \text{(Eq G)}$$

$$\text{Return Loss (dB)} = -20 \log |\rho| \qquad \text{(Eq H)}$$

$$SWR = \frac{1 + |\rho|}{1 - |\rho|} \qquad \text{(Eq I)}$$

$$V \text{ peak} = \frac{(1.15\,S\,d)(\log D/d)}{K} \qquad \text{(Eq J)}$$

$$A = \frac{0.435}{Z_0 D}\left(\frac{D}{d}(K1+K2)\right)\sqrt{f} + 2.78\sqrt{\varepsilon}\,(PF)\,(f) \qquad \text{(Eq K)}$$

where

- A = attenuation in dB/100 foot
- d = OD of inner conductor
- D = ID of outer conductor
- S = max voltage gradient of insulation in volts/mil
- ε = dielectric constant
- K = safety factor
- K1 = strand factor
- K2 = braid factor
- f = freq in MHz
- PF = power factor

Note: Obtain K1 and K2 data from manufacturer.

and chemicals over time contaminates the center insulation and increases cable losses. Newer types of foam-dielectric cables are less prone to contamination than are older types of solid-polyethylene insulated cables.

Impregnated cables, such as Times Wire LMR-400-DB, are immune to water and chemical damage, and may be buried if desired. They also have a self-healing property that is valuable when rodents chew into the line. Cable loss

should be checked at least every two years if the cable has been outdoors or buried. See the section on testing transmission lines.

The outer insulating jacket of the cable (usually PVC) is used solely as protection from dirt, moisture and chemicals. (The jacket's only electrical function is compressing the shield braid to keep the strands in good contact with each other.) If the jacket is breached, it generally leads to corrosion of the shield and contamination of the center insulation, again causing high losses.

The ultra-violet (UV) radiation in sunlight causes a chemical reaction in standard PVC jacket material that causes the plastic to break down into products that migrate from the jacket into the braid and center insulation, degrading the electrical properties of both. If your cable will be exposed to strong sunlight, use a cable with a non-contaminating jacket.

Cable Capacitance

The capacitance between the conductors of coaxial cable varies with the impedance and dielectric constant of the line. Therefore, the lower the impedance, the higher the capacitance per foot, because the conductor spacing is decreased. Capacitance also increases with dielectric constant.

Bending Radius

A normal amateur installation will create bends and turns in the feed line run. It is common to wind coax into a coil to form a common-mode RF choke or to store excess cable. Bending coax is acceptable as long as the *minimum bending radius* is not violated. A typical minimum bending radius is a multiple of the coax diameter. For example, a common minimum bending radius specification for RG-8 is 4 inches, which is a multiple of 8 (½ inch OD × 8). Coax with more rigid shield materials such as hardline or Heliax will have a larger bending radius.

If the cable will be subjected to regular flexing, such as if it is attached to a rotating antenna, use a cable with a stranded center conductor. When repeatedly bent or flexed, solid center conductors will develop *metal fatigue* and break.

Shielded Balanced Lines

Shielded balanced lines made from parallel coaxial cables have several advantages over open-wire lines. They can be buried and they can be routed through metal buildings or inside metal piping the same as for single coaxial lines. The outer surface of the shields can pick up noise and common-mode signals just as for single coaxial lines, as well.

The characteristic impedance of a balanced shielded line is twice that of each single line — as if they were in series. Shielded balanced lines having impedances of 140 or 100 Ω can be constructed from two equal lengths of 70-Ω or 50-Ω cable (RG-59 or RG-58 would be satisfactory for amateur power levels). Paralleled RG-63 (125-Ω) cable would make a balanced transmission line more in accord with traditional 300-Ω twin-lead feed line ($Z_0 = 250$ Ω). Note that the losses for these shielded types of balanced lines will generally be

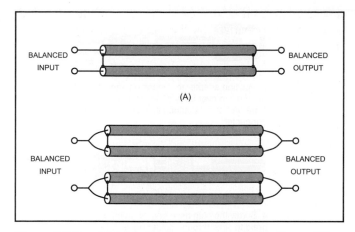

Figure 23.25 — Shielded balanced transmission lines utilizing standard small-size coaxial cable, such as RG-58 or RG-59. These balanced lines may be routed inside metal conduit or near large metal objects without adverse effects.

higher than those for classic open-wire lines.

The shields are connected together (see **Figure 23.25A**), and the two inner conductors constitute the balanced line. At the input, the coaxial shields should be connected to chassis ground; at the output (the antenna side), they are joined but left floating.

A high power, low-loss, low-impedance 70-Ω (or 50-Ω) balanced line can be constructed from four coaxial cables as in Figure 23.25B. In this case, the characteristic impedance of each pair of cables is one-half that of the single lines because the signal divides equally between them — they are in parallel. The net result is that the overall characteristic impedance is that of a single cable. Again, the shields are all connected together. The center conductors of the two sets of coaxial cables that are connected in parallel provide the balanced feed.

23.4 RF CONNECTORS

There are many different types of RF connectors for coaxial cable, but the three most common for amateur use are the UHF, Type N and BNC families. Type F connectors are becoming popular for use with receiving antennas and low-loss RG-6 coaxial cable. Type SMA connectors are commonly found on hand-held transceivers and microwave equipment. The type of connector used for a specific job depends on the size of the cable, the frequency of operation and the power levels involved.

If the connector is to be exposed to the weather, select a waterproof design such as Type N or take care to thoroughly waterproof the connector as discussed in the chapter **Building Antenna Systems and Towers.**

23.4.1 UHF CONNECTORS

The so-called UHF connector (the series name is not related to frequency) is found on most HF and some VHF equipment. It is the only connector many hams will ever see on coaxial cable. PL-259 is another name for the UHF male, and the female is also known as the SO-239. These connectors are rated for full legal amateur power at HF. They are poor for UHF work because they do not present a constant impedance, so the UHF label is a misnomer. PL-259 connectors are designed to fit RG-8 and RG-11 size cable (0.405-inch OD). Adapters are available for use with smaller RG-58, RG-59 and RG-8X size cable. UHF connectors are not weatherproof.

Figure 23.26 shows how to install the solder type of

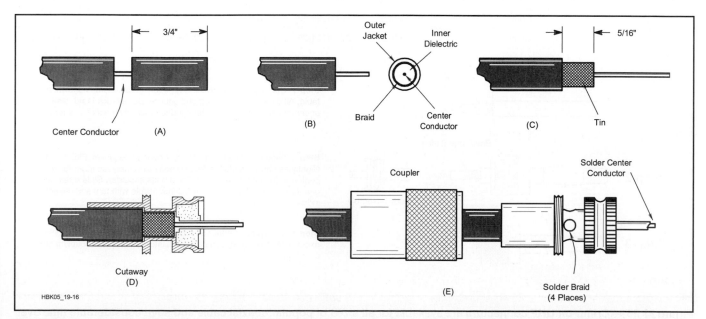

Figure 23.26 — The PL-259 plug of the UHF family of connectors is almost universal for amateur HF use and is popular for equipment operating in the VHF range. Steps A through E are described in detail in the text.

83-1SP (PL-259) Plug with adapters
(UG-176/U OR UG-175/U)

COUPLING RING   ADAPTER   ⊢ 3/4 ⊣

1. Cut end of cable even. Remove vinyl jacket 3/4" - don't nick braid. Slide coupling ring and adapter on cable.

2. Fan braid slightly and fold back over cable.

Figure 23.27 — Installing PL-259 plugs on RG-58 or RG-59 cable requires the use of UG-175 or UG-176 reducing adapters, respectively. The adapter screws into the plug body using the threads of the connector to grip the jacket on larger cables. (*Courtesy Amphenol Electronic Components*)

3. Position adapter to dimension shown. Press braid down over body of adapter and trim to 3/8". Bare 5/8" of conductor. Tin exposed center conductor.

PLUG ASSEMBLY   SOLDER HOLE

4. Screw the plug assembly on adapter. Solder braid to shell through solder holes. Solder conductor to contact sleeve.

5. Screw coupling ring on plug assembly.

HBK0460

UHF Connectors
Braid Crimp - Solder Center Contact

Ferrule   Coupling Nut   Body assembly

Amphenol	Cable RG-/U	Cable Attachment		Hex Crimp Data			Stripping Dims, inches (mm)		
		Outer	Inner	Cavity for Outer Ferrule	Die Set Tool 227-994	CTL Series Tool No.	a	b	c
83-58SP	58, 141	Crimp	Solder	0.213(5.4)	227-1221-11	CTL-1	1.14 (29.0)	0.780 (19.9)	0.250 (6.4)
83-58SP-1002	400	Crimp	Solder	0.213(5.4)	227-1221-11	CTL-1	1.14 (29.0)	0.780 (19.9)	0.250 (6.4)
83-59DCP-RFX	59	Crimp	Solder	0255(6.5)	227-1221-13	CTL-1	1.22 (30.9)	0.574 (22.6)	0.543 (13.8)
83-58SCP-RFX	58	Crimp	Solder	0.213(5.4)	227-1221-11	CTL-1	1.22 (30.9)	0.574 (22.6)	0.543 (13.8)
83-59SP	59	Crimp	Solder	0.255(6.5)	227-1221-13	CTL-1	1.22 (30.9)	0.574 (22.6)	0.543 (13.8)
83-8SP-RFX	8	Crimp	Solder	0.429(10.9)	227-1221-25	CTL-3	1.22 (30.9)	0.574 (22.6)	0.543 (13.8)

Step 1

Step 1 Cut end of cable even. Strip cable to dimensions shown in table. All cuts are to be sharp and square. Do not nick braid, dielectric or center conductor. Tin center conductor avoiding excessive heat.

Braid after flaring

Step 2

Body assembly

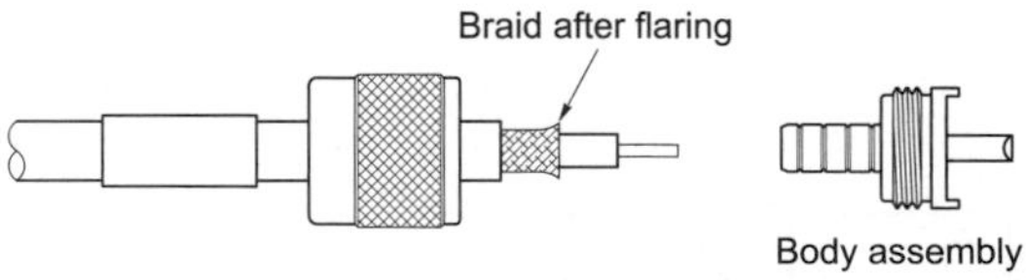

Step 2 Slide coupling nut and ferrule over cable jacket. Flair braid slightly as shown. Install cable into body assembly, so inner ferrule portion slides under braid, until braid butts shoulder. Slide outer ferrule over braid until it butts shoulder. Crimp ferrule with tool and die set indicated in table.

Step 3

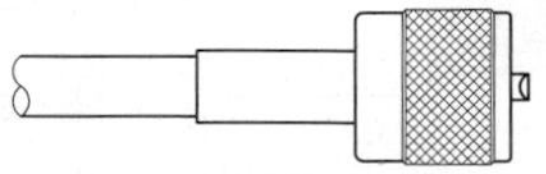

Step 3 Soft solder center conductor to contact. Avoid heating contact excessively to prevent damaging insulator. Slide/screw coupling nut over body.

HBK0475

Figure 23.28 — Crimp-on UHF connectors are available for all sizes of popular coaxial cable and save considerable time over soldered connectors. The performance and reliability of these connectors is equivalent to soldered connectors, if crimped properly. (*Courtesy Amphenol Electronic Components*)

PL-259 on RG-8 cable. Proper preparation of the cable end is the key to success. Follow these simple steps. Measure back about ¾-inch from the cable end and slightly score the outer jacket around its circumference. With a sharp knife, cut through the outer jacket, through the braid, and through the dielectric — almost to the center conductor. Be careful not to score the center conductor. Cutting through all outer layers at once keeps the braid from separating. (Using a coax stripping tool with preset blade depth makes this and subsequent trimming steps much easier.)

Pull the severed outer jacket, braid and dielectric off the end of the cable as one piece. Inspect the area around the cut, looking for any strands of braid hanging loose and snip them off. There won't be any if your knife was sharp enough. Next, score the outer jacket about ⁵⁄₁₆-inch back from the first cut. Cut through the jacket lightly; do not score the braid. This step takes practice. If you score the braid, start again. Remove the outer jacket.

Tin the exposed braid and center conductor, but apply the solder sparingly and avoid melting the dielectric. Slide the coupling ring onto the cable. Screw the connector body onto the cable. If you prepared the cable to the right dimensions, the center conductor will protrude through the center pin, the braid will show through the solder holes, and the body will actually thread onto the outer cable jacket. A very small amount of lubricant on the cable jacket will help the threading process.

Solder the braid through the solder holes. Solder through all four holes; poor connection to the braid is the most common form of PL-259 failure. A good connection between connector and braid is just as important as that between the center conductor and connector. Use a large soldering iron for this job. With practice, you'll learn how much heat to use. If you use too little heat, the solder will bead up, not really flowing onto the connector body. If you use too much heat, the dielectric will melt, letting the braid and center conductor touch. Most PL-259s are nickel plated, but silver-plated connectors are much easier to solder and only slightly more expensive.

Solder the center conductor to the center pin. The solder should flow on the inside, not the outside, of the center pin. If you wait until the connector body cools off from soldering the braid, you'll have less trouble with the dielectric melting. Trim the center conductor to be even with the end of the center pin. Use a small file to round the end, removing any solder that built up on the outer surface of the center pin. Use a sharp knife, very fine sandpaper or steel wool to remove any solder flux from the outer surface of the center pin. Screw the coupling ring onto the body, and you're finished.

Figure 23.27 shows how to install a PL-259 connector on RG-58 or RG-59 cable. An adapter is used for the smaller cable with standard RG-8 size PL-259s. (UG-175 for RG-58 and UG-176 for RG-59) Prepare the cable as shown. Once the braid is prepared, screw the adapter into the PL-259 shell and finish the job as you would a PL-259 on RG-8 cable.

Figure 23.28 shows the instructions and dimensions for crimp-on UHF connectors that fit all common sizes of coaxial cable. While amateurs have been reluctant to adopt crimp-on connectors, the availability of good quality connectors and inexpensive crimping tools make crimp technology a good choice, even for connectors used outside. Soldering the center conductor after crimping in the connector tip is optional. UHF connectors are not waterproof and must be waterproofed whether soldered or crimped.

23.4.2 OTHER RF CONNECTORS
BNC Connectors

The BNC connectors illustrated in **Figure 23.29** are popular for low power levels at VHF and UHF. They accept RG-58 and RG-59 cable and are available for cable mounting in both male and female versions. Several different styles are available, so be sure to use the dimensions for the type you have. Follow the installation instructions carefully. If you prepare the cable to the wrong dimensions, the center pin will not seat properly with connectors of the opposite gender. Sharp scissors are a big help for trimming the braid evenly. Crimp-on BNC connectors are also available, with a large number of variations, including a twist-on version. A guide to installing these connectors is available on the CD-ROM accompanying this book.

Type N Connectors

The Type N connector, illustrated in **Figure 23.30**, is a must for high-power VHF and UHF operation. N connectors are available in male and female versions for cable mounting and are designed for RG-8 size cable. Unlike UHF connectors, they are designed to maintain a constant impedance at cable joints. Like BNC connectors, it is important to prepare the cable to the right dimensions. The center pin must be positioned correctly to mate with the center pin of connectors of the opposite gender. Use the right dimensions for the connector style you have. Crimp-on N connectors are also available, again with a large number of variations. A guide to installing these connectors is available on the CD-ROM accompanying this book.

Type F Connectors

Type F connectors, used primarily on cable TV connections, are also popular for receive-only antennas and can be used with RG-59 or the increasingly popular RG-6 cable available at low cost. Crimp-on is the only option for these connectors and **Figure 23.31** shows a general guide for installing them. The exact dimensions vary between connector styles and manufacturers — information on crimping is generally provided with the connectors. There are two styles of crimp — ferrule and compression. The ferrule crimp method is similar to that for UHF, BNC and N connectors in which a metal ring is compressed around the exposed coax shield. The compression crimp forces a bushing into the back of the connector, clamping the shield against the connector body. In all cases, the exposed center conductor of the cable — a solid wire — must end flush with the end of the connector. A center conductor that is too short may not make a good connection.

BNC CONNECTORS

Standard Clamp

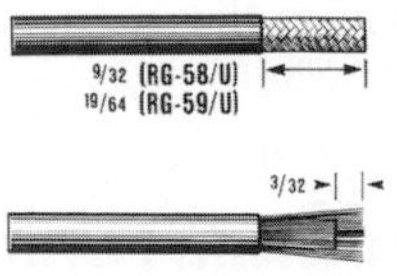

1. Cut cable even. Strip jacket. Fray braid and strip dielectric. **Don't nick braid or center conductor.** Tin center conductor.

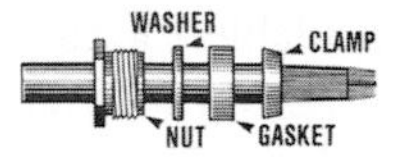

2. Taper braid. Slide nut, washer, gasket and clamp over braid. Clamp inner shoulder should fit squarely against end of jacket.

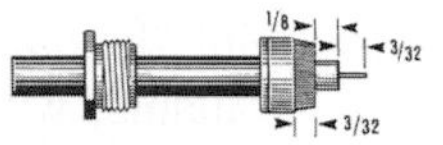

3. With clamp in place, comb out braid, fold back smooth as shown. Trim center conductor.

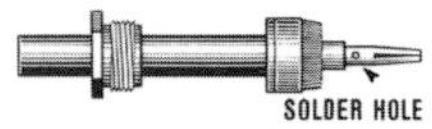

4. Solder contact on conductor through solder hole. Contact should butt against dielectric. Remove excess solder from outside of contact. Avoid excess heat to prevent swollen dielectric which would interfere with connector body.

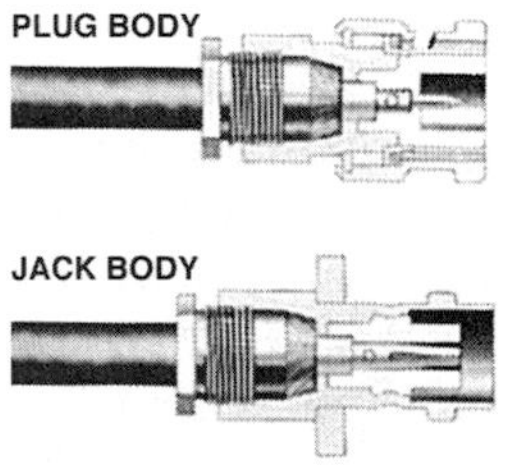

5. Push assembly into body. Screw nut into body with wrench until tight. **Don't rotate body on cable to tighten.**

Improved Clamp

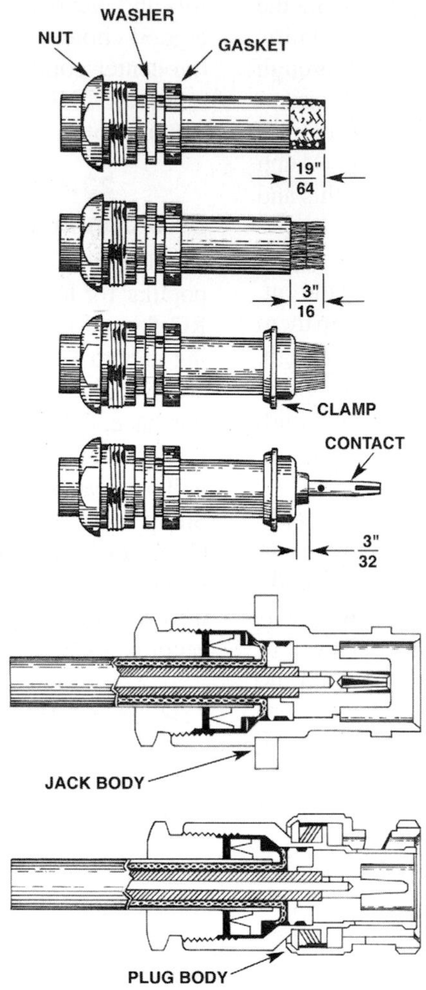

Follow 1, 2, 3 and 4 in BNC connectors (standard clamp) exceptas noted. Strip cable as shown. Slide gasket on cable *with groove facing clamp*. Slide clamp *with sharp edge facing gasket*. Clamp *should* cut gasket to seal properly.

HBK05_19-18

C. C. Clamp

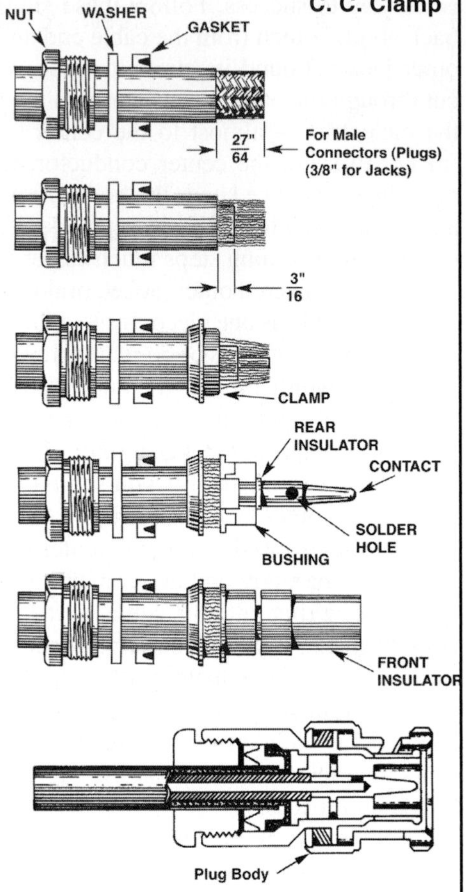

1. Follow steps 1, 2, and 3 as outlined for the standard-clamp BNC connector.

2. Slide on bushing, rear insulator and contact. The parts must butt securely against each other, as shown.

3. Solder the center conductor to the contact. Remove flux and excess solder.

4. Slide the front insulator over the contact, making sure it butts against the contact shoulder.

5. Insert the prepared cable end into the connector body and tighten the nut. Make sure the sharp edge of the clamp seats properly in the gasket.

Figure 23.29 — BNC connectors are common on VHF and UHF equipment at low power levels. (*Courtesy Amphenol Electronic Components*)

Type N assembly instructions

CLAMP TYPES

     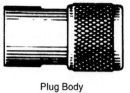 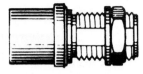

Nut   Washer   Gasket   Clamp   Male Contact   Plug Body   Female Contact   Jack Body

Step 1

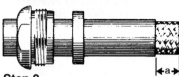

Step 2

Step 3

Step 4

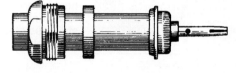

Step 5

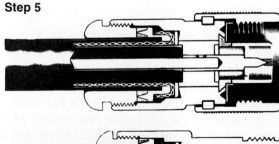

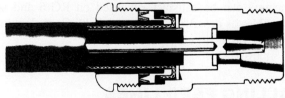

Amphenol Number	Connector Type	Cable RG-/U	Strip Dims., inches (mm) a	c
82-61	N Plug	8, 9, 144, 165, 213, 214, 216, 225	0.359(9.1)	0.234(6.0)
82-62	N Panel Jack		0.312(7.9)	0.187(4.7)
82-63	N Jack	8, 9, 87A, 144, 165, 213, 214, 216, 225	0.281(7.1)	0.156(4.0)
82-67	N Bulkhead Jack			
82-202	N Plug	8, 9, 144, 165, 213, 214, 216, 225	0.359(9.1)	0.234(6.0)
82-202-1006	N Plug	Belden 9913	0.359(9.1)	0.234(6.0)
82-835	N Angle Plug	8, 9, 87A, 144, 165, 213, 214, 216, 225	0.281(7.1)	0.156(4.0)
18750	N Angle Plug	58, 141, 142	0.484(12.3)	0.234(5.9)
34025	N Plug		0.390(9.9)	0.203(5.2)
34525	N Plug	59, 62, 71, 140, 210	0.410(10.4)	0.230(5.8)
35025	N Jack	58, 141, 142	0.375(9.5)	0.187(4.7)
36500	N Jack	59, 62, 71, 140, 210	0.484(12.3)	0.200(5.1)

Step 1 Place nut and gasket, with "V" groove toward clamp, over cable and cut off jacket to dim. a.

Step 2 Comb out braid and fold out. Cut off cable dielectric to dim. c as shown.

Step 3 Pull braid wires forward and taper toward center conductor. Place clamp over braid and push back against cable jacket.

Step 4 Fold back braid wires as shown, trim braid to proper length and form over clamp as shown. Solder contact to center conductor.

Step 5 Insert cable and parts into connector body. Make sure sharp edge of clamp seats properly in gasket. Tighten nut.

Figure 23.30 — Type N connectors are required for high-power VHF and UHF operation. (*Courtesy Amphenol Electronic Components*)

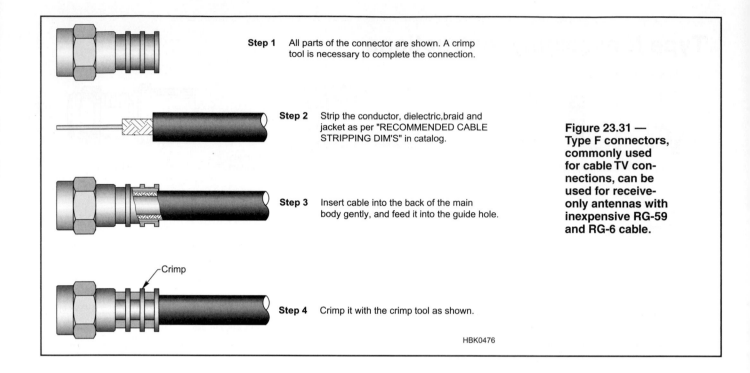

Step 1   All parts of the connector are shown. A crimp tool is necessary to complete the connection.

Step 2   Strip the conductor, dielectric,braid and jacket as per "RECOMMENDED CABLE STRIPPING DIM'S" in catalog.

Step 3   Insert cable into the back of the main body gently, and feed it into the guide hole.

Crimp

Step 4   Crimp it with the crimp tool as shown.

HBK0476

Figure 23.31 — Type F connectors, commonly used for cable TV connections, can be used for receive-only antennas with inexpensive RG-59 and RG-6 cable.

SMA Connectors

The SMA connector in **Figure 23.32** is the most common microwave connector. The cable center insulation is taken directly to the connector interface without air gaps. A standard SMA is rated for use to 12.4 GHz but high-quality connectors, properly installed, can be used to 24 GHz. For more information about SMA and other microwave connectors, see the Bibliography entry for Williams (the article is also available on this book's CD-ROM).

Hardline Connectors

Surplus hardline cable comes in various sizes (½, ⅝, ¾, 1 inch and so on) that are not compatible with standard RF connectors such as UHF or N. There have been dozens of inventive schemes published over the years that use plumbing hardware or other materials to fabricate an adaptor compatible with a standard connector. If you decide to make your own adapter, be cautious about using dissimilar metals and waterproof the connector carefully. Otherwise, use the recommended connectors from the manufacturer — these are often available as surplus on Internet websites.

Figure 23.32 — A pair of SMA connectors, with male on the left and female on the right. SMA connectors are available in nickel, stainless steel, or gold finish.

Using RG-6 with RG-58 Crimp Connectors

RG-6 coaxial cable is readily and cheaply available as it is commonly used for domestic cable and satellite TV. Crimp-type BNC, N, PL-259 and others are readily obtainable for RG-58 cables. Crimp connectors for RG-6 other than Type F are becoming difficult to find. However RG-58 crimp connectors can be satisfactorily used on RG-6 and some other cables as described on the article by Garth Jenkinson, VK3BBK, on this book's CD-ROM.

23.5 CHOOSING AND INSTALLING FEED LINES

23.5.1 COMPARING FEED LINES

The usual two primary considerations for choosing a feed line are loss at the frequency of use and cost. Starting with the impedance of the load attached to the feed line (usually an antenna feed point) determine the matched loss for types of feed line you are considering. **Table 23-3** and **Table 23-4**, published by Frank Donovan, W3LPL in 2008 give typical losses for various types of coaxial cable at frequencies in

the amateur bands by using the VK1OD online calculator at **vk1od.net/calc/tl/tllc.php**. (Most manufacturers specify losses at 1, 10, 100 and 1000 MHz.) Table 23-4 specifies the length of line that will exhibit a loss of 1 dB.

To use Table 23-3, multiply the loss figure by the length of your feed line divided by 100 feet. For example, to find the loss of a 250-foot run of RG-213 at 28.4 MHz, multiply the table loss (1.2 dB) by 250/100 = 1.2 × 2.5 = 3.0 dB. Now use

Table 23-3
Cable Attenuation (dB per 100 feet)

MHz	1.8	3.6	7.1	14.2	21.2	28.4	50.1	144	440	1296
LDF7-50A	0.03	0.04	0.06	0.08	0.10	0.12	0.16	0.27	0.5	0.9
FHJ-7	0.03	0.05	0.07	0.10	0.12	0.15	0.20	0.37	0.8	1.7
LDF5-50A	0.04	0.06	0.09	0.14	0.17	0.19	0.26	0.45	0.8	1.5
FXA78-50J	0.06	0.08	0.13	0.17	0.23	0.27	0.39	0.77	1.4	2.8
3/4" CATV	0.06	0.08	0.13	0.17	0.23	0.26	0.38	0.62	1.7	3.0
LDF4-50A	0.09	0.13	0.17	0.25	0.31	0.36	0.48	0.84	1.4	2.5
RG-17	0.10	0.13	0.18	0.27	0.34	0.40	0.50	1.3	2.5	5.0
LMR-600	0.10	0.15	0.20	0.29	0.35	0.41	0.55	0.94	1.7	3.1
SLA12-50J	0.11	0.15	0.20	0.28	0.35	0.42	0.56	1.0	1.9	3.0
FXA12-50J	0.12	0.16	0.22	0.33	0.40	0.47	0.65	1.2	2.1	4.0
FXA38-50J	0.16	0.23	0.31	0.45	0.53	0.64	0.85	1.5	2.7	4.9
9913	0.16	0.23	0.31	0.45	0.53	0.64	0.92	1.6	2.7	5.0
LMR-400	0.16	0.23	0.32	0.46	0.56	0.65	0.87	1.5	2.7	4.7
RG-213	0.25	0.37	0.55	0.75	1.0	1.2	1.6	2.8	5.1	10.0
RG-8X	0.49	0.68	1.0	1.4	1.7	1.9	2.5	4.5	8.4	13.2
RG-58	0.56	0.82	1.2	1.7	2.0	2.4	3.2	5.6	10.5	20.0
RG-174	1.1	1.5	2.1	3.1	3.8	4.4	5.9	10.2	18.7	34.8

Table 23-4
Cable Attenuation (feet per dB)

MHz	1.8	3.6	7.1	14.2	21.2	28.4	50.1	144	440	1296
LDF7-50A	3333	2500	1666	1250	1000	833	625	370	200	110
FHJ-7	2775	2080	1390	1040	833	667	520	310	165	92
LDF5-50A	2108	1490	1064	750	611	526	393	227	125	69
FXA78-50J	1666	1250	769	588	435	370	256	130	71	36
3/4" CATV	1666	1250	769	588	435	385	275	161	59	33
LDF4-50A	1145	809	579	409	333	287	215	125	70	39
RG-17	1000	769	556	370	294	250	200	77	40	20
LMR-600	973	688	492	347	283	244	182	106	59	33
SLA12-50J	909	667	500	355	285	235	175	100	53	34
FXA12-50J	834	625	455	300	250	210	150	83	48	25
FXA38-50J	625	435	320	220	190	155	115	67	37	20
9913	625	435	320	220	190	155	110	62	37	20
LMR-400	613	436	310	219	179	154	115	67	38	21
RG-213	397	279	197	137	111	95	69	38	19	9
RG-8X	257	181	128	90	74	63	47	27	14	8
RG-58	179	122	83	59	50	42	30	18	9	5
RG-174	91	67	48	32	26	23	17	10	5	3

Equation 16 or one of the charts in Figure 23.14 to determine the total loss of the line at that frequency and SWR. If one of the cables is acceptable to you in performance and affordability, your job is done.

If you are operating with full power, you must also consider the peak voltage and power handling capability of the line. There may be other considerations in special circumstances. For example, operators who carry QRP equipment may elect to use RG-174 coax, even though it has high losses, because of its low weight.

For situations in which SWR is very high (such as for a nonresonant doublet used on multiple bands) or a very long run of feed line is required, open-wire line may be the best solution. Be sure to include the cost of impedance transformers in your system budget to connect the higher-impedance open-wire line to 50-Ω equipment and antennas.

If you are considering replacing a long run of cable with hardline or Heliax, **Table 23-5** should be helpful. This is a common situation for stations with antennas far from the transceiver and for VHF/UHF stations of any size. The cable lengths in the table are the lengths for which replacing them with Heliax would yield a 1-dB benefit. For example, replacing a 146-foot run of RG-213 with ½-inch Heliax would yield a 1 dB benefit on 10 meters. Similarly, an 85-foot run of Belden 9913 used on 2 meters could be replaced by ⅞-inch Heliax for a 1 dB benefit. The longer the cable run, the greater the benefit of replacing them with the lower loss of Heliax. (LDF4-50A and LDF5-50A are available at reasonable prices on auction websites, ham websites such as **www.eham.net** or **www.qrz.com**, and at hamfests.)

Table 23-5
Advantage from Upgrading Feed Line

Feet Required For 1 dB Advantage If Replaced By LDF5-50A (7/8-inch Heliax)

MHz	1.8	3.6	7.1	14.2	21.2	28.4	50.1	144	440	1296
LDF4-50A	2500	1430	1250	910	715	625	475	279	158	90
RG-17	1666	1430	1110	770	560	475	420	120	60	30
FXA12-50J	1250	1000	770	525	435	355	255	120	75	40
9913	935	590	455	320	280	220	150	85	53	29

Feet Required For 1 dB Advantage If Replaced By LDF4-50A (1/2-inch Heliax)

MHz	1.8	3.6	7.1	14.2	21.2	28.4	50.1	144	440	1296
RG-17	-	-	-	-	-	-	-	220	90	40
FXA12-50J	-	-	2000	1250	1100	835	625	250	145	65
9913	1430	1000	715	500	455	345	235	135	75	40
RG-213	618	434	306	212	171	146	106	58	29	14

23.5.2 INSTALLING COAXIAL CABLE

One great advantage of flexible coaxial line is that it can be installed with almost no regard for its surroundings. It requires no insulation, can be run on or in the ground or in piping, can be bent around corners with a reasonable radius, and can be snaked through places such as the space between walls where it would be impractical to use other types of lines. In addition, coaxial lines are unaffected by proximity to other conductors and can be run inside metal conduit or attached to metal structures.

Coax must still be treated with care as described in the following paragraphs, especially when being pulled through a conduit. Cable grips should be used to spread the gripping force over a large area of the cable's surface and the amount of force should be limited to prevent distorting the cable's cross section.

Jacket Protection

When installing coaxial cable, it is important to protect the cable jacket to prevent water from entering the cable at any point. First, handle the cable with care during storage and installation so that the jacket is not damaged. If damage to the jacket is noticed immediately and no water is allowed to enter the cable, limited amounts of damage can be repaired using the same technique for waterproofing splices made with RF connectors as described in the **Building Antenna Systems and Towers** chapter.

Secure the cable after it has been connected to the antenna so that the jacket is not abraded or chafed by motion due to wind or antenna rotation. Cables hanging vertically should be supported in such a way that any bending is gradual and with a radius comfortably above the minimum bending radius. Cable grips are available that clamp over a short length, spreading the pressure and avoiding damage to the jacket. If wire or plastic cable ties are used, do not over-tighten them so that the jacket is crimped.

An important part of jacket protection is the waterproofing of RF connectors. Exposed coaxial cable braid will act as

Using Coax Braid

It is common to loosen and strip the shield braid from old coax and reuse it as a ground strap. Unfortunately, cable braid is not a very good RF conductor without its jacket! What makes braid work well in coaxial cable is the continuous pressure of the jacket that compresses the braid and keeps all of the strands in good contact. This allows the braid to act as a continuous conducting surface. When braid is removed from the cable, the jacket is no longer present to protect and compress the strands. This allows them to move away from each other and for contaminants to corrode the strand surface, greatly reducing the effectiveness of the braid at RF. Braid may be used for dc and low-frequency connections but for a reliable RF connection use copper strap or heavy wire. The cable's inner conductor and center insulation can be used as a high-voltage wire to the rating of the coaxial cable as long as the insulation is not cracked or compromised in some other way.

a wick, drawing in moisture. To a lesser extent, cables with stranded center conductors or partially hollow center insulation will draw in moisture as well. Coaxial cable infiltrated by water or moisture, either in the braid or center conductor, rapidly becomes unusable due to loss. Coax with a discolored or tarnished shield is not repairable and should be discarded.

Burying Coax

There are several reasons why you might choose to bury coaxial cable feed lines. One is that buried cable is virtually free from storm and UV damage, and usually has lower maintenance costs than cable that is exposed to the weather. Another reason might be that underground cable interacts less with the radiation pattern of antennas, picks up less noise, and carries less common-mode RF on the outside of the shield. A buried cable will be aesthetically acceptable in almost all communities, as well.

Although any cable can be buried, a cable that is specifically designed for burial will have a longer life. *Direct-burial* cable has a high-density polyethylene jacket because it is both nonporous and will withstand a relatively high amount of compressive loads. In impregnated direct burial cables, an additional moisture barrier of polyethylene grease may be applied under the jacket; this allows the material to leak out, thus "healing" small jacket penetrations. These are referred to as "flooded" cables and the grease can make installing connectors more difficult. Neither RG-8/U or RG-213/U are automatically rated for direct burial — the cable vendor must specify the direct burial rating. The cable jacket is usually stamped with "Direct Burial" or the equivalent.

Here are some direct burial tips:

1) Because the outer jacket is the cable's first line of defense, any steps which can be taken to prevent damage to it will go a long way toward maintaining cable quality.

2) Bury the cable in sand or finely pulverized soil, free of sharp stones, cinders or rubble. If the soil in the trench does not meet these requirements, tamp four to six inches of sand into the trench and lay the cable. Tamp in another six to eleven inches of sand above the cable. Place a creosoted or pressure-treated board in the trench above the sand prior to the final filling of the trench. This will provide some protection against damage that could be caused by digging or driving stakes.

3) When laying buried cable, leave some slack in the cable. A tightly stretched cable is more likely to be damaged as it is being covered with fill material.

4) Examine the cable as it is being installed to be sure the jacket has not been damaged during storage or by being dragged over sharp edges.

5) It is important that burial is below the frost line to avoid damage by the expansion and contraction of the soil and water during freezing and thawing cycles.

Using Conduit

You may want to consider burying the coax in plastic pipe or electrical conduit. While plastic pipe provides a mechanical barrier, water incursion is practically guaranteed — water will either leak in directly or will condense from moisture in the air. Be careful to drill holes in the bottom of solid conduit at all low spots so that any moisture can drain out or use the perforated pipe that allows the water to drain out into the surrounding ground.

Whether the conduit is above or below ground, use large-radius sweeps to create bends instead of elbows. It is much easier to pull cable through the gradual bend of a sweep and pulling cables through too sharp a bend can damage it. Metal conduit and fittings frequently have sharp edges and burrs that will cut or even strip the jacket from coax being pulled over them. Before assembling each section, file off sharp or rough edges.

When choosing the size of the conduit, leave plenty of extra space — at least double the expected total diameter of your cable bundle. A 3 to 4 inch-diameter pipe is recommended. This greatly eases the pulling process and gives the cables plenty of room to move around connectors and joints in the conduit. Be sure to include a "fish rope" or "fish wire" with the final cable you pull so you can add or replace cables later.

If you also have rotator or other control cables, there may be local building codes that limit the number and type of cables that can share the same conduit.

23.5.3 INSTALLING PARALLEL-WIRE LINE
Open-Wire Line

In installing an open-wire line, care must be used to prevent it from being affected by moisture, snow and ice. If the line is home-made, only spacers that are impervious to moisture and are unaffected by sunlight and weather should be used on air-insulated lines. Ceramic spacers meet this requirement although they are somewhat heavy. The wider the line spacing, the longer the leakage path across the spacers, but this cannot be carried too far without running into line radiation, particularly at the higher frequencies. Six inches should be considered a maximum practical spacing for HF use.

The line should be kept away from other conductors, including downspouts, metal window frames, flashing, etc, by a distance of two or three times the line spacing. Conductors that are very close to the line will be coupled to it to some degree, and the effect is that of placing an additional load across the line at the point where the coupling occurs. Reflections take place from this coupled load, raising the SWR. The effect is at its worst when one wire is closer than the other to the external conductor. In such a case one wire carries a heavier load than the other, with the result that the line currents are no longer equal. The line then becomes unbalanced.

Twin-lead and Window Lines

Solid dielectric, two-wire lines have a relatively small external field because of the small spacing, and can be mounted within a few inches of other conductors without much danger of coupling between the line and such conductors. Standoff insulators are available for supporting lines of this type when run along walls or similar structures.

As with open-wire lines, avoid installing the line in such a way that snow, ice, or liquid water can build up on the line. This presents an additional dielectric to the conductors and can change the line impedance or create loss.

Mechanical Issues

Where a parallel-wire line must be anchored to a building or other structure, standoff insulators of a height comparable with the line spacing should be used if mounted in a spot that is open to the weather. Lead-in bushings for bringing the line into a building also should have a long leakage path.

When running any kind of parallel-wire line down the side of a tower or other conducting surface, balance can be preserved by twisting the line every few feet. This results in approximately equal coupling by each conductor. Twisting the line also reduces the tendency of the line to move in the wind.

Parallel-line also has more wind resistance than coaxial cable and tends to move quite a bit more. The continual flexing can cause the conductors to break at soldered or otherwise fixed joints. This is a particular problem for lines with solid conductors as is common with window line. Support the line where it is attached to an antenna with insulators designed to provide stress relief to parallel-wire lines. (See the **Antenna Materials and Construction** chapter.)

Sharp bends should be avoided in any type of parallel-wire line, because it causes a change in the characteristic impedance at that point. The result is that reflections take place from each bend. This is of less importance when the SWR is high than when an attempt is being made to match the load to the line Z_0. It may be impossible to get the SWR to the desired figure until bends in the line are made very gradual.

23.5.4 TESTING TRANSMISSION LINES

Coaxial cable loss should be checked at least every two years if the cable is installed outdoors or buried. (See earlier sections on losses and deterioration.) Testing of any type of line can be done using the technique illustrated in **Figure 23.33**. If the measured loss in watts equates to more than 1 dB over the rated matched-line loss per 100 feet, the line should be replaced. The matched-line loss in dB can be determined from

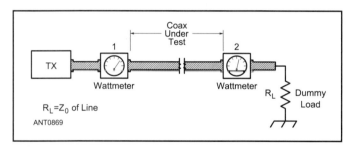

Figure 23.33 — Method for determining losses in transmission lines. The impedance of the dummy load must equal the Z_0 of the line for accurate results.

$$dB = 10 \log \frac{P_1}{P_2} \qquad \text{(Eq 33)}$$

where

P_1 is the power at the transmitter output
P_2 is the power measured at R_L of Figure 23.33.

Yet other methods of determining line losses may be used. If the line input impedances can be measured accurately with a short- and then an open-circuit termination, the electrical line length (determined by velocity factor) and the matched-line loss may be calculated for the frequency of measurement.

Determining line characteristics as just mentioned requires the use of a laboratory style of impedance bridge, or at least an impedance or noise bridge calibrated to a high degree of accuracy. But useful information about a transmission line can also be learned with just an SWR indicator, if it offers reliable readings at high SWR values.

A lossless line theoretically exhibits an infinite SWR when terminated in an open or a short circuit. A practical line will have losses, and therefore will limit the SWR at the line input to some finite value. Provided the signal source can operate safely into a severe mismatch, an SWR indicator can be used to determine the line loss. The instruments available to most amateurs lose accuracy at SWR values greater than about 5:1, so this method is useful principally as a go/no-go check on lines that are fairly long. For short, low-loss cables, only significant deterioration can be detected by the open-circuit SWR test.

First, either open or short circuit one end of the line. It makes no difference which termination is used, as the terminating SWR is theoretically infinite in either case. Then measure the SWR at the other end of the line. The matched-line loss for the frequency of measurement may then be determined from

$$ML = 10 \log \left(\frac{SWR + 1}{SWR - 1} \right) \qquad \text{(Eq 34)}$$

where SWR = the SWR value measured at the line input.

23.6 BIBLIOGRAPHY

Source material and more extended discussion of topics covered in this chapter can be found in the references given below and in the textbooks listed at the end of Chapter 2.

C. Brainard and K. Smith, "Coaxial Cable — The Neglected Link," *QST*, Apr 1981, pp 28-31.

J. Brown, "Transmission Lines at Audio Frequencies, and a Bit of History," Audio Systems Group (**www.audiosystemsgroup.com**).

D. DeMaw, "In-Line RF Power Metering," *QST*, Dec 1969, pp 11-16.

A. Ferreira, Jr., W. Pereira, J. Ribeiro, "Determine Twisted-Line Characteristic Impedance," *Microwaves & RF*, Jan 2008, **www.mwrf.com/Articles/ArticleID/18027/18027.html**

D. Geiser, "Resistive Impedance Matching with Quarter-Wave Lines," *QST*, Feb 1963, pp 56-57.

H. Jasik, *Antenna Engineering Handbook*, 1st ed. (New York: McGraw-Hill, 1961).

R. C. Johnson and H. Jasik, *Antenna Engineering Handbook*, 2nd ed. (New York: McGraw-Hill, 1984), pp 43-27 to 43-31.

E. Jordan, Ed., *Reference Data for Engineers: Radio, Electronics, Computer, and Communications*, 7th Edition (Howard W. Sams, 1985).

R. W. P. King, H. R. Mimno and A. H. Wing, *Transmission Lines, Antennas and Waveguides* (New York: Dover Publications, Inc., 1965).

J. D. Kraus, *Antennas* (New York: McGraw-Hill Book Co., 1950).

Kurokawa, "Power Waves and the Scattering Matrix," *IEEE Transactions on Microwave Theory and Techniques*, Vol MTT-13, Mar 1965, pp 194-202.

Z. Lau, "RF: Mounting RF Connectors," *QEX*, Nov 1996, pp 21-22.

J. Reisert, "RF Connectors, Part I and Part II," *Ham Radio*, Sep 1986, pp 77-80, and Oct 1986, pp 59-64.

W. Silver, "Hands-On Radio: Experiment 94 — SWR and Transmission Line Loss," *QST*, Nov 2010, pp 63-64.

W. Silver, "Hands-On Radio: Experiment 96: Open Wire Transmission Lines," *QST*, Jan 2011, pp 59-60.

M. W. Maxwell, "Another Look at Reflections (Parts 1-7)," *QST*, Apr 1973, pp 35-41; Jun 1973, pp 20-23, 27; Aug 1973, pp 36-43; Oct 1973, pp 22-29; Apr 1974, pp 26-29, 160-165; Dec 1974, pp 11-14, 158-166; Aug 1976, pp 15-20.

M. W. Maxwell, *Reflections III* (New York: CQ Communications, 2010).

T. McMullen, "The Line Sampler, an RF Power Monitor for VHF and UHF," *QST*, Apr 1972, pp 21-25.

H. Weinstein, "RF Transmission Cable for Microwave Applications," *Ham Radio*, May 1985, pp 106-112.

T. Williams, "Microwavelengths: Coaxial RF Connectors for Microwaves," *QST*, Nov 2004, pp 92-94.

TABLE OF CONTENTS

Chapter 24

Transmission Line Coupling and Impedance Matching

The **Transmission Lines** chapter presented the fundamentals of transmission line operation and characteristics. This chapter covers methods of getting energy into and out of the transmission line at the transmitter and at the antenna. This requires *coupling* — the transfer of energy between two systems — from a transmitter to the feed line or from the feed line to the antenna. For coupling to be the most efficient, both systems should have the same ratio of voltage to current (impedance) wherever the two systems meet so that no energy is reflected at that interface. This often requires *impedance matching* to convert energy at one ratio of voltage to current to another ratio — all as efficiently as possible. This can be done with LC circuits, special structures, and even transmission lines themselves.

The initial portions of this chapter discuss methods used at the transmitter to effectively transfer power into the antenna system feed line using LC impedance-matching circuits and antenna tuners. The subject then turns to choosing a transmission line and deciding the best configuration of feed line and impedance-matching devices. Finally, at the "other end" of the feed line, several sections address methods of impedance matching at the antenna and minimizing unwanted interaction between the feed line and antenna.

24.1 COUPLING THE TRANSMITTER AND LINE

A lot of effort is expended to ensure that the impedance presented to the transmitter by the antenna system feed line is close to 50 Ω. Is all that effort worthwhile? Like most broadly phrased questions, the answer begins, "It depends…" Vacuum-tube transmitters, with the wide adjustment range of the output amplifier's pi-network, could comfortably deliver rated output power into a wide variety of loads. The drawback was that the output network needed to be readjusted whenever the operating frequency changed significantly.

The modern amateur transceiver does not require output tuning adjustment at all for its broadband, untuned solid-state final amplifiers that are designed to operate into 50 Ω. Such a transmitter is able to deliver its rated output power — at the rated level of distortion — only when it is operated into the load for which it was designed. Generating full power from such a transmitter into loads far from 50 Ω can result

in distortion products causing interference to other stations.

Further, modern radios often employ protection circuitry to reduce output power automatically if the SWR rises above 2:1. Protective circuits are needed because the higher voltages or currents encountered at such loads can quickly destroy solid-state amplifier transistors. Modern solid-state transceivers often include built-in antenna tuners to match impedances when the SWR isn't 1:1.

The impedance at the input of a transmission line is determined by the frequency, the characteristic impedance (Z_0) of the line, the physical length, velocity factor and the matched-line loss of the line, as well as the impedance of the load (the antenna) at the output end of the line. If the impedance at the input of the transmission line connected to the transmitter differs appreciably from the load resistance into which the transmitter output circuit is designed to operate, an impedance-matching circuit must be inserted between the transmitter and the line input terminals.

These circuits, called *networks* in professional literature, have one of several configurations with the L, pi, and T being the most common. The name of the network reflects the letter (L, Π or T) that the usual shape of the circuit schematic most closely resembles.

The use of impedance-matching networks in a stand-alone piece of equipment is usually referred to as an *antenna tuner* or just *tuner*. This is somewhat of a misnomer since the network does not "tune" the antenna at all, even if located directly at the terminals of the antenna. The network only transforms the impedance presented to its output terminals into a different impedance at its input terminals. Many modern transceivers feature an internal antenna tuner that can compensate for SWR up to 3:1 (sometimes more).

In many publications, such an impedance-matching network is often called a *transmatch*, meaning a "transmitter matching" network. Another common name is *matchbox* (after the E.F. Johnson product line). A network operated automatically by a microprocessor is often called an *auto tuner*. Regardless of the name, the function of an antenna tuner is to transform the impedance at the input end of the transmission line — whatever it may be — to the 50 Ω needed for the transmitter to operate properly. An antenna tuner does *not* alter the SWR between its output terminals and the load, such as on the transmission line going to the antenna. It only ensures that the transmitter sees the 50-Ω load for which it was designed.

Antenna tuners come in three basic styles: *manual* (adjusted by the operator), *automatic* (adjusted under the control of a microprocessor) and *remote* (an automatic version designed to be mounted away from the operating position). Manual tuners are the most common and often include an SWR or power meter to aid the operator in adjusting the tuner. Automatic tuners may be internal to the transmitter or external, standalone equipment. Since the controlling microprocessor measures SWR on its own, there is rarely a need for power or SWR metering on automatic antenna tuners. Automatic models are available that are activated manually, or that sense the RF frequency and tune immediately, or that tune based on a computer control input or control link to the host transceiver. Remote antenna tuners are essentially automatic antenna tuners in enclosures designed to be mounted outside or out of sight of the operator and have no operating controls or displays.

As an example of the impedance-matching task, column one of **Tables 24-1** and **24-2** list the computed impedance at the center of two common dipoles mounted over average ground (with a conductivity of 5 mS/m and a dielectric constant of 13). The dipole in Table 24-1 is 100 feet long, and is mounted as a flattop, 50 feet high. The dipole in Table 24-2 is 66 feet long overall, mounted as an inverted-V whose apex is 50 feet high and whose legs have an included angle of 120°. The second column in Tables 24-1 and 24-2 shows the computed impedance at the transmitter end of a 100-foot long transmission line using 450-Ω window open-wire line. Please

Table 24-1
Impedance of Center-Fed 100 Foot Flattop Dipole, 50 Feet High Over Average Ground

Frequency (MHz)	Antenna Feed point Impedance (Ω)	Impedance at Input of 100 ft 450-Ω Line (Ω)
1.83	4.5 − j 1673	2.0 − j 20
3.8	39 − j 362	888 − j 2265
7.1	481 + j 964	64 − j 24
10.1	2584 − j 3292	62 − j 447
14.1	85 − j 123	84 − j 65
18.1	2097 + j 1552	2666 − j 884
21.1	345 − j 1073	156 + j 614
24.9	202 + j 367	149 − j 231
28.4	2493 − j 1375	68 − j 174

Table 24-2
Impedance of Center-Fed 66 Foot Inv-V Dipole, 50 Feet at Apex, 120° Included Angle Over Average Ground

Frequency (MHz)	Antenna Feed point Impedance (Ω)	Impedance at Input of 100 ft 450-Ω Line (Ω)
1.83	1.6 − j 2257	1.6 − j 44
3.8	10 − j 879	2275 + j 8980
7.1	65 − j 41	1223 − j 1183
10.1	22 + j 648	157 − j 1579
14.1	5287 − j 1310	148 − j 734
18.1	198 − j 820	138 − j 595
21.1	103 − j 181	896 − j 857
24.9	269 + j 570	99 − j 140
28.4	3089 + j 774	74 − j 223

recognize that there is nothing special or "magic" about these antennas — they are merely representative of typical antennas used by real-world amateurs.

The intent of the tables is to show that the impedance at the input of the transmission line varies over an extremely wide range when antennas like these are used over the entire range of amateur bands from 160 to 10 meters. The impedance at the input of the line (that is, at the antenna tuner's output terminals) *will be different* if the length of the line or the frequency of operation is changed. It should be obvious that an antenna tuner used with such a system must be very flexible to match the wide range of impedances encountered under ordinary circumstances — and it must do so without arcing from high voltage or overheating from high current.

24.1.1 THE IMPEDANCE MATCHING SYSTEM

Over the years, radio amateurs have derived a number of circuits for use as antenna tuners. At one time, when parallel-wire transmission line was more widely used, link-coupled tuned circuits were in vogue. With the increasing popularity of coaxial cable used as feed lines, other circuits have become more prevalent. The most common form of antenna tuner in recent years is some variation of a *T-network* configuration.

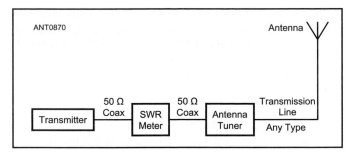

Figure 24.1 — Essentials of an impedance-matching system between transmitter and transmission line. The SWR meter indicates the quality of the match provided by the antenna tuner and may be part of the antenna tuner or the transmitter.

The basic system of a transmitter, impedance-matching network, transmission line and antenna is shown in **Figure 24.1**. As usual, we assume that the transmitter is designed to deliver its rated power into a load of 50 Ω. The problem is one of designing a matching circuit that will transform the actual line impedance at the input of the transmission line into a resistive impedance of $50 + j0$ Ω. This impedance will be unbalanced; that is, one side will be grounded, since modern transmitters universally ground one side of the output connector to the chassis. The line to the antenna, however, may be unbalanced (coaxial cable) or balanced (parallel-wire line), depending on whether the antenna itself is unbalanced or balanced.

The antenna tuner in such a system may only consist of the LC network necessary to transform impedance. This is typical of custom LC networks constructed to match an antenna used on a single band that may be located away from the transmitter. An antenna tuner used on multiple bands and located in the shack usually includes some type of SWR bridge or meter. (See the **Transmission Line and Antenna Measurements** chapter.)

Other features common in commercial antenna tuners include directional wattmeters, switches for the use of multiple feed lines and for bypassing the tuner, and balanced and single-wire outputs. An overview of antenna tuner functions and features is provided in *The ARRL Guide to Antenna Tuners* by Joel Hallas, W1ZR. (See Bibliography)

24.1.2 HARMONIC ATTENUATION

This is a good place to bring up the topic of harmonic attenuation, as it is related to antenna tuners. One potentially desirable characteristic of an antenna tuner is the degree of extra harmonic attenuation it can provide by acting as a tuned circuit. While this is desirable in theory, it is not always achieved in practice. For example, if an antenna tuner is used with a single, fixed-length antenna on multiple bands, the impedances presented to the tuner at the fundamental frequency and at the harmonics will often be radically different as shown in Table 24-2. For example, at 7.1 MHz, the impedance seen by the antenna tuner for the 66-foot inverted-V dipole is $1223 - j\,1183$ Ω. At 14.1 MHz, roughly the second harmonic, the impedance is $148 - j\,734$ Ω. The amount of harmonic attenuation for a particular network will vary dramatically with the impedances presented at the different frequencies.

Harmonics and Multiband Antennas

There are some antennas for which the impedance at the second harmonic is essentially the same as that for the fundamental. This often involves *trap* antenna systems or wideband log-periodic designs. For example, a system used by many amateurs is a *triband* Yagi that works on 20, 15 and 10 meters. The second harmonic of a 20 meter transmitter feeding such a tribander can be objectionably strong for nearby amateurs operating on 10 meters such as at a Field Day or other multi-position special event or contest station, even with the approximately 60 dB of attenuation of the second harmonic provided by the low-pass filters at the output of modern solid-state transceivers. The third harmonic of a 144.2 MHz fundamental can cause interference on the 432 MHz band, as well. A linear amplifier can exacerbate the problem, since its second harmonic may be suppressed only about 46 dB by the typical pi-network output circuit used in many older amplifiers.

Most amateur antenna tuners will not attenuate the 10 meter harmonic much at all, especially if the tuner uses a high-pass T-network. This is the most common network used commercially because of the wide range of impedances it will match. Some T-network designs have attempted to improve the harmonic attenuation using parallel inductors and capacitors instead of a single inductor for the center part of the tee. Unfortunately, this often leads to more loss and more critical tuning at the fundamental, while providing little, if any, additional harmonic suppression in actual installations. The lesson here is to not depend on the antenna tuner for harmonic suppression — use filters at the transmitter.

Harmonics and Pi-Network Tuners

If a low-pass pi network is used for an antenna tuner, there will be additional attenuation of harmonics, perhaps as much as 30 dB for a loaded Q of 3. The exact degree of harmonic attenuation, however, is often limited due to the stray inductance and capacitance present in most tuners at harmonic frequencies. Further, the matching range for a pi-network tuner is fairly limited because of the range of input and output capacitance needed for widely varying loads.

Harmonics and Stubs

Far more reliable suppression of harmonics can be achieved using quarter-wave and half-wave transmission line stubs at the transmitter output. For example, a typical 20 meter λ/4 shorted stub (which is an open circuit at 20 meters, but a short circuit at 10 meters) will provide about 25 dB of attenuation to the second harmonic. It will handle full legal amateur power too. The characteristics of such stubs are covered in the sections of this chapter on impedance matching at the antenna. The use of stubs as filters is covered in the *ARRL Handbook* and the excellent book *Managing Interstation Interference* by George Cutsogeorge, W2VJN. (See Bibliography.)

24.1.3 MYTHS ABOUT SWR

There are some enduring and quite misleading myths in Amateur Radio concerning SWR.

■ Despite some claims to the contrary, a high SWR *does not by itself* cause RF interference, or TVI or telephone interference. While it is true that an antenna located close to such devices can cause overload and interference, the SWR on the feed line to that antenna has nothing to do with it, providing of course that the tuner, feed line or connectors are not arcing. The antenna is merely doing its job, which is to radiate. The transmission line is doing its job, which is to convey power from the transmitter to the radiator.

■ A second myth, often stated in the same breath as the first one above, is that a high SWR will cause excessive radiation from a transmission line. SWR has nothing to do with excessive radiation from a line. Common-mode currents on feed lines cause radiation, but they are not directly related to SWR. An asymmetric arrangement of a transmission line and antenna can result in common-mode currents being induced on the outside of the shield of coax or as an imbalance of currents in an open-wire line. Common-mode current will radiate just as if it were on an antenna. If that current is flowing close to electronic equipment such as a telephone or entertainment system, RFI can result. A *choke balun* is used on coaxial feed lines to reduce these currents

as described in the section on baluns later in this chapter.

■ A third and perhaps even more prevalent myth is that you can't "get out" if the SWR on your transmission line is higher than 1.5:1 or 2:1 or some other such arbitrary figure. On the HF bands, if you use reasonable lengths of good coaxial cable (or even better yet, open-wire line), the truth is that you need not be overly concerned if the SWR at the load is kept below about 6:1. This sounds pretty radical to some amateurs who have heard horror story after horror story about SWR. The fact is that if you can load up your transmitter without any arcing inside, or if you use a tuner to make sure your transmitter is operating into its rated load resistance, you can enjoy a very effective station, using antennas with feed lines having high values of SWR on them. For example, a 450-Ω open-wire line connected to the multiband dipole shown in Table 24-1 would have a 19:1 SWR on it at 3.8 MHz. Yet time and again this antenna has proven to be a great performer at many installations.

■ A fourth myth is that changing the length of a feed line changes the SWR. Changing a feed line's length does *not* change the SWR (except for losses) inside the line. When someone tells you that adding or subtracting length changes the SWR, they are really telling you that their SWR meter reading was affected by the changing impedance in the line or that common-mode currents were affecting the measurement. Changing the feed line length can affect the impedance of the line to common-mode current and thus how much common-mode current is flowing at a particular point.

24.2 IMPEDANCE MATCHING NETWORKS

This section reviews the operation of several common impedance matching networks that are used as antenna tuners. As a supplement to this chapter, a review of impedance-matching circuit designs and characteristics contributed by Robert Neece, KØKR is included on this book's CD-ROM. The material includes:

■ Factors to be Considered in Creating or Assessing Matching-Unit Designs for the MF/HF Spectrum
■ Comparison Table of Matching-Unit Designs
■ Baluns in Matching Units

Along with the discussion is an extensive collection of references. The student of impedance matching will find the material to supplement and complement the material here, giving examples of commercial equipment and addressing the general advantages and disadvantages of each type.

24.2.1 THE L-NETWORK

A comparatively simple but very useful matching circuit for unbalanced loads is the L-network, as shown in **Figure 24.2A**. L-network antenna tuners are normally used for only a single band of operation, although multiband versions can be made with switched or variable coil taps. To determine

the range of circuit values for a matched condition, the input and load impedance values must be known or assumed. Otherwise a match may be found by trial and error.

There are several versions of the L-network. In Figure 24.2A, L is shown as the series reactance, X_S, and C1 as the shunt or parallel reactance, X_P. However, a capacitor may be used for the series reactance and an inductor for the shunt reactance, to satisfy mechanical or other considerations. The version shown in Figure 24.2A is the most popular with amateurs because of its low-pass characteristics that reduce harmonics, reasonable component values, and convenient construction from available component styles. A complete discussion of L-networks is available in the *ARRL Handbook*.

The ratio of the series reactance to the series resistance, X_S/R_S, is defined as the network Q. The four variables, R_S, R_P, X_S and X_P, for lossless components are related as given in the equations below. When any two values are known, the other two may be calculated.

$$Q = \sqrt{\frac{R_P}{R_S} - 1} = \frac{X_S}{R_S} = \frac{R_P}{X_P} \qquad \text{(Eq 1)}$$

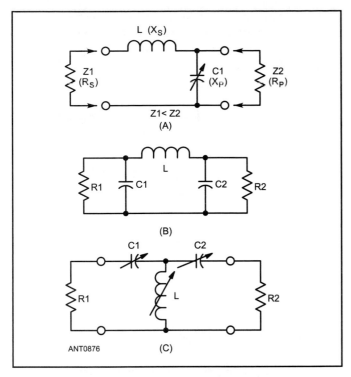

Figure 24.2 — At A, the L-matching network, consisting of L and C1, to match Z1 and Z2. The lower of the two impedances to be matched, Z1, must always be connected to the series-arm side of the network and the higher impedance, Z2, to the shunt-arm side. The positions of the inductor and capacitor may be interchanged in the network. At B, the Pi-network tuner, matching R1 to R2. The Pi provides more flexibility than the L as an antenna-tuner circuit. See equations in the text for calculating component values. At C, the T-network tuner. This has more flexibility in that components with practical values can match a wide variety of loads. The drawback is that this network can be inefficient, particularly when the output capacitor is small.

$$X_S = QR_S = \frac{QR_P}{1+Q^2} \qquad (Eq\ 2)$$

$$X_P = \frac{R_P}{Q} = \frac{R_P R_S}{X_S} = \frac{R_S^2 + X_S^2}{X_S} \qquad (Eq\ 3)$$

$$R_S = \frac{R_P}{Q^2 + 1} = \frac{X_S X_P}{R_P} \qquad (Eq\ 4)$$

$$R_P = R_S(1+Q^2) = QX_P = \frac{R_S^2 + X_S^2}{R_S} \qquad (Eq\ 5)$$

The reactance of loads that are not purely resistive may be taken into account and absorbed or compensated for in the reactances of the matching network. Inductive and capacitive reactance values may be converted to inductor and capacitor values for the operating frequency with standard reactance equations.

It is important to recognize that Eq 1 through 5 are for *lossless* components. When real components with real unloaded Qs are used, the transformation changes and you must compensate for the losses. Real coils are represented by a perfect inductor in series with a loss resistance, and real capacitors by a perfect capacitor in parallel with a loss resistance. At HF, a physical coil will have an unloaded Q_U between 100 and 400, with an average value of about 200 for a high-quality airwound coil mounted in a spacious metal enclosure. A variable capacitor used in an antenna tuner will have an unloaded Q_U of about 1000 for a typical air-variable capacitor with wiper contacts. An expensive vacuum-variable capacitor can have an unloaded Q_U as high as 5000.

The power loss in coils is generally larger than in variable capacitors used in practical antenna tuners. The circulating RF current in both coils and capacitors can also cause severe heating. The ARRL Laboratory has seen coils forms made of plastic melt when pushing antenna tuners to their extreme limits during product testing. The RF voltages developed across the capacitors can be pretty spectacular at times, leading to severe arcing.

Note that L-networks cannot match all impedances to 50 Ω. The load and source impedances must have the proper relationship for the equations to solve to obtainable component values. The reactance at the load must also be cancellable by the reactance of the L-network. If the load impedance is such that it cannot be matched by an L-network try (a) reversing the network or (b) adding λ/8 to λ/4 of transmission line between the load and network. This does not change the SWR but it does transform the load impedance to a new combination of resistance and reactance that the L-network may be able to match.

24.2.2 THE PI-NETWORK

The impedances at the feed point of an antenna used on multiple HF bands varies over a very wide range, particularly if thin wire is used. This was described in detail in the **Dipoles and Monopoles** chapter. The transmission line feeding the antenna transforms the wide range of impedances at the antenna's feed point to another wide range of impedances at the transmission line's input. This often mandates the use of a more flexible antenna tuner than an L-network.

The pi-network, shown in Figure 24.2B, offers more flexibility than the L-network, since there are three variables instead of two. The only limitation on the circuit values that may be used is that the reactance of the series arm, the inductor L in the figure, must not be greater than the square root of the product of the two values of resistive impedance to be matched. The following equations are for lossless components in a pi-network.

For R1 > R2

$$X_{C1} = \frac{R_1}{Q} \qquad (Eq\ 6)$$

$$X_{C2} = R2 \sqrt{\frac{R1/R2}{Q^2 + 1 - R1/R2}} \qquad (Eq\ 7)$$

$$X_L = \frac{(Q \times R1) + \dfrac{R1 \times R2}{X_{C2}}}{Q^2 + 1} \qquad \text{(Eq 8)}$$

The pi-network may be used to match a low impedance to a rather high one, such as 50 to several thousand ohms. Conversely, it may be used to match 50 Ω to a quite low value, such as 1 Ω or less. For antenna-tuner applications, C1 and C2 may be independently variable. L may be a roller inductor or a coil with switchable taps.

Alternatively, a lead fitted with a suitable clip may be used to short out turns of a fixed inductor. In this way, a match may be obtained through trial. It will be possible to match two values of impedances with several different settings of L, C1 and C2. This results because the Q of the network is being changed. If a match is maintained with other adjustments, the Q of the circuit rises with increased capacitance at C1.

Of course, the load usually has a reactive component along with resistance. You can compensate for the effect of these reactive components by changing one of the reactive elements in the matching network. For example, if some reactance were shunted across R2, the setting of C2 could be changed to compensate for inductive or capacitive shunt reactance.

As with the L-network, the effects of real-world unloaded Q for each component must be taken into account in the pi-network to evaluate real-world losses.

Pi-networks are used in vacuum-tube amplifiers to match the high tube output impedance to the 50-Ω impedance of most feed lines and antenna systems. See the *ARRL Handbook* chapter **RF Power Amplifiers** for more information on and design software for the pi-network.

24.2.3 THE T-NETWORK

Both the pi-network and the L-network often require unwieldy values of capacitance — that is, *large* capacitances are often required at the lower frequencies — to make the desired transformation to 50 Ω. Often, the range of capacitance from minimum to maximum must be quite wide when the impedance at the output of the network varies radically with frequency, as is common for multiband, single-wire antennas.

The high-pass T-network shown in Figure 24.2C is capable of matching a wide range of load impedances and uses practical values for the components. However, as in almost everything in radio, there is a price to be paid for this flexibility. The T-network can be very lossy compared to other network types. This is particularly true at the lower frequencies, whenever the load resistance is low. Loss can be severe if the maximum capacitance of the output capacitor C2 in Figure 24.2C is low.

For example, **Figure 24.3** shows the computed values for the components at 1.8 MHz for four types of networks into a load of 5 + *j* 0 Ω. In each case, the unloaded Q of the inductor used is assumed to be 200, and the unloaded Q of the capacitor(s) used is 1000. The component values were computed using the program *TLW* (described later in this chapter).

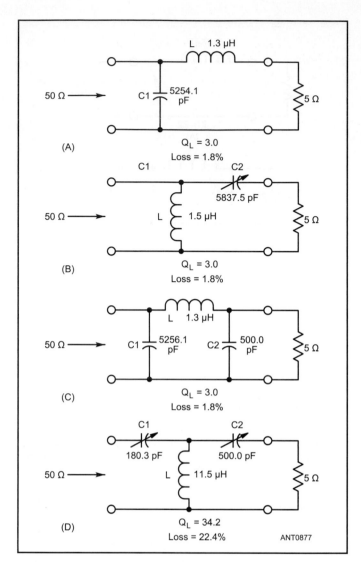

Figure 24.3 — Computed values for real components (Q_U = 200 for coil, Q_U = 1000 for capacitor) to match 5-Ω load resistance to 50-Ω line. At A, low-pass L-network, with shunt input capacitor, series inductor. At B, high-pass L-network, with shunt input inductor, series capacitor. Note how large the capacitance is for these L-networks. At C, low-pass pi-network and at D, high-pass T-network. The component values for the T-network are practical, although the loss is highest for this particular network, at 22.4% of the input power.

Figure 24.3A is a low-pass L-network; Figure 24.3B is a high-pass L-network and Figure 24.3C is a pi-network. At more than 5200 pF, the capacitance values are pretty unwieldy for the first three networks. The loaded Q_L for all three is only 3.0, indicating that the network loss is small. In fact, the loss is only 1.8% for all three because the loaded Q_L is much smaller than the unloaded Q_U of the components used.

The T-network in Figure 24.3D uses more practical, realizable component values. Note that the output capacitor C2 has been set to 500 pF and that dictates the values for the other two components. The drawback is that the loaded Q in this configuration has risen to 34.2, with an attendant loss of

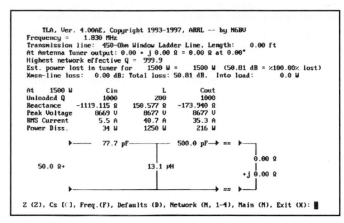

Figure 24.4 — Screen print of *TLA* program (a DOS predecessor of *TLW*) for a T-network antenna tuner with short at output terminals. The tuner has been "loaded up into itself," dissipating all input power internally!

22.4% of the power delivered to the input of the network. For the legal limit of 1500 W, the loss in the network is 335 W. Of this, 280 W ends up in the inductor, which will probably melt! Even if the inductor doesn't burn up, the output capacitor C2 might well arc over, since it has more than 3800 V peak across it at 1500 W into the network.

Due to the losses in the components in a T-network, it is quite possible to "load it up into itself," causing real damage inside. For example, see **Figure 24.4**, where a T-network is loaded up into a short circuit at 1.8 MHz. The component values look quite reasonable, but unfortunately *all* the power is dissipated in the network itself. The current through the output capacitor C2 at 1500 W input to the antenna tuner would be 35 A, creating a peak voltage of more than 8700 V across C2. Either C1 (also at more than 8700 V peak) or C2 will probably arc over before the power loss is sufficient to destroy the coil. However, the loud arcing might frighten the operator pretty badly.

The point you should remember is that the T-network is indeed very flexible in terms of matching to a wide variety of loads. However, it must be used judiciously, lest it burn itself up. Even if it doesn't fry itself, it can waste that precious RF power you'd rather put into your antenna. Additional discussion of the T-network as an antenna tuner is provided in the article by Sabin listed in the Bibliography.

Adjusting T-Network Antenna Tuners

The process of adjusting an antenna tuner can be simplified greatly by using a process that not only results in minimum SWR to the transmitter, but also minimizes power losses in the tuner circuitry. If you have a commercial tuner and read the user's manual, the manufacturer will likely provide a method of adjustment that you should follow, including initial settings. If you do not have a user's manual, first open the tuner and determine the circuit for the tuner. To adjust a T-network type of tuner:

1) Set the series capacitors to maximum value. This may

not correspond to the highest number on the control scale — verify that the capacitor's plates are fully meshed.

2) Set the inductor to maximum value. This corresponds to placing a switch tap or roller inductor contact so that it is electrically closest to circuit ground.

3) If you have an SWR analyzer, connect it to the TRANSMITTER connector of the tuner. Otherwise, connect the transceiver and tune it to the desired frequency, but do not transmit.

4) Adjust the inductor throughout its range watching the SWR analyzer for a dip in the SWR or listen for a peak in the received noise. Return the inductor to the setting for lowest SWR or highest received noise.

a) If no SWR minimum or noise peak is detected, reduce the value of the capacitor closest to the transmitter in steps of about 20% and repeat.

b) If still no SWR minimum or noise peak is detected, return the input capacitor to maximum value and reduce the output capacitor value in steps of about 20%.

c) If still no SWR minimum or noise peak is detected, return the output capacitor to maximum value and reduce both input and output capacitors in 20% steps.

5) Once a combination of settings is found with a definite SWR minimum or noise peak:

a) If you are using an SWR analyzer, make small adjustments to find the combination of settings that produce minimum SWR with the maximum value of input and output capacitance.

b) If you do not have an SWR analyzer, set the transmitter output power to about 10 W, ensure that you won't cause interference, identify with your call sign, and transmit a steady carrier by making the same adjustments as in step 5a.

c) For certain impedances, the tuner may not be able to reduce the SWR to an acceptable value. In this case, try adding feed line at the output of the tuner from ⅛- to ½-λ electrical wavelength long. This will not change the feed line SWR, but it may transform the impedance to a value more suitable for the tuner components.

In general, for any type of tuner, begin with the maximum reactance to ground (maximum inductance or minimum capacitance) and the minimum series reactance between the source and load (minimum inductance or maximum capacitance). The configuration that produces the minimum SWR with maximum reactance to ground and minimum series reactance will generally have the highest efficiency and broadest tuning bandwidth.

24.2.4 THE *TLW* (TRANSMISSION LINE FOR *WINDOWS*) PROGRAM AND ANTENNA TUNERS

The ARRL program *TLW* (Transmission Line for *Windows*) on the CD-ROM included with this book does calculations for transmission lines and antenna tuners. *TLW* evaluates four different networks: a low-pass L-network, a high-pass L-network, a low-pass pi-network, and a high-pass T-network. **Figure 24.5** shows the *TLW* output screen for an L-network design example.

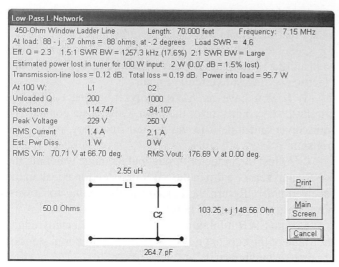

Figure 24.5 — Antenna tuner output screen of *TLW* software. Note the tuner schematic with parts values shown. The data above the schematic provide additional important information.

Not only does *TLW* compute the exact values for network components, but also the full effects of voltage, current and power dissipation for each component. Depending on the load impedance presented to the antenna tuner, the internal losses in an antenna tuner can be disastrous. See the documentation file TLW.PDF for further details on the use of *TLW*, which some call the "Swiss Army Knife" of transmission line software.

24.2.5 THE *AAT* (ANALYZE ANTENNA TUNER) PROGRAM

As you might expect, the limitations imposed by practical components used in actual antenna tuners depends on the individual component ratings, as well as on the range of impedances presented to the tuner for matching. ARRL has developed a program called *AAT*, standing for "Analyze Antenna Tuner," to map the range over which a particular design can achieve a match without exceeding certain operator-selected limits. *AAT* may be downloaded from **www.arrl.org/antenna-book**.

Let's assume that you want to evaluate a T-network on the ham bands between 1.8 to 29.7 MHz. First, you select suitable variable capacitors for C1 and C2. You decide to try the Johnson 154-16-1, a commonly available surplus or used component rated for a minimum to maximum range from 32 to 241 pF at 4500 V peak. Stray capacitance in the circuit is estimated at 10 pF, making the actual range from 42 to 251 pF, with an unloaded Q of 1000. This value of Q is typical for an air-variable capacitor with wiping contacts. Next, you choose a variable inductor with a maximum inductance of, let's say, 28 μH and an unloaded Q of 200, again typical values for a practical inductor. Set a power-loss limit of 20%, equivalent to a power loss of about 1 dB. Then let *AAT* do its computations.

AAT tests matching capability over a very wide range

of load impedances, in octave steps of both resistance and reactance. For example, it starts out with $3.125 - j\ 3200\ \Omega$, and checks whether a match is possible. It then proceeds to $3.125 - j\ 1600\ \Omega$, $3.125 - j\ 800\ \Omega$, etc, down to $3.125 + j\ 0\ \Omega$. Then *AAT* checks matching with positive reactances: $3.125 + j\ 3.125$, $3.125 + j\ 6.25$, $3.125 + j\ 12.5$, etc on up to $3.125 + j\ 3200\ \Omega$. Then it repeats the same process, over the same range of negative and positive reactances, for a series resistance of $6.25\ \Omega$. It continues this process in octave steps of resistance, all the way up to $3200\ \Omega$ resistive. A total of 253 impedances are thus checked for each frequency, giving a total of 2277 combinations for nine amateur bands from 1.8 to 29.7 MHz.

If the program determines that the chosen network can match a particular impedance value, while staying within the limits of voltage, component values and power loss imposed by the operator, it stores the lost-power percentage in memory and proceeds to the next impedance. If *AAT* determines that a match is possible, but some parameter is violated (for example, the voltage limit is exceeded), it stores the out-of-specification problem to memory and tries the next impedance.

For the pi-network and the T-network, which have three variable components, the program varies the output capacitor in discrete steps of capacitance. It is possible for *AAT* to miss very critical matching combinations because of the size of the steps necessary to hold execution time down. You can sometimes find such critical matching points manually using the *TLW* program, which uses the same algorithms to determine matching conditions.

Once all impedance points have been tried, *AAT* writes the results to two disk files — one is a summary file (TEENET.SUM, in this example) and the other is a detailed log (TEENET.LOG) of successful matches, and matche that came close except for exceeding a voltage rating. **Figure 24.6** is a sample printout of part of the summary *AAT* output for the 3.5 MHz band and one for the 29.7 MHz band. (The printouts for 1.8 MHz, and the bands from 7.1 to 24.9 MHz are not shown here.) This is for a T-network whose variable capacitors C1 and C2 (including 10 pF stray) range from 42 to 251 pF, each with a voltage rating of 4500 V. The coil is assumed to go up to 28 μH and has an unloaded Q of 200.

The numbers in the matching map grid represent the power loss percentage for each impedance where a match is indeed possible. Where a "C–" appears, *AAT* is saying that a match can't be made because the minimum capacitance of one or the other variable capacitors is too large. This often happens on the higher frequency bands, but can occur on the lower bands when the power loss is greater than the specified limit and *AAT* continues to try to find a condition where the power loss is lower. It does this until it runs into the minimum-capacitance limit of the input capacitor C1.

Similarly, where a "C+" appears, a match can't be made because the maximum capacitance of one or the other variable capacitors is too small. Where an "L+" is placed in the grid, the match fails because more inductance is needed. Where a "V" is shown, the voltage limit for some component

Loss percentage for Tee-network, series cap., shunt inductor, series cap.
Freq: 3.5 MHz, Z0: 50, 1500W, Vmax: 4500 V, Qu: 200 , Qc: 1000
Var. Cap: 42 to 251 pF with switched 160/80 m output cap.: 0 pF

Xa	3.125	6.25	12.5	25	50	100	200	400	800	1600	3200	Ra
- 3200	L+	L+	L+	L+		L+	L+	L+	L+	V	7.2	
- 1600	L+	L+	L+	L+		L+	V	V	6.7	5.4	5.6	
- 800	L+	L+	C-	C-	V	V	8.1	5.5	4.3	4.2	5.0	
- 400	C-	C-	C-	V	12.0	7.6	5.0	3.6	3.2	3.7	4.8	
- 200	C-	C-	P	13.3	8.2	5.2	3.5	2.7	2.8	3.5	4.7	
- 100	C-	C-	16.7	10.2	6.3	3.9	3.1	2.9	2.6	3.4	4.7	
- 50	C-	C-	14.3	8.6	5.2	3.6	3.3	2.9	2.6	3.4	4.7	
- 25	C-	C-	13.1	7.8	4.7	3.6	3.1	2.8	2.5	3.4	4.7	
- 12.5	C-	C-	12.4	7.4	4.5	3.9	3.5	2.8	2.5	3.4	4.7	
- 6.25	C-	C-	12.1	7.2	4.4	3.8	3.5	2.7	2.5	3.4	4.7	
-3.125	C-	19.8	11.9	7.1	4.7	3.8	3.5	2.7	2.5	3.4	4.7	
0	C-	19.6	11.8	7.0	4.7	3.7	3.4	2.7	2.5	3.4	4.7	
3.125	C-	19.3	11.6	6.9	4.6	3.7	3.4	2.7	2.5	3.4	4.7	
6.25	C-	19.1	11.4	6.8	4.5	3.7	3.4	2.9	2.5	3.4	4.7	
12.5	C-	18.6	11.1	6.6	4.4	4.2	3.3	2.9	2.5	3.4	4.7	
25	C-	17.6	10.4	6.2	4.7	4.0	3.2	2.8	2.5	3.4	4.7	
50	C-	15.5	9.1	6.1	4.9	3.7	3.4	2.7	2.4	3.3	4.7	
100	P	11.0	7.6	6.5	4.9	3.9	3.4	2.9	2.4	3.3	4.7	
200	V	V	8.3	7.0	5.3	3.9	3.6	2.8	2.3	3.3	4.7	
400	P	V	V	V	V	5.4	3.6	3.5	2.3	3.3	4.6	
800	P	P	P	V	V	V	2.3	2.3	2.6	3.4	4.7	
1600						L+	2.5	3.6	3.9	4.0	4.9	
3200						L+	L+	L+	L+	5.5	5.9	

Loss percentage for Tee-network, series cap., shunt inductor, series cap.
Freq: 29.7 MHz, Z0: 50, 1500W, Vmax: 4500 V, Qu: 200 , Qc: 1000
Var. Cap: 42 to 251 pF with switched 160/80 m output cap.: 0 pF

Xa	3.125	6.25	12.5	25	50	100	200	400	800	1600	3200	Ra
- 3200	C-	C-	C-	C-	C-	C-	C-	C-	C-	C-	C-	
- 1600	C-	C-	C-	C-	C-	C-	C-	C-	C-	C-	C-	
- 800	C-	C-	C-	C-	C-	C-	C-	C-	C-	C-	C-	
- 400	C-	C-	C-	C-	C-	C-	C-	C-	C-	C-	C-	
- 200	C-	C-	C-	C-	C-	C-	C-	C-	C-	C-	C-	
- 100	C-	C-	C-	C-	2.7	1.8	1.6	C-	C-	C-	C-	
- 50	C-	C-	C-	2.6	1.6	1.2	1.3	C-	C-	C-	C-	
- 25	C-	5.3	2.9	1.7	1.1	1.0	1.2	C-	C-	C-	C-	
- 12.5	7.1	3.9	2.1	1.1	0.8	0.9	1.1	C-	C-	C-	C-	
- 6.25	6.0	3.2	1.7	1.0	0.6	0.8	1.1	C-	C-	C-	C-	
-3.125	5.4	2.8	1.4	1.0	0.6	0.8	1.1	C-	C-	C-	C-	
0	4.7	2.5	1.6	1.0	0.6	0.8	1.1	C-	C-	C-	C-	
3.125	4.1	2.4	1.7	1.1	0.6	0.7	1.1	C-	C-	C-	C-	
6.25	3.4	2.4	1.5	1.0	0.6	0.7	1.1	C-	C-	C-	C-	
12.5	3.4	2.9	2.0	1.1	0.6	0.7	1.1	C-	C-	C-	C-	
25	4.6	3.2	2.0	1.3	0.6	0.6	1.0	C-	C-	C-	C-	
50	5.2	3.9	2.0	1.6	0.7	0.5	1.0	C-	C-	C-	C-	
100	8.9	4.8	2.5	C+	0.9	0.5	1.0	C-	C-	C-	C-	
200						0.7	1.1	C-	C-	C-	C-	
400						C-	C-	C-	C-	C-	C-	
800						C-	C-	C-	C-	C-	C-	
1600						C-	C-	C-	C-	C-	C-	
3200						L+	C-	C-	C-	C-	C-	

Figure 24.6 — Sample printout from the *AAT* program, showing 3.5 and 29.7-MHz simulations for a T-network antenna tuner using 42-251 pF variable tuning capacitors (including 10 pF of stray), with voltage rating of 4500 V and 28 μH roller inductor. The load varies from 3.125 – *j* 3200 Ω to 3200 + *j* 3200 Ω in geometric steps. Symbol "L+" indicates that a match is impossible because more inductance is needed. "C–" indicates that the minimum capacitance is too large. "V" indicates that the voltage rating of a capacitor has been exceeded. "P" indicates that the power rating limit set by the operator to 20% has been exceeded. A blank indicates that matching is not possible at all, probably for a variety of simultaneous reasons.

Loss percentage for Tee-network, series cap., shunt inductor, series cap.
Freq: 3.5 MHz, Z0: 50, 1500W, Vmax: 3000 V, Qu: 200 , Qc: 1000
Var. Cap: 25 to 402 pF with switched 160/80 m output cap.: 400 pF

Xa	3.125	6.25	12.5	25	50	100	200	400	800	1600	3200	Ra
- 3200	L+	L+	L+	L+		L+	L+	L+	L+	V	V	
- 1600	L+	L+	L+	L+		L+	V	V	V	V	V	
- 800	C-	L+	L+	L+	V	V	V	4.9	3.9	4.0	V	
- 400	C-	L+	L+	V	V	6.0	4.0	3.0	2.9	3.6	V	
- 200	C-	L+	V	9.0	5.5	3.5	2.5	2.2	2.6	3.4	V	
- 100	C-	V	9.6	5.7	3.5	2.3	1.8	1.9	2.4	3.4	V	
- 50	19.7	11.7	6.8	4.0	2.6	2.2	1.8	1.8	2.4	3.3	V	
- 25	16.1	9.3	5.4	3.3	2.7	2.3	1.8	1.7	2.4	3.3	V	
- 12.5	14.1	8.1	4.6	3.4	2.9	2.4	1.9	1.7	2.4	3.3	V	
- 6.25	13.1	7.5	4.2	3.5	2.8	2.4	1.9	1.7	2.3	3.3	V	
-3.125	12.6	7.2	4.3	3.3	2.7	2.3	1.8	1.7	2.3	3.3	V	
0	12.1	6.9	4.4	3.6	3.0	2.3	1.8	1.7	2.3	3.3	V	
3.125	11.6	6.5	4.6	3.4	3.0	2.3	2.0	1.7	2.3	3.3	V	
6.25	11.0	6.2	4.4	3.7	2.9	2.6	2.0	1.7	2.3	3.3	V	
12.5	10.0	6.0	4.4	3.5	2.8	2.5	1.9	1.7	2.3	3.3	V	
25	8.5	5.8	4.7	3.6	3.0	2.4	1.9	1.6	2.3	3.3	V	
50	8.6	6.9	4.7	4.2	3.2	2.3	1.8	1.6	2.3	3.3	V	
100	V	V	6.3	4.4	3.2	2.5	1.9	1.5	2.3	3.3	V	
200	V	V	V	V	4.2	2.6	2.0	1.5	2.3	3.3	V	
400	P	V	V	V	V	1.1	1.5	1.7	2.3	3.3	V	
800	P	P	P	V	V	V	2.3	2.6	2.7	3.4	V	
1600	P	P	P	V	V	V	V	V	V	4.1	V	
3200						L+	L+	L+	V	V	V	

Loss percentage for Tee-network, series cap., shunt inductor, series cap.
Freq: 29.7 MHz, Z0: 50, 1500W, Vmax: 3000 V, Qu: 200 , Qc: 1000
Var. Cap: 25 to 402 pF with switched 160/80 m output cap.: 400 pF

Xa	3.125	6.25	12.5	25	50	100	200	400	800	1600	3200	Ra
- 3200	C-	C-	C-	C-		C-	C-	C-	C-	C-	C-	
- 1600	C-	C-	C-	C-	C-	C-	C-	C-	C-	C-	C-	
- 800	C-	C-	C-	C-	C-	C-	C-	C-	C-	C-	C-	
- 400	C-	C-	C-	C-	C-	C-	C-	2.8	C-	C-	C-	
- 200	C-	C-	C-	C-	4.6	2.9	2.2	2.1	2.5	C-	C-	
- 100	C-	C-	C-	4.1	2.5	1.7	1.5	1.8	2.4	C-	C-	
- 50	C-	6.9	3.9	2.3	1.4	1.1	1.3	1.7	2.3	C-	C-	
- 25	7.7	4.3	2.4	1.3	0.9	0.9	1.2	1.6	2.3	C-	C-	
- 12.5	5.4	2.9	1.5	0.8	0.6	0.8	1.1	1.6	2.3	C-	C-	
- 6.25	4.1	2.1	1.3	0.8	0.5	0.7	1.1	1.6	2.3	C-	C-	
-3.125	3.5	1.9	1.4	0.8	0.4	0.7	1.1	1.6	2.3	C-	C-	
0	2.8	1.9	1.4	1.0	0.4	0.7	1.1	1.6	2.3	C-	C-	
3.125	3.2	2.0	1.4	0.9	0.4	0.7	1.1	1.6	2.3	C-	C-	
6.25	3.4	1.9	1.5	1.0	0.4	0.6	1.1	1.6	2.3	C-	C-	
12.5	3.4	2.1	1.4	1.1	0.4	0.6	1.0	1.6	2.3	C-	C-	
25	4.6	2.3	1.5	1.0	0.5	0.6	1.0	1.6	2.3	C-	C-	
50	5.2	3.9	2.0	1.6	0.5	0.5	1.0	1.5	2.3	C-	C-	
100	V	5.6	3.0	1.6	1.0	0.5	0.9	1.5	2.3	C-	C-	
200	V				0.7	0.8	1.1	1.5	2.2	C-	C-	
400						1.2	1.6	1.8	2.3	C-	C-	
800						C-	C-	C-	C-	C-	C-	
1600						C-	C-	C-	C-	C-	C-	
3200						L+	C-	C-	C-	C-	C-	

Figure 24.7 — Another sample *AAT* program printout, using a dual-section variable capacitor whose overall tuning range when in parallel varies from 25 to 402 pF, but with a 3000-V rating. The same 28 μH roller is used, but an auxiliary 400 pF fixed capacitor can now be manually switched across the output variable capacitor. Note that the overall matching range has in effect been shifted over to the left from that in Figure 24.6 for the lower frequency because the maximum output capacitance is higher. The range has been extended on the highest frequency because the minimum capacitance is smaller.

has been exceeded. It may be possible in such a circumstance to reduce the power to eliminate arcing. Where "P" is shown, the power limit has been exceeded, meaning that the loss would be excessive. Where a blank occurs, no combination of matching components resulted in a match.

It should be clear that with this particular set of capacitors, the T-network suffers large losses when the load resistance is less than about 12.5 Ω at 3.5 MHz. For example, for a load impedance of $12.5 - j\,100$ Ω the loss is 16.7%. At 1500 W into the tuner, 250 W would be burned up inside, mainly in the coil. It should also be clear that as the reactance increases, the power loss increases, particularly for capacitive reactance. This occurs because the series capacitive reactance of the load adds to the series reactance of C2, and losses rise accordingly.

For most loads, a larger value for the output capacitor C2 decreases losses. Typically, there is a tradeoff between the range of minimum-to-maximum capacitance and the voltage rating for the variable capacitors that determines the effective impedance-matching range. See **Figure 24.7**, which assumes that capacitors C1 and C2 have a larger range between minimum to maximum capacitance, but with a lower peak voltage rating. Each tuning capacitor is representative of a Johnson 154-507-1 dual-section capacitor, which has a range from 15 to 196 pF in each section, at a peak voltage rating of 3000 V. The two sections are placed in parallel for the lower frequencies. Again, a stray capacitance of 10 pF is assumed for each variable capacitor.

The result at 3.5 MHz in Figure 24.7 is a shift of the matching map toward the left. This means that lower values of series load resistance can be matched with lower power loss. However, it also means that the highest value of load resistance, 3200 Ω, now runs into the limitation of the voltage rating of the output capacitor, something that did not happen when the 4500-V capacitors were used in Figure 24.6.

Now, compare Figure 24.6 and Figure 24.7 at 29.7 MHz. The smaller minimum capacitance (25 pF) of the capacitors in Figure 24.7 allows for a wider range of matching impedance, compared with the circuit of Figure 24.6, where the minimum capacitance is 42 pF. This circuit can't match loads with resistances greater than 200 Ω.

Note that *AAT* also allows the operator to specify a switchable fixed-value capacitor across the output capacitor C2 to aid in matching low-resistance loads on the lower frequency bands. In Figure 24.7, a 400 pF fixed capacitor C4 was assumed to be switched across C2 for the 1.8 and 3.5 MHz bands. **Figure 24.8** shows the schematic for such a T-network antenna tuner.

The power loss in Figure 24.7 on 3.5 MHz at a load of $6.25 - j\,3.125$ Ω is 7.2%, while in Figure 24.6 the loss is 19.7%. On the other hand, the voltage rating of one (or both) capacitors is exceeded for a load with a 3200 Ω resistance. By the way, it isn't exceeded by very much: the computed voltage is 3003 V at 1500 W input, just barely exceeding the 3000-V rating for the capacitor. This is, after all, a strictly literal computer program. Turning down the power just a small amount would stop any arcing.

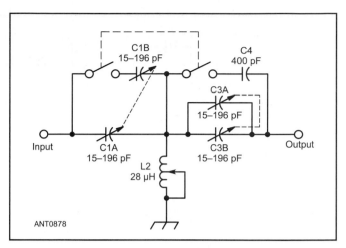

Figure 24.8 — Schematic for the T-network antenna tuner whose tuning range is shown in Figure 24.7.

AAT produces similar tables for pi-network and L-network configurations, mapping the matching capabilities for the component combinations chosen. All computations are, of course, only as accurate as the assumed values for unloaded Q_U in the components. The unloaded Q_U of variable inductors can vary quite a bit over the full amateur MF and HF frequency range. Computations produced by *AAT* have been compared to measured results on real antenna tuners and they correlate well when measured values for unloaded inductor Q_U are plugged into *AAT*. Individual antenna tuners may well vary, depending on what sort of stray inductance or capacitance is introduced during construction.

24.2.6 BALANCED ANTENNA TUNERS

Modern antenna tuners often include a toroid-wound balun at their output for use with balanced or parallel-wire feed lines. This allows a transmitter's unbalanced coaxial output to be connected to the balanced feed line. (Baluns are discussed later in this chapter.) Be aware that at very high or very low impedances, the balun's power rating may be exceeded at high transmitted power levels.

The inductive- or link-coupling circuits seen in **Figure 24.9** are sometimes used but have largely been replaced by the toroid-wound balun. A more detailed discussion on inductive coupling is available on this book's CD-ROM as is a low-power link-coupled tuner project that uses the configuration shown in Figure 24.9D and instructions for building the 100-W "Z-Match" antenna tuner designed by Phil Salas, AD5X. The article "*FilTuners*-a New (Old) Approach to Antenna Matching" by John Stanley, K4ERO (see Bibliography) also discusses tuned link-coupling from the standpoint of the matching network providing both filtering and impedance matching.

A fully-balanced tuner has a symmetrical internal circuit with a tuner circuit for each side of the feed line and the balun at the input to the tuner where the impedance is close to 50 Ω. Several examples are shown in **Figure 24.10** that can be recognized as being formed from the unbalanced

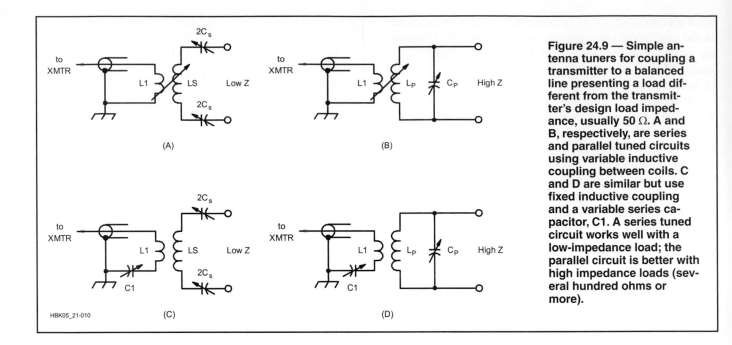

Figure 24.9 — Simple antenna tuners for coupling a transmitter to a balanced line presenting a load different from the transmitter's design load impedance, usually 50 Ω. A and B, respectively, are series and parallel tuned circuits using variable inductive coupling between coils. C and D are similar but use fixed inductive coupling and a variable series capacitor, C1. A series tuned circuit works well with a low-impedance load; the parallel circuit is better with high impedance loads (several hundred ohms or more).

networks described earlier with a mirror-image of the network being inserted in the "ground" side of the circuit.

A balun is inserted on the 50-Ω side of the circuit to allow connection to unbalanced coaxial feed lines. Some tuners are designed to use a 1:1 balun for this purpose while others transform the load impedance to 200 Ω and use a 4:1 balun. This allows the balun to operate at its design impedances regardless of load impedance. A balun at the output of an unbalanced tuner must operate at whatever load impedance is presented, which can lead to significant losses or arcing in the balun.

A disadvantage of balanced tuners is the higher cost from the additional components and the more complex mechanical arrangements to adjust more than one component at the same time with a single control.

The hairpin tuner configuration in **Figure 24.11** is a balanced tuner for use at VHF and UHF where solenoid-wound

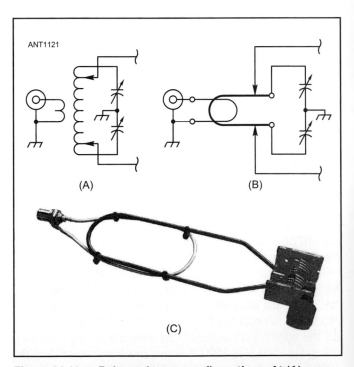

Figure 24.11 — Balanced tuner configurations. At (A) conventional tapped coil based tuner, at (B) the hairpin equivalent. (C) shows a hairpin tuner for 144 MHz. The technique can be used from 10 meters through 70 cm.

Figure 24.10 — Configurations of balanced antenna tuners.

coils may have too much inductance. The tuner is described in the April 2009 *QST* article "Hairpin Tuners for Matching Balanced Antenna Systems" by John Stanley, K4ERO, that is included on this book's CD-ROM.

24.2.7 Project: HIGH-POWER ARRL ANTENNA TUNER

Dean Straw, N6BV designed this antenna tuner with three objectives in mind: First, it would operate over a wide range of loads at full legal power. Second, it would be a high efficiency design, with minimal losses, including losses in the balun. This led to the third objective: Include a balun operating within its design impedances. For that reason this unit was designed with the balun at the input of the tuner.

This antenna tuner is designed to handle full legal power from 160 to 10 meters, matching a wide range of either balanced or unbalanced impedances. The network configuration is a high-pass T-network, with two series variable capacitors and a variable shunt inductor. See **Figure 24.12** for the schematic of the tuner. Note that the schematic is drawn in a somewhat unusual fashion. This is done to emphasize that the common connection of the series input and output capacitors and the shunt inductor is actually the subchassis used to mount these components away from the tuner's cabinet. The subchassis is insulated from the main cabinet using four heavy-duty 2-inch steatite (ceramic) stand-off insulators.

While a T-network type of tuner can be very lossy if care isn't taken, it is very flexible in the range of impedances it can match. Special attention has been paid to minimize power loss in this tuner — particularly for low-impedance loads on the lower-frequency amateur bands. Preventing arcing or excessive power dissipation for low-impedance loads on 160 meters represents the most challenging conditions for an antenna tuner designer. To see the computed range of impedances it can handle, look over the tables in the ASCII file called TUNER.SUM on this book's CD-ROM. The tables were created using the program *AAT*, described previously in this chapter.

For example, assume that the load at 1.8 MHz is $12.5 + j \, 0 \, \Omega$. For this example, the output capacitor C3 is set by the program to 750 pF. This dictates the values for the other two components. At 1.8 MHz, for typical values of component unloaded Q (200 for the coil), 7.9% of the power delivered to the input of the network is lost as heat. For 1500 W at the input, the loss in the network is thus 119 W. Of this, 98 W ends up in the inductor, which must be able to handle this without melting or detuning. The T-network must be used judiciously, lest it burn itself up or arc over internally.

One of the techniques used to minimize power lost in this tuner is the use of a relatively large output capacitor. (The output variable capacitor has a maximum capacitance of approximately 400 pF, including an estimated 20 pF of stray capacitance.) An additional 400 pF of fixed capacitance

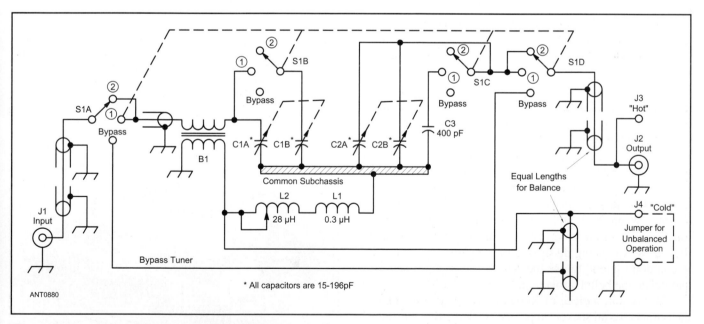

Figure 24.12 — Schematic diagram of the ARRL Antenna Tuner.

C1, C2 — 15-196 pF transmitting variable with voltage rating of 3000 V peak, such as the Cardwell-Johnson 154-507-1 (www.cardwellcondenser.com).

C3 — Home-made 400 pF capacitor; more than 10 kV voltage breakdown. Made from plate glass from a 5 × 7-inch picture frame, sandwiched in between a 4 × 6-inch, 0.030-inch thick aluminum plate and the electrically floating subchassis that also forms the common connection between C1, C2 and L1.

L1 — Fixed inductor, approximately 0.3 μH, 4 turns of ¼-inch copper tubing formed on 1-inch OD tubing.

L2 — Rotary inductor, 28 μH inductance, Cardwell 229-203-1, with steatite coil form (www.cardwellcondenser.com).

B1 — Balun, 12 turns bifilar wound #10 AWG Formvar wire side-by-side on 2.4-inch OD Type 43 core, Amidon FT240-43.

can be switched across the output variable capacitor on 80 or 160 meters. At 750 pF output capacitance at 1.8 MHz and a 12.5-Ω load, enough heat is generated at 1500 W input to make the inductor uncomfortably warm to the touch after 30 seconds of full-power key-down operation, but not enough to destroy the roller inductor.

For a variable capacitor used in a T-network tuner, there is a trade-off between the range of minimum to maximum capacitance and the voltage rating. This tuner uses two identical Cardwell-Johnson dual-section 154-507-1 air-variable capacitors, rated at 3000 V. Each section of the capacitor ranges from 15 to 196 pF, with an estimated 10 pF of stray capacitance associated with each section. Both sections are wired in parallel for the output capacitor, while they are switched in or out using switch S1B for the input capacitor. This strategy allows the minimum capacitance of the input capacitor to be smaller to match high-impedance loads at the higher frequencies.

The roller inductor is a high-quality Cardwell 229-203-1 unit, with a steatite body to enable it to dissipate heat without damage. The roller inductor is augmented with a series 0.3 μH coil made of four turns of ¼-inch copper tubing formed on a 1-inch OD form (which is then removed). This fixed coil can dissipate more heat when low values of inductance are needed for low-impedance loads at high frequencies. Both variable capacitors and the roller inductor use ceramic-insulated shaft couplers, since all components are hot electrically. Each shaft goes through a grounded bushing at the front panel to make sure none of the knobs is hot for the operator.

The balun allowing operation with balanced loads is placed at the input of this antenna coupler, rather than at the output where it is commonly placed in other designs. Putting the balun at the input stresses the balun less, since it is operating into its design resistance of 50 Ω, once the network is tuned. For unbalanced (coax) operation, the common point at the bottom of the roller inductor is grounded using a jumper at the feedthrough insulator at the rear of the cabinet. In the prototype antenna tuner, the balun was wound using 12 turns of #10 AWG Formvar insulated wire, wound side-by-side in bifilar fashion on a 2.4-inch OD core of type 43 material. After 60 seconds of key-down operation at 1500 W on 29.7 MHz, the wire becomes warm to the touch, although the core itself remains cool. We estimated that 25 W was being dissipated in the balun. Alternatively, if you don't intend to use the tuner for balanced lines, you can delete the balun altogether.

In our unit, a piece of RG-213 coax is used to connect the output coaxial socket (in parallel with the "hot" insulated feedthrough insulator) to S1D common. This adds approximately 15 pF fixed capacitance to ground. An equal length of RG-213 is used at the "cold" feedthrough insulator so that the circuit remains balanced to ground when used with balanced transmission lines. When the cold terminal is jumpered to ground for unbalanced loads (that is, using the coax connector), the extra length of RG-213 is shorted out and is thus out of the circuit.

Construction

The prototype antenna tuner was mounted in a Hammond model 14151 heavy-duty, painted steel cabinet. This is an exceptionally well-constructed cabinet that does not flex or jump around on the operating table when the roller inductor shaft is rotated vigorously. The electrical components inside were spaced well away from the steel cabinet to keep losses down, especially in the variable inductor. There is also lots of clearance between components and the chassis itself to prevent arcing and stray capacitance to ground. See **Figures 24.13** and **24.14** showing the layout inside the cabinet of

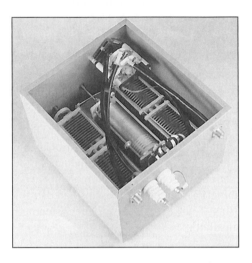

Figure 24.13 — Interior view of the ARRL Antenna Tuner. The balun is mounted near the input coaxial connector. The two feedthrough insulators for balanced-line operation are located near the output coaxial unbalanced connector. The Radioswitch Corporation high-voltage switch is mounted to the front panel. Ceramic-insulated shaft couplers through ground ¼-inch panel bushings couple the variable components to the knobs.

Figure 24.14 — Bottom view of the subchassis, showing the four white insulators used to isolate the subchassis from the cabinet. The homemade 400-pF fixed capacitor C3 is epoxied to the bottom of the subchassis, sandwiching a piece of plate glass as the dielectric between the subchassis and a flat piece of aluminum.

Figure 24.15 — Front panel view of the ARRL Antenna Tuner. The high-quality turns counter dial is from Surplus Sales of Nebraska.

the prototype tuner. **Figure 24.15** shows a view of the front panel. The turns-counter dial for the roller inductor was purchased from Surplus Sales of Nebraska.

The 400-pF fixed capacitor is constructed using low-cost plate glass from a 5 × 7-inch picture frame, together with an approximately 4 × 6-inch flat piece of sheet aluminum that is 0.030-inch thick. The tuner's 10½ × 8-inch subchassis forms the other plate of this homebrew capacitor. For mechanical rigidity, the subchassis uses two ¹⁄₁₆-inch thick aluminum plates. The ¹⁄₁₆-inch thick glass is epoxied to the bottom of the subchassis. The 4 × 6-inch aluminum sheet forming the second plate of the 400-pF fixed capacitor is in turn epoxied to the glass to make a stable, high-voltage, high-current fixed capacitor. Two strips of wood are screwed down over the assembly underneath the subchassis to make sure the capacitor stays in place. The estimated breakdown voltage is 12,000 V. See **Figure 24.16** for a bottom view of the subchassis.

Figure 24.16 — Bottom view of subchassis, showing the two strips of wood ensuring mechanical stability of the C3 capacitor assembly.

Note: The dielectric constant of the glass in a cheap ($2 at Wal-Mart) picture frame can vary. The final dimensions of the aluminum sheet secured with one-hour epoxy to the glass was varied by sliding it in and out until 400 pF was reached, while the epoxy was still wet, using an Autek RF-1 antenna analyzer as a capacitance meter. Don't let epoxy slop over the edges — this can arc and burn permanently!

S1 is bolted directly to the front of the cabinet. S1 is a special high-voltage RF switch from Radio Switch Corporation, with four poles and three positions. It is not inexpensive, but we wanted to have no weak points in the prototype unit. A more frugal ham might want to substitute two more common surplus DPDT switches for S1. One switch would bypass the tuner when the operator desires to do that. The other would switch the additional 400-pF fixed capacitor across variable C3 and also parallel both sections of C1 together for the lower frequencies. Both switches would have to be capable of handling high RF voltages, of course.

Operation

The ARRL Antenna Tuner is designed to handle the output from transmitters that operate up to 1.5 kW. An external SWR indicator is used between the transmitter and the antenna tuner to show when a matched condition is attained. Most often the SWR meter built into the transceiver is used to tune the tuner and then the amplifier is switched on. The builder may want to integrate an SWR meter in the tuner circuit between J1 and the arm of S1A.

Never *hot switch* an antenna tuner, as this can damage both transmitter and tuner. For initial setting below 10 MHz, set S1 to position 2 and C1 at midrange, C2 at full mesh. With a few watts of RF, adjust the roller inductor for a decrease in reflected power. Then adjust C1 and L2 alternately for the lowest possible SWR, also adjusting C2 if necessary. If a satisfactory SWR cannot be achieved, try S1 at position 3 and repeat the steps above. Finally, increase the transmitter power to maximum and touch up the tuner's controls if necessary. When tuning, keep your transmissions brief and identify your station.

For operation above 10 MHz, again initially use S1 set to position 2, and if SWR cannot be lowered properly, try S1 set to position 3. This will probably be necessary for 24 or 28-MHz operation. In general, you want to set C2 for as much capacitance as possible, especially on the lower frequencies. This will result in the least amount of loss through the antenna tuner. The first position of S1 permits switched-through operation direct to the antenna when the antenna tuner is not needed.

Comments

Surplus coils and capacitors are suitable for use in this circuit. L2 should have at least 25 µH of inductance and be constructed with a steatite body. There are roller inductors on the market made with Delrin plastic bodies but these are very prone to melting under stress and should be avoided. The tuning capacitors need to have 200 pF or more of capacitance per section at a breakdown voltage of at least 3000 V. You could save some money by using a single-section variable capacitor for the output capacitor, rather than the dual-section unit we used. It should have a maximum capacitance of 400 pF and a voltage rating of 3000 V.

Measured insertion loss for this antenna tuner is low. The worst-case load tested was four 50-Ω dummy loads in parallel to make a 12.5-Ω load at 1.8 MHz. Running 1500 W key down for 30 seconds heated the variable inductor enough so that you wouldn't want to keep your hand on it for long. None of the other components became hot in this test.

At higher frequencies (and into a 50-Ω load at 1.8 MHz), the roller inductor was only warm to the touch at 1500 W key down for 30 seconds. The #10 AWG balun wire, as mentioned previously, was the warmest component in the antenna tuner for frequencies above 14 MHz, although it was far from catastrophic.

24.2.8 GENERAL PURPOSE TUNER DESIGNS

Several antenna tuner designs were created by Joel Hallas, W1ZR, for the book *The ARRL Guide to Antenna Tuners*. The *TLW* program was used to determine component values for a set of common load impedances and three popular antenna tuner circuits shown in **Figure 24.17**. **Tables 24-3** to **24-5** show the required component values to match those load impedances at 1.8, 3.5 and 30 MHz, the extremes of HF operation for antenna tuners.

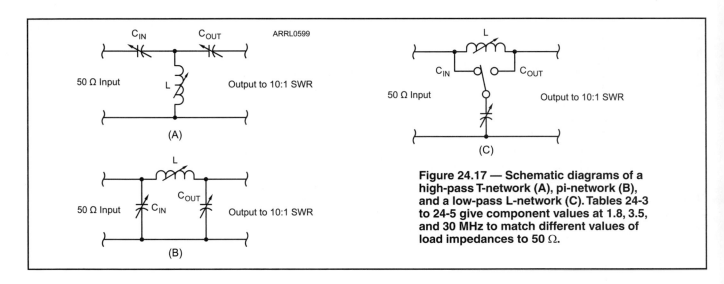

Figure 24.17 — Schematic diagrams of a high-pass T-network (A), pi-network (B), and a low-pass L-network (C). Tables 24-3 to 24-5 give component values at 1.8, 3.5, and 30 MHz to match different values of load impedances to 50 Ω.

Table 24-3

Component Requirements for High-Pass (Shunt L) T-Network Antenna Tuners at 10:1 SWR

Frequency/Z (Ω)	Capacitor		Inductor (µH)	Capacitor Voltage (V_P)		Efficiency (%)
1.8 MHz	Input (pF)	Output (pF)		100 W	1500 W	
5	1136	3000	2.1	180	710	96
500	548	500	13.9	323	1250	98
25 + j100	343	300	10.3	790	3070	92
25 − j100	170	300	20	1040	4030	86
250 + j250	308	200	10.5	380	1470	98
250 − j250	337	300	16.9	525	2030	96

Frequency/Z (Ω)	Capacitor		Inductor (µH)	Capacitor Voltage (V_P)		Efficiency (%)
3.5 MHz	Input (pF)	Output (pF)		100 W	1500 W	
5	563	1500	1.1	190	720	96
500	265	200	7.3	343	1330	98
25 + j100	275	200	3.5	613	2373	95
25 − j100	104	200	8.6	880	3403	88
250 + j250	333	100	5.6	381	1475	98
250 − j250	136	100	10.8	670	2600	94

Frequency/Z (Ω)	Capacitor		Inductor (µH)	Capacitor Voltage (V_P)		Efficiency (%)
30 MHz	Input (pF)	Output (pF)		100 W	1500 W	
5	79	200	0.12	160	640	96
500	29	50	0.77	370	1470	97
25 + j100	91	30	0.24	400	1560	98
25 − j100	24	100	0.46	440	1710	93
250 + j250	36	100	0.9	300	1150	98
250 − j250	29	100	0.6	360	1410	97

Table 24-4

Component Requirements for Low-Pass (Series L) L-Network Antenna Tuners at 10:1 SWR

Frequency/Z (Ω) 1.8 MHz	Capacitor Input (pF)	Output (pF)	Inductor (μH)	Capacitor Voltage (V_P) 100 W	1500 W	Efficiency (%)
5	5254	n/a	1.34	100	390	98
500	n/a	536	13.5	310	1210	98
25 + j100	n/a	1408	12	290	1120	98
25 − j100	1760	n/a	11	100	390	97
250 + j250	n/a	713	13	310	1210	98
250 − j250	n/a	359	13	310	1210	98

Frequency/Z (Ω) 3.5 MHz	Capacitor Input (pF)	Output (pF)	Inductor (μH)	Capacitor Voltage (V_P) 100 W	1500 W	Efficiency (%)
5	2700	n/a	0.69	100	400	98
500	n/a	275	6.8	310	1200	98
25 + j100	n/a	720	6.2	290	1120	98
25 − j100	926	n/a	5.6	100	390	97
250 + j250	n/a	367	6.8	310	1210	98
250 − j250	n/a	184	6.8	310	1210	98

Frequency/Z (Ω) 30 MHz	Capacitor Input (pF)	Output (pF)	Inductor (μH)	Capacitor Voltage (V_P) 100 W	1500 W	Efficiency (%)
5	315	n/a	0.08	100	390	98
500	n/a	32	0.79	310	1210	98
25 + j100	n/a	85	0.72	290	1120	98
25 − j100	140	n/a	0.58	100	390	97
250 + j250	n/a	43	0.79	310	1210	98
250 − j250	n/a	22	0.79	310	1210	98

Table 24-5

Component Requirements for Low-Pass Pi-Network Antenna Tuners at 10:1 SWR

Frequency/Z (Ω) 1.8 MHz	Capacitor Input (pF)	Output (pF)	Inductor (μH)	Capacitor Voltage (V_P) 100 W	1500 W	Efficiency (%)
5	5256	500	1.4	100	390	98
500	2602	1000	9.6	310	1200	96
25 + j100	966	1500	12.5	280	1110	97
25 − j100	3410	500	7.5	280	1100	96
250 + j250	1931	1000	11.3	310	1210	97
250 − j250	1284	500	12.9	310	1210	97

Frequency/Z (Ω) 3.5 MHz	Capacitor Input (pF)	Output (pF)	Inductor (μH)	Capacitor Voltage (V_P) 100 W	1500 W	Efficiency (%)
5	2706	500	0.7	100	390	98
500	1287	500	5.1	310	1200	96
25 + j100	643	800	6.2	280	1110	97
25 − j100	1886	300	3.7	280	1430	95
250 + j250	934	500	6.0	310	1200	97
250 − j250	859	300	6.2	310	1200	97

Frequency/Z (Ω) 30 MHz	Capacitor Input (pF)	Output (pF)	Inductor (μH)	Capacitor Voltage (V_P) 100 W	1500 W	Efficiency (%)
5	321	200	0.08	100	390	98
500	118	50	0.7	310	1200	97
25 + j100	103	100	0.7	290	1100	97
25 − j100	205	30	0.5	285	1100	96
250 + j250	71	50	0.8	310	1200	97
250 − j250	77	30	0.8	310	1200	97

24.3 TRANSMISSION LINE SYSTEM DESIGN

The previous sections of this chapter looked at system design from the point of view of the transmitter, examining what could be done to ensure that the transmitter load is its design load of 50 Ω. In this section, we will look at antenna system design from the point of view of the transmission line. We will examine what should be done to ensure that the transmission line operates at best efficiency, once a particular antenna is chosen to do a particular job.

24.3.1 TRANSMISSION LINE SELECTION

Until you get into the microwave region where waveguides become practical, there are only two practical choices for transmission lines: coaxial cable and parallel-conductor lines such as open wire or ladder line, window line and twinlead.

The shielding of coaxial cable offers advantages in incidental radiation and routing flexibility. Coax can be tied or taped to the legs of a metal tower without problem, for example. Some varieties of coax can even be buried underground. Coaxial cable can perform acceptably even with significant SWR. (Refer to information in the **Transmission Lines** chapter.) A drawback of coaxial line is its loss, particularly at moderate to high SWR. For example, a 100-foot length of RG-8 coax has 1.1 dB matched-line loss at 30 MHz. If this line were used with a load of $250 + j\,0\,\Omega$ (an SWR of 5:1), the total line loss would be 2.2 dB. This represents about a half S unit on most receivers.

On the other hand, open-wire line has the advantage of both lower loss and lower cost compared to coax. At 30 MHz, 600-Ω open-wire line has a matched loss of only 0.1 dB. If you use such open-wire line with the same 5:1 SWR, the total loss would about 0.3 dB. In fact, even if the SWR rose to 20:1, the total loss would be less than 1 dB. Typical open-wire line sells for about ⅓ the cost of good quality coax cable.

Despite their inherently low-loss characteristics, open-wire lines are not often employed above about 100 MHz. This is because the physical spacing between the two wires begins to become an appreciable fraction of a wavelength, leading to undesirable radiation by the line itself. Some form of coaxial cable is almost universally used in the VHF and UHF amateur bands.

Open-wire line is enjoying a renaissance of sorts with amateurs wishing to cover multiple HF bands with a single-wire antenna. This is particularly true since the bands at 30, 17 and 12 meters became available in the early 1980s. The 102-foot long dipole fed with open-wire line into an antenna tuner has become popular as a simple all-band antenna. The simple 135-foot long flattop dipole, fed with 450-Ω window line, is also very popular as an all-band antenna.

So, apart from concerns about convenience and the matter of cost, how do you go about choosing a transmission line for a particular antenna? Let's start with some simple cases.

Feeding a Single-Band Antenna

If the antenna system is only required to operate on a single band and if the feed point impedance of the antenna doesn't vary too radically across the band, then the choice of transmission line is easy. Most amateurs would opt for convenience — they would use coaxial cable to feed the antenna, usually without an antenna tuner.

An example of such an installation is a half-wave 80 meter dipole fed with 50-Ω coax. The matched-line loss for 100 feet of 50-Ω RG-8 coax at 3.5 MHz is only 0.33 dB. At each end of the 80 meter band, this dipole will exhibit an SWR of about 6:1. The additional loss caused by this level of SWR at this frequency is less than 0.6 dB, for a total line loss of 0.9 dB. Since 1 dB represents an almost undetectable change in signal strength at the receiving end, it does not matter whether the line is "flat" (low SWR) or not for this 80 meter system.

This is true provided that the transmitter can operate properly into the load presented to it by the impedance at the input of the transmission line. Even if the feed line loss is low, an antenna tuner is sometimes required to ensure that the transmitter operates into its design load impedance. On the other amateur bands, where the percentage bandwidth is smaller than that on 75/80 meters, a simple dipole fed with coax will provide an acceptable SWR for most transmitters without an antenna tuner.

If you want a better match at the antenna feed point of a single-band antenna to coax, you can provide some sort of matching network at the antenna. We'll look further into schemes for achieving matched antenna systems later in this chapter, when we'll examine single-band methods of matching feed point and feed line impedances.

Feeding a Multiband Antenna

A *multiband antenna* is one where special measures are used to make a single antenna present a consistent feed point impedance on each of several amateur bands. Often, *trap* circuits are employed. (Information on traps is given in the **Multiband HF Antennas** chapter.) For example, a trap dipole presents a feed point impedance similar to that of a λ/2 dipole on each of the bands for which it is designed.

Note that "resonance" only means that the self-impedance of the antenna is completely resistive (no reactance) and does not imply that the value of the impedance is low. For example, the 135-foot dipole may be resonant on 3.5 MHz and all harmonics but its feed point impedance will vary from low values at the fundamental and odd harmonics (10.5, 17.5, 24.5 MHz) to very high impedances at even harmonics (7.0, 14.0, 21.0, 28.0 MHz). Yet it may be resonant at all of those frequencies.

Another common multiband antenna is constructed from several dipoles cut for different frequencies and connected in parallel at a common feed point and fed with a single coaxial cable. This arrangement acts as an independent λ/2 dipole on each band. (Interaction between the individual dipoles is discussed in the **Multiband HF Antennas** chapter.)

Another type of multiband antenna is a *log-periodic dipole array* (LPDA), which features moderate gain and pattern with a low SWR across a fairly wide band of frequencies. See the **Log-Periodic Dipole Arrays** chapter for more details.

Yet another popular multiband antenna is the trap *trib-and* Yagi, or a multiband interlaced quad. On the amateur HF bands, the triband Yagi is almost as popular as the simple λ/2 dipole. See the **HF Yagis and Quads** chapter for more information on this antenna.

A multiband antenna doesn't present much of an antenna system design challenge — you simply feed it with coax that has characteristic impedance close to the antenna's feed point impedance. Usually, 50-Ω cable, such as RG-8, is used.

Feeding a Multiband Nonresonant Antenna

Let's say that you wish to use a single antenna, such as a 100-foot long dipole, on multiple amateur bands. You know from the **Antenna Fundamentals** chapter that since the physical length of the antenna is fixed, the feed point impedance of the antenna will vary on each band. In other words, except by chance, the antenna will *not* be resonant — or even close to resonant — on multiple bands. This presents special challenges with regard to feed line selection.

For multiband nonresonant antenna systems, the most appropriate transmission line is often a parallel-wire line, because of the inherently low matched-line loss characteristic of these types of lines. Such a system is called an *unmatched* system, because no attempt is made to match the impedance at the antenna's feed point to the Z_0 of the transmission line. Commercial 450-Ω window ladder line has become popular for this kind of application. It is almost as good as traditional open-wire or ladder-line for most amateur systems.

The transmission line will be mismatched most of the time and on some frequencies it will be severely mismatched. Because of the mismatch, the SWR on the line will vary widely with frequency. As shown in the **Transmission Lines** chapter, such a variation in load impedance has an impact on the loss suffered in the feed line. Let's look at the losses suffered in a typical multiband nonresonant system.

Table 24-6 summarizes the feed point information over the HF amateur bands for a 100-foot long dipole, mounted as a flattop, 50 feet high over typical earth. In addition, the table shows the total line loss for 100 feet of 450-Ω ladder line and the SWR at the antenna feed point. As usual, there is nothing particularly significant about the choice of a 100-foot long antenna or a 100-foot long transmission line. Both are practical lengths that could very well be encountered in a real-world situation. At 1.8 MHz, the loss in the transmission line is large — 8.9 dB. This is due to the fact that the SWR at the feed point is a very high 793:1, a direct result of the fact that the antenna is extremely short in terms of wavelength.

Table 24-7 summarizes the same information as in Table 24-6, but this time for a 66-foot long inverted-V dipole, whose apex is 50 feet over typical earth and whose included angle between its two legs is 120°. The situation at 1.83 MHz is even worse, as might be expected because this antenna is even shorter electrically than its 100-foot flattop cousin. The line loss has risen to 15.1 dB!

Under such severe mismatches, another problem can

Table 24-6
Impedance of Center-Fed 100-Foot Flattop Dipole, 50 Feet High Over Average Ground

Frequency MHz)	Antenna Feed point Impedance (Ω)	Loss for 100 ft 450-Ω Line (dB)	SWR
1.83	4.5 − j 1673	8.9	792.9
3.8	39 − j 362	0.5	18.3
7.1	481 + j 964	0.2	6.7
10.1	2584 − j 3292	0.6	16.8
14.1	85 − j 123	0.3	5.2
18.1	2097 + j 1552	0.4	8.1
21.1	345 − j 1073	0.6	10.1
24.9	202 + j 367	0.3	3.9
28.4	2493 − j 1375	0.6	8.1

Table 24-7
Impedance of Center-Fed 66-Foot Inv-V Dipole, 50-Foot High Apex Over Average Ground

Frequency (MHz)	Antenna Feed point Impedance (Ω)	Loss for 100 ft 450-Ω Line (dB)	SWR
1.83	1.6 − j 2257	15.1	1627.7
3.8	10 − j 879	3.9	195.7
7.1	65 − j 41	0.2	6.3
10.1	22 + j 648	1.9	68.3
14.1	5287 − j 1310	0.6	13.9
18.1	198 − j 820	0.6	10.8
21.1	103 − j 181	0.3	4.8
24.9	269 + j 570	0.3	4.9
28.4	3089 + j 774	0.6	8.1

arise. Transmission lines with solid dielectric have voltage and current limitations. At lower frequencies with electrically short antennas, this can be a more compelling limitation than the amount of power loss. The ability of a line to handle RF power is inversely proportional to the SWR. For example, a line rated for 1.5 kW when matched, should be operated at only 150 W when the SWR is 10:1. At the mismatch on 1.83 MHz illustrated for the 66-foot inverted-V dipole in Table 24-7, the line may well arc over, burning the insulation, due to the extremely high level of SWR (at 1627.7:1).

A feed line of 450-Ω window-type ladder line using two #16 AWG conductors should be safe up to the 1500 W level for frequencies where the antenna is nearly a half-wavelength long. For the 100-foot dipole, this would be above 3.8 MHz, and for the 66-foot long dipole, this would be above 7 MHz. For the very short antennas illustrated above, however, even 450-Ω window line may not be able to take full amateur legal power. Check the line's maximum rated voltage in the table in the **Transmission Lines** chapter and compare with that expected at your maximum power and expected maximum SWR.

24.3.2 ANTENNA TUNER LOCATION

To meet the goal of presenting a 50-Ω load to the transmitter, in many antenna systems it is necessary to place an

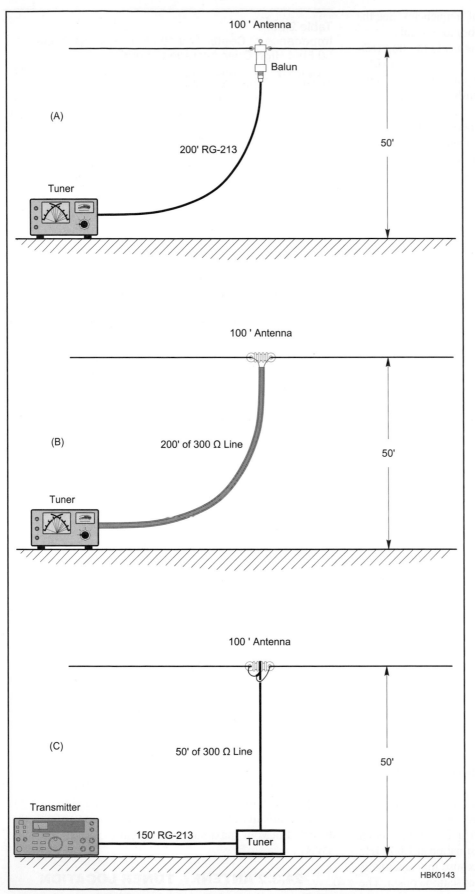

Figure 24.18 — Variations of an antenna system with different losses. The examples are discussed in the text.

antenna tuner between the transmitter and the transmission line going to the antenna. This is particularly true for a single-wire antenna used on multiple amateur bands.

The tuner is usually located near the transmitter in order to adjust it for different bands or antennas. If a tuner is in use for one particular band and does not need to be adjusted once set up for minimum VSWR, it can be placed in a weatherproof container near the antenna. Some automatic tuners are designed to be installed at the antenna, for example. For some situations, placing the tuner at the base of a tower can be particularly effective and eliminates having to climb the tower to perform maintenance on the tuner.

It is useful to consider the performance of the entire antenna system when deciding where to install the antenna tuner and what types of feed line to use in order to minimize system losses. Here is an example, using the program *TLW*. Let's assume a flattop antenna 50 feet high and 100 feet long and not resonant on any amateur band. As extreme examples, we will use 3.8 and 28.4 MHz with 200 feet of transmission line. There are many ways to configure this system, but three examples are shown in **Figure 24.18**.

Example 1 in Figure 24.18A shows a 200-foot run of RG-213 going to a 1:1 balun that feeds the antenna. A tuner in the shack reduces the VSWR for proper matching in the transmitter. Example 2 (Figure 24.18B) shows a similar arrangement using 300-Ω transmitting twin lead. Example 3 (Figure 24.18C) shows a 50-foot run of 300-Ω line dropping straight down to a remote tune near the ground and 150 feet of RG-213 going to the shack. **Table 24-8** summarizes the losses and the L-network component values required.

Some interesting conclusions can be drawn. First, direct feeding this antenna with coax through a balun is very lossy — a poor solution. If the flattop were λ/2 long — a resonant half-wave dipole — direct

Table 24-8
Tuner Settings and Performance

Example (Fig 24.18)	Frequency (MHz)	Tuner Type	L (μH)	C (pF)	Total Loss (dB)
1	3.8	Rev L	1.46	2308	8.53
	28.4	Rev L	0.13	180.9	12.3
2	3.8	L	14.7	46	2.74
	28.4	L	0.36	15.6	3.52
3	3.8	L	11.37	332	1.81
	28.4	L	0.54	94.0	2.95

coax feed would be a good method. In the second example, direct feed with 300-Ω low-loss line does not always give the lowest loss. The combination method in Example 3 provides the best solution.

Example 3 has some additional advantages. It feeds the antenna in a symmetrical arrangement which is best to reduce common-mode current pickup on the shield of the feed line. The shorter feed line will not weigh down the antenna as much, and the balun's additional weight and expense are also avoided. The coax back to the transmitter can be buried or laid on the ground and it is perfectly matched. Burial of the cable will also prevent any additional

common-mode currents from being induced on the coax shield. The tuner is then adjusted for minimum SWR on the cable as measured in the shack at the transmitter.

24.3.3 USING *TLW* TO DETERMINE SWR

The program *TLW* can be used in two important ways to determine SWR and impedance on the "other end" of transmission lines. The first case occurs when you are given a certain load impedance, such as that of an antenna feed point, and wish to know what the SWR and impedance will be at the input of the feed line. This type of information is used to design impedance-matching networks and antenna tuners for use in the shack. From the program's main screen, select the feed line type and length. Enter frequency and the load resistance and reactance, specifying LOAD for the location of the impedance. The SWR and impedance at the input of the feed line will be displayed at the bottom of the window. The additional loss due to SWR is also calculated.

The second case works in reverse. It occurs when you know the SWR (or impedance) at the input to the feed line and want to know the SWR (or impedance) at the load (antenna) end of the feed line. Enter the cable type and length, frequency, and a value for RESISTANCE equal to SWR × Z_0. (If you know the input impedance, enter it instead.) Specify INPUT for the location where SWR is specified. The SWR (and impedance) will be displayed at the bottom of the window along with the additional line loss due to SWR.

24.4 TRANSMISSION LINE MATCHING DEVICES

24.4.1 QUARTER-WAVE TRANSFORMERS

The impedance-transforming properties of a λ/4 transmission line *synchronous transformer* or *Q-section* shown in **Figure 24.19A** can be used to good advantage for matching the feed point impedance of an antenna to the characteristic impedance of the line. As described in the **Transmission Lines** chapter, the input impedance of a λ/4 line terminated in a resistive impedance Z_R is

$$Z_i = \frac{Z_0^{\,2}}{Z_L} \qquad \text{(Eq 9)}$$

where
  Z_i = the impedance at the input end of the line
  Z_0 = the characteristic impedance of the line
  Z_L = the impedance at the load end of the line

Rearranging this equation gives

$$Z_0 = \sqrt{Z_i Z_L} \qquad \text{(Eq 10)}$$

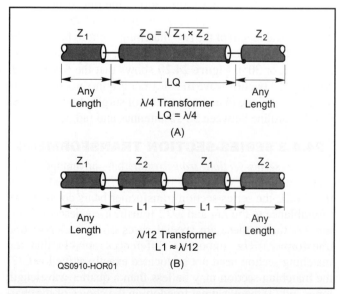

Figure 24.19 — The ¼-wave (A) Q-section and ¹/₁₂-wave (B) synchronous transformers.

This means that any value of load impedance Z_L can be transformed into any desired value of impedance Z_i at the input terminals of a λ/4 line, provided the line can be constructed to have a characteristic impedance Z_0 equal to the square root of the product of the other two impedances. The factor that limits the range of impedances that can be matched by this method is the range of values for Z_0 that is physically realizable. The latter range is approximately 50 to 600 Ω. Practically any type of line can be used for the matching section, including both air-insulated and solid-dielectric lines.

The λ/4 transformer may be adjusted to resonance before being connected to the antenna by following the procedures for determining line length in the chapter **Transmission Line and Antenna Measurements**.

Yagi Driven Elements

Another application for the λ/4 transformer is in matching the low antenna impedance encountered in close-spaced, monoband Yagi arrays to a 50-Ω transmission line. The impedances at the antenna feed point for typical Yagis range from about 8 to 30 Ω. Let's assume that the feed point impedance is 25 Ω. A matching section is needed. Since there is no commercially available cable with a Z_0 of 35.4 Ω, a pair of λ/4-long 75-Ω RG-11 coax cables connected in parallel will have a net Z_0 of 75/2 = 37.5 Ω, close enough for practical purposes.

24.4.2 TWELFTH-WAVE TRANSFORMERS

The Q-section is really a special case of series-section matching described below. There's no restriction (other than complexity) that there be just one matching section. In fact, the two-section variation shown in Figure 24.19B is quite handy for matching two different impedances of transmission line, such as 50-Ω coax and 75-Ω hardline. Best of all, special transmission line impedances are not required, only sections of line with the same impedances that are to be matched.

This configuration is referred to as a *twelfth-wave transformer* because when the ratio of the impedances to be matched is 1.5:1 (as is the case with 50- and 75-Ω cables), the electrical length of the two matching sections between the lines to be matched is 0.0815 λ (29.3°), quite close to λ/12 (0.0833 λ or 30°). **Figure 24.20** shows that the SWR bandwidth of the twelfth-wave transformer is quite broad. You can use this technique to make good use of surplus low-loss 75-Ω CATV hardline between 50-Ω antennas and radios.

24.4.3 SERIES-SECTION TRANSFORMERS

The *series-section transformer* has advantages over either stub tuning or the λ/4 transformer. Illustrated in **Figure 24.21**, the series-section transformer bears considerable resemblance to the λ/4 and λ/12 transformers described earlier. (Actually, these are special cases of the series-section transformer.) The important differences are (1) that the matching section need not be located exactly at the load, (2) the matching section may be less than a quarter wavelength long, and (3) there is great freedom in the choice of the characteristic impedance of the matching section.

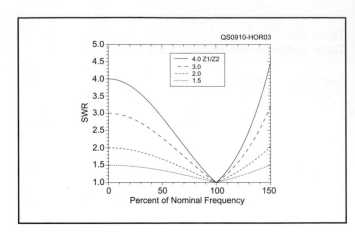

Figure 24.20 — The bandwidth of the λ/12 transformer is fairly broad as shown in this family of curves for different impedance transformation ratios. For 75- and 50-Ω impedances (a ratio of 1.5:1), the points at which an SWR of 1.2:1 are reached are approximately 75% and 125% of the design frequency.

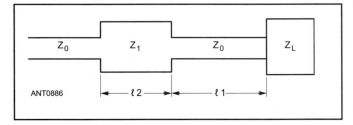

Figure 24.21 — Series section transformer Z_1 for matching transmission line Z_0 to load Z_L.

In fact, the matching section can have *any* characteristic impedance that is not too close to that of the main line. Because of this freedom, it is almost always possible to find a length of commercially available line that will be suitable as a matching section. As an example, consider a 75-Ω line, a 300-Ω matching section, and a pure-resistance load. It can be shown that a series-section transformer of 300-Ω line may be used to match *any* resistance between 5 Ω and 1200 Ω to the main line.

Frank Regier, OD5CG, described series-section transformers in July 1978 *QST*. (See Bibliography.) This information is based on that article. The design of a series-section transformer consists of determining the length $\ell 2$ of the series or matching section and the distance $\ell 1$ from the load to the point where the section should be inserted into the main line. Three quantities must be known. These are the characteristic impedances of the main line and of the matching section, both assumed purely resistive, and the complex-load impedance. Either of two design methods may be used. One is a graphic method using the Smith Chart, and the other is algebraic. You can take your choice. (Of course the algebraic method may be adapted to obtaining a computer solution.) The Smith Chart graphic method is described in an article included on this book's CD-ROM.

Algebraic Design Method

The two lengths $\ell 1$ and $\ell 2$ are to be determined from the characteristic impedances of the main line and the matching section, Z_0 and Z_1, respectively, and the load impedance $Z_L = R_L + j\,X_L$. The first step is to determine the normalized impedances.

$$n = \frac{Z_1}{Z_0} \qquad\qquad\qquad (\text{Eq 11})$$

$$r = \frac{R_L}{Z_0} \qquad\qquad\qquad (\text{Eq 12})$$

$$x = \frac{X_L}{Z_0} \qquad\qquad\qquad (\text{Eq 13})$$

Next, $\ell 2$ and $\ell 1$ are determined from

$\ell 2 = \arctan B$, where

$$B = \pm \sqrt{\frac{(r-1)^2 + x^2}{r\left(n - \frac{1}{n}\right)^2 - (r-1)^2 - x^2}} \qquad (\text{Eq 14})$$

$\ell 1 = \arctan A$, where

$$A = \frac{\left(n - \dfrac{r}{n}\right)B + x}{r + xnB - 1} \qquad\qquad (\text{Eq 15})$$

Lengths $\ell 2$ and $\ell 1$ as thus determined are electrical lengths in degrees (or radians). The electrical lengths in wavelengths are obtained by dividing by 360° (or by 2π radians). The physical lengths (main line or matching section, as the case may be), are then determined from multiplying by the free-space wavelength and by the velocity factor of the line.

The sign of B may be chosen either positive or negative, but the positive sign is preferred because it results in a shorter matching section. The sign of A may not be chosen but can turn out to be either positive or negative. If a negative sign occurs and a computer or electronic calculator is then used to determine $\ell 1$, a negative electric length will result for $\ell 1$. If this happens, add 180°. The resultant electrical length will be correct both physically and mathematically.

In calculating B, if the quantity under the radical is negative, an imaginary value for B results. This would mean that Z_1, the impedance of the matching section, is too close to Z_0 and should be changed.

Limits on the characteristic impedance of Z_1 may be calculated in terms of the SWR produced by the load on the main line without matching. For matching to occur, Z_1 should either be greater than $Z_0\sqrt{\text{SWR}}$ or less than $Z_0 / \sqrt{\text{SWR}}$.

An Example

As an example, suppose we want to feed a 29-MHz ground-plane vertical antenna with RG-58 type foam-dielectric coax. We'll assume the antenna impedance to be 36 Ω,

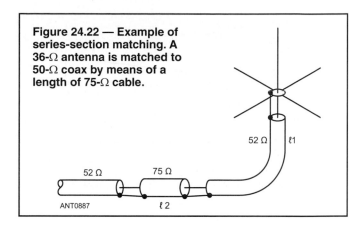

Figure 24.22 — Example of series-section matching. A 36-Ω antenna is matched to 50-Ω coax by means of a length of 75-Ω cable.

pure resistance, and use a length of RG-59 foam-dielectric coax as the series section. See **Figure 24.22**.

Z_0 is 50 Ω, Z_1 is 75 Ω, and both cables have a velocity factor of 0.79. Because the load is a pure resistance we may determine the SWR to be 50/36 = 1.389. From the above, Z_1 must have an impedance greater than $50\sqrt{1.389}$. From the earlier equations, n = 75/50 = 1.50, r = 36/50 = 0.720, and x = 0.

Further, B = 0.431 (positive sign chosen), and $\ell 2 = 23.3°$ or 0.065 λ. The value of A is −1.570. Calculating $\ell 1$ yields −57.5°. Adding 180° to obtain a positive result gives $\ell 1 = 122.5°$, or 0.340 λ.

To find the physical lengths $\ell 1$ and $\ell 2$ we first find the free-space wavelength.

$$\lambda = \frac{984}{f(\text{MHz})} = 33.93 \text{ feet}$$

Multiply this value by 0.79 (the velocity factor for both types of line), and we obtain the electrical wavelength in coax as 26.81 feet. From this, $\ell 1 = 0.340 \times 26.81 = 9.12$ feet, and $\ell 2 = 0.065 \times 26.81 = 1.74$ feet.

This completes the calculations. Construction consists of cutting the main coax at a point 9.12 feet from the antenna and inserting a 1.74-foot length of the 75-Ω cable.

The antenna in the preceding example could also have been matched by a $\lambda/4$ transformer at the load. Such a transformer would use a line with a characteristic impedance of 42.43 Ω. It is interesting to see what happens in the design of a series-section transformer if this value is chosen as the characteristic impedance of the series section.

Following the same steps as before, we find n = 0.849, r = 0.720, and x = 0. From these values we find B = 8 and $\ell 2 = 90°$. Further, A = 0 and $\ell 1 = 0°$. These results represent a $\lambda/4$ section at the load, and indicate that, as stated earlier, the $\lambda/4$ transformer is indeed a special case of the series-section transformer.

24.4.4 TAPERED LINES

A tapered line is a specially constructed transmission line in which the impedance changes gradually from one end of the line to the other. Such a line operates as a broadband impedance transformer. Because tapered lines are used almost

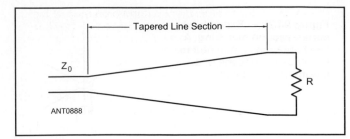

Figure 24.23 — A tapered line provides a broadband frequency transformation if it is one wavelength long or more. From a practical construction standpoint, the taper may be linear.

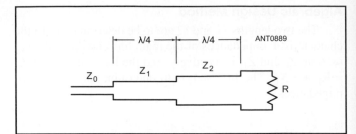

Figure 24.24 — Multiple quarter-wave matching sections approximate the broadband matching transformation provided by a tapered line. Two sections are shown here, but more may be used. The more sections in the line, the broader is the matching bandwidth. Z_0 is the characteristic impedance of the main feed line, while Z_1 and Z_2 are the intermediate impedances of the matching sections. See text for design equations.

exclusively for matching applications, they are discussed in this chapter.

The characteristic impedance of an open-wire line can be tapered by varying the spacing between the conductors, as shown in **Figure 24.23**. Coaxial lines can be tapered by varying the diameter of either the inner conductor or the outer conductor, or both. The construction of coaxial tapered lines is beyond the means of most amateurs, but open-wire tapered lines can be made rather easily by using spacers of varied lengths. In theory, optimum broadband impedance transformation is obtained with lines having an exponential taper, but in practice, lines with a linear taper as shown in Figure 24.23 work very well.

A tapered line provides a match from high frequencies down to the frequency at which the line is approximately 1 λ long. At lower frequencies, especially when the tapered line length is λ/2 or less, the line acts more as an impedance lump than a transformer. Tapered lines are most useful at VHF and UHF, because the length requirement becomes unwieldy at HF.

Air-insulated open-wire lines can be designed from the equation

$$S = \frac{d \times 10^{Z_0/276}}{2} \qquad \text{(Eq 16)}$$

where
    S = center-to-center spacing between conductors
    d = diameter of conductors (same units as S)
    Z_0 = characteristic impedance, Ω.

For cases where S < 3d, see the **Transmission Lines** chapter.

For example, for a tapered line to match a 300-Ω source to an 800-Ω load, the spacing for the selected conductor diameter would be adjusted for a 300-Ω characteristic impedance at one end of the line, and for an 800-Ω characteristic impedance at the other end of the line. The disadvantage of using open-wire tapered lines is that characteristic impedances of 100 Ω and less are impractical.

24.4.5 MULTIPLE QUARTER-WAVE SECTIONS

An alternate to the smooth-impedance transformation of

the tapered line is provided by using two or more λ/4 transformer sections in series, as shown in **Figure 24.24**. Each section has a different characteristic impedance, selected to transform the impedance at its input to that at its output. Thus, the overall impedance transformation from source to load takes place as a series of gradual transformations. The frequency bandwidth with multiple sections is greater than for a single section. This technique is useful at the upper end of the HF range and at VHF and UHF. Here, too, the total line length that is required may become unwieldy at the lower frequencies.

A multiple-section line may contain two or more λ/4 transformer sections; the more sections in the line, the broader is the matching bandwidth. Coaxial transmission lines may be used to make a multiple-section line, but standard coax lines are available in only a few characteristic impedances. Open-wire lines can be constructed rather easily for a specific impedance, designed from Eq 16 above.

The following equations may be used to calculate the intermediate characteristic impedances for a two-section line.

$$Z_1 = \sqrt[4]{RZ_0{}^3} \qquad \text{(Eq 17)}$$

$$Z_2 = \sqrt[3]{R^2 Z_1} \qquad \text{(Eq 18)}$$

where terms are as illustrated in Figure 24.24. For example, assume we wish to match a 75-Ω source (Z_0) to an 800-Ω load. From Eq 17, calculate Z_1 to be 135.5 Ω. Then from Eq 18, calculate Z_2 to be 442.7 Ω. As a matter of interest, for this example the virtual impedance at the junction of Z_1 and Z_2 is 244.9 Ω. (This is the same impedance that would be required for a single-section λ/4 matching section.)

Multisection λ/4 transformers are discussed by Randy Rhea in *High-Frequency Electronics* magazine. (See Bibliography.) This technique is related to the "equal delay" transmission line transformers.

Double Quarter-Wave Transformer

The double λ/4 transformer is a special case of the

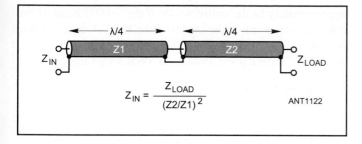

Figure 24.25 — The impedance transformation ratio of the double quarter-wave transformer is the square of the difference between the characteristic impedances of the two λ/4 sections.

multisection λ/4 transformer. If two λ/4 sections of feed line, one with impedance Z_0 followed by another with an impedance of $2Z_0$ as the input impedance as in **Figure 24.25**, the input to the transformer will be the load impedance divided by 4. The transformer can be "turned around" to step up the load impedance. In general, the transformation ratio is the square of the impedance ratio of the two λ/4 sections and it is independent of the impedances of the input and output. The

larger the difference in Z_0 between the sections, the smaller the bandwidth of the impedance transformation.

You are not restricted to the Z_0 of single cables. Paralleled cables with characteristic impedances of Z_0 act as a combined cable with a characteristic impedance of $Z_0/2$. So for example, a λ/4 section of two 50-Ω cables in parallel ($Z_0 = 25$ Ω) connected to a λ/4 section of 50-Ω line has an impedance ratio of 2:1 and an impedance transformation ratio of 4:1. This design could match 75-Ω line to a 300-Ω load — using 50-Ω cable! If the input section were composed of three cables in parallel, the impedance ratio would be 3:1 and the transformation ratio 9:1 — this could match 50 Ω at the input to 450 Ω at the output.

24.5 MATCHING IMPEDANCE AT THE ANTENNA

Since operating a transmission line at a low SWR requires that the line be terminated in a load matching the line's characteristic impedance, the problem can be approached from two standpoints:

(1) selecting a transmission line having a characteristic impedance that matches the antenna impedance at the point of connection, or

(2) transforming the antenna resistance to a value that matches the Z_0 of the line selected.

The first approach is simple and direct, but its application is obviously limited — the antenna impedance and the line impedance are alike only in a few special cases. Commercial transmission lines come in a limited variety of characteristic impedances while antenna feed point impedances vary over a wide range.

The second approach provides a good deal of freedom in that the antenna and line can be selected independently. The disadvantage of the second approach is that it is more complicated in terms of actually constructing the matching system at the antenna. Further, this approach sometimes calls for a tedious routine of measurement and adjustment before the desired match is achieved.

24.5.1 ANTENNA IMPEDANCE MATCHING

Impedance Change with Frequency

Most antenna systems show a marked change in impedance when the frequency is changed greatly. For this reason it is usually possible to match the line impedance only on one frequency. A matched antenna system is consequently a one-band affair, in most cases. It can, however, usually be

operated over a fair frequency range within a given band.

The frequency range over which the SWR is low is determined by how rapidly the impedance changes as the frequency is changed. If the change in impedance is small for a given change in frequency, the SWR will be low over a fairly wide band of frequencies. However, if the impedance change is rapid (implying a sharply resonant or high-Q antenna), the SWR will also rise rapidly as the operating frequency is shifted away from antenna resonance, where the line is matched. See the discussion of Q in the **Dipoles and Monopoles** chapter in the section dealing with changes of impedance with frequency.

Antenna Resonance

In general, achieving a good match to a transmission line means that the antenna is resonant. (Some types of long-wire antennas, such as rhombics, are exceptions. Their input impedances are resistive over a wide band of frequencies, making such systems essentially nonresonant.) Antennas that are not resonant may also be matched to transmission lines, of course, but the additional cancellation of reactance complicates the task.

The higher the Q of an antenna system, the more essential it is that resonance be established before an attempt is made to match the line. This is particularly true of close-spaced parasitic arrays. With simple dipole antennas, the tuning is not so critical, and it is usually sufficient to cut the antenna to the length given by the appropriate equation. The frequency should be selected to be at the center of the range of frequencies (which may be the entire width of an amateur band) over which the antenna is to be used.

24.5.2 CONNECTING DIRECTLY TO THE ANTENNA

As discussed previously, the impedance at the center of a resonant λ/2 antenna at heights of the order of λ/4 and more is resistive and is in the neighborhood of 50 to 70 Ω. The dipole may be fed through 75-Ω coaxial cable such as RG-11, as shown in **Figure 24.26**. Cable having a characteristic impedance of 50 Ω, such as RG-8, may also be used. RG-8 may actually be preferable, because at the heights many amateurs install their antennas, the feed point impedance is closer to 50 Ω than it is to 75 Ω.

With a parallel-wire feed line the system would be symmetrical but with coaxial line it is inherently *unbalanced*. Stated broadly, the unbalance with coaxial line is caused by the fact that the outside surface of the outer braid is not coupled to the antenna in the same way as the inner conductor and the inner surface of the outer braid. The overall result is that common-mode current will flow on the outside of the outer conductor in the simple arrangement shown in Figure 24.26. The unbalance is small if the line diameter is very small compared with the length of the antenna, a condition that is met fairly well at the lower amateur frequencies. It is not negligible in the VHF and UHF range, however, nor should it be ignored at 28 MHz. If the feed line is oriented asymmetrically with respect to the antenna so that it is closer to one side of the antenna than the other, higher common-mode currents will flow on the outside of the feed line.

The system can be detuned for currents on the outside of the line by using a choke balun later in this chapter for more details about balanced loads used with unbalanced transmission lines.

This system is designed for single-band operation, although it can be operated at *odd* multiples of the fundamental. For example, an antenna that is resonant near the low-frequency end of the 7-MHz band will operate with a relatively low SWR across the 21-MHz band.

At the fundamental frequency, the SWR should not exceed about 2:1 within a frequency range ±2% from the frequency of exact resonance. Such a variation corresponds approximately to the entire width of the 7-MHz band, if the antenna is resonant at the center of the band. A wire antenna is assumed. Antennas having a greater ratio of diameter to length will have a lower change in SWR with frequency.

Direct-Feed Yagis

Direct-feed Yagis are designed to have a feed point impedance of 50- or 75-Ω so that a coaxial feed line can be connected directly to the antenna without additional impedance matching. These have become more common in recent years as antenna modeling has produced designs without the gain and pattern tradeoffs previously required for the higher feed point impedances required for direct-feed.

There is some question as to whether a choke balun is required for direct-feed antennas. The same questions of symmetry and radiation from common-mode current apply to direct-feed Yagis as to dipoles and other types of antennas. If re-radiation is an issue, a choke balun should be used. For commercial antennas, if the manufacturer specifies that a balun be used or makes no recommendation, use a choke balun at the feed point. If the manufacturer specifies that *no* balun be used, that is an indication that the feed line affects antenna performance in some way and the manufacturer's instructions for feed line placement and attachment should be followed exactly.

24.5.3 THE DELTA MATCH

Among the properties of a coil and capacitor resonant circuit is that of transforming impedances. If a resistive impedance, Z_1 in **Figure 24.27**, is connected across the outer terminals AB of a resonant LC circuit, the impedance Z_2 as viewed looking into another pair of terminals such as BC will also be resistive, but will have a different value depending on the mutual coupling between the parts of the coil associated with each pair of terminals. Z_2 will be less than Z_1 in the circuit shown. Of course this relationship will be reversed if Z_1 is connected across terminals BC and Z_2 is viewed from terminals AB.

As stated in the **Antenna Fundamentals** chapter, a

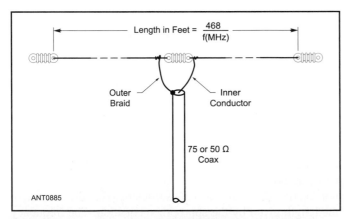

Figure 24.26 — A ½-λ antenna fed with 75-Ω coaxial cable. The outside of the shield of the line acts as a "third wire" connected to the dipole's left leg. A choke balun can be used to reduce current flowing on this conductor.

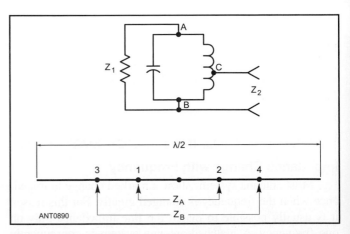

Figure 24.27 — Impedance transformation with a resonant circuit, together with antenna analogy.

resonant antenna has properties similar to those of a tuned circuit. The impedance presented between any two points symmetrically placed with respect to the center of a $\lambda/2$ antenna will depend on the distance between the points. The greater the separation, the higher the value of impedance, up to the limiting value that exists between the open ends of the antenna. This is also suggested in Figure 24.27, in the lower drawing. The impedance Z_A between terminals 1 and 2 is lower than the impedance Z_B between terminals 3 and 4. Both impedances, however, are purely resistive if the antenna is resonant.

This principle is used in the *delta matching system* shown in **Figure 24.28**. The center impedance of a $\lambda/2$ dipole is too low to be matched directly by any practical type of air-insulated parallel-conductor line. However, it is possible to find, between two points, a value of impedance that can be matched to such a line when a "fanned" section or delta is used to couple the line and antenna. The antenna length ℓ is that required for resonance. The ends of the delta or "Y" should be attached at points equidistant from the center of the antenna. When so connected, the terminating impedance for the line will be resistive. Obviously, this technique is useful only when the Z_0 of the chosen transmission line is higher than the feed point impedance of the antenna.

Based on experimental data for the case of a typical $\lambda/2$ antenna coupled to a 600-Ω line, the total distance, A, between the ends of the delta should be 0.120 λ for frequencies below 30 MHz, and 0.115 λ for frequencies above 30 MHz. The length of the delta, distance B, should be 0.150 λ. These values are based on a wavelength in air, and on the assumption that the center impedance of the antenna is approximately 70 Ω. The dimensions will require modifications if the actual impedance is very much different.

The delta match can be used for matching the driven element of a directive array to a transmission line, but if the impedance of the element is low — as is frequently the case — the proper dimensions for A and B must be found by experimentation.

The delta match is somewhat awkward to adjust when the proper dimensions are unknown, because both the length and width of the delta must be varied. An additional disadvantage is that there is always some radiation from the delta. This is because the conductor spacing does not meet the requirement for negligible radiation: The spacing should be very small in comparison with the wavelength.

24.5.4 FOLDED DIPOLES

Basic information on the folded dipole antenna appears in chapter **Dipoles and Monopoles**. The input impedance of a two-wire folded dipole is so close to 300 Ω that it can be fed directly with 300-Ω twinlead or with open-wire line without any other matching arrangement, and the line will operate with a low SWR. The antenna itself can be built like an open-wire line; that is, the two conductors can be held apart by regular feeder spreaders. TV ladder line is quite suitable. It is also possible to use 300-Ω line for the antenna, in addition to using it for the transmission line.

Since the antenna section does not operate as a transmission line, but simply as two wires in parallel, the velocity factor of twinlead can be ignored in computing the antenna length. The reactance of the folded-dipole antenna varies less rapidly with frequency changes away from resonance than a single-wire antenna. Therefore it is possible to operate over a wider range of frequencies, while maintaining a low SWR on the line, than with a simple dipole. This is partly explained by the fact that the two conductors in parallel form a single conductor of greater effective diameter.

A folded dipole will not accept power at twice the fundamental frequency. However, the current distribution is correct for harmonic operation on odd multiples of the fundamental. Because the feed point resistance is not greatly different for a $3\lambda/2$ antenna and one that is $\lambda/2$, a folded dipole can be operated on its third harmonic with a low SWR in a 300-Ω line. A 7-MHz folded dipole, consequently, can be used for the 21-MHz band as well.

Folded dipoles are sometimes used as the driven element of Yagi antennas at VHF and UHF. The low feed point impedance of a Yagi, often less than 20 Ω, when multiplied by four presents a good match to 75-Ω coaxial cable.

24.5.5 THE T AND GAMMA MATCHES

The T Match

The current flowing at the input terminals of the T match consists of the normal antenna current divided between the radiator and the T conductors in a way that depends on their relative diameters and the spacing between them, with a superimposed transmission line current flowing in each half of the T and its associated section of the antenna. See **Figure 24.29**. Each such T conductor and the associated antenna conductor can be looked upon as a section of transmission line shorted at the end. Because it is shorter than $\lambda/4$ it has inductive reactance. As a consequence, if the antenna itself is exactly resonant at the operating frequency, the input impedance of the T will show inductive reactance as well as

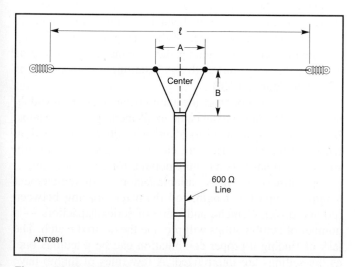

Figure 24.28 — The delta matching system.

resistance. The reactance must be tuned out if a good match to the transmission line is to be obtained. This can be done either by shortening the antenna to obtain a value of capacitive reactance that will reflect through the matching system to cancel the inductive reactance at the input terminals, or by inserting a capacitance of the proper value in series at the input terminals as shown in **Figure 24.30A**.

Theoretical analyses have shown that the part of the

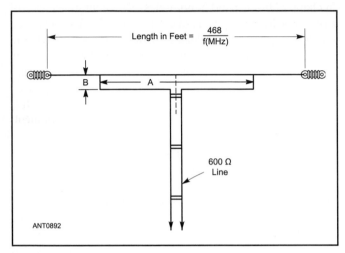

Figure 24.29 — The T matching system, applied to a ½-λ antenna and 600-Ω line.

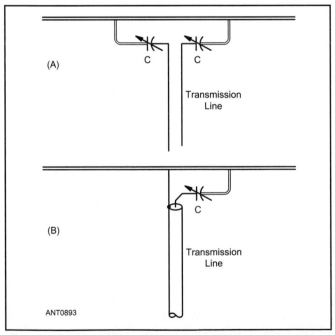

Figure 24.30 — Series capacitors for tuning out residual reactance with the T and gamma matching systems. A maximum capacitance of 150 pF in each capacitor should provide sufficient adjustment range, in the average case, for 14-MHz operation. Proportionately smaller capacitance values can be used on higher frequency bands. Receiving-type plate spacing will be satisfactory for power levels up to a few hundred watts.

impedance step-up arising from the spacing and ratio of conductor diameters is approximately the same as given for a folded dipole. The actual impedance ratio is, however, considerably modified by the length A of the matching section (Figure 24.29). The trends can be stated as follows:

1) The input impedance increases as the distance A is made larger, but not indefinitely. In general there is a distance A that will give a maximum value of input impedance, after which further increase in A will cause the impedance to decrease.

2) The distance A at which the input impedance reaches a maximum is smaller as d2/d1 is made larger, and becomes smaller as the spacing between the conductors is increased. (d1 is the diameter of the lower T conductor in Figure 24.29 and d2 is the diameter of the antenna.)

3) The maximum impedance values occur in the region where A is 40% to 60% of the antenna length in the average case.

4) Higher values of input impedance can be realized when the antenna is shortened to cancel the inductive reactance of the matching section.

The T match has become popular for transforming the balanced feed point impedance of a VHF or UHF Yagi up to 200 Ω. From that impedance a 4:1 balun is used to transform down to the unbalanced 50 Ω level for the coax cable feeding the Yagi. See the various K1FO-designed Yagis in the **VHF and UHF Antenna Systems** chapter and the section later in this chapter concerning baluns.

The structure of the T-match also affects the length of the driven element by increasing the element's electrical diameter. A typical T-match is approximately 5 to 10 times greater in diameter than the element alone. This results in the need to extend the length of the driven element by 2-3% to return it to resonance.

The Gamma Match

The gamma-match arrangement shown in Figure 24.30B is an unbalanced version of the T, suitable for use directly with coaxial lines. Except for the matching section being connected between the center and one side of the antenna, the remarks above about the behavior of the T apply equally well. The inherent reactance of the matching section can be canceled either by shortening the antenna appropriately or by using the resonant length and installing a capacitor C, as shown in Figure 24.30B.

For a number of years the gamma match has been widely used for matching coaxial cable to all-metal parasitic beams. Because it is well suited to *plumber's delight* construction, where all the metal parts are electrically and mechanically connected, it has become quite popular for amateur arrays.

Because of the many variable factors — driven-element length, gamma rod length, rod diameter, spacing between rod and driven element, and value of series capacitors — a number of combinations will provide the desired match. The task of finding a proper combination can be a tedious one, as the settings are interrelated. A few rules of thumb have evolved that provide a starting point for the various factors.

For matching a multielement array made of aluminum tubing to 50-Ω line, the length of the rod should be 0.04 to 0.05 λ, its diameter ⅓ to ½ that of the driven element, and its spacing (center-to-center from the driven element), approximately 0.007 λ. The capacitance value should be approximately 7 pF per meter of wavelength. This translates to about 140 pF for 20 meter operation. The exact gamma dimensions and value for the capacitor will depend on the radiation resistance of the driven element, and whether or not it is resonant. These starting-point dimensions are for an array having a feed point impedance of about 25 Ω, with the driven element shortened approximately 3% from resonance.

Calculating Gamma Dimensions

A starting point for the gamma dimensions and capacitance value may be determined by calculation. H. F. Tolles, W7ITB, has developed a method for determining a set of parameters that will be quite close to providing the desired impedance transformation. (See Bibliography.) The impedance of the antenna must be measured or computed for Tolles's procedure. If the antenna impedance is not accurately known,

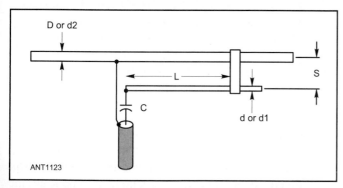

ANT1123

Figure 24.31 — The gamma match, as used with tubing elements. Parameters are those used for the *GAMMA* dimension calculation software. Note that S is a center-to-center value, not surface-to-surface. The transmission line may be either 50-Ω or 75-Ω coax.

modeling calculations provide a very good starting point for initial settings of the gamma match.

The math involved in Tolles's procedure is tedious, especially if several iterations are needed to find a practical set of dimensions. The procedure has been adapted for computer calculations by R. A. Nelson, WB0IKN, who wrote his program in Applesoft BASIC (see Bibliography). A similar program for *Windows*-compatible computers called *GAMMA* in BASIC source code, with modifications suggested by Dave Leeson, W6NL, may be downloaded from **www.arrl.org/antenna-book**. The program can be used for calculating a gamma match for a dipole (or driven element of an array) or for a vertical monopole, such as a shunt-fed tower.

The inputs to *GAMMA* are as shown in **Figure 24.31**:

Z_a — the complex impedance of the unmatched antenna ($Z_a = R_a + j X_a$, normally measured with dipole halves split)

S — center-to-center spacing of the circular antenna element to the circular gamma rod

D or d2 — diameter of the circular antenna element

d or d1 — diameter of the circular gamma rod

L — length of the gamma rod

C — the added series capacitance used to null any resulting inductive reactance

Note that S is a *center-to-center* dimension, not a surface-to-surface value.

As an example of computer calculations, assume a 14.3-MHz Yagi beam is to be matched to 50-Ω line. The driven element is 1½ inches in diameter, and the gamma rod is a length of ½-inch tubing, spaced 6 inches from the element (center to center). The driven element has been shortened by 3% from its resonant length. Assume the antenna has a radiation resistance of 25 Ω and a capacitive reactance component of 25 Ω (about the reactance that would result from the 3% shortening). The overall impedance of the driven element is therefore 25 – j 25 Ω. At the program prompts enter the frequency, the feed point resistance and reactance (don't forget the minus sign), the line characteristic impedance (50 Ω), and

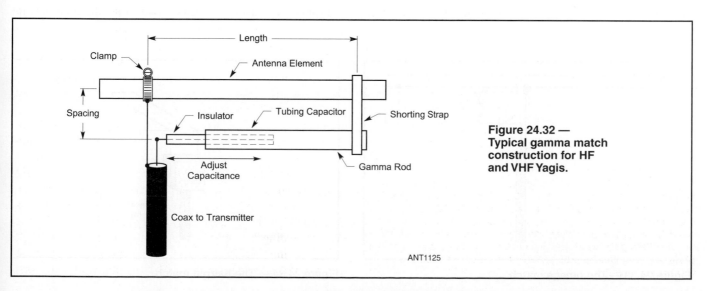

Figure 24.32 — Typical gamma match construction for HF and VHF Yagis.

ANT1125

the element and rod diameters and center-to-center spacing. *GAMMA* computes that the gamma rod is 38.9 inches long and the gamma capacitor is 96.1 pF at 14.3 MHz.

As another example, say we wish to shunt feed a tower at 3.5 MHz with 50-Ω line. The driven element (tower) is 12 inches in diameter, and #12 AWG wire (diameter = 0.0808 inch) with a spacing of 12 inches from the tower is to be used for the "gamma rod." The tower is 50 feet tall with a 5-foot mast and beam antenna at the top. The total height, 55 feet, is approximately 0.19 λ. We assume its electrical length is 0.2 λ or 72°. Modeling shows that the approximate base feed point impedance is $20 - j\,100$ Ω. *GAMMA* says that the gamma rod should be 57.1 feet long, with a gamma capacitor of 32.1 pF.

Immediately we see this set of gamma dimensions is impractical — the rod length is greater than the tower height. So we make another set of calculations, this time using a spacing of 18 inches between the rod and tower. The results this time are that the gamma rod is 49.3 feet long, with a capacitor of 43.8 pF. This gives us a practical set of starting dimensions for the shunt-feed arrangement.

The preferred method of building a gamma match is illustrated in **Figure 24.32**. The feed line is connected directly to the center element. This is usually done using a clamp or strap from an RF connector but depends on the physical size of the antenna. The gamma capacitor is created from an insulated wire inside the tube that forms the gamma rod. For ½ inch OD aluminum tube and the center conductor and insulation from RG-8 or RG-213, the capacitance is approximately 25 pF/ft of wire inserted into the tube. Do not use the center conductor and insulation from foam-dielectric coax as it will absorb water. Seal the end of the wire inserted into the tube to reduce the tendency to arc when wet or if insects or debris are present. After a satisfactory match has been obtained by adjusting the gamma capacitor as described below, the variable capacitor may be replaced with an equivalent length of wire in the gamma rod.

Adjustment

After installation of the antenna, the proper constants for the T and gamma generally must be determined experimentally. The use of the variable series capacitors, as shown in Figure 24.30, is recommended for ease of adjustment. With a trial position of the tap or taps on the antenna, measure the SWR on the transmission line and adjust C (both capacitors simultaneously in the case of the T) for minimum SWR. If it is not close to 1:1, try another tap position and repeat. It may be necessary to try another size of conductor for the matching section if satisfactory results cannot be brought about. Changing the spacing will show which direction to go in this respect.

24.5.6 THE OMEGA MATCH

The omega match is a slightly modified form of the gamma match. In addition to the series capacitor, a shunt capacitor is used to aid in canceling a portion of the inductive reactance introduced by the gamma section. This is shown in **Figure 24.33**. C1 is the usual series capacitor. The addition of C2 makes it possible to use a shorter gamma rod, or makes it easier to obtain the desired match when the driven element is resonant. During adjustment, C2 will serve primarily to determine the resistive component of the load as seen by the coax line, and C1 serves to cancel any reactance.

24.5.7 THE HAIRPIN AND BETA MATCHES

The usual form of the *hairpin match* is shown in **Figure 24.34**. Basically, the hairpin is a form of an L-matching network in which the feed point's capacitive reactance forms the shunt capacitor. Because it is somewhat easier to adjust for the desired terminating impedance than the gamma match, it is preferred by many amateurs. Its disadvantages, compared with the gamma, are that it must be fed with a balanced line (a balun may be used with a coax feeder, as shown in Figure 24.34 — see the section later in this chapter about baluns), and the driven element must be split at the center and insulated from the boom. This latter requirement complicates the mechanical mounting arrangement for the element, by ruling out plumber's delight construction.

As indicated in Figure 24.34, the center point of the hairpin is electrically neutral. As such, it may be grounded or connected to the remainder of the antenna structure, restoring dc ground to the feed line and driven element. The hairpin itself is usually secured by attaching this neutral point

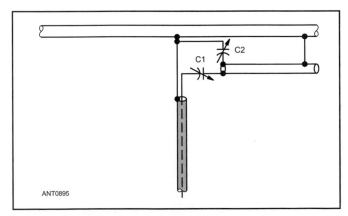

Figure 24.33 — The omega match.

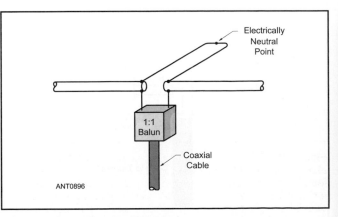

Figure 24.34 — The hairpin match.

to the boom of the antenna array. The Hy-Gain *beta match* is electrically identical to the hairpin match, the difference being in the mechanical construction of the matching section. With the beta match, the conductors of the matching section straddle the Yagi's boom, one conductor being located on either side, and the electrically neutral point consists of a sliding or adjustable shorting clamp placed around the boom and the two matching-section conductors.

The capacitive portion of the L-network circuit is produced by slightly shortening the antenna driven element, shown in **Figure 24.35A**. For a given frequency the impedance of a shortened $\lambda/2$ element appears as the antenna resistance and a capacitance in series, as indicated schematically in Figure 24.35B. The inductive portion of the resonant circuit at C is a hairpin of heavy wire or small tubing that is connected across the driven-element center terminals. The diagram of C is redrawn in D to show the circuit in conventional L-network form. R_A, the resistive component of the feed point impedance, must be a smaller value than R_{IN}, the impedance of the feed line, usually 50 Ω.

If the approximate value of R_A for the antenna system is known, **Figures 24.36** and **24.37** may be used to gain an idea of the hairpin dimensions necessary for the desired match. The required value of X_A, the feed point impedance's capacitive reactance component is

$$X_A = -\sqrt{R_A(R_{IN} - R_A)} \qquad \text{(Eq 19)}$$

The curves of Figure 24.36 were obtained from design equations for L-network matching presented earlier in this chapter. Figure 24.37 is based on the equation, $X_I/Z_0 = j \tan \theta$, which gives the inductive reactance as normalized to the characteristic impedance, Z_0, of the hairpin, looking at it as a length of transmission line terminated in a short circuit. For example, if an antenna-system impedance of 20 Ω is to be matched to 50-Ω line, Figure 24.36 shows that the inductive reactance required for the hairpin is +41 Ω. If the hairpin is constructed of ¼-inch tubing spaced 1½ inches, its characteristic impedance is 300 Ω (from equations in the **Transmission Lines** chapter). Normalizing the required 41-Ω reactance to this impedance, 41/300 = 0.137.

By entering the graph of Figure 24.37 with this value, 0.137, on the scale at the bottom, you can see that the hairpin length should be 7.8 electrical degrees, or 7.8/360 λ. For purposes of these calculations, taking a 97.5% velocity factor into account, the wavelength in inches is 11,508/f (MHz). If the antenna is to be used on 14 MHz, the required hairpin length is 7.8/360 × 11,508/14.0 = 17.8 inches. The length of the hairpin affects primarily the resistive component of the

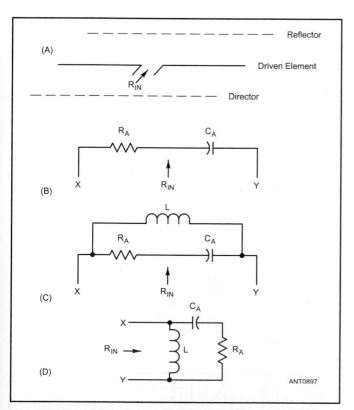

Figure 24.35 — For the Yagi antenna shown at A, the driven element is shorter than its resonant length with a capacitive feed point impedance as represented at B. By adding an inductor, as shown at C, the low value of R_A is made to appear as a higher impedance at terminals XY. At D, the diagram of C is redrawn in the usual L-network configuration.

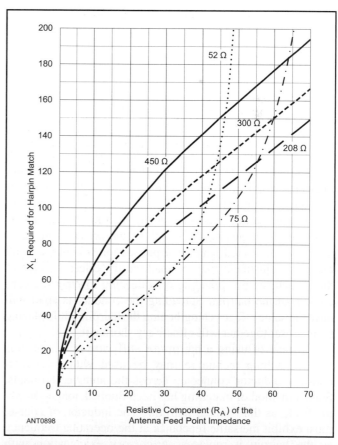

Figure 24.36 — Reactance required for a hairpin to match various antenna resistances to common line or balun impedance. The driven element's feed point impedance must exhibit a specific amount of capacitive reactance as shown in the text.

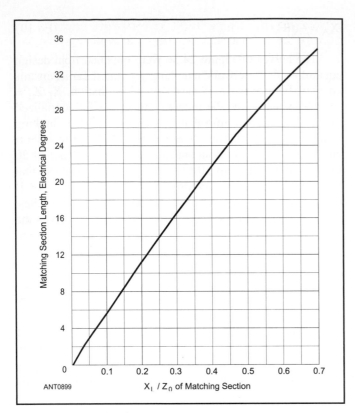

Figure 24.37 — Inductive reactance (normalized to Z_0 of matching section), scale at bottom, versus required hairpin matching section length, scale at left. To determine the length in wavelengths divide the number of electrical degrees by 360. For open-wire line, a velocity factor of 97.5% should be taken into account when determining the electrical length.

terminating impedance, as seen by the feed line. Greater resistances are obtained with longer hairpin sections — meaning a larger value of shunt inductor — and smaller resistances with shorter sections.

The remaining reactance at the feed point terminals is tuned out by adjusting the length of the driven element, as necessary. If a fixed-length hairpin section is in use, a small range of adjustment may be made in the effective value of the inductance by spreading or squeezing together the conductors of the hairpin. Spreading the conductors apart will have the same effect as lengthening the hairpin, while placing them closer together will effectively shorten it.

Instead of using a hairpin of stiff wire or tubing, this same matching technique may be used with a lumped-constant inductor connected across the antenna terminals. Such a method of matching has been dubbed, tongue firmly in cheek, as the "helical hairpin." The inductor, of course, must exhibit the same reactance at the operating frequency as the hairpin it replaces. A cursory examination with computer calculations indicates that a helical hairpin may offer a very slightly improved SWR bandwidth over a true hairpin.

24.5.8 MATCHING STUBS

As explained in the **Transmission Lines** chapter, a mismatch-terminated transmission line less than $\lambda/4$ long has an input impedance that is both resistive and reactive. The equivalent circuit of the line input impedance at any one frequency can be formed either of resistance and reactance in series, or resistance and reactance in parallel. Depending on the line length, the series resistance component, R_S, can have any value between the terminating resistance Z_R (when the line has zero length) and Z_0^2/Z_R (when the line is exactly $\lambda/4$ long). The same thing is true of R_P, the parallel-resistance component.

R_S and R_P do not have the same values at the same line length, however, other than at zero and $\lambda/4$. With either equivalent there is some line length that will give a value of R_S or R_P equal to the characteristic impedance of the line. However, there will be reactance along with the resistance. But if provision is made for canceling or tuning out this reactive part of the input impedance, only the resistance will remain. Since this resistance is equal to the Z_0 of the transmission line, the section from the reactance-cancellation point back to the generator will be properly matched.

Tuning out the reactance in the equivalent series circuit requires that a reactance of the same value as X_S (but of opposite kind) be inserted in series with the line. Tuning out the reactance in the equivalent parallel circuit requires that a reactance of the same value as X_P (but of opposite kind) be connected across the line. In practice it is more convenient to use the parallel-equivalent circuit. The transmission line is simply connected to the load (which of course is usually a resonant antenna) and then a reactance of the proper value is connected across the line at the proper distance from the load. From this point back to the transmitter there are no standing waves on the line.

A convenient type of reactance to use is a section of

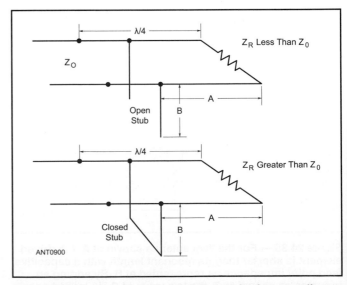

Figure 24.38 — Use of open or closed stubs for canceling the parallel reactive component of input impedance.

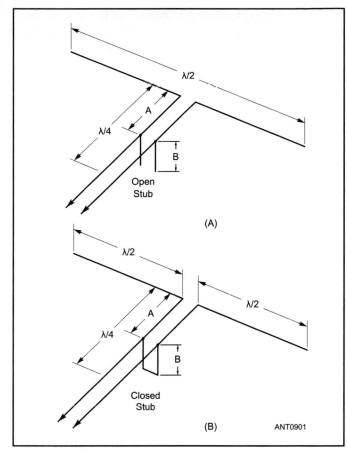

Figure 24.39 — Application of matching stubs to common types of antennas.

than Z_0 and therefore requires a closed stub.

A Smith Chart may be used to determine the length of the stub and its distance from the load as described on the supplement on this book's CD-ROM or the ARRL program *TLW* also included on the CD-ROM may be used. If the load is a pure resistance and the characteristic impedances of the line and stub are identical, the lengths may be determined by equations. For the closed stub when Z_R is greater than Z_0, they are

$$A = \arctan \sqrt{SWR} \qquad \text{(Eq 20)}$$

$$B = \arctan \frac{\sqrt{SWR}}{SWR - 1} \qquad \text{(Eq 21)}$$

For the open stub when Z_R is less than Z_0

$$A = \arctan \frac{1}{\sqrt{SWR}} \qquad \text{(Eq 22)}$$

$$B = \arctan \frac{SWR - 1}{\sqrt{SWR}} \qquad \text{(Eq 23)}$$

In these equations the lengths A and B are the distance from the stub to the load and the length of the stub, respectively, as shown in Figure 24.39. These lengths are expressed in electrical degrees, equal to 360 times the lengths in wavelengths.

In using the above equations it must be remembered that the wavelength along the line is not the same as in free space. If an open-wire line is used the velocity factor of 0.975 will apply. When solid-dielectric line is used, the free-space wavelength as determined above must be multiplied by the appropriate velocity factor to obtain the actual lengths of A and B (see the **Transmission Lines** chapter.)

Although the equations above do not apply when the characteristic impedances of the line and stub are not the same, this does not mean that the line cannot be matched under such conditions. The stub can have any desired characteristic impedance if its length is chosen so that it has the proper value of reactance. Correct lengths can be determined using *TLW* or the Smith Chart for dissimilar types of line.

In using matching stubs it should be noted that the length and location of the stub should be based on the SWR at the load. If the line is long and has fairly high losses, measuring the SWR at the input end will not give the true value at the load. This point is discussed in the section on attenuation in the **Transmission Lines** chapter.

transmission line less than $\lambda/4$ long, terminated with either an open circuit or a short circuit, depending on whether capacitive reactance or inductive reactance is called for. Reactances formed from sections of transmission line are called *matching stubs*, and are designated as *open* or *closed* depending on whether the free end is open or short circuited. The two types of matching stubs are shown in the sketches in **Figure 24.38**.

The distance from the load to the stub (dimension A in Figure 24.38) and the length of the stub, B, depend on the characteristic impedances of the line and stub and on the ratio of Z_R to Z_0. Since the ratio of Z_R to Z_0 is also the standing-wave ratio in the absence of matching (and with a resonant antenna), the dimensions are a function of the SWR. If the line and stub have the same Z_0, dimensions A and B are dependent on the SWR only. Consequently, if the SWR can be measured before the stub is installed, the stub can be properly located and its length determined even though the actual value of load impedance is not known.

Typical applications of matching stubs are shown in **Figure 24.39**, where open-wire line is being used. From inspection of these drawings it will be recognized that when an antenna is fed at a current loop, as in Figure 24.39A, Z_R is less than Z_0 (in the average case) and therefore an open stub is called for, installed within the first $\lambda/4$ of line measured from the antenna. Voltage feed, as at B, corresponds to Z_R greater

Reactive Loads

In this discussion of matching stubs it has been assumed that the load is a pure resistance. This is the most desirable condition, since the antenna that represents the load preferably should be tuned to resonance before any attempt is made to match the line. Nevertheless, matching stubs can be used even when the load is considerably reactive. A reactive load simply means that the loops and nodes of the standing waves of voltage and current along the line do not occur at integral multiples of λ/4 from the load. If the reactance at the load is known, the Smith Chart or *TLW* may be used to determine the correct dimensions for a stub match.

Stubs on Coaxial Lines

The principles outlined in the preceding section apply also to coaxial lines. The coaxial cases corresponding to the open-wire cases shown in Figure 24.39 are given in **Figure 24.40**. The equations given earlier may be used to determine dimensions A and B. In a practical installation the junction of the transmission line and stub would be a T connector.

A special case is the use of a coaxial matching stub, in which the stub is associated with the transmission line in such a way as to form a balun. This is described in detail later on in this chapter. The antenna is shortened to introduce just enough reactance at its feed point to permit the matching stub to be connected there, rather than at some other point along the transmission line as in the general cases discussed here. To use this method the antenna resistance must be lower than the Z_0 of the main transmission line, since the resistance is transformed to a higher value. In beam antennas such as Yagis, this will nearly always be the case.

Matching Sections

If the two antenna systems in Figure 24.39 are redrawn in somewhat different fashion, as shown in **Figure 24.41**, a system results that differs in no consequential way from the matching stubs described previously, but in which the stub formed by A and B together is called a *quarter-wave matching section*. The justification for this is that a λ/4 section of line is similar to a resonant circuit, as described earlier in this chapter. It is therefore possible to use the λ/4 section to transform impedances by tapping at the appropriate point along the line.

Earlier equations give design data for matching sections, A being the distance from the antenna to the point at which the line is connected, and A + B being the total length of the matching section. The equations apply only in the case where the characteristic impedance of the matching section and transmission line are the same. Equations are available for the case where the matching section has a different Z_0 than the line, but are somewhat complicated. A graphic solution for different line impedances may be obtained with the Smith Chart (see the supplement on this book's CD-ROM).

Adjustment

In the experimental adjustment of any type of matched line it is necessary to measure the SWR with fair accuracy in order to tell when the adjustments are being made in the proper direction. In the case of matching stubs, experience has shown that experimental adjustment is unnecessary, from a practical standpoint, if the SWR is first measured with the stub not connected to the transmission line, and the stub is then installed according to the design data.

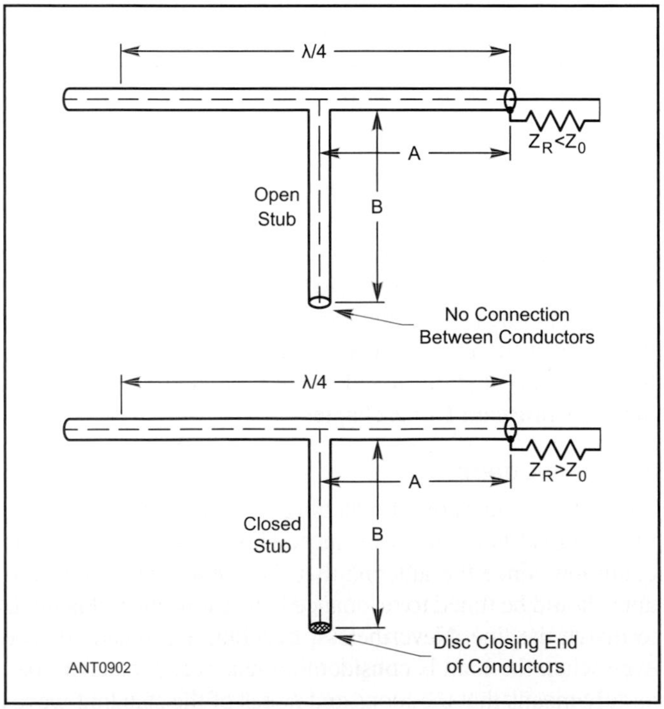

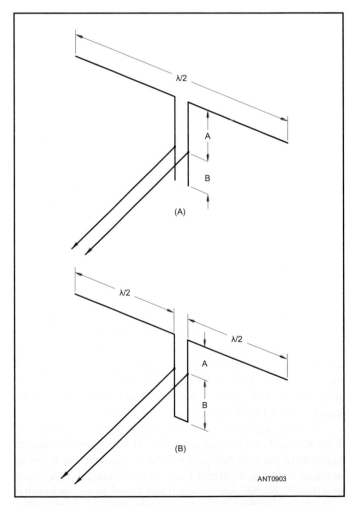

Figure 24.41 — Application of matching sections to common antenna types.

Figure 24.40 — Open and closed stubs on coaxial lines.

24.5.9 RESONANT CIRCUIT MATCHING

Antennas with a high feed point impedance, such as end-fed wires close to $\lambda/2$ in length and "voltage-fed" antennas such as the Bobtail Curtain often use a parallel-tuned circuit at the feed point to effect an impedance match. The circuit is adjusted to resonance and then the feed line attached to a tap on the inductor that is moved until an SWR minimum is obtained. The circuit may need a slight retuning following by a final position adjustment of the feed line. (See the chapters **Multiband HF Antennas** and **Broadside and End-Fire Arrays** for more information on these antennas and typical feed systems.)

The matching bandwidth of this technique is quite narrow, requiring frequent retuning or operation over a narrow bandwidth. In addition, the voltages at the "hot" or ungrounded end of the tank circuit can be very high. Caution must be used in construction to prevent contact with the high voltages and adequately rated components must be used.

24.5.10 BROADBAND MATCHING

Material from previous editions in the chapter "Broadband Antenna Matching" by Frank Witt, AI1H, is included for reference on this book's CD-ROM. It presents and analyzes various techniques used to increase the bandwidth of antenna feed point impedance.

Broadband Matching Transformers

Broadband transformers have been used widely because of their inherent bandwidth ratios (as high as 20,000:1) from a few tens of kilohertz to over a thousand megahertz. This is possible because of the transmission line nature of the windings. The interwinding capacitance is a component of the characteristic impedance and therefore, unlike a conventional transformer, forms no resonances that seriously limit the bandwidth.

At low frequencies, where interwinding capacitances can be neglected, these transformers are similar in operation to a conventional transformer. The main difference (and a very important one from a power standpoint) is that the windings tend to cancel out the induced flux in the core. Thus, high permeability ferrite cores, which are not only highly nonlinear but also suffer serious damage even at flux levels as low as 200 to 500 gauss, can be used. This greatly extends the low frequency range of performance. Since higher permeability also permits fewer turns at the lower frequencies, HF performance is also improved since the upper cutoff is determined mainly from transmission line considerations. At the high frequency cutoff, the effect of the core is negligible.

Bifilar matching transformers lend themselves to unbalanced operation. That is, both input and output terminals can have a common ground connection. This eliminates the third magnetizing winding required in balanced to unbalanced (*voltage balun*) operation. By adding third and fourth windings, as well as by tapping windings at appropriate points, various combinations of broadband matching can be obtained. **Figure 24.42** shows a 4:1 unbalanced to unbalanced configuration using #14 AWG wire. It will easily handle

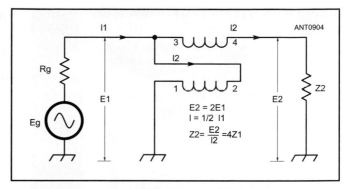

Figure 24.42 — Broadband bifilar transformer with a 4:1 impedance ratio. The upper winding can be tapped at appropriate points to obtain other ratios such as 1.5:1, 2:1, and 3:1. Terminal numbering corresponds to the ends of the wires of the windings. Odd numbered wire ends (1 and 3) are at the same end of the winding.

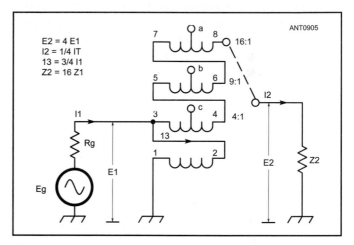

Figure 24.43 — Four-winding, broadband, variable impedance transformer. Connections a, b and c can be placed at appropriate points to yield various ratios from 1.5:1 to 16:1. See Figure 24.42 for an explanation of the wire numbering scheme.

1000 W of power. By tapping at points ¼, ½ and ¾ of the way along the top winding, ratios of approximately 1.5:1, 2:1 and 3:1 can also be obtained. One of the wires should be covered with vinyl electrical tape in order to prevent voltage breakdown between the windings. This is necessary when a step-up ratio is used at high power to match antennas with impedances greater than 50 Ω.

Figure 24.43 shows a transformer with four windings, permitting wideband matching ratios as high as 16:1. **Figure 24.44** shows a four-winding transformer with taps at 4:1, 6:1, 9:1, and 16:1. In tracing the current flow in the windings when using the 16:1 tap, one sees that the top three windings carry the same current. The bottom winding, in order to maintain the proper potentials, sustains a current three times greater. The bottom current cancels out the core flux caused by the other three windings. If this transformer is used to match into low impedances, such as 3 to 4 Ω, the

Figure 24.44 — A 4-winding, wideband transformer (with front cover removed) with connections made for matching ratios of 4:1, 6:1, 9:1 and 16:1. The 6:1 ratio is the top coaxial connector and, from left to right, 16:1, 9:1 and 4:1 are the others. There are 10 quadrifilar turns of #14 AWG enameled wire on a Q1, 2.5-inch OD ferrite core. (see text for numbers of turns on different core materials)

current in the bottom winding can be as high as 15 amperes. This value is based on the high side of the transformer being fed with 50-Ω cable handling a kilowatt of power. If one needs a 16:1 match like this at high power, then cascading two 4:1 transformers is recommended. In this case, the transformer at the lowest impedance side requires each winding to handle only 7.5 A. Thus, even #14 AWG wire would suffice in this application.

The popular cores used in these applications are 2.5-inch OD ferrites of Q1 and Q2 material, and powdered-iron cores of 2 inches OD. The permeabilities of these cores, μ, are nominally 125, 40 and 10 respectively. Powdered-iron cores of permeabilities 8 and 25 are also available.

In all cases these cores can be made to operate over the 1.8 to 28-MHz bands with full power capability and very low loss. The main difference in their design is that lower permeability cores require more turns at the lower frequencies. For example, Q1 material requires 10 turns to cover the 1.8-MHz band. Q2 requires 12 turns, and powdered-iron (μ = 10) requires 14 turns. Since the more common powdered iron core is generally smaller in diameter and requires more turns because of lower permeability, higher ratios are sometimes difficult to obtain because of physical limitations. When you are working with low impedance levels, unwanted parasitic inductances come into play, particularly on 14 MHz and above. In this case lead lengths should be kept to a minimum.

24.6 COMMON-MODE TRANSMISSION LINE CURRENTS

In discussions so far about transmission line operation, it was always assumed that the two conductors carry equal and opposite currents throughout their length. This is an ideal condition that may or may not be realized in practice. In the average case, the chances are rather good that the currents will not be balanced unless special precautions are taken. The degree of imbalance — and whether that imbalance is actually important — is what we will examine in the rest of this chapter, along with measures that can be taken to restore balance in the system.

There are two common conditions that will cause an imbalance of transmission line currents. Both are related to the symmetry of the system. The first condition involves the lack of symmetry when an inherently *unbalanced* coaxial line feeds a *balanced* antenna (such as a dipole or a Yagi driven element) directly. The second condition involves asymmetrical routing of a transmission line near the antenna it is feeding.

24.6.1 UNBALANCED COAX FEEDING A BALANCED ANTENNA

Figure 24.45 shows a coaxial cable feeding a hypothetical balanced dipole fed in the center. The coax has been drawn highly enlarged to show all currents involved. In this

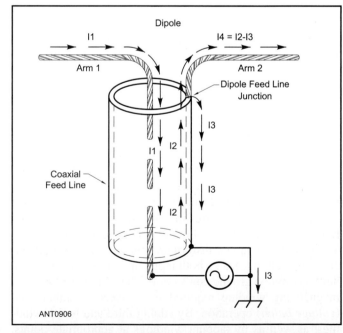

Figure 24.45 — Drawing showing various current paths at feed point of a balanced dipole fed with unbalanced coaxial cable. The diameter of the coax is exaggerated to show currents clearly.

drawing the feed line drops at right angles down from the feed point and the antenna is assumed to be perfectly symmetrical. Because of this symmetry, one side of the antenna induces current on the feed line that is completely canceled by the current induced from the other side of the antenna.

Currents I1 and I2 from the transmitter flow on the inside of the coax. I1 flows on the *outer surface* of the coax's inner conductor and I2 flows on the *inner surface* of the shield. Skin effect keeps I1 and I2 inside the transmission line confined to where they are within the line. The field outside the coax is zero, since I1 and I2 have equal amplitudes but are 180° out of phase with respect to each other.

The currents flowing on the antenna itself are labeled I1 and I4, and both flow in the same direction at any instant in time for a resonant half-wave dipole. On Arm 1 of the dipole, I1 is shown going directly into the center conductor of the feed coax. However, the situation is different for the other side of this dipole. Once current I2 reaches the end of the coax, it splits into two components. One is I4, going directly into Arm 2 of the dipole. The other is I3 and this flows down the *outer surface* of the coax shield. Again, because of skin effect, I3 is separate and distinct from the current I2 on the inner surface. The antenna current in Arm 2 is thus equal to the difference between I2 and I3.

The magnitude of I3 is proportional to the relative impedances in each current path beyond the split. The feed point impedance of the dipole by itself is somewhere between 50 to 75 Ω, depending on the height above ground. The impedance seen looking into one half of the dipole is half, or 25 to 37.5 Ω. The impedance seen looking down the outside surface of the coax's outer shield to ground is called the *common-mode impedance*, and I3 is aptly called the *common-mode current*. (The term common mode is more readily appreciated if parallel-conductor line is substituted for the coaxial cable used in this illustration. Current induced by radiation onto both conductors of a two-wire line is a common-mode current, since it flows in the *same direction* on both conductors, rather than in opposite directions as it does for transmission line current. The outer braid for a coaxial cable shields the inner conductor from such an induced current, but the unwanted current on the outside braid is still called *common-mode* current.)

The common-mode impedance will vary with the length of the coaxial feed line, its diameter and the path length from the transmitter chassis to whatever is actually "RF ground." Note that the path from the transmitter chassis to ground may go through the station's grounding bus, the transmitter power cord, the house wiring and even the power-line service ground. In other words, the overall length of the coaxial outer surface and the other components making up ground can actually be quite a bit different from what you might expect by casual inspection.

The worst-case common-mode impedance occurs when the overall effective path length to ground is a multiple of λ/2, making this path half-wave resonant. In effect, the line and ground-wire system acts like a sort of transmission line, transforming the short circuit to ground at its end to a low

impedance at the dipole's feed point. This causes I3 to be a significant part of I2.

I3 not only causes an imbalance in the amount of current flowing in each arm of the otherwise symmetrical dipole, but it also radiates by itself. The radiation in Figure 24.45 due to I3 would be mainly vertically polarized, since the coax is drawn as being mainly vertical. However the polarization is a mixture of horizontal and vertical, depending on the orientation of the ground wiring from the transmitter chassis to the rest of the station's grounding system.

Pattern Distortion for a Dipole with Symmetrical Coax Feed

Figure 24.46 compares the azimuthal radiation pattern for two λ/2-long 14-MHz dipoles mounted horizontally λ/2 above average ground. Both patterns were computed for a 28° elevation angle, the peak response for a λ/2-high dipole. The model for the first antenna, the reference dipole shown as a solid line, has no feed line associated with it — it is as though the transmitter were somehow remotely located right at the center of the dipole. This antenna displays a classical figure-8 pattern. Both side nulls dip symmetrically about 10 dB below the peak response, typical for a 20 meter dipole 33 feet above ground (or an 80 meter dipole placed 137 feet above ground).

The second dipole, shown as a dashed line, is modeled

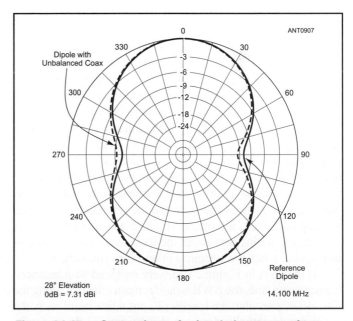

Figure 24.46 — Comparison of azimuthal patterns of two λ/2-long 14-MHz dipoles mounted λ/2 over average ground. The reference dipole without effect of feed line distortion (modeled as though the transmitter were located right at the feed point) is the solid line. The dashed line shows the pattern for the dipole affected by common-mode current on its feed line due to the use of unbalanced coax to feed a balanced antenna. The feed line is dropped directly from the feed point to ground in a symmetrical manner. The feed point impedance in this symmetrical configuration changes only a small amount compared to the reference antenna.

using a λ/2-long coaxial feed line dropped vertically to the ground below the feed point. Now, the azimuthal response of the second dipole is no longer perfectly symmetrical. It is shifted to the left a few dB in the area of the side nulls and the peak response is down about 0.1 dB compared to the reference dipole. Many would argue that this sort of response isn't all that bad! However, do keep in mind that this is for a feed line placed in a symmetrical manner, at a right angle below the dipole. Asymmetry in dressing the coax feed line will result in more pattern distortion.

SWR Change with Common-Mode Current

If an SWR meter is placed at the bottom end of the coax feeding the second dipole, it would show an SWR of 1.38:1 for a 50-Ω coax such as RG-213, since the antenna's feed point impedance is 69.20 + j 0.69 Ω. The SWR for the reference dipole would be 1.39:1, since its feed point impedance is 69.47 − j 0.35 Ω. As could be expected, the common-mode impedance in parallel with the dipole's natural feed point impedance has lowered the net impedance seen at the feed point, although the degree of impedance change is miniscule in this particular case with a symmetrical feed line dressed away from the antenna.

In theory at least, we have a situation where a change in the length of the unbalanced coaxial cable feeding a balanced dipole will cause the SWR on the line to change also. This is due to the changing common-mode impedance to ground at the feed point. The SWR may even change if the operator touches the SWR meter, since the path to RF ground is subtly altered when this happens. Even changing the length of an antenna to prune it for resonance may also yield unexpected, and confusing, results on the SWR meter because of the common-mode impedance.

When the overall effective length of the coaxial feed line to ground is not a multiple of a λ/2 resonant length but is an odd multiple of λ/4, the common-mode impedance transformed to the feed point is high in comparison to the dipole's natural feed point impedance. This will cause I3 to be small in comparison to I2, meaning that radiation by I3 itself and the imbalance between I1 and I4 will be minimal. Modeling this case produces no difference in response between the dipole with unbalanced feed line and the reference dipole with no feed line. Thus, a multiple of a half-wave length for coax and ground wiring represents the *worst case* for this kind of imbalance, when the system is otherwise symmetrical.

If the coax in Figure 24.45 were replaced with balanced transmission line, the SWR would remain constant along the line, no matter what the length. (To put a fine point on it, the SWR would actually decrease slightly toward the transmitter end. This is because of line loss with SWR. However, the decrease would be slight, because the loss in open-wire balanced transmission line is small, even with relatively high SWR on the line. See the **Transmission Lines** chapter for a thorough discussion on additional line loss due to SWR.)

Size of Coax

At HF, the diameter of the coax feeding a λ/2 dipole

is only a tiny fraction of the length of the dipole itself. In the case of Figure 24.45 above, the model of the coax used assumed an exaggerated 9-inch diameter, just to simulate a worst-case effect of coax spacing at HF.

However, on the higher UHF and microwave frequencies, the assumption that the coax spacing is not a significant portion of a wavelength is no longer true. The plane bisecting the feed point of the dipole in Figure 24.45 down through the space below the feed point and in-between the center conductor and shield of the coax is the "center" of the system. If the coax diameter is a significant percentage of the wavelength, the center is no longer symmetrical with reference to the dipole itself and significant imbalance will result. Measurements done at microwave frequencies showing extreme pattern distortion for balunless dipoles may well have suffered from this problem.

24.6.2 ASYMMETRICAL ROUTING OF THE FEED LINE

Figure 24.45 shows a symmetrically located coax feed line, one that drops vertically at a 90° angle directly below the feed point of the symmetrical dipole. What happens if the feed line is not dressed away from the antenna in a completely symmetrical fashion — that is, not at a right angle to the dipole?

Figure 24.47 illustrates a situation where the feed line goes to the transmitter and ground at a 45° angle from the dipole. Now, one side of the dipole can radiate more strongly onto the feed line than the other half can. Thus, the currents radiated onto the feed line from each half of the symmetrical dipole won't cancel each other. In other words, the antenna itself radiates a common-mode current onto the transmission line. This is a different form of common-mode current from what was discussed above in connection with an unbalanced

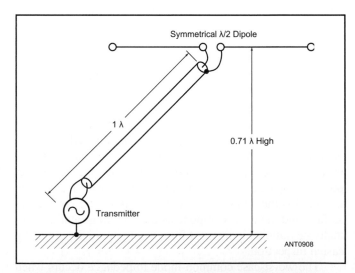

Figure 24.47 — Drawing of λ/2 dipole, placed 0.71 λ above average ground, with a 1-λ long coax feed line connected at far end to ground through a transmitter. Worst-case feed line radiation due to common-mode current induced on the outer shield braid occurs for lengths that are multiples of λ/2.

coax feeding a balanced dipole, but it has similar effects.

Figure 24.48 shows the azimuthal response of a 0.71-λ-high reference dipole with no feed line (as though the transmitter were located right at the feed point) compared to a 0.71-λ-high dipole that uses a 1-λ-long coax feed line, slanted 45° from the feed point down to ground through the transmitter. The 0.71-λ height was used so that the slanted coax could be exactly 1 λ long, directly grounded at its end through the transmitter and so that the low-elevation angle response could be emphasized to show pattern distortion. The feed line was made 1 λ long in this case, because when the feed line length is only 0.5 λ and is slanted 45° to ground, the height of the dipole is only 0.35 λ. This low height masks changes in the nulls in the azimuthal response due to feed line common-mode currents. Worst-case pattern distortion occurs for lengths that are multiplies of λ/2, as before.

The degree of pattern distortion is now slightly worse than that for the symmetrically placed coax, but once again, the overall effect is not really severe. Interestingly enough, the slanted-feed line dipole actually has about 0.2 dB more gain than the reference dipole. This is because the left-hand side null is deeper for the slanted-feed line antenna, adding power to the frontal lobes at 0° and 180°.

The feed point impedance for this dipole with slanted feed line is $62.48 - j\,1.28\ \Omega$ for an SWR of 1.25:1, compared to the reference dipole's feed point impedance of $72.00 + j\,16.76\ \Omega$ for an SWR of 1.59:1. Here, the reactive part of the net feed point impedance is smaller than that for the reference dipole, indicating that detuning has occurred due to mutual coupling to its own feed line. This change of SWR is slightly larger than for the previous case and could be seen on a typical SWR meter.

You should recognize that common-mode current arising from radiation from a balanced antenna back onto its transmission line due to a lack of symmetry occurs for *both* coaxial or balanced transmission lines. For a coax, the inner surface of the shield and the inner conductor are shielded from such radiation by the outer braid. However, the outer surface of the braid carries common-mode current radiated from the antenna and then subsequently reradiated by the line. For a balanced line, common-mode currents are induced onto both conductors of the balanced line, again resulting in reradiation from the balanced line.

If the *antenna or its environment* are not perfectly symmetrical in all respects, there will also be some degree of common-mode current generated on the transmission line, either coax or balanced. Perfect symmetry means that the ground would have to be perfectly flat everywhere under the antenna, and that the physical length of each leg of the antenna would have to be exactly the same. It also means that the height of the dipole must be exactly symmetrical all along its length, and it even means that nearby conductors, such as power lines, must be completely symmetrical with respect to the antenna.

In the real world, where the ground isn't always perfectly flat under the whole length of a dipole and where wire legs aren't cut with micrometer precision, a balanced line feeding

a supposedly balanced antenna is no guarantee that common-mode transmission line currents will not occur! However, dressing the feed line so that it is symmetrical to the antenna will lead to fewer problems in all cases.

24.6.3 COMMON-MODE CURRENT EFFECTS ON DIRECTIONAL ANTENNAS

For a simple dipole, many amateurs would look at Figure 24.46 or Figure 24.48 and say that the worst-case pattern asymmetry doesn't look very important, and they would be right. Any minor, unexpected change in SWR due to common-mode current would be shrugged off as inconsequential — if indeed it is even noticed. All around the world, there are many thousands of coax-fed dipoles in use, where no special effort has been made to smooth the transition from unbalanced coax to balanced dipole.

For antennas that are specifically designed to be highly directional, however, pattern deterioration resulting from common-mode currents is a very different matter. Much care is usually taken during design of a directional antenna like a Yagi or a quad to tune each element in the system for the best compromise between directional pattern, gain and SWR bandwidth. What happens if we feed such a carefully tailored antenna in a fashion that creates common-mode feed line currents?

Figure 24.49 compares the azimuthal response of two five-element 20 meter Yagis, each located horizontally λ/2

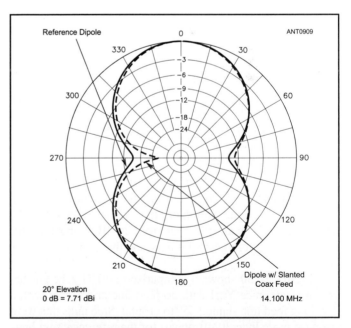

Figure 24.48 — Azimuthal response for two dipoles placed as shown in Figure 24.47. The solid line represents a reference dipole with no feed line (modeled as though the transmitter were located directly at the feed point). The dashed line shows the response of the antenna with feed line slanted 45° down to ground. Current induced on the outer braid of the 1-λ-long coax by its asymmetry with respect to the antenna causes the pattern distortion. The feed point impedance also changes, causing a different SWR from that for the unaffected reference dipole.

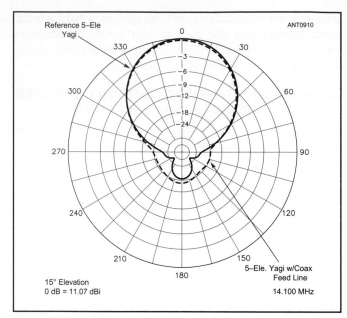

Figure 24.49 — Azimuthal response for two five-element 20 meter Yagis placed λ/2 over average ground. The solid line represents an antenna fed with no feed line, as though the transmitter were located right at the feed point. The dashed line represents a dipole fed with a λ/2 length of un-balanced coax line directly going to ground (through a transmitter at ground level). The distortion in the rearward pattern is evident, and the Yagi loses a small amount of forward gain (0.3 dB) compared to the reference antenna. In this case, placing a common-mode choke of + j 1000 Ω at the feed point eliminated the pattern distortion.

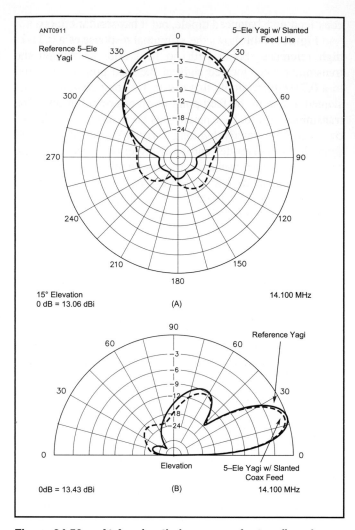

Figure 24.50 — At A, azimuthal response for two five-element 20 meter Yagis placed 0.71 λ over average ground. The solid line represents an antenna fed with no feed line. The dashed line represents a dipole fed with a 1-λ length of un-balanced coax line slanted at 45° to ground (through a transmitter at ground level). The distortion in the rearward pattern is even more evident than in Figure 24.49. This Yagi loses a bit more forward gain (0.4 dB) compared to the reference antenna. At B, elevation response comparison. The slant of the feed line causes more common-mode current due to asymmetry. In this case, placing a common-mode choke of + j 1000 Ω at the feed point was not sufficient to eliminate the pattern distortion substantially. Another choke was required λ/4 farther down the transmission line to eliminate common-mode currents of all varieties.

above average ground. The solid line represents the reference antenna, where it is assumed that the transmitter is located right at the balanced driven element's feed point without the need for an intervening feed line. The dashed line represents the second Yagi, which is modeled with a λ/2-long unbalanced coaxial feed line going to ground directly under the balanced driven element's feed point.

Minor pattern skewing evident in the case of the dipole now becomes definite deterioration in the rearward pattern of the otherwise superb pattern of the reference Yagi. The side nulls deteriorate from more than 40 dB to about 25 dB. The rearward lobe at 180° goes from 26 dB to about 22 dB. In short, the pattern gets a bit ugly and the gain decreases as well.

Figure 24.50 shows a comparison at 0.71 λ height between a reference Yagi with no feed line and a Yagi with a 1-λ-long feed line slanted 45° to ground. Side nulls that were deep (at more than 30 dB down) for the reference Yagi have been reduced to less than 18 dB in the common-mode afflicted antenna. The rear lobe at 180° has deteriorated mildly, from 28 dB to about 26 dB. The forward gain of the antenna has fallen 0.4 dB from that of the reference antenna. As expected, the feed point impedance also changes, from 22.3 − j 25.2 Ω for the reference Yagi to 18.5 − j 29.8 Ω for the antenna with the unbalanced feed. The SWR will also change with line length on the balanced Yagi fed with unbalanced line, just as

it did for the simple dipole.

Clearly, the pattern of what is supposed to be a highly directional antenna can be seriously degraded by the presence of common-mode currents on the coax feed line. As in the case of the simple dipole, multiples of λ/2-long resonant feed line to ground represents the worst-case feed system, even when the feed line is dressed symmetrically at right angles below the antenna. And as found with the dipole, the pattern deterioration becomes even worse if the feed line is dressed at a slant under the antenna to ground, although this sort of installation with a Yagi is not very common. For least interaction, the feed line still should be dressed so that it is symmetrical with respect to the antenna.

In the computer models used to create Figures 24.46, 24.48 and 24.49, placing a *common-mode choke* (described in the next sections) whose reactance is $+j\,1000\ \Omega$ at the antenna's feed point removed virtually all traces of the problem. This was always true for the simple case where the feed line was dressed symmetrically, directly down under the feed point. Certain slanted-feed line lengths required additional common-mode chokes which should be placed at $\lambda/4$ intervals beginning $\lambda/2$ down the transmission line from the feed point. (Placing the first choke $\lambda/2$ from the antenna feed point avoids creating a low impedance point on the outside of the coax shield at the feed point.) Remember that the free-space wavelength is used on the *outside* of coax while the VF must be applied *inside* the coax.

24.7 CHOKE BALUNS

In the preceding sections, the problems of directional pattern distortion and unpredictable SWR readings were traced to common-mode currents on transmission lines. Such common-mode currents arise from several types of asymmetry in the antenna-feed line system — either a mismatch between unbalanced feed line and a balanced antenna, or lack of symmetry in placement of the feed line. A device called a *balun* can be used to eliminate these common-mode currents.

The word balun is a contraction of the words *bal*anced to *un*balanced. Its primary function is to prevent common-mode currents, while making the transition from an unbalanced transmission line to a balanced load such as an antenna. Baluns come in a variety of forms, which we will explore in this section.

The term balun applies to any device that transfers differential-mode signals between a balanced system and an unbalanced system while maintaining symmetrical energy distribution at the terminals of the balanced system. The term only applies to the function of energy transfer, not to how the device is constructed. It doesn't matter whether the balanced-unbalanced transition is made through symmetrical transmission line structures, flux-coupled transformers, or simply by blocking unbalanced current flow. A common-mode choke balun described below, for example, performs the balun function by putting impedance in the path of common-mode currents and is therefore a balun.

A *current balun* forces symmetrical current at the balanced terminals, regardless of voltage. This is of particular importance in feeding antennas, since antenna currents determine the antenna's radiation pattern. A *voltage balun* forces symmetrical voltages at the balanced terminals, regardless of current. Voltage baluns are less effective in causing equal currents at their balanced terminals, such as at an antenna's feed point.

An impedance transformer may or may not perform the balun function. Impedance transformation (changing the ratio of voltage and current) is not required of a balun nor is it prohibited. There are balanced-to-balanced impedance transformers (transformers with isolated primary and secondary windings, for example) just as there are unbalanced-to-unbalanced impedance transformers (autotransformer and transmission-line designs). A transmission-line transformer is a device that performs the function of power transfer (with or without impedance transformation) by utilizing the characteristics of transmission lines.

Multiple devices are often combined in a single package called a "balun." For example, a "4:1 balun" can be a 1:1 current balun in series with a 4:1 impedance transformer. Other names for baluns are common, such as "line isolator" for a choke balun. Baluns are often referred to by their construction — "bead balun," "coiled-coax balun," "sleeve balun," etc. What is important is to separate the function (power transfer between balanced and unbalanced systems) from the construction.

Schematic Representation of a Choke Balun

The choke balun has the hybrid properties of a tightly coupled transmission line transformer (with a 1:1 transformation ratio) and a coil. The transmission line transformer action forces the current at the output terminals to be equal, and the coil portion chokes off common-mode currents.

See **Figure 24.51** for a schematic representation of such a balun. This characterization is attributed to Frank Witt, AI1H. Z_W is the winding impedance that chokes off common-mode currents. The winding impedance is mainly inductive if a high-frequency ferrite core is involved, while it is mainly resistive if a low-frequency ferrite core is used. The *ideal transformer* in this characterization models what

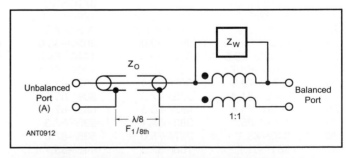

Figure 25.51 — Choke balun model, also known as a 1:1 current balun. The transformer is an ideal transformer. Z_W is the common-mode winding impedance. Sources of loss are the resistive part of the winding impedance and loss in the transmission line. This model is by Frank Witt, AI1H.

happens either inside a coax or for a pair of perfectly coupled parallel wires in a two-wire transmission line. Although Z_W is shown here as a single impedance, it could be split into two equal parts, with one placed on each side of the ideal transformer.

Note that you can compute the amount of power lost in a balun by transforming the polar representation (impedance magnitude and phase angle) shown in **Table 24-9** to the equivalent parallel form (R_p resistance and X_p shunt reactance). The power lost in the balun is then the square of half the voltage across the load divided by the equivalent parallel resistance: $(E/2)^2/R_p$. For example, in Table 24-9 the balun made with 8 turns of RG-213 on a 6⅝-inch diameter coil form at 14 MHz has an impedance of $262 \angle -86.9°$. Converting polar to rectangular, this is equal to $14.17 - j\,261.62\ \Omega$ and converting series to parallel, we have $4844 - j\,262.38$. For an RF voltage of 273.9 V RMS, the power lost in the balun is $(273.9/2)^2/(4844.8) = 3.9$ W, while for a 50-Ω load the power

is $273.9^2/50 = 1500$ W. The amount of power lost in the balun is very small compared to the power delivered to the load.

24.7.1 THE COAXIAL CHOKE BALUN

The following sections were updated by Jim Brown, K9YC, originally for the *2010 ARRL Handbook*. The simplest construction method for a choke balun is simply to wind a portion of the coaxial cable feed line into a coil (see **Figure 24.52**), creating an inductor from the shield's outer surface. This type of choke balun is simple, cheap and effective. Currents on the outside of the shield encounter the coil's impedance, while currents on the inside are unaffected.

A scramble-wound flat coil (like a coil of rope) shows a broad resonance that easily covers three octaves, making it reasonably effective over the entire HF range. If particular problems are encountered on a single band, a coil that is resonant on that band may be added. The choke baluns described in **Table 24-10** were constructed to have a high

Table 24-9
K2SQ Measurements on Coiled-Coax Baluns

Freq. MHz	6 T, 4.25 in. 1 Layer Z, Phase $\Omega/°$	12 T, 4.25 in. 1 Layer Z, Phase $\Omega/°$	4 T, 6.625 in. 1 Layer Z, Phase $\Omega/°$	8 T, 6.625 in. 1 Layer Z, Phase $\Omega/°$	8 T, 6.625 in. Bunched Z, Phase $\Omega/°$
1	26/88.1	65/89.2	26/88.3	74/89.2	94/89.3
2	51/88.7	131/89.3	52/88.8	150/89.3	202/89.2
3	77/88.9	200/89.4	79/89.1	232/89.3	355/88.9
4	103/89.1	273/89.5	106/89.3	324/89.4	620/88.3
5	131/89.1	356/89.4	136/89.2	436/89.3	1300/86.2
6	160/89.3	451/89.5	167/89.3	576/89.1	8530/59.9
7	190/89.4	561/89.5	201/89.4	759/89.1	2120/–81.9
8	222/89.4	696/89.6	239/89.4	1033/88.8	1019/–85.7
9	258/89.4	869/89.5	283/89.4	1514/87.3	681/–86.5
10	298/89.3	1103/89.3	333/89.2	2300/83.1	518/–86.9
11	340/89.3	1440/89.1	393/89.2	4700/73.1	418/–87.1
12	390/89.3	1983/88.7	467/88.9	15840/–5.2	350/–87.2
13	447/89.2	3010/87.7	556/88.3	4470/–62.6	300/–86.9
14	514/89.3	5850/85.6	675/88.3	2830/–71.6	262/–86.9
15	594/88.9	42000/44.0	834/87.5	1910/–79.9	231/–87.0
16	694/88.8	7210/–81.5	1098/86.9	1375/–84.1	203/–87.2
17	830/88.1	3250/–82.0	1651/81.8	991/–82.4	180/–86.9
18	955/86.0	2720/–76.1	1796/70.3	986/–67.2	164/–84.9
19	1203/85.4	1860/–80.1	3260/44.6	742/–71.0	145/–85.1
20	1419/85.2	1738/–83.8	3710/59.0	1123/–67.7	138/–84.5
21	1955/85.7	1368/–87.2	12940/–31.3	859/–84.3	122/–86.1
22	3010/83.9	1133/–87.7	3620/–77.5	708/–86.1	107/–85.9
23	6380/76.8	955/–88.0	2050/–83.0	613/–86.9	94/–85.5
24	15980/–29.6	807/–86.3	1440/–84.6	535/–86.3	82/–85.0
25	5230/–56.7	754/–82.2	1099/–84.1	466/–84.1	70/–84.3
26	3210/–78.9	682/–86.4	967/–83.4	467/–81.6	60/–82.7
27	2000/–84.4	578/–87.3	809/–86.5	419/–85.5	49/–81.7
28	1426/–85.6	483/–86.5	685/–87.1	364/–86.2	38/–79.6
29	1074/–85.1	383/–84.1	590/–87.3	308/–85.6	28/–75.2
30	840/–83.2	287/–75.0	508/–87.0	244/–82.1	18/–66.3
31	661/–81.7	188/–52.3	442/–85.7	174/–69.9	9/–34.3
32	484/–78.2	258/20.4	385/–83.6	155/–18.0	11/37.2
33	335/–41.4	1162/–13.5	326/–78.2	569/–0.3	21/63.6
34	607/–32.2	839/–45.9	316/–63.4	716/–57.6	32/71.4
35	705/–58.2	564/–56.3	379/–69.5	513/–72.5	46/76.0

Table 24-10
Coiled Coax Choke Baluns
Wind the indicated length of coaxial feed line into a coil (like a coil of rope) and secure with electrical tape.
The balun is most effective when the coil is near the antenna. Lengths are not critical.

Single Band (Very Effective)

Freq (MHz)	RG-213, RG-8	RG-58
3.5	22 ft, 8 turns	20 ft, 6-8 turns
7	22 ft, 10 turns	15 ft, 6 turns
10	12 ft, 10 turns	10 ft, 7 turns
14	10 ft, 4 turns	8 ft, 8 turns
21	8 ft, 6-8 turns	6 ft, 8 turns
28	6 ft, 6-8 turns	4 ft, 6-8 turns

Multiple Band

Freq (MHz)	RG-8, 58, 59, 8X, 213
3.5-30	10 ft, 7 turns
3.5-10	18 ft, 9-10 turns
1.8-3.5	40 ft, 20 turns
14-30	8 ft, 6-7 turns

Figure 24.52 — RF choke balun formed by coiling the feed line at the point of connection to the antenna. The inductance of the choke isolates the antenna from the outer surface of the feed line.

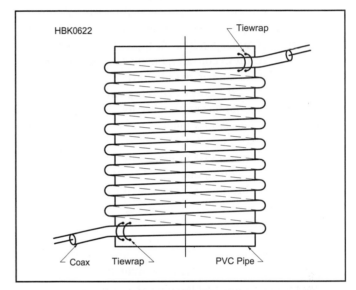

Figure 24.53 — Winding a coaxial choke balun as a single-layer solenoid may increase impedance and self-resonant frequency compared to a flat-coil choke.

impedance at the indicated frequencies as measured with an impedance meter. This construction technique is not effective with open-wire or twinlead line because of coupling between adjacent turns.

The inductor formed by the coaxial cable shield is self-resonant due to the distributed capacitance between the turns of the coil. The self-resonant frequency can be found by using a dip meter. Leave the ends of the choke open, couple the coil to the dip meter, and tune for a dip. This is the parallel resonant frequency and the impedance will be very high.

Ed Gilbert, K2SQ, measured a series of coaxial-coil baluns with a Hewlett-Packard 4193A vector-impedance meter. He constructed the coiled-coax baluns using either 4-inch or 6-inch plastic pipe. Table 24-9 lists the results.

The distributed capacitance of a flat-coil choke balun can be reduced (or at least controlled) by winding the cable as a single-layer solenoid around a section of plastic pipe, an empty bottle or other suitable cylinder (**Figure 24.53**). The coil form is then removed if desired. The cable is secured with electrical tape as shown in Figure 24.52. A coil diameter of about 5 inches is reasonable for RG-8X or RG-58/59 cable. Use a diameter of 8 inches or more for larger cable. This type of construction reduces the stray capacitance between the ends of the coil.

For both types of coiled-coaxial chokes, use cable with solid insulation, not foamed, to minimize migration of the center conductor through the insulation toward the shield. The diameter of the coil should be at least ten times the cable diameter to avoid mechanically stressing the cable.

24.7.2 TRANSMITTING FERRITE-CORE CHOKE BALUNS

A ferrite choke is simply a very low-Q parallel-resonant circuit tuned to the frequency where the choke should be effective. Passing a conductor through most ferrite cores (that is, one turn) produces a resonance around 150 MHz. By choosing a suitable core material, size and shape, and by adding multiple turns and varying their spacing, the choke can be "tuned" (optimized) for the required frequency range. (A table of ferrite and powdered-iron core toroid data is provided on this book's CD-ROM.)

Transmitting chokes differ from other common-mode chokes because they must be designed to work well when the line they are choking carries high power. They must also be physically larger so that the bend radius of the coax is large enough that the line is not deformed. Excellent common-mode chokes having very high power handling capability can be formed simply by winding multiple turns of coax through a sufficiently large ferrite core or multiple cores. (Chokes made by winding coaxial cable on ferrite cores will be referred to as "wound-coax chokes" to distinguish them from the coiled-coax chokes of the preceding section.) Because of the isolation between the inside and outside conducting surfaces of coaxial cable, all of the magnetic flux associated with differential mode current is confined to the dielectric (the insulating material between the center conductor and the shield). The external ferrite core carries only flux associated with common-mode current.

If the line is made up of parallel wires (a bifilar winding), a significant fraction of the flux associated with differential current will leak outside the line to the ferrite core. Leakage flux can exceed 30% of the total flux for even the most tightly-spaced bifilar winding. In addition to this leakage flux, the core will also carry the flux associated with common-mode current.

When a transformer (as opposed to a choke) is wound on a magnetic core, all of the field associated with current in the windings is carried by the core. Similarly, all forms of voltage baluns require all of the transmitted power to couple to the ferrite core. Depending on the characteristics of the core, this can result in considerable heating and power loss. Only a few ferrite core materials have loss characteristics suitable for use as the cores of high power RF transformers. Type 61 material has reasonably low dissipation below about 10 MHz, but its loss tangent rises rapidly above that frequency. The loss tangent of type 67 material makes it useful in high power transformers to around 30 MHz.

Leakage flux, corresponding to 30-40% of the transmitter power, causes heating in the ferrite core and attenuates the transmitted signal by a dB or so. At high power levels, temperature rise in the core also changes its magnetic properties, and in the extreme case, can result in the core temporarily losing its magnetic properties. A flux level high enough to make the core hot is also likely to saturate the core, producing distortion (harmonics, splatter, clicks).

Flux produced by common-mode current can also heat the core — if there is enough common-mode current. Dissipated power is equal to I^2R, so it can be made very small by making the common-mode impedance so large that the common-mode current is very small.

Design Criteria

It can be shown mathematically and experience confirms that wound-coax chokes having a resistive impedance at the transmit frequency of at least 5000 Ω and wound with RG-8 or RG-11-size cable on five toroids are conservatively rated for 1500 W under high duty-cycle conditions, such in contesting or digital mode operation. While chokes wound with smaller coax (RG-6, RG-8X, RG-59, RG-58 size) are conservatively rated for dissipation in the ferrite core, the voltage and current ratings of those smaller cables suggests a somewhat lower limit on their power handling. Since the chokes see only the common-mode voltage, the only effect of high SWR on power handling of wound-coax chokes is the peaks of differential current and voltage along the line established by the mismatch.

Experience shows that 5000 Ω is also a good design goal to prevent RFI, noise coupling and pattern distortion. While 500-1000 Ω has long been accepted as sufficient to prevent

pattern distortion, Chuck Counselman, W1HIS, has correctly observed that radiation and noise coupling from the feed line should be viewed as a form of pattern distortion that fills in the nulls of a directional antenna, reducing its ability to reject noise and interference.

Chokes used to break up a feed line into segments too short to interact with another antenna should have a choking impedance on the order of 1000 Ω to prevent interaction with simple antennas. A value closer to 5000 Ω may be needed if the effects of common-mode current on the feed line are filling the null of directional antenna.

Building Wound-Coax Ferrite Chokes

Coaxial chokes should be wound with a bend radius sufficiently large that the coax is not deformed. When a line is deformed, the spacing between the center conductor and the shield varies, so voltage breakdown and heating are more likely to occur. Deformation also causes a discontinuity in the impedance; the resulting reflections may cause some waveform distortion and increased loss at VHF and UHF.

Chokes wound with any large diameter cable have more stray capacitance than those wound with small diameter wire. There are two sources of stray capacitance in a ferrite choke: the capacitance from end-to-end and from turn-to-turn via the core; and the capacitance from turn-to-turn via the air dielectric. Both sources of capacitance are increased by increased conductor size, so stray capacitance will be greater with larger coax. Turn-to-turn capacitance is also increased by larger diameter turns.

At low frequencies, most of the inductance in a ferrite choke results from coupling to the core, but some is the result of flux outside the core. At higher frequencies, the core has less permeability, and the flux outside the core makes a greater contribution.

The most useful cores for wound-coax chokes are the 2.4-inch OD, 1.4-inch ID toroid of type 31 or 43 material, and the 1-inch ID × 1.125-inch long clamp-on of type 31 material. Seven turns of RG-8 or RG-11 size cable easily fit through these toroids with no connector attached, and four turns fit with a PL-259 attached. Four turns of most RG-8 or RG-11 size cable fit within the 1-inch ID clamp-on. The toroids will accept at least 14 turns of most RG-6, RG-8X or RG-59 size cables.

Practical Chokes

Joe Reisert, W1JR, introduced the first coaxial chokes wound on ferrite toroids. He used low-loss cores, typically type 61 or 67 material. **Figure 24.54** shows that these high-Q chokes are quite effective in the narrow frequency range near their resonance. However, the resonance is quite difficult to measure and it is so narrow that it typically covers only one or two ham bands. Away from resonance, the choke becomes far less effective, as choking impedance falls rapidly and its reactive component resonates with the line.

Figure 24.55 shows typical wound-coax chokes suitable for use on the HF ham bands. **Figures 24.56**, **24.57** and **24.58** are graphs of the magnitude of the impedance for HF

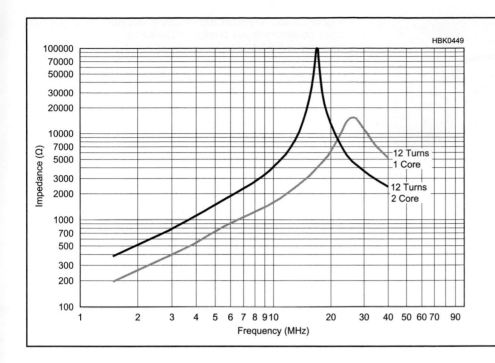

HBK0449

**Figure 24.54 —
Impedance versus frequency for HF wound-coax transmitting chokes wound with RG-142 coax on toroid cores of #61 material.**

**For the 1-core choke:
R = 15.6 kΩ, L = 25 μH, C = 1.4 pF, Q = 3.7.**

**For the 2-core choke:
R = 101 kΩ, L = 47 μH, C = 1.9 pF, Q = 20.**

Table 24-11
Transmitting Choke Designs

Freq Band(s) (MHz)	Mix	RG-8, RG-11		RG-6, RG-8X, RG-58, RG-59	
		Turns	Cores	Turns	Cores
1.8, 3.8	#31	7	5 toroids	7	5 toroids
				8	Big clamp-on
3.5-7		6	5 toroids	7	4 toroids
				8	Big clamp-on
10.1	#31 or #43	5	5 toroids	8	Big clamp-on
				6	4 toroids
7-14		5	5 toroids	8	Big clamp-on
14		5	4 toroids	8	2 toroids
		4	6 toroids	5-6	Big clamp-on
21		4	5 toroids	4	5 toroids
		4	6 toroids	5	Big clamp-on
28		4	5 toroids	4	5 toroids
				5	Big clamp-on
7-28, 10.1-28 or 14-28	#31 or #43	Use two chokes in series: #1 — 4 turns on 5 toroids #2 — 3 turns on 5 toroids		Use two chokes in series: #1 — 6 turns on a big clamp-on #2 — 5 turns on a big clamp-on	
14-28		Two 4-turn chokes, each w/one big clamp-on		4 turns on 6 toroids, or 5 turns on a big clamp-on	
50		Two 3-turn chokes, each w/one big clamp-on			

Notes: Chokes for 1.8, 3.5 and 7 MHz should have closely spaced turns.
Chokes for 14-28 MHz should have widely spaced turns.
Turn diameter is not critical, but 6 inches is good.

Figure 24.55 — Typical transmitting wound-coax common-mode chokes suitable for use on the HF bands.

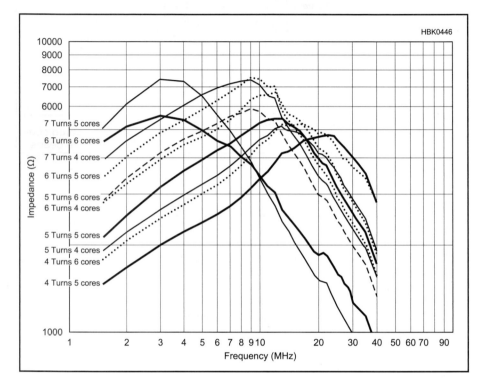

HBK0446

Figure 24.56 — Impedance versus frequency for HF wound-coax transmitting chokes using 2.4-inch toroid cores of #31 material with RG-8X coax.

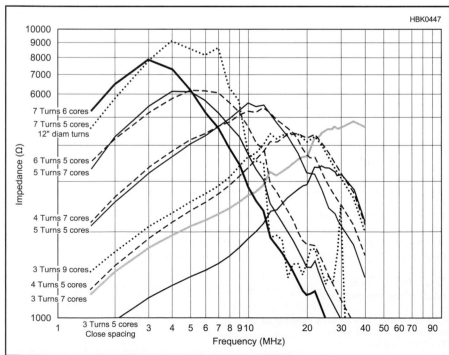

HBK0447

Figure 24.57 — Impedance versus frequency for HF wound-coax transmitting chokes using toroid cores of #31 material with RG-8 coax. Turns are 5-inch diameter and wide-spaced unless noted.

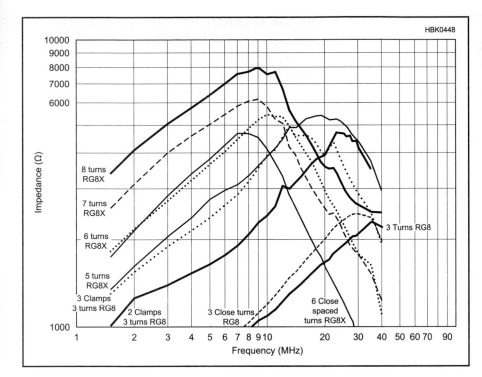

Figure 24.58 — Impedance versus frequency for HF wound-coax transmitting chokes wound on big clamp-on cores of #31 material with RG-8X or RG-8 coax. Turns are 6-inch diameter, wide-spaced except as noted.

Figure 24.59 — W2DU bead balun consisting of 50 FB-73-2041 ferrite beads over a length of RG-303 coax. See text for details.

transmitting chokes of various sizes. Fourteen close-spaced, 3-inch diameter turns of RG-58 size cable on a #31 toroid is a very effective 300-W choke for the 160 and 80 meter bands.

Table 24-11 summarizes designs that meet the 5000-Ω criteria for the 160 through 6 meter ham bands and several practical transmitting choke designs that are "tuned" or optimized for ranges of frequencies. The table entries refer to the specific cores in the preceding paragraph. If you construct the chokes using toroids, remember to make the diameter of the turns large enough to avoid deformation of the coaxial cable. (Coaxial cable has a specified "minimum bend radius.") Space turns evenly around the toroid to minimize inter-turn capacitance.

24.7.3 USING FERRITE BEADS IN CHOKE BALUNS

The ferrite bead current baluns developed by Walt Maxwell, W2DU, formed simply by stringing multiple beads in series on a length of coax to obtain the desired choking impedance, are really common-mode chokes. Maxwell's designs utilized 50 very small beads of type 73 material as shown in **Figure 24.59**. Product data sheets show that a single type 73 bead has a very low-Q resonance around 20 MHz, and has a predominantly resistive impedance of 10-20 Ω on all HF ham bands. Stringing 50 beads in series simply multiples the impedance of one bead by 50, so the W2DU balun has a choking impedance of 500-1000 Ω and because it is strongly resistive, any resonance with the feed line is minimal.

This is a fairly good design for moderate power levels, but suitable beads are too small to fit most coax. A specialty coaxial cable such as RG-303 must be used for high-power applications. Even with high-power coax, the choking

impedance is often insufficient to limit current to a low enough value to prevent overheating. Equally important — the lower choking impedance is much less effective at rejecting noise and preventing the filling of nulls in a radiation pattern.

Newer bead balun designs use type 31 and 43 beads that are resonant around 150 MHz, are inductive below resonance, and have only a few tens of ohms of strongly inductive impedance on the HF bands. Even with 20 of the type 31 or 43 beads in the string, the choke is still resonant around 150 MHz, is much less effective than a wound coaxial ferrite choke, and is still inductive on the HF bands (so it will be ineffective at frequencies where it resonates with the line).

Be aware that the heat-dissipating capability of small-diameter ferrite beads can be exceeded where there is a serious imbalance that results in large common-mode currents. Beads nearest the feed point can become very warm and can even shatter under extreme conditions of imbalance. Be careful not to skimp on using sufficient beads to choke off common-mode currents in the first place.

Adding Ferrite Beads to Air-Wound Coaxial Chokes

Air-wound coaxial chokes are less effective than bead baluns. Their equivalent circuit is also a simple high-Q parallel resonance and they must be used below resonance. They are simple, inexpensive and unlikely to overheat. Choking impedance is purely inductive and not very great, reducing their effectiveness. Effectiveness is further reduced when the inductance resonates with the line at frequencies where the line impedance is capacitive and there is almost no resistance to damp the resonance.

Adding ferrite cores to a coiled-coax balun is a way

Table 24-12
Combination Ferrite and Coaxial Coil

Freq (MHz)	7 ft, 4 turns of RG-8X	1 Core	2 Cores
1.8	—	—	520 Ω
3.5	—	660	1.4 kΩ
7	—	1.6 kΩ	3.2 kΩ
14	560 Ω	1.1 kΩ	1.4 kΩ
21	42 kΩ	500 Ω	670 Ω
28	470 Ω	—	—

to increase their effectiveness. The resistive component of the ferrite impedance damps the resonance of the coil and increases its useful bandwidth. The combinations of ferrite and coil baluns shown in **Table 24-12** demonstrate this very effectively. Eight feet of RG-8X in a 5-turn coil is a great balun for 21 MHz, but it is not particularly effective on other bands. If one type 43 core (Fair-Rite 2643167851) is inserted in the same coil of coax, the balun can be used from 3.5 to 21 MHz. If two of these cores are spaced a few inches apart on the coil as in **Figure 24.60**, the balun is more effective from 1.8 to 7 MHz and usable to 21 MHz. If type 31 material was used (the Fair-Rite 2631101902 is a similar core), low-frequency performance would be even better. The 20-turn, multiple-band, 1.8-3.5 MHz coiled-coax balun in Table 24-11 weighs 1 pound, 7 ounces. The single ferrite core combination balun weighs 6.5 ounces and the two-core version weighs 9.5 ounces.

Figure 24.60 — Choke balun that includes both a coiled cable and ferrite beads at each end of the cable.

24.7.4 MEASURING CHOKE BALUN IMPEDANCE

A ferrite RF choke creates a parallel resonant circuit from inductance and resistance coupled from the core and stray capacitance resulting from interaction of the conductor that forms the choke with the permittivity of the core. If the choke is made by winding turns on a core (as opposed to single-turn bead chokes) the inter-turn capacitance also becomes part of the choke's circuit.

These chokes are very difficult to measure for two fundamental reasons. First, the stray capacitance forming the parallel resonance is quite small, typically 0.4-5 pF, which is often less than the stray capacitance of the test equipment used to measure it. Second, most RF impedance instrumentation measures the reflection coefficient (see the **Transmission Lines** chapter) in a 50-Ω circuit.

As a result, reflection-based measurements have increasingly poor accuracy when the unknown impedance is more than about three times the characteristic impedance of the analyzer, because the value of the unknown is computed by differencing analyzer data. When the differences are small, as they are for high impedances measured this way, even very small errors in the raw data cause very large errors in the computed result. While the software used with reflection-based systems use calibration and computation methods to remove systemic errors such as fixture capacitance from the measurement, these methods have generally poor accuracy when the impedance being measured is in the range of typical ferrite chokes.

The key to accurate measurement of high impedance ferrite chokes is to set up the choke as the series element, Z_X, of a voltage divider. Impedance is then measured using a well-calibrated voltmeter to read the voltage across a well-calibrated resistor that acts as the voltage divider's load resistor, R_{LOAD}. The fundamental assumption of this measurement method is that the unknown impedance is much higher than the impedance of both the generator and the load resistor.

The RF generator driving the high impedance of the voltage divider must be terminated by its calibration impedance because the generator's output voltage, V_{GEN}, is calibrated only when working into its calibration impedance. An RF spectrum analyzer with its own internal termination resistor can serve as both the voltmeter and the load. Alternatively, a simple RF voltmeter or scope can be used, with the calibrated load impedance being provided by a termination resistor of known value in the frequency range of the measurement.

With the ferrite choke in place, obtain values for the voltage across the load resistor (V and the generator in frequency increments of about 5% over the range of interest, recording the data in a spreadsheet. If multiple chokes are being measured, use the same frequencies for all chokes so that data can be plotted and compared. Using the spreadsheet, solve the voltage divider equation backwards to find the unknown impedance.

$$|Z_X| = R_{LOAD} [V_{GEN} / V_{LOAD}]$$

Plot the data as a graph of impedance (on the vertical axis) vs frequency (on the horizontal axis). Scale both axes to display logarithmically.

Obtaining R, L, and C Values

This method yields the magnitude of the impedance, $|Z_X|$, but no phase information. Accuracy is greatest for large values of unknown impedance (worst case 1% for 5000 Ω, 10% for 500 Ω). Accuracy can be further improved by correcting for variations in the loading of the generator by the test circuit. Alternatively, voltage at the generator output can be measured with the unknown connected and used as V_{GEN}. The voltmeter must be un-terminated for this measurement.

In a second spreadsheet worksheet, create a new table that computes the magnitude of the impedance of a parallel resonant circuit for the same range of frequencies as your choke measurements. (The required equations can be found in the section Parallel Circuits of Moderate to High Q of the **Electrical Fundamentals** chapter in the *ARRL Handbook.*) Set up the spreadsheet to compute resonant frequency and Q from manually-entered values for R, L, and C. The spreadsheet should also compute and plot impedance of the same range of frequencies as the measurements and with the same plotted scale as the measurements.

1) Enter a value for R equal to the resonant peak of the measured impedance.

2) Pick a point on the resonance curve below the resonant frequency with approximately one-third of the impedance at resonance and compute L for that value of inductive reactance.

3) Enter a value for C that produces the same resonant frequency of the measurement.

4) If necessary, adjust the values of L and C until the computed curve most closely matches the measured curve.

The resulting values for R, L, and C form the equivalent circuit for the choke. The values can then be used in circuit modeling software (*NEC, SPICE*) to predict the behavior of circuits using ferrite chokes.

Accuracy

This setup can be constructed so that its stray capacitance is small but it won't be zero. A first approximation of the stray capacitance can be obtained by substituting for the unknown a noninductive resistor whose resistance is in the same general range as the chokes being measured, then varying the frequency of the generator to find the -3 dB point where $X_C = R$. This test for the author's setup yielded a stray capacitance value of 0.4 pF. A thin-film surface-mount or chip resistor will have the lowest stray reactances. If a surface-mount resistor is not available, use a ¼-W carbon composition leaded resistor with leads trimmed to the minimum amount necessary to make the connections.

Since the measured curve includes stray capacitance, the actual capacitance of the choke will be slightly less than the computed value. If you have determined the value of stray capacitance for your test setup, subtract it from the computed value to get the actual capacitance. You can also use this corrected value in the theoretical circuit to see how the choke will actually behave in a circuit — that is, without the stray capacitance of your test setup. You won't see the change in your measured data, only in the theoretical RLC equivalent.

Dual Resonances

In NiZn ferrite materials (#61, #43), there is only circuit resonance, but MnZn materials (#77, #78, #31) have both circuit resonance and dimensional resonance. (See the **RF Techniques** chapter of the *ARRL Handbook* for a discussion of ferrite resonances.) The dimensional resonance of #77 and #78 material is rather high-Q and clearly defined, so R, L, and C values can often be computed for both resonances. This is not practical with chokes wound on #31 cores because the dimensional resonance occurs below 5 MHz, is very low-Q, is poorly defined, and blends with the circuit resonance to broaden the impedance curve. The result is a dual-sloped resonance curve — that is, curve fitting will produce somewhat different values of R, L, and C when matching the low-frequency slope and high frequency slope. When using these values in a circuit model, use the values that most closely match the behavior of the choke in the frequency range of interest.

24.8 TRANSMISSION-LINE BALUNS

The properties of transmission lines, explored in the **Transmission Lines** chapter can be put to work isolating loads and transforming impedances. Here are a few useful designs for use with your antenna projects.

24.8.1 DETUNING SLEEVES

The detuning sleeve shown in **Figure 24.61B** is essentially an air-insulated λ/4 line, but of the coaxial type, with the sleeve constituting the outer conductor and the outside of the coax line being the inner conductor. Because the impedance at the open end is very high, the unbalanced voltage on the coax line cannot cause much current to flow on the outside of the sleeve. Thus the sleeve acts just like a choke to isolate the remainder of the line from the antenna. (The same viewpoint can be used in explaining the action of the λ/4 arrangement shown at Figure 24.61A, but is less easy to understand in the case of baluns less than λ/4 long.)

A sleeve of this type may be resonated by cutting a small longitudinal slot near the bottom, just large enough to take a single-turn loop which is, in turn, link-coupled to a dip meter. If the sleeve is a little long to start with, a bit at a time can be cut off the top until the stub is resonant.

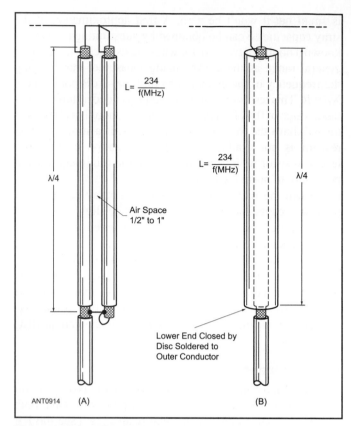

$$L = \frac{234}{f(MHz)}$$

$$L = \frac{234}{f(MHz)}$$

λ/4

λ/4

Air Space
1/2" to 1"

Lower End Closed by
Disc Soldered to
Outer Conductor

ANT0914   (A)   (B)

Figure 24.61 — Fixed-balun methods for balancing the termination when a coaxial cable is connected to a balanced antenna. These baluns work at a single frequency. The balun at B is known as a "sleeve balun" and is often used at VHF.

sleeve. This is particularly important at VHF and UHF.

In both the balancing methods shown in Figure 24.61 the λ/4 section should be cut to be resonant at exactly the same frequency as the antenna itself. These sections tend to have a beneficial effect on the impedance-frequency characteristic of the system, because their reactance varies in the opposite direction to that of the antenna. For instance, if the operating frequency is slightly below resonance the antenna has capacitive reactance, but the shorted λ/4 sections or stubs have inductive reactance. Thus the reactances tend to cancel, which prevents the impedance from changing rapidly and helps maintain a low SWR on the line over a band of frequencies.

24.8.2 QUARTER/THREE-QUARTER-WAVE BALUN

The coaxial balun in **Figure 24.62** is a 1:1 decoupling balun made from two pieces of coaxial cable. One leg is λ/4 long and the other 3λ/4 long. The two coaxes and the feed line are joined together with a T connector. At the antenna, the shields of the cables are connected together and the center conductors connected to the terminals of the antenna feed point. The balun has very little loss and is reported to have a bandwidth of more than 10%.

The balun works because of the current-forcing function of a transmission line an odd number of λ/4 long. The current at the output of such a transmission line is V_{IN} / Z_0 regardless of the load impedance, similarly to the behavior of a current source. Because both lines are fed with the same voltage, being connected in parallel, the output currents will also be equal.

The current out of the 3λ/4 line is delayed by λ/2 from the current out of the λ/4 line (and so is out of phase). The result is that equal and opposite currents are forced into the terminal of the load.

24.8.3 COMBINED BALUN AND MATCHING STUB

In certain antenna systems the balun length can be considerably shorter than λ/4; the balun is, in fact, used as

The diameter of the coaxial detuning sleeve in Figure 24.61B should be fairly large compared with the diameter of the cable it surrounds. A diameter of two inches or so is satisfactory with half-inch cable. The sleeve should be symmetrically placed with respect to the center of the antenna so that it will be equally coupled to both sides. Otherwise a current will be induced from the antenna to the outside of the

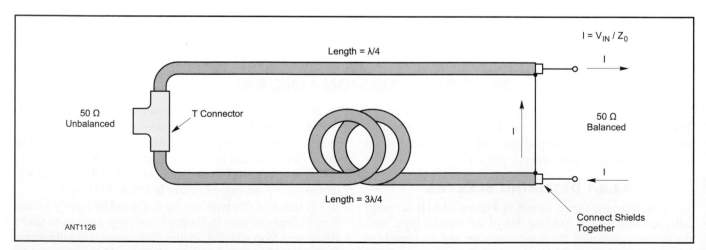

$$I = V_{IN} / Z_0$$

Length = λ/4

I

50 Ω
Unbalanced

T Connector

50 Ω
Balanced

I

I

Length = 3λ/4

Connect Shields
Together

ANT1126

Figure 24.62 — The λ/4-3λ/4 balun uses the current-forcing function of odd-λ/4 feed lines and the λ/2 delay of the longer line to cause equal and opposite currents to flow in the antenna terminals.

part of the matching system. This requires that the radiation resistance be fairly low as compared with the line Z_0 so that a match can be brought about by first shortening the antenna to make it have a capacitive reactance, and then using a shunt inductor across the antenna terminals to resonate the antenna and simultaneously raise the impedance to a value equal to the line Z_0. This is the same principle used for hairpin matches. The balun is then made the proper length to exhibit the desired value of inductive reactance.

The basic matching method is shown in **Figure 24.63A** for parallel-wire line, and the balun adaptation to coaxial feed is shown in Figure 24.63B. The matching stub in Figure 24.63B is a parallel-line section, one conductor of which is the outside of the coax between point X and the antenna; the other stub conductor is an equal length of wire. (A piece of coax may be used instead, as in the balun in Figure 24.61A.) The spacing between the stub conductors can be 2 to 3 inches. The stub of Figure 24.63 is ordinarily much shorter than $\lambda/4$, and the impedance match can be adjusted by altering the stub length along with the antenna length. With simple coax feed, even with a $\lambda/4$ balun as in Figure 24.61, the match depends entirely on the actual antenna impedance and the Z_0 of the cable; no adjustment is possible.

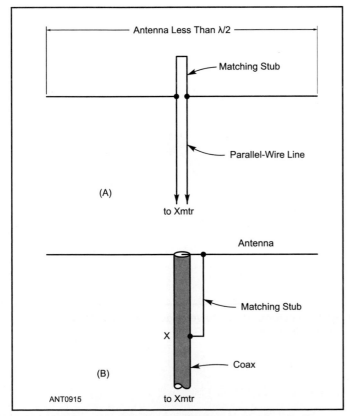

Figure 24.63 — Combined matching stub and balun. The basic arrangement is shown at A. At B, the balun arrangement is achieved by using a section of the outside of the coax feed line as one conductor of a matching stub.

ANT0915

Adjustment

When a $\lambda/4$ balun is used it is advisable to resonate it before connecting the antenna. This can be done without much difficulty if a dip meter or impedance analyzer is available. In the system shown in Figure 24.61A, the section formed by the two parallel pieces of line should first be made slightly longer than the length given by the equation. The shorting connection at the bottom may be installed permanently. With the dip meter coupled to the shorted end, check the frequency and cut off small lengths of the shield braid (cutting both lines equally) at the open ends until the stub is resonant at the desired frequency. In each case leave just enough inner conductor remaining to make a short connection to the antenna. After resonance has been established, solder the inner and outer conductors of the second piece of coax together and complete the connections indicated in Figure 24.61A.

Another method is to first adjust the antenna length to the desired frequency, with the line and stub disconnected, then connect the balun and recheck the frequency. Its length may then be adjusted so that the overall system is again resonant at the desired frequency.

Construction

In constructing a balun of the type shown in Figure 24.61A, the additional conductor and the line should be maintained parallel by suitable spacers. It is convenient to use a piece of coax for the second conductor; the inner conductor can simply be soldered to the outer conductor at both ends since it does not enter into the operation of the device. The two cables should be separated sufficiently so that the vinyl covering represents only a small proportion of the dielectric between them. Since the principal dielectric is air, the length of the $\lambda/4$ section is based on a velocity factor of 0.95, approximately.

24.8.4 IMPEDANCE STEP-UP/STEP-DOWN BALUN

A coax-line balun may also be constructed to give an impedance step-up ratio of 4:1. This form of balun is shown in Figure 24.64. If 75-Ω line is used, as indicated, the balun will provide a match for a 300-Ω terminating impedance. If 50-Ω line is used, the balun will provide a match for a 200-Ω terminating impedance. The U-shaped section of line must be an electrical length of $\lambda/2$ long, taking the velocity factor of the line into account. In most installations using this type of balun, it is customary to roll up the length of line represented by the U-shaped section into a coil of several inches in diameter. The coil turns may be bound together with electrical tape.

Because of the bulk and weight of the balun, this type is seldom used with wire-line antennas suspended by insulators at the antenna ends. More commonly it is used with multielement Yagi antennas, where its weight may be supported by the boom of the antenna system. See the K1FO designs in the **VHF and UHF Antenna Systems** chapter, where 200-Ω T-matches are used with such a balun.

24.9 VOLTAGE BALUNS

The voltage baluns shown in **Figure 24.65A** and Figure 24.65B, cause equal and opposite voltages to appear at the two output terminals, relative to the voltage at the cold side of the input. They are flux-linked impedance transformers, similar to power transformers.

If the impedances of the two antenna halves are perfectly balanced with respect to ground, the currents flowing from the output terminals will be equal and opposite and no common-mode current will flow on the line. This means if the line is coaxial, there will be no current flowing on the outside of the shield; if the line is balanced, the currents in the two conductors will be equal and opposite. These are the conditions for a nonradiating line.

Under this condition, the 1:1 voltage balun of Figure 24.65A performs exactly the same function as the current balun of **Figure 24.66A**, as there is no current in winding b. If the antenna isn't perfectly balanced, however, unequal currents will appear at the balun output, causing antenna current to flow on the line, an undesirable condition. Voltage baluns can be used as impedance transformers in this application if a 1:1 current or choke balun is added at the unbalanced input to prevent the common-mode current flow.

Another potential shortcoming of the 1:1 voltage balun is that winding b appears across the line. If this winding has insufficient impedance (a common problem, particularly near the lower frequency end of its range), the impedance transformation ratio will be degraded.

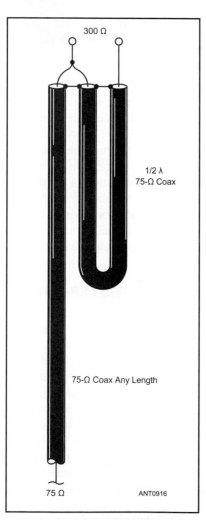

Figure 24.64 — A balun that provides an impedance step-up ratio of 4:1. The electrical length of the U-shaped section of line is λ/2.

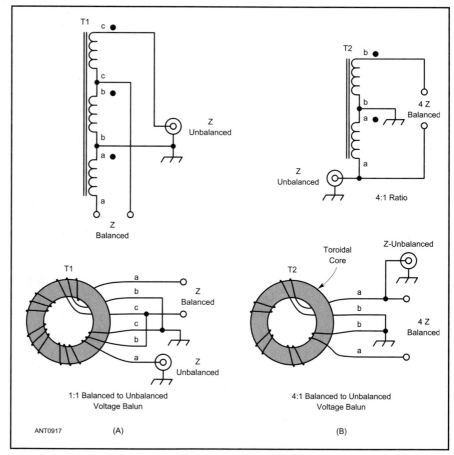

Figure 24.65 — Voltage-type baluns. These have largely been supplanted by the current (choke) type of balun.

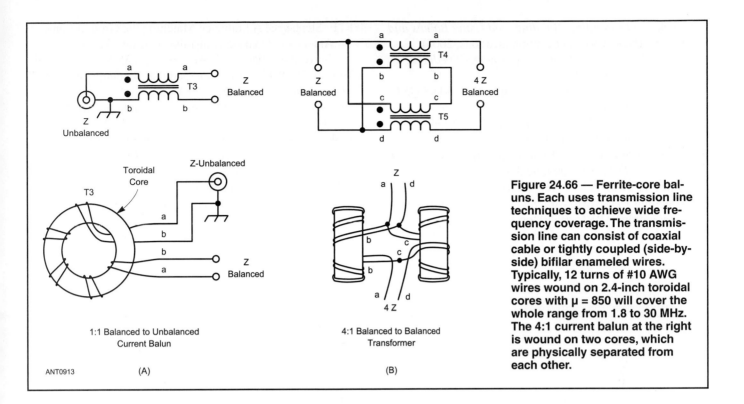

Figure 24.66 — Ferrite-core baluns. Each uses transmission line techniques to achieve wide frequency coverage. The transmission line can consist of coaxial cable or tightly coupled (side-by-side) bifilar enameled wires. Typically, 12 turns of #10 AWG wires wound on 2.4-inch toroidal cores with μ = 850 will cover the whole range from 1.8 to 30 MHz. The 4:1 current balun at the right is wound on two cores, which are physically separated from each other.

1:1 Balanced to Unbalanced
Current Balun

4:1 Balanced to Balanced
Transformer

ANT0913   (A)   (B)

24.10 BIBLIOGRAPHY

Source material and more extended discussion of topics covered in this chapter can be found in the references given below and in the textbooks listed at the end of the **Antenna Fundamentals** chapter.

G. Barrere, "Magnetic Coupling in Transmission Lines and Transformers," *QEX*, Sep/Oct 2006, pp 28-36.

D. K. Belcher, "RF Matching Techniques, Design and Example," *QST*, Oct 1972, pp 24-30.

W. Bruene, "Introducing the Series-Parallel Network," *QST*, Jun 1986, pp 21-23.

W. Caron, *Antenna Impedance Matching* (Newington: ARRL, 1989). [out of print]

G. Cutsogeorge, *Managing Interstation Interference, 2nd edition*, International Radio, 2009.

T. Dorbuck, "Matching-Network Design," *QST*, Mar 1979, pp 26-30.

B. A. Eggers, "An Analysis of the Balun," *QST*, Apr 1980, pp 19-21.

D. Emerson, "Try a Twelfth-Wave Transformer," *QST*, Jun 1997, pp 43-44.

D. Geiser, "Resistive Impedance-matching with Quarter-Wave Lines," *QST*, Feb 1963, pp 63-67.

J. D. Gooch, O. E. Gardner, and G. L. Roberts, "The Hairpin Match," *QST*, Apr 1962, pp 11-14, 146, 156.

G. Grammer, "Simplified Design of Impedance-Matching Networks," *QST*, Part 1, Mar 1957, pp 38-42; Part 2, Apr 1957, pp 32-35; Part 3, May 1957, pp 29-34.

J. Hallas, *The ARRL Guide to Antenna Tuners* (Newington: ARRL, 2010).

D. J. Healey, "An Examination of the Gamma Match," *QST*, Apr 1969, pp 11-15, 57.

J. D. Kraus and S. S. Sturgeon, "The T-Matched Antenna," *QST*, Sep 1940, pp 24-25.

R. W. Lewallen, "Baluns: What They Do and How They Do It," *The ARRL Antenna Compendium, Vol 1* (Newington: ARRL, 1985), pp 157-164.

R. Lindquist, "*QST* Compares: Four High-Power Antenna Tuners," Product Review, *QST*, Mar 1997, pp 73-77.

M. W. Maxwell, "Some Aspects of the Balun Problem," *QST*, Mar 1983, pp 38-40.

M. W. Maxwell, *Reflections III* (New York: CQ Communications, 2010).

R. A. Nelson, "Basic Gamma Matching," *Ham Radio*, Jan 1985, pp 29-31, 33.

B. Pattison, "A Graphical Look at the L Network," *QST*, Mar 1979, pp 24-25.

F. A. Regier, "Series-Section Transmission line Impedance-matching," *QST*, Jul 1978, pp 14-16.

R. Rhea, "Yin-Yang of Matching, Parts 1 and 2," *High Frequency Electronics,* Mar and Apr 2006. Also available from Agilent Technologies (**www.agilent.com**) as application notes 5989-9012EN and 5989-9015EN.

W. Sabin, "Understanding the T-tuner (C-L-C) Transmatch," *QEX*, Dec 1997, pp 13-21.

J. Sevick, *Understanding, Building, and Using Baluns and Ununs,* (New York: CQ Communications, 2003).

J. Sevick, *Transmission Line Transformers, 4th edition,* Noble Publishing, 2001.

J. Sevick, "Simple Broadband Matching Networks," *QST,* Jan 1976, pp 20-23.

W. Silver, ed., *2011 ARRL Handbook,* 88th edition (Newington: ARRL, 2011).

J. Stanley, "Hairpin Tuners for Matching Balanced Antenna Systems," *QST,* Apr 2009, pp 34-35.

J. Stanley, "*FilTuners* — a New (Old) Approach to Antenna Matching," *The ARRL Antenna Compendium, Vol. 6* (Newington: ARRL, 1999), pp 168-173.

R. E. Stephens, "Admittance Matching the Ground-Plane Antenna to Coaxial Transmission Line," Technical Correspondence, *QST,* Apr 1973, pp 55-57.

H. F. Tolles, "How to Design Gamma-Matching Networks," *Ham Radio,* May 1973, pp 46-55.

E. Wingfield, "New and Improved Formulas for the Design of Pi and Pi-L Networks," *QST,* Aug 1983, pp 23-29.

F. Witt, "Baluns in the Real (and Complex) World," *The ARRL Antenna Compendium, Vol 5* (Newington: ARRL, 1997), pp 171-181.

F. Witt, "How to Evaluate Your Antenna Tuner," *QST,* Part 1, Apr 1995, pp 30-34 and May 1995, pp 33-37.

B. S. Yarman, *Design of Ultra Wideband Antenna Matching Networks,* (New York: Springer, 2008).

TABLE OF CONTENTS

Chapter 25

Antenna Materials and Construction

This chapter contains information on materials and techniques amateurs use to construct antennas. Included is a discussion of useful material types that are readily available at reasonable cost, and tips on working with and using these materials. The list of manufacturers on the CD-ROM included with this book contains information on where to purchase these materials.

The National Electric Code (NEC) of the National Fire Protection Association contains a section on amateur stations in which a number of recommendations are made concerning minimum size of antenna wire and the manner of bringing the transmission line into the station. The code in itself does not have the force of law but it is frequently made a part of local building regulations, which are enforceable. The provisions of the code may also be written into, or referred to, in fire and liability insurance documents. See the chapter **Building Antenna Systems and Towers** for more information on applying the NEC to your station's antenna system.

Although antennas are relatively simple structures, they can constitute a potential hazard unless properly constructed. Antennas and supporting ropes or wires should *never* be run under or over public utility (telephone or power) lines. Stay well clear of utility lines when erecting antennas and give yourself plenty of safety margins. Amateurs have lost their lives by failing to observe these precautions.

Basically any conductive material can be used as the radiating element of an antenna. Almost any insulating material can be used as an antenna insulator. An antenna system must also include some means to support those conductors and maintain their relative positions — the boom for a Yagi antenna, for example. The materials used for antenna construction are limited mainly by physical considerations (required strength and resistance to outdoor exposure) and by the availability of materials. Don't be afraid to experiment with radiating materials and insulators.

The two types of material most often used for antenna conductors are wire and tubing. Wire antennas are generally simple and therefore easier to construct, although arrays of multiple wire elements can become rather complex. When tubing is required, aluminum tubing is used most often because of its light weight, reasonable cost and strength. Aluminum tubing is discussed in a subsequent section of this chapter.

25.1 WIRE ANTENNAS

25.1.1 WIRE TYPES

Solid copper wire is used for most wire antennas although the use of stranded wire is common. Solid wire is less flexible than stranded wire, but it is available "hard-drawn," which offers good tensile strength and negligible stretch. Special stranded wire with a larger-than-usual number of fine strands (such as Flex-Weave) is available for building antennas. It withstands vibration and bending in the wind better than common stranded wire and better than solid wire. Galvanized steel and aluminum wire are generally not used for antennas because of higher electrical resistance than copper. Galvanized wire also has a strong tendency to rust and making good electrical connections to aluminum wire is difficult — it cannot be directly soldered without special solder fluxes.

Solid wire is also available with and without enamel coating. Enamel coating resists oxidation and corrosion, but bare wire is far more common. Solid wire is also available with a variety of different insulating coatings, including plastics, rubbers and PVC. Unless specifically rated for outdoor use however, wire insulation, including enamel, tends to break down when exposed to the UV in sunlight. Insulation also lowers the velocity factor of wire by a few percent (see the **Transmission Lines** chapter) making it electrically longer than its physical length — this will lower the resonant frequency of an antenna compared to one made of bare wire of equivalent diameter. In addition, insulation increases wind loading without increasing strength. If enameled or insulated wire is used, care should be taken to not nick the wire when removing the coating for an electrical connection. Wire will break at a nick when flexed repeatedly, such as by wind.

"Soft-drawn" or annealed copper wire is easy to handle and obtain. Common THHN-insulated "house wire" is soft-drawn. Unfortunately, soft-drawn wire stretches considerably under load. Soft-drawn wire should only be used in applications where there will be little or no tension, or where some change in length can be tolerated. For example, the length of a horizontal antenna fed at the center with open-wire line is not critical, although a change in length may require some readjustment of an impedance matching unit. Similarly, if the wire stretches significantly, it can be re-trimmed to the desired length. Repeated cycles of stretching followed by trimming and re-tensioning will result in loss of strength and possibly in mechanical failure.

"Hard-drawn" copper wire and CCS (copper-clad steel, usually sold as the trademarked product Copperweld) wire are more difficult to handle because of their mechanical stiffness and, in the case of CCS, the tendency to have "memory" when unrolled. These types of wire are ideal for applications where high strength for a given weight is required and/or significant stretch cannot be tolerated. Care should be exercised to make sure kinks do not develop in hard-drawn and CCS wire — the wire will have a far greater tendency to break at a kink. The "memory" or tendency of CCS wire to coil up can be reduced by suspending it a few feet above ground for a few days before final use. The wire should not be recoiled before it is installed.

The electrical quality of CCS wire varies considerably. A conductivity class of 30% or higher is desirable, meaning the wire has 30% of the conductivity of copper wire of the same diameter but for RF applications at HF it will have close to 100% conductivity due to skin effect. Copper cladding can be damaged by abrasion (typically at insulators) or sharp bends. Plastic insulators of sufficient strength are preferable to ceramic insulators when using CCS; they are soft in comparison and less likely to degrade the copper cladding over time. Induced defects in copper cladding eventually result in mechanical failure due to rusting of the steel core. Breaks in the copper cladding also form high resistance points to RF and will heat considerably when running high power. Heat accelerates oxidation (rusting).

25.1.2 WIRE SIZE AND TENSION

Many factors influence the choice of wire type and size (gage or gauge). Important considerations include the length of the unsupported span, the amount of sag that can be tolerated, the stability of the supports under wind pressure, the

Table 25-1
Copper-Wire Table

Wire Size AWG (B&S)	Dia in Mils[1]	Dia in mm	Turns per Linear Inch Enamel	Feet per Pound Bare	Ohms per 1000 ft 25°C[3]	Cont.-duty current[2,3] Single Wire in Open Air
1	289.3	7.348	—	3.947	0.1264	—
2	257.6	6.544	—	4.977	0.1593	—
3	229.4	5.827	—	6.276	0.2009	—
4	204.3	5.189	—	7.914	0.2533	—
5	181.9	4.621	—	9.980	0.3195	—
6	162.0	4.115	—	12.58	0.4028	—
7	144.3	3.665	—	15.87	0.5080	—
8	128.5	3.264	7.6	20.01	0.6405	73
9	114.4	2.906	8.6	25.23	0.8077	—
10	101.9	2.588	9.6	31.82	1.018	55
11	90.7	2.305	10.7	40.12	1.284	—
12	80.8	2.053	12.0	50.59	1.619	41
13	72.0	1.828	13.5	63.80	2.042	—
14	64.1	1.628	15.0	80.44	2.575	32
15	57.1	1.450	16.8	101.4	3.247	—
16	50.8	1.291	18.9	127.9	4.094	22
17	45.3	1.150	21.2	161.3	5.163	—
18	40.3	1.024	23.6	203.4	6.510	16
19	35.9	0.912	26.4	256.5	8.210	—
20	32.0	0.812	29.4	323.4	10.35	11
21	28.5	0.723	33.1	407.8	13.05	—
22	25.3	0.644	37.0	514.2	16.46	—
23	22.6	0.573	41.3	648.4	20.76	—
24	20.1	0.511	46.3	817.7	26.17	—
25	17.9	0.455	51.7	1031	33.00	—
26	15.9	0.405	58.0	1300	41.62	—
27	14.2	0.361	64.9	1639	52.48	—
28	12.6	0.321	72.7	2067	66.17	—
29	11.3	0.286	81.6	2607	83.44	—
30	10.0	0.255	90.5	3287	105.2	—
31	8.9	0.227	101	4145	132.7	—
32	8.0	0.202	113	5227	167.3	—
33	7.1	0.180	127	6591	211.0	—
34	6.3	0.160	143	8310	266.0	—
35	5.6	0.143	158	10480	335	—
36	5.0	0.127	175	13210	423	—
37	4.5	0.113	198	16660	533	—
38	4.0	0.101	224	21010	673	—
39	3.5	0.090	248	26500	848	—
40	3.1	0.080	282	33410	1070	—

[1]A mil is 0.001 inch.
[2]Max wire temp of 212° F and max ambient temp of 135° F.
[3]Ratings are for dc measurements and currents without skin effect.

amount of wind and ice loading anticipated and whether or not a transmission line will be suspended from the span. Some sag is desirable. Removing most or all sag requires additional unnecessary tension and increases the likelihood of failure. **Table 25-1** shows the wire diameter, current-carrying capacity and resistance of various sizes of copper wire. **Table 25-2** shows the recommended maximum working tension of hard-drawn and CCS wire of various sizes. The recommended working tension is approximately 10% of the minimum guaranteed breaking strength of the wire. Together with a calculation of span sag, these two tables can

Table 25-2
Stressed Antenna Wire

American Wire Gauge	Recommended Tension[1] (pounds)		Weight (pounds per 1000 feet)	
	Copper-clad steel[2]	Hard-drawn copper	Copper-clad steel[2]	Hard-drawn copper
4	495	214	115.8	126.0
6	310	130	72.9	79.5
8	195	84	45.5	50.0
10	120	52	28.8	31.4
12	75	32	18.1	19.8
14	50	20	11.4	12.4
16	31	13	7.1	7.8
18	19	8	4.5	4.9
20	12	5	2.8	3.1

[1]Approximately one-tenth the guaranteed breaking strength. Might be increased 50% if end supports are firm and there is no danger of ice loading.
[2] Copperweld, 40% copper

be used to select the appropriate wire size for an antenna.

The National Electrical Code (see the chapter **Building Antenna Systems and Towers**) specifies minimum conductor sizes for different span-length wire antennas. For hard-drawn copper wire, the Code specifies #14 AWG wire for open (unsupported) spans less than 150 feet, and #10 AWG for longer spans. CCS, bronze or other high-strength conductors may be #14 AWG for spans less than 150 feet and #12 AWG for longer runs. Lead-in conductors (for open-wire transmission line) should be at least as large as those specified for antennas.

The RF resistance of copper wire increases as the size of the wire decreases. In most common wire antenna designs however, the antenna's radiation resistance will be much higher than the wire's RF resistance and the efficiency of the antenna will be adequate. Wire sizes as small as #30 AWG, or even smaller, have been used successfully in the construction of "invisible" antennas in areas where more conventional antennas cannot be erected. In most cases, the selection of wire for an antenna will be based primarily on the mechanical properties of the wire, since the suspension of wire from elevated supports places the wire in tension.

If the tension on a wire can be adjusted to a known value, the expected sag of the wire (**Figure 25.1**) may be determined using Table 25-2 and the nomograph of **Figure 25.2**. Alternately, sag can be adjusted to achieve a desired tension. Even though there may be no convenient method to determine the tension in pounds, calculation of the expected sag for practical working tension is often desirable. If the calculated sag is greater than allowable it may

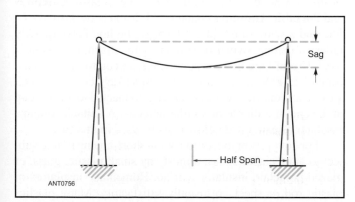

Figure 25.1 — The half span and sag of a long-wire antenna.

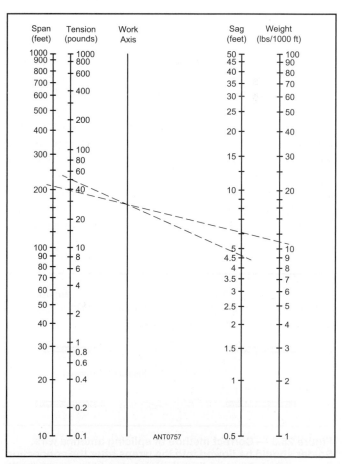

Figure 25.2 — Nomograph for determining wire sag. (*courtesy John Elengo, W1DQ*)

be reduced by any one or a combination of the following:

    1) Providing additional supports, thereby decreasing the span

    2) Increasing the tension in the wire

    3) Decreasing the size (gage or gauge) of the wire

Instructions for Using the Nomograph

    1) From Table 25-2, find the weight (pounds/1000 feet) for the particular wire size and material to be used.

    2) Draw a line from the value obtained above, plotted on the weight axis, to the desired span (feet) on the span axis, Figure 25.2. Note in Figure 25.1 that the span is one half the distance between the supports.

    3) Choose an operating tension in pounds, consistent with the values presented in Table 25-2 (preferably less than that recommended).

    4) Draw a line from the tension value chosen (plotted on the tension axis) through the point where the work axis crosses the original line constructed in step 2, and continue this new line to the sag axis.

    5) Read the sag in feet on the sag axis.

Example:

Weight = 11 pounds/1000 feet

Span = 210 feet

Tension = 50 pounds

Answer: Sag = 4.7 feet

These calculations do not take into account the weight of a feed line supported by the antenna wire.

25.1.3 WIRE SPLICING

Wire antennas should preferably be made with unbroken lengths of wire. In instances where this is not feasible, wire sections should be spliced as shown in **Figure 25.3**. Any insulation should be removed for a distance of about 6 inches from the end of each section (take care not to nick the wire). Enamel may be removed by scraping with a knife or rubbing with sandpaper until the copper underneath is bright. The turns of wire should be brought up tight around the standing part of the wire by twisting with broad-nose pliers.

The crevices formed by the wire should be completely filled by using solder that does not contain an acid-core flux.

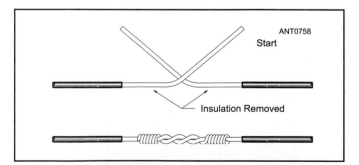

Figure 25.3 — Correct method of splicing antenna wire. Solder should be flowed into the wraps after the connection is completed. After cooling, the joint should be sprayed with acrylic to prevent oxidation and corrosion.

A soldering iron or gun may not be sufficient for heavy wire or in cold temperatures; use a propane or butane torch instead. The joint should be heated sufficiently so the solder flows freely into the joint when the source of heat is removed momentarily. After the joint has cooled completely, it should be wiped clean with a cloth and then sprayed generously with acrylic to prevent corrosion.

25.1.4 ANTENNA INSULATORS

To prevent loss of RF power, the antenna should be well insulated from ground, unless of course it is a shunt-fed system. This is particularly important at the outer end or ends of wire antennas, since these points are always at a comparatively high RF potential. If an antenna is to be installed indoors (in an attic, for instance) the antenna may be suspended directly from the wood rafters without additional insulation if the wood is permanently dry. Much greater care should be given to the selection of proper insulators when the antenna is located outside where it is exposed to wet weather.

Antenna insulators should be made of material that will not absorb moisture. The best insulators for antenna use are made of glass or glazed porcelain although plastic insulators are widely available and suitable for most antennas.

The length of an insulator relative to its surface area is indicative of its comparative voltage stand-off and RF leakage abilities. A long thin insulator will have less leakage than a short thick insulator. Some antenna insulators are deeply ribbed to increase the surface leakage path without increasing the physical length of the insulator. Shorter insulators can be used at low-potential points, such as at the center of a dipole. If such an antenna is to be fed with open-wire line and used on several bands however, the center insulator should be the same as those used at the ends, because high RF potential may exist across the center insulator on some bands.

Insulator Stress

As with the antenna wire, the insulator must have sufficient physical strength to carry the mechanical load of the antenna without danger of breaking. Elastic line ("bungee cord" or "shock cord") or woven fishing line can provide long leakage paths and be used to provide both the end-insulator and support functions at antenna ends, subject to their ability to carry mechanical load. They are often used in antennas of the "invisible" type mentioned in the **Stealth Antennas** and **Portable Antennas** chapters. Abrasion between a woven line and a wire loop will cut through the line fairly quickly unless a fishing swivel or similar metal attachment point is used. Use of high power approaching and up to the US legal limit of 1500 W may cause sufficient leakage current to melt woven or monofilament line directly connected to a wire loop at the end of a dipole or similar antenna. A suitable antenna insulator as explained below must be used in this case.

For low-power operation with short antennas not subject to appreciable stress, almost any small plastic, glass, or glazed-porcelain insulator will do. Homemade insulators of plastic rod or sheet are usually satisfactory. Many plastics rated for outdoor use make good insulators — this includes

Lucite (polycarbonate), Delrin, plexiglass, and even the high-density polyethylene (HDPE) used in cutting boards. More care is required in the selection of insulators for longer spans and higher transmitter power.

For a given material, the breaking tension of an insulator will be proportional to its cross-sectional area. It should be remembered that the wire hole at the end of the insulator decreases the effective cross-sectional area. For this reason, insulators designed to carry heavy strains are fitted with heavy metal end caps, the eyes being formed in the metal cap, rather than in the insulating material itself.

The following stress ratings of ceramic antenna insulators are typical:

- ⅝ inch square by 4 inches long — 400 pounds
- 1 inch diameter by 7 or 12 inches long — 800 pounds
- 1½ inches diameter by 8, 12 or 20 inches long, with special metal end caps — 5000 pounds

These are rated breaking tensions. The actual working tensions should be limited to not more than 25% of the breaking rating. Plastic insulators have significantly lower tension ratings.

The antenna wire should be attached to the insulators as shown in **Figure 25.4**. Care should be taken to avoid sharp angular bends in the wire when it is looped through the insulator eye. The loop should be generous enough in size that it will not bind the end of the insulator tightly. If the length of the antenna is critical, the length should be measured to the outward end of the loop, where it passes through the eye of the insulator. (See the note below about the loop area affecting the antenna's electrical length.) Soldering should be done as described earlier for the wire splice. If CCS wire is used, care should be taken to ensure insulator holes and edges are smooth. Any roughness at contact points between the wire and the insulator will cause the copper to be abraded away over time, exposing the wire's steel core and eventually leading to mechanical failure from rust. Assuming they are of sufficient size to handle the mechanical load, plastic insulators are a good choice for use with CCS wire.

Note that the large area of the loop through the insulator adds capacitance to the antenna. The larger the insulator loop, the more capacitance is created, and the greater its effect in lowering the resonant frequency of the antenna. This effect increases with operating frequency. When building a wire antenna, attach the insulators temporarily (without soldering) and adjust the resonant frequency of the antenna before soldering the insulator loop.

Strain Insulators

Strain or "egg" insulators have their holes at right angles, since they are designed to be connected as shown in **Figure 25.5**. It can be seen that this arrangement places the insulating material in compression rather than tension. An insulator connected this way can withstand very high mechanical load.

The principal attribute of strain insulators is that the wire will not fall or fail to carry load if the insulator breaks, since the two loops are interlocked. Insulator failure may go unnoticed however — strain insulators should be visually checked periodically. Because the wires are wrapped around each other, the leakage path is shorter than it would be otherwise and both leakage and capacitive end effects are higher compared to insulators where the wires are not interlinked. For this reason, strain insulators are typically confined to applications such as breaking up resonances in guy wires, where there is high mechanical load and where RF insulation is of minor importance.

Strain insulators are suitable for use at low-potential points on an antenna, such as at the center of a dipole. They may also be used at the ends of antennas used for low power operation.

Feed Point Insulators

Often referred to as "center insulators," the insulators used at the feed point of a wire antenna often have special features that help attach and support feed lines. A "dog bone" style insulator as in **Figure 25.6A** is the most common. To attach a coaxial feed line using this style of insulator, the cable's shield and center conductor are separated into "pigtails" that are soldered to the wire at each eye. The cable can be supported by looping it over the insulator and securing it with tape as shown in the figure. Note that the length of the separated shield and center conductor count as part of the antenna length — that may be significant at higher frequencies. The cable must be carefully waterproofed with a coating such as silicone sealant or Liquid Electrical Tape to prevent water from being wicked into the cable by the exposed shield. The "Budwig" style of insulator in Figure 25.6B includes an SO-239 so that the coaxial cable can be attached with a con-

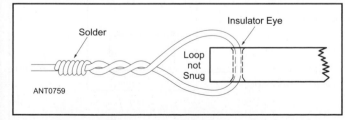

Figure 25.4 — When fastening antenna wire to an insulator, do not make the wire loop too snug. After the connection is complete, flow a non-acid core solder into the turns. When the joint has cooled completely, spray it with acrylic.

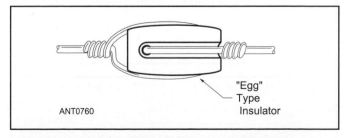

Figure 25.5 — Conventional manner of fastening wire to a strain insulator. This method decreases the leakage path and increases capacitance, as discussed in the text.

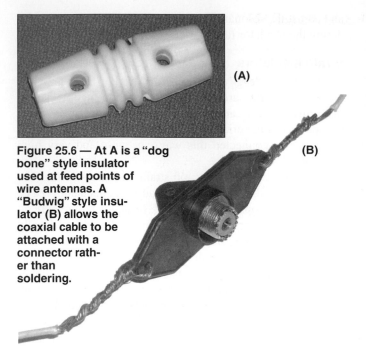

Figure 25.6 — At A is a "dog bone" style insulator used at feed points of wire antennas. A "Budwig" style insulator (B) allows the coaxial cable to be attached with a connector rather than soldering.

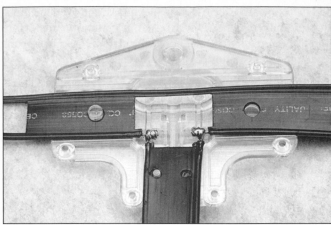

Figure 25.7 — The Ten-Tec "Acro-Bat" is made for attaching parallel-wire feed line to a wire antenna. It provides strain relief and reinforcement to the feed line to keep the conductors from breaking due to repeated flexing and bending in the wind.

nector instead of soldered to the antenna. The PL-259 and exposed portion of the SO-239 connectors in this case should be waterproofed. This type of center insulator can be made from a PVC pipe cap or other plumbing fittings as shown later in this chapter.

Figure 25.7 shows a feed point insulator intended for use with parallel-wire feed line. The dog bone style of insulator may be used but cannot support the feed line in the same way as for coaxial cable. Parallel-wire line cannot be looped back on itself with the conductors close together. If left unsupported, the conductors of the feed line continually flex and bend in the wind which causes them to break. The tee-style of insulator in the figure captures the parallel-wire feed line and provides mechanical support, greatly reducing breakage.

Insulators for Ribbon-Line Antennas

Figure 25.8A shows the sketch of an insulator designed to be used at the ends of a folded dipole or a multiple dipole made of parallel conductor line. It should be made approximately as shown, out of insulating material about ¼ inch thick. The advantage of this arrangement is that the strain of the antenna is shared by the conductors and the plastic webbing of the line, which adds considerable strength. After soldering, the screw should be sprayed with acrylic.

Figure 25.8B shows a similar arrangement for suspending one dipole from another in a stagger-tuned dipole system. If better insulation is desired, these insulators can be wired to a conventional insulator.

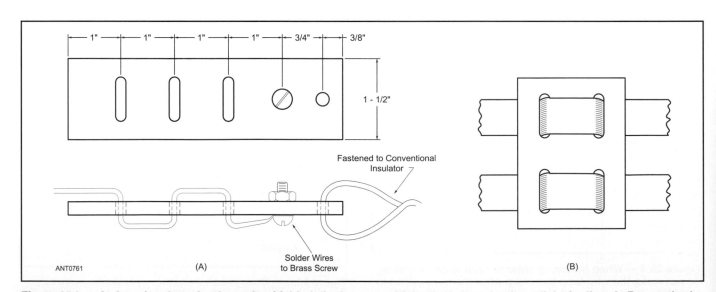

Figure 25.8 — At A, an insulator for the ends of folded dipoles, or multiple dipoles made of parallel-wire line. At B, a method of suspending one ribbon dipole from another in a multiband dipole system.

25.2 ANTENNAS OF ALUMINUM TUBING

Aluminum is a non-toxic, malleable, ductile metal with a density approximately 35% that of iron and 30% that of copper. Aluminum can be polished to a high brightness, and it will retain this polish in dry air. In the presence of oxygen, aluminum forms an oxide coating (Al_2O_3) that protects the metal from further corrosion. Direct contact between aluminum and certain metals (particularly ferrous metals such as iron or steel) in an outdoor environment can bring about galvanic corrosion of aluminum and its alloys. Some protective coating such as Noalox or Penetrox should be applied to any point of contact between dissimilar metals. (See the section on Corrosion in the chapter **Building Antenna Systems and Towers**.)

The ease with which aluminum can be drilled or sawed makes it a pleasure to work with. Aluminum alloys can be used to build amateur antennas, towers and supports. Light weight and high conductivity make aluminum ideal for these applications. Alloying typically lowers conductivity, but significantly increases tensile strength. Aluminum is typically alloyed with metals such as manganese, silicon, copper, magnesium and zinc. Cold rolling can be employed to further increase the strength.

A four-digit system is used to identify aluminum alloys, such as 6061. Aluminum alloys starting with a 6 contain di-magnesium silicide (Mg_2Si). The second digit indicates modifications of the original alloy or impurity limits. The last two digits designate different aluminum alloys within the category indicated by the first digit.

In the 6000-series, the 6061 and 6063 alloys are commonly used for antenna applications. Both types have good resistance to corrosion, medium strength and are widely available. A further designation like T6 denotes thermal treatment (heat tempering). In recent years 6063-T832 drawn aluminum tubing has become an attractive alternative to 6061-T6, given its good mechanical properties (typical yield strength of 35,000 psi) and comparatively low cost. Often found in commercial antennas, this alloy's low cost is derived from ubiquitous use in household items including aluminum folding chairs. More information on the available aluminum alloys can be found in **Table 25-3**.

25.2.1 SELECTING ALUMINUM TUBING

Table 25-4 shows the standard sizes of aluminum tubing that are stocked by most aluminum suppliers or distributors in the United States and Canada. Note that all tubing comes in 12-foot lengths (local hardware stores sometimes stock 6- and 8-foot lengths) and larger-diameter sizes may be available in lengths up to 24 feet. Note also that any diameter tubing will fit snugly into the next larger size, if the larger size has a 0.058-inch wall thickness. For example, ⅝-inch tubing has an outside diameter of 0.625 inch. This will fit into ¾-inch tubing with a 0.058-inch wall, which has an inside diameter of 0.634 inch. A clearance of 0.009 inch is just right for a slip fit or for slotting the tubing and then using hose clamps. Always get the next larger size and specify a

Table 25-3
Aluminum Numbers for Amateur Use
Common Alloy Numbers

Type	Characteristics
2024	Good formability, high strength
5052	Excellent surface finish, excellent corrosion resistance, normally not heat treatable for high strength
6061	Good machinability, good weldability
6063	Good machinability, good weldability
7075	Good formability, high strength

Common Tempers

Type	Characteristics
T0	Special soft condition
T3	Hard
T6	Hardest, possibly brittle
TXXX	Three digit tempers — usually specialized high strength heat treatments, similar to T6

General Uses

Type	Uses
2024-T3	Chassis boxes, antennas, anything that will be bent or
7075-T3	Flexed repeatedly
6061-T6	Tubing and pipe; angle channel and bar stock
6063-T832	Tubing and pipe; angle channel and bar stock

0.058-inch wall to obtain the 0.009-inch clearance.

A little figuring with **Table 25-5** will give you all the information you need to build a beam, including what the antenna will weigh. 6061-T6 aluminum has relatively high strength and good workability. It is highly resistant to corrosion and will bend without taking a "set."

25.2.2 SOURCES OF ALUMINUM TUBING

Aluminum tubing can be purchased new; suppliers are listed in the manufacturers table on the CD-ROM. Don't overlook sources for used tubing however, such as a local metal scrap yard. Some items to look for include aluminum vaulting poles, tent poles, tubing and fittings from scrapped antennas, and aluminum angle stock. Occasionally, aluminum tower sections can be found in scrap yards. Garage sales are also good sources of used tubing. By being a good scavenger, you can build up a "bone yard" of materials for antenna construction.

Aluminum vaulting poles are 12 or 14 feet long and range in diameter from 1½ to 1¾ inches. These poles are suitable for element center-sections of large beams or as booms for smaller antennas. Tent poles range in length from 2½ to 4 feet, are usually tapered and can be split on the larger end and mated with the smaller end of another pole of the same diameter. A small stainless-steel hose clamp can be used to fasten the poles at this junction. A 14- or 21-MHz element can be constructed from several tent poles in this fashion.

Longer continuous pieces of tubing can be used for center sections to decrease the number of junctions and clamps.

For vertical antennas, consumer items such as window-washing and painter's poles can sometimes be used. These are not made of structural-strength tubing but are often suitable and are low cost. For larger low-band verticals, surplus irrigation pipe is often available in rural areas.

25.2.3 CONSTRUCTION WITH ALUMINUM TUBING

Although there is endless variation in the type of antennas designed and built with aluminum tubing, Yagis are by far the most common. Yagi antennas can be successfully built using rules-of-thumb for element and boom material and sizing. Some of these approaches and a set of element point designs are provided in the following paragraphs. *YagiStress*, a commercially available software program developed and supported by Kurt Andress, K7NV (**k7nv.com/yagistress**), can be used to accurately calculate the loads and survivability of Yagi designs. Designers and builders of large Yagi antennas are well advised to use modeling software such as *YagiStress* to ensure survivability of the antenna while at the same not using more material than required to achieve desired mechanical performance. *YagiStress* was used to calculate the wind-speed ratings of the half-element designs in this chapter and is based on the EIA-222-C "Structural Standard for Antenna Supporting Structures and Antennas." Antenna mechanical design spreadsheets from *Physical Design of Yagi Antennas* by David Leeson, W6NL (see Bibliography), are available from **www.realhamradio.com/Download.htm** (the URL is case-sensitive) and have been updated to EIA-222-F.

Antennas for frequencies of 14 MHz and above are usually made to be rotated. Rotatable antennas require materials that are strong, lightweight and easy to obtain. Material selection is dependent on many factors, with weather conditions typically being the most demanding requirement. High winds alone may not cause as much damage to an antenna as does ice loading. Ice in combination with high wind is typically the worst-case condition.

As explained in Section 25.2.1, elements and booms can be made from telescoping tubing to provide the necessary total length. This is referred to as tapering. The boom diameter for a rotatable Yagi or quad should be selected

Table 25-4
Aluminum Tubing Sizes
6061-T6 (61S-T6) Round Aluminum Tube In 12-Foot Lengths

Tubing Diameter	Wall Thickness Inches	Stubs ID, Ga.	Stubs ID, Inches	Approximate Weight Pounds	Pounds Per Foot	Per Length
³⁄₁₆ in.	0.035	(#20)	0.117	0.019	0.228	
(0.1875 in.)	0.049	(#18)	0.089	0.025	0.330	
¼ in.	0.035	(#20)	0.180	0.027	0.324	
(0.25 in.)	0.049	(#18)	0.152	0.036	0.432	
	0.058	(#17)	0.134	0.041	0.492	
⁵⁄₁₆ in.	0.035	(#20)	0.242	0.036	0.432	
(0.3125 in.)	0.049	(#18)	0.214	0.047	0.564	
	0.058	(#17)	0.196	0.055	0.660	
³⁄₈ in.	0.035	(#20)	0.305	0.043	0.516	
(0.375 in.)	0.049	(#18)	0.277	0.060	0.720	
	0.058	(#17)	0.259	0.068	0.816	
	0.065	(#16)	0.245	0.074	0.888	
⁷⁄₁₆ in.	0.035	(#20)	0.367	0.051	0.612	
(0.4375 in.)	0.049	(#18)	0.339	0.070	0.840	
	0.065	(#16)	0.307	0.089	1.068	
½ in.	0.028	(#22)	0.444	0.049	0.588	
(0.5 in.)	0.035	(#20)	0.430	0.059	0.708	
	0.049	(#18)	0.402	0.082	0.984	
	0.058	(#17)	0.384	0.095	1.040	
	0.065	(#16)	0.370	0.107	1.284	
⁵⁄₈ in.	0.028	(#22)	0.569	0.061	0.732	
(0.625 in.)	0.035	(#20)	0.555	0.075	0.900	
	0.049	(#18)	0.527	0.106	1.272	
	0.058	(#17)	0.509	0.121	1.452	
	0.065	(#16)	0.495	0.137	1.644	
¾ in.	0.035	(#20)	0.680	0.091	1.092	
(0.75 in.)	0.049	(#18)	0.652	0.125	1.500	
	0.058	(#17)	0.634	0.148	1.776	
	0.065	(#16)	0.620	0.160	1.920	
	0.083	(#14)	0.584	0.204	2.448	
⁷⁄₈ in.	0.035	(#20)	0.805	0.108	1.308	
(0.875 in.)	0.049	(#18)	0.777	0.151	1.810	
	0.058	(#17)	0.759	0.175	2.100	
	0.065	(#16)	0.745	0.199	2.399	
1 in.	0.035	(#20)	0.930	0.123	1.476	
	0.049	(#18)	0.902	0.170	2.040	
	0.058	(#17)	0.884	0.202	2.424	
	0.065	(#16)	0.870	0.220	2.640	
	0.083	(#14)	0.834	0.281	3.372	

Table 25-5
Hose-Clamp Diameters

Size No.	Clamp Diameter (In.) Min	Max	Size No.	Clamp Diameter (In.) Min	Max
06	⁷⁄₁₆	⁷⁄₈	44	2⁵⁄₁₆	3¼
08	⁷⁄₁₆	1	48	2⅝	3½
10	½	1⅛	52	2⅞	3¾
12	⅝	1¼	56	3⅛	4
16	¾	1½	64	3½	4½
20	⅞	1¾	72	4	5
24	1⅛	2	80	4½	5½
28	1⅜	2¼	88	5⅛	6
32	1⅝	2½	96	5⅝	6½
36	1⅞	2¾	104	6-⅛	7
40	2⅛	3			

Tubing Diameter	Wall Thickness Inches	Stubs Ga.	Stubs ID, Inches	Pounds Per Foot	Per Length
1⅛ in.	0.035	(#20)	1.055	0.139	1.668
(1.125 in.)	0.058	(#17)	1.009	0.228	2.736
1¼ in.	0.035	(#20)	1.180	0.155	1.860
(1.25 in.)	0.049	(#18)	1.152	0.210	2.520
	0.058	(#17)	1.134	0.256	3.072
	0.065	(#16)	1.120	0.284	3.408
	0.083	(#14)	1.084	0.357	4.284
1⅜ in.	0.035	(#20)	1.305	0.173	2.076
(1.375 in.)	0.058	(#17)	1.259	0.282	3.384
1½ in.	0.035	(#20)	1.430	0.180	2.160
(1.5 in.)	0.049	(#18)	1.402	0.260	3.120
	0.058	(#17)	1.384	0.309	3.708
	0.065	(#16)	1.370	0.344	4.128
	0.083	(#14)	1.334	0.434	5.208
	*0.125	1/8 in.	1.250	0.630	7.416
	*0.250	1/4 in.	1.000	1.150	14.832
1⅝ in.	0.035	(#20)	1.555	0.206	2.472
(1.625 in.)	0.058	(#17)	1.509	0.336	4.032
1¾ in.	0.058	(#17)	1.634	0.363	4.356
(1.75 in.)	0.083	(#14)	1.584	0.510	6.120
1⅞ in.	0.058	(#17)	1.759	0.389	4.668
(1.875 in.)					
2 in.	0.049	(#18)	1.902	0.350	4.200
	0.065	(#16)	1.870	0.450	5.400
	0.083	(#14)	1.834	0.590	7.080
	*0.125	1/8 in.	1.750	0.870	9.960
	*0.250	1/4 in.	1.500	1.620	19.920
2¼ in.	0.049	(#18)	2.152	0.398	4.776
(2.25 in.)	0.065	(#16)	2.120	0.520	6.240
	0.083	(#14)	2.084	0.660	7.920
2½ in.	0.065	(#16)	2.370	0.587	7.044
(2.5 in.)	0.083	(#14)	2.334	0.740	8.880
	*0.125	1/8 in.	2.250	1.100	12.720
	*0.250	1/4 in.	2.000	2.080	25.440
3 in.	0.065	(#16)	2.870	0.710	8.520
	*0.125	1/8 in.	2.700	1.330	15.600
	*0.250	1/4 in.	2.500	2.540	31.200

*These sizes are extruded. All other sizes are drawn tubes.

to provide required structural strength and to stably support the elements. The appropriate tubing diameter for a boom depends on many factors. Among them are element weight, element length, number of elements and environmental loads, including static loads such as ice and dynamic loads, principally from wind gusts. Tubing of 1¼-inch diameter can easily support a three-element 28-MHz antenna and marginally a two-element 21-MHz antenna. A 2-inch diameter boom will be adequate for larger 28-MHz antennas or for harsh weather conditions and for antennas up to three elements on 14 MHz or four elements on 21 MHz. It is not recommended that 2-inch diameter booms be made any longer than 24 feet unless additional support is added to carry both vertical and horizontal loads. Suitable reinforcement for a long 2-inch boom can consist of a truss or a truss and lateral support, as shown in **Figure 25.9**.

For boom lengths in excess of 24 feet, 3-inch diameter material is usually required. Three-inch diameter booms provide considerable mechanical stability as well as large clamping surface area for boom-to-element hardware. Clamping surface area is particularly important if heavy icing is anticipated, and helps prevent rotation of elements around the axis of the boom. Pinning an element to the boom with a bolt or, preferably, a swaged, hardened pin, can eliminate this possibility, but the hole introduces a stress riser that can materially reduce the strength of the boom. Element rotation about the boom axis can be minimized by mounting elements under the boom rather than on top. Pinned elements sometimes work loose and elongate the pinning holes in both the element and the boom. This is a progressive condition resulting in elements that can be so loose-fitting to the boom that their rotational positions change frequently. Although this condition typically does not adversely affect the electrical performance of a Yagi, the mechanical strength of the members involved degrades as the holes elongate. A Yagi with elements at various angles is unsightly as well.

A 3-inch diameter boom with a wall thickness of 0.065 inch is satisfactory for antennas up to about a five-element, 14-MHz array that is spaced on a 40-foot long boom. A truss is recommended for any boom longer than 24 feet.

Per theory, there is no RF voltage at the center of a parasitic element and insulation is not required at the boom-to-element interface for elements centered on the boom. Driven

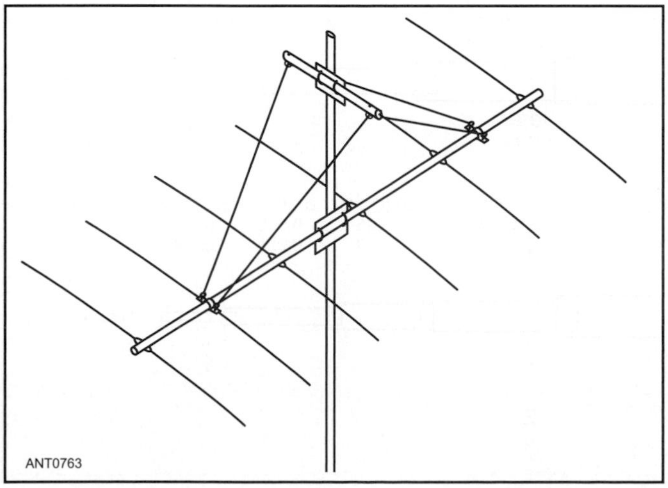

ANT0763

Figure 25.9 — A long boom needs both vertical and horizontal support. The cross bar mounted above the boom can support a double truss to help keep the antenna in position.

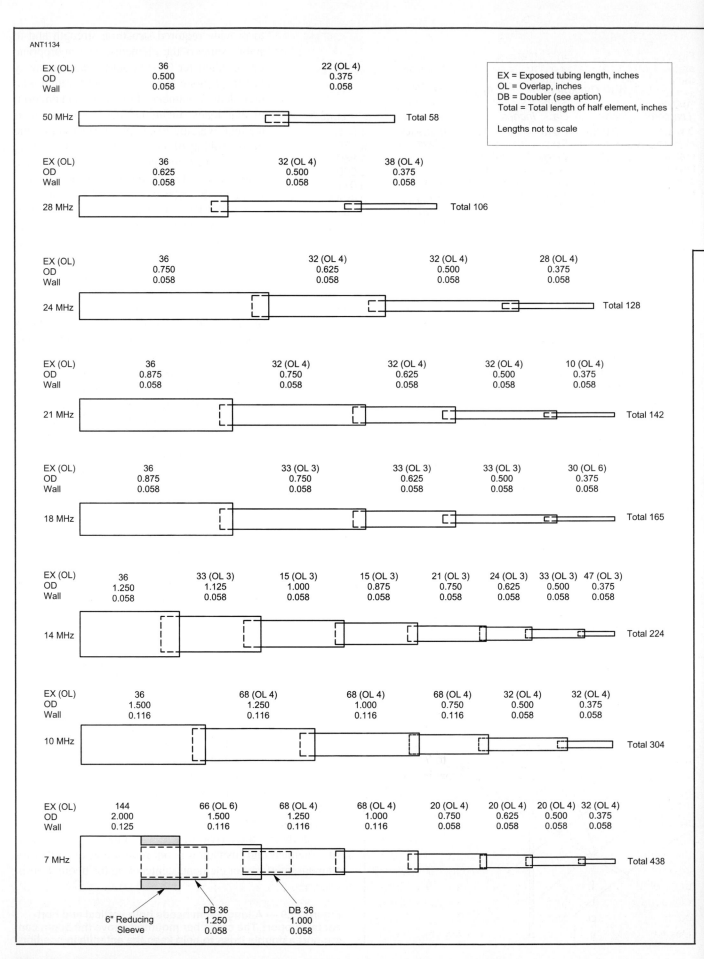

EX = Exposed tubing length, inches
OL = Overlap, inches
DB = Doubler (see aption)
Total = Total length of half element, inches

Lengths not to scale

50 MHz

EX (OL)	36	22 (OL 4)
OD	0.500	0.375
Wall	0.058	0.058

Total 58

28 MHz

EX (OL)	36	32 (OL 4)	38 (OL 4)
OD	0.625	0.500	0.375
Wall	0.058	0.058	0.058

Total 106

24 MHz

EX (OL)	36	32 (OL 4)	32 (OL 4)	28 (OL 4)
OD	0.750	0.625	0.500	0.375
Wall	0.058	0.058	0.058	0.058

Total 128

21 MHz

EX (OL)	36	32 (OL 4)	32 (OL 4)	32 (OL 4)	10 (OL 4)
OD	0.875	0.750	0.625	0.500	0.375
Wall	0.058	0.058	0.058	0.058	0.058

Total 142

18 MHz

EX (OL)	36	33 (OL 3)	33 (OL 3)	33 (OL 3)	30 (OL 6)
OD	0.875	0.750	0.625	0.500	0.375
Wall	0.058	0.058	0.058	0.058	0.058

Total 165

14 MHz

EX (OL)	36	33 (OL 3)	15 (OL 3)	15 (OL 3)	21 (OL 3)	24 (OL 3)	33 (OL 3)	47 (OL 3)
OD	1.250	1.125	1.000	0.875	0.750	0.625	0.500	0.375
Wall	0.058	0.058	0.058	0.058	0.058	0.058	0.058	0.058

Total 224

10 MHz

EX (OL)	36	68 (OL 4)	68 (OL 4)	68 (OL 4)	32 (OL 4)	32 (OL 4)
OD	1.500	1.250	1.000	0.750	0.500	0.375
Wall	0.116	0.116	0.116	0.116	0.058	0.058

Total 304

7 MHz

EX (OL)	144	66 (OL 6)	68 (OL 4)	68 (OL 4)	20 (OL 4)	20 (OL 4)	20 (OL 4)	32 (OL 4)
OD	2.000	1.500	1.250	1.000	0.750	0.625	0.500	0.375
Wall	0.125	0.116	0.116	0.116	0.058	0.058	0.058	0.058

Total 438

6" Reducing
Sleeve

DB 36
1.250
0.058

DB 36
1.000
0.058

Figure 25.10 — Light-duty half-element designs for Yagi antennas. The other side of the element is identical and the center section should be a single piece twice as long as the length shown here for the largest diameter section. Tubing with 0.116-inch wall thickness consists of doubled 0.058-inch wall sections of the same length. Tubing with 0.125-inch or 0.250-inch wall thickness is 6061-T6 alloy, all other tubing is 6063-T832. Doubler (DB) sections consist of a length of tubing inserted completely into the next larger segment, flush with the inner end of that larger segment. The CD-ROM text file "K5GO Half-Element Designs" gives complete specifications for each half-element along with survivability ratings for ½ inch and 1 inch of radial ice loading.

elements may or may not be electrically connected to the boom depending on the feed system employed. In practice, parasitic elements are usually directly connected to the boom both mechanically and electrically for designs from HF through lower UHF. At upper UHF grounded elements are subject to detuning because the element-to-boom contact no longer acts as a point but rather as a complex shape of significant area. At HF, unanticipated and unwanted resonances, though very unlikely, can occur in center-grounded elements. Highly conservative HF designs and many UHF designs insulate all elements from the boom, typically using Garolite at HF and suitable materials such as Teflon at UHF and above.

Metal booms have a small "shortening effect" on elements that run through them. With materials sizes commonly employed, this is not more than one percent of the element length, and may not be noticeable. It is just perceptible with ½-inch tubing booms used on 432 MHz, for example. At VHF and UHF, standard design-formula lengths can be used as given and driven element matching can be adjusted at the desired operating frequency. The center frequency of an all-metal array will tend to be 0.5 to 1 percent higher than a similar system built with insulated elements.

Element Assembly

Figure 25.10 shows tapered Yagi element designs contributed by Stan Stockton, K5GO, that will survive winds in excess of 80 mi/h. With a ½-inch thickness of radial ice, these designs will withstand winds from 45 to 77 mi/h. Ice increases the surface area subject to wind loading but does not increase the strength of the element. More rugged designs are shown in **Figure 25.11**. With no ice loading, these elements will survive in 118 to 172-mi/h winds, and in winds from 78 to 92 mi/h with ½ inch of radial ice. Deviations from the designs provided require analysis with a program such as *YagiStress* to ensure survivability in the environmental conditions of interest. Except for the very largest 40 meter elements, all required tubing lengths are 6 feet or shorter that can be shipped by parcel services. The file "K5GO Half-Element Designs" showing all element segment lengths, overlaps,

tubing specifications and more information on ice loading is included on this book's CD-ROM.

Figures 25.10 and 25.11 show only half elements. When the element is assembled, the largest size tubing for each element should be double the length shown in the drawing, with its center being the point of attachment to the boom. These designs are somewhat conservative, in that they are self-resonant slightly below the frequency indicated for each design. Telescoping the outside end sections to shorter lengths for resonance will increase the survival wind speeds. Conversely, lengthening the outside end sections will reduce the survival wind speeds. [See Bibliography listing for David Leeson, W6NL (ex-W6QHS), at the end of this chapter.]

Figure 25.12 shows several methods of fastening antenna element sections together. The slot and hose-clamp method shown in Figure 25.12A works well for joints that require adjustment. Generally, one adjustable joint per element half is sufficient to tune an antenna. Stainless-steel hose clamps work well and are inexpensive. Some do not have stainless steel screws however. This can be checked with a magnet. Table 25-5 shows available hose-clamp sizes. Wherever tubing sections overlap, a small amount of anti-oxidation compound such as Noalox or Penetrox should be used. This prevents aluminum oxide from forming between the tubing surfaces that can create a high impedance electrical connection and/or mechanically "freeze" the joint.

Figures 25.12B, 12C and 12D show possible fastening methods for joints that do not require adjustment. At B, machine screws and nuts hold the elements in place. At C, sheet metal screws are used. At D, rivets secure the tubing. If the antenna is to be assembled permanently, rivets are the best choice. Once in place they are permanent, although they can be drilled out if necessary. They will not work free, regardless of vibration or wind, if properly installed and seated. If aluminum rivets with aluminum mandrels are used, they will never rust. In addition, there is no danger of dissimilar-metal corrosion with aluminum rivets and aluminum antenna elements. If the antenna is to be disassembled and moved periodically, either B or C will work. If machine screws are used, however, take all possible precautions to keep the nuts from vibrating free. Use Nylock nuts or lock washers and a thread-locking compound.

Very strong elements can be made by using a double thickness of tubing, made by telescoping one size inside another for a portion of, or for the total length. This is usually done at the center of an element where more strength is desired at the boom support point, as in the 14-MHz element in Figure 25.11. Other materials can be used as well, such as wood dowels, fiberglass rods, etc.

Metal antenna elements have high mechanical Q, resulting in a tendency to vibrate in the wind. One way to dampen vibrations is by placing a piece of polypropylene or similar material line inside the element throughout its entire length. Choice of damping line material is not critical — the line will not be exposed to the sun's UV. The line will mildew or rot however if something like inexpensive clothesline is used.

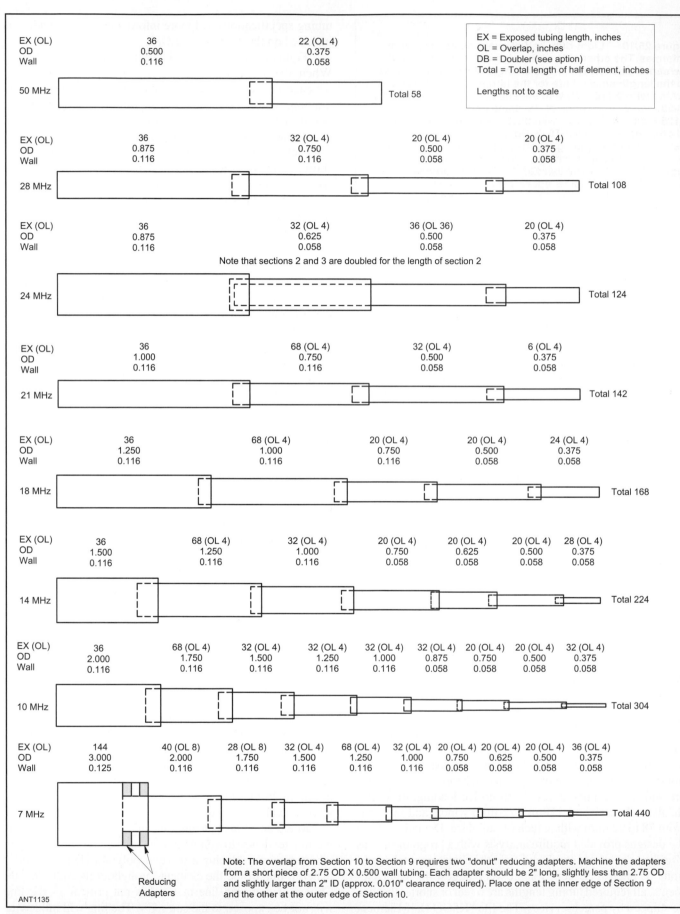

Figure 25.11 — A heavy-duty schedule of Yagi half-element segments. See the Figure 25.10 caption for details. Table 25-4 gives details of aluminum tubing sizes.

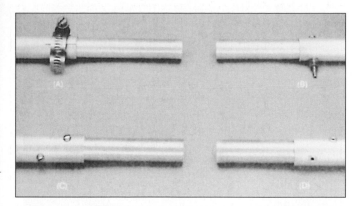

Figure 25.12 — Methods of connecting telescoping tubing sections to build beam elements. See text for a discussion of each method.

Cap or tape the end of the element to secure the damping line. If mechanical requirements dictate (a U-bolt going through the center of the element, for instance), the line may be cut into separate pieces for each element half.

Antennas for 50 MHz need not have elements larger than ½-inch diameter, although up to 1 inch is used occasionally. At 144 and 222 MHz the elements are usually ⅛ to ¼ inch in diameter. For 432 MHz, elements as small as 1/16 inch diameter work well if made of stiff rod. Aluminum welding rod of 3/32 to ⅛ inch diameter is fine for 432-MHz arrays, and ⅛ inch or larger is good for the 222-MHz band. Aluminum rod or hard-drawn wire works well at 144 MHz.

Tubing and rod sizes recommended in the paragraph above are usable with most formula dimensions for VHF/UHF antennas. Larger diameter material reduces Q and increases bandwidth; smaller diameter material raises element and overall antenna Q and reduces bandwidth. Much smaller diameters than those recommended will require longer elements, particularly for antennas for 50-MHz and above.

Element Taper and Electrical Length

The builder should be aware of one important aspect of telescoping or tapered elements. When the element diameter tapers, as shown in Figures 25.10 and 25.11, the electrical length is not the same as it would be for a constant diameter element of the same total length. Length corrections for tapered elements are discussed in the chapter on **HF Yagi and Quad Antennas**.

25.3 OTHER MATERIALS FOR ANTENNA CONSTRUCTION

25.3.1 WOOD AND BAMBOO

Wood is very useful in antenna work. It is available in a great variety of types and sizes. Rug poles of wood or bamboo make fine booms. Bamboo is quite satisfactory for spreaders in quad antennas.

Round wood stock (doweling) is found in many hardware stores in sizes suitable for small arrays. Wood is good for the framework of multi-bay arrays for the higher bands, as it keeps down the amount of metal in the active area of the array. Square or rectangular boom and frame materials can be cut to order in most lumber yards if they are not available from the racks in suitable sizes.

Wood used for antenna construction should be well seasoned and free of knots or damage. Available materials vary, depending on local sources. Your lumber dealer can help you better than anyone else in choosing suitable materials. Joining wood members at right angles can be done with gusset plates, as shown in **Figure 25.13**. These can be made of thin outdoor-grade plywood. Construction with round material can be handled in ways similar to those used with metal components, such as with U-bolts.

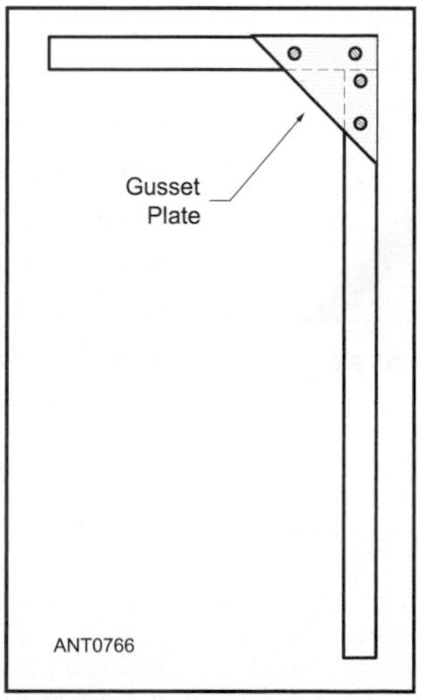

In the early days of radio, hardwood was used as insulating material for antennas, such

Gusset Plate

ANT0766

Figure 25.13 — Wood members can be joined at right angles using gusset plates.

as at the center and ends of dipoles, or for the center insulator of a driven element made of tubing. Wood dowels cut to length were the most common approach. To drive out moisture and prevent the subsequent absorption of moisture into the wood, it was treated before use by boiling in paraffin. Of course today's technology has produced superior materials for insulators in terms of both strength and insulating qualities. However, the technique is worth consideration in an emergency situation or if low cost is a prime requirement. "Baking" the wood in an oven for a short period at 200° F should drive out any moisture. Then treatment as described in the next paragraph should prevent moisture absorption. The use of wood insulators should be avoided at high-voltage points if high power is being used.

All wood or bamboo used in outdoor installations should be protected from the weather with varnish or paint. A good grade of marine spar varnish or UV-stable polyurethane varnish will offer protection for years in mild climates, and one or more seasons in harsh climates. Epoxy-based paints also offer good protection. Bamboo can also be protected by wrapping it with electrical tape. Spray varnish is sometimes applied after wrapping with tape and will provide excellent longevity.

25.3.2 PLASTICS

Plastic tubing and rods of various sizes are available from many building-supply stores. The uses for the available plastic materials are limited only by your imagination. PVC pipe and electrical conduit is quite useful for antenna construction at VHF and UHF. For permanent antennas, be sure the plastic will withstand UV exposure or paint it.

Plastic plumbing and irrigation fittings can also be used to enclose baluns and as the center insulator or end insulators of a dipole, as shown in **Figure 25.14**. The same fittings and adapters can be used to create a portable antenna that is assembled using friction fits between pipe and fittings.

Plastic or Teflon rod can be used as the core of antenna loading coils, including for mobile antennas (**Figure 25.15**), but the material for this use should be selected carefully. Some plastics, particularly PVC, become warm in the presence of a strong RF field. This can result in the core deforming or even catching fire. Where high RF fields are anticipated, fiberglass or Teflon solid rod, or open polycarbonate cylinders are recommended. Home goods stores frequently carry inexpensive drinking glasses made of polycarbonate, in a variety of sizes. These make excellent coil forms for high-power RF applications.

25.3.3 FIBERGLASS

Fiberglass is lightweight, withstands harsh weather well, and has excellent insulating qualities. Fiberglass rod and tubing are excellent for the nonconductive structure of an antenna. Fiberglass poles are the preferred material for spreaders for quad antennas, for example. Fiberglass rod or tubing can be used as the boom for VHF and UHF antennas. Extendable fiberglass poles have become very popular as supports for portable wire antennas. The SteppIR family of tunable Yagi

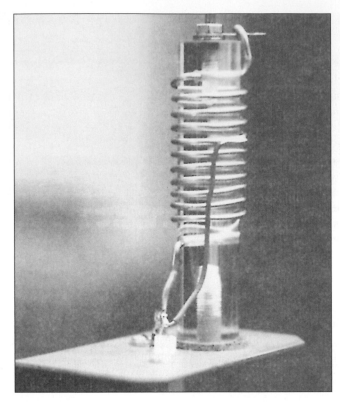

Figure 25.15 — A mobile-antenna loading coil wound on a polystyrene rod.

antennas use fiberglass tubes with flexible metal tape inside as the elements.

Fiberglass should be painted or coated to protect it from exposure to UV when used outdoors. UV breaks down the resin holding the glass fibers together and the surface begins to shed fibers, leading to cracks and water ingress.

Whenever working with fiberglass materials — sawing, cutting, sanding, drilling — gloves and eye protection against loose fiber fragments should be used. If heavy dust is being generated, a dust mask should be worn.

A disadvantage of hollow fiberglass poles is that they may be crushed rather easily. Fracturing occurs at the point where the pole is crushed, causing it to lose its strength. A crushed pole is next to worthless. Some amateurs have repaired crushed poles with fiberglass cloth and epoxy, but the original strength is nearly impossible to regain. Inserting a wooden dowel into the tubing provides additional crush resistance.

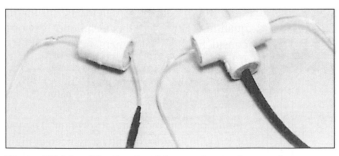

Figure 25.14 — Plastic plumbing parts can be used as antenna center and end insulators.

25.4 HARDWARE

Antennas should be assembled with good quality hardware intended for outdoor use. Stainless steel is a good choice for long life. Rust will quickly attack plated steel hardware, making nuts difficult, if not impossible, to remove. If stainless-steel muffler clamps and hose-clamps are not available, steel hardware can be plated or painted with a good zinc-chromate primer and a one or more finish coats. Rust inhibiting paints are also good protection. When using stainless-steel hardware, use an anti-seize compound on the threads to prevent the threads from jamming due to galling of the thread surfaces.

Galvanized steel generally has a longer life than plated steel, but this depends on the thickness of the galvanizing coat. In harsh climates rust will usually develop on galvanized fittings in a few years. For the ultimate in long-term protection, galvanized steel should be further protected with zinc-chromate primer and then paint or enamel before exposing it to the weather. Cold-galvanizing spray is useful in repairing damage to galvanized surfaces and preventing rust. It is available in home goods stores.

Good quality hardware is expensive, but over time is less expensive and much less frustrating than poor quality "equivalents." Antennas built of high quality hardware need to be taken down and refurbished much less often. When the time does come to repair or modify an antenna, rusty hardware, particularly at the top of a tower, will seem in retrospect to have been a very poor investment.

25.5 BIBLIOGRAPHY

Source material and more extended discussion of topics covered in this chapter can be found in the following references:

ARRL's Wire Antenna Classics, (Newington, CT: ARRL)

More Wire Antenna Classics, (Newington, CT: ARRL)

ARRL's Yagi Antenna Classics, (Newington, CT: ARRL)

D. Daso, K4ZA, *Antenna Towers for Radio Amateurs* (Newington, CT: ARRL, 2010)

J. Elengo, K1AFR, "Predicting Sag in Long Wire Antennas," *QST*, Jan 1966, pp 57-58.

D. Leeson, W6NL, *Physical Design of Yagi Antennas* (Newington, CT: ARRL). [out of print]

D. Leeson, W6NL, "Joint Design for Yagi Booms," *QEX*, Jun 1993, pp 6-8.

D. Leeson, W6NL, "Strengthening the Cushcraft 40-2CD," *QST*, Nov 1991, pp 36-42.

S. Morris, K7LXC, *Up the Tower* (Seattle: Champion Radio Products, 2009)

R. Weber, K5IU, "More on Strengthening Yagi Elements," *QST*, Oct 1992, pp 65-66

R. Weber, K5IU, "Structural Evaluation of Yagi Elements," *Ham Radio*, Dec 1988, pp 29-46.

TABLE OF CONTENTS

Chapter 26

Building Antenna Systems and Towers

Getting an antenna in the air and keeping it there comes with decisions and challenges. For example, what kind of antenna support? How do you build it? What are the tools and techniques? There are many other questions. In this chapter, experienced tower climber Steve Morris, K7LXC, updates and expands the material from previous editions. (Unless otherwise noted, photos were provided by K7LXC.)

The information here is by no means exhaustive. For a more complete treatment, the reader is directed to two new books written specifically for the ham putting up or working on towers and antennas:

- *Up the Tower: The Complete Guide to Tower Construction* by Steve Morris, K7LXC, and published by Champion Radio Products (**www.championradio.com**).
- *Antenna Towers for Radio Amateurs: A Guide for Design, Installation and Construction* by Don Daso, K4ZA and published by the ARRL.

These books are great tutorials on working successfully and safely with antennas, towers, masts and trees. They provide complementary perspectives on many subjects, reinforcing perspectives on others. If you are contemplating a significant tower or antenna project, you should read either or both these books before beginning. You are also encouraged to read the articles listed in the Bibliography and to attend hamfest and convention presentations by these and other experienced individuals. Consider hiring professional assistance if you are not comfortable with doing the work yourself.

Many of the safety and tower work products mentioned in this chapter are available from numerous *QST* advertisers and from Champion Radio Products. The CD-ROM supplied with this book also includes a directory of manufacturers and distributors for all manner of antenna-related products. You should be able to find everything you need in order to do the job correctly and safely, resulting in years of good service at the lowest possible risk.

Learn and practice the right way to do things — it will save you time, money and worries. Let's start with safety!

Equipment and Materials

A list of vendors for equipment and materials for antennas and towers is available on the CD-ROM that comes with this book. Printed in previous editions, the list is now changed to electronic form in order to allow more frequent updates.

26.1 SAFETY AND SAFETY EQUIPMENT

Climbing and working on towers is potentially dangerous, as is handling and installing antennas. Safety and safety equipment are the keys to the safe and reliable installation, maintenance and enjoyment of your tower and antenna system. What you use and how you use it is up to you. As long as you've got the right safety equipment and follow the basic rules you won't have any problems. Don't cut corners on buying or using safety equipment; you bet your life on it every time you use it!

OSHA and Tower Work

OSHA is the federal Occupation Safety and Health Agency (**www.osha.gov**) that sets minimum safety standards for workers. Each state has an agency that is responsible for enforcing the OSHA regulations in that state. In addition, your state agency may have stricter regulations than OSHA; OSHA regulations are just the minimum requirements.

If you are getting paid or paying someone to do tower work, you or they must comply with the federal and state regulations. If you are simply working on your own system, or someone else's without pay, then you don't fall under the OSHA/state laws. But you should still observe them! You should use only OSHA/state approved safety equipment and follow the regulations applicable to your activity. By doing this, you'll be giving yourself a large and acceptable safety margin while working.

26.1.1 FALL-ARREST EQUIPMENT

The most important pieces of safety equipment are the *fall-arrest harness* (FAH) and the accompanying lanyards (see **Figure 26.1**). Leather safety equipment was outlawed years ago by OSHA so please don't use any of it. This includes the old-fashioned safety belt that was used for years but offers no fall-arrest capability.

If you drop down while wearing a safety belt, your body weight can cause the safety belt to rise up your waist to your ribcage where it will immobilize your diaphragm, potentially suffocating you! On the other hand you can use your safety belt for positioning when it's used in conjunction with your FAH. Just don't depend on it to catch you in case of a fall.

The FAH is the part that you wear and to which the lanyards attach. The FAH has leg loops and suspenders to help spread the fall forces over more of your body. It has the ability to catch you in a natural position with your arms and legs hanging below your body so you're able to breathe normally. Plan on spending $150 or more for a new FAH and lanyards.

There are two primary types of lanyards. One is the *positioning lanyard* shown in **Figure 26.2**. That is, it holds you in working position and attaches to the D-rings at your waist. Positioning lanyards can be adjustable or fixed and are made from materials such as nylon rope, steel chain or special synthetic materials. An adjustable positioning lanyard will adjust to almost any situation whereas a fixed-length one is typically either too long or too short for the job. The rope type is the least expensive version.

The other lanyard is the *fall-arrest lanyard* that attaches to a D-ring between your shoulder blades. The other end attaches to the tower above your work position and catches you in case of a fall. The simplest is a 6-foot rope lanyard that is inexpensive but doesn't offer any shock absorption. There are also shock absorbing varieties that typically have bar-tacked stitches that pull apart under force and decelerate you (see **Figure 26.3**).

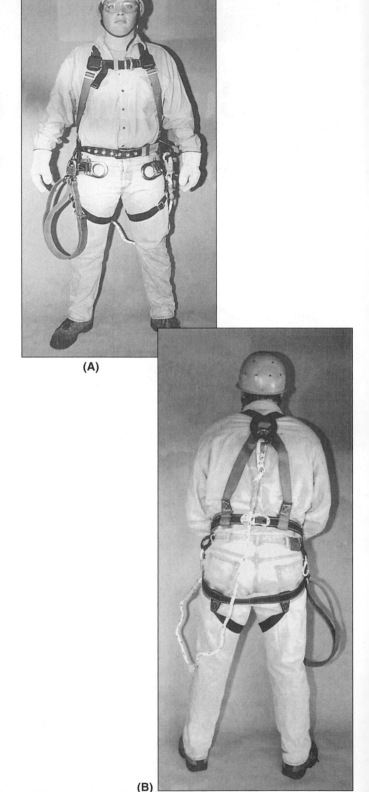

(A)

(B)

Figure 26.1 — **(A) The well-dressed tower climber. The fall-arrest harness has waist D-rings for positioning lanyard attachment as well as suspenders and leg loops. At (B) note the D-ring between the shoulder blades. This is where the fall arrest lanyard attaches to the climber. The other end attaches to the tower above the climber. The climber also has working boots, gloves, safety glasses and hardhat.**

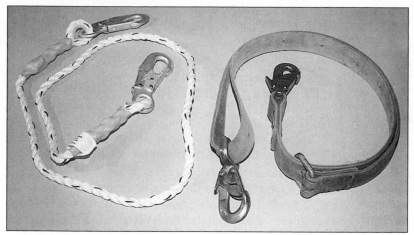
Figure 26.2 — A fixed-length rope positioning lanyard on the left and a versatile Klein adjustable lanyard on the right. They both use double-locking snap-hooks.

Figure 26.4 — A climber on a tower. Note the fall arrest lanyard attached to the tower above him.

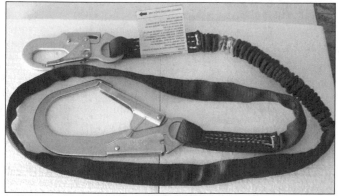
Figure 26.3 — A shock absorbing fall arrest lanyard. Portions of the nylon webbing are sewn together and pull apart under the weight of a climber falling on it, thus decelerating the fall.

26.1.2 SAFELY CLIMBING A TOWER

OSHA rules and common sense say you should be attached to the tower 100% of the time. You can do this several ways. One is to attach the fall-arrest lanyard above you and climb up to it as shown in **Figure 26.4**. Use your positioning lanyard to hold you while you detach the fall-arrest lanyard and move it up again. Repeat as necessary. An alternative is to use two fall-arrest lanyards, alternating them as you climb.

It's not a race! Take your time and climb safely. If you become tired or uncomfortable, stop and rest with your lanyards securely fastened to the tower. If you feel unsafe at any time for any reason — stop and return to a safe position or configuration!

Safety Climb Systems

Most commercial towers have a safety climb system, typically a ⅜-inch steel cable that runs from the top to the bottom of the tower. The climber attaches to a special trolley

with a cable from the climber's FAH. The trolley will slide up freely but clamps the safety cable if weight is put on it, thus preventing you from sliding down the cable and tower. They are rare on amateur towers but are worth considering.

Mountain Climbing Harnesses — Problems

Some amateurs feel that mountain climbing harnesses offer a less-expensive option for a safety belt. The first problem with using a mountain climbing harness is that most require you to tie the harness directly to a rope or to a carabiner and most hams are not skilled at tying climbing knots properly. You could use a locking carabiner as an attachment point but it is another piece of hardware that could fail or open up at the wrong time.

Second, there are no D-rings for attaching any sort of positioning lanyard; you can only connect one carabiner to the loops in the front. The nylon loop on the front of the climbing harness is only designed to position the leg loops and is intended to be used only with a climbing rope or carabiner, not the metal snaps of your lanyard that are frequently snapped on and off.

Mountain climbing belts are designed to be used only with climbing ropes and hardware, not with tower tools or equipment. They also don't have any provisions for convenient attachment of tool or bolt bags.

The final problems are that a mountain climbing harness may be designed for a force of only 1000 pounds while OSHA-approved fall-arrest gear must be designed for 5000 pounds of strength and the mountain climbing harness has no fall-arrest capability. Although the main advantage of a mountain climbing harness is low cost, its limitations prevent it from being recommended for tower work. Use only the tools designed specifically for the job!

Working on a Crank-up Tower

One of the advantages of a crank-up is the ability to bring the antennas down to roof or close to ground level where it's easier for the station owner to work on it. For this convenience, the price that you pay is the added mechanical complexity and cost of the crank-up apparatus. They can cost two to three times the cost of a guyed tower of the same height.

Another limitation is the fact that a crank-up cannot be climbed safely once it is extended. Do not climb a crank-up tower unless it is totally nested and locked in the lowered position! Again, all of the weight of the system is on the cable and pulley systems and if something breaks or comes loose, your toes and fingers are in the path of the tower sections as they make their rapid descent. If the tower is jammed and won't come down, don't climb it to fix it. Get a boom truck or crane in to lift you up to work on it. Better yet, get professional help.

It is possible to climb a crank-up if you can lock it into place. One method is to use 3 to 4 foot long pieces of 2×4s or pipes. Another is to place a U-bolt on at least one leg under each section. Insert them at the bottom of each section through the bracing and they'll catch each section before it can move down very far. You can also gently lower the tower until it rests on the safety pieces, thus jamming them into place and eliminating any tower movement at all.

26.1.3 WORKING SAFELY

The Mental Game

One of the most important aspects of safety is having the knowledge and awareness that will enable you to do a job safely and efficiently. You must have the mental ability to climb and work at altitude while constantly rethinking all connections, techniques and safety factors. Climbing and working on towers safely is 90% mental. Mental preparedness is something that must be learned. This is an occasion when there is no substitute for experience.

When it comes to tower climbing, only a small percentage of people will climb and work at altitude. The biggest obstacle for anyone is making the mental adjustment. Properly installed towers are inherently safe and accidents are relatively rare. The only thing stopping most people is their own mind and attitude.

Would you have any trouble standing on a 24 × 24 inch piece of plywood on the ground? Of course not! Could you stand on that same four-square-foot platform 100 feet in the air? The only difference is in your mind. It's easier said than done but you must make the mental adjustment if you are going to do any tower work.

An important lesson learned from mountain climbing that is directly applicable to tower climbing is that when you climb, you have four points of attachment and security — two hands and two feet. When climbing, move only one point at a time. That leaves you with three points of contact and a wide margin of safety if you ever need it. This is in addition to having your fall-arrest lanyard connected at all times.

Another recommended technique to excel at the mental game is to always do everything the same way every time. That is, always wear your positioning lanyard on the same D-ring and always connect it in the same way. Always look at your belt D-ring while clipping in with your safety strap. This way you'll always confirm that you're belted in. Don't assume you're belted in and clipped on. Always look — always!

Check Your Safety Equipment

You should also check your safety equipment every time before you use it. Inspect it for any nicks or cuts to your belt and safety strap. Professional tower workers are required to check their safety equipment every day.

Inclement Weather

Tower work is the easiest when the weather is nice and the sun is shining. Unfortunately, that doesn't always coincide with your construction schedule or repair priority. Don't hesitate to call off your project. If you're not sure if the weather is good enough, it probably isn't.

For raising tower sections or antennas, a relatively windless day is preferred. Professional climbers usually do their trickiest lifts first thing in the morning when the chance of wind is the least. Don't push on in marginal conditions; you may wind up doing more harm than good. Obviously you don't ever want to climb during a lightning storm.

As far as rain goes, unless it's coming in horizontally it's more of a nuisance. For ham towers, you'll always be belted in and you won't be walking across any rain-slicked surfaces, so working in the rain is possible. Just dress with good rain gear and you'll be able to still get some work done.

Electrical Safety

Electrocution due to metal antenna or tower parts touching power lines is the biggest cause of tower related electricity injuries. *Be very careful if you're anywhere near power lines.*

Even without touching a power line, you can still be electrocuted while working on a tower, which is a large, grounded conductor. A major cause of tower injuries and deaths is electrocution. While there usually isn't much 120 V ac circuitry on amateur towers, care should still be taken around ac power. Use battery-powered equipment if possible, both for the convenience and safety. If you do use ac extension cords, make sure they're plugged into a GFCI (ground fault circuit interrupter) for your protection. Power tools operated from ac should be double-insulated. Part of your pre-work safety meeting should be pointing out where the circuit breaker box is in case someone has to turn off the power.

Safety Tips for Tower Work

- Don't climb with anything in your hands; attach it to your safety belt if you must climb with it or have your ground crew send it up in a bucket after you're in position.
- Don't put any hardware in your mouth; you could swallow it or choke on it.
- Remove any rings and/or neck chains; they can get hooked on things.

The National Electrical Code (NEC)

The National Electrical Code (a.k.a. — "the Code") is a comprehensive document that details safety requirements for all types of electrical installations. In addition to setting safety standards for house wiring and grounding, the Code also contains a section on Radio and Television Equipment — Article 810. Sections C and D specifically cover "Amateur Transmitting and Receiving Stations". Highlights of the section concerning Amateur Radio stations follow. If you are interested in learning more about electrical safety, you may purchase a copy of *The National Electrical Code* or *The National Electrical Code Handbook*, edited by Peter Schram, from the National Fire Protection Association, Batterymarch Park, Quincy, MA 02269.

Antenna installations are covered in some detail in the Code. It specifies minimum conductor sizes for different length wire antennas. For hard-drawn copper wire, the Code specifies #14 AWG wire for open (unsupported) spans less than 150 feet, and #10 AWG for longer spans. Copper-clad steel, bronze or other high-strength conductors may be #14 AWG for spans less than 150 feet and #12 AWG wire for longer runs. Lead-in conductors (for open-wire transmission line) should be at least as large as those specified for antennas.

The Code also says that antenna and lead-in conductors attached to buildings must be firmly mounted at least 3 inches clear of the surface of the building on nonabsorbent insulators. The only exception to this minimum distance is when the lead-in conductors are enclosed in a "permanently and effectively grounded" metallic shield. The exception covers coaxial cable.

According to the Code, lead-in conductors (except those covered by the exception) must enter a building through a rigid, noncombustible, nonabsorbent insulating tube or bushing, through an opening provided for the purpose that provides a clearance of at least 2 inches or through a drilled window pane. All lead-in conductors to transmitting equipment must be arranged so that accidental contact is difficult.

Transmitting stations are required to have a means of draining static charges from the antenna system. An antenna discharge unit (lightning arrester) must be installed on each lead-in conductor (except where the lead-in is protected by a continuous metallic shield that is permanently and effectively grounded, or the antenna is permanently and effectively grounded). An acceptable alternative to lightning arrester installation is a switch that connects the lead-in to ground when the transmitter is not in use.

Grounding conductors are described in detail in the Code. Grounding conductors may be made from copper, aluminum, copper-clad steel, bronze or similar erosion-resistant material. Insulation is not required. The "protective grounding conductor" (main conductor running to the ground rod) must be as large as the antenna lead-in, but not smaller than #10 AWG. The "operating grounding conductor" (to bond equipment chassis together) must be at least #14 AWG. Grounding conductors must be adequately supported and arranged so they are not easily damaged. They must run in as straight a line as practical between the mast or discharge unit and the ground rod.

■ Be on the lookout for bees, wasps and their nests; there aren't too many bigger surprises when you're climbing a tower. If you do get stung, apply a meat tenderizing powder containing the enzyme papain, such as Adolph's Meat Tenderizer, directly on the sting moistened with a little water or saliva. The enzyme neutralizes the venom and reduces the pain within a minute or two. Keep a bottle in your tower tool kit.

■ Don't climb when tired; that's when most accidents occur.

■ Don't try to lift anything by yourself; one person on a tower has very little leverage or strength. Let the ground crew use their strength; save your strength for when you really need it or you'll quickly run out of arm strength.

■ If something doesn't work one way, re-rig, then try again.

26.1.4 SAFETY EQUIPMENT

Boots

Boots should be leather with a steel or fiberglass shank. Diagonal bracing on Rohn 25G tower is only ⁵⁄₁₆-inch rod — spending all day standing on that small step will take a toll on your feet. The stiff shank will support your weight and protect your feet; tennis shoes will not. Leather boots are mandatory on towers like Rohn BX that have sharp X-cross braces, plus your feet are always on a slant and that combination is hard on feet.

Hard Hats

The hard hat is highly recommended. Just make sure hard hats are OSHA-approved and that you and your crew wear them. As you'll be looking up and down a lot while wearing your hard hat, a chin strap is essential to keep it from falling off. Look for the ANSI or OSHA label on the hard hat; that should be the minimum safety compliance for your helmet.

Safety Goggles

Approved safety goggles should be worn to prevent eye injury. Look for ANSI or OSHA approval.

Gloves

If you do a lot of tower work, your hands will take a beating — gloves are essential. Keep several spare pairs for ground crew members who show up without them. Cotton gloves are fine for gardening but not for tower work; they don't provide enough friction for climbing or working with a haul rope. Leather gloves are the only kind to use; either full leather or leather-palmed are fine.

The softer the gloves the more useful they'll be. Stiff leather construction gloves are fine for the ground crew but the pigskin and other soft leathers allow you to thread a nut or do just about any other delicate job without removing (and possibly dropping) your gloves.

Safety Equipment Suppliers

Chances are that you've got a safety equipment store in your area but your best bet is to search the Internet for what you need since tower climbing equipment is not very common. Manufacturers such as Klein, Petzl, DBI-Sala and others all provide OSHA-approved safety equipment. These are more expensive products but they're preferred by professionals who wear and work in them all day. These companies will have many other useful accessories, such as canvas buckets, tool pouches and other hardware.

26.1.5 INSURANCE

It is important that you have insurance that covers any potential liabilities (someone getting hurt on the tower, damage caused by tower failure, and so on) as well as the physical equipment itself.

The ARRL also offers the Ham Radio Equipment Insurance Plan (**www.arrlinsurance.com**). Your mobile and home station equipment is covered on an all-risk form which includes fire, lightning, theft, collision, and other accidents and natural hazards. Loss or damage to antennas, towers or rotators is covered. Review the policy's coverage at the insurance plan's website for complete information.

Ray Fallen, ND8L, an agent for State Farm Insurance for over 20 years, wrote a terrifically informative article on insurance in the February 2009 issue of *QST*, titled "Homeowners Insurance and Your Antenna System." The article is included on this book's CD-ROM for reference.

26.2 TREES AND MASTS

26.2.1 TREES

Trees were the first antenna supports and have been used successfully by many amateurs over the years. If you're in an area with suitable trees — congratulations! They're free (compared to towers) and generally unregulated for use as antenna supports. Trees make good temporary antenna supports and with care can support an antenna for many years — even a large one. When attaching an antenna to a tree, it's important to traumatize the tree as little as possible. This will ensure a strong, enduring attachment.

Although it's relatively easy to get a wire up into a tree, it's certainly more difficult to keep it there for the long term. Tree-mounted antennas require more maintenance but their height and low cost more than make up for the added work. (Although uncommon, even Yagi antennas have been installed in trees using the techniques in the short article "Installing Yagis in Trees" included on the CD-ROM for this book.)

Using a Line Launcher

In this method, you use some sort of line launcher from the ground by which a lightweight line (usually fishing line of a few pounds capacity) with a weight on the end of it is propelled over a branch high up in the tree. Hopefully the weight drops to the ground and you use the small line to pull up a bigger line with your antenna attached. These launchers include slingshots, compressed air cannons, fishing rod and reel, bow and arrow, and even tennis ball throwing aids.

Keep people out of the fall zone around the tree since there will be falling weights, plus lines and antennas at some point. Safety glasses and gloves are always a good idea for these kinds of activities.

Attaching an Anchor

A stouter method of securing a rope in a tree is to climb the tree to install an anchor. For light antenna loads, such as the end of a dipole, a threaded eye-screw is the method of choice. (Use welded or cast eye-screws and bolts to prevent them from opening up under load.) Just drill a hole into the tree about 1/16 inch smaller than the screw diameter, then twist

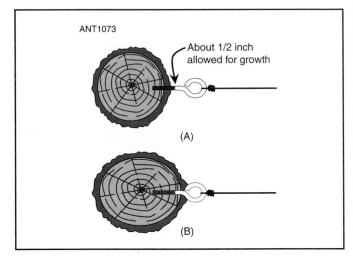

Figure 26.5 — The best way to secure a wire to a tree is with an eye-screw threaded into the wood (A). As the tree grows and expands, however, the eye-screw will become embedded (B) and must be removed and replaced.

in the eye-screw as shown in **Figure 26.5**. Be certain you use a cadmium-plated eye-screw threaded for use in wood. A screw thread length of two or three inches should secure most antennas. Allow ½ inch of space or more between the trunk and the eye; this allows for outward growth of the tree with time.

For stouter antennas, such as multielement wire beams, a different method for securing wires to trees is recommended (see **Figure 26.6**). This procedure involves using an eyebolt longer than the tree diameter, drilling completely through the tree, and securing the eyebolt on each side of the tree with flat washers and nuts. Drilling a hole through a tree causes much less trauma to the tree than wrapping something around it. Much of the core of a tree is dead tissue, used mainly for physical support.

Although there will be some wounding of the tree at the site of a bolt or screw, such trauma will be far less than that which occurs from wrapping a wire around the trunk. Wrapping a line around a tree's branch or trunk strangles

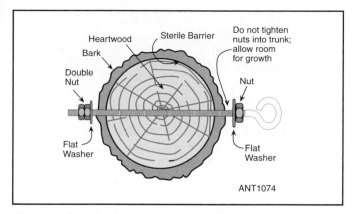

Figure 26.6 — For heavy antenna loads, an eyebolt passed through the trunk or limb will support more weight than an eye-screw. Allow about ½ inch of play between the bolt and trunk or limb. Don't tighten the bolt completely; this allows for tree growth.

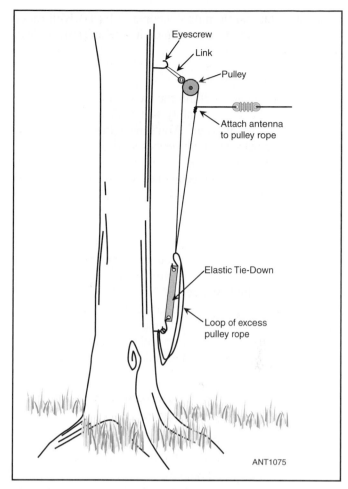

Figure 26.7 — By using a pulley, raising and lowering the antenna for repairs can be done without the need to climb the tree. Elastic cords or straps can be used to apply tension to the antenna. Loop the excess pulley rope to a second eye-screw in case the cord or strap fails.

the veins in the sapwood the same way a noose around your neck would strangle you. It's important not to wrap anything around the trunk.

You can find a professional tree climber/arborist in the *Yellow Pages* or perhaps use the services of a talented friend to install a pulley and rope system in your trees of choice. A ⅜ or ½ inch eyebolt screwed into the tree as described above with a pulley attached is the best method. Use a threaded chain link or "cold shut" (a type of chain attachment link) to attach the pulley to the eye.

A non-swiveling pulley is preferred because the lay of the rope can cause the pulley to turn, twisting the rope and possibly jamming the pulley. Use only all-metal pulleys for permanent installations, preferably ones made from stainless or galvanized materials. Plastic parts will either break or be damaged by UV (ultraviolet) radiation from sunlight. Check your local hardware stores for inexpensive stainless steel pulleys.

Keep in mind that with pulleys and haul ropes there should be minimal clearance between the sheave (the wheel in the pulley) and the pulley body; the rope or halyard should be larger in diameter than that clearance so it can't get jammed between the sheave and the pulley — a major annoyance. Use ¼ inch rope; only a very sloppy pulley will allow it to jam. The best type of rope for this purpose is black Dacron UV-resistant line because it doesn't deteriorate when used outdoors. (See the section "Ropes and Rope Care" later in this chapter for more information.)

Have the climber go up the tree to the desired location, screw in the eye-screw, then attach the pulley. It's all but certain that the tree will have to be pruned to clear a decent window through which the line can travel. It's better to over-prune since new growth will invariably grow back in just a few years. Small branches are incredibly strong and resilient and can cause major problems in any tree project or installation.

Having brought the line along, the climber will put the line through the *back* side of the newly installed pulley (closest side to the tree), attach a weight to the end of the line, and throw it out in the direction that your wire antenna will take. The wire antenna must clear all branches to successfully install your antenna. It's very difficult to install an inverted V in a tree from the ground because it's just about impossible to get both sides of the antenna through the branches. A climber can help by throwing each leg of the antenna through the branches separately.

When the end of the line reaches the ground, remove the weight, then tie the ends of the line together, making the rope into a loop (see **Figure 26.7**). This is because in almost all cases it is the antenna that breaks, not the rope. Without the loop, when the antenna breaks the end of the support rope will be at the top of the pulley and you'll have to send someone up to retrieve it. If you have a loop system, all you have to do is pull the line down and reattach the antenna. Tie an overhand knot loop to form the antenna attachment point (this is usually an insulator) where the rope ends are tied together and you're ready to start hoisting.

In a strong wind that will get the trees swaying, you'll want to have a method that allows the trees to move without breaking the antenna. You can attach a weight of some sort (cement block, plastic milk container, a bucket with rocks, etc.) to the rope or place tension on it with an elastic cord or strap.

Tree Climbing

If you're going to climb the tree yourself, you'll need sturdy boots, hard hat, a safety belt with two lanyards and possibly tree climbing spurs. You'll need the two lanyards to leapfrog your belts around branches so that you'll be belted to the tree 100% of the time.

Newer tree climbing techniques don't use steel climbing spikes as it's deemed harmful to the tree. The latest methods use a line thrown or shot over a branch and then the rope is used to climb the tree using rope ascenders like the ones used by mountain climbers and cavers. You don't even touch the trunk of the tree using this technique. The same techniques used to get a line over a branch for an antenna can be used to position a tree-climbing line.

Tree climbing has even become a recreational activity similar to the way that rock climbing has. There are clubs and resources available and you can find them online. Be sure to check out the equipment and techniques and you can do this yourself.

26.2.2 GROUND-MOUNTED MASTS AND POLES

TV and Push-up Masts

Stacking TV mast is available in 5- and 10-foot lengths, 1¼ inches diameter, in both steel and aluminum. These sections are swaged or crimped at one end to permit sections to be joined together. This type of mast is usually mounted on a chimney or some sort of house-mounted bracket and is not intended to be permanently guyed. This mast is suitable for VHF/UHF verticals and small beams and holding up light wire antennas for HF.

Galvanized steel push-up masts such as Rohn H30 or H40 are intended primarily for TV antennas and wireless Internet antennas. The masts may be obtained with three, four or five 10-foot sections and come complete with guying rings and a means of locking the sections in place after they have been extended. These masts are inherently more suitable for guyed mast installations than the non-telescoping type because the diameters of the sections increase toward the bottom of the mast. For instance, the top section of a 50-foot mast is 1¼ inches diameter, and the bottom section is 2½ inches diameter. The mast can be mounted on the ground or on a roof.

While tricky to install (each 10-foot segment must be guyed separately while pushing the mast up section by section), they can provide years of reliable service if not overloaded with anything larger than small VHF/UHF beams and verticals or HF wire antennas. If you are unfamiliar with push-up masts, a local TV antenna installer can perform the actual installation quickly and properly. They cannot be climbed and must be lowered to work on the antennas. Do not attempt to "walk up" these masts when extended.

Push-up masts are available from numerous sources but

Figure 26.8 — An AB-577 temporary tower system in its transport case. (Photo by Alan Biocca, WB6ZQZ)

Figure 26.9 — Installation of surplus AB-577 tower with tribander at 45 feet at K7NV. (Photo by Kurt Andress, K7NV)

the shipping cost often exceeds the cost of the mast. These masts can be ordered online (search for antenna, pushup and mast), through hardware stores and from TV antenna installers.

AB-577/GRC Masts

The AB-577 mast is an all-aluminum mast kit available primarily as military surplus. It is designed to be field deployed by one or more people and does not require a prepared surface or foundation of any kind. The complete kit in **Figure 26.8** consists of a "launcher" (the base section), eight tube sections, guy wires and all hardware and tools to assemble the 50-foot mast. The standard AB-577 system, with three sets of guys, will support a modest triband Yagi at 45 feet (see **Figure 26.9**).

A total height of 75 feet is possible with the addition of the MK-806 extension kit. It's useful for any application requiring a temporary or permanent tower such as lighting, surveillance, emergency communications or RF survey work. The quick erection time also makes the mast very useful in neighborhoods where a permanently installed tower is not allowed.

The system consists of several short sections of aluminum tubing, with special end connections for joining them. These can be erected from the base fixture, which has a crank-up type winch-driven elevator platform. The tubing sections are installed in the base fixture and connected to the section above it with an over-center locking *Marmon*-style clamp. Then, the elevator platform is raised with the winch and the new tube is locked in place, high on the base fixture. Then the elevator is lowered to accept the next section. While the tower is extended, the supporting guys are adjusted via the unique *snubber* assemblies at the anchor connection. One person can erect this system, even in windy conditions, when special care is given to keeping the guys properly adjusted during each extension.

Fiberglass Poles

Telescoping fiberglass poles have become widely available in recent years. While they are too light to support rotatable antennas, they are popular as supports for wire antennas. Primarily intended for portable use, if you decide to use one in a permanent installation make sure the surface is coated to resist UV from sunlight or paint it. There is more information on these poles in the **Portable Antennas** chapter.

Wooden Poles

A seldom-used but sturdy alternative is to use a wooden utility pole. They vary from new ones to used poles that have been pulled from service by utility companies. Make some inquiries to find out the availability and installed cost in your area. You'll need to add pole steps to climb it and will have to fabricate your own antenna mounting hardware. Nevertheless, they are very sturdy, require no guys, and might satisfy your use and budget.

26.2.3 MAST GUYING

Three guy wires in each set are usually adequate for a mast. These should be spaced equally around the mast. The required number of sets of guys depends on the height of the mast, its stiffness, and the required antenna tension if supporting a wire antenna in one end. A 30-foot-high mast usually requires two sets of guys, and a 50-foot mast needs at least three sets. If supporting the end of a wire antenna, one guy of the top set should be anchored to a point directly opposite the antenna. The other two guys of the same set should be spaced 120° with respect to the first, as shown in **Figure 26.10**.

Generally, the top guys should be anchored at distances from the base of the mast at least 60% of the mast height. The separation of the guy anchors from the mast determines the guy loads and the vertical load compressing the mast. At an anchor distance of 60% of the mast height, the load on the guy wire opposite the wire antenna is approximately twice the antenna tension. The compression in the mast will be 1.66 times the antenna tension. For 80% of the mast height, the guy tension will be 1.6 times larger than the antenna load and the mast compression will be 1.25 times larger.

The largest available and practical anchor spacing should be used. Additional compression on the mast caused by closer

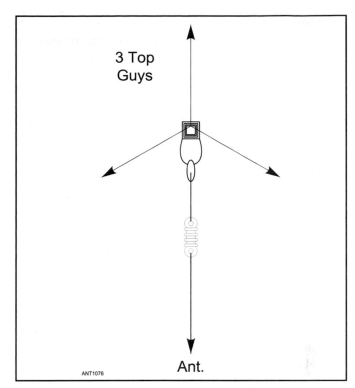

Figure 26.10 — For a mast supporting a wire antenna, the guys should be equally spaced at 120 degrees around the mast with one guy directly in line with the antenna.

anchor spacing increases the tendency of the mast to buckle. Buckling occurs when the compression on the unsupported spans between guys become too great for the unsupported length. The section then bows out laterally and will usually fold over, collapsing the mast. Additional sets of guys reduce the tendency for the mast to buckle under the compression by decreasing the unsupported span lengths and stabilizing the mast, keeping it straight where it best withstands compression.

A natural phenomenon, called *vortex shedding*, can occur when the wind passes over the sections of a guyed mast. For every section size, shape, and length, there is a wind speed that can cause the sections to oscillate mechanically. When all the sections of an antenna support mast are close to the same size and length, it is possible for all of the mast sections to vibrate simultaneously between the guys. To reduce the potential for this, you can place the guys at locations along the mast that will result in different span lengths. This creates different mechanical resonant frequencies for each span, eliminating the possibility of all sections oscillating at the same time.

When determining the guy locations along the mast to treat this problem, you also need to consider the mast buckling requirements. Since compression of the mast is greatest in the bottom span and the least in the top span, the guys should be placed to make the bottom span the shortest and the top span the longest. A general guide for determining the different span lengths is to make the unguyed lengths increase by 10 to 20% with increasing height.

Guy Material

When used within their safe load ratings, you may use any of the ropes listed later in the chapter for mast guys. Nonmetallic materials have the advantage that there is no need to break them up into sections to avoid unwanted resonant interactions, also discussed later in the chapter. All of these materials are subject to *stretching*, however, which causes mechanical problems in permanent installations. At rated working loads, dry manila rope stretches about 5%, while nylon rope stretches about 20%. Usually, after a period of wind load and wet/dry cycles, the lines will become fairly stable and require less frequent adjustment.

Solid galvanized steel wire is also widely used for guying. This wire has approximately twice the load ratings of similar sizes of copper-clad wire, but it is more susceptible to corrosion. Stranded galvanized wire sold for guying TV masts is also suitable for light-duty applications, but is also susceptible to corrosion. It is prudent to inspect the guys every six months for signs of deterioration or damage. **Figure 26.11** shows how to attach guy wire to strain insulators.

Guy Anchors

Figures 26.12 and **26.13** show two different kinds of guy anchors. In Figure 26.12 one or more pipes are driven into the ground at right angles to the guy wire. If a single pipe proves to be inadequate, another pipe can be added in tandem, as shown, and connected with a galvanized steel cable. Heavy-gauge galvanized pipe is preferred for corrosion resistance. Steel fence posts may be used in the same manner. Figure 26.13 shows a *dead-man* type of anchor. The buried anchor may consist of one or more pipes 5 or 6 feet long, or scrap automobile parts, such as bumpers or wheels. The anchors

should be buried 3 or 4 feet in the ground. The cable connecting the dead-man to the guys should be galvanized wire rope, such as EHS guy cable. You should coat the buried part of the cable with roofing tar to well above the ground and thoroughly dry it prior to burial to enhance resistance to corrosion.

Heavy auger-type anchors that screw into the ground are also used and are commonly used by utilities to anchor power poles. These anchors are usually heavier than required for guying a mast, although they may be more convenient to install. You should conduct annual inspections of the anchors by digging several inches below grade around the anchor to inspect for corrosion.

Trees and buildings may also be used as guy anchors if they are located appropriately. Care should be exercised, however, to make sure that the tree is of adequate size and that any fastening to a building can be made sufficiently secure. See the section above on using trees as antenna supports regarding anchoring to trees.

Guy Tension

Many troubles encountered in mast guying are a result of pulling the guy wires too tight. Guy-wire tension should never be more than necessary to correct for obvious bowing or movement under wind pressure. Approximately 10% to 15% of the working load is sufficient. In most cases, achieving

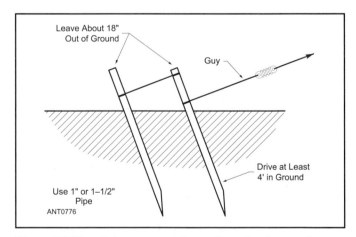

Figure 26.12 — Driven guy anchors. One pipe is usually sufficient for a small mast. For added strength, a second pipe may be added as shown.

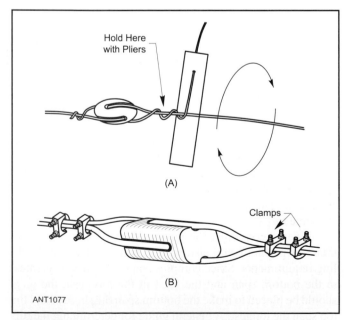

Figure 26.11 — Attaching guy wires to strain insulators. At (A) a simple lever is used to twist solid wire and at (B) standard cable clamps are used for stranded wire.

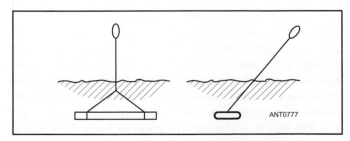

Figure 26.13 — Buried "dead-man" guy anchors (see text).

the necessary tension does not require the use of turnbuckles, with the possible exception of the guy opposite a wire antenna. If any great difficulty is experienced in eliminating bowing from the mast, the guy tension should be reduced or additional sets of guys are required. The mast should be checked periodically, especially after strong winds, to ensure the guys and anchors have not stretched or moved, allowing the mast to bend away from the required straight alignment.

In the case of rope guys, use of a "trucker's hitch" (see the section on knots) will provide much more tension than can be obtained by just pulling on the rope since it has a 2:1 mechanical advantage.

26.3 TYPES OF TOWERS

A tower is the best answer to a reliable, permanent antenna support structure and they basically come in two types — self-supporting and guyed. Beginning with the small, roof-mounted "four-footed tripod" models, amateurs use towers up to and beyond 200-foot broadcast-size "big iron." This section is an overview of the various common types of towers with some of their key characteristics.

Lattice towers consist of two kinds of *members*: *legs* and diagonal and horizontal *braces*. Members can either be round, such as for Rohn 25G (**www.rohnnet.com**), or 90- or 60-degree angled metal. Round-member towers are the most common for amateur towers. The *tower face* is that outward facing area between the legs with the braces between them. Free-standing and guyed lattice towers are built of pre-assembled *sections*, usually 8 to 10 feet long that are stacked on top of each other to reach the desired height. Lattice towers are constructed from steel or aluminum with steel the most common for guyed towers. *Tubular* towers are constructed from telescoping sections of steel tubing.

26.3.1 ROOF-MOUNTED TOWERS

The self-supporting roof-mounted tower is a modest way to support small to mid-sized antennas. This might be your first foray into a tower and directional antenna and a roof-mounted tower offers an inexpensive way to get started. Glen Martin Engineering (**www.glenmartin.com**) offers several models of four-leg aluminum towers and is a representative source of roof-mounted towers ranging in height from 4.5 to 26 feet. **Figure 26.14** shows a typical installation. Follow the manufacturer's recommendations for installation and grounding.

A roof-mounted tower is attached to the roof with anchor bolts that extend completely through the roof. Do not use lag bolts into the roof trusses. Use a 2×4 or 2×6 across the trusses in the attic for a backing plate and attach the anchor bolts to them as in **Figure 26.15**. Another similar board can be placed on top of the roof to spread the load. Any wood exposed to the weather should be pressure-treated or coated with roofing tar. Roofing tar is used to seal around the mounting bolt holes to prevent leaks (see **Figure 26.16**).

Roof-mounted antennas and structures are handy but roofs can be dangerous. State and federal safety laws require fall-arrest equipment and it's highly recommended that you use it as well. A fall-arrest harness (FAH) should be attached to an anchor point on the peak of the roof.

26.3.2 SELF-SUPPORTING TOWERS

Self-supporting towers have a smaller footprint but are generally more expensive to install. Significantly more concrete is required for the base of a free-standing tower and the amount of steel or aluminum (which ultimately determines the cost of a tower) is higher. The advantage of a self-supporting tower is that no guy wires are required. This appeals to hams without enough room for the necessary guying system and the cleaner "look" sometimes helps with esthetic concerns.

Because there are no guys to keep them standing, self-supporting towers depend on bending strength and a large concrete base. The base is generally required to have a volume of at least five to six cubic yards, requiring significant

Figure 26.14 — A roof mounted tower will give your antennas a chance to get up in the air with a minimal impact and cost. (Photo by Redd Swindells, AI2N)

Figure 26.15 — The strengthened anchoring for the roof-mounted tower. Bolts run through the roof and through the anchor plate (2 × 6) between joists. (Photo by Jane Wolfert)

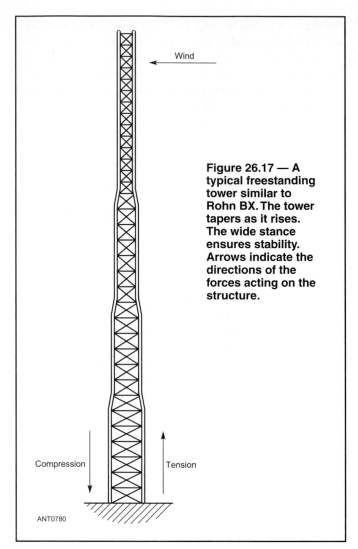

Figure 26.17 — A typical freestanding tower similar to Rohn BX. The tower tapers as it rises. The wide stance ensures stability. Arrows indicate the directions of the forces acting on the structure.

Wind

Compression

Tension

ANT0780

Figure 26.16 — Lengths of 2 × 6 on the roof act as footing for the tower legs and are coated by roofing tar to protect against weathering and prevent leaks. (Photo by Jane Wolfert)

digging and preparation. The weight of the base keeps the tower system's center of gravity low or below ground level, minimizing the overturning force from wind. The soil around the base must be solid enough to withstand the pressure from overturning forces on the tower system. If you have any questions about your ability to properly construct the base, consult a professional engineer or hire a concrete contractor.

Freestanding Towers

Towers specifically designed and installed for TV antennas are at the low end of suitability for typical HF beams. TV antenna towers have a maximum height of 40 to 60 feet.

The most common are the Rohn AX, BX and HDBX series and a tubular-legged type similar to but lighter than Rohn 25G. Universal Manufacturing (**www.universaltowers.com**) offers similar towers made of aluminum.

The common BX-series towers sketched in **Figure 26.17** are made from stamped steel with X-bracing of the legs. The X braces are not connected to each other and the most common failure point is between the braces. Also, the rotator and top plates are made from sheet metal and can crack from wind-induced metal fatigue. For small triband HF beams and VHF arrays they are fine, but be careful of overloading towers using the smaller stacking sections. These towers should be limited to antennas with boom lengths of less than 10 feet since they have minimal resistance to torsion (twisting).

For larger antenna arrays, heavier towers are available that are designed for broadcast and commercial applications. These look much the same as the "TV antenna" towers but are made of heavier material and have heavier and stiffer bracing. The most common models of these towers are the Rohn SSV, Trylon (**www.trylon.com**), Universal and AN Wireless (**www.anwireless.com**). While significantly more expensive, they can handle very large loads including high winds and icing conditions.

Crank-up Towers

Crank-ups are a popular type of self-supporting tower. These towers use a motorized or manual system of cables and pulleys to extend or retract the tower. They are the most expensive tower for the height due to more materials and hardware but satisfy many hams with limited space. When cranked down, a telescoping tower can maintain a low-profile system, out of sight of the neighbors and family.

Tubular crank-ups are generally limited to a single antenna since the rotator is mounted on a plate at the top of the tower without any additional bracing. This limits the size of the antenna and how far above the rotator it can be mounted. Lattice crank-ups generally have the same top structure as a guyed tower and can support much larger antenna and mast combinations.

US Tower (**www.ustower.com**) dominates the market for crank-ups, manufacturing good products and offering good customer support. Both lattice- and tubular-type crank-up towers are available as shown in **Figure 26.18**.

Do not use guys with normal crank-up towers (those that have no locking devices between sections)! The increased tower compression will be carried by the hoisting cable, which will eventually cause it to fail.

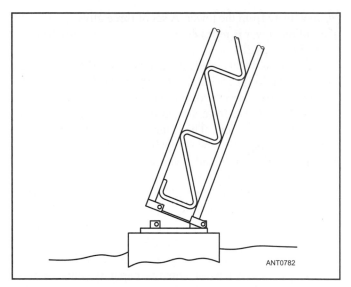

Figure 26.19 — Fold-over or tilting base. There are several different kinds of hinged sections permitting different types of installation. Great care should be exercised when raising or lowering a tilting tower.

Tilt-over Towers

Some free-standing towers have another convenience feature — a hinged section that permits the owner to fold over all or a portion of the tower. The primary benefit is in allowing antenna work to be done close to ground level, without the necessity of removing the antenna and lowering it for service. **Figure 26.19** shows a hinged base used with stacked, guyed tower sections. Many crank-up towers come with optional tilt-over base fixtures that are equipped with a winch and cable system for tilting the fully nested tower between horizontal and vertical positions.

The hinged section can also be designed for portions of the tower above the base. These are usually referred to as *guyed tilt-over towers*, where a conventional guyed tower can be tilted over for installing and servicing antennas.

Misuse of hinged sections during tower erection is a dangerously common practice among radio amateurs. Unfortunately, these episodes can end in accidents. If you do not have a good grasp of the fundamentals of physics, it might be wise to avoid hinged towers or to consult an expert if there are any questions about safely installing and using such a tower. It is often far easier (and safer) to erect a regular guyed tower or self-supporting tower with gin pole and climbing belt than it is to try to walk up an unwieldy hinged tower.

26.3.3 GUYED TOWERS

Guyed tubular-leg lattice towers are strong, reliable, relatively easy to erect, and have a wide array of accessories compatible with amateur use.

They are usually less expensive to install but need a big footprint for the guying system. Since the typical recommended guy anchor distance from the tower is 80% of the height, the guys for a 100-foot tower need to be anchored

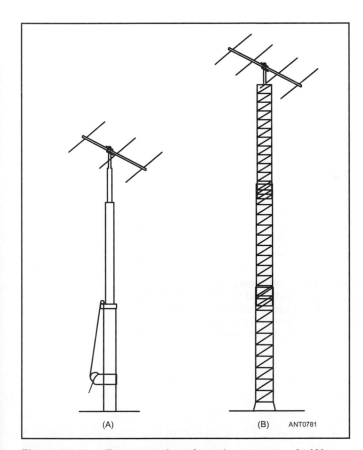

Figure 26.18 — Two examples of crank-up towers. At (A) a tubular style and at (B) a lattice style.

80 feet away from the tower. A set of three guys spaced 120° around the tower is repeated every 30 to 40 feet up the tower (see **Figure 26.20**).

The most widely used guyed towers for amateur applications are the Rohn 25G and 45G. They are well constructed, are hot-dipped galvanized, and have enough accessory items for any use. These towers have tubular legs and Z-bracing rods welded to the legs. The Rohn product catalog (available for downloading from the company website) provides calculations for rated wind load at various heights and all base and guying requirements.

Rohn 25G has a face width of 12 inches and a 10-foot section weighs 40 pounds. A gin pole and a ground crew is the recommended way to install these towers. A practical height limit of 190 feet at 90 MPH wind speed provides 7.8 square feet of antenna load capacity. A 100-foot tower yields 9.1 square feet of antenna capacity, enough for a small stack of monoband Yagis or a high-performance trib-and beam. An experienced crew can erect up to a hundred feet a day of this popular tower.

Rohn 45G is 18 inches across the face and a 10-foot section weighs 70 pounds. This robust tower is rated up to 240 feet in 90 MPH winds, with a wind load rating of 16.3 square feet. At a height of 100 feet the wind loading is 21.5 square feet.

Rohn 55G is also 18 inches across the face, weighs 90 pounds per section, and can be installed up to 300 feet in 90 MPH winds. It has a gross capacity of 17.4 square feet in that maximum configuration. The standard Rohn gin pole is not rated for 55G because of its weight.

Tubular-leg towers can also be supported by attaching them to a building with a *house bracket*. The manufacturer will specify how far above a bracket the tower can be extended without guys.

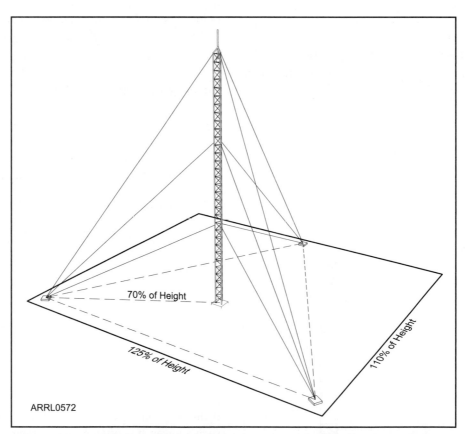

70% of Height

125% of Height

110% of Height

ARRL0572

Figure 26.20 — Guyed towers are built from stackable sections that are usually identical except for the base that attaches to the concrete and the top section that supports the rotator and mast. Guy requirements are specified by the manufacturer, but spacing the anchors 70 to 80% of the tower height is typical. As seen in the drawing, the tower and guy wires do take up quite a bit of space.

26.4 ENGINEERING THE TOWER PROJECT

Engineering in this sense means to plan, construct, or manage the practical applications of your tower project. The engineering should be done *before* you begin digging, pouring, or constructing!

The process you go through to design your system may begin with site selection ("What is a suitable location for a tower?") or it may start with selecting a tower ("What tower can I put up on this site?"). Everyone's circumstances are different.

It's not unusual to repeat the process of planning and tower selection for several iterations as you work through the various types of towers and associated costs and constraints. The important thing is to work through the various interacting issues until you are satisfied that you have addressed all of them.

It is often very helpful to the novice tower installer to visit other local amateurs who have installed towers. Look over their hardware and ask questions. Ask about local permitting processes and requirements. If possible, have a few local experienced amateurs look over your plans — before you commit yourself. They may be able to offer a great deal of help. If someone in your area is planning to install a tower and antenna system, be sure to offer your assistance. There is no substitute for experience when it comes to tower work and your experience there may prove invaluable to you later.

26.4.1 SITE PLANNING AND PERMITTING

Local Ordinances and CC&Rs

Local ordinances, deed restrictions, and any CC&Rs (Covenants, Conditions and Restrictions) should be checked to determine if any legal restrictions affect the proposed installation. While compliance with local building regulations may be pretty straightforward, your CC&Rs may specifically rule out any type of outdoor structure that would make tower or antenna installation impossible.

The FCC's PRB-1 memorandum specifies that local regulations must make "reasonable accommodation" for Amateur Radio antennas and support structures, but does not pre-empt local regulations. For more information on PRB-1, consult the information at **www.arrl.org/prb-1**.

The best book for Amateur Radio tower zoning issues is the *Antenna Zoning for the Radio Amateur* by Fred Hopengarten, K1VR, now in its second edition and available from the ARRL or Radioware (**www.radio-ware.com**). Fred is a telecommunications attorney and this book is full of valuable information on legal issues. Besides covering the legal issues, it also contains many insights and examples of the practical aspects of working with the building department and navigating the permitting process.

Building permits will dictate setbacks from property lines and are likely to place other constraints on where your tower can be located. For example, you may have to stay a certain distance from septic systems or buried utilities.

Safety

You must consider the safety aspects of your installation. For example, a tower should not be installed in a location where it could fall onto a neighbor's property. Imagine what would happen if your tower or antenna fell — where would it be likely to land? What could it hit on the way down? You may not be able to mitigate every possible outcome but thinking about it before construction may lead to a better plan.

The antenna must be located in such a position that it cannot possibly come in contact with power lines, either during normal operation or if the structure should fall. Consider the proximity of power lines to the tower. Safety rules dictate that all parts of a tower and antenna must remain at least 10 feet from power lines when being erected or after being installed. This is the smallest separation you should consider and more safety margin is strongly recommended.

Area and Access

For a guyed tower, there must be sufficient space for proper guying. The guy anchors should be between 70% and 80% of the tower height in distance from the base of the tower on level ground — sloping terrain may require larger areas (see Figure 26.20).

Erecting the tower and installing the antennas will require some space. Is there enough room to lay out a tower on a tilt-over base and how should the hinged base be oriented? Think about where antennas will be assembled and how they'll be hoisted to the top of the tower. Where will any necessary equipment need to be positioned and how will it get there?

Another part of choosing a tower site has to do with arranging for access. That is, access for base excavation and access for concrete. If you aren't sure, ask a local contractor to evaluate your site and make suggestions. They may spot something important that you've overlooked.

26.4.2 SELECTING A TOWER

The selection of a tower, its height, and the type of antennas and rotator is probably one of the more complex issues faced by station builders. All aspects of the tower, antenna, and rotator system are interrelated, and you should consider the overall system before making any decisions regarding specific system components.

Selecting a tower must be based on your requirements for what the tower must support and other considerations such as total budget, permit restrictions, esthetics, and the specifics of where you intend to install the tower. You should also consider the climate and your ability to maintain a tower. You may already know what general type of tower you want — self-supporting or guyed, lattice or tubular, etc. Or you may have to select a tower based on the constraints of the available site or other factors.

One of the first things you need to determine in the tower selection process is the type of specification required by the local authorities, if any. Then, you must determine the

Basic Wind Speed appropriate for the site. The Basic Wind Speed used in most specifications is the average wind speed for one mile of wind passing across the structure. It will be a lower value than the peak readings from an anemometer (wind gauge) installed at the site. For example, a Basic Wind Speed of 70 mph could have a maximum value of 80 mph and a minimum of 60 mph, equally distributed during the passage of the mile of wind. Basic wind speeds can be found in tables or maps contained in the appropriate specifications. Often, the basic wind speed used for the location may be obtained from the local permit authority.

Many building regulations base their specifications for maximum wind speed on TIA-222, "Structural Standard for Antenna Supporting Structures and Antennas." (TIA-222G is the latest revision as of mid-2011.) County wind speeds for all 3076 counties in the US from TIA-222 are also online at **www.championradio.com** under Tech Notes. Remember — these are the minimums and some building departments use a slightly higher figure for issuing building permits.

Add up the total square feet of antenna area (commercial antennas include area in the antenna specifications) you plan on installing. Compare that combination of wind area and your maximum wind speed rating to manufacturer specifications for the specific models of acceptable towers.

Most tower manufacturers provide catalogues or data packages that represent engineered tower configurations. These are provided as a convenience for users to help determine the most suitable tower configurations. The most commonly used design specifications for towers are the previously mentioned TIA-222 and the UBC (Uniform Building Code). These specifications define how the tower, antenna and guy loads are determined and applied to the system, and establish general design criteria for the analysis of the tower. Local authorities often require the review and approval of the installation by a state licensed Professional Engineer (P.E.) to obtain building permits. All local authorities in the United States do not subscribe to the same design standards, so often the manufacturers' general-purpose engineering is not applicable.

Determining Tower Load

Most manufacturers rate their towers in terms of the maximum allowable antenna load that can safely be carried at a specific wind speed. Ensuring that the specific antennas you plan to install meet the tower's design criteria, however, may not always be a straightforward task.

For most towers, the manufacturer assumes that the allowable antenna load is a horizontal force applied at the top of the tower. The allowable load represents a defined amount of exposed antenna area, at a specified wind velocity. Most tower manufacturers rate the load in terms of *Flat Projected Area* (FPA). This is simply the equivalent area of a flat rectangular surface at right angles to the wind. The FPA is not related to the actual shape of the antenna itself, only its rectangular projected area. Some manufacturers provide separate FPAs for antennas made from cylindrical sections and those made from rectangular sections.

In the realm of antenna manufacturers, however, you may encounter another wind load rating called the *Effective Projected Area* (EPA). This attempts to take into account the actual shape of antenna elements. The problem is that there is no agreed-upon standard for the conversion from EPA to load numbers. Different manufacturers may use different conversion factors.

Since most tower manufacturers have provided FPA figures for their towers — allowing us in effect to ignore design-specification details — it would be easiest for us to work only with FPA values for our antennas. This would be fine, if indeed we had good FPA figures for the specific antennas we plan to use! Unfortunately, FPAs are rarely specified for commercially built amateur antennas. Instead, most antenna manufacturers provide effective areas in their specification sheets. You may need to contact the antenna manufacturer directly for the FPA antenna area or for the antenna dimensions so that you can do your own FPA calculations as discussed in **Appendix A** of this chapter.

26.4.3 DESIGNING THE GUYS

The configuration shown in **Figure 26.21A** is taken from an older (1983) Unarco-Rohn catalog. This configuration has the top set of guys placed at the top of the tower with the lower set halfway up the tower. This configuration is best for most amateur installations, which usually have the antennas mounted on a rotatable mast extending out the top of the tower — thereby placing the maximum lateral loads when the wind blows at the top of the tower (and the bottom of the rotating mast).

The configuration shown in Figure 26.21B is from the current Rohn catalog (Catalog 2). It shows 5 feet of unsupported tower extending above the top guy set. The lower guy set is approximately halfway between the top guys and the base. The newer configurations are tailored for commercial users who populate the top region of the tower with fixed arrays and/or dishes. The installation in Figure 26.21B cannot safely withstand the same amount of horizontal top load as can the configuration shown in Figure 26.21A, simply because the guys start farther down from the top of the tower.

An overhead view of a guyed tower is given in Figure 26.21C. Common practice is to use equal angular spacings of 120° between guy wires. If you must deviate from this spacing, the engineering staff of the tower manufacturer or a civil engineer should be contacted for advice.

Amateurs should understand that most catalogs show generic examples of tower configurations that work within the cited design specifications. They are by no means the only solution for any specific tower/antenna configuration. You can usually substantially change the load capability of any given tower by varying the size and number of guys. Station builders are encouraged to utilize the services of professional engineers to get the most out of their guyed towers.

26.4.4 DESIGNING THE BASE

Tower manufacturers can provide customers with detailed plans for properly constructing tower bases. **Figure 26.22** is

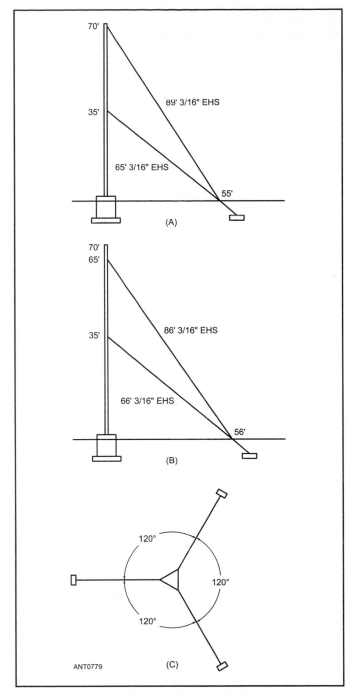

Figure 26.21 — The proper method of installation of a guyed tower. At (A) is the method recommended for most amateur installations. At (B), the method shown in current Rohn catalogs that places considerable stresses on the top section of the tower when large antennas are mounted above the tower (see text). (C) shows the recommended orientation of guy wires, symmetrically spaced around the tower.

an example of one such plan. This plan calls for a hole that is $3.5 \times 3.5 \times 6$ feet. Steel reinforcement bars are tied together to form a cage and placed in the hole.

A strong wooden form is constructed around the top of the hole. The hole and the wooden form are filled with concrete so that the resultant block will be 4 inches above grade. Before it hardens, the anchor bolts are embedded in

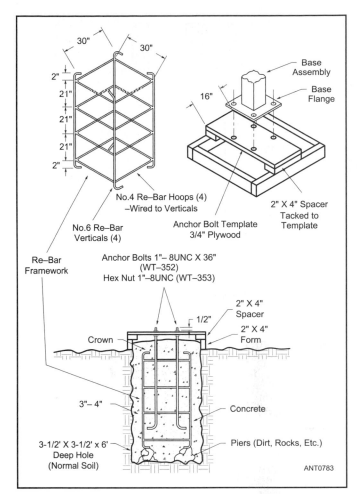

Figure 26.22 — Plans for installing concrete base for a 70-foot tubular crank-up tower. Although the instructions vary from tower to tower, this is representative of the type of concrete base specified by most manufacturers.

the concrete, and aligned with the plywood template. The template serves to align the anchor bolts to properly mate with the tower itself. Once the concrete has cured, the tower base is installed on the anchor bolts and the base connection is adjusted to bring the tower into vertical alignment.

For a tower that bolts to a flat base plate mounted to the footing bolts (as shown in Figure 26.22), you can bolt the first tower section on the base plate to ensure that the base is level and properly aligned. Use temporary guys or wooden braces to hold things exactly vertical while the concrete cures. (The use of such temporary guys also works well when you place the first tower section in the base hole and plumb it vertically before pouring in the concrete.) Manufacturers can provide specific, detailed instructions for the proper mounting procedure. **Figure 26.23** shows a slightly different design for a tower base.

The one assumption so far is that *normal* soil is predominant in the area in which the tower is to be installed. Normal soil is a mixture of clay, loam, sand and small rocks. More conservative design parameters for the tower base should be adopted (usually, using more concrete) if the soil is sandy, swampy or extremely rocky. If there are any doubts about the

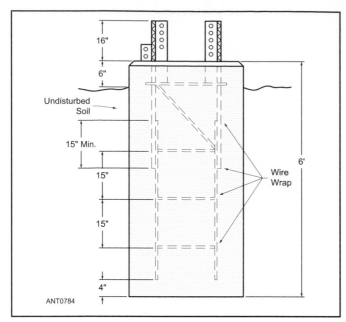

Figure 26.23 — Another example of a concrete base for a 70-foot lattice crank-up tower.

soil, the local agricultural extension office can usually provide specific technical information about the soil in a given area. When this information is in hand, contact the engineering department of the tower manufacturer or a civil engineer for specific recommendations with regard to compensating for any special soil characteristics.

Pier-Pin Bases

An important phenomenon in a guyed tower is stretching of the guy cables. All guys stretch under load and when the wind blows the elongated guys allow the tower to lean over somewhat. If the tower base is buried in the concrete footing — as is commonly done in amateur installations — the bending stress at the tower base can become a significant factor. Towers that have been installed with tapered pier-pin bases much more freely absorb tower leaning, and they are far less sensitive to guy-elongation problems.

The tapered pier-pin tower installation is not without some drawbacks. These installations often require torque-arm guy brackets or six-guy torque-arm assemblies to control tower rotation due to antenna torque. They also require temporary guys when they are being installed to hold the base steady until the permanent guys are mounted. Some climbers also don't like the flexing when they start to climb these types of towers.

On the positive side, pier-pin base towers have all structural members above the concrete footing, eliminating concerns about hidden corrosion that can occur with buried towers. Most decisions regarding the type of base installation are made according to the preference of the tower builder/maintainer. While either type of base configuration can be successfully used, you would be wise to do the stress calculations (or have a professional engineer do them) to ensure safety, particularly when large antenna loads are contemplated

Table 26-1
Yield Strengths of Mast Materials

Material Specification	Yield Strength (lb/in.^{2})
Drawn aluminum tube	
6063-T5	15,000
6063-T832	35,000
6061-T6	35,000
6063-T835	40,000
2024-T3	42,000
Aluminum pipe	
6063-T6	25,000
6061-T6	35,000
Extruded alum. tube	
7075-T6	70,000
Aluminum sheet and plate	
3003-H14	17,000
5052-H32	22,000
6061-T6	35,000
Structural steel	
A36	33,000
Carbon steel, cold drawn	
1016	50,000
1022	58,000
1027	70,000
1041	87,000
1144	90,000
Alloy steel	
2330 cold drawn	119,000
4130 cold worked	75,000
4340 1550 °F quench	162,000
1000 °F temper Stainless steel	
AISI 405 cold worked	70,000
AISI 440C heat-treated	275,000

(From *Physical Design of Yagi Antennas* by David B. Leeson, W6NL)

and particularly if guys that can easily stretch are used, such as Phillystran guys.

26.4.5 DESIGNING THE ANTENNA MAST

The antenna mast is the pipe or tubing that extends from the top of the rotator through the top of the tower. Wind loading on the mast can be significant for large antenna systems or for antennas mounted well above the top of the tower. This requires careful selection of the mast material and is an important part of completing your tower system design. **Table 26-1** gives yield strengths for various mast materials. For all but the smallest systems, do not depend on unknown materials for this critical component!

There are two types of round material used for masts — pipe and structural tubing. Pipe is commonly water pipe or conduit and is of limited value. Pipe is designed to carry liquids and is not rated for bending strength. While pipe may have a *yield strength* of 30,000 psi (pounds-per-square-inch), that will only accommodate small loads and wind speeds. Another problem is that the OD (outside diameter) of pipe is 1.9 inches which is smaller than the 2.0 inch ham hardware standard. Conduit should not be used as antenna mast at all except for very small antennas.

Tubing on the other hand does come in 2.0 inch sizes and is rated for strength. There are many different materials and manufacturing processes for tubing that may be used for a mast. Yield strengths range from 25,000 psi to nearly 100,000 psi. Knowing the minimum yield strength of the material used for a mast is an important part of determining if it will be safe.

When evaluating a mast with multiple antennas attached to it, special care should be given to finding the worst-case condition (wind direction) for the system. What may appear to be the worst load case, by virtue of the combined flat projected antenna areas, may not always be the exposure that creates the largest mast bending moment. Masts with multiple stacked antennas should always be examined to find the exposure that produces the largest mast bending moment. The antenna flat projected areas at 0° and 90° azimuths are particularly useful for this evaluation.

A manual procedure for determining the mast bending stress is available in **Appendix B** of this chapter. There are also several online calculators and the *MARC* (Mast, Antenna and Rotator Calculator) program is available from Champion Radio Products for a modest price. If you have any doubts about the strength requirements for your antenna mast, consult a professional installer or engineer.

When selecting the length of the mast, allow for four feet or more of mast extending above the top of the highest antenna on the tower. This extra mast can then be used as a gin pole/pulley attachment point for other antenna or tower work.

26.4.6 ROTATORS

Rotators (not "rotors") are electric motors with sturdy gear trains and bearings in a weatherproof housing. They are used to turn directional antennas attached to a mast sitting directly on the rotator. A control unit in the ham shack allows the operator to turn the antenna. Allow plenty of margin for rated wind load when selecting a rotator — this will improve reliability. A table of rotator specifications is available on this book's CD-ROM.

Light-duty TV antenna rotators can handle loads such as small VHF and UHF antenna systems but only have minimal torque and little or no braking capability.

Medium-duty rotators such as the Hy-Gain Ham-V in **Figure 26.24** have the largest array of choices available. Some use a conventional circular gear train and a solenoid-controlled brake. Several use worm gear drive which has the advantages of fewer gears in the gear train, a significant gear reduction ratio, and do not require a separate brake, all of which improve reliability.

Heavy-duty rotators come in several configurations, from larger amateur rotators to surplus "prop pitches" to

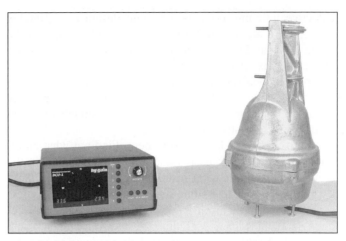

Figure 26.24 — This Ham-V model uses a DCU-1 digital controller.

commercial versions capable of handling extremely large antenna systems. Prop pitch rotators are military surplus motors that varied the pitch of the propellers in propeller driven aircraft. They have tremendous torque and worm gear drive. They require special control boxes and sensors for use as antenna rotators but are extremely powerful and reliable.

Light and medium-duty rotators can be mounted on top of a mast or tubular crank-up tower with the antenna sitting directly above the rotator but this limits them to turning one mid-sized antenna. Lattice towers designed for ham radio use have shelves or plates for rotator and a bearing plate or sleeve at the top of the tower for supporting the antenna mast against horizontal loads. This support allows the rotator to turn much larger antenna systems to the limits of its torque specifications.

Antennas can also be mounted along a tower and rotated with an orbital or ring rotator. These rotators hold the antenna in a carriage mounted on a circular track that clamps to the tower. Ring rotators are available from TIC General and KØXG Systems.

Thrust Bearings

A thrust bearing is mounted at the top of the tower and the antenna mast passes through it to the rotator. The thrust bearing clamps the mast and supports the weight of the antenna system, leaving the rotator to handle the torque load without carrying any weight. Except in unusual circumstances, this is unnecessary since rotator bearings are designed to operate properly at full vertical load. A substitute for an actual thrust bearing is a bushing of heavy plastic or wood that supports a collar clamped to the antenna mast.

Do not use machine shop type pillow-blocks for thrust bearings. They are not intended to be exposed to the weather and will quickly rust solid. Use only outdoor grade (Rohn, galvanized, etc.) thrust bearings.

26.4.7 GROUND SYSTEMS

The following section is taken from the **Safety** chapter of *The ARRL Handbook*, and was written by Jim Lux, W6RMK.

Effective lightning protection system design is a complex topic. There are a variety of system tradeoffs that must be made and that determine the type and amount of protection needed. Hams can easily follow some general guidelines that will protect their stations against high-voltage events that are induced by nearby lightning strikes or that arrive via utility lines. Let's talk about where to find professionals first, and then consider construction guidelines.

Start with your local government. Find out what building codes apply in your area and have someone explain the regulations about antenna installation and safety. For more help, look in your telephone directory or online for professional engineers, lightning protection suppliers and contractors. Companies that sell lightning-protection products may offer considerable help to apply their products to specific installations. One such source is PolyPhaser Corporation. Look in the Bibliography of this chapter for a partial list of PolyPhaser's publications. Electrical safety equipment and materials are listed in the lost of vendors and dealers provided on this book's CD-ROM.

Bonding Conductors

Copper strapping (or flashing) comes in a number of sizes. 1.5 inches wide and 0.051 inch thick or #6 AWG stranded wire, is the minimum recommended grounding conductor for lightning protection. Do not use braided strap because the individual strands oxidize over time, greatly reducing the effectiveness of braid as an ac conductor. Use bare copper for buried ground wires. (There are some exceptions; seek an expert's advice if your soil is corrosive.) Exposed runs above ground that are subject to physical damage may require additional protection (such as a conduit) to meet code requirements. Wire size depends on the application but never use anything smaller than #6 AWG for bonding conductors. Local lightning-protection experts or building inspectors can recommend sizes for each application.

Tower and Antennas

Because a tower is usually the highest metal object on the property, it is the most likely strike target. Proper tower grounding is essential to lightning protection. The goal is to establish short multiple paths to the Earth so that the strike energy is divided and dissipated.

Connect each tower leg and each fan of metal guy wires to a separate ground rod. Space the rods at least 6 feet apart. Bond the leg ground rods together with #6 AWG or larger copper bonding conductor (form a ring around the tower base, see **Figure 26.25**). Connect a continuous bonding conductor between the tower ring ground and the entrance panel. Make all connections with fittings approved for grounding applications. Do not use solder for these connections. Solder will be destroyed in the heat of a lightning strike.

Because galvanized steel (which has a zinc coating) reacts with copper when combined with moisture, use stainless steel hardware between the galvanized metal and the copper grounding materials.

To prevent strike energy from entering a shack via the

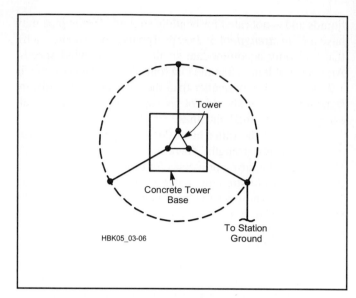

Figure 26.25 — Schematic of a properly grounded tower. A bonding conductor connects each tower leg to a ground rod and a buried (1 foot deep) bare, tinned copper ring (dashed line), which is also connected to the station ground and then to the ac safety ground. Locate ground rods on the ring, as close as possible to their respective tower legs. All connectors should be compatible with the tower and conductor materials to prevent corrosion. See text for conductor sizes and details of lightning and voltage transient protection.

feed line, ground the feed line outside the home. Ground the coax shield to the tower at the antenna and the base to keep the tower and line at the same potential. Several companies offer grounding blocks that make this job easy.

All grounding media at the home must be bonded together. This includes lightning protection conductors, electrical service, telephone, antenna system grounds and underground metal pipes. Any ground rods used for lightning protection or entrance-panel grounding should be spaced at least 6 feet from each other and the electrical service or other utility grounds and then bonded to the ac system ground as required by the NEC.

A Cable Entrance Panel

The basic concept with transient protection is to make sure that all the radio and other equipment is tied together and "moves together" in the presence of a transient voltage. It's not so important that the shack be at "ground" potential, but, rather, that everything is at the same potential. For fast rise-time transients such as the individual strokes that make up a lightning strike, even a short wire has enough inductance that the voltage drop along the wire is significant, so whether you are on the ground floor, or the 10th floor of a building, your shack is "far" from Earth potential.

The easiest way to ensure that everything is at the same potential is to tie all the signals to a common reference. In large facilities, this reference would be provided by a grid of large diameter cables under the floor, or by wide copper bars, or even a solid metal floor. A more practical approach for smaller facilities like a ham shack is to have a single "tie point" for all the signals. This is often, but erroneously, called a "single-point ground," but what's really important is not only the shields (grounds) for the signals, but the signal wires as well are referenced to that common potential.

We want to control the flow of the energy in a strike and eliminate any possible paths for surges to enter the building. This involves routing the feed lines, rotator control cables, and so on at least six feet away from other nearby grounded metal objects.

A commonly used approach to ensuring that all the connections are tied together is to route all the signals through a single "entrance panel" which will serve as the "single point ground" although it may not actually be at ground potential. A convenient approach is to use a standard electrical box installed in the exterior wall.

Both balanced line and coax arrestors should be mounted to a secure ground connection on the outside of the building. The easiest way to do this is to install a large metal enclosure or a metal panel as a bulkhead and grounding block. The panel should be connected to the lightning dissipation ground with a short wide conductor (for minimum impedance), and, like all grounds, bonded to the electrical system's ground. Mount all protective devices, switches and relay disconnects on the outside facing wall of the bulkhead. The enclosure or panel should be installed in a way that if lightning currents cause a component to fail, the molten metal and flaming debris do not start a fire.

Every conductor that enters the structure, including antenna system control lines, should have its own surge suppressor on an entrance panel. Suppressors are available from a number of manufacturers, including Industrial Communication Engineers (ICE) and PolyPhaser, as well as the usual electrical equipment suppliers such as Square-D.

Lightning Arrestors

Feed line lightning arrestors are available for both coax cable and balanced line. Most of the balanced line arrestors use a simple spark gap arrangement, but a balanced line impulse suppressor is available from ICE.

DC blocking arrestors for coaxial cable have a fixed frequency range. They present a high-impedance to lightning (less than 1 MHz) while offering a low impedance to RF.

DC continuity arrestors (gas tubes and spark gaps) can be used over a wider frequency range than those that block dc. Where the coax carries supply voltages to remote devices (such as a mast-mounted preamp or remote coax switch), dc-continuous arrestors must be used.

26.5 TOOLS AND EQUIPMENT

Any job anywhere is easier and safer if you've got the right tools and tower work is no exception. If you are a weekend mechanic or handyman, you've probably already got most of what you need; all you need to do is add a few specialized items and you're good to go. If, on the other hand, all you have is a hammer, pair of pliers and a screwdriver, you'll need to make a trip or two to the tool store before you can really do anything. Once you have them, you'll be all set whenever any of your friends need help on their tower, too. Have the right tools and be prepared; you'll never go wrong.

26.5.1 THE TOWER TOOLBOX

Most amateur tower and antenna work can be done with a minimum of hand tools. Nut sizes of ⁷⁄₁₆, ½ and ⁹⁄₁₆ inch are all you'll usually need. **Table 26-2** lists the tools necessary for building and working on a typical ham tower. Your club may have a gin pole or guy wire tension gauge for members to borrow or you may be able to rent one.

26.5.2 SPECIALIZED TOWER TOOLS

Come-alongs

A come-along or hand cable winch, is very useful for pulling tower sections together, tightening tramlines and tensioning guy wires. You'll probably find more uses for it. Cheap ones are fifteen to twenty dollars and are fine for occasional use. The best ones for tower work have spring-loaded safety latches over the end of the hooks.

Cable Grips

The cable grip in **Figure 26.26** complements the come-along to tighten guy wires. It is a spring-loaded device that slides up the guy wire but clamps down when you put tension on it. Klein is the primary supplier of cable grips and they come in lots of sizes and designs for use with various materials. For amateur use, the Klein 1613-40 is for ³⁄₁₆ and ¼ inch EHS guy material — used on the majority of amateur towers.

Figure 26.26 — Klein Chicago cable grip on the left and Klein Haven's grip on the right.

Table 26-2
Essential tools

1	set of combination wrenches: ⁷⁄₁₆, ½ and ⁹⁄₁₆ inch
1	set of sockets ⅜ inch drive
1 each	deep sockets: ⁷⁄₁₆, ½, ⁹⁄₁₆ inch
1 each	screwdrivers (blade and Phillips)
2	adjustable pliers
1	diagonal cutter
1	razor blade utility knife
2	pulleys
1	drift pin or centering punch (for lining up tower sections)
1	hammer (attach some line for hanging on the tower)
3 each	adjustable wrenches — small, medium, and large
1	bubble level
6	carabiners
6	one-inch nylon webbing slings — 2 feet long
250 ft	rope (or more — this is enough for working on a 100 ft tower)
1	canvas bucket (for parts hauling and storage)
1	Loos PT-2 Tension Gauge
1 set	nutdrivers
1 (or more)	come-along or hand cable winch
1 (or more)	cable grips
1	circular saw with aggregate blade or hand grinder (for cutting metal, including guywires)
1	tag line (¼ inch is fine — you chose the size and length)
1	cordless ½ inch drill, with assorted bits and socket driver, 18 V recommended
1	set drill bits including step-drill, e.g. Uni-Bit
1	antenna analyzer
1	gin pole
1	soldering gun and solder

If you have three come-alongs and cable grips you can put initial tension on a full set of three guy wires at the same time.

Steel Cutter

A circular saw with a steel-cutting aggregate blade will work but the best cutting tool is a 4½ inch hand grinder with ⅛-inch steel-cutting blades. Always use safety goggles when cutting metal!

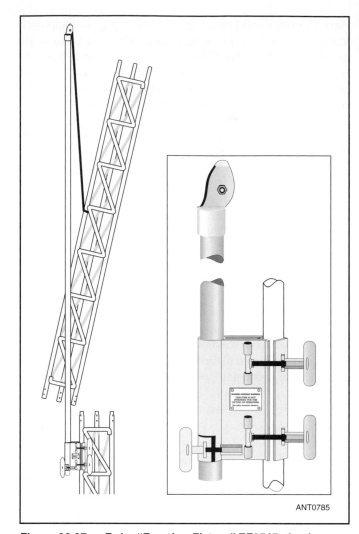

ANT0785

Figure 26.27 — Rohn "Erection Fixture" EF2545 also known commonly as a "gin pole."

Gin Pole

The purpose of a gin pole (see **Figure 26.27**) is to provide a support point high above the top of the tower for lifting and positioning an object. This allows the necessary work to be done on the object without whoever is doing the work having to support its weight at the same time. The Rohn gin pole (Rohn Erection Fixture EF2545) is rated for sections of Rohn 25G and 45G and comes with clamps to secure it to a leg of the assembled sections. Towers made of angled legs require a special gin pole — contact the manufacturer.

Typical gin pole loads are tower sections (10 feet long) and masts (6 to 22 feet long). Pick up these loads just above their balance point so they will hang naturally in the correct upright position for installation. The Rohn gin pole is 12 feet long, just right for lifting a 10-foot tower section. For 20-foot masts, a 12-foot gin pole is marginal because there is barely 10 feet of working length available from the gin pole. A large mast will probably exceed the rating for the Rohn gin pole which is rated for 70 pounds. Large, heavy-duty masts require special handling; consult an experienced tower worker for instructions on installing large masts.

Carabiners

Carabiners are steel or aluminum snap-links with spring loaded gates as seen in **Figure 26.28A** and **B**; they are invaluable for dozens of tower work tasks. A carabiner at the end of your haul rope can be attached to virtually anything that needs to be raised or lowered. A carabiner can be a third hand on the tower; you can clip a carabiner to almost anything with a rung or diagonal brace. You can instantly hang a pulley from a tower rung. Lightweight, they can be clipped on to your climbing harness for easy access. Experienced tower workers may carry twelve to fifteen carabiners on typical jobs. They typically cost $6 to $10 and will last for years with little or no maintenance. If the gate no longer opens and closes smoothly, the carabiner should be discarded.

A word of caution: mountain climbing carabiners are considered to be for private use and not OSHA-approved. Current ratings for mountain climbing carabiners are typically in the 6 to 10 kN (1350-2250 pounds of force) range with the gate open and 18-25 kN (4050-5625 pounds) with the gate closed. A typical rating for an OSHA-approved commercial carabiner — called a *safety hook* — is 40kN (9000 pounds). If you don't feel that mountain-climbing carabiners are adequately rated, safety hooks are available from safety equipment vendors.

Larger carabiners are available with locking gates; these will give you an added degree of safety, particularly if you are using them for your own protection or if you just want to be doubly safe. They're only a couple of dollars more than the standard, non-locking types.

Big carabiners are used for rescue work and other applications where a wider gate opening is needed. These are sometimes called *gorilla hooks* or *rebar hooks* and are used for larger tower rungs (Rohn BX, etc.) and larger loads. OSHA-compliant devices are offered by safety equipment vendors.

Using Carabiners

Here are some common ways that carabiners are used on tower projects:

1) Attach a sling to a guy anchor rod as an attachment point for the come-along when pulling guy wires.

2) Clip a carabiner onto a rung at the bottom of the tower then attach the haul rope snatch block pulley to it. This will change the direction of the haul rope from vertical to horizontal, making it much easier to pull. It also allows the pullers to watch the load as it goes up or down the tower and it removes them from the fall danger zone at the bottom of the tower.

3) Dedicate a sling and carabiner to the gin pole for easy lifting as the tower is assembled.

4) Put a loop through a frequently used tool, then clip it to your belt with a carabiner.

5) Always have a carabiner clipped into the bowline at the end of your haul rope and tag line for quick load attachment.

6) Clip a carabiner into the U-bolt on your rotator to haul it up.

Slings

A loop sling is made from one-inch nylon tubular webbing as seen in Figure 26.28C. Mountain-climbing slings are a continuous loop of webbing. A configuration with a sewn loop at each end is also useful. Slings can be wrapped around large or irregularly shaped objects and attached to a rope or tower member with a carabiner. Slings have around the same breaking strength as carabiners (approximately 4000 pounds, or 18.1 kN force) and are very handy for amateur applications and loads. Wrapping one around a tower rung or leg provides a convenient place to hang tools, parts or a pulley. Like carabiners, slings are not OSHA-approved but they're used for

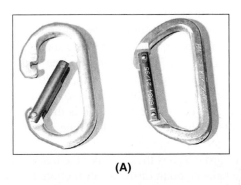

(A)

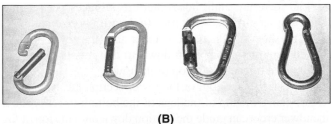

(B)

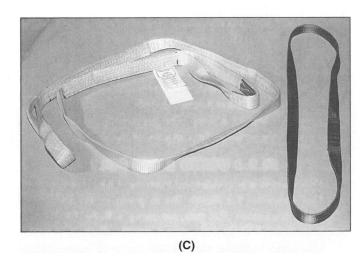

(C)

Figure 26.28 — (A) Oval mountain climbing type carabiners are ideal for tower workloads and attachments. The gates are spring loaded — the open gate is shown for illustration. (B) An open aluminum oval carabiner; a closed oval carabiner; an aluminum locking carabiner; a steel snap link. (C) A heavy duty nylon sling of the left for big jobs and a lighter-duty loop sling on the right for everything else.

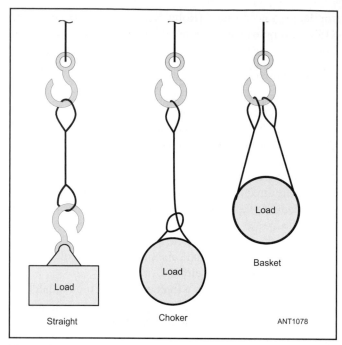

Figure 26.29 — Three basic lifting hitches used with slings and ropes.

mountain climbing protection. OSHA-approved slings are available from a safety equipment vendor.

Lifting Loads with Slings

Slings are typically used in one of three rigging configurations shown in **Figure 26.29**:

1) *Straight pull* — A simple direct vertical attachment such as for a tower section. Run the sling around a tower member and clip both ends in a carabiner for lifting.

2) *Choker* — Wrap the sling around the load one or more times, insuring that you pull the loop through itself on each wrap, cinch it tight, clip it into a carabiner and pull it up. The more tension you put on the sling, the tighter it gets. Chokers are the best way to lift a mast.

A choker will work in many other cases where you have an irregular load to haul, not just masts. Using a sling as a choker reduces the lifting capacity of the sling by as much as 30% though. A U-clamp can be installed above the sling when raising a mast for redundant protection if desired.

3) *Basket* — Basket hitches distribute a load equally between the two legs of a sling. The greater the angle between the two legs, the smaller the capacity of the sling.

26.5.3 USING A GIN POLE

This section was condensed from the ARRL book *Simple and Fun Antennas for Hams*. We're going to assume in the following discussion that you are using a Rohn EF2545 to install sections of Rohn 45G, which weighs about 70 pounds.

The main working part of the gin pole is the pulley mounted at the top of the 12-foot long heavy-wall aluminum tubing. This pulley has a haul rope going down to the ground crew through the center of the aluminum tube.

An adjustable, sliding clamp toward the bottom of the aluminum tubing is clamped to the tower using a swinging L-bracket-type clamp with two clamping bolts. These have T-bar handles that can be tightened by hand. In fact, this gin pole can be moved and deployed without any tools. The clamp is positioned just below the top braces of the tower section onto which the next tower section is to be installed. Once clamped to the top of the tower, you would loosen the T-bar handle that tightens the clamp against the sliding aluminum tube and slide the tubing up to its maximum extent.

In practice, the following steps are taken as each 10-foot section of tower is installed, one-by-one. We're assuming here that the gin pole starts out on the ground, with at least one person harnessed safely at the top of the tower. We're also assuming that the haul rope has been threaded through the aluminum tube and the top pulley, with a carabiner to prevent it from falling back down the tube.

Here's a rope tip — If the wind is blowing it may be difficult to lower the end of the rope to the ground. Attach a weight to the end of the rope; a wrench works well. If added weight isn't enough, use a carabiner to clip the free end of the haul rope around the other side of the rope. The carabiner will guide the free end back down the haul rope without blowing around.

1) The clamp holding the aluminum tubing is loosened so that the pulley on the tube can be lowered to where it is just above the bottom clamp. Then the T-bar handle for the tube clamp is tightened.

2) The climber lowers a tag rope for the ground crew to tie to the gin-pole pull rope. (This tag rope has been looped through a temporary pulley clipped to the top of the tower. It is also used to pull up tools and other materials.) The ground crew then pulls the gin pole up to the climber, using the tag line rope. Once the gin-pole head reaches the top of the tower, the climber clamps the gin pole clamp securely to the top of the tower. The tag line is then removed from the gin pole.

3) The T-bar handle for the tube clamp is loosened, and the aluminum tube is extended to its maximum height, as shown in Figure 26.27. Make sure the free end of the haul rope cannot slip through the top pulley, or else you'll have to lower the gin pole and go through this step again.

4) The free end of the haul rope is then dropped to the ground, often using a weight to keep the rope from waving about. (See the rope tip above.)

5) The ground crew then attaches the free end of the rope *above* the balance point of the tower section. For Rohn 25G or 45G there are eight horizontal cross braces per section. The crew should attach the rope to the fifth horizontal brace from the bottom. Please remember that the tower section should hang with its bottom down so that it is properly oriented when it reaches the top of the tower.

6) Once the bottom of the tower section has been lifted to just above the top of the legs of the bottom tower section, the tower crew can guide the section down onto the top of the three legs, while calling out to the ground crew instructions about *slowly lowering* the new section down onto the legs. See **Figure 26.30**, which illustrates guiding the new section

Figure 26.30 — Tower worker lowering a new section onto the top of the assembled stack of sections. The gin pole attached to the left leg is bearing the weight as the tower worker gives verbal instructions to the ground crew pulling on the haul rope. (Photo by Mike Hammer, N2VR)

of tower onto the previous section's legs.

7) Once the new tower section has been guided down onto the male ends, the pinning bolts are inserted and tightened with nuts. Note that Rohn uses two different sized bolts on the 25G and 45G section, with the larger diameter bolt on the bottom.

8) Finally, reposition the gin pole for the next section of tower. The T-bar at the clamp is loosened, the tube is dropped down to the level of the clamp, and the climber walks the gin pole up to the top of the section just installed and clamps it there, ready to pull up the next tower section.

26.5.4 ROPES AND ROPE CARE

If you are going to do tower and antenna work, you'll be using ropes. The most common uses are for haul rope, tag lines and temporary guys. A *halyard* is a rope used for hoisting.

Manila

Manila is the best known natural fiber rope. Manila must be handled and stored with care as any dampness will cause it to rot and damage its effectiveness and safety.

Polypropylene

Polypropylene makes lightweight, strong ropes that float on water, are rot-proof and are unaffected by water, oil, gasoline and most chemicals. Polypropylene rope is relatively stiff and doesn't take a knot well.

Nylon

Nylon is the strongest fiber rope commercially available. Due to its elasticity, nylon ropes can absorb sudden shock loads that would break ropes of other fibers. Nylon is particularly recommended for antennas using trees as supports. A disadvantage of new nylon rope is that it stretches by a significant percentage.

Nylon has very good resistance to abrasion and will last four to five times longer than natural fiber ropes. Nylon ropes are rot-proof and are not damaged by oils, gasoline, grease, marine growth or most chemicals.

Dacron

Dacron rope comes in three sizes ($\frac{3}{32}$, $\frac{3}{16}$ and $\frac{5}{16}$ inch) and is UV resistant. This is an excellent candidate for any rope used permanently outside such as for wire antenna halyards.

Rope Lay

All rope is twisted, or laid; and nearly all laid rope is *three-strand* construction, typically what you'll find at your local hardware store. Another type of rope is known as *braid-on-braid*, or *kernmantle*. This rope has a laid core covered with a braided jacket to produce a strong, easy-handling rope. In most instances, braid-on-braid rope is stronger than twisted rope of the same material and diameter. It is available in various synthetic fibers. Marine supply stores and mountain climbing stores carry a large variety of braid-on-braid types as well as a variety of types and sizes.

Which Rope to Use

The best rope for holding up wire antennas with spans up to 150 or 200 feet is ¼-inch nylon rope. Nylon is somewhat more expensive than ordinary rope of the same size, but it weathers much better. UV-resistant Dacron rope is also popular. After an installation with any new rope, it will be necessary to repeatedly take up the slack created by stretching. This process will continue over a period of several weeks, at which time most of the stretching will have taken place. Even a year after installation, however, some slack may still arise from stretching.

For ropes to be used on tower work, first decide which size will suit your needs based on working load. Most amateur loads are less than 100 pounds and very rarely do they exceed 250 pounds. A haul rope having a working load between 100 and 250 pounds will handle just about anything. **Table 26-3** summarizes the sizes and working loads for different types of rope.

Second, choose the type and material of your rope. Polypropylene rope is stiffer and more difficult to knot than nylon. Nylon and braid-on-braid ropes are softer and will take a knot very easily. The softer ropes also coil more easily and are more resistant to kinking.

Finally choose the length that will be most useful for you. If you double the height of your tower and add 25%, you'll have plenty. A 100-foot tower requires $(100 \times 2) + (100 \times 2 \times 0.25) = 200 + 50 = 250$ feet.

Price varies from less than $20 for 600 feet of ¼ inch polypropylene rope to more than $100 for 165 feet of high quality kernmantle climbing rope. K7LXC carries two lengths of $\frac{9}{16}$-inch braid-on-braid for haul ropes. One is approximately 175 feet long and can be used on towers up to 80 feet. The other haul rope is around 350 feet long and can be used for tower work up to 165 feet. The shorter rope is coiled when not in use and the longer one is simply fed into a plastic container

Table 26-3
Rope Sizes and Safe Working Load Ratings in Pounds

3-strand twisted line

Diameter	Manila	Nylon	Dacron	Polypropylene
¼	120	180	180	210
⅜	215	405	405	455
½	420	700	700	710
⅝	700	1140	1100	1050

Double braided line

Diameter	Nylon	Dacron
¼	420	350
⅜	960	750
½	1630	1400
⅝	2800	2400

for storage. If you feed the rope into the container it will pull back out without kinking or knotting.

Make certain that the rope ends will not unravel. Most supply stores will cut the length with a hot knife; that will do the best job of sealing the ends. You can do it at home by simply melting the ends with a lighter. An alternative is to tightly wrap a few layers of electrical tape around the ends. Be sure to tape the ends of all your ropes to protect them.

Rope Care

Inspect your rope periodically and replace it if there is any visible serious abrasion or damage. Here are some additional tips for using ropes:

1) Be certain your rope size is adequate for the job; don't use a rope that is too small.

2) Dry your rope before storing it. Natural fiber (Manila) ropes will mildew and rot if stored wet. You can put nylon ropes in the clothes dryer on low heat if they are really soaked.

3) Don't store ropes in direct sunlight; UV deterioration will significantly weaken them.

4) Cut out and discard any badly worn or abraded portions of a rope; better to have two shorter ropes you can trust than one long one that is suspect.

5) Keep your rope clean. Don't drag it through the mud, or over a rough or gritty surface. Try not to even step on your ropes.

6) Watch for kinks; they can cause permanent damage and weakening.

7) Protect ropes from all chemicals such as acids, oils, gasoline, paints, solvents, etc.

8) Avoid sudden strains; shock loading or jerking may cause failure.

9) Avoid overloading. A safe working load for a rope is 10-20% of its breaking strength.

10) Avoid abrasion. If the rope must run over a tower leg or any surface with a sharp edge, protect it with a layer or two of canvas or other such material.

11) Avoid bending a rope around corners or at sharp angles.

26.5.5 KNOTS

You can do about 98% of your tower and antenna work with only three knots — and you already know one of them. Remember that any knot will decrease the breaking strength of the rope — usually 40% or more. Choose and use the correct rope and knots for the job, and you should have no problems. Knots not listed here and additional knot-tying know-how can be found online at Animated Knots (**www.animatedknots.com**) and Real Knots (**www.realknots.com/knots**). **Figure 26.31** shows several common knots.

Overhand Knot

Start with an overhand loop, then passing the end under and up through the loop and then tightening. To form an overhand loop in the middle of a rope, double the rope for about two feet and tie an overhand knot with the doubled rope.

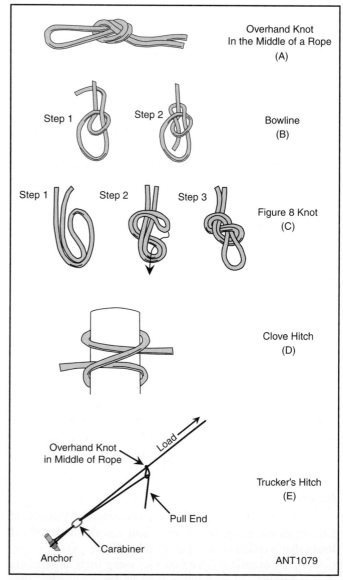

Figure 26.31 — Common knots used in tower and antenna work.

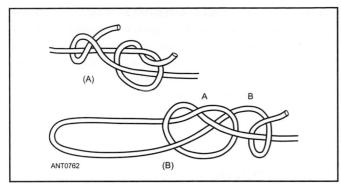

Figure 26.32 — This is one type of knot that will hold with slick types of line. Avoid these types of lines for lifting or safety uses. Shown at A, the knot for splicing two ends. B shows the use of a similar knot in forming a loop, as might be needed for attaching an insulator to a halyard. Knot A is first formed loosely 10 or 12 in. from the end of the rope; then the end is passed through the eye of the insulator and knot A. Knot B is then formed and both knots pulled tight. (Richard Carruthers, K7HDB)

Bowline

The bowline forms a loop that will not slip or jam, yet unties easily. It is used for hoisting, joining two ropes and fastening a rope to a ring or carabiner. To tie it, form a small loop in the rope. Run the end up through the loop, behind the standing part, then back down through the loop. Pull tight. Practice this one until you can make it almost automatically.

Figure-eight

Simpler than the bowline, a figure-eight knot may be used in most situations in place of a bowline. It is tied like a doubled overhand except that the rope is twisted an additional half-turn before the knot is pulled through the loop. It is one of the few knots that can be easily untied after holding a severe impact load, such as a falling tower section. Its only disadvantage for tower work is that it is a physically larger knot, and it takes a bit more rope than a bowline.

Clove Hitch

The clove hitch can be invaluable when you're working with round objects, and it can be put on or around almost any object very quickly.

Truckers' Hitch

The trucker's hitch allows you to tighten the rope as much as you can without a come-along. Tie an overhand loop (see above) toward the load end, run the end of the rope through a carabiner or shackle at a convenient anchor point, pass the end through the loop and then pull to tighten the rope. This technique gives twice the mechanical advantage of pulling on the single rope.

Plastic Line

For types of plastic line that are too slick to hold common knots well, **Figure 26.32** shows a more suitable knot. Needless to say, these lines should probably not be used for lifting loads or holding climbers.

26.5.6 PULLEYS

Pulleys are used constantly in tower and antenna projects. One should always be placed at the top of the tower for a haul rope to bring up materials. Steel pulleys costing $25-35 are found in many hardware stores or rigging shops but are heavy. K7LXC recommends the lightweight nylon pulleys used by utility company line crews for tower work. Wood-sheathed pulleys used in "block and tackle" devices and for sail hoisting should work well for very heavy loads.

Two important things to consider when shopping for pulleys are sheave size and sheave clearance. A sheave is the pulley wheel with a groove in it. A two-inch diameter sheave is the minimum size to use and larger sizes are better. Use a jam-proof pulley with minimal clearance between the sheave and the pulley body. If there is any way for your haul rope or cable to jump the pulley and get jammed, it almost certainly will.

A *snatch-block* is a pulley with a body that opens up so that it can be placed directly anywhere on a rope without

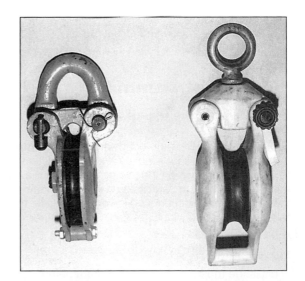

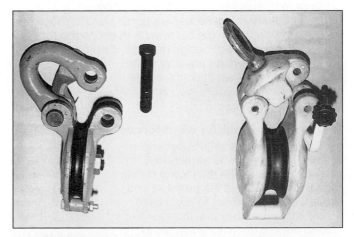

Figure 26.33 — (A) closed snatch-block pulleys. (B) open snatch-block pulleys.

needing one end of the rope to be free. This is useful when the rope is under tension (see **Figure 26.33**).

For supporting wire antennas, avoid small galvanized pulleys designed for awnings and clothesline pulleys. Use heavier and stronger pulleys intended for outdoor and marine installations with good-quality bearings.

An important consideration for pulleys to be constantly exposed to the weather is corrosion resistance. Use a good-quality pulley made entirely of alloys and materials that do not corrode readily. Galvanized pulleys will quickly rust. Marine pulleys have good weather-resisting qualities since they are usually made of bronze but they are comparatively expensive and the smaller pulleys are not designed to carry heavy loads.

26.6 TOWER CONSTRUCTION

Now that you have done all the planning and purchased the materials, it's time to start "growing" your tower. We'll start at the bottom!

26.6.1 THE LXC PRIME DIRECTIVE

After working on more than 225 Amateur Radio tower and antenna systems over the last 20 years, Steve Morris, K7LXC, has seen many problems and failures that could have, and should have, been avoided. By avoiding these mistakes, your tower and antenna system will be safer and more reliable. You'll sleep better when that big storm blows through, too.

When it comes to tower construction, you are strongly advised to always observe the 'LXC Prime Directive; that is, to "DO what the manufacturer says." Similarly, "DON'T do what the manufacturer doesn't say to do." Follow the specifications for materials, concrete and wind load and you'll minimize the chances for failure, small or large. Follow the directions for assembling equipment and using tools and supplies. Professional engineers have designed every aspect of these systems for safe, long-term and reliable use and it's in your best interests to follow their specifications and directions.

26.6.2 BASE EXCAVATION AND REBAR

To avoid underground utility lines, please don't dig

The 10 Most Common Tower Building Mistakes

1. Not following the manufacturer's specifications

Commercially manufactured towers have to comply with current standards for wind loading and structural integrity. Engineers design the towers and make the calculations to make them safe. If you don't follow their specifications at a minimum, the tower will not take the stresses and loads to which it is subjected. In other words, it'll probably fail.

2. Overloading

This is the most common reason for amateur tower failure. You must not exceed the wind load rating. This is even more important for self-supporting and crank-up towers. While you might get away with exceeding the ratings due to built-in design margins, it's never a good idea to overload any part of the tower system. When in doubt, err on the conservative side — you won't regret it.

3. Underestimating wind forces

Wind pressure on a tower and antenna system can be tremendous. Unless you've been on a tower during a windstorm to feel the pressure and the forces, it's difficult to appreciate how significant they are. Increases in wind pressure are not linear; wind loading goes up with the *cube* of wind speed. An increase of 10 MPH in wind speed can increase the wind force by almost 50% in some cases as shown in **Table 26-A**.

4. Not building for the wind speed rating in your county

While many counties and even whole states in the US are only rated for 70 MPH winds (the minimum rating), many other counties have ratings much higher. For example, Dade and Broward counties in Florida have ratings of 140 MPH. Find out what the wind speed rating is for your county or your specific location and use that as the *minimum* wind speed design parameter for your tower and antenna system. Champion Radio Tech Notes provides the wind speed ratings for all 3076 counties (**www.championradio.com/tech.notes.html**).

5. Using the wrong mast for the job

This is an all too common failure. Stacks of medium to large HF beams can put huge stresses on your mast. Pipe may be fine for small installations where you don't have much wind speed or loading or when there is only one antenna at the top of the tower. Structural tubing is carbon alloy steel rated for strength and is the preferred material.

Table 26-A
Wind Speed and Pressure

Mean Velocity	Wind Pressure
50.0 MPH	10.0 PSF
60.0 MPH	14.4 PSF
70.7 MPH	20.0 PSF
86.6 MPH	30.0 PSF
100.0 MPH	40.0 PSF
111.8 MPH	50.0 PSF
122.5 MPH	60.0 PSF

without calling one of the utility locator services. There are several websites such as **www.call811.com** that can help or you can call your local utility for assistance. Avoid expensive and embarrassing surprises. It may even be illegal in your area to begin digging without determining the location of buried utilities!

Hand-digging the hole for a large self-supporting tower base entails a lot of work! Excavating the necessary hole can be done quickly and effectively by a professional contractor. You can also rent excavating equipment and do the job yourself. No matter how you dig the hole, extreme caution should be used when someone is in the hole due to the risk of wall collapse. Many building regulations make it illegal to be in a hole or trench more than 4 feet deep without shoring up the sides of the hole. If you're doing the work yourself, never work alone in a hole that is deeper than your waist.

Building a Rebar Cage

Once the hole is dug you'll be installing the reinforcing bar, or rebar. The tower manufacturer will provide a recommended design for the rebar "cage" in the concrete base. **Figure 26.34** shows a typical completed cage.

Rebar is sized in eighths of an inch. For example, #4 rebar is ⅛ of an inch, or ½ inch, and #6 rebar is ⅝, or ¾ inch. Rebar vendors will cut and bend the rebar to your

Figure 26.34 — The rebar cage for KX8D's tower base. (Photo by Duane Durflinger, KX8D)

order which is a lot easier than buying long lengths of it at your local hardware store and trying to cut it yourself.

You can either build the rebar cage on the ground or in the hole. You'll need a backhoe or other piece of equipment to lift the completed cage up and lower it into the hole.

6. Not having the guy wires tensioned properly

Proper guy wire tension is a critical part of a tower's ability to handle wind stresses. Having the wrong tension can be like driving your car with over or under-inflated tires; it is potentially dangerous and is not the proper specification from the manufacturer. Having too little tension can result in wind slamming of the tower and guys as the tower is blown back and forth. Too much tension puts excess preload on the guys and lowers the safety margin significantly.

Around 90% of ham towers use ³⁄₁₆ inch EHS steel guy wires. Guy wire tension is typically 10% of the breaking strength — in the case of ³⁄₁₆ inch EHS that would be 400 pounds. The only inexpensive and accurate way to measure this is to use a Loos Tension Gauge such as the Loos PT-2 for ³⁄₁₆ and ¼ inch wire rope sizes.

7. Not having a proper ground system

A good ground system is necessary not only for lightning protection but will also protect your equipment, your home and your life. Proper grounding is discussed elsewhere in this chapter and in *The ARRL Handbook's* chapter on safety.

8. Not doing an annual inspection

Your tower and antennas are undergoing a slow, but constant process of deterioration. The best way to find and fix small problems before they grow into big problems and potential calamities is by doing an annual inspection.

Look at everything and push and pull on the hardware. You also want to put a wrench on 10% or more of the tower nuts to check for tightness as well as all of the nuts on accessories like antennas, mounts, U-bolts, etc.

9. Not fitting the tower sections on the ground

Tower sections, new or used, may not fit together easily. It's much easier to correct alignment problems on the ground than up on the tower during construction. A handy tool for getting tower sections together (or apart) is the Tower*Jack Combo that combines a leg aligner along with a lever for pulling sections together or pushing them apart.

10. Using the wrong hardware

To slow the process of deterioration, use only hardware that minimizes corrosion. Galvanized or stainless steel materials are the only ones that will survive outdoor use reliably. (See the section on "Corrosion" in this chapter.)

Substituting the wrong hardware can also lead to failure, for example using general hardware store bolts for tower legs when the manufacturer calls for a specific SAE grade. Using hardware totally unsuited for the task is common, i.e. installing the wrong type of 'screw-in' anchor or anchor rods; use of non-closed-eye eyebolts (use only welded or forged ones); use of the wrong guy material (EHS only!); and more.

Building the cage in the hole is harder since the room to work is really restricted. Remember to shore up the hole and don't work by yourself.

To tie the rebar together to form the cage use bailing/tie wire at each joint. Take about 2 feet of bailing wire and bend it in half. Wrap the tie wire through one of the Xs of the joint twice. Next wrap it twice through the other axis of the joint, bring the ends together and wrap them together several times. Use a large pair of pliers to twist it until snug. To stiffen the cage, add an X of two pieces of rebar across each face.

Guy anchors are easy to deal with since they're smaller, take less concrete and you don't have to move as much soil. The easiest way to locate the anchors is to temporarily put up a tower section at the desired location and then sight through each face across the opposite leg — that'll give you the angle. Then run your measuring tape out the appropriate distance to the anchor location.

Once the rebar cage has been placed in the hole any forms should be built and braced. A wooden form surrounding the top of the base hole provides for a neater appearance and also raises the top of the base above ground for a few inches. This allows water to run off the base and not pool around the legs or bolts of the tower.

Installing the Base Section

If you're installing a guyed tower such as Rohn 25G or 45G with tubular legs, be sure to put 4 inches or so of gravel at the bottom for drainage and set the legs of the base in the gravel. Water will condense in the legs and if there's no place for the water to drain out, it will build up and split the leg when it freezes.

Place the base section, if used, in the hole without touching the rebar cage and use wooden braces to hold it precisely vertical. Alternately, you can join one of the tower sections to the base section and use temporary guys to hold it up. For bigger tower bases, it's sometimes convenient to attach the leg(s) to the rebar cage with tie wire. A properly constructed rebar cage will be strong enough to support it and you can stand on it if needed.

If anchor bolts are being used a piece of plywood with the proper hole pattern can be used to hold the bolts when the concrete is being poured.

26.6.3 CONCRETE FOR BASES

The tower manufacturer will specify the type of concrete required for the base and your building permit may also impose some requirements. The strength specification is generally 2500 to 4000 PSI for tower bases and a slump (a measure of the concrete's workability) of 4. Consult an engineer if you are unfamiliar with ordering or working with concrete. The Wikipedia entry for concrete (**en.wikipedia.org/wiki/Concrete**) provides a great deal of good information.

You can mix the concrete yourself by using bags of premixed concrete and a powered mixer. It takes about 45 80-pound bags of concrete mix to make one cubic yard of concrete so for large bases ordering ready-mix concrete is more practical. The delivery truck will need to be relatively close to the hole (within 10 to 15 feet) to be able to position the delivery chute properly. If the truck cannot get close enough to the hole, you'll have to move the concrete yourself.

To avoid moving tons of concrete in long runs to the hole with a wheelbarrow, use a concrete line pumper — a truck-mounted pump that uses 2-inch hoses laid on the ground for concrete distribution. They're not that expensive and can pump for distances up to 400 feet. There are big hydraulic boom pumpers that can go over obstacles such as buildings and fences but they are more expensive to hire. In either case, using professional equipment makes the job of moving tons of concrete much easier.

Concrete takes a long time to cure to its rated strength — at least three weeks until it reaches 90% of its rated strength. The concrete supplier can give you complete instructions on how long to wait and whether the concrete needs to be kept damp during the curing period or any other special treatment. It's hard to sit and wait a month before beginning work on the tower but be safe and don't put any load on the base until it is ready to support it. Your building permit may require inspection of the base before tower work can begin.

26.6.4 WORKING WITH GUY WIRES

Guy wires are the heart of a reliable guyed tower system. Almost any tall amateur tower is going to be guyed. Rohn 25G, 45G and 55G are the most common towers used by amateurs and they all need to be guyed. Before you begin building the tower, familiarize yourself with guy wires and the associated equipment, hardware and techniques. Practice until you are confident of being able to handle guy wires correctly.

Guy Wire Grades

Steel guy wire comes in several different grades. Rohn specifications call for EHS (Extra High Strength) cable exclusively. As you can see from **Table 26-4**, this is the strongest steel cable available.

Guy Wire Terminations

The three most common methods of terminating guy wires are to use cable clamps, swaged or crimped pressed

Table 26-4
Guy Wire Specifications

Typical ³⁄₁₆ inch steel guy wire breaking strengths

Common Grade	1540 pounds
Utility Grade	2400 pounds
Siemens-Martin Grade	2550 pounds
High Strength Grade	2850 pounds
Stainless Steel Aircraft	3700 pounds
Extra High Strength Grade	3990 pounds
Phillystran HPTG4000	4000 pounds

EHS guy wire sizes and breaking strengths

³⁄₁₆ inch	3990 pounds
¼ inch	6650 pounds
⁵⁄₁₆ inch	11,200 pounds
³⁄₈ inch	15,400 pounds

fittings, or preformed guy grips. With the advent of the Preformed Guy Grips, cable clamp and swage fitting use has declined dramatically.

Cable Clamps

The least expensive and most common cable fittings are cable clamps consisting of two parts; the U-bolt and the saddle. The guy wire is put through a thimble or insulator and doubled back for clamping (this is called a *turnback*) as shown in **Figure 26.35**. A thimble is used to prevent the wire from breaking because of a sharp bend at the point of intersection. Conventional wisdom strongly recommends the use of thimbles that are at least one wire size larger than the cable to provide a more gentle wire bend radius.

Wrapping the wire around the thimble results in two parallel guy wires. The wire that bears the tension of the guy wire forces is called the "live" end and the short piece that is turned back is called the "dead" end. It's "dead" because it is not load bearing.

Always use three cable clamps per joint and make certain that the saddle is on the live (load-bearing) side of the guy wire. The saddle portion provides the majority of the holding capacity of the clamp and goes on the "live" side of the cable. To remember the correct method, use the saying "Don't saddle a dead horse." In other words, don't put the saddle on the dead side of the turnback. A clamp mounted backwards loses 40% of the holding capacity of a properly installed clamp.

As a final backup measure, the individual strands of the free end are unraveled and wrapped around the guy wire. It is a lot of work, but it is necessary to ensure a safe and permanent connection.

Swaged Fittings

Swaged fittings produce a strong, clean connection. If you don't like the look of lots of cable clamps, swaging may be for you. The most common swages are *Nicopress* fittings shown in **Figure 26.36**. While the fittings themselves are relatively inexpensive, you have to buy or rent a Nicopress tool to crimp them onto the guy wire. Once they're crimped on they can't be removed.

Preformed Guy Grips

Preformed guy grips (or *Big-Grip Dead-Ends* from Preformed Line Products — **www.preformed.com**) are the easiest to use and the most expensive. (see **Figure 26.37**) You

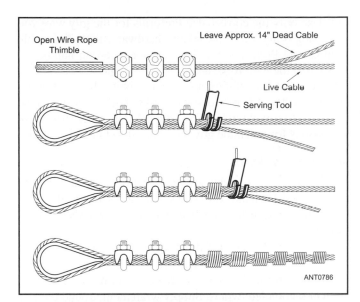

Figure 26.35 — Traditional method for securing the end of a guy wire. This technique is becoming increasingly uncommon as Preforms replace cable clamps.

Figure 26.36 — Swaged guy wire end using Nicopress fitting.

simply curl them onto the end of the guy wire to produce a permanent termination. Preformed cable grips have virtually replaced cable clamps for power, telephone, and communications companies. Factory specs say that you can remove and reapply the grips twice. If removal is necessary after a guy grip has been installed for a period greater than three months, it must be replaced. If you can't find them locally, they are available from several *QST* advertisers.

Preforms are color-coded for guy wire sizes, as follows:

$\frac{1}{8}$ inch — blue
$\frac{3}{16}$ inch — red
$\frac{1}{4}$ inch — yellow
$\frac{9}{32}$ inch — blue
$\frac{5}{16}$ inch — black
$\frac{3}{8}$ inch — orange

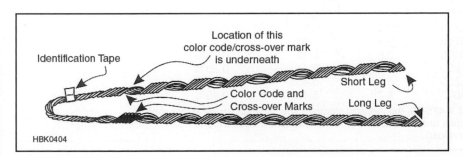

Figure 26.37 — Preformed guy wire "dead end" grip. The grip is wound around the guy wire and holds the load through friction.

Use only the correct size Preforms for the guy wire you are using. Guy wire and related hardware, including cable clamps and Preforms, are designed for a certain number of strands in the wire rope, and for a specific lay for each cable size. Do not mix different hardware. Note that Preformed grips have two sets of crossover marks. The set closest to the loop is for normal guy wire attachment. The set farthest from the loop is for when the guy wire goes through an insulator.

Installing Preforms

Preformed guy grips are precision devices, designed to be installed by hand; do not use any tools to install them. They should be installed only in conjunction with heavy-duty wire rope thimbles.

1) Insert a heavy-duty thimble into the eye of the Preform then through the attaching hardware (shackle, etc.).

2) Wrap the first leg (either one) around the guy wire with two complete wraps. Simply wrap them around the guy wire. Line up the crossover marks, then wrap the second leg with two complete wraps, ending opposite the first leg.

3) Complete the installation by either simultaneously wrapping both legs (keeping the legs opposite each other) or alternating between the legs a couple of wraps at a time. Bending the EHS guy wire as you wrap the Preform leg around it will make it easier to attach.

4) Finish the short leg first, then the long leg.

5) Seat the ends of the legs by hand or use a flat blade screwdriver under the end of the strands. For Phillystran guy wire you may need to separate the strands to finish the ends of the Preform.

6) Attach a black tie-wrap or end sleeve around the grip at the end to secure it.

Cutting Guy Cable

Many different methods have been used over the years to cut guy cable. These days, EHS (extra high strength) guy wire is the standard and special cutters are needed to cut this hard wire. Always wear safety goggles when working with guy wires. There can be lots of metal chips floating around when you cut them or the guy wire can easily whip around and hit you in the face or other body parts.

To cut the guy wire, rent or borrow a bolt cutter. Be certain it will cut EHS, not just soft metal. Another method is to use a circular power saw or hand grinder with a metal cutting aggregate blade. These blades are less than $4 at your neighborhood hardware store and will cut pipe mast material as well. Use electrical tape not only to mark where you want to cut but also to prevent the guy wire from unraveling after it's cut.

Phillystran

Introduced in 1973, Phillystran offers the strength of EHS guy wire with the added advantage that it is nonconducting and electrically transparent to RF. It consists of a polyurethane resin-impregnated aramid fiber rope with a thick extruded jacket of specially formulated polyurethane. Its non-conductivity makes it ideal for tower systems where some antennas will be under or close to guy wires. Guy wire interaction with stacks and wire antennas will be eliminated by using Phillystran. **Table 26-5** compares EHS, Phillystran and fiberglass rod guying material.

Recommended Phillystran installation calls for at least 10 to 25 feet of steel cable from the end of the Phillystran to the anchor. This prevents damage from vandalism, accidents and ground fires that can weaken Phillystran and cause a tower failure.

Phillystran Cable Grips

Preformed Line Products now manufactures Phillystran-compatible Preformed guy grips. These are different from those used with ¼ or ⅜ inch EHS with a different lay (twist) to match the characteristics of Phillystran. The grips for Phillystran cannot be interchanged with the grips for EHS.

The guy grips are installed generally the same way, except that you must keep some tension on the *Phillystran* while installing them, and you may have to split the strands on the end of the Preform in order to finish wrapping them on. This is because the *Phillystran* is very flexible, particularly when compared to EHS. Other than that, they're installed just like the Preforms for steel guys.

Table 26-5
Guy Cable Comparisons

Cable	Nominal Dia. (inches)	Breaking Strength (lbs)	Weight (lbs/100 ft)	Elongation (inches/100 ft)	Elongation (%)
³⁄₁₆ inch 1×7 EHS	0.188	3990	7.3	6.77	0.56%
¼ inch 1×7 EHS	0.250	6700	12.1	3.81	0.32%
HPTG6700	0.220	6700	3.1	13.20	1.10%
HPTG8000	0.290	8000	3.5	8.90	0.74%
⁵⁄₁₆ inch 1×7 EHS	0.313	11200	20.5	2.44	0.20%
HPTG11200	0.320	11200	5.5	5.45	0.45%
⅜ inch fiberglassrod	0.375	13000	9.7	5.43	0.45%

EHS steel cable information is taken from ASTM A 475-89, the industry standard specification for steel wire rope.
The HPTG listings are for Phillystran aramid cables, and are based on the manufacturers' data sheets. The elongation (stretch) values are for 100 feet of cable with a 3000-pound load.

Resonance in Guy Wires

If steel guy wires are resonant at or near the operating frequency, they can receive and reradiate RF energy. By behaving as parasitic elements, the guy wires may alter and thereby distort the radiation pattern of a nearby antenna. For low frequencies where a dipole or other simple antenna is used, this is generally of little or no consequence. But at the higher frequencies where a unidirectional antenna is installed, it is desirable to avoid pattern distortion if at all possible. The symptoms of re-radiating guy wires are usually a lower front-to-back ratio and a lower front-to-side ratio than the antenna is capable of producing. The gain of the antenna and the feed point impedance will usually not be significantly affected, although sometimes changes in SWR can be noted as the antenna is rotated. (Of course other conductors in the vicinity of the antenna can also produce these same symptoms.)

The amount of re-radiation from a guy wire depends on two factors — its resonant frequency, and the degree of coupling to the antenna. Resonant guy wires near the antenna will have a greater effect on performance than those that are farther away. Therefore, the upper portion of the top level of guy wires should warrant the most attention with horizontally polarized arrays. The lower guy wires are usually closer to horizontal than the top level, but by virtue of their increased distance from the antenna, are not coupled as tightly to the antenna.

To avoid resonance, the guys should be broken up by means of egg or strain insulators.

Figure 26.A shows wire lengths that fall within 10% of ½-λ resonance (or a multiple of ½ λ) over all the HF amateur bands.

Unfortunately, no single length greater than about 14 feet avoids resonance in all bands. If you operate just a few bands, you can locate greater lengths from the chart that will avoid resonance. For example, if you operate only the 14-, 21- and 24-MHz bands, guy wire lengths of 27 feet or 51 feet would be suitable, along with any length less than 16 feet.

Of course, you could neutralize the whole problem by using Phillystran at some expense. One way to minimize the cost is to use Phillystran on only the top or top two sets of guys. Further, it's not necessary to use Phillystran all the way down to the anchor. Even using Phillystran for the top 50% will reap benefits.

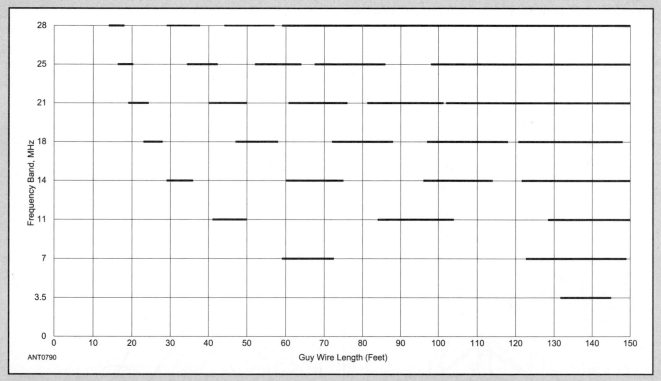

Figure 26.A — The black bars indicate ungrounded guy wire lengths to avoid for the eight HF amateur bands. This chart is based on resonance within 10% of any frequency in the band. Grounded wires will exhibit resonance at odd multiples of a quarter wavelength. (*by Jerry Hall, K1TD.*)

Attaching Guy Wires to the Tower

Figure 26.38 shows two different methods for attaching guy wires to towers. At Figure 26.38A, the guy wire is simply looped around the tower leg and terminated in the usual manner. At Figure 26.38B, a *guy bracket*, with *torque arms* has been added. Even if the torque arms are not required, it is preferred to use the guy bracket to distribute the load from the tower/guy connection to all three tower legs, instead of just one. The torque bracket is more effective at resisting torsion on the tower than the simpler installation. Rohn offers another guy attachment bracket, called a *Torque Arm Assembly*, that allows six guys to be connected between the bracket and anchors. This is by far the best method of stabilizing a tower against high torque loads, and is recommended for installations with large antennas.

Attaching Guys to Anchors

Turnbuckles and associated hardware are used to attach guy wires to anchors and to provide a convenient method for adjusting tension. **Figure 26.39A** shows a turnbuckle with a single guy wire attached to the eye of the anchor. Turnbuckles are usually fitted with either two eyes, or one eye and one jaw. The eyes are the oval ends, while the jaws are U-shaped with a bolt through each tip. Figure 26.39B shows two turnbuckles attached to the eye of an anchor. The procedure for installation is to remove the bolt from the jaw, pass the jaw over the eye of the anchor and reinstall the bolt through the jaw, through the eye of the anchor and through the other side of the jaw.

If two or more guy wires are attached to one anchor, *equalizer plates* should be installed (Figure 26.39C). In addition to providing a convenient point to attach the turnbuckles, the plates pivot slightly to equalize the various guy loads and produce a single load applied to the anchor. Once the installation is complete, a safety wire should be passed through

the turnbuckles in a figure-eight fashion to prevent the turnbuckles from turning and getting out of adjustment (Figure 26.39D).

Pulling and Tensioning Guy Wires

Once the guys are cut to their appropriate lengths and are attached to the tower, you need to pull them so you can attach them to the turnbuckle at the guy anchor. One method is to pull them by hand with a moderate amount of force (100-200 pounds of pre-tension will stabilize the tower under construction) and then secure them to the anchor. This will deflect the tower slightly but will put some initial tension on them. Another method shown in **Figure 26.40** is to use a come-along and cable grip. Place a nylon sling around the guy anchor for attachment of the other end of the come-along.

A rule of thumb is for final tension of the guy wire to be 10% of its breaking strength. That amount of tension is necessary to eliminate looseness in the cable caused by the spiral wire construction and to eliminate excessive dynamic guy and tower motion under wind loading. For ³⁄₁₆-inch EHS that amount of tension would be approximately 400 pounds.

How do you know when you've got the right amount of

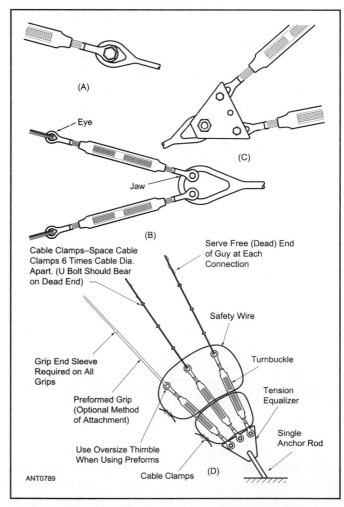

Figure 26.39 — Variety of means available for attaching guy wires and turnbuckles to anchors.

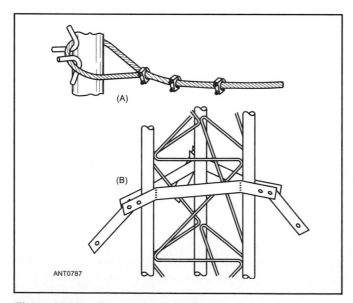

Figure 26.38 — Two methods of attaching guy wires to tower. See text for discussion.

Figure 26.40 — To tighten guy wires a nylon sling (see at the lower right of the photo) is attached to the guy anchor and a come-along. The come-along is then hooked to a Klein cable grip on the guy wire. The come-along is then tightened until the required guy tension is achieved as measured with a Loos tension gauge or dynamometer. The guy wire can then be attached to the guy anchor and the Klein grip released. (Photo courtesy of Dale Boggs, K7MJ.)

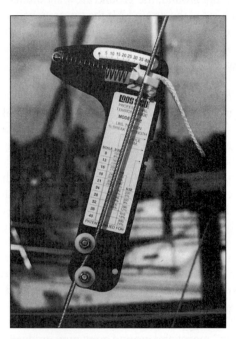

Figure 26.41 — Loos PT-2 guy wire tension gauge.

Figure 26.42 — A length of guy cable is used to assure that the turnbuckles do not loosen after they are tightened. This procedure is an absolute requirement in guyed tower systems, as shown by Jodi Morin, KA1JPA (left) and Helen Dalton, KB1HLF.

tension? A calibrated dynamometer can be used but they are expensive. The Loos Tension Gauge in **Figure 26.41** is an accurate, inexpensive device for measuring guy tension. It works by measuring the deflection of the guy wire and does not need to be inserted into the guy wire. (If you are using Phillystran, measure tension in the recommended section of steel EHS between the Phillystran and the ground anchor.)

The guy is gripped with a cable grip, which is connected to the anchor below the eye (or equalizer plate) with a block and tackle arrangement (see Figure 26.40) or a come-along. Then the turnbuckle is adjusted to take up the load, the cable grip is released and the final guy tension is adjusted and checked.

Regardless of how you measure guy tension, the important thing is to tighten all the guys so tension is approximately the same within each set of guys. Having all tensions equal avoids pulling the tower out of alignment. When you adjust

the guys at each level, you should check the tower for vertical alignment and straightness. This is often done with a transit from two ground points located 90° from each other. After plumbing the tower up to the first set of guys, another method is to look up the face of the tower from the bottom. It will be obvious if the sections above the guys are out of plumb.

Safety Wiring Turnbuckles

The final step in installing guy wires is to safety wire them as shown in **Figure 26.42**. This keeps turnbuckles from loosening from normal vibration and discourages vandalism. Use some pieces of leftover guy cable and loop it through the anchor shackle and the turnbuckles, securing the ends with a cable clamp.

26.6.5 BEFORE WORKING ON A TOWER

The Work Crew

For small antenna jobs, two people (one on the tower and one on the ground) are usually enough. Even erecting 25G tower (40 pounds per section) can be accomplished with two people but a third person to handle the tag line is very handy. For 45G, it takes two people on the haul rope as these sections weigh 70 pounds each and a section with guy brackets is close to 100 pounds.

Commercial riggers commonly use some type of winch or windlass to haul up heavy loads. For working with large antennas, such as 40 meter beams, two people on the tower along with one or two tag line handlers plus two to four on the haul rope requires a large crew.

Take care of your crew! Roll out the red carpet for them. They're giving up their time to help you and they deserve it. Make an effort to provide lots of water or iced tea and by all means feed everybody a nice lunch. *No alcohol* until after the work is done!

Pre-Work Meeting

On project day, the first thing you should do is have a session with the entire crew and go over what is going to be accomplished and the order and manner in which it is going to be done. Cover all safety issues, commands and equipment related to the job. Identify any hazards in the work area, such as power lines. Explain any specialized equipment or tools, including carabiners and slings, come-alongs, hoisting grips and so on. If a come-along or other special tool is going to be used, be sure that someone on the tower and ground crews knows how to use it properly.

One of the most important jobs for the ground crew is to act as a spotter and take care of the safety of the tower crew and the whole team. Point out where a phone is and any phone numbers that may be needed in an emergency. Also discuss and understand what to do in an emergency situation. For minor emergencies, knowing where the closest medical facility is will be valuable. Since just about everyone will have a mobile phone, calling 911 won't present any problems for bigger emergencies. Not many emergency services professionals have been trained for high-angle rescue such as lowering someone off of a tower so you're probably going to be on your own at least initially. Search and rescue crews are used to working with ropes and other hardware for extrications so hopefully your 911 operator will be able to put you in touch with them. Physical trauma can set in quickly even with a fall-arrest harness so fast action is vital.

Let your ground crew know not to be standing around the bottom of the tower unless they must specifically be there. This is the danger zone for dropped tools and hardware which reaches high speeds and can bounce a long way from the tower.

Rule #1. The tower crew is in charge. The ground crew should do what the tower crew tells them and not do what the tower crew doesn't tell them. Being on the ground crew is usually pretty boring, but they should not do anything that would have any impact up on the tower. With very few exceptions, the ground crew shouldn't do anything unless directed to. If they are not sure about something, ask the tower crew.

Rule #2. When the ground crew is talking to the tower crew, look up and talk in a loud, concise voice. Although it may be still and quiet on the ground, the ambient noise level on the tower is always significantly higher 50 feet or more in the air and you have major communication obstacles. VHF/UHF handhelds, FRS handhelds, or VOX-operated 47 MHz headsets all work. Make sure that all have fully charged batteries before work begins.

Rule #3. Really communicate. Insist that the ground crew keeps the tower crew really informed. If something is lowered to the ground, the ground crew should tell the tower crew that it's "on the ground." If the tower crew is waiting for the ground crew to do something, they should keep the tower crew informed about status. This prevents the "everybody waiting on everybody" problem.

Commands

Make certain that everyone understands each of the commands — whether they are the ones given here as examples or your own preferred set — and that they all use the same ones. All of the following commands refer to the "load" (antenna, tower section, etc.) and are applied to the "haul rope" (the line to which the load is attached). There are also several common hand signals to use. Simple ones for up, down and stop can be useful, particularly in high-noise situations. Make certain everyone knows what they are. For example:

- "Tension" tells the ground crew to put tension on the line, to take up any slack. Once you have some tension, move the load with "Up" or "Down" commands. Add "Slow" for slower lifting and lowering.
- "Slack" means giving the load some slack.
- "All slack" means the ground crew may gradually and gently release their grip on the load.
- "Stop" is obvious and "Stand by" indicates that they should maintain their assignment while awaiting the next command. Again, the tower crew is in charge; don't do anything without their instruction.

If something drops or falls, alert the ground crew immediately. Yell "Look out below!" or "Headache!" so that they can get out of the way of the wayward bolt, nut or tool. Their hardhats only provide minimal protection against this occurrence. Dropped items are not only dangerous but it also means sloppy work. Take your time and concentrate on not dropping anything.

The Tower Crew

If you're on the tower crew, you should know what you're doing or be working with someone who does. If you are working on a standing tower, before climbing walk around it and make a thorough visual inspection. Look at the base for cracked or rusted legs or missing hardware. Go out to the anchors to check the turnbuckles, clamps and other hardware. Look for bee or wasp nests. Never assume that any tower is safe to climb — always inspect it thoroughly before you take that first step.

Before beginning any maneuver, discuss how you're going to do it and the sequence that will be used. This way, everyone will understand the process and will hopefully do the right thing at the right time. This is particularly important if you're up there with someone that you've never worked with before. Sometimes you both assume that the other person is going to do something obvious that needs doing and then neither of you does it — this can be dangerous. Go over everything. This trains an inexperienced person and makes it easier the next time you work together.

Keep your tools either in your bucket or tool bags on your belt or tied to the tower. Try to avoid putting anything on a flat surface such as the rotator plate or thrust bearing plate; they can roll off.

Avoid using ac-powered tools on the tower. Battery powered tools are safer; you can buy, borrow or rent them. If you must use ac-powered tools, make certain they are insulated and that the extension cords are suitable. Zip cord extensions are dangerous. Make certain the ground crew knows where to disconnect the extension cords and where the breaker box is located.

The LXC Maxim of Manageability

Break everything down into bite-sized pieces and just do one step at a time. Trying to combine two or more steps in the same task is asking for trouble. For example, don't try to bring up the guy wires already attached to the tower section; bring them up after the section and guy brackets are installed. Trying to combine too many steps often results in doing things twice, along with undoing what you've already done. You'll be more efficient and safe by doing things one step at a time.

Prepping the Materials

Many tasks are a lot easier to do on the ground than up on the tower. Take the time to prepare all of the materials before hoisting them so that the tower crew's job is as simple as possible.

For a tubular-legged lattice tower, there are several things you can do to make the job easier while the tower sections are still on the ground. First, there will be excess galvanizing from the hot-dip process in many of the leg bolt holes on new tower sections. This will prevent a bolt from going through the hole. Except as a last resort, do not drill out the holes as it exposes the steel. Use a drift pin or taper punch and a hammer to enlarge the hole only enough for a bolt to clear the hole. Next, check the inside of each lower leg for that same excess galvanizing and remove it carefully with a round file. These steps are much easier to do on the ground than on the tower.

Check that the sections fit together. It's not uncommon that one leg won't line up, particularly with new sections. Using a piece of pipe or another tower section as a lever, gently bend the out-of-line leg until it slips on properly. This also is easier to do on the ground. Lay out the sections in order of fit and mark one pair of the mating legs with tape or

a felt marker to ensure they can be assembled the same way they were on the ground. Be sure to send the sections up the tower in the same order they were checked for fit.

Put some grease around the *inside* of each *lower* leg of a tubular-legged tower section. Not only will they slide on more easily during installation but the grease will help minimize corrosion and oxidation between the sections and make removal easier. Skipping this step at assembly makes disassembly harder to the point where a jack may be required to get the sections apart! If the tower is to be conductive, for example if it's to be used as a vertical antenna, then use a conductive antioxidant compound instead.

Inspect all of the remaining metal pieces and parts for blocked holes, damaged threads, bent braces or arms — anything that will make it hard to assemble on the tower. These are much easier to repair on the ground. Use a file to round the sharp edges of all plates, steps, brackets or arms to keep them from damaging you.

If more than one antenna is to be installed on the mast, measure and mark where each antenna will be mounted and where the thrust bearing, if any, will be.

Hook the rotator up to its control box and test its operation. Turn the rotator until it indicates North or another known direction then get it ready for hoisting. It doesn't really matter which way the rotator is physically installed in the tower as the antennas can be oriented when mounting them on the mast. By knowing the rotator's indicated direction the antennas can be aligned properly without stopping work.

If you are assembling an antenna for the project, let it sit overnight then retighten all of the nuts and bolts the next day. The hardware will have temperature cycled from warm to cold and warm again and some of the hardware will have loosened up during that temperature-induced expansion and contraction. This is the time to be sure it's all tight!

Antenna element hose clamps invariably catch on anything — wire antennas, guy wires, cables, and so on. To minimize this annoying characteristic, wrap the hose clamp with a layer or two of electrical tape while it's still on the ground. This is another good reason to use rivets instead of hose clamps.

If your rotator doesn't have a connector for the control cable, you can add one using vehicle trailer connectors — they come in a flat 4-wire polarized configuration. Get two sets and install a pigtail to the rotator terminated in one male and one female connector. Do the opposite at the end of your control cable to the shack. This will ensure that the cable is always connected correctly.

When putting something together "temporarily," always install it as though you won't be coming back; "temporary" sometimes means it will be up and used for years!

Hardware Prep

Make sure all hardware is stainless or galvanized hardware. Avoid plated hardware.

Never place a load on eyebolts with eyes that can open. Only eyebolts that are cast or welded closed should be use on tower or antenna projects if they will be carrying a load.

Always take extra hardware, nuts and bolts up the tower in case you run short or drop something. If you don't have them, you'll invariably need them.

26.6.6 ASSEMBLING THE TOWER

Route the haul rope through a snatch block at the bottom of the tower to transfer the hoisting effort from pulling down to pulling horizontally. Pulling vertically is all arm strength plus the ground crew is exposed to falling objects. Pull horizontally by putting the rope around your hips and walking backwards to hoist the load. This uses larger muscle groups and hoisting will be much easier. In addition, those hoisting can watch the load while staying out of the danger zone. Anyone working with ropes under load should be wearing leather gloves.

To hold onto a haul rope, put it around your hips then bring the tail or dead end in front of you. *Do not* tie the rope around your waist — this is potentially dangerous. Aiming the tail end in the same direction as the load rope, grasp both ropes with one or both hands. This is the best way to hold or brake a rope load. Don't depend on just using your hands; it's not as reliable and your hands and arms will quickly tire. With the rope secured around you, it can be held comfortably for quite some time.

Section Stacking

After rigging the gin pole as in Figure 26.27 (the haul rope goes up the middle of the pipe, across the pulley, then down to the load), attach the leg bracket to the top of the top section, *below* the top brace. Make certain that it's secure before you push the gin pole mast up to the extended position where it'll be ready for the lift. (This is a good procedure to rehearse on the first section above the base with the ground crew watching.)

The tower section should be rigged so that it hangs more or less vertically; the heavier the section, the more important this becomes. Put a sling around a leg at about ¾ of the way up the section (double-check for proper top and bottom orientation) to establish the pick-point. Attach the haul rope just above the section midpoint and, on the command of the tower crew, start to pull on the haul rope.

As soon as it clears the top of the tower, the tower crew should yell "stop," then "down slow" when ready to have the section lowered onto the top of the tower.

If leg alignment problems are discovered (see item 9 in the sidebar on tower building mistakes), use a come-along around the bottom of the whole section and tighten it up to pull the legs together. (This is common practice when putting up angle-legged self-supporting towers.) If you don't have a come-along, a ratchet-operated truck strap will work great. One person on a tower doesn't have a whole lot of leverage and if the sections line up but won't slide down, use a come-along or Tower*Jack and pull the section down into place.

Stack an appropriate number of sections (typically up to the next guy point), then bring up the first set of guys and attach them. Your ground crew can use their cable grips and

come-alongs to put the initial tension on them, then attach them to the anchors. You'll be able to tell them which ones to tighten and which ones to loosen by using a level on the leg to plumb the tower. Once that's done, repeat the same steps until all the sections are in place and guyed.

It's important to plumb the first set of sections including the first set of guys. Once that segment is plumb, you can look up the face of the tower to see if everything above it lines up — it'll be pretty obvious. If it doesn't, just adjust the come-alongs or turnbuckles to get it straight.

Installing the Mast

For small and medium masts, use the gin pole to bring it up using a sling as a choker. The choker should be above the balance point so that the mast goes up vertically. Lower the mast into the tower from the top.

Large and heavy masts more than 20 feet long are bigger than the usual gin pole can control properly. When building the tower, put the mast inside the bottom sections. Remove any rotator shelves or other obstructions so the gin pole can lift the mast up through the tower. Once the mast is captured at the top of the tower, it can be raised gradually. The books referenced at the beginning of this chapter provide more details.

Once the mast extends slightly above the top of the tower and is captured by the thrust bearing or a clamp acting as a collar, install the top antenna on the mast if more than one is to be installed. Once the first antenna is installed, pull the mast up with a come-along to where the next antenna is to be installed. Repeat the sequence until all the antennas are installed.

Installing the Rotator

Clip a carabiner and haul rope onto a U-bolt on the rotator clamp or lift it with a bucket. Bring up the rotator, install it under the mast, and lower the mast into the rotator clamp. To haul up the control cable, tie an overhand knot in the cable and snap that into the haul rope carabiner.

To minimize the possibility of binding in the rotator/mast/thrust bearing system, work down when doing the final tightening. Do the thrust bearing first, the rotator mast clamps next, the rotator shelf bolts, and the rotator base bolts last.

When connecting the multiconductor control cable, one way to keep wire colors straight and consistent is to use the resistor color code: black, brown, red, orange, yellow, green, blue, violet, grey and white.

Rotation Loops

There are two ways to make a rotation loop for your cables. One way is to tape all the cables coming down the mast into a bundle, leaving an extra 4-5 feet of slack before securing the bundle to a tower leg. The bundle will have some rigidity that will help keep it out of harm's way. Make sure that it doesn't snag on anything as the system rotates and you'll be good to go. If you have a flat-topped tower, wind the cable around the mast 2-3 times in a diameter smaller than the top plate so that the coil lays on the flat surface.

Tower Climbing Shield

A tower can be legally classified as an "attractive nuisance" that could cause injuries and/or lawsuits. You should take some precautions to ensure that "unauthorized climbers" can't get hurt on your tower.

Generally, the attractive-nuisance doctrine applies to your responsibility to trespassers on your property. (The law is much stricter with regard to your responsibility to an invited guest.) You should expect your tower to attract children, whether they are already technically trespassing or whether the tower itself lures them onto your property. A tower is dangerous to children, especially because of their inability to appreciate danger. (What child could resist trying to climb a tower once they see one?) Because of this danger, you have a legal duty to exercise reasonable care to eliminate the danger or otherwise protect children against the perils of the attraction.

An article describing such a tower shield by Baker Springfield, W4HYY and Richard Ely, WA4VHM was published in September 1976 QST. It has been added to this book's CD-ROM, including construction diagrams. Installing it should eliminate the worry.

26.7 RAISING AND LOWERING ANTENNAS

While small antennas can simply be pulled up directly on a haul rope, working with HF beams requires some technique. If done properly, the actual work of getting the antenna into position can be executed quite easily with only one person at the top of the tower. The ground crew does all the lifting by using a large pulley attached to the antenna mast or a gin pole with its pulley a foot or two above the point at which the antenna is to be mounted. Because raising an antenna often requires the load to be pulled away from the tower — either to avoid guy wires or as part of a tram or V-track system — this places significant bending forces on a mast or gin pole and may bend them if the pulley is too far above where they are attached to the tower.

The advice and suggestions in this section also apply to removing antennas by following the procedures in reverse. An antenna should probably be removed the same way it was installed. If installing it required a crane, it will most likely have to be removed by a crane.

26.7.1 AVOIDING GUY WIRES

Guy wires often obstruct the antenna's path to the top of the tower. One method of avoiding them is to tie a tag line to the middle of the boom and to a middle element for leverage (but within reach of the tower crew). The ground crews then pull the antenna out away from the guys as the antenna is raised. With this method, some crew members are pulling up the antenna to raise it while others are pulling down and out to keep the beam clear of the guys. Obviously, the opposing crews must act in coordination to avoid damaging the antenna.

A second method is to tie the haul rope to the center of the antenna. A crew member, wearing a climbing harness, walks the antenna up the tower as the ground crew raises it. Because the haul rope is tied at the balance point, the tower climber can rotate the elements around the guys. A tag line can be tied to the bottom end of the boom so that a ground crew member can help move the antenna around the guys. The tag line must be removed while the antenna is still vertical.

The third method is characterized as the "wig-wag" system by Tom Schiller, N6BT in his book *Array of Light*. It is particularly useful when other antennas are already installed on the antenna mast. The new antenna is lifted until it is immediately below the lowest antenna on the mast and rotated so that its elements are parallel to the boom of the installed antenna. The new antenna's elements are then tipped up to clear the elements of the installed antenna so that the new antenna is rotated around the installed antenna until its boom is above that of the installed antenna. Once above the installed antenna, the new antenna can be lifted so that its elements can be rotated to clear those of the installed antenna and then returned to horizontal and lowered for installation. This can be difficult if more than one antenna is already installed on the antenna mast.

26.7.2 USING A TRAM SYSTEM

Sometimes one of the top guys can provide a track to support the antenna as it is pulled upward. Insulators in the guys, however, may obstruct the movement of the antenna. A better track made with rope is an alternative. One end of the rope is secured outside the guy anchors. The other end is passed over the top of the tower and back down to an anchor near the first anchor. So arranged, the rope forms a narrow V-track strung outside the guy wires. Once the V-track is secured, the antenna may simply be pulled up, resting on the track. This is known as the trolley or V-track system. It is not an easy method to use. It requires two trolley cables spread apart some distance with the same tension on each line or the beam will tip. Plus there is a lot of added friction to the system from the weight of the antenna on the lines.

A much easier system is the tram line in which one line runs from the top of the tower to an anchor on the ground and the antenna is slung below the tramline. The system is illustrated in **Figure 26.43**.

Install one long (6-foot) sling on each side of the center mounting point of the antenna with two or three wraps around the boom; then bring them together to form a truss with the pick point is directly above where the boom plate will attach to the mast.

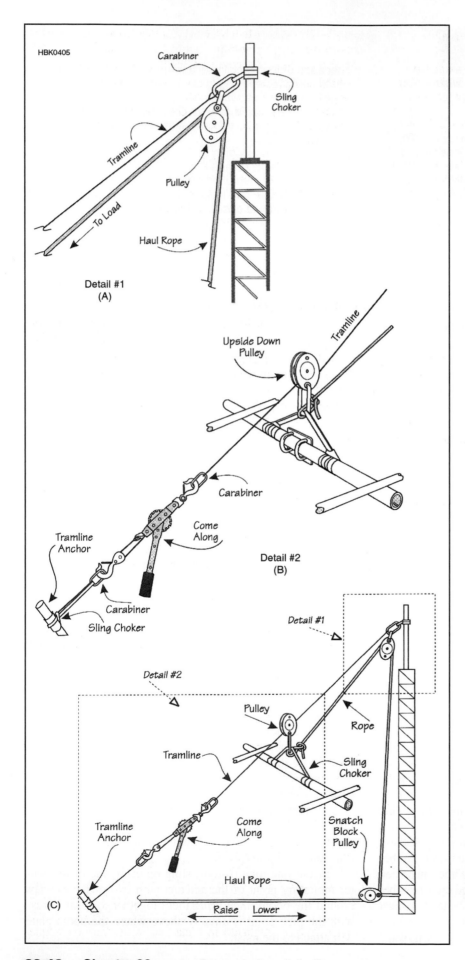

HBK0405

Carabiner

Sling Choker

Tramline

Pulley

To Load

Haul Rope

Detail #1
(A)

Upside Down Pulley

Tramline

Carabiner

Tramline Anchor

Come Along

Detail #2
(B)

Carabiner

Sling Choker

Detail #1

Detail #2

Pulley

Rope

Tramline

Sling Choker

Tramline Anchor

Come Along

Snatch Block Pulley

Haul Rope

Raise   Lower

(C)

This assures that the antenna is balanced and will arrive in the correct mounting position. Using two slings on the boom enables you to hoist the beam while it remains horizontal. Even if the antenna is mechanically off balance, you can adjust the slings so that it will remain basically horizontal.

You'll need three pulleys, a haul rope, a length of wire rope for the tram line, an anchor on the ground and miscellaneous slings and carabiners. K7LXC's preference is to use a wire rope tram line with the antenna suspended below the tram wire. Small diameter aircraft cable or wire rope such as ⅛ inch or ³⁄₁₆ inch is sufficient to take the static load of just about any amateur antenna.

To set up the tram line, first secure a sling choker on the antenna mast about three feet above the place where the antenna will be mounted. Use two or three wraps and bring the choker through itself as described earlier.

Clip a carabiner or shackle to the tail of the sling. Then clip a large pulley into the carabiner. Bring up one end of the tram line and clip it into the same carabiner.

Secure the other end of the tram line to an anchor. You can use a tree, a fence post, a car, a stake driven into the ground or any other convenient strong point. Use a come-along and cable gripper to tighten the cable until most of the slack is taken up. Do not over-tighten; you could damage your mast. If the sling on the mast is now high enough to create a significant bending force on your mast (more than four or five feet), back guy it in the opposite direction with another wire line or rope that is anchored to a convenient spot.

Run the haul rope through the back of the antenna mast pulley and out the front in the direction of the ground anchor. Lower

Figure 26.43 — A schematic drawing of the tram line system. At A, rigging the top of the tower for tramming antennas. Note the use of a sling and carabiner. (B) Rigging the anchor of the tramline. A come-along is used to tension the tramline. (C) The tram system for getting antennas up and down. Run the antenna part way up the tramline for testing before installation. It just takes a couple of minutes to run an antenna up or down once the tramline is rigged.

Figure 26.44 — A sturdy all-metal pulley suitable for tramming. (Photo by K4ZA)

the end of the haul rope directly to the ground or tie it to a carabiner clipped onto the tram line and let it slide down the wire. Figure 26.43A shows how the system should look at the top of the tower.

You may have to drop one or two of the top guy wires or any wire antennas closest to the antenna tram path if the antenna is going to be installed close to the top of the tower. Guys should be detached at ground level.

On the ground, attach the tram pulley (**Figure 26.44**) to the tramline. Turn the pulley upside-down (the antenna will be suspended under the tramline) then clip in the load end of the haul rope. Lift the two slings forming the antenna truss to the tram pulley and clip it in. The boom should be at a right angle to the tram line (elements parallel to the line) with the boom-to-mast bracket pointed toward the mast ready to accept U-bolts.

At this point, the haul rope should be attached to the tramline pulley. It goes up through the pulley on the mast, then down the tower to the ground. The third pulley is used at the bottom of the tower to change the direction of the haul rope from vertical to horizontal. At this point the system should look like Figure 26.43.

Figure 26.45 — Photo of the tram suspension system used by K7NV. Note that the tiller is attached to the haul rope in this system. The boom of the antenna can be rotated in the U-bolt holding it to the tiller to adjust the tilt of the elements to clear guy wires. (Photo by Kurt Andress, K7NV)

With antennas that have the elements mounted above the boom the antenna will attempt to flip over or "turn turtle." Minimize that tendency by tying the slings with opposite wraps (one around the boom in one direction, the other wrapped in the other direction).

Another method that helps counteract this unwanted tendency is to use a "tiller" as shown in **Figure 26.45**. It's a 4-foot long or so piece of angle iron or aluminum that is U-bolted to the boom on one end and has a small U-bolt on the front that captures the tramline and acts as a guide. Alternately, the front of the tiller can be attached to the haul rope. The tiller holds the antenna boom in a relatively fixed position, thus preventing it from turning over. Once the antenna has been lifted off the ground, the boom can be rotated in the tiller's U-bolt so that the element halves facing the tower are raised to clear the guy wires.

Next, attach any tag lines. Use a small line such as 1/4 inch polypropylene because it's light and stiff enough to resist hanging up on any clamps or hardware sticking out on the elements. Tie one end to the boom at a convenient spot that the tower crew can reach to untie it. Wrap the tag line around an adjacent element two or three times. You can add one or two wraps of electrical tape to hold it in place on the element to keep the fulcrum out on the element and away from the boom. The tag line will pull easily through the tape when you're done. If the tag line does hang up on a guy wire, lower the antenna to free it then tram it back up again.

When it's time to launch the antenna, have the ground crew pull the haul rope while another person helps the antenna off the ground. Once the antenna is launched, crew members holding the tag lines can guide it as it goes up.

Use the tag lines to pull the element halves pointing away from the tower down so that they'll clear the guys. You'll be pulling against the haul rope so don't pull too hard on the tagline. The tag lines can also be used to move the boom so that the antenna will be in the proper mast-mounting orientation.

The tower crew can guide the antenna when it gets close to the tower. Once the antenna has cleared all obstacles and if everything was rigged correctly, the antenna should come right up to the mast.

Another advantage is that while on the tram line you can run any on-the-air tests you'd like. Just attach a run of coax before you lift the antenna. To make any adjustments, lower the antenna, make the changes and pull it up again. Make measurements with the boom 90° to the tram line if possible (elements parallel to the tramline).

To take antennas down, rig everything the same way, then lower the antenna down the tram line. Be certain as it comes up from the ground, the haul rope goes behind the boom before it goes through the mast pulley.

26.7.3 BUILDING ANTENNAS ON THE TOWER

A fourth method is to build the antenna on the tower and then swing it into position. Building the Yagi on the tower works particularly well for Yagis mounted partway up the tower, as you might do in a stacked array. The technique

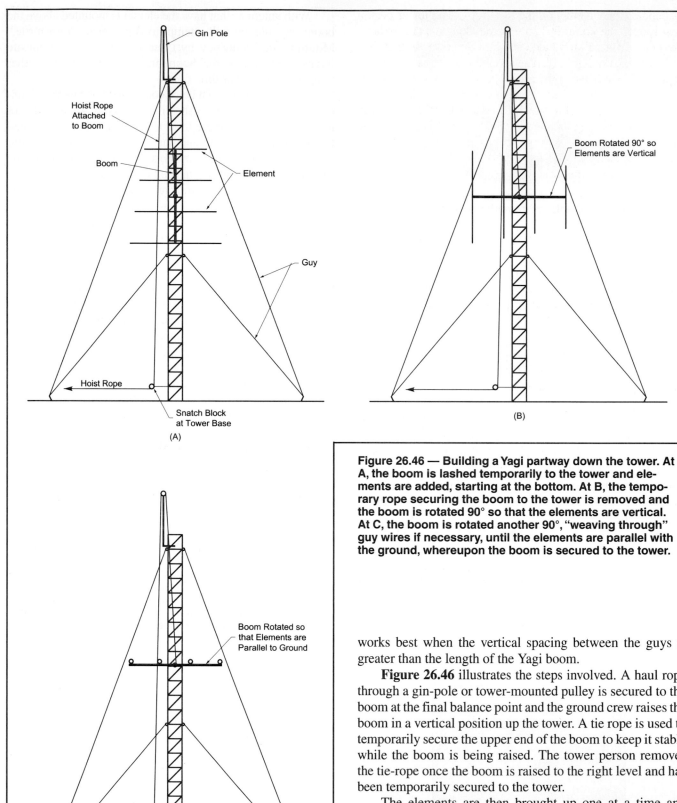

Figure 26.46 — Building a Yagi partway down the tower. At A, the boom is lashed temporarily to the tower and elements are added, starting at the bottom. At B, the temporary rope securing the boom to the tower is removed and the boom is rotated 90° so that the elements are vertical. At C, the boom is rotated another 90°, "weaving through" guy wires if necessary, until the elements are parallel with the ground, whereupon the boom is secured to the tower.

works best when the vertical spacing between the guys is greater than the length of the Yagi boom.

Figure 26.46 illustrates the steps involved. A haul rope through a gin-pole or tower-mounted pulley is secured to the boom at the final balance point and the ground crew raises the boom in a vertical position up the tower. A tie rope is used to temporarily secure the upper end of the boom to keep it stable while the boom is being raised. The tower person removes the tie-rope once the boom is raised to the right level and has been temporarily secured to the tower.

The elements are then brought up one at a time and mounted to the boom. It helps if you have a 2- or 3-foot long spotting mast temporarily attached to the boom to form a 90° frame of reference. This allows the ground crew to spot from below so that the elements are all lined up in the same plane. After all the elements are mounted and aligned properly, the temporary rope securing the boom to the tower is released, suspending the antenna on the haul rope. The tower person then rotates the boom 90° so that the elements are vertical. Next the elements are rotated 90° into the tower so that they are parallel to the ground. The ground crew then moves the boom up or down using the haul rope to the final point where it is mounted to the tower.

A modification of this technique also works for building a medium-sized Yagi on the top of the tower. This technique will work if the length of the gin pole at maximum safe extension is long enough (see **Figure 26.47**).

As usual, the gin pole haul rope is attached to the balance point of the boom and the boom is pulled up the tower in the vertical position, using a rope to temporarily tie the haul rope to the top end of the boom for stability. The boom is temporarily secured to the tower with rope in the vertical position so that the top end is just higher than the top of the tower. In order to clear the gin pole when the elements are mounted and the boom is raised higher to mount the next element, you must tilt the boom slightly so that the element mounted to the top end of the boom will be behind the mast. This is very important!

The elements are first mounted to the bottom side of the boom to provide weight down below for stability. Then the top-most element is mounted to the boom. The tower person removes the temporary rope securing the boom to the tower and the ground crew uses the haul rope to move the mast vertically upwards to the point where the next element from the top can be mounted. Once all the elements are mounted and aligned in the same plane (the center element closest to the mast-to-boom bracket can be left off until the boom is in place), the temporary securing rope is removed. The boom is now swung so that the elements can be maneuvered to clear the top guy wires. Once the elements are horizontal the boom is secured to the mast and the center element is mounted if necessary.

A special boom-to-mast mounting plate that supports working on antennas at the top of the tower was designed by the Potomac Valley Radio Club and is described in a short article ("The PVRC Mount") on the CD-ROM for this book.

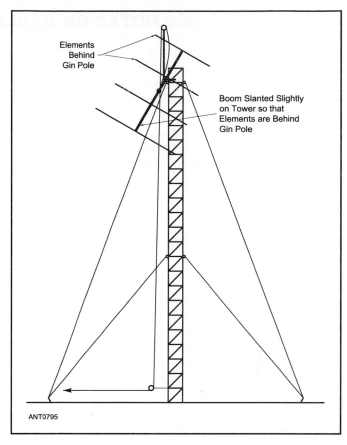

Figure 26.47 — Building a Yagi at the top of the tower. The length of the gin pole must be longer than ½ the boom so that the boom can be hoisted upwards to the place where it is mounted to the mast. Usually the boom is initially lashed to the tower slanted slightly from vertical so that the top element ends up behind the gin pole. The elements are mounted at the bottom end of the boom first to provide stability. Then the element at the top of the boom is mounted and the boom is moved upwards using the gin-pole hoist rope so that the next-to-top element may be mounted, again behind the gin pole. This process is repeated until all elements are mounted (save possibly the middle element if it can be reached easily from the tower once the beam has been mounted to the mast). Then the boom is tilted to the final position, weaving the elements to clear guy wires if necessary.

26.8 NOTES ON CABLES AND CONNECTORS

The following sections contain information that applies to the construction of antenna and tower systems. For more information on the characteristics of coaxial cable and RF connectors, including cable selection, see the **Transmission Lines** chapter.

A general tip for handling cable and wire — when removing it from a roll, unroll it so that it lies straight and flat along the ground. Pulling it straight out of the coil gives it a full twist with turn, leading to strength-reducing kinks in wire and endless aggravation as you attempt to get it untwisted and untangled.

26.8.1 COAXIAL CABLE

Bending Radius

Bending coax is acceptable as long as the radius of the bend is larger than the specified minimum bending radius. For example, a common minimum bending radius specification for RG-8 is 4 inches (8 times the cable diameter). Coax with more rigid shield materials will have a larger bending radius. Bending the coax tighter than the minimum bending radius can cause impedance "bumps" in the line by distorting the geometry of the conductors. It can also cause the center conductor to migrate through the plastic insulation and eventually short to the outer shield.

Burying Coax

There are several reasons why you might choose to go to all the work of burying your coax. One is that direct burial cable is virtually free from storm and UV damage, and usually has lower maintenance cost than cable that is out in the open. Another reason might be aesthetics; a buried cable will be acceptable in almost all communities. Also, being underground reduces common-mode feed line current on the outside of the shield, helping to reduce interstation interference and RFI.

Although any cable can be buried, a cable that is specifically designed for direct burial will have a longer life. The best cable to use is one that has a high-density polyethylene jacket because it is both nonporous and will take a relatively high amount of compressive loads. "Flooded" direct burial cables contain an additional moisture barrier of non-conductive grease under the jacket; this allows the material to leak out, thus "healing" small jacket penetrations. (These can be messy to work with when installing connectors.)

Here are some direct burial tips:

1) Because the outer jacket is the cable's first line of defense, any steps that can be taken to protect it will go a long way toward maintaining the internal quality of the cable.

2) Bury the cable in sand or finely pulverized dirt, without sharp stones, cinders or rubble. If the soil in the trench does not meet these requirements, tamp four to six inches of sand into the trench, lay the cable and tamp another six to eleven inches of sand above it. A pressure-treated board placed in the trench above the sand prior to backfilling will provide some protection against subsequent damage that could be caused by digging or driving stakes.

3) Lay the cable in the trench with some slack. A tightly stretched cable is more likely to be damaged as the fill material is tamped.

4) Examine the cable as it is being installed to be sure the jacket has not been damaged during storage or by being dragged over sharp edges.

5) You may want to consider burying it in plastic pipe or conduit. Be careful to drill holes in the bottom of the pipe at all low spots so that any moisture can drain out. While PVC pipe provides a mechanical barrier, water incursion is practically guaranteed — you can't keep it out. It will leak in directly or condense from moisture in the air. Use the perforated type so that any water will just drain out harmlessly.

6) It is important that direct burial is below the frost line to avoid damage by the expansion and contraction of the earth during freezing and thawing of the soil and any water surrounding the buried cables.

Coax Jumpers

With many beam antennas, the feed point is out of reach from the tower and should be connected to a jumper just long enough to reach from the feed point to the antenna mast. That way, the feed line connection and waterproofing can be done at the most convenient location. If you ever have to remove the antenna in the future you can just disconnect the jumper and lower the antenna.

Coax "Pigtails"

Most manufacturers use some type of feed point system that accepts a PL-259 or N connector. Some antennas require you to split the coax and attach the shield and center conductor to attachment points on the driven element. The exposed end of the coax is very difficult to seal. Water will wick down the outer shield and into your shack unless you take great pains to weatherproof it. Coating the entire pigtail and attachment terminals with Liquid Electrical Tape or some other conformal sealant is a good approach. Another approach for HF beams is to use a "Budwig HQ1" style insulator with the integral SO-239 and wires for connecting to the terminals (See the **Antenna Materials and Construction** chapter.) As always, follow the manufacturer's directions.

26.8.2 CONTROL CABLES

In addition to coaxial cables, most towers will have some sort of control cable for rotators, antenna switches or other accessories. The manufacturer should provide the size that is necessary and again, you should follow their specifications.

In the case of rotator cables, some rotators are sensitive to voltage drop so bigger sizes should be used. For really long runs, some amateurs use THHN house wire from the local hardware store to get reasonably-priced bigger wire. Only the motor and solenoid conductors typically require the larger wire.

26.8.3 WEATHERPROOFING RF CONNECTORS

The primary purpose of weatherproofing is to keep moisture and contaminants out of your coaxial cable connections. Whether it is rain or condensation, water in a connector can put you off the air.

Properly sealed connector joints will be very effective and reliable in maintaining electrical and mechanical integrity. Here's how to do it as illustrated in **Figure 26.48**:

1) Install the connector correctly on the end of the coax.

2) Use pliers when attaching a PL-259 to a SO-239 or PL-258 barrel connector. Hand-tightened connections are not tight enough! Do not crimp or deform the connector.

3) Apply two wraps of premium electrical tape such as Scotch 33+ or 88.

4) Apply a layer of vapor-wrap material. Vapor-wrap is a butyl rubber material that comes in rolls or sheets and does an excellent job of isolating the joint from the elements. A commercial vapor-wrap, such as from Andrew Solutions or Decibel Products won't stick to connectors and comes off easily. By putting one or two wraps of tape over the joint first, your connector will be protected from the vapor-wrap and it will look as good as new if you ever have to take it apart. To remove, simply take your razor knife, slice down the joint and peel off the weatherproofing.

Putty-type "coax seals" are not recommended as the surface can crack and dry out with age. If applied directly to a connector, the connector will become unusable as the inner putty forms a sticky mess. If you want to use putty-type sealants, wrap the connector with a layer of tape first.

5) Apply two or three layers of tape over the vapor wrap.

6) When your coax joint will be vertical, always apply the final layer of tape in an upward direction. This way the tape will overlap in such a way that water will not be conducted into the tape layers (like the shingles on your house). Tape wrapped downward will form little pockets that will trap the rain and conduct it right into your joint.

7) Do not stretch the tape when applying the final few inches. If you put it on under tension, it will eventually "flag," meaning to come loose and blow around in the wind.

8) Paint the whole joint with a UV-resistant protective layer; e.g., clear acrylic spray paint. That joint should never fail.

Shrink-Fit Tubing

A recent product for coax joints is shrink-fit tubing impregnated with glue along the inside. As you apply heat to the shrink-fit tubing, it shrinks while the glue melts and oozes inside between the fitting and the tubing. It not only keeps the tubing from slipping, but it also fills in the voids in the joint and provides an additional seal. It's an expensive alternative (approximately $1 per inch) but is very simple to use and remove if necessary.

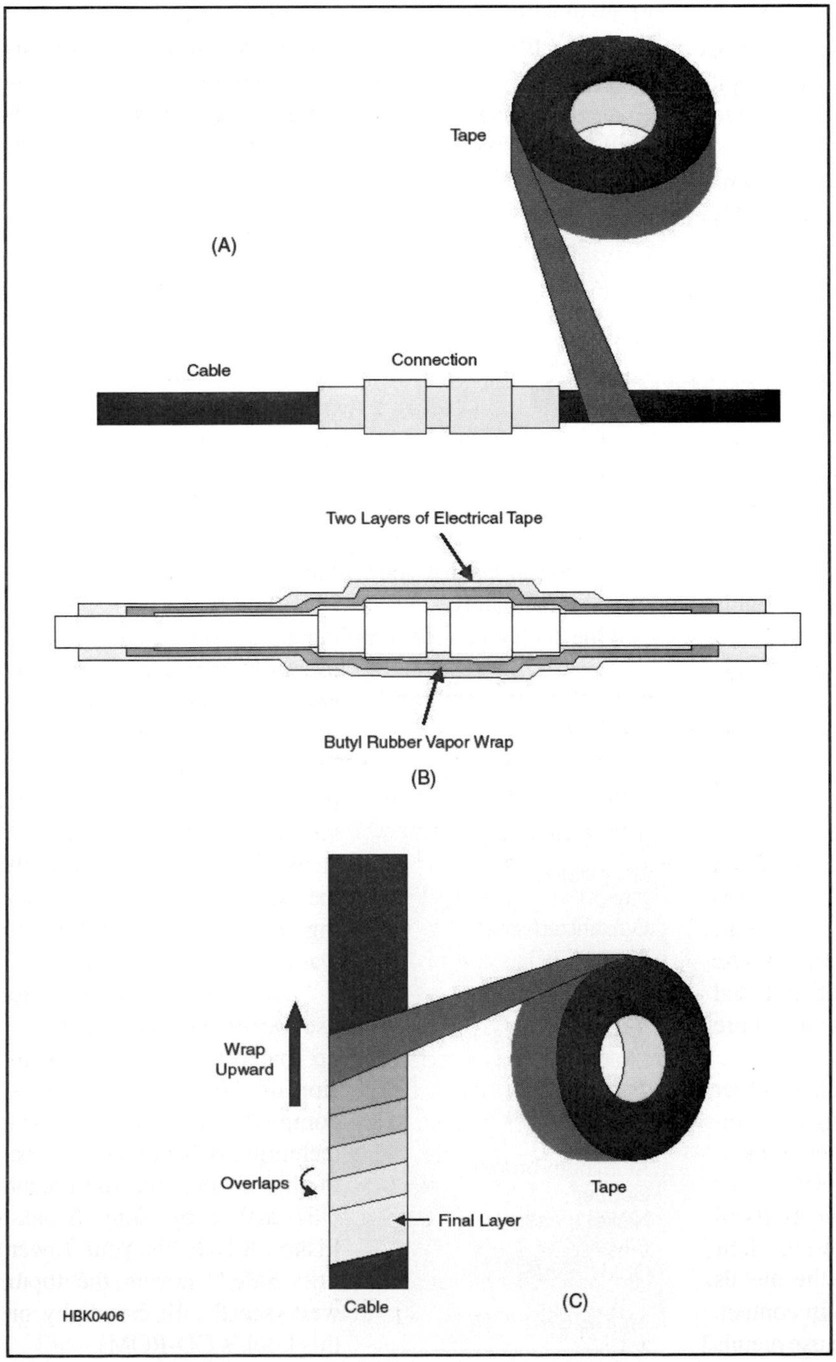

Figure 26.48 — Waterproofing a connector in three steps. At A, cover the connectors with a layer of good-quality electrical tape. B shows a layer of butyl rubber vapor wrap between the two layers of electrical tape. C shows how to wrap tape of a vertical cable so that the tape sheds water away from the connection. (Drawing (C) reprinted courtesy of *Circuitbuilding for Dummies*, Wiley Press)

Silicone Sealants

Do not use silicone sealant that gives off acetic acid (a vinegary smell) and absorbs water when curing. Acid and water will migrate into the connection causing problems later. Use only aquarium-type sealants or Dow-Corning 3145 for reliable connections. Be aware that once cured, silicone sealants are very hard to remove from connectors — practically impossible.

26.8.4 TAPE AND TIES

Every amateur installation has many feet of electrical tape used outdoors in a variety of applications. The "3 rolls for $1" bargain specials are not recommended for demanding outdoor use, particularly for weatherproofing. Scotch Super 88 is the recommended standard for waterproofing connectors. Besides being conformable to 0 °F (–18 °C), it will perform continuously in ambient temperatures of up to 220 °F (105 °C) and it is UV-resistant. The data sheet says it provides "moisture-tight electrical protection" and it retails in the $4 to $5 range per roll. Another Scotch tape, Super 33+, is another "premium grade, all-weather vinyl insulating tape" with many of the same properties and specs as the Super 88.

The only difference is that Super 88 is slightly thicker than Super 33+ (10 mils for 88 vs 7 mils for 33+). Both tapes are easily applied at low temperatures, and will even stick to a wet aluminum antenna boom.

Another specialized tape is the Scotch 130C Linerless Rubber Splicing Tape. This is a fairly thick (30 mils vs 7 mils for Super 33+) tape intended for high-voltage splices and is moisture-sealing. 3M makes many products for demanding electrical use — these are just several of them. You may have your own favorite.

Cable ties or tie-wraps are locking plastic fasteners intended to bundle cables and secure them to brackets and other supports, such as tower legs. They come in a variety of lengths, strengths, and materials at the local hardware store. For outside work, do not use white or translucent tie-wraps; they'll deteriorate quickly from UV exposure, often in just a year or two. Black, UV-resistant tie-wraps are better but they still eventually breakdown. A wrap of electrical tape will protect the tie.

A tie-wrap also makes a simple drip loop for coax and control cables. Attach a medium-size tie to the cable just before it enters the building with the tie's free end pointing down.

26.9 CORROSION

Corrosion is one of the biggest problems in tower and antenna installations. Knowing more about it will help you to use appropriate materials and stay away from problematic combinations. For detailed information on corrosion, visit the website of Corrosion Source (**www.corrosionsource.com**) where there a number of free reports and other downloadable documents on corrosion.

Any metal by itself will eventually oxidize due to exposure to the oxygen in the atmosphere. The aluminum in our antennas combines with oxygen to create the powdery aluminum oxide you find when you take an antenna apart, while oxidation of steel (which is iron) produces the rust that you want to avoid.

When two metals with the right properties are in contact in the presence of an electrolyte, *bimetallic corrosion* takes place. It's the same chemical process that takes place in batteries. Specifically, ions from one metal (called the *anodic* metal) flow across the joint or junction to the other metal (called the *cathodic* metal). In bimetallic joints, the more anodic metal is the one that loses material.

The electrolyte is typically some kind of salt or other compound (such as zinc) dissolved in water making the solution conductive. Rain (particularly acid rain), mist or condensation are sufficient for bimetallic corrosion to begin.

Galvanically incompatible metals are combinations of metals that readily corrode when in contact because of their ranking on the galvanic chart. The farther apart the metals are in the table, the faster they will corrode when in contact. When you must use different materials, it is best to use metals

that are close together in **Table 26-6**. You can see that on a zinc galvanized tower, aluminum and mild steel are the most compatible. If you use materials such as copper and brass when installing your tower ground system on a galvanized tower, you can see that you will have problems with corrosion almost immediately.

One technique for avoiding corrosion on towers is to use an intermediate corrosion-resistant material between two otherwise incompatible metals. For example, to connect a copper ground conductor to a galvanized tower, use a stainless steel washer or shim between the copper and zinc galvanizing and stainless steel hardware to hold them together.

Another technique is to use *sacrificial anodes* that give up material to prevent corrosion of the main structure. A complete discussion of this technique is beyond the scope of this chapter but the recent *QST* article by Tony Brock-Fisher, K1KP, "Is Your Tower Still Safe?" covers the topic well (see the Bibliography or this book's CD-ROM).

Table 26-6
Relative Galvanic Series In Sea Water

MORE ANODIC

Magnesium
Zinc
Galvanized steel
Aluminum
Mild Steel
Iron
50-50 lead/tin solder
Stainless Steel
Tin
Nickel (active)
Brass
Aluminum-bronze
Copper
Nickel (passive)
Silver
Gold

MORE CATHODIC

26.9.1 ANTIOXIDANTS

Various compounds are available for combating corrosion. These are *antioxidants* and most commonly-used metals such as copper, aluminum, and steel have several products designed specifically for each of them.

For aluminum antennas, most manufacturers provide a packet of antioxidant with their products. Retarding oxidation is not only a good electrical idea but the compound also functions as an anti-seize coating, aiding you in taking the antenna apart.

Antioxidants are sometimes incorrectly called "conductive pastes or greases." In general, these antioxidant compounds are comprised of a carrier material with metallic chips in suspension. It is these conductive chips, not the carrier, that give the compound its conductive properties. What happens is that the particles will pierce the layer of oxidation while preventing corrosion by isolating the joint from the air. The compound that comes with Butternut antennas, *Butter-It's-Not*, uses copper dust in a molybdenum suspension while the paste supplied by M^2 Antennas uses copper and graphite flakes in a petroleum base. There are other commercial products available for copper joints which should be used on ground systems. Just be certain to use the right one for the job. **Table 26-7**

lists several compounds and their manufacturers. In addition to using antioxidants on towers and antennas, they should be used in ground system joints as well as in marine environments.

26.9.2 RUST

Steel towers and hardware will rust unless steps are taken to prevent it. In the case of towers, use galvanized steel or aluminum. Hardware, including U-bolts, nuts, bolts and other fasteners should either be made out of stainless steel (SS) or be galvanized. Because the galvanizing process deposits a thin coating of zinc on the hardware, you can't interchange SS and galvanized nuts and bolts.

Surface rust is rust that is either deposited when you have water from a rusted piece of hardware run down a surface such as a tower leg or active rust that hasn't yet penetrated the layer of galvanizing. Neither condition is serious but you should repair those spots during your annual inspection. Use a wire brush to scrub off the rust and then spray the spot with a cold-galvanizing paint. "Cold-galv" paint is available at almost any spray paint rack. Check the contents to make sure that it contains zinc. The LPS Company (**www.lpslabs.com**) makes a very good cold-galvanizing spray that is relatively expensive but adheres very well.

Table 26-7
Antioxidant Compounds

Product	Manufacturer	Use with
Butter-It's-Not	Bencher, Inc — **www.bencher.com**	Aluminum-aluminum
OX-GARD	GB Electrical — **www.gardnerbender.com**	Aluminum-aluminum, aluminum-copper
NOALOX	Ideal Industries, Inc — **www.idealindustries.com**	Aluminum-aluminum
NO-OX-ID "A-SPECIAL"	Sanchem, Inc. — **www.sanchem.com**	Steel rust preventative
Penetrox	FCI — **fciconnect.com**	Aluminum-aluminum, aluminum-copper
DE-OX	ILSCO Corporation — **www.ilsco.com**	Aluminum-aluminum, aluminum-copper

26.10 GENERAL MAINTENANCE

Now that you've spent all that time and money on installing your dream antenna and tower system, you'll need to do periodic preventive maintenance (PM) and inspection to catch anything before it turns into a problem.

If you've followed the directives and steps described in this chapter you've already taken the most important steps in ensuring the safety and reliability of your tower and antenna system. Following the manufacturer's specifications, using the right hardware, using antioxidants and conservative design are the keys to success.

26.10.1 ANNUAL INSPECTION

An annual inspection is a critical part of your PM program. Most commercial companies do it religiously; many insurance companies require it as a condition of insurance coverage. An annual inspection entails examining everything

in the tower and antenna system, including the ground system, concrete anchors and footings, and the tower structure. In addition to annual inspections, all installations should be inspected after ice storms or wind storms that exceed 60 mph.

You should correct any problems that you discover in your inspection. If you're not sure about the seriousness of something you've found, talk to a knowledgeable friend or contact the manufacturer for advice. When you do a tower inspection, you should have enough supplies to redo several coax connector joints if necessary, as well as a note pad and pencil to write down any discrepancies that may require further action. You'll be able to take care of most problems on the spot as well as to know what else you might need to finish the repairs. I always push and pull on antennas and appurtenances (anything that's attached to the tower) to see if anything is loose. Something might look okay but pushing on it might reveal loose hardware or some other problem.

You should get in the habit of doing a quick visual check every time that you climb the tower. Carry a wire brush, a can of cold-galvanizing spray, a roll of electrical tape, and a utility knife to perform small repairs along the way. A log book of inspections, exceptions and repairs is a handy reference item. The information that follows is based on commercial and *TIA-222* tower inspection standards.

Tower Structure

1) Check for damaged or faulty tower legs and braces. With welded towers such as Rohn *25G* and *45G*, the members cannot be replaced without replacing the whole section; minor bends or damage that do not alter the structural integrity can usually be tolerated.

2) Check all welds for integrity.

3) Examine the condition of the finish and any corrosion. Look for rust patches; use a wire brush and cold galvanizing paint to repair it.

4) In addition to visually checking any bolted connections, you should put a wrench to at least 10% of them to check for tightness. Any loose nuts or bolts should be retightened. Also look for missing hardware and replace it immediately.

Tower Alignment

1) The tower should be checked for plumb. A guyed tower is allowed a maximum deviation of one part in 400, or three inches per 100 feet. While a transit is the best way to check tower alignment, an electronic level will give you 0.1° accuracy, or a bubble level will indicate relative plumb. Even simpler is a long piece of string with a weight on the end, held at arm's-length away from the tower; sight the string along the tower leg for a very quick and fairly accurate indication of tower plumb. For self-supporting towers, the allowed deviation allowed is 1 part in 250 or 4.8 inches in 100 feet.

2) Check the guy wires and guy insulators, using binoculars for the ones that aren't close to the ground or the tower.

3) Examine all guy wire and guy wire hardware including Preformed grips, turnbuckles, clamps, and clevises for damage. Make sure that all turnbuckle safeties are intact.

4) Check guy wire tension with an instrument or another technique.

5) Examine the tower base and guy anchors. Look for any cracking of the concrete. Also look for evidence of movement in the soil of the anchor rods or base. Check for rust and/ or corrosion. Excavate a buried anchor rod for twelve inches to inspect for hidden corrosion — some sources recommend inspecting anchor rods all the way to the concrete anchor.

Antennas, Cables and Appurtenances

1) Inspect antenna, boom-to-mast bracket and boom truss hardware for loose or missing hardware. Test nuts for tightness.

2) Look at each feed point joint and coax cable joint for compromised weatherproofing.

3) Check all cables for abrasion, binding and attachment.

Removing and Refurbishing Towers

Sooner or later every tower must come down and you may become the proud owner of such a tower! The article "Removing and Refurbishing Towers" on the CD-ROM for this book discusses some of the special concerns and techniques involved.

---

4) Examine all appurtenances for missing hardware or corrosion.

Rotator

1) Check that all mounting bolts are tight and that they are not slipping in the rotator shelf or plate.

2) Check that the rotator mast clamp is securely holding the mast.

Grounding System

Do a visual inspection of the grounding system. Redo any connections that are corroded.

26.10.2 CRANK-UP MAINTENANCE

Crank-up towers are complex mechanical contrivances. While some are hand cranked, many have a motor, gearbox, cables, pulleys and limit switches — all of which should be carefully inspected twice a year.

The electric motors and gearbox are generally bulletproof and the only inspections are to check the oil level in the gearbox, the condition of the drive belt or chain (some sort of conditioner is helpful for each), and the operation of the cable drum (there are probably some Zerk grease fittings that need attention).

Pulleys are sometimes custom made by the manufacturer so you may not be able to run down to the local store and buy one. Some sheaves are made by the manufacturer and then an off-the-shelf bearing is inserted in the middle. This one you probably can replace.

Pulleys need to turn and not bind so a good thing to do is to watch the pulleys if they're exposed enough while the tower is being raised or lowered and see if there are any problems.

Crank-Up Cables

Crank-up towers depend almost entirely on their cables to operate reliably and safely. Exercise the cables by running the tower up and down a couple of times a month and don't always leave the tower in the same spot all the time, for example at the limit switches. Over time the cable can take a set if it's always at the same place so leaving it at different places spreads the wear over much more of the cable.

The cables should be lubricated at least annually; twice a year would be even better. Do not use heavy grease or motor oil which will just attract grime and particles. Use a cable lubricant such as PreLube 6 and be sure to check for damage while you're doing the lube job. If you see any of the following, the cables should be replaced:

1) Damage in which a cable is significantly kinked or flattened.

2) Rust. This means serious rust, not surface rust that can be easily scraped off.

3) Excessive broken strands. Most crank-ups use 7×19 galvanized cable which means it has 133 strands in it. You're allowed to have six total broken strands and three in the same bundle before replacing the cable.

26.10.3 ROTATOR MAINTENANCE

Most rotator problems are first noticed as misalignment of the antennas with regard to where the control box indicator says they are pointing. With a light duty rotator, this happens frequently when the wind blows the antenna to a different heading. With no brake, the force of the wind can move the gear train and motor of the rotator, while the indicator remains fixed. Such rotator systems have a mechanical stop to prevent continuous rotation during operation, and provision is usually included to realign the indicator against the mechanical stop from inside the shack. During installation, the antenna must be oriented correctly for the mechanical stop position, which is usually north.

In larger rotator systems with an adequate brake, indicator misalignment is caused by mechanical slippage in the antenna boom-to-mast hardware. Many texts suggest that the boom be pinned to the mast with a heavy-duty bolt and the rotator be similarly pinned to the mast. There is a trade-off here. If there is sufficient wind to cause slippage in the couplings without pins, with pins the wind could break a rotator casting or transmission parts. The slippage will act as a clutch release, which may prevent serious damage to the rotator. On the other hand, you might not like to climb the tower and realign the system after each heavy windstorm.

26.10.4 WHEN SOMETHING FAILS

Failures to your installation can come in many forms but wind is generally the common denominator. Rust, metal fatigue and overloading aren't usually a problem until the wind starts to blow. Other causes of failure could be lightning strikes, ice, vandalism or accidents.

Assess the Damage

The first thing to do is a visual inspection. Using binoculars if possible, take a look at everything from the ground to see if anything is bent or broken. If something is swinging in the wind, that's a major problem. If there is obvious damage, try to determine if it is in danger of falling. If so, evacuate the endangered area immediately and alert local emergency services. This is especially true if it looks as though it could fall on power lines, sidewalks or roadways. If you have damage that isn't an imminent danger to life or property, keep an eye on it until the storm is over to ensure that it doesn't get worse. If you have the opportunity, take some snapshots or video of the damage for documentation.

Prevent Further Damage

Your next task is to take prudent steps to prevent further damage, both to your property and to the property of others. This is not only common sense but also a requirement of the insurance company. You want to avoid or minimize the possibility of liability lawsuits for personal injury or the property damage of others. Tie anything off you can but *do not* attempt to climb the tower!

File an Insurance Claim

After the storm is over, call your homeowner's or renter's insurance agent and notify them of the loss. Do it orally first, then follow up with a letter. The insurance company may require a *"Proof of Loss."* They'll give you a claim number that you'll need to use in all written and verbal communications. Start a file with all your documentation, plus the other paperwork that you'll start accumulating. (See the article on insurance by Ray Fallen, ND8L, on this book's CD-ROM.)

Keep notes of every conversation with your insurance agent or claims adjuster with dates and times; you may have to refer to them in the future. At this point, you may want to write down all pertinent facts surrounding the loss for reference also. Send copies of your photos with your loss letter.

Estimate of Repairs

You'll make things very easy for your claims adjuster if you include an estimate of repair along with your letter and photos. The adjuster has probably never run into a tower loss before and would appreciate your help in getting a quote. Contact your local commercial rigger or antenna installation company and they'll give you the quote.

Insurance companies will want professional workers to perform professional repairs to your loss; they expect to pay the going rate and they expect licensed contractors to do the work. Be sure that your estimate for tower repair covers *all* of the work including: dismantling damaged parts, hauling away damaged parts and disposal, clean-up, labor for reinstallation including assembly of antennas, labor for reinstallation of tower, replacing all damaged materials including hardware, cables, rotators, etc.

Don't be surprised if the estimate comes in quite a bit higher than you expect. Not only are you paying professionals to do all of the work, but a damaged tower or antenna system can be hazardous and a crane or other piece of equipment may be needed to remove it safely.

Stay in Your Comfort Zone

Needless to say, don't consider getting involved in the removal and repair of the damage unless you feel comfortable with it. If there is *any* doubt at all in your mind, either get the professionals in or bring in a piece of equipment such as a crane or boom truck. If anything is at a precarious or dangerous angle, don't touch it — send for the professionals!

26.11 BIBLIOGRAPHY

Source material and more extended discussions of the topics covered in this chapter can be found in the references listed below and in the texts listed at the end of the **Antenna Fundamentals** chapter.

L. H. Abraham, "Guys for Guys Who Have To Guy," *QST*, Jun 1955, pp 33-34, 142.

K. Andress, "The K7NV Notebook", **k7nv.com/notebook**

R.W. Block, "Lightning Protection for the Amateur Radio Station," Parts 1-3, *QST*, Jun 2002, pp 56-59; Jul 2002, pp 48-52; Aug 2002, pp 53-55.

G. Brede, "The Care and Feeding of the Amateur's Favorite Antenna Support — The Tree," *QST*, Sep 1989, pp 26-28, 40.

T. Brock-Fisher, "Is Your Tower Still Safe?," *QST*, Oct 2010, p 43-47.

D. Daso, "Antenna Towers for Radio Amateurs" (Newington: ARRL, 2010).

D. Daso, "Workshop Chronicles," columns in *National Contest Journal*.

W. R. Gary, "Toward Safer Antenna Installations," *QST*, Jan 1980, p 56.

S. F. Hoerner, "Fluid Dynamic Drag," (Bricktown, NJ: Hoerner Fluid Dynamics, 1993), pp 1-10.

C. L. Hutchinson, R. D. Straw, *Simple and Fun Antennas for Hams* (Newington: ARRL, 2002).

M. P. Keown and L. L. Lamb, "A Simple Technique for Tower-Section Separation," *QST*, Sep 1979, pp 37-38.

S. Morris, *Up the Tower*, (Seattle: Champion Radio Products, 2009).

S. Morris, "Up the Tower," columns in *National Contest Journal*.

P. O'Dell, "The Ups and Downs of Towers," *QST*, Jul 1981, pp 35-39.

S. Phillabaum, "Installation Techniques for Medium and Large Yagis," *QST*, Jun 1979, pp 23-25.

PolyPhaser, see **www.protectiongroup.com** and look for the Knowledge Base for articles on lightning protection.

C. J. Richards, "Mechanical Engineering in Radar and Communications" (London: Van Nostrand Reinhold Co., 1969), pp 162-165.

T. Schiller, *Array of Light*, Third edition, **www.n6bt.com**.

D. Weber "Determination of Yagi Wind Loads Using the Cross-Flow Principle," *Communications Quarterly*, Spring 1993.

B. White, E. White and J. White, "Assembling Big Antennas on Fixed Towers," *QST*, Mar 1982, pp 28-29.

L. Wolfert, "The Tower Alternative," *QST*, Nov 1980, pp 36-37.

W. C. Young., "Roark's Formulas for Stress & Strain" (New York: McGraw-Hill Co., 1989), pp 67, 96.

National Electrical Code, NFPA 70, National Fire Protection Association, Quincy, MA (**www.nfpa.org**).

Standard for the Installation of Lightning Protection Systems, NFPA 780, National Fire Protection Association, Quincy, MA (**www.nfpa.org**).

Structural Standards for Steel Antenna Towers and Antenna Supporting Structures, TIA Standard TIA-222-G, Telecommunications Industry Association, Aug 2005 (**www.tiaonline.org**). May be purchased from IHS/ Global Engineering Documents, 15 Inverness Way East, Englewood, CO, 80112-5704, 1-800-854-7179 (**www.global.ihs.com**).

APPENDIX A
DETERMINING ANTENNA AREAS AND WIND LOAD

The method for determining the flat projected area of an antenna is quite simple. We'll use a Yagi antenna as an example. There are two worst-case areas that should be considered here. The first is the FPA of all the elements when the wind blows in the direction along the boom; that is, at right angles to the elements. The second FPA for a Yagi is when the wind is at right angles to the boom. One of these two orientations produces the worst-case exposed antenna area — all other wind angles present lower exposed areas. The idea is to take the highest of the FPAs for these two wind directions and call that the FPA of the antenna structure. See **Figure 26.49A.**

The element FPA is calculated by multiplying each element's dimension of length by its diameter and then summing the FPAs for all elements. The boom's FPA is computed by multiplying the boom's length by its diameter.

The reason for considering two potential peak-load orientations becomes clear when different frequency antennas are stacked on a mast or tower. Some antennas produce peak loads when the elements are broadside to the wind. This is typical of low-frequency Yagis, where the elements are long lengths of aluminum tubing. On the other hand, the boom can dominate the surface area computations in higher-frequency Yagis.

The fundamentals responsible for the need to examine both potential FPAs for Yagis relates to how wind flows over a structure and develops loads. Called *The Cross-Flow Principle*, this was introduced to the communications industry by Dick Weber, K5IU, in 1993. The principle is based on the fact that the loads created by wind flowing across an antenna member only produce forces that are normal to (or perpendicular to) the major axis of the member. The resultant and component load calculations for this method are shown in Figure 26.49A.

For a Yagi, this means that wind forces on the elements act in-line with the boom, while forces on the boom act in-line with the elements. Figure 26.49B shows a force diagram for a typical Yagi. Figure 26.49C shows the FPA for a Yagi rotated through 90° of azimuth.

Antenna Placement on the Mast/Tower

Another important consideration is where the antenna(s) will be placed on the tower. As mentioned before, most generic tower specifications assume that the entire antenna load is applied at the top of the tower. Most amateur installations have a tubular mast extending above the tower top, turned by a rotator mounted down inside the tower. Multiple Yagi antennas are often placed on the mast above the tower top, and you must make sure that both the tower and the mast can withstand the wind forces on the antennas.

For freestanding towers, you can determine how a proposed antenna configuration compares to the tower manufacturer's rating by using an *Equivalent Moment* method. The method computes the bending moment generated at the base

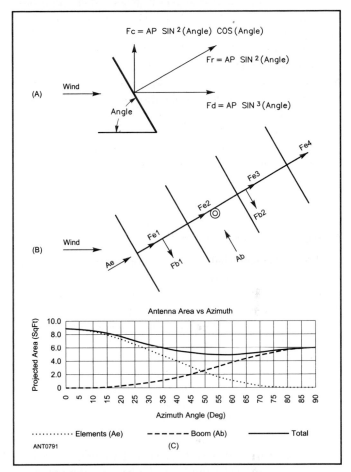

Figure 26.49 — Description of how loads are developed on a Yagi. At A, F_r is the resultant force from the wind load on a generalized member. F_d is the load acting downwind (drag) that creates the load on the tower. F_c is the lateral component of the wind load. The term A is the flat projected area (FPA), which is the broadside area normal to the wind. The term P is the wind pressure. At B, A_e is the total element area, while Ab is the total boom area. All the loads due to the wind act normal to the antenna sections—the force on element #1 (F_{e1}) acts along the axis of the boom, for example. At C, a plot of the effective FPA as a function of the azimuthal wind direction for a Yagi, ignoring drag coefficients. The Yagi in this example has 9.0 square feet of element FPA and 6.0 square feet of boom FPA. The worst-case FPAs occur with the beam pointed in the wind and with the boom broadside to the wind. To determine the actual tower loading, the actual drag coefficients and wind pressures must be used.

of the tower by wind loads on the tower's rated antenna area located right at the top of the tower and compares that to the case when the antenna is mounted on a mast sticking out of the top of the tower.

The exact value of wind pressure is not important, so long as it is the same for both comparisons. The wind load on the tower itself can be ignored because it is the same in both comparisons and the drag coefficients for the antennas can also be ignored if all calculations are performed using flat projected antenna areas, as we've recommended previously.

Keep in mind that this approach does not calculate *actual* loads and moments relevant to any specific tower design standard, but it does allow equivalent comparisons when the wind pressure is constant and all the antenna areas are of the same type. An example is in order.

Figure 26.50A shows a generic tower configuration, with a concentrated antenna load at the top of the tower. We'll assume that the tower manufacturer rates this tower at 20 square feet of flat projected antenna area. Figure 26.50B shows a typical amateur installation with a rotating mast and an antenna mounted 7 feet above the top of the tower. To make the calculations easy, we select a wind pressure of 1 pound per square foot (1 psf). This makes the tower base moment calculation for Figure 26.50A:

Antenna load = 20 feet^2 × 1 psf = 20 pounds
Base moment = 70 feet × 20 pounds = 1400 foot-pounds.

This is the target value for the comparison. An equivalent configuration would produce the same base moment. For the configuration in Figure 26.50B, we assume a tubular 2-inch diameter mast that is 20 feet long, mounted 5 feet down inside the tower. Note that the lattice structure of the tower allows the wind to "see" the whole length of the mast and that we can consider the force distributed along the mast as being a single force concentrated at the mast's center. The flat projected area of the mast by itself, without the antenna, is:

Mast area = 20 feet × 2 inches / 12 inches/foot =
3.33 square feet

The center of the mast is located at a height of 75 feet. Using the same 1-psf-wind load, the base bending moment due to the mast alone is:

Base moment (due to mast) = 3.33 feet^2 × 1 psf × 75 feet =
249.75 foot-pounds

Including the mast in the configuration reduces the allowable antenna load. The remaining target base moment left for the antenna is found by subtracting the moment due to the mast from the original target value:

New base target moment = 1400 − 249.75 foot-pounds =
1150.25 foot-pounds.

The antenna in Figure 26.50B is located at a height of 77 feet. To obtain the allowable antenna area at this elevation we divide the new base target moment by the antenna height, yielding an allowable antenna load of:

1150.25 foot-pounds / 77 feet = 14.94 pounds.

Since we chose a wind load of 1 psf, the allowable antenna FPA has been reduced to 14.94 square feet from 20 square feet. If the projected area of the antenna we are planning to mount in the new configuration is less than or equal to this value, we have satisfied the requirements of the original design. You can use this equivalent-moment method to evaluate different configurations, even ones involving multiple

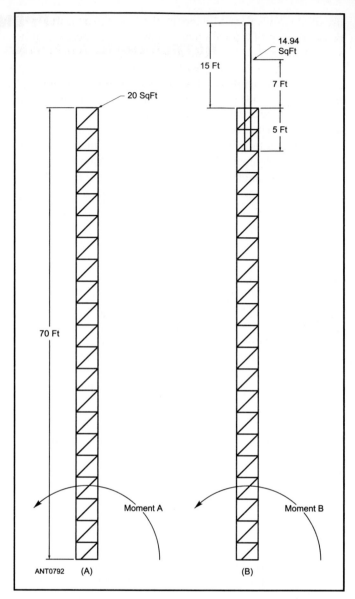

Figure 26.50 — At A, a 70-foot tower rated for 20 square feet of antenna load at the top. At B, the same tower with a 2-inch OD, 20-foot long mast, with an antenna mounted 7 feet above the top of the tower. Both configurations produce the same tower load.

antennas on the mast or situations with additional antennas placed along the tower below the tower top.

For guyed towers, the analyses become much more rigorous to solve. Because the guys and their behaviors are such a significant portion of the tower support mechanism, these designs can become very sensitive to antenna load placements. A general rule of thumb for guyed towers is never to exceed the original tower-top load rating, regardless of distributed loads along its length. Once you redistribute the antenna load placements along a guyed tower, you should do a fresh analysis, just to be sure.

You can run evaluations using the above method for antennas placed on the mast above a guyed tower top. The use of the Equivalent-Moment method for antennas mounted below the top of a guyed tower, however, can become quite suspect, since many generic tower designs have their intermediate guys sized for zero antenna loads lower down the tower. The proper approach in this case is to have a qualified mechanical engineer check the configuration, to see if guy placement and strength is adequate for the additional antennas down the tower.

Mounting the mast and antenna as shown in Figure 26.50B increases tower loads in the region of the mast. You should investigate these loads to ensure that the tower bracing in that area is sufficient.

APPENDIX B — CALCULATING THE REQUIRED MAST STRENGTH

When you mount antennas on a mast above the tower top, you should examine the bending loads on the mast to ensure that it will be strong enough. This section explains how to perform mast stress calculations for a single sustained wind speed. This procedure does not include height, exposure and gust-response factors found in most tower design standards.

Here are some fundamental formulas and values used to calculate the bending stress in a mast mounted in the top of a tower. The basic formula for wind pressure is:

$$P = 0.00256 \, V^2 \qquad \text{(Eq 1)}$$

where

P is the wind pressure is in pounds per square foot (psf)
V = wind speed in miles per hour (mph)

This assumes an air density for standard temperature and atmospheric pressure at sea level. The wind speed is not the Basic Wind Speed discussed in other sections of this chapter. It is simply a steady state (static) wind velocity.

The formula for calculating the force created by the wind on a structure is:

$$F = P \times A \times C_d \qquad \text{(Eq 2)}$$

where

P = the wind pressure from Eq 1
A = the flat projected area of the structure (square feet)
C_d = drag coefficient for the shape of the structure's members.

The commonly accepted *drag coefficient* for long cylindrical members like the tubing used for the mast and antenna is 1.20. The coefficient for a flat plate is 2.0.

The formula used to find the *bending stress* in a simple beam like our mast is:

$$\sigma = \frac{M \times c}{I} \qquad \text{(Eq 3)}$$

where

σ = the stress in pounds per square inch (psi)
M = *bending moment* at the base of the mast (inch-pounds)
c = ½ of the mast outside diameter (inches)
I = *moment of inertia* of the mast section (inches[4])

In this equation you must make sure that all values are in the same units. To arrive at the mast stress in pounds per square inch (psi), the other values need to be in inches and pounds also. The equation used to find the moment of inertia for the round tubing mast section is:

$$I = \frac{\pi}{4}(R^4 - r^4) \qquad \text{(Eq 4)}$$

where

I = Moment of Inertia of the section (inches[4])
R = Radius of tube outside diameter (inches)
r = Radius of tube inside diameter (inches)

This value describes the distribution of material about the mast *centroid*, which determines how it behaves under load. The equation used to compute the *bending moment* at the base of the mast (where it is supported by the tower) is:

$$M = (F_M \times L_M) + (F_A \times L_M) \qquad \text{(Eq 5)}$$

where

F_M = wind force from the mast (pounds)
L_M = Distance from tower top to center of mast (inches)
F_A = Wind force from the antenna (pounds)
L_A = Distance from tower top to antenna attachment (inches)
L_M is the distance to the center of the portion of the mast extending above the tower top. Additional antennas can be added to this formula by including their F × L. In the installation shown in Figure 26.50B, a wind speed of 90 mph, and a mast that is 2 inches OD, with a 0.250-inch wall thickness, the steps for calculating the mast stress are:

1) Calculate the wind pressure for 90 mph, from Eq 1:

$$P = .00256 \, V^2 = .00256 \times (90)^2 = 20.736 \text{ psf}$$

2) Determine the flat projected area of the mast. The portion of the mast above the tower is 15 feet long and has an outside diameter of 2 inches, which is 2/12 feet.

Mast FPA, A_M = 15 feet × (2 inches / 12 inches/feet) = 2.50 square feet.

3) Calculate the wind load on the mast, from Eq 2:

Mast Force, F_M = P × A × C_d = 20.736 psf × 2.50 feet² × 1.20 = 62.21 pounds

4) Calculate the wind load on the antenna: From Eq 2:

Antenna Force, $F_A = P \times A \times C_d = 20.736$ psf $\times 14.94$ feet^2 $\times 1.20 = 371.76$ pounds

5) Calculate the mast *Bending Moment*, from Eq 5:

$M = (F_M \times L_M) + (F_A \times L_A) = (62.21$ pounds $\times 90$ inches$) + (371.76$ pounds $\times 84$ inches$) = 36827$ inch-pounds

where
  $L_M = 7.5$ feet $\times 12$ inches/foot $= 90$ inches
  $L_A = 7.0$ feet $\times 12$ inches/foot $= 84$ inches.

6) Calculate the mast *Moment of Inertia*, from Eq 4:

$I = \dfrac{\pi}{4}(R^4 - r^4) = \dfrac{\pi}{4}(1.0^4 - 0.75^4) = 0.5369$ inches^4

where, for a 2.0-inch OD and 0.250-inch wall thickness tube, R= 1.0 and r = 0.75.

7) Calculate the mast *Bending Stress*, from Eq 3:

$\sigma = \dfrac{M \times c}{I} = \dfrac{36827 \text{ inch-pounds} \times 1.0 \text{ inches}}{0.5369} = 68592$ psi

If the yield strength of the mast material is greater than the calculated bending stress, the mast is considered safe for this configuration and wind speed. If the calculated stress is higher than the mast yield strength, a stronger alloy, or a larger mast, or one with a thicker wall is required.

When evaluating a mast with multiple antennas attached to it, special care should be given to finding the worst-case condition (wind direction) for the system. What may appear to be the worst load case, by virtue of the combined flat projected antenna areas, may not always be the exposure that creates the largest mast bending moment. Masts with multiple stacked antennas should always be examined to find the exposure that produces the largest mast bending moment. The antenna flat projected areas at 0° and 90° azimuths are particularly useful for this evaluation.

One way of reducing the net wind torque on a mast holding multiple antennas is to mount antennas on opposite sides of the mast. This alternate mounting scheme causes the wind torque from each antenna to cancel at least partially, reducing the total torque experienced by the mast.

TABLE OF CONTENTS

Chapter 27

Antenna and Transmission Line Measurements

The principal quantities measured on transmission lines are current or voltage, including phase. From these measurements, forward and reflected power and standing wave ratio (SWR) may be obtained. For antennas, the primary measurement of interest to amateurs is field strength in order to determine an antenna's radiation pattern or to compare relative antenna performance. It is important to note that for most practical purposes, a relative measurement is sufficient. An uncalibrated indicator that shows when the largest possible amount of power is being put into the line is just as useful, in most cases, as an instrument that measures the power accurately. It is seldom necessary to know the actual number of watts going into the line unless the overall efficiency of the system is being investigated. An instrument that shows when the SWR is close to 1:1 is all you need for most impedance-matching adjustments.

Absolute quantitative measurements of amplitude or time (phase) become increasingly difficult at frequencies above a few MHz with numerous sources of error becoming more and more significant. Quantitative measurements of reasonable accuracy demand good design and careful construction in the measuring instruments. They also require intelligent use of the equipment, including knowledge not only of its limitations but also of stray effects in the instrument and also of the test configuration that often lead to false results. Until you know the complete conditions of the measurements, a certain amount of skepticism regarding numerical data resulting from amateur measurements with simple equipment is justified.

Accurate measurement of SWR, for example, is necessary only in studies of antenna characteristics such as bandwidth, or for the design of some types of matching systems, such as a stub match. If such measurements are required, surplus lab equipment of very high quality is commonly available although usually not "in calibration."

On the other hand, purely qualitative or relative measurements, such as comparing one antenna to another, before-and-after, or max/min adjustments are easy to make and quite useful. This chapter presents methods and devices for making these measurements.

27.1 LINE CURRENT AND VOLTAGE

A current or voltage indicator that can be used with coaxial line is a useful piece of equipment. It need not be elaborate or expensive. Its principal function is to show when the maximum power is being taken from the transmitter for any given set of line conditions (length, SWR, etc). This will occur when you adjust the transmitter output circuits for maximum current or voltage into the transmission line. Although a final-amplifier plate or collector current meter is frequently used for this purpose, it is not always a reliable indicator. In many cases, particularly with a screen-grid tube in the final stage, minimum loaded plate current does not occur simultaneously with maximum power output.

27.1.1 RF VOLTMETERS

You can combine a germanium or Schottky diode in conjunction with a low-range milliammeter and a few resistors to form an RF voltmeter suitable for connecting across the two conductors of a coaxial line, as shown in **Figure 27.1**. It

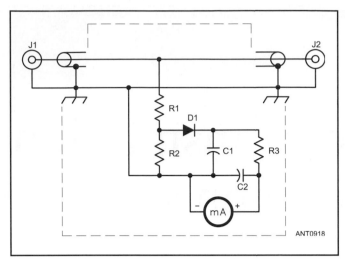

Figure 27.1 — RF voltmeter for coaxial line.
C1, C2 — 0.005- or 0.01-μF disc ceramic.
D1 — 1N34A germanium or 1N5817 Schottky diode.
J1, J2 — Coaxial fittings, chassis-mounting type.
M1 — 0-1 milliammeter (more sensitive meter may be used if
  desired; see text).
R1 — 6.8 kΩ, metal-oxide, 1 W for each 100 W of RF power.
R2 — 680 Ω, ½ or 1 W carbon-film or metal-oxide.
R3 — 10 kΩ, ½ W (see text).

consists of a voltage divider, R1-R2, having a total resistance about 100 times the Z_0 of the line (so the power consumed will be negligible) with a diode rectifier and milliammeter connected across part of the divider to read relative RF voltage. The purpose of R3 is to make the meter readings directly proportional to the applied voltage, as nearly as possible, by swamping the resistance of D1, since the diode resistance will vary with the amplitude of the current through the diode.

You may construct the voltmeter in a small metal box, indicated by the dashed line in the drawing, and fitted with coax receptacles. R1 and R2 should be noninductive resistors such as carbon-film or metal-oxide types. The power rating for R1 should be 1 W for each 100 W of carrier power in the matched line; separate 1- or 2-W resistors should be used to make up the total power rating required, to the total resistance as given. Any type of resistor can be used for R3; the total resistance should be such that about 10 V dc will be developed across it at full scale. For example, a 0-1 milliammeter would require 10 kΩ, a 0-500 microammeter would take 20 kΩ, and so on. R1 may be a variable resistor so the sensitivity can be adjusted for various power levels.

If more than one resistor is used for R1, the units should be arranged end-to-end with very short leads. R1 and R2 should be kept ½ inch or more from metal surfaces parallel to the body of the resistor. These precautions must be observed if consistent measurements are to be obtained above a few MHz. Stray capacitance and stray coupling limit the accuracy at higher frequencies but do not affect the utility of the instrument for comparative measurements.

Calibration

You may calibrate the meter for RF voltage at low

frequencies by comparison with a standard such as an RF ammeter, wattmeter or oscilloscope. If a wattmeter is used, the line must be well matched so the impedance at the point of measurement is equal to the actual Z_0 of the line. The power can be calculated as $E = \sqrt{P Z_0}$. By making voltage measurements at a number of different power levels, you can obtain enough points to draw a calibration curve for your particular setup. Be advised that stray effects and nonlinearities inherent in this simple circuit make a true calibration questionable above a few MHz.

27.1.2 RF CURRENT METERS

The following project was designed by Tom Rauch, W8JI (**w8ji.com/building_a_current_meter.htm**). The circuit of **Figure 27.2** is based on a current transformer (T1) consisting of a T157-2 powdered-iron toroid core with a 20-turn winding. The meter is used with the current-carrying wire or antenna inserted through the middle of the core as a one-turn primary

When 1 A is flowing in the single-turn primary, the secondary current will be 50 mA (equal to primary current

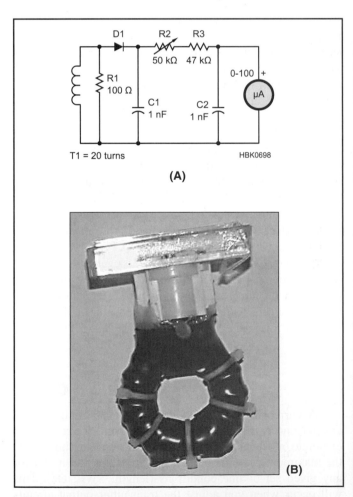

(A)

(B)

Figure 27.2 — The schematic of the RF current probe (A) and assembly of the RF current probe (B). Use an all-plastic meter and mount the circuits and toroid directly on the back of the meter case.

divided by the turns ratio of 20:1). R1 across the transformer flattens the frequency response and limits the output voltage. The RF voltage is then detected and filtered by D1 (a low-threshold Schottky diode for minimum voltage drop) and C1. The adjustable sum of R2 and R3 allow for full-scale (FS) calibration of the 100 μA meter. C2 provides additional filtering. The toroid core and all circuitry are glued to the back of the meter case with only R2 exposed — a screwdriver-adjustable calibration pot.

It is important to minimize stray capacitance by using a meter with all-plastic construction except for the electrical parts. The meter in Figure 27.2B has an all-plastic case including the meter scale. The meter movement and all metallic areas are small. The lack of large metallic components minimizes stray capacitance from the proximity of the meter. Low stray capacitance ensures the instrument has the least possible effect on the circuit being tested.

A value of 100 Ω for R1 gave the flattest response from 1.8 to 30 MHz. With 50 mA of secondary current, the voltage across R1 is $0.05 \times 100 = 5$ V_{RMS}. The peak voltage is then $1.414 \times 5 = 7.1$ V. At full current, power dissipation in R1 = 50 mA $\times$ 5 V_{RMS} = 0.25 W so a ½-W or larger resistor should be used.

The meter used here was a 10,000 Ω/V model so for full-scale deflection from a primary current of 1 A producing a secondary voltage of ~7 V, the sum of R2 and R3 must be set to $7 \times 10,000 = 70$ kΩ. The low-current meter combined with high detected voltage improves detector linearity.

Calibration of the meter can be performed by using a calibrated power meter and a test fixture consisting of two RF connectors with a short piece of wire between them and through the transformer core. With 50 W applied to a 50-Ω load, the wire will be carrying 1 A of current. Full-scale accuracy is not required in comparison measurements, since the meter references against itself, but linearity within a few percent is important.

This transformer-based meter is much more reliable and linear than thermocouple RF ammeters and perturbs systems much less. Stray capacitance added to the system being tested is very small because of the proximity of the meter and the compact wiring area. Compared to actually connecting a meter with its associated lead lengths and capacitance in line with the load, the advantages of a transformer-coupled meter become apparent.

Clamp-on RF Current Probe

Sometimes it is not practical to disconnect a wire in order to sense RF current on it, such as a power cord or speaker wire. In such cases a *clamp-on* probe can be used as described in the February 1999 *QST* article by Steve Sparks, N5SV, and shown in **Figure 27.3**. The core is a split-core type — any common material will suffice (type 31, 75, 61, 43, etc) for HF use. If the enclosure is hand-held size, the instrument can be used as a handy detector and "sniffer" for RFI troubleshooting. Because the split core does not close completely and consistently every time, this is not a precision instrument but is effective for relative comparison.

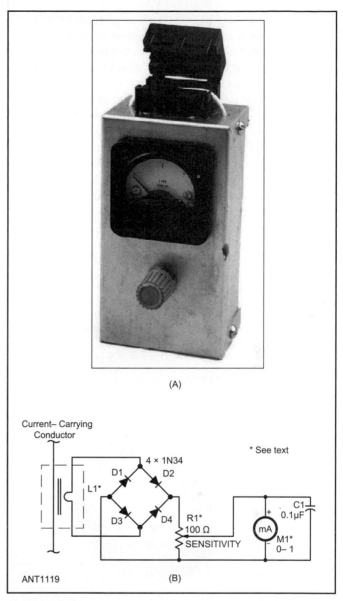

Figure 27.3 — The RF current probe at A is small enough to be hand-carried as an effective RF "sniffer." At B is the schematic of the RF current probe. Use a metal enclosure for the probe.
C1 — 0.1 μF disc ceramic.
D1-D4 — 1N34A germanium or 1N5817 Schottky diodes.
L1 — Single turn of #14 AWG wire through a snap-on ferrite split-core, type 31, 43, 61, 73, or 75 material will work. Glue core to top of metal enclosure.
M1 — 1 mA analog meter. Substitute lower full-scale current for higher sensitivity.
R1 — 100 to 500 Ω panel-mount potentiometer.

27.1.3 RF AMMETERS

An RF ammeter is a good way to gauge output power. You can mount an RF ammeter in any convenient location at the input end of the transmission line, the principal precaution being that the capacitance to ground, chassis and nearby conductors should be low. A Bakelite-case instrument can be mounted on a metal panel without introducing enough shunt capacitance to ground to cause serious error up to 30 MHz. When installing a metal-case instrument on a metal panel, you should mount it on a separate sheet of insulating material so that there is ⅛ inch or more separation between the edge of the case and the metal.

A 2-inch instrument can be mounted in a 2 × 4 × 4-inch metal box, as shown in **Figure 27.4**. This is a convenient arrangement for use with coaxial line. Installed this way, a good quality RF ammeter will measure current with an accuracy that is entirely adequate for calculating power in the line. As discussed above in connection with calibrating RF voltmeters, the line must be closely matched by its load so the actual impedance is resistive and equal to Z_0. The scales of such instruments are cramped at the low end, however, which limits the range of power that can be measured by a single meter. The useful current range is about 3 to 1, corresponding to a power range of about 9 to 1.

Figure 27.4 — A convenient method of mounting an RF ammeter for use in a coaxial line. This is a metal-case instrument mounted on a thin bakelite panel. The cutout in the metal clears the edge of the meter by about ⅛ inch.

New RF ammeters are expensive and even surplus pricing can vary widely between $10 and $100 in today's market. AM radio stations are the main users of new units. The FCC defines the output power of AM stations based on the RF current in the antenna, so new RF ammeters are made mainly for that market. They are quite accurate, and their prices reflect that!

The good news is that used RF ammeters are often available. For example, Fair Radio Sales in Lima, Ohio, has been a consistent source of RF ammeters. Ham flea markets are also worth trying. Some grubbing around in your nearest surplus store or an older ham's junk box may provide just the RF ammeter you need.

Before buying a used RF ammeter, check to be sure it is actually an RF ammeter — it is common to find meters labeled "RF Amps" that are simple current meters intended to be used with an external RF current sensing unit.

RF Ammeter Substitutes

Don't despair if you can't find a used RF ammeter. It's possible to construct your own. Both hot-wire and thermocouple units can be homemade. Pilot lamps in series with antenna wires, or coupled to them in various ways, can indicate antenna current or even forward and reflected power. (See the Bibliography entries for Sutter and Wright.)

Another approach is to use a small low-voltage lamp as the heat/light element and use a photodetector driving a meter as an indicator. (Your eyes and judgment can serve as the indicating part of the instrument.) A feed line balance checker could be as simple as a couple of lamps with the right current rating and the lowest voltage rating available. You should be able to tell fairly well by eye which bulb is brighter or if they are about equal. You can calibrate a lamp-based RF ammeter with 60-Hz or dc power.

The optical approach is often taken in QRP portable equipment where an LED is used to replace a meter in an SWR bridge as described by Phil Salas, AD5X, in his Z-Match antenna tuner described in the **Transmission Line Coupling and Impedance Matching** chapter.

As another alternative, you can build an RF ammeter that uses a dc meter to indicate rectified RF from a current transformer that you clamp over a transmission line wire as described by Zack Lau, W1VT. (See Bibliography.)

27.2 SWR MEASUREMENTS

On parallel-conductor lines it is possible to measure the standing wave ratio by moving a current (or voltage) indicator along the line, noting the maximum and minimum values of current (or voltage) and then computing the SWR from these measured values. This cannot be done with coaxial line since it is not possible to make measurements of this type inside the cable. The technique is, in fact, seldom used with open lines because it is not only inconvenient but sometimes impossible to reach all parts of the line conductors. Also, the method is subject to considerable error from antenna currents flowing on the line.

Present-day SWR measurements made by amateurs practically always use some form of *directional coupler* or RF-bridge circuit. The indicator circuits themselves are fundamentally simple, but they require considerable care in construction to ensure accurate measurements. The requirements for indicators used only for the adjustment of impedance-matching circuits, rather than actual SWR measurement, are not so stringent, and you can easily make an instrument for this purpose.

27.2.1 BRIDGE CIRCUITS

Two commonly used bridge circuits are shown in **Figure 27.5**. The bridges consist essentially of two voltage dividers in parallel, with an RF voltmeter connected between the junctions of each pair of *arms*, as the individual elements are called. When the equations shown to the right of each circuit are satisfied there is no potential difference between the two junctions, and the RF voltmeter indicates zero voltage. The bridge is then said to be in *balance*.

Taking Figure 27.5A as an illustration, if R1 = R2, half the applied voltage, E, will appear across each resistor. Then if $R_S = R_X$, ½ E will appear across each of these resistors and the RF voltmeter reading will be zero. Remember that a matched transmission line has essentially a purely resistive input impedance. Suppose that the input terminals of such a line are substituted for R_X. Then if R_S is a resistor equal to the Z_0 of the line, the bridge will be balanced.

If the line is not perfectly matched, its input impedance will not equal Z_0 and hence will not equal R_S, since you chose the latter to be equal to Z_0. There will then be a difference in potential between points X and Y, and the RF voltmeter will show a reading. Such a bridge therefore can be used to show the presence of standing waves on the line, because the line input impedance will be equal to Z_0 only when there are no standing waves.

Considering the nature of the incident and reflected components of voltage that make up the actual voltage at the input terminals of the line, as discussed in the **Transmission Lines** chapter, it should be clear that when $R_S = Z_0$, the bridge is always in balance for the incident component. Thus the RF voltmeter does not respond to the incident component at any time but reads only the reflected component. The incident component can be measured across either R1 or R2, if they are equal resistances. The standing wave ratio is then

$$SWR = \frac{E1 + E2}{E1 - E2} \qquad (Eq\ 1)$$

where E1 is the incident voltage and E2 is the reflected voltage. It is often simpler to normalize the voltages by expressing E2 as a fraction of E1, in which case the formula becomes

$$SWR = \frac{1 + k}{1 - k} \qquad (Eq\ 2)$$

where k = E2/E1.

The operation of the circuit in Figure 27.5B is essentially the same, although this circuit has arms containing reactance as well as resistance.

It is not necessary that R1 = R2 in Figure 27.5A; the bridge can be balanced, in theory, with any ratio of these two resistances provided R_S is changed accordingly. In practice, however, the accuracy is highest when the two are equal; this circuit is most commonly used.

A number of types of bridge circuits appear in **Figure 27.6**, many of which have been used in amateur products or amateur construction projects. The bridge at E is most often used in common low-cost SWR meters. (See the Bibliography entry for Silver for a description of how these meters work.) All circuits except that at G can have the ground returns of the generator and load at a common potential. At G, the generator and detector ground returns are at a common potential. You may interchange the positions of the detector and transmitter (or generator) in the bridge, and this may be advantageous in some applications.

The bridges shown at D, E, F and H may have one terminal of the generator, detector and load common. Bridges

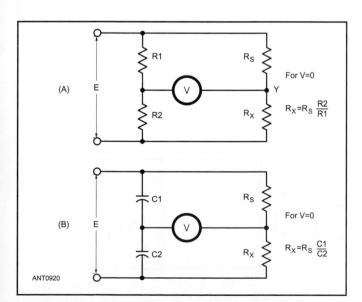

Figure 27.5 — Bridge circuits suitable for SWR measurement. At A, Wheatstone type using resistance arms. At B, capacitance-resistance bridge ("Micromatch"). Conditions for balance are independent of frequency in both types. The voltmeter must be an RF voltmeter.

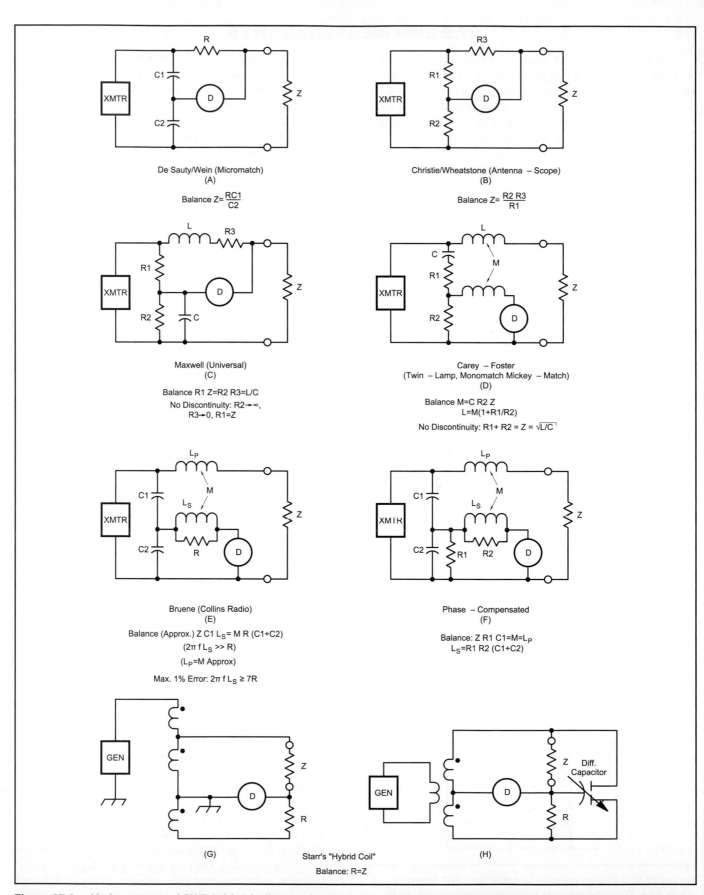

Figure 27.6 — Various types of SWR bridge indicator circuits and commonly known names of bridge circuits or devices in which they have been used. Detectors (D) are usually semiconductor diodes with meters, isolated with RF chokes and capacitors. However, the detector may be a radio receiver. In each circuit, Z represents the load being measured. (*This information provided by David Geiser, WA2ANU*)

at A, B, E, F, G and H have constant sensitivity over a wide frequency range. Bridges at B, C, D and H may be designed to show no discontinuity (impedance bump) with a matched line, as shown in the drawing. Discontinuities with A, E and F may be small.

Bridges are usually most sensitive when the detector bridges the midpoint of the generator voltage, as in G or H, or in B when each resistor equals the load impedance. Sensitivity also increases when the currents in each leg are equal.

27.2.2 SWR RESISTANCE BRIDGE

The basic bridge configuration shown in Figure 27.5B may be home constructed and is reasonably accurate for SWR measurement at HF. A practical circuit for such a bridge is given in **Figure 27.7A** and a representative layout is shown in Figure 27.7B. Properly built, a bridge of this design can be used for measurement of SWRs up to about 15:1 with good accuracy. Resistance bridges cannot be left in the transmission during regular operation due to the power dissipation limits of the resistors. This bridge should be used for test purposes only.

You must also observe these important construction points:

1) Keep leads in the RF circuit short, to reduce stray inductance.

2) Mount resistors two or three times their body diameter away from metal parts, to reduce stray capacitance.

3) Place the RF components so there is as little inductive and capacitive coupling as possible between the bridge arms.

In the instrument shown in Figure 27.7B, the input and line connectors, J1 and J2, are mounted fairly close together so the standard resistor, R_S, can be supported with short leads directly between the center terminals of the connectors. R2 is mounted at right angles to R_S, and a shield partition is used between these two components and the others.

The two 47-kΩ resistors, R5 and R6 in Figure 27.7A, are voltmeter multipliers for the 0-100 microammeter used as an indicator. This is sufficient resistance to make the voltmeter approximately linear (that is, the meter reading is directly proportional to the RF voltage) and no voltage calibration curve is needed. D1 is the rectifier for the reflected voltage and D2 is for the incident voltage. Because of manufacturing variations in resistors and diodes, the readings may differ slightly with two multipliers of the same nominal resistance value, so a correction resistor, R3, is included in the circuit. You should select its value so that the meter reading is the same with S1 in either position, when RF is applied to the bridge with the line connection open. In the instrument shown, a value of 1000 Ω was required in series with the multiplier for reflected voltage; in other cases different values probably would be needed and R3 might have to be put in series with the multiplier for the incident voltage. You can determine this by experiment.

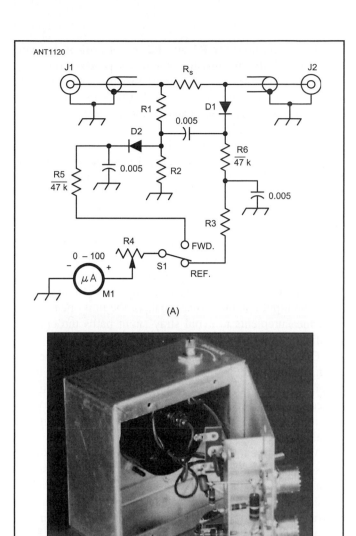

(A)

(B)

Figure 27.7 — At A, schematic of the resistance bridge for SWR measurement. Capacitors are disc ceramic. Resistors are ½-W composition except as noted below.

D1, D2 — 1N34A germanium or 1N5817 Schottky diodes.
J1, J2 — Coaxial connectors, chassis-mounting type.
M1 — 0-100 dc microammeter.
R1, R2 — 47 Ω, ½-W carbon-film or metal-oxide (see text).
R3 — See text.
R4 — 50-kΩ volume control.
R_s — Resistance equal to line Z_0 (½ or 1 W composition).
S1 — SPDT toggle.

At B, a 2 × 4 × 4-inch aluminum box is used to house this SWR bridge. The variable resistor, R4, is mounted on the side. The bridge components are mounted on one side plate of the box and a subchassis formed from a piece of aluminum. The input connector is at the top in this view. R_s is connected directly between the two center posts of the connectors. R2 is visible behind it and perpendicular to it. One terminal of D1 projects through a hole in the chassis so the lead can be connected to J2. R1 is mounted vertically to the left of the chassis in this view, with D2 connected between the junction of R1-R2 and a tie point.

The value used for R1 and R2 is not critical, but you should match the two resistors within 1% or 2% if possible. Keep the resistance of R_S as close as possible to the actual Z_0 of the line you use (generally 50 or 75 Ω). Select the resistor by actual measurement with an accurate resistance bridge, if you have one available.

R4 is for adjusting the incident-voltage reading to full scale in the measurement procedure described below. Its use is not essential, but it offers a convenient alternative to exact adjustment of the RF input voltage.

Testing

Measure R1, R2 and R_S with a reliable digital ohmmeter or resistance bridge after completing the wiring. This will ensure that their values have not changed from the heat of soldering. Disconnect one side of the microammeter and leave the input and output terminals of the unit open during such measurements to avoid stray shunt paths through the rectifiers.

Check the two voltmeter circuits as described above, applying enough RF (about 10 V peak, 1 V RMS) to the input terminals to give a full scale reading with R4 set for maximum deflection and with the line terminals open. If necessary, try different values for R3 until the reading is the same with S1 in either position.

With J2 open, adjust the RF input voltage and R4 for full-scale reading with S1 in the incident-voltage position. Then switch S1 to the reflected-voltage position. The reading should remain at full scale. Next, short-circuit J2 by touching a screwdriver between the center terminal and the frame of the connector to make a low-inductance short. Switch S1 to the incident-voltage position and readjust R4 for full scale, if necessary. Then throw S1 to the reflected-voltage position, keeping J2 shorted, and the reading should be full scale as before. If the readings differ, R1 and R2 are not the same value, or there is stray coupling between the arms of the bridge. You must read the reflected voltage at full scale with J2 either open or shorted, when the incident voltage is set to full scale in each case, to make accurate SWR measurements.

The circuit should pass these tests at all frequencies at which it is to be used. It is sufficient to test at the lowest and highest frequencies, usually 1.8 or 3.5 and 28 or 50 MHz. If R1 and R2 are poorly matched but the bridge construction is otherwise good, discrepancies in the readings will be substantially the same at all frequencies. A difference in behavior at the low and high ends of the frequency range can be attributed to stray coupling between bridge arms, or stray inductance or capacitance in the arms.

To check the bridge for balance, apply RF and adjust R4 for full scale with J2 open. Then connect a resistor identical with R_S (the resistance should match within 1% or 2%) to the line terminals, using the shortest possible leads. It is convenient to mount the test resistor inside a cable connector (PL-259), a method of mounting that also minimizes lead inductance. When you connect the test resistor the reflected-voltage reading should drop to zero. The incident voltage should be reset to full scale by means of R4, if necessary.

The reflected reading should be zero at any frequency in the range to be used. If a good null is obtained at low frequencies but some residual current shows at the high end, the trouble may be the inductance of the test resistor leads, although it may also be caused by stray coupling between the arms of the bridge itself.

If there is a constant low (but not zero) reading at all frequencies the problem is poor matching of the resistance values. Both effects can be present simultaneously. You should make sure you obtain a good null at all frequencies before using your bridge.

Bridge Operation

You must limit the RF power input to a bridge of this type to 2 W at most, because of the power-dissipation ratings of the resistors. If the transmitter has no provision for reducing power output to this value a simple power-absorber circuit can be made up, as shown in **Figure 27.8**. Lamp DS1 changes resistance as it heats up — from a few ohms when cold to more than 100 Ω at full power. This increasing resistance tends to maintain constant current through the resistor over a fairly wide power range, so the voltage drop across the resistor also tends to be constant. This voltage is applied to the bridge, and with the constants given is in the right range for resistance-type bridges.

To make a measurement, connect the unknown load to J2 and apply sufficient RF voltage to J1 to give a full-scale incident-voltage reading. Use R4 to set the indicator to exactly full scale. Then throw S1 to the reflected voltage position and note the meter reading. The SWR is then found by using these readings in Eq 1.

For example, if the full-scale calibration of the dc instrument is 100 μA and the reading with S2 in the reflected-voltage position is 40 μA, the SWR is

$$SWR = \frac{100 + 40}{100 - 40} = \frac{140}{60} = 2.33 : 1$$

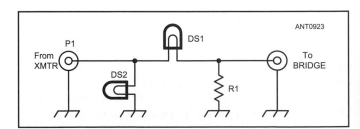

Figure 27.8 — Power-absorber circuit for use with resistance-type SWR bridges when the transmitter has no special provisions for power reduction. For RF powers up to 50 W, DS1 is a 120-V 40-W incandescent lamp and DS2 is not used. For higher powers, use sufficient additional lamp capacity at DS2 to load the transmitter to about normal output; for example, for 250-W output DS2 may consist of two 100-W lamps in parallel. R1 is made from three 1-W 68-Ω resistors connected in parallel. P1 and P2 are cable-mounting coaxial connectors. Leads in the circuit formed by the lamps and R1 should be kept short, but convenient lengths of cable may be used between this assembly and the connectors.

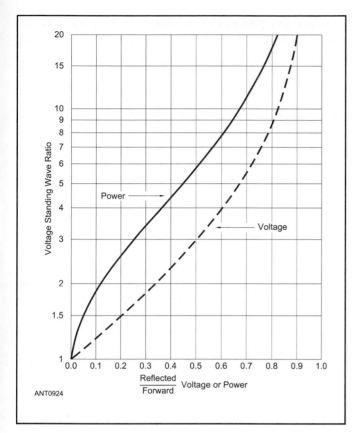

Figure 27.9 — Chart for finding voltage standing wave ratio when the ratio of reflected-to-forward voltage or reflected-to-forward power is known.

Instead of calculating the SWR value, you could use the voltage curve in **Figure 27.9**. In this example the ratio of reflected to forward voltage is 40/100 = 0.4, and the SWR value is about 2.3:1.

You may calibrate the meter scale in any arbitrary units, so long as the scale has equal divisions. It is the ratios of the voltages, and not the actual values, that determine the SWR.

27.2.3 AVOIDING ERRORS IN SWR MEASUREMENTS

The principal causes of inaccuracies within the bridge are differences in the resistances of R1 and R2, stray inductance and capacitance in the bridge arms, and stray coupling between arms. If the checkout procedure described above is followed carefully, the bridge in Figure 27.6 should be sufficiently accurate for practical use. The accuracy is highest for low standing wave ratios because of the nature of the SWR calculation; at high SWR the divisor in the equation above represents the difference between two nearly equal quantities, so a small error in voltage measurement may mean a considerable difference in the calculated SWR.

Detector nonlinearity is another source of error. A diode peak detector is approximately linear if the load impedance is high enough, and the signal is much greater than the diode forward-conduction voltage, but it will still have significant nonlinearity at the low end of the scale.

The standard resistor R_S must equal the actual Z_0 of the line. The actual Z_0 of a sample of line may differ by a few percent from the nominal figure because of manufacturing variations, but this has to be tolerated. In the 50- to 75-Ω range, the RF resistance of a noninductive resistor of ½- or 1-W rating is essentially identical with its dc resistance at VHF and below.

Common-Mode Currents

As explained in the **Transmission Line Coupling and Impedance Matching** chapter, there are two ways in which unwanted *common-mode* (sometimes called *antenna*) currents can flow on the outside of a coaxial line — currents induced onto the line because of its spatial relationship to the antenna and currents that result from the direct connection between the coax outer conductor and (usually) one side of the antenna. Such currents can cause significant SWR measurements error and SWR that changes with line length but for different reasons.

Induced current usually will not be troublesome if the bridge and the transmitter (or other source of RF power for operating the bridge) are shielded so that any RF currents flowing on the outside of the line cannot find their way into the bridge. This point can be checked by inserting an additional section of line (⅛ to ¼ electrical wavelength preferably) of the same Z_0. The SWR indicated by the bridge should not change except for a slight decrease because of the additional line loss. If there is a marked change, you may need better shielding.

Common-mode currents can also flow on the outside of coaxial transmission lines if the outside surface of the shield is connected directly to one side of the antenna. Even if the antenna itself is balanced, this "extra" conductor will unbalance the system and common-mode current will flow on the outside of the line. In such cases, the SWR will vary with line length, even though the bridge and transmitter are well-shielded and the shielding is maintained throughout the system by the use of coaxial fittings. Often, merely moving the transmission line around will cause the indicated SWR to change. This is because the outside of the coax has become part of the antenna system by being connected to the antenna at the feed point. The outside shield of the line thus constitutes a load, along with the desired load represented by the antenna itself. The SWR on the line then is determined by the composite load of the antenna and the outside of the coax. Since changing the line length (or position) changes one component of this composite load, the SWR changes too. This is an undesirable condition since the line is usually operating at a higher SWR than it should — and would if the common-mode current on the outside of the coax were eliminated.

The remedy for both situations is generally to use a common-mode choke balun as described in the **Transmission Line Coupling and Impedance Matching** chapter or to detune the outside of the line by proper choice of length so that it presents a high impedance at the frequency of operation. Note that this is not a *measurement error*, since what the instrument reads is the actual SWR on the line.

Spurious Frequencies

Off-frequency components in the RF voltage applied to the bridge may cause considerable error. The principal components of this type are harmonics and low-frequency subharmonics that may be fed through the final stage of the transmitter driving the bridge. The antenna is almost always a fairly selective circuit, and even though the system may be operating with a very low SWR at the desired frequency, it is almost always mismatched at harmonic and subharmonic frequencies. If such spurious frequencies are applied to the bridge in appreciable amplitude, the SWR indication will be very much in error. In particular, it may not be possible to obtain a null on the bridge with any set of adjustments of the matching circuit. The only remedy is to filter out the unwanted components by increasing the selectivity of the circuits between the transmitter final amplifier and the bridge.

27.2.4 REFLECTOMETERS

A reflectometer consists of a coupled pair of transmission-line impedance bridges (see Figure 27.6) operated back-to-back so that the generator and load are reversed in one bridge. The resulting imbalance between bridges is displayed on a meter with a scale calibrated so as to convert the imbalance to SWR. Various simple reflectometers have been described from time to time in *QST* and in *The ARRL Handbook*. (See Bibliography.)

Bridges of this type are usually frequency-sensitive — that is, the meter response increases with increasing frequency for the same applied voltage so that a CAL (calibration) potentiometer is required to set the meter sensitivity for each use.

Because most of these designs are frequency sensitive, it is difficult to calibrate them accurately for power measurement. Similarly, without a guaranteed power calibration, they cannot make accurate quantitative measurements of SWR but their low cost and suitability for use at moderate power levels, combined with the ability to show accurately when a matching circuit has been properly adjusted, make them a worthwhile addition to the amateur station.

A pair of typical reflectometer designs are given in **Figures 27.10** and **27.11**. (Both original *QST* articles are included on this book's CD-ROM.) The classic circuit by DeMaw in Figure 27.10 is a very useful circuit at low power levels. It can be scaled up to be used at higher power levels by reducing the number of turns on the toroid primary and increasing the voltage ratings of the voltage sensing capacitors, C1 and C2. (The article by Bruene in the Bibliography should be consulted, as well.) The design by Brown in Figure 27.11 is for use with 300-Ω twin-lead and may be used with parallel-wire feed lines of other characteristic impedances such as 450-Ω window line by changing R1 and R2 to match the impedance of the line.

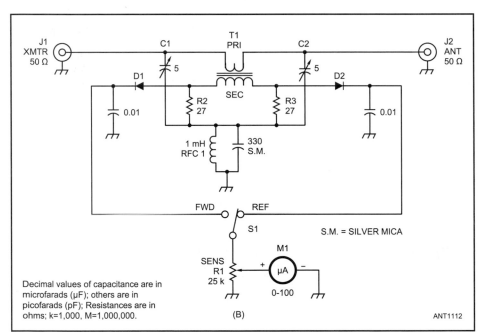

Figure 27.10 — Schematic diagram of the QRP VSWR indicator. Fixed-value capacitors are disc ceramic except those marked with S.M., which are silvered-mica. R2 and R3 and ¼-W carbon-film or metal-film units.

C1, C2 — Miniature PC board mount air trimmer.
D1, D2 — Silicon switching diode, 1N4148 type, matched for equivalent forward resistance by using an ohmmeter.
J1, J2 — RF connector receptacle (phono jack, BNC, UHF).
M1 — Miniature 50- or 100-µA dc meter.
R1 — Linear-taper miniature control, 25 kΩ.
RFC1 — Miniature 1-mH RF choke.
S1 — Miniature SPDT slide or toggle switch.
T1 — Toroidal transformer. Secondary: 60 turns #30 AWG enameled wire on a T68-2 powdered-iron core. Primary is two turns over secondary winding (see text).

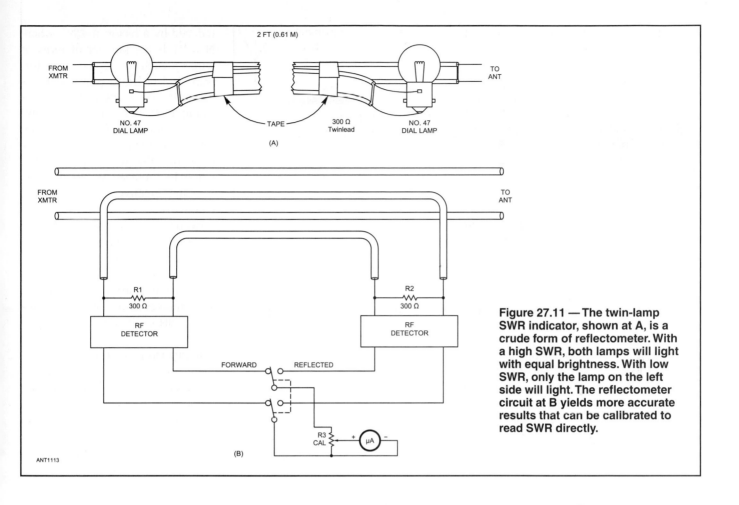

Figure 27.11 — The twin-lamp SWR indicator, shown at A, is a crude form of reflectometer. With a high SWR, both lamps will light with equal brightness. With low SWR, only the lamp on the left side will light. The reflectometer circuit at B yields more accurate results that can be calibrated to read SWR directly.

27.3 RF POWER MEASUREMENT

The standard commercial instruments amateurs use to measure RF power are the various models of the Thruline *directional wattmeters* from Bird Electronics (**www.bird-technologies.com**) such as the popular Model 43. The meter consists of a section of transmission into which is inserted a selectable power-sensing element, popularly referred to as a "slug." The transmission line in the wattmeter is designed to have an element inserted without disrupting normal power flow through the meter.

The element consists of a pickup loop and terminating resistor that form a *directional coupler* — a circuit that couples to a transmission line and extracts a small amount of power flowing in one direction. (See the Bibliography entry by Wade for a tutorial on directional couplers, also include on this book's CD-ROM.) The construction of the Bird transmission line and sensing element are shown as Figure 3 in the Model 43 operating manual, available for download at **www.bird-technologies.com/products/manuals/920-43.pdf**. The element can be rotated so that the directional coupler picks up either forward or reflected power.

The energy from the directional coupler in the element then passes through a rectifying diode and filter capacitor that form an RF detector as described earlier in this chapter. The

output of the RF detector then drives a meter that is calibrated in watts. The standard series of elements covers from 2 to 1000 MHz and from 5 W to 5000 W full-scale. A variety of specialty elements are also available.

For a close look at the construction of the Bird Thruline wattmeter and a typical power sensing element, see the Repeater Builders website article, "Photo Tour of a Bird Wattmeter Element," by Robert Meister, WA1MIK at **www.repeater-builder.com/projects/bird-element-tour/bird-element-tour.html**. A number of excellent white papers and application notes on the use of these ubiquitous instruments are available on the Bird Electronics website under "Resources."

27.3.1 DIRECTIONAL POWER/SWR METER

The following section is an overview of the January 2011 *QST* article by Bill Kaune, W7IEQ, "A Modern Directional Power/SWR Meter." The complete article including firmware and printed circuit board artwork is available on the CD-ROM included with this book.

The primary use for this unit is to monitor the output power and tuning of a transceiver. The author's station configuration is shown in **Figure 27.12**. RF power generated by the transmitter is routed via RG-8 coaxial cable through a

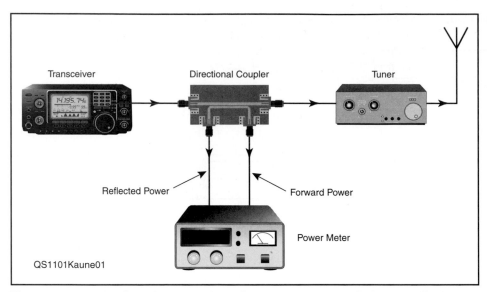

Figure 27.12 — W7IEQ station setup, including the power meter being described here.

reduced by a factor of $1/N^2$, where N = 31 is the number of turns of wire on each toroid. Thus the forward and reflected power samples are reduced by about 30 dB. For example, if a transceiver were delivering a power of 100 W to a pure 50 Ω load, the forward power sample from the directional coupler would be about 0.1 W (20 dBm).

The directivity of a directional coupler is defined as the ratio of the forward power sample divided by the reflected power sample when the coupler is terminated in 50 Ω. In this coupler, the directivity measured using an inexpensive network analyzer is at least 35 dB at 3.5 MHz and 28 dB at 30 MHz.

directional coupler to an antenna tuner, which is connected to the antenna with RG-8. The directional coupler contains circuits that sample the RF power flowing from the transmitter to the tuner (the forward power) and the RF power reflected back from the tuner to the transmitter (the reflected power). These samples are sent via RG-58 cable to the two input channels of the power meter. This project includes the directional coupler and the power meter. Enough detail is provided in the full article so that an amateur can duplicate the device or modify the design.

Directional Coupler

The directional coupler is based on the unit described in "The Tandem Match" by John Grebenkemper, KI6WX in the January 1987 issue of *QST* and also included on this book's CD-ROM. A pair of FT-82-67 toroids with 31 turns of #26 AWG magnet wire over lengths of RG-8 form the basis of the directional coupler shown in **Figure 27.13**.

The forward and reflected power samples coupled are

Power/SWR Meter — Circuit Description

Figure 27.14 shows a front panel view of the power meter. An LCD displays the measured peak (PEP) and average (AEP) envelope powers as well as the standing wave ratio (SWR). The power meter calculates either the peak and average envelope power traveling from the transceiver to load (the forward power) or the peak and average envelope powers actually delivered to the load (the forward power minus reflected power). The average envelope power (AEP) represents an average of the forward or load powers over an averaging period of either 1.6 or 4.8 seconds.

A 1 mA-movement analog meter on the front panel facilitates antenna tuning. This meter continuously displays the quantity 1 – 1/SWR, where SWR is the standing wave ratio on the line. Thus, an SWR of 1.0 corresponds to a meter reading of 0 — no deflection of the meter. An SWR of 2 results in a 50% deflection of the meter, while an SWR of 5 produces an 80% deflection of the meter.

The forward and reflected power samples from the directional coupler are applied to a pair of Analog Devices

Figure 27.13 — Completed directional coupler.

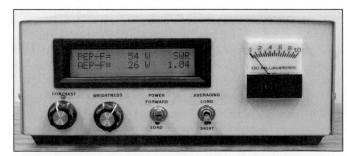

Figure 27.14 — Front panel of power meter. The LCD shows the peak envelope power (PEP), the average envelope power (AEP) and the SWR. The two knobs control the contrast and back lighting of the LCD. One toggle switch determines whether forward or load powers are displayed. A second switch sets the averaging time for the AEP calculation. The meter displays SWR and is used for tuning purposes.

AD8307 logarithmic detectors. External 20 dB attenuators (Mini-Circuits HAT-20) reduce the signals from the directional coupler to levels compatible with the AD8307. As noted earlier, the directional coupler has an internal attenuation of about 30 dB, so the total attenuation in each channel is about 50 dB. Thus, a rig operating at a power level of 1 kW (60 dBm) will result in an input to the forward power channel of about 10 dBm. (The schematic diagram and parts list of the power meter are provided on the CD-ROM version of the article.) The detectors are configured such that the time constant of their output follows the modulation envelope of the RF signal.

LF398 sample-and-hold ICs stabilize the voltages from the forward and reflected power logarithmic detectors. In this way both voltages can be sampled at the exact same time and held for subsequent analog-to-digital conversion and calculation of power and SWR by the PIC16F876A microprocessor (**www.microchip.com**). The processor also includes a pulse-width-modulated (PWM) output used to drive the analog SWR meter on the front panel.

27.3.2 HIGH-POWER RF SAMPLERS

If one wants to measure characteristics of a transmitter or high-power amplifier, some means of reducing the power of the device to 10 or 20 dBm must be used. The most straightforward way to do this is to use a 30 or 40 dB attenuator capable of handling the high power. A 30 dB attenuator will reduce a 100 W transmitter to 20 dBm. A 40 dB attenuator will reduce a 1 kW amplifier to 20 dBm. If further attenuation is needed, a simple precision attenuator may be used after the signal has been reduced to the 20 dBm level.

The problem with high-power attenuators is that they are expensive to buy or build because the front end of the attenuator must handle the output power of the transmitter or amplifier. If one already has a dummy load, an RF sampler may be used to produce a replica of the signal at a reduced power level. The sampler described here was originally presented in *QST* Technical Correspondence for May 2011 by Tom Thompson, WØIVJ. (The original article with construction information plus some supplemental information is available on this book's CD-ROM.)

A transformer sampler passes a single conductor (usually the insulated center conductor from a piece of coaxial cable) from the transmitter or amplifier to the dummy load through a toroidal inductor forming a transformer with a single turn primary. The secondary of the transformer is connected to a resistor network and then to the test equipment as shown in **Figure 27.15** The source, whether a transmitter or amplifier, is assumed to be a pure voltage source in series with a 50-Ω resistor. This most likely is not exactly the case but is sufficient for analysis.

If a current, I, flows into the dummy load, then a current, I / N flows in the secondary of the transformer, where N is the number of turns on the secondary. Figure 27.15 also shows the equivalent circuit, substituting a current source for the transformer. 40 dB is selected for the attenuation and 15 turns for the secondary of the transformer. If R_{SHUNT} = 15 Ω, and R_{SERIES} = 35 Ω, then the voltage across a 50-Ω load resistor, R_{SAMPLE}, is 1/100 of the voltage across the dummy load, which is 40 dB of attenuation.

Reflecting this resistor combination back through the transformer yields 0.06 Ω in series with the 50-Ω dummy load impedance. This is an insignificant change. Furthermore, reflecting 100 Ω from the primary to the secondary places 22.5 kΩ in parallel with R_{SHUNT}, which does not significantly affect its value. The test equipment sees a 50-Ω load looking back into the sampler. Even at low frequencies, where the reactance of the secondary winding is lower than 15 Ω, the impedance looking back into the sample port remains close to 50 Ω.

The samplers described here use an FT37-61 ferrite core followed by two resistors as described above. The through-line SWR is good up to 200 MHz, the SWR is fair looking into the sampled port, and the useful bandwidth extends

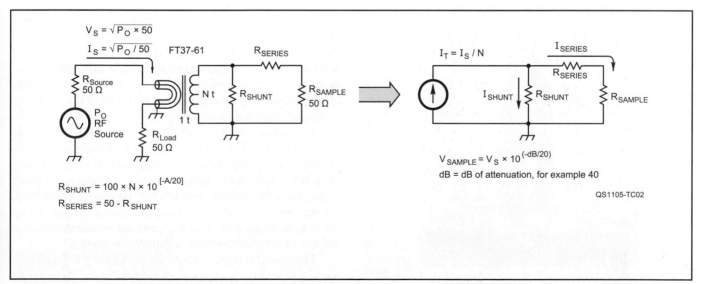

Figure 27.15 — RF sampler circuit diagram and equivalent circuit showing calculations.

Figure 27.16 — RF sampler using box construction.

Figure 27.17 — RF sampler using tube construction.

from 0.5 MHz to about 100 MHz. If you are interested in an accurate representation of the third harmonic of your HF transmitter or amplifier, it is important for the sampler to give accurate attenuation into the VHF range.

Figure 27.16 shows a photo of a sampler built into a 1.3 × 1.3 × 1 inch (inside dimensions) box constructed from single-sided circuit board material. The through-line connection is made with a short piece of UT-141 semi-rigid coax with the shield grounded only on one side to provide electrostatic shielding between the toroid and the center conductor of the coax. (Do not ground both ends of the shield or a shorted turn is created.) R_{SHUNT} is hidden under the toroid, and R_{SERIES} is shown connected to the sample port. This construction technique looks like a short piece of 200-Ω transmission line in the through-line which affects the SWR at higher frequencies. This can be corrected by compensating with two 3 pF capacitors connected to the through-line input and output connectors as shown in the photo. The through-line SWR was reduced from 1.43:1 to 1.09:1 at 180 MHz by adding the capacitors. This compensation, however, causes the attenuation to differ at high frequencies depending on the direction of the through-line connection. A sampler constructed using the box technique is useable from below 1 MHz through 30 MHz.

Figure 27.17 shows a different approach using 9⁄16 inch diameter, 0.014 inch wall thickness, hobby brass tubing. This lowers the impedance of the through-line so that no compensation is needed. The through-line SWR for the tube sampler is 1.08:1 at 180 MHz which is as good as the box sampler and the sensitivity to through-line direction is reduced. Although the high frequency attenuation is not as good as the box sampler, the construction technique provides a more consistent result. A sampler constructed using the tube technique should be usable through 200 MHz.

27.3.3 AN INEXPENSIVE VHF DIRECTIONAL COUPLER

Precision inline metering devices capable of reading forward and reflected power over a wide range of frequencies are very useful in amateur VHF and UHF work, but their rather high cost puts them out of the reach of many VHF enthusiasts. The device shown in **Figures 27.18** through **27.20** is an inexpensive adaptation of their basic principles. It can be made for the cost of a meter, a few small parts, and bits of copper pipe and fittings that can be found in the plumbing section at many hardware stores.

The sampler consists of a short section of handmade coaxial line, in this instance, of 50-Ω impedance, with a reversible probe coupled to it. A small pickup loop built into the probe is terminated with a resistor at one end and a diode at the other. The resistor matches the impedance of the loop, not the impedance of the line section. Energy picked up by the loop is rectified by the diode, and the resultant current is fed to a meter equipped with a calibration control.

The principal metal parts of the device are a brass plumbing T, a pipe cap, short pieces of ¾-inch ID and 5⁄16-inch OD copper pipe, and two coaxial fittings. Other available tubing

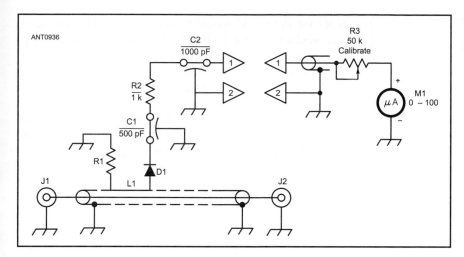

Figure 27.18 — Circuit diagram for the line sampler.
C1 — 500-pF feedthrough capacitor, solder-in type.
C2 — 1000-pF feedthrough capacitor, threaded type.
D1 — 1N34A germanium or 1N5817 Schottky diode.
J1, J2 — Coaxial connector, type N (UG-58A).
L1 — Pickup loop, copper strap 1-inch long × ³⁄₁₆-inch wide. Bend into "C" shape with flat portion ⅝-inch long.
M1 — 0-100 μA meter.
R1 — 82 to 100 Ω, carbon-film or metal film.
R3 — 50-kΩ composition control, linear taper.

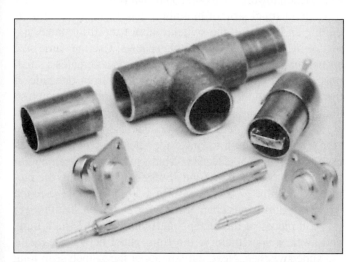

Figure 27.19 — Major components of the line sampler. The brass T and two end sections are at the upper left in this picture. A completed probe assembly is at the right. The N connectors have their center pins removed. The pins are shown with one inserted in the left end of the inner conductor and the other lying in the right foreground.

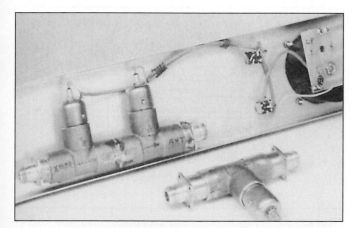

Figure 27.20 — Two versions of the line sampler. The single unit described in detail here is in the foreground. Two sections in a single assembly provide for monitoring forward and reflected power without probe reversal.

combinations for 50-Ω line may be usable. The ratio of outer conductor ID to inner conductor OD should be 2.4/1. (The complete article with more detail is available on this book's CD-ROM.)

The sampler is very useful for many jobs even if it is not accurately calibrated, although it is desirable to calibrate it against a wattmeter of known accuracy as described in the complete article.

27.3.4 RF STEP ATTENUATOR

A good RF step attenuator is one of the key pieces of equipment that belongs on your workbench. The attenuator in this project offers good performance yet can be built with a few basic tools. The attenuator is designed for use in 50-Ω systems, provides a total attenuation of 71 dB in 1-dB steps, offers respectable accuracy and insertion loss through 225 MHz and can be used at 450 MHz as shown in **Table 27-1**. This material was originally published as "An RF Step Attenuator" by Denton Bramwell, K7OWJ, in the June 1995 *QST*.

The attenuator consists of 10 resistive pi (π) attenuator sections such as the one in **Figure 27.21**. Each section consists of a DPDT slide switch and three ¼-W, 1%-tolerance metal-film resistors. The complete unit contains single 1, 2,

Table 27-1
Step Attenuator Performance at 148, 225, and 250 MHz
Measurements made in the ARRL Laboratory

Attenuator set for Maximum attenuation (71 dB)		Attenuator set for minimum attenuation (0 dB)	
Frequency (MHz)	Attenuation (dB)	Frequency (MHz)	Attenuation (dB)
148	72.33	148	0.4
225	73.17	225	0.4
450	75.83	450	0.84

Note: Laboratory-specified measurement tolerance of ±1 dB

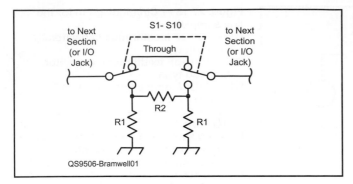

Figure 27.21 — Schematic of one section of the attenuator. All resistors are ¼-W, 1%-tolerance metal-film units. See Table 27-2 for the resistor values required for each attenuator section. There are six 10 dB sections and one each of 1, 2, 3, and 5 dB.

Table 27-2
Closest 1%-Tolerance Resistor Values

Attenuation (dB)	R1 (Ω)	R2 (Ω)
1.00	866.00	5.60
2.00	436.00	11.50
3.00	294.00	17.40
5.00	178.00	30.10
10.00	94.30	71.50

3 and 5-dB sections, and six 10-dB sections. **Table 27-2** lists the resistor values required for each section.

The enclosure is made of brass sheet stock, readily available at hardware and hobby stores. By selecting the right stock, you can avoid having to bend the metal and need only perform a minimum of cutting.

Construction

The enclosure can be built using only a nibbling tool, drill press, metal shears, and a soldering gun or heavy soldering iron. (Use a regular soldering iron on the switches and resistors.) One method of cutting the small pieces of rectangular tubing to length is to use a drill press equipped with a small abrasive cutoff wheel.

Brass is easy to work and solder. For the enclosure, you'll need two precut 2 × 12 × 0.025-inch sheets and two 1 × 12 × 0.025-inch sheets. The 2-inch-wide stock is used for the front and back panels; the 1-inch-wide stock is used for the ends and sides. For the internal wiring, you need a piece of ⁵⁄₃₂ × ⁵⁄₁₆-inch rectangular tubing, a ¼ × 0.032-inch strip, and a few small pieces of 0.005-inch-thick stock to provide interstage shields and form the 50-Ω transmission lines that run from the BNC connectors to the switches at the ends of the step attenuator.

For the front panel, nibble or shear a piece of 2-inch-wide brass to a length of about 9½ inches. Space the switches from each other so that a piece of the rectangular brass tubing lies flat and snugly between them. See **Figure 27.22**. Drill

holes for the #4-40 mounting screws and nibble or punch rectangular holes for the bodies of the slide switches.

Before mounting any parts, solder in place one of the 1-inch-wide chassis side pieces to make the assembly more rigid. Solder the side piece to the edge of the top plate that faces the "through" side of the switches; this makes later assembly easier (see **Figure 27.23**). Although the BNC input and output connectors are shown mounted on the top (front) panel, better lead dress and high-frequency performance may result from mounting the connectors at the ends of the enclosure.

DPDT slide switches designed for sub-panel mounting often have mounting holes tapped for #4-40 screws. Enlarge the holes to allow a #4-40 screw to slide through. Before mounting the switches, make the "through" switch connection (see Figure 27.21) by bending the two lugs at one end of each switch toward each other and soldering the lugs together or solder a small strip of brass between the lugs and clip off the lug ends. Mount the switches above the front panel, using ⁵⁄₃₂-inch-high by ⁷⁄₃₂-inch-OD spacers. Use the same size spacer on the inside. On the inside, the spacer creates a small post that helps reduce capacitive coupling from one side of the attenuator to the other. The spacers position the switch so that the 50-Ω stripline can be formed later.

The trick to getting acceptable insertion loss in the "through" position is to make the attenuator look as much as possible like 50-Ω coax. That's where the rectangular tubing and the ¼ × 0.032-inch brass strip come into the picture (see Figure 27.22); they form a 50-Ω stripline. (See the **Transmission Lines** chapter for information on stripline.)

Cut pieces of the rectangular tubing about ¾-inch long, and sweat solder them to the front panel between each of the slide switches. Next, cut lengths of the ¼-inch strip long enough to conveniently reach from switch to switch, then cut one more piece. Drill ¹⁄₁₆-inch holes near both ends of all but one of the ¼-inch strips. The undrilled piece is used as a temporary spacer, so make sure it is flat and deburred.

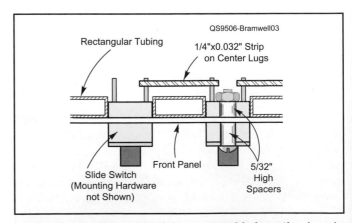

Figure 27.22 — Key to obtaining acceptable insertion loss in the "through" position is to make the whole device look as much as possible like 50-Ω coax. The rectangular tubing and the ¼ × 0.032-inch brass strip between the switch sections form a 50-Ω stripline.

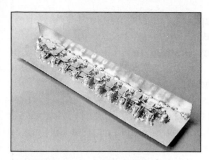

Figure 27.23 — Solder one of the 1-inch-wide chassis side pieces in place to make the assembly more rigid during construction. Solder the side piece to the edge of the top plate that faces the "through" side of the switches; this makes the rest of the assembly easier.

Figure 27.24 — The attenuator before final mechanical assembly. The ¼-inch strips are spaced 0.033 inch apart to form a 50-Ω connection from the BNC connector to the stripline. There are ½-inch square shields between 10-dB sections. The square shields have a notch in one corner to accommodate the end of the rectangular tubing.

Figure 27.25 — The completed step attenuator in the enclosure of brass sheet. The BNC connectors may be mounted on the front panel at the end of the switches or on the end panels.

Lay the temporary spacer on top of the rectangular tubing between the first two switches, then drop one of the drilled ¼-inch pieces over it, with the center switch lugs through the ¹⁄₁₆-inch holes. Before soldering, check the strip to make sure there's sufficient clearance between the ¼-inch strip and the switch lugs; trim the corners if necessary. Use a screwdriver blade to hold the strip flat and solder the lugs to the strip. Remove the temporary spacer. Repeat this procedure for all switch sections. This creates a 50-Ω stripline running the length of the attenuator.

Next, solder in place the three 1%-tolerance resistors of each section, keeping the leads as short as possible. Use a generous blob of solder on ground leads to make the lead less inductive. Install a ½-inch-square brass shield between each 10-dB section to ensure that signals don't couple around the sections at higher frequencies.

Use parallel ¼-inch strips of 0.005-inch-thick brass spaced 0.033 inch apart to form 50-Ω feed lines from the BNC connectors to the switch contacts at each end of the stripline as shown in Figure 27.23. (Use the undrilled piece of 0.032-inch-thick brass to insure the proper line spacing.) The attenuator with all switches and shields in place is shown ready for final mechanical assembly in **Figure 27.24**

Finally, solder in place the remaining enclosure side, cut and solder the end pieces, and solder brass #4-40 nuts to the inside walls of the case to hold the rear (or bottom) panel. Drill and attach the rear panel and round off the sharp corners to prevent scratching or cutting anyone or anything. Add stick-on feet and labels and your step attenuator of **Figure 27.25** is ready for use.

Remember that the unit is built with ¼-W resistors, so it can't dissipate a lot of power. Remember, too, that for the attenuation to be accurate, the input to the attenuator must be a 50-Ω source and the output must be terminated in a 50-Ω load.

27.4 FIELD STRENGTH METERS

Few amateur stations, fixed or mobile, are without need of a *field-strength meter* (*FSM*). An instrument of this type serves many useful purposes during antenna experiments and adjustments. In its simplest form, the field strength meter is simply a diode detector and a sensitive meter with a potentiometer wired as a resistive divider to act as a sensitivity control as in **Figure 27.26**. This type of meter is commonly and inexpensively available both new and used. (See the Bibliography and this book's CD-ROM for the *QST* article describing how to build this simple FSM.)

When work is to be done from many wavelengths away from the antenna, however, such a simple instrument lacks the necessary sensitivity. Further, such a device has a serious fault because its linearity leaves much to be desired and it is very wideband so that the measurement may be upset from any other strong nearby transmitter, such as an AM broadcast station. Thus, a more capable instrument is needed.

27.4.1 PORTABLE FIELD STRENGTH METER

The field-strength meter described here takes care of the problems associated with a simple FSM. Additionally, it is small, measuring only 4 × 5 × 8 inches. The power

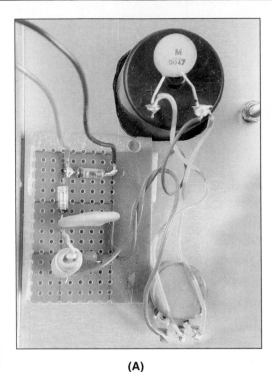

(A)

Figure 27.26 — With the sensitivity control at mid-range, the simple FSM shown at A can easily detect a 1-W, 2 meter signal. B gives the schematic and parts list for the FSM. A metal enclosure is mandatory.

C1-C3 — 0.01 µF disc ceramic capacitor.
D1, D2 — 1N34A (germanium) or 1N5817 (Schottky) diode.
L1 — 100 µH inductor.
M1 — 50 µA analog meter.
R1 — 68 kΩ, ¼-W carbon-film or metal-film resistor.
R2 — 10 kΩ linear or audio taper potentiometer.
Antenna — BNC chassis-mount receptacle.

QS0208-Noakes01

Antenna

C1 0.01 µF R1 68 k D1 1N34A D2 1N34A L1 100 µH C2 0.01 µF C3 0.01 µF R2 10 k 0 - 50 µA M1

(B)

supply consists of two 9-V batteries. Sensitivity can be set for practically any amount desired. However, from a usefulness standpoint, the circuit should not be too sensitive or it will respond to unwanted signals. This unit also has excellent linearity with regard to field strength. (The field strength of a received signal varies inversely with the distance from the source, all other things being equal.) The frequency range includes all amateur bands from 3.5 through 148 MHz, with band-switched circuits, thus avoiding the use of plug-in inductors. All in all, it is a quite useful instrument. The information in this section is based on a January 1973 *QST* article by Lew McCoy, W1ICP. (See the Bibliography.)

The unit is pictured in **Figures 27.27** and **27.28**, and the schematic diagram is shown in **Figure 27.29**. A type 741 op-amp IC is the heart of the unit. (Any general-purpose op-amp can be substituted for the 741.) The antenna is connected to J1, and a tuned circuit is used ahead of a diode detector. The rectified signal is coupled as dc and amplified in the op amp. Sensitivity of the op amp is controlled by inserting resistors R3 through R6 in the circuit by means of S2.

Figure 27.27 —The linear field strength meter. The control at the upper left is for C1 and the one to the right for C2. At the lower left is the band switch, and to its right the sensitivity switch. The zero-set control for M1 is located directly below the meter.

Figure 27.28 — Inside view of the field-strength meter. At the upper right is C1 and to the left, C2. The dark leads from the circuit board to the front panel are the shielded leads described in the text.

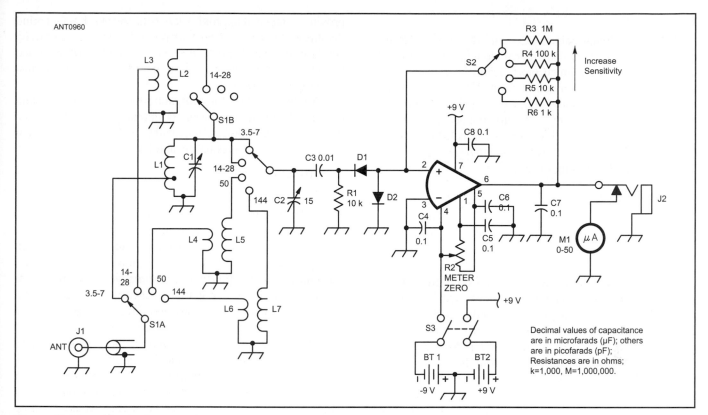

Figure 27.29 — Circuit diagram of the linear field strength meter. All resistors are ¼- or ½-W carbon-film or metal-film types.

C1 — 140 pF variable.
C2 — 15-pF variable
D1, D2 — 1N4148 or equiv.
L1 — 34 turns #24 AWG enameled wire wound on an T-68-2 core, tapped 4 turns from ground end.
L2 — 12 turns #24 AWG enameled wire wound on T-68-2 core.
L3 — 2 turns #24 AWG enameled wire wound at ground end of L2.
L4 — 1 turn #26 AWG enameled wire wound at ground end of L5.

L5 — 12 turns #26 AWG enameled wire wound on T-25-12 core.
L6 — 1 turn #26 AWG enameled wire wound at ground end of L7.
L7 — 1 turn #18 AWG enameled wire wound on T-25-12 core.
M1 — 50 or 100 μA dc.
R2 — 10-kΩ control, linear taper.
S1 — Rotary switch, 3 poles, 5 positions, 3 sections.
S2 — Rotary switch, 1 pole, 4 positions.
S3 — DPST toggle.
U1 — Type 741 op amp or equivalent. Pin numbers shown are for a 14-pin package.

With the circuit shown, and in its most sensitive setting, M1 will detect a signal from the antenna on the order of 100 μV. Linearity is poor for approximately the first ⅓ of the meter range, but then is almost straight-line from there to full-scale deflection. The reason for the poor linearity at the start of the readings is because of nonlinearity of the diodes at the point of first conduction. However, if gain measurements are being made this is of no real importance, as accurate gain measurements can be made in the linear portion of the readings.

The 741 op amp requires both a positive and a negative voltage source. This is obtained by connecting two 9-V batteries in series and grounding the center. One other feature of the instrument is that it can be used remotely by connecting an external meter at J2. This is handy if you want to adjust an antenna and observe the results without having to leave the antenna site.

L1 is the 3.5/7 MHz coil and is tuned by C1. The coil is wound on a toroid form. For 14, 21 or 28 MHz, L2 is

switched in parallel with L1 to cover the three bands. L5 and C2 cover approximately 40 to 60 MHz, and L7 and C2 from 130 MHz to approximately 180 MHz. The two VHF coils are also wound on toroid forms.

Construction Notes

The majority of the components may be mounted on an etched circuit board. A shielded lead should be used between pin 4 of the IC and S2. The same is true for the leads from R3 through R6 to the switch. Otherwise, parasitic oscillations may occur in the IC because of its very high gain.

In order for the unit to cover the 144-MHz band, L6 and L7 should be mounted directly across the appropriate terminals of S1, rather than on a circuit board. The extra lead length adds too much stray capacitance to the circuit. It isn't necessary to use toroid forms for the 50- and 144 MHz coils. They were used in the version described here simply because they were available. You may substitute air-wound coils of the appropriate inductance.

Calibration

The field strength meter can be used as is for a relative-reading device. A linear indicator scale will serve admirably. However, it will be a much more useful instrument for antenna work if it is calibrated in decibels, enabling the user to check relative gain and front-to-back ratios. If you have access to a calibrated signal generator, connect it to the field-strength meter and use different signal levels fed to the device to make a calibration chart. Convert signal-generator voltage ratios to decibels by using the equation

$$dB = 20 \log (V1/V2) \tag{Eq 3}$$

where V1/V2 is the ratio of the two voltages and log is the common logarithm (base 10).

Let's assume that M1 is calibrated evenly from 0 to 10. Next, assume we set the signal generator to provide a reading of 1 on M1, and that the generator is feeding a 100 µV signal into the instrument. Now we increase the generator output to 200 µV, giving us a voltage ratio of 2:1. Also let's assume M1 reads 5 with the 200 µV input. From the equation above, we find that the voltage ratio of 2 equals 6.02 dB between 1 and 5 on the meter scale. M1 can be calibrated more accurately between 1 and 5 on its scale by adjusting the generator and figuring the ratio. For example, a ratio of 126 µV to 100 µV is 1.26, corresponding to 2.0 dB. By using this method, all of the settings of S2 can be calibrated. In the instrument shown here, the most sensitive setting of S2 with R3, 1 MΩ,

provides a range of approximately 6 dB for M1. Keep in mind that the meter scale for each setting of S1 must be calibrated similarly for each band. The degree of coupling of the tuned circuits for the different bands will vary, so each band must be calibrated separately.

Another method for calibrating the instrument is using a transmitter and measuring its output power with an RF wattmeter. In this case we are dealing with power rather than voltage ratios, so this equation applies:

$$dB = 10 \log (P1/P2) \tag{Eq 4}$$

where P1/P2 is the power ratio.

With most transmitters the power output can be varied, so calibration of the test instrument is rather easy. Attach a pickup antenna to the field-strength meter (a short wire a foot or so long will do) and position the device in the transmitter antenna field. Let's assume we set the transmitter output for 10 W and get a reading on M1. We note the reading and then increase the output to 20 W, a power ratio of 2. Note the reading on M1 and then use Eq 4. A power ratio of 2 is 3.01 dB. By using this method the instrument can be calibrated on all bands and ranges.

With the tuned circuits and coupling links specified in Figure 27.29, this instrument has an average range on the various bands of 6 dB for the two most sensitive positions of S2, and 15 dB and 30 dB for the next two successive ranges. The 30-dB scale is handy for making front-to-back antenna measurements without having to switch S2.

27.5 NOISE BRIDGE AND ANTENNA ANALYZER MEASUREMENTS

27.5.1 USING NOISE BRIDGES

The *noise bridge*, sometimes referred to as an *antenna (R-X) noise bridge*, is an instrument for measuring the impedance of an antenna or other electrical circuits. The unit shown here in **Figure 27.30**, designed for use in the 1.8 through 30-MHz range, provides adequate accuracy for most measurements. Battery operation and small physical size make this unit ideal for remote-location use.

Tone modulation is applied to the wide-band noise generator as an aid for obtaining a null indication. With an unknown impedance connected, the R and X controls are

Figure 27.30 — A noise bridge contains a noise source and an external receiver serves as the detector. The bridge is adjusted for minimum noise in the receiver and values for R and X are read from calibrated dials.

adjusted for minimum noise in a receiver that acts as the bridge detector. (See the Bibliography and this book's CD-ROM for an article by Grebenkemper on using R-X noise bridges.) The values of resistance and reactance are then read from the R and X dials.

Measuring Cable Electrical Length with a Noise Bridge

With a noise bridge and a general-coverage receiver, you can easily locate frequencies at which the line in question is a multiple of ½ λ, because a shorted ½ λ line has a 0-Ω impedance (neglecting line loss). By locating two adjacent null frequencies, you can solve for the length of line in terms of ½ λ at one of the frequencies and calculate the line length (overall accuracy is limited by bridge accuracy and line loss, which broadens the nulls). As an interim variable, you can express cable length as the frequency at which a cable is 1 λ long. This length will be represented by f_λ. Follow these steps to determine f_λ for a coaxial cable. You will need calibrated test loads as shown in **Figure 27.31**.

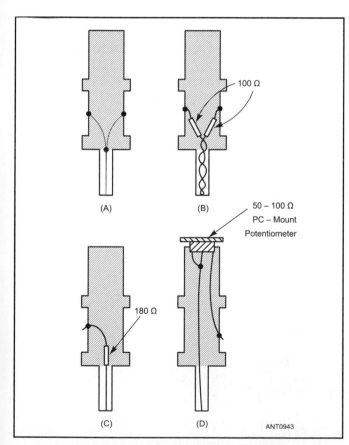

(A)   (B)

100 Ω

50 – 100 Ω
PC – Mount
Potentiometer

(C)   (D)

180 Ω

ANT0943

Figure 27.31 — Construction details of the resistive loads used to check and calibrate the noise bridge. Each of the loads is constructed inside a coaxial connector that matches those on the bridge. (Views shown are cross-sections of PL-259 bodies; the shells are not shown.) Leads should be kept as short as possible to minimize parasitic inductance. A is a 0-Ω load; B depicts a 50-Ω load; C is a 180-Ω load; D shows a variable-resistance load used to determine the loss in a coaxial cable. Use noninductive carbon-film or metal-film resistors.

1) Tune the receiver to the frequency range of interest. Attach the short-circuit load to the noise bridge UNKNOWN connector and null the bridge.

2) Disconnect the far end of the coaxial cable from its load (the antenna) and connect it to the 0-Ω test load. Connect the near end of the cable to the bridge UNKNOWN connector.

3) Adjust the receiver frequency and the noise-bridge resistance control for a null. *Do not change the noise bridge reactance-control setting during this procedure.* Note the frequency at which the null is found; call this frequency f_n. The noise-bridge resistance at the null should be relatively small (less than 20 Ω).

4) Tune the receiver upward in frequency until the next null is found. Adjust the resistance control, if necessary, to improve the null, *but do not adjust the reactance control.* Note the frequency at which this second null is found; this is f_{n+2}.

5) Solve Eq 5 for n and the electrical length of the cable.

$$n = \frac{2f_0}{f_{n+2} - f_0} \qquad \text{(Eq 5)}$$

$$f_\lambda = \frac{4f_n}{n} \qquad \text{(Eq 6)}$$

$$\ell = \frac{f_0}{f_\lambda} \qquad \text{(Eq 7)}$$

where

n = cable electrical length in quarter waves, at f_n
f_λ = frequency at which the cable is 1λ
f_0 = frequency at which electrical length is to be determined
ℓ = cable electrical length, in λ

For example, consider a 74-foot length of Carol C1188 foam-dielectric cable (velocity factor = 0.78) to be used on the 10 meter band. Based on the manufacturer's specification, the cable is 2.796 λ at 29 MHz (f_0). Nulls were found at 24.412 (f_n) and 29.353 (f_{n+2}) MHz. Eq 5 yields n = 9.88, which produces f_λ = 9.883 MHz from Eq 6 and ℓ = 2.934 λ from Eq 7. If the manufacturer's specification is correct, the measured length is off by less than 5%, which is very reasonable. Ideally, n would yield an integer. The difference between n and the closest integer indicates that there is some error.

This procedure also works for lines with an open circuit as the termination (n will be close to an odd number). End effects from the PL-259 increase the effective length of the coaxial cable; however, this decreases the calculated f_λ.

27.5.2 USING ANTENNA ANALYZERS

Antenna or SWR analyzers that employ a low-level variable frequency signal source and wideband RF detectors have become very popular for antenna and transmission line measurements, largely displacing the noise bridge and dip meter as the preferred tool for antenna system measurements. The basic operation of the instrument is well-covered by the instrument user's manual and supplemented by descriptions of its use in several measurement techniques described in this chapter.

Peter Shuch, WB2UAQ contributes methods for the first three common analyzer tasks. The Sep 1996 *QST* article by George Badger, W6TC, and others, "SWR Analyzer Tips, Tricks and Techniques: SWR Analyzer Hints" provides other interesting applications of SWR analyzers and the *QST* article by Frederick Hauff, W3NZ, "The Gadget — An SWR Analyzer Add-on" describes a useful test accessory. (Articles are included on this book's CD-ROM and listed in the Bibliography.)

Amateur antenna analyzers are not intended to be precision instruments — values for impedance and reactance should be considered to have accuracy of a few percent. If precision measurements are required use calibrated, laboratory-grade test instrumentation.

Common-mode currents and load imbalance can also cause errors in measurements involving lengths of cable. Use a good-quality choke balun when measuring antenna characteristics so that the outside surface of the cable does not influence the measurement. It may also be necessary to use RF choke techniques if the cable is long enough to pick up significant levels of RF from any nearby transmitters, such as broadcast stations or paging transmitters.

Measuring Line Length

In addition to the analyzer, you'll need a coaxial tee adaptor and a 50-Ω load (see Figure 27.31). Connect the tee adapter to the analyzer. To one arm of the tee, connect the 50-Ω load. Connect the cable under test (CUT) to the other arm. Short the far end of the line with the minimum length connection. Starting at a frequency too low for the line to be $\lambda/4$ long, slowly tune the analyzer frequency upward until the SWR decreases to a minimum or reaches 1:1. (The lossier the cable, the higher SWR will be at the minimum.) At that frequency the CUT will be $\lambda/4$ long because a shorted $\lambda/4$ line is an open-circuit at the other end and the analyzer will only see the 50-Ω load, regardless of the line's characteristic impedance.

Measuring Velocity Factor

Start by determining the frequency at which the line is $\lambda/4$ long as described above. To find the velocity factor, divide the line's physical length by the free-space wavelength at the frequency at which the line is $\lambda/4$ long. For example, if an 86-foot piece of line is $\lambda/4$ long at 7.58 MHz, the velocity factor (VF) = 86 / (984 / 7.58) = (86 × 7.58) / 984 = 0.662.

Measuring Characteristic Impedance

Characteristic impedance changes slowly as a function of frequency, so this measurement must be done near the frequency of interest, f_λ. The characteristic impedance of the coaxial cable is found by measuring its input impedance at two frequencies separated by $\frac{1}{4} f_\lambda$. This must be done when the cable is terminated in a resistive load.

If your analyzer can measure the magnitude of impe-

dance, a $\lambda/4$ line's characteristic impedance, Z_0, can be measured by using the formula

$$Z_0 = \sqrt{Z_i \times Z_L}$$

where

Z_i = the input impedance to the line
Z_L = the load impedance.

Terminate the line with a 50-Ω load. At the frequency for which the line is $\lambda/4$ long, measure input impedance, Z_i. If the input impedance is 50 Ω, so is the line's characteristic impedance. If the input impedance is some other value, use the equation above. For example, if $Z_i = 100\ \Omega$, then

$$Z_0 = \sqrt{100 \times 50} = 70.7\,\Omega$$

The preceding procedure yields only the magnitude of the characteristic impedance which actually includes some reactance. The measurement procedure to determine complex characteristic impedance follows.

1) Place the 50-Ω load on the far end of the coaxial cable and connect the near end to the analyzer. (Measurement error is minimized when the load resistance is close to the characteristic impedance of the cable. This is the reason for using the 50-Ω load.)

2) Tune the analyzer approximately $\frac{1}{8}$ f_λ below the frequency of interest. Call this frequency f1. Read R_{f1} and X_{f1}. Remember, the reactance reading must be scaled to the measurement frequency.

3) Increase the frequency by exactly $\frac{1}{4}$ f_λ. Call this frequency f2 and note the readings as R_{f2} and X_{f2}.

4) Calculate the characteristic impedance of the coaxial cable using Eqs 8 through 13. A scientific calculator or spreadsheet is helpful for this.

$$R = R_{f1} \times R_{f2} - X_{f1} \times X_{f2} \qquad \text{(Eq 8)}$$

$$X = R_{f1} \times X_{f2} + X_{f1} \times R_{f2} \qquad \text{(Eq 9)}$$

$$Z = \sqrt{R^2 + X^2} \qquad \text{(Eq 10)}$$

$$R_0 = \sqrt{Z} \cos\left[\frac{1}{2}\tan^{-1}\left(\frac{X}{R}\right)\right] \qquad \text{(Eq 11)}$$

$$X_0 = \sqrt{Z} \tan\left[\frac{1}{2}\tan^{-1}\left(\frac{X}{R}\right)\right] \qquad \text{(Eq 12)}$$

$$Z_0 = R_0 + jX_0 \qquad \text{(Eq 13)}$$

where Z_0 is the characteristic impedance of the transmission line.

Let's continue with the example used earlier for cable length. The measurements are:

f1 = 29.000 − (9.883/8) = 27.765 MHz

R_{f1} = 64 Ω

X_{f1} = −22 Ω × (10/27.765) = −7.9 Ω

f2 = 27.765 + (9.883/4) = 30.236 MHz

R_{f2} = 50 Ω

X_{f2} = −24 Ω × (10/30.236) = −7.9 Ω

When used in Eqs 8 through 13, these data yield:

R = 3137.59 Ω

X = −900.60 Ω

Z = 3264.28 Ω

R_0 = 56.58 Ω

X_0 = −7.96 Ω

Remember the limitations on accuracy for inexpensive test equipment and be skeptical of data or calculations beyond two significant figures. The level of precision implied here is for illustration purposes only.

Cable Attenuation

Cable loss can be measured once the cable electrical length and characteristic resistance are known. The measurement must be made at a frequency where the cable presents no reactance. Reactance is zero when the cable electrical length is an integer multiple of λ/4. You can easily meet that condition by making the measurement frequency an integer multiple of ¼ f_λ. Loss at other frequencies can be interpolated with reasonable accuracy. This procedure employs a resistor-substitution method using the test loads in Figure 27.31 that provides much greater accuracy than is achieved by directly reading the resistance from the analyzer. (You can also measure loss directly by using a wattmeter to measure power into and out of the line.)

1) Determine the approximate frequency at which you want to make the loss measurement by using

$$n = \frac{4f_0}{f_\lambda} \qquad \text{(Eq 14A)}$$

where f_0 is the nominal frequency.

Round n to the nearest integer, then

$$f1 = \frac{n}{4}f_\lambda \qquad \text{(Eq 14B)}$$

2) If n is odd, leave the far end of the cable open; if n is even, connect the 0-Ω load to the far end of the cable. Attach the near end of the cable to the analyzer and read resistance and reactance.

3) Disconnect the cable from the analyzer and connect the variable-resistance calibration load in its place. Without changing analyzer frequency, adjust the load resistor to obtain the same resistance and reactance.

5) Remove the variable-resistance load from the analyzer and measure the load resistance using an ohmmeter that's accurate at low resistance levels. Refer to this resistance as R_i.

6) Calculate the cable loss in decibels using

$$loss = 8.69\frac{R_i}{R_0} \qquad \text{(Eq 15)}$$

To continue this example, Eq 14A gives n = 11.74, so measure the attenuation at n = 12. From Eq 14B, f1 = 29.649 MHz. The input resistance of the cable measures 12.1 Ω with 0-Ω load on the far end of the cable; this corresponds to a loss of 1.86 dB.

Antenna Impedance

The impedance at the end of a transmission line can be easily measured using an SWR analyzer, as shown in **Figure 29.32**. In many cases, however, you really want to measure the impedance of an antenna — that is, the impedance of the load at the far end of the line. There are several ways to handle this.

1) Measurements can be made with the bridge at the antenna. This is usually not practical because the antenna must be in its final position for the measurement to be accurate. Even if it can be done, making such a measurement is certainly not very convenient.

2) Measurements can be made at the source end of a coaxial cable — if the cable length is an exact integer multiple of ½ λ. This effectively restricts measurements to a single frequency.

3) Measurements can be made at the source end of a coaxial cable and corrected using a Smith Chart. (See this book's CD-ROM for an article on the Smith Chart.) This graphic method can result in reasonable estimates of antenna impedance — as long as the SWR is not too high and the cable is not too lossy. However, it doesn't compensate for the complex impedance characteristics of real-world coaxial cables. Also, compensation for cable loss can be tricky to

Figure 27.32 — When using an antenna analyzer to measure impedance data, use the numeric display and not the analog meters. In this example, the load impedance is 39 Ω (R_s) in series with a reactance (X_s) of 10 Ω. The sign of the reactance is not given by this instrument.

apply. These problems, too, can lead to significant errors.

4) Last, measurements can be corrected using the transmission-line equation. The *TLW* program included on this book's CD-ROM can do these complicated computations for you. This is the best method for calculating antenna impedances from measured parameters, but it requires that you measure the feed line characteristics beforehand — measurements for which you need access to both ends of the feed line.

The procedure for determining antenna impedance is to first measure the electrical length, characteristic impedance, and attenuation of the coaxial cable connected to the antenna. After making these measurements, connect the antenna to the coaxial cable and measure the input impedance of the cable at a number of frequencies. Then use these measurements in the transmission-line equation to determine the actual antenna impedance at each frequency.

When doing the conversions, be careful not to introduce measurement errors as discussed earlier. Such errors will be carried through into the corrected data. This problem is most significant when the transmission line is near an odd multiple of a ¼ λ and the line SWR and/or attenuation is high. Measurement errors are probably present if small changes in the input impedance or transmission-line characteristics appear as large changes in antenna impedance or if changing the physical orientation of the line or instruments cause significant changes in the measured data. These effects can be minimized by decoupling the line from the antenna and by making the measurements with a transmission line that is approximately an integer multiple of ½ λ. Another clue that there is something amiss with the system is final data that changes erratically with frequency or in ways that aren't typical of antennas or transmission lines. If the data "looks funny," apply extra scrutiny before accepting it as fact.

27.6 TIME-DOMAIN REFLECTOMETER

A time-domain reflectometer (TDR) is a simple but powerful tool used to evaluate transmission lines. When used with an oscilloscope, a TDR displays impedance "bumps" (open and short circuits, kinks and so on) in transmission lines. Commercially produced TDRs cost from hundreds to thousands of dollars each, but you can add the TDR described here to your shack for much less. This material is based on a *QST* article by Tom King, KD5HM, (see Bibliography), and supplemented with information from the references.

A handy "free" TDR is sometimes available from oscilloscopes with a trigger output pulse synchronized with the start of the sweep. The output pulse generally has a very fast rise time and although not adjustable, does serve the same purpose as an external TDR pulse generator.

27.6.1 HOW A TDR WORKS

A simple TDR consists of a square-wave generator and an oscilloscope. See **Figure 27.33**. The generator sends a train of dc pulses down a transmission line, and the oscilloscope lets you observe the incident and reflected waves from the pulses (when the scope is synchronized to the pulses).

A little analysis of the scope display tells the nature and location of any impedance changes along the line. The nature of an impedance disturbance is identified by comparing its pattern to those in **Figure 27.34**. The patterns are based on the fact that the reflected wave from a disturbance is determined by the incident-wave magnitude and the reflection coefficient of the disturbance. (The patterns shown neglect losses; actual patterns may vary somewhat from those shown.)

The location of a disturbance is calculated with a simple proportional method: The round-trip time (to the disturbance) can be read from the oscilloscope screen (graticule). Thus, you need only read the time, multiply it by the velocity of the radio wave (the speed of light adjusted by the velocity factor

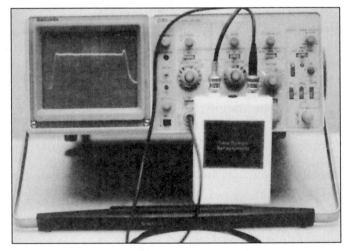

Figure 27.33 — The time-domain reflectometer shown here is attached to a small portable oscilloscope.

of the transmission line) and divide by two. The distance to a disturbance is given by:

$$\ell = \frac{983.6 \times VF \times t}{2} \qquad \text{(Eq 16)}$$

where
ℓ = line length in feet
VF = velocity factor of the transmission line (from 0 to 1.0)
t = time delay in microseconds (μs).

The Circuit

The time-domain reflectometer circuit in **Figure 27.35** consists of a CMOS 555 timer configured as an astable

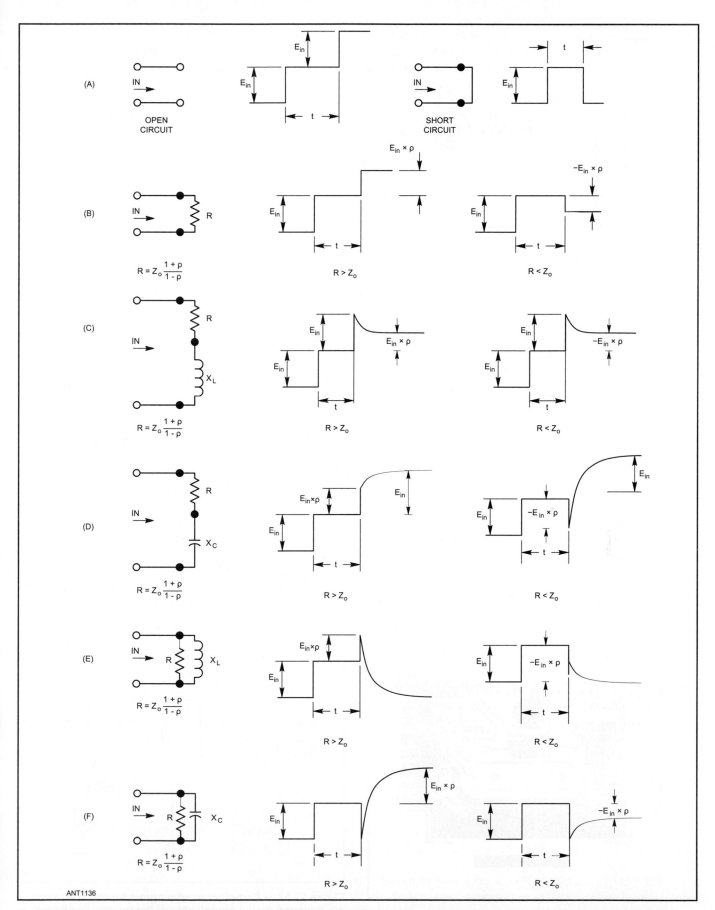

Figure 27.34 — Characteristic TDR patterns for various loads. The location of the load can be calculated from the transit time, t, which is read from the oscilloscope (see text). R values can be calculated as shown (for purely resistive loads only — $\rho < 0$ when $R < Z_0$; $\rho > 0$ when $R > Z_0$). Values for reactive loads cannot be calculated simply.

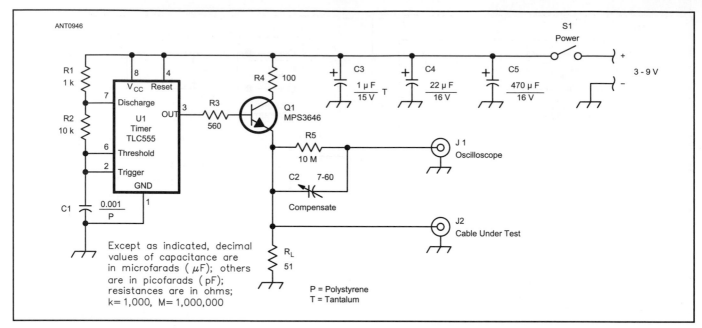

Figure 27.35 — Schematic diagram of the time-domain reflectometer. All resistors are ¼-W, 5% tolerance. U1 is a CMOS 555 timer. Circuit current drain is 10 to 25 mA. When building the TDR, observe the construction cautions discussed in the text.

multivibrator, followed by an MPS3646 transistor acting as a 15-ns-risetime buffer. The timer provides a 71-kHz square wave. This is applied to the 50-Ω transmission line under test (connected at J2). The oscilloscope is connected to the circuit at J1.

Construction

An etching pattern for the TDR is shown in **Figure 27.36**. **Figure 27.37** is the part-placement diagram. The TDR is designed for a $4 \times 3 \times 1$-inch enclosure (including the batteries). S1, J1 and J2 are right-angle-mounted components. Two aspects of construction are critical. First use *only* an MPS3646

for Q1. This type was chosen for its good performance in this circuit. If you substitute another transistor, the circuit may not perform properly.

Second, for the TDR to provide accurate measurements, the cable connected to J1 (between the TDR and the oscilloscope) must not introduce impedance mismatches in the circuit. *Do not make this cable from ordinary coaxial cable.* Oscilloscope-probe cable is the best thing to use for this connection.

(It took KD5HM about a week and several phone calls to determine that scope-probe cable isn't "plain old coax." Probe cable has special characteristics that prevent

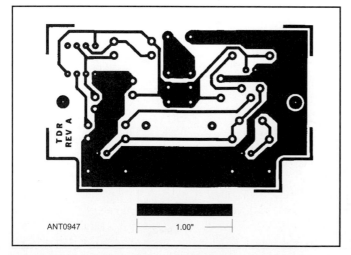

Figure 27.36 — Full-size PC-board etching pattern for the TDR. Black areas represent unetched copper foil. (A PC-board is available from FAR Circuits at www.farcircuits.net.)

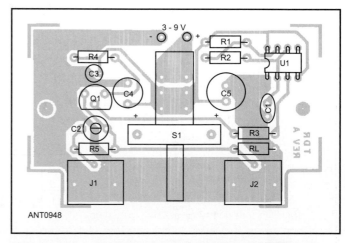

Figure 27.37 — Part-placement diagram for the TDR. Parts are mounted on the nonfoil side of the board; the shaded area represents an X-ray view of the copper pattern. Be sure to observe the polarity markings of C3, C4 and C5.

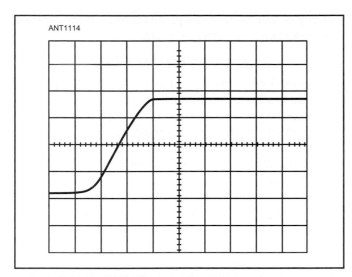

Figure 27.38 — TDR calibration trace as shown on an oscilloscope. Adjust C2 (See Figures 27.35 and 27.37) for maximum deflection and sharpest waveform corners during calibration. See text.

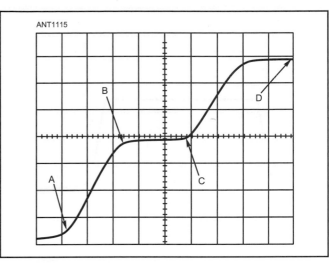

Figure 27.39 — Open-circuited test cable. The scope is set for 0.01 ms per division. See text for interpretation of the waveform.

undesired ringing and other problems.)

Mount a binding post at J1 and connect a scope probe to the binding post when testing cables with the TDR. R5 and C2 form a compensation network — much like the networks in oscilloscope probes — to adjust for effects of the probe wire.

An alternative that avoids issues associated with loading of the TDR's OSCILLOSCOPE output is to attach the TDR's CABLE UNDER TEST output and the cable under test to a BNC tee connector mounted on the scope input. (In this configuration the OSCILLOSCOPE output is not used.)

The TDR is designed to operate from dc between 3 and 9 V. Two C cells (in series — 3 V) supply operating voltage in this version. The circuit draws only 10 to 25 mA, so the cells should last a long time (about 200 hours of operation). U1 can function with supply voltages as low as 2.25 to 2.5.

If you want to use the TDR in transmission-line systems with characteristic impedances other than 50 Ω, change the value of R_L to match the system impedance as closely as possible.

27.6.2 CALIBRATING AND USING THE TDR

Just about any scope with a bandwidth of at least 10 MHz should work fine with the TDR, but for tests in short-length cables, a scope with at least 50 MHz bandwidth provides for much more accurate measurements. To calibrate the TDR, terminate CABLE UNDER TEST connector, J2, with a 51-Ω resistor. Connect the scope vertical input to J1. Turn on the TDR, and adjust the scope timebase so that the rise time from the TDR fills as much of the scope display as possible (without uncalibrating the timebase). The waveform should resemble **Figure 27.38**. Adjust C2 to obtain maximum amplitude and sharpest corners on the observed waveform. That's all there is to the calibration process!

To use the TDR, connect the cable under test to J2, and connect the scope vertical input to J1. If the waveform you observe is different from the one you observed during calibration, there are impedance variations in the load you're testing. See **Figure 27.39**, showing an unterminated test cable connected to the TDR. The beginning of the cable is shown at point A. (AB represents the TDR output-pulse rise time.)

Segment AC shows the portion of the transmission line that has a 50-Ω impedance. Between points C and D, there is a mismatch in the line. Because the scope trace is higher than the 50-Ω trace, the impedance of this part of the line is higher than 50 Ω — in this case, an open circuit.

To determine the length of this cable, read the length of time over which the 50-Ω trace is displayed. The scope is set for 0.01 μs per division, so the time delay for the 50-Ω section is (0.01 μs × 4.6 divisions) = 0.046 μs. The manufacturer's specified velocity factor (VF) of the cable is 0.8. Eq 16 tells us that the 50-Ω section of the cable is

$$\ell = \frac{983.6 \times 0.8 \times 0.046 \; \mu s}{2} = 18.1 \; \text{feet}$$

The TDR provides reasonable agreement with the actual cable length — in this case, the cable is really 16.5 feet long. (Variations in TDR-derived calculations and actual cable lengths can occur as a result of cable VFs that can vary considerably from published values. Many cables vary as much as 10% from the specified values.)

A second example is shown in **Figure 27.40**, where a length of ¾-inch hardline is being tested. The line feeds a 432-MHz vertical antenna at the top of a tower. Figure 27.40 shows that the 50-Ω line section has a delay of (6.6 divisions × 0.05 μs) = 0.33 μs. Because the trace is straight and level at the 50-Ω level, the line is in good shape. The trailing edge at the right-hand end shows where the antenna is connected to the feed line.

To determine the actual length of the line, use the same

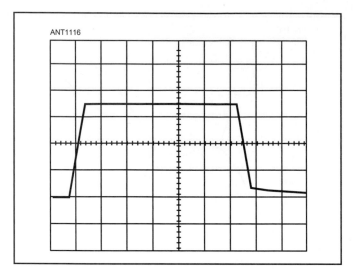

Figure 27.40 — TDR display of the impedance characteristics of the 142-foot hardline run to the 432-MHz antenna at KD5HM. The scope is set for 0.05 ms per division. See text for discussion.

procedure as before: Using the published VF for the hardline (0.88) in Eq 16, the line length is

$$\ell = \frac{983.6 \times 0.88 \times 0.33\ \mu s}{2} = 142.8\ \text{feet}$$

Again, the TDR-derived measurement is in close agreement with the actual cable length (142 feet).

Final Notes

The time-domain reflectometer described here is not frequency specific; its measurements are not made at the frequency at which a system is designed to be used. Because of this, the TDR cannot be used to verify the impedance of an antenna, nor can it be used to measure cable loss at a specific frequency. Just the same, in two years of use, it has never failed to help locate a transmission-line problem. The vast majority of transmission-line problems result from improper cable installation or connector weathering.

27.6.3 TDR LIMITATIONS

Certain limitations are characteristic of TDRs because the signal used to test the line differs from the system operating frequency and because an oscilloscope is a broadband device. In the instrument described here, measurements are made with a 71-kHz square wave. That wave contains components at 71 kHz and odd harmonics thereof, with the majority of the energy coming from the lower frequencies. The leading edge of the trace indicates that the response drops quickly above 6 MHz. (The leading edge in Figure 27.40 is 0.042 µs, corresponding to a period of 0.168 µs and a frequency of 5.95 MHz.) The result is dc pulses of approximately 7 µs duration. The scope display combines the circuit responses to all of those frequencies. Hence, it may be difficult to interpret any disturbance which is narrowband in nature (affecting only a small range of frequencies, and thus a small portion of the total power), or for which the travel time plus pattern duration exceeds 7 µs. The 432-MHz vertical antenna in Figure 27.40 illustrates a display error resulting from narrow-band response.

The antenna shows as a major impedance disturbance because it is mismatched at the low frequencies that dominate the TDR display, yet it is matched at 432 MHz. For an event that exceeds the observation window, consider a 1-µF capacitor across a 50-Ω line. You would see only part of the pattern shown in Figure 27.34C because the time constant ($1 \times 10^{-6} \times 50 = 50$ ms) is much larger than the 7-µs window.

In addition, TDRs are unsuitable for measurements where there are major impedance changes inside the line section to be tested. Such major changes mask reflections from additional changes farther down the line.

Because of these limitations, TDRs are best suited for spotting faults in dc-continuous systems that maintain a constant impedance from the generator to the load. Happily, most amateur stations would be ideal subjects for TDR analysis, which can conveniently check antenna cables and connectors for short and open-circuit conditions and locate the position of such faults with fair accuracy.

27.7 VECTOR NETWORK ANALYZER

Professionals make transmission line measurements by employing a *vector network analyzer* (VNA) or the somewhat simpler *reflection-transmission test set* (more on this later). These instruments can make all the necessary measurements quickly and with great accuracy. However, in the past VNAs have been very expensive, out of reach for general amateur use. But thanks to modern digital technology VNAs that work with a laptop computer are now becoming available at prices an amateur might consider. As Paul Kiciak, N2PK (**n2pk.com**) and others have demonstrated, it's even possible to homebrew a VNA with performance that approaches a professional instrument. In addition, the data taken in the frequency domain by the VNA can be transformed to the time domain as a type of time-domain reflectometry as described in the Agilent application note "Comparison of Measurement Performance between Vector Network Analyzer and TDR Oscilloscope." (See Bibliography.)

VNAs are based on reflection and transmission measurements. To use a VNA it is very helpful to have a basic understanding of *scattering parameters* (S-parameters). Microwave engineers have long used these because they have to work with circuits that are large in terms of wavelength, where measurements of forward and reflected power are not easy.

27.7.1 S-PARAMETERS

In the chapter **Transmission Lines**, the reflection coefficient rho (ρ) is defined as the ratio of the reflected voltage (V_r) to the incident voltage (V_i):

$$\rho = \frac{V_r}{V_i} \qquad \text{(Eq 17)}$$

If we know the load impedance (Z_L) and the transmission line impedance (Z_0) we can calculate ρ from:

$$\rho = \frac{Z_L - Z_0}{Z_L + Z_0} \qquad \text{(Eq 18)}$$

Keep in mind that ρ is a complex number (a vector), which we represent by either amplitude and phase ($|Z|$, θ) or by real and imaginary parts ($R \pm j\,X$). The two representations are equivalent. Neglecting phase, from $|\rho|$ (the magnitude of ρ) we can then calculate SWR. That's very handy, but here we want to do something different. If we have an instrument that measures ρ and we know Z_0 then we can determine Z_L from:

$$Z_L = Z_0 \left(\frac{1+\rho}{1-\rho} \right) \qquad \text{(Eq 19)}$$

Measuring ρ is one of the things that VNAs do very well. With a VNA, the measurement can be made at one end of a long transmission line with the load at the other end. The effect of the line can be calibrated out, as mentioned above, so that we are in effect measuring right at the load. Note that the symbol Γ (gamma) is also used to represent the reflection coefficient. The two symbols may be used interchangeably.

This approach can be used directly to measure the impedance and resonant frequency of a single antenna element. By open and short circuiting elements in an array of antenna elements we can determine the mutual as well as self impedances for, and between, all the elements. We can also use this approach to measure component values, inductor Q, etc.

This is an example of a *one-port* measurement; that is, a load at the end of a transmission line. However, to get the most out of a VNA, you need to generalize the above procedure. This is where S-parameters come into play.

VNAs usually have at least two RF connections: the transmit port (T) and the receive port (R). Professional units may have more RF connections. The T output provides a signal from a 50-Ω source and the R port is a detector with a 50-Ω input impedance. Basically we have a transmitter and a receiver. The transmit port uses a directional coupler to provide measurements of the forward and reflected signals at that output. The receive port measures the signal transmitted through the network.

Using incident and reflected voltages, the two-port network representation is now changed, as shown in **Figure 27.41**, where:

V_{1i} = incident voltage at port 1
V_{1r} = reflected voltage at port 1

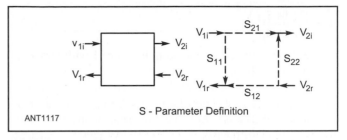

Figure 27.41 — Two-port network with incident and reflected waves.

V_{2i} = incident voltage at port 2
V_{2r} = reflected voltage at port 2

We can write an expression in terms of the incident and reflected voltages:

$$b_1 = S_{11}a_1 + S_{12}a_2$$
$$b_2 = S_{21}a_1 + S_{22}a_2 \qquad \text{(Eq 20)}$$

where:

$$a_1 \frac{V_{1i}}{\sqrt{Z_0}} \quad b_1 \frac{V_{1r}}{\sqrt{Z_0}}$$
$$a_2 \frac{V_{2i}}{\sqrt{Z_0}} \quad b_2 \frac{V_{2r}}{\sqrt{Z_0}} \qquad \text{(Eq 21)}$$

We see that a_n and b_n are simply the incident and reflected voltages at the two ports divided by $\sqrt{Z_0}$. Because this is a linear network, $S_{21} = S_{12}$.

What are the S_{ij} quantities? These are called the *S-parameters*, which are defined by:

$$S_{11} \equiv \left.\frac{b_1}{a_1}\right|_{a_2=0} = \left.\frac{V_{1r}}{V_{1i}}\right|_{V_{2i}=0}$$

$$S_{21} \equiv \left.\frac{b_2}{a_1}\right|_{a_2=0} = \left.\frac{V_{2r}}{V_{1i}}\right|_{V_{2i}=0}$$

$$\text{(Eq 22)}$$

$$S_{12} \equiv \left.\frac{b_1}{a_2}\right|_{a_1=0} = \left.\frac{V_{1r}}{V_{2i}}\right|_{V_{1i}=0}$$

$$S_{22} \equiv \left.\frac{b_2}{a_2}\right|_{a_1=0} = \left.\frac{V_{2r}}{V_{2i}}\right|_{V_{1i}=0}$$

Note that the S_{ij} parameters are all ratios of reflected and incident voltages, and they are usually complex numbers. The condition that $a_2 = 0 = V_{2i}$ is the same as saying that port 2 is terminated in a load equal to Z_0 and the network is excited at port 1. This means there is no reflection from the load on port 2, which makes $V_{2i} = 0$. Similarly, if we terminate port 1 with Z_0 and excite port 2, then $V_{1i} = 0 = a_1$.

If we compare Eq 17 to the first line of Eq 22 we see that $S_{11} = \rho_1$, the reflection coefficient at port 1. We can now restate Eq 19 in terms of S_{11}:

$$Z = Z_0 \left(\frac{1 + S_{11}}{1 - S_{11}} \right) \qquad \text{(Eq 23)}$$

where Z is the impedance looking into port 1 with port 2 terminated in Z_0. In the case where port 2 does not exist — that is, you are measuring a single impedance (for example, measuring an impedance at port 1 with port 2 open-circuited) or a component, then Z is simply the impedance at that port. Since S_{11} is a standard measurement for VNAs you can calculate Z using Eq 23. In many cases the VNA software will do this calculation for you automatically. You can also measure an impedance at port 2 with port 1 open and determine Z_{22}.

S_{21} represents the ratio of the signal coming out of port 2 (V_{2r}) to the input signal on port 1 (V_{1i}) and is another standard VNA measurement. S_{21} is a measurement of the signal transmission between the ports through the network with port 2 terminated in Z_0; forward gain in most applications.

A full-feature VNA will measure all the S_{ij} parameters at once, but most of the lower-cost units of interest to amateurs are what we call reflection-transmission test sets. What this means is that they only measure S_{11} and S_{21}. To obtain S_{22} and S_{12} we have to interchange the test cables at the ports and run the measurements again. Normally the software will accommodate this as a second entry and we end up with the full set of S_{ij} parameters.

If we do run a full set of S_{ij} parameters then we can transform these to Z_{ij} using the following expressions, assuming that $S_{21} = S_{12}$:

$$Z_{11} = \frac{(1 + S_{11})(1 - S_{22}) + S_{12}{}^2}{(1 - S_{11})(1 - S_{22}) - S_{12}{}^2}$$

$$Z_{22} = \frac{(1 - S_{11})(1 + S_{22}) + S_{12}{}^2}{(1 - S_{11})(1 - S_{22}) - S_{12}{}^2} \qquad \text{(Eq 24)}$$

$$Z_{12} = \frac{2 S_{12}}{(1 - S_{11})(1 - S_{22}) - S_{12}{}^2}$$

27.7.2 RETURN LOSS

Return loss (RL) is another term for S_{11}, the ratio of the reflected voltage to the incident voltage, usually expressed in dB.

$$RL = -20 \log\left(\frac{V_{1i}}{V_{1r}}\right) = -10 \log\left(\frac{P_{1i}}{P_{1r}}\right)$$

RL is measured as S_{11} by a VNA.

The name stems from measuring how much voltage is returned from a transmission line wave encountering a termination or impedance discontinuity. If the line is terminated in its characteristic impedance, the entire wave is absorbed and none is returned so the "loss" at the reflection is total and RL is infinite. If the line is open- or short-circuited, the entire wave is returned to the source and RL is 0. Note that RL is a positive quantity range from 0 (no transfer of wave energy

at the termination) to infinite (all wave energy transferred to the termination). Negative RL would describe a voltage gain.

To convert from return loss to SWR, the following formulas are used:

$$|\rho| = 10^{-\frac{RL}{20}}$$

and

$$SWR = \frac{1 + |\rho|}{1 - |\rho|}$$

So, for example, a return loss of 20 dB is a reflection coefficient of 0.1, and an SWR of 1.22. A return loss of 10 dB is a reflection coefficient of 0.316, and an SWR of 1.92.

One of the most common measurements made is the standing wave ratio of an antenna. A low SWR means that the antenna input impedance is close to that of the measuring reference impedance. These measurements are from the July/August 2004 *QEX* article by McDermott and Ireland (see Bibliography) and show the magnitude of the return loss versus frequency for a KT34XA triband Yagi antenna at the end of 300 feet of hardline cable.

The resonance points are clearly visible. **Figure 27.42** shows the return loss of the antenna swept from 1 MHz to 50 MHz. The 20 meter, 15 meter and 10 meter band resonances are easily seen. (RL increases toward the bottom of the chart.) **Figure 27.43** shows a close-up of the return loss from 13.5 to 14.5 MHz. **Figure 27.44** shows this same close-up on a Smith Chart.

27.7.3 USING A VECTOR NETWORK ANALYZER

Discussing how to use a VNA is beyond the scope of this chapter but the user's manual for a VNA will explain the technique of calibrating that particular VNA and using it to make measurements. The second step will be the use of the measurements by computer software to display and transform the measurements into the desired parameters.

In addition, there are many online tutorials and application notes (see the Bibliography entries for Agilent) and the text *Microwave Electronics* by Pozar also goes into some detail about what the various measurements are and how they are made.

Array Measurement Example

The process of building and properly tuning a phased array often involves making a number of different measurements to achieve a desired level of performance, as was pointed out in the **Multielement Arrays** chapter. This section is adapted from material written by Rudy Severns, N6LF.

After erecting an array we would like to measure the resonant frequency of each element, the self-impedances of each element and the mutual impedances between the elements. We will also want to know these impedances over the whole operating band to help design a feed network. When building the feed network, we may need to check the values and Qs

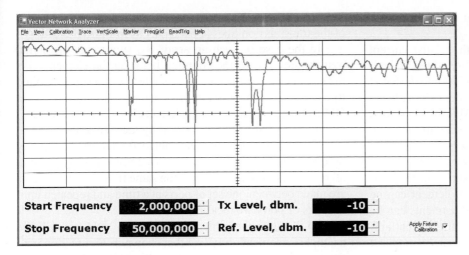

Figure 27.42 — Return loss of KT34XA antenna through 300 feet of hardline. Vertical scale is 5 dB/div. The three resonances at 20, 15, and 10 meters are clearly visible.

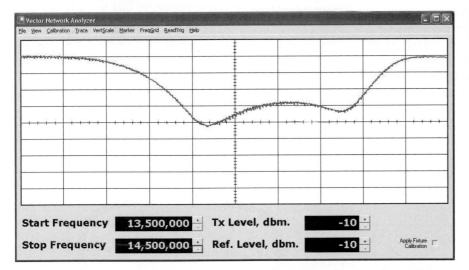

Figure 27.43 — Return loss of Figure 27.42 from 13.5 MHz to 14.5 MHz. A 26 dB return loss (best case at 13.94 MHz) is an SWR of 1.105 (at the ham-shack end of the feed line). Vertical scale is 5 dB/div.

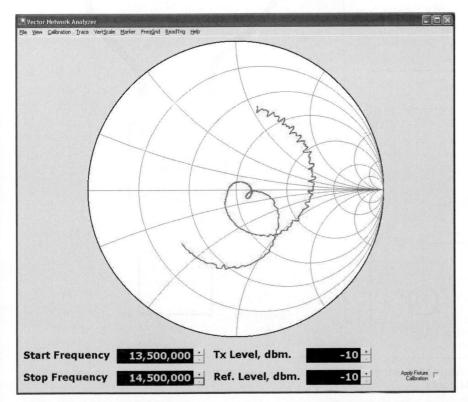

Figure 27.44 — Return loss of Figure 27.43 on a Smith Chart.

of the network elements and we will want to determine the electrical lengths of transmission lines.

Final tuning of the array requires that the relative current amplitudes and phases in each element be measured and adjusted, if necessary. We also will want to determine the SWR at the feed point. Doing all of this even moderately well can require quite a bit of equipment, some of which is heavy and requires ac line power. This can be a nuisance in the field, especially if the weather is not cooperating.

In a completed array with its feed network, the network can be excited by the VNA at the feed point and the relative current amplitudes and phases at each element can be measured over a frequency band. Then, adjustments can be made as needed. When the final values for the current amplitudes and phases are known, these values can be put back into an array model in a program like *EZNEC* to determine the pattern of the array across the whole frequency band. A multielement array actually behaves as a multiport network, so using a VNA is a natural solution to the measurement problem.

HF arrays are also large in terms of wavelength. The techniques for measuring forward and reverse powers work well even at 160 meters. For example, even though the array elements may be 100 feet apart, you can place your instruments in a central location and run cables out to each element. The effect of the cables from the VNA to the elements can be absorbed in the initial calibration procedure so the measurements read out at the VNA are effectively those at each element. In other words, the measurement reference points can be placed electrically at the base of the element, regardless of the physical location of the instrumentation and the interconnecting cables.

The discussion of S-parameters in the previous section can be viewed as measuring the characteristics of a 2-element array (see **Figure 27.45**) if one element is attached to the end of the transmission lines at each port as in **Figure 27.46**.

In the case of such an array, S_{21} represents the signal transmission due to the coupling between the elements. i.e. the signal coupled to element 2 as a result of a signal applied to element 1. Transmission lines are assumed to have $Z_0 = 50 \Omega$ (or the characteristic impedance of the overall system) and may be of any length required by the size of the array.

S-parameters can be determined for an array with any number of elements. In an n-port S-parameter measurement, all ports are terminated in Z_0 at the same time. Measurements are made between one set of ports at a time and repeated until all pairs of ports are measured.

To illustrate the principles of using a VNA we will use a simple 2-element array like that shown in Figure 27.45. To design a feed network to drive this array we need to know the input impedance of each element (Z_1 and Z_2) as a function of the drive currents (I_1 and I_2). The input impedances will depend on the self impedance of each element, the coupling

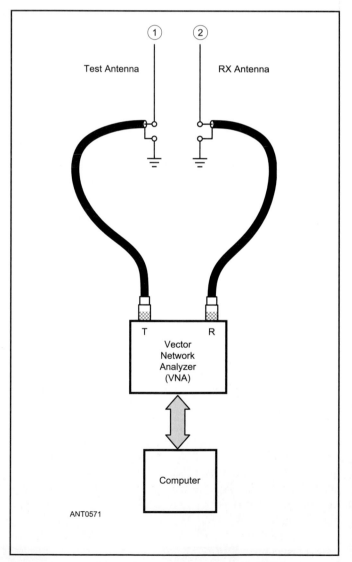

Figure 27.46 — Test setup to measure a 2-element array using a VNA.

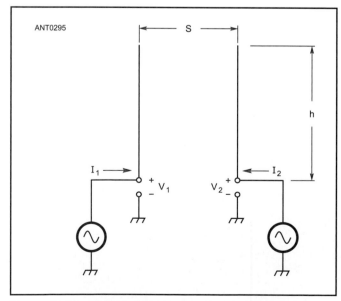

Figure 27.45 — A 2-element array, where h is the element height and S is the spacing between the elements.

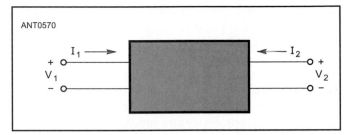

Figure 27.47 — Two-port representation of currents and voltages in the 2-element array in Figure 27.45.

Figure 27.48 — 2-element 20 meter phased array (*Photo courtesy N7MQ*).

between them (the mutual impedance) and the drive currents in each element. To manage this problem we can represent a 2-element array as a two-port network, as shown in **Figure 27.47**. And we can relate the port voltages, currents and impedances with Eq 25:

$$V_1 = Z_{11}I_1 + Z_{12}I_2$$

$$V_2 = Z_{21}I_1 + Z_{22}I_2$$

(Eq 25)

Normally we know I_1 and I_2 from the design of the array, but we need to determine the resulting element impedances. That's the challenge. Fortunately, an array is a linear network, so $Z_{12} = Z_{21}$, which means we need only determine three variables: the self impedances Z_{11} and Z_{22} and the mutual impedance, Z_{12}.

Once we know Z_{11}, Z_{12}, Z_{22} and are given I_1 and I_2, we can determine the feed point impedances at each element from:

$$Z_1 = Z_{11} + \left(\frac{I_2}{I_1}\right)Z_{12}$$

(Eq 26)

$$Z_2 = Z_{22} + \left(\frac{I_1}{I_2}\right)Z_{12}$$

This is the conventional approach. However, there are some problems here. We have to be able to accurately measure either voltages and currents or impedances in multiple elements that may be separated by large fractions of a wavelength. In addition, accurate measurements of current, voltage and impedance become increasingly more difficult as we go up in frequency.

It turns out that we can get the information more easily by measuring incident and reflected voltages at the ports and from those measurements determine the feed point impedances. A VNA is an instrument for measuring these voltages. It turns out to be easier to measure the ratios of two voltages rather than their absolute values.

The measurement setup using a VNA for a 2-element array is shown in Figure 27.46. A good way to illustrate the use of a VNA for array measurements is to work through an example with a real array. **Figure 27.48** is a picture of

a 2-element 20 meter phased array built by Mark Perrin, N7MQ.

Each element is λ/4 (self resonant at 14.150 MHz) and spaced λ/4 (17 feet 5 inches). In the ideal case, both elements would have the same current amplitude with a 90° phase difference. This gives the cardioid pattern shown in the **Multielement Arrays** chapter. There are many schemes for correctly feeding such an array. The one used in this example uses two different 75-Ω transmission lines (one λ/4 and the other λ/2, electrically), as described by Roy Lewallen, W7EL and in Orr and Cowan. (See Bibliography.)

The first task is to resonate the elements individually. With the VNA set to measure S_{11} phase, we will get a graph like that shown in **Figure 27.49**.

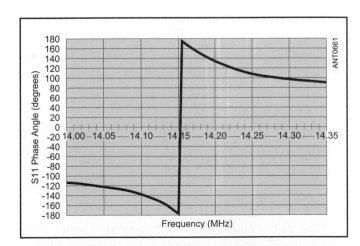

Figure 27.49 — S_{11} phase plot for an individual element.

At the λ/4 resonant frequency (f_r) we will see a sharp phase transition as we go from −180° to +180°. This is typical of any series resonant circuit. The length of each element is adjusted until the desired f_r is achieved. This is a very sensitive measurement. You can see the shift in f_r due to the wind blowing, the length of the element changing as it heats up in the sun or any interactions between the feed line and the antenna as you move the feed line around. In fact this is a very good point in the process to make sure everything is mechanically stable and free of unexpected couplings. Usually you will find it necessary place choke baluns on each element to reduce stray coupling.

The next step is to determine the self (Z_{11} and Z_{22}) and mutual (Z_{12}) impedances from which the actual driving point impedances present when the array is excited can be determined. There are two ways to go.

First, we can simply use the VNA as an impedance bridge — ie, make two S_{11} measurements at one element, first with the other element open (Z_{11} or Z_{22}) and then with it shorted (Z_1 or Z_2). We can convert the S_{11} measurements to impedances using Eq 23. The value for Z_{12} can be obtained from:

$$Z_{12} = \pm\sqrt{Z_{11}(Z_{11} - Z_1)}$$

(Eq 27)

$$Z_{12} = \pm\sqrt{Z_{22}(Z_{22} - Z_2)}$$

The second approach is to do a full two-port S-parameter measurement (S_{11}, S_{21}, S_{12} and S_{22}) and derive the impedances using Eq 23. Both approaches will work but the second approach has the advantage that the ± ambiguity in Eq 27 is eliminated.

For this example, the impedance values from the measurements at 14.150 MHz, turn out to be:

$$Z_{11} = 51.4 + j0.35$$

$$Z_{22} = 50.3 + j0.299$$

(Eq 28)

$$Z_{12} = 15.06 + j19.26$$

With these values we can now determine the feed point impedances from:

$$Z_1' = Z_{11} + \frac{I_2}{I_1} Z_{12}$$

$$Z_2' = Z_{22} + \frac{I_1}{I_2} Z_{12}$$

(Eq 29)

$$\frac{I_1}{I_2} = -j$$

Note that −j represents the 90° phase shift between the currents. Substituting the values from Eq 28 into Eq 29:

$$Z_1 = 32.09 - j14.7$$

(Eq 30)

$$Z2 = 69.61 + j15.32$$

With these impedances in hand we can now design the feed network. In this particular example however, we have decided to use the λ/4 and λ/2 cables as described by Lewallen and accept the results. So we now proceed to cut and trim the two cables to length.

Again, there are two ways to go. First we can determine the frequency at which each cable is λ/4 long. At this point the input impedance of the cable will be equivalent to a series-resonant circuit and we can simply measure the phase of S_{11} as we did earlier for f_r and get a plot like that shown in Figure 27.49. In this example the λ/4 resonant frequencies of the two cables are 7.075 MHz and 14.150 MHz.

The second approach would be to measure S_{21} for each cable at 14.150 MHz. The phase shift in S_{21} tells you how long the cable is, in degrees, at a given frequency. Because there is a small variation in cable characteristics with frequency (dispersion) this approach is slightly more accurate since it is done at the desired operating frequency. But this is not very large effect at HF.

This brings us down to the final measurements, which are to check that the relative current amplitudes and phases between the two elements are correct. We can then determine the feed point SWR. The phase and amplitude ratios are made using the S_{12} capability of the VNA and the test setup shown in **Figure 27.50**.

The VNA transmit port is connected to the normal feed point. A current sensor (see the **Multielement Arrays** chapter for a discussion of current sensors) is inserted at the base of element 1 and the output of the sensor is returned to the

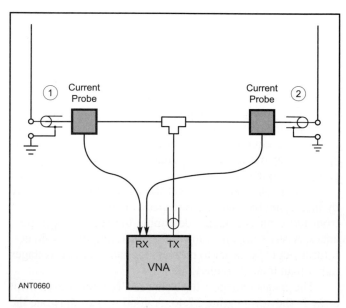

Figure 27.50 — Current phase and amplitude ratio test setup.

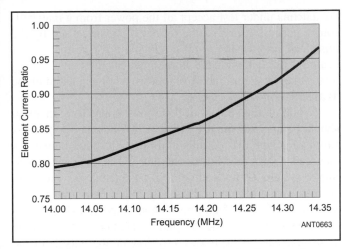

Figure 27.51 — Measured element current ratio over the 20 meter band.

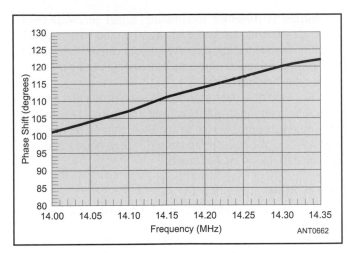

Figure 27.52 — Measured relative current phase shift over the 20 meter band.

detector or receive port of the VNA. A calibration run is then made to normalize this path. That makes it the reference.

Next, the current sensor is shifted to element 2. The amplitude and phase plots for S_{12} obtained at this point will be the desired relative phase shift and amplitude ratio between the currents in the array when driven at the normal feed point. **Figures 27.51** and **27.52** show the behavior of the example array over the 20 meter band. Note that the amplitude ratio has been converted from dB. We can now use these values in a *EZNEC* model of the array to determine the actual radiation pattern.

Obviously the W7EL feed scheme is not perfect, but it

has a definite advantage of simplicity. If better performance is desired we can use the values of Z_1' and Z_2' determined earlier to design and fabricate a new feed network and then proceed to evaluate its performance in the same way.

The final measurement is to connect the transmit port of the VNA to the feed point and measure S_{11}. From this we can calculate the SWR:

$$SWR = \frac{1+|S_{11}|}{1-|S_{11}|}$$

In this example, the return loss, $|S_{11}|$, is about 19 dB over the entire 20 meter band. This corresponds to SWR= 1.25:1.

27.8 ANTENNA FIELD MEASUREMENTS

Of all the measurements made in Amateur Radio systems, perhaps the most difficult and least understood are various measurements of the radiated field from antennas. For example, it is relatively easy to measure the frequency and CW power output of a transmitter, the response of a filter, or the gain of an amplifier. These are all what might be called *bench measurements* because, when performed properly, all the factors that influence the accuracy and success of the measurement are under control. In making antenna measurements, however, the "bench" is probably your backyard. In other words, the environment surrounding the antenna can affect the results of the measurement.

Control of the environment is not at all as simple as it was for the bench measurement, because now the work area may be rather spacious. This section describes antenna measurement techniques that are closely allied to those used in an antenna measuring event or contest. With these procedures you can make measurements successfully and with meaningful results. These techniques should provide a better understanding of the measurement problems, resulting in

a more accurate and less difficult task. The information in this section was provided by Dick Turrin, W2IMU, and was originally published in November 1974 *QST*. The conventions used by amateurs to plot radiation patterns and antenna measurements are covered in the **Antenna Fundamentals** chapter.

27.8.1 FIELD MEASUREMENT BASICS

An antenna is simply a transducer or coupler between a suitable feed line and the environment surrounding it. In addition to the efficient transfer of power from feed line to environment, an antenna at VHF or UHF is most frequently required to concentrate the radiated power into a particular region of the environment.

To be consistent while comparing different antennas, you must standardize the environment surrounding the antenna. Ideally, you want to make measurements with the measured antenna so far removed from any objects causing environmental effects that it is literally in outer space — a very impractical situation. The purpose of the measurement techniques is therefore to simulate, under practical conditions, a *controlled environment*. At VHF and UHF, and with practical-size antennas, the environment can be controlled so that successful and accurate measurements can be made in a reasonable amount of space.

The electrical characteristics of an antenna that are most desirable to obtain by direct measurement are: (1) gain (relative to an isotropic source, which by definition has a gain of unity); (2) space-radiation pattern; (3) feed point impedance (mismatch) and (4) polarization.

Polarization

In general the polarization can be assumed from the geometry of the radiating elements. That is to say, if the antenna consists of a number of linear elements (straight lengths of rod or wire that are resonant and connected to the feed point) the polarization of the electric field will be linear and polarized parallel to the elements. If the elements are not consistently parallel with each other, then the polarization cannot easily be assumed. The following techniques are directed to antennas having polarization that is essentially linear (in one plane), although the method can be extended to include all forms of elliptic (or mixed) polarization.

Feed Point Mismatch

The feed point mismatch, although affected to some degree by the immediate environment of the antenna, does not affect the gain or radiation characteristics of an antenna. If the immediate environment of the antenna does not affect the feed point impedance, then any mismatch intrinsic to the antenna tuning reflects a portion of the incident power back to the source. In a receiving antenna this reflected power is reradiated back into the environment, and can be lost entirely.

In a transmitting antenna, the reflected power travels back down the feed line to the transmitter, where it changes the load impedance presented to that transmitter. The amplifier output controls are customarily altered during the normal tuning procedure to obtain maximum power transfer to the antenna. You can still use a mismatched antenna to its full gain potential, provided the mismatch is not so severe as to cause heating losses in the system, especially the feed line and matching devices. (See also the discussion of additional loss caused by SWR in the **Transmission Lines** chapter.)

Similarly, a mismatched receiving antenna may be matched into the receiver front end for maximum power transfer. In any case you should clearly keep in mind that the feed point mismatch does not affect the radiation characteristics of an antenna. It can only affect the system efficiency when heating losses are considered.

Why then do we include feed point mismatch as part of the antenna characteristics? The reason is that for efficient system performance, most antennas are resonant transducers and present a reasonable match over a relatively narrow frequency range. It is therefore desirable to design an antenna, whether it be a simple dipole or an array of Yagis, such that the final single feed point impedance is essentially resistive and matched to the feed line. Furthermore, in order to make accurate, absolute gain measurements, it is vital that

the antenna under test accept all the power from a matched-source generator, or that the reflected power caused by the mismatch be measured and a suitable error correction for heating losses be included in the gain calculations. Heating losses may be determined from information contained in the **Transmission Lines** chapter.

While on the subject of feed point impedance, mention should be made of the use of baluns in antennas. A balun is simply a device that permits a lossless transition between a balanced system feed line or antenna and an unbalanced feed line or system. If the feed point of an antenna is symmetric, such as with a dipole, and it is desired to feed this antenna with an unbalanced feed line such as coax, you should provide a balun between the line and the feed point. Without the balun, current will be allowed to flow on the outside of the coax. The current on the outside of the feed line will cause radiation, and thus the feed line will become part of the antenna radiation system. In the case of beam antennas, where it is desired to concentrate the radiated energy is a specific direction, this extra radiation from the feed line will be detrimental, causing distortion of the expected antenna pattern. See the **Transmission Line Coupling and Impedance Matching** for additional details on this problem.

27.8.2 TEST SITE SET-UP AND EVALUATION

Since an antenna is a reciprocal device, measurements of gain and radiation patterns can be made with the test antenna used either as a transmitting or as a receiving antenna. In general and for practical reasons, the test antenna is used in the receiving mode, and the source or transmitting antenna is located at a specified fixed remote site and unattended. In other words the source antenna, energized by a suitable transmitter, is simply required to illuminate or flood the receiving site in a controlled and constant manner.

As mentioned earlier, antenna measurements ideally should be made under free-space conditions. A further restriction is that the illumination from the source antenna be a *plane wave* over the effective aperture (capture area) of the test antenna. A plane wave by definition is one in which the magnitude and phase of the fields are uniform, and in the test-antenna situation, *uniform over the effective area plane of the test antenna*. Since it is the nature of all radiation to expand in a spherical manner at great distance from the source, it would seem to be most desirable to locate the source antenna as far from the test site as possible. However, since for practical reasons the test site and source location will have to be near the Earth and not in outer space, the environment must include the effects of the ground surface and other obstacles in the vicinity of both antennas. These effects almost always dictate that the test range (spacing between source and test antennas) be as short as possible consistent with maintaining a nearly error-free plane wave illuminating the test *aperture*.

A nearly error-free plane wave can be specified as one in which the phase and amplitude, from center to edge of the illuminating field over the test aperture, do not deviate by more than about 30° and 1 dB, respectively. These conditions will result in a gain-measurement error of no more than a few percent less than the true gain. Based on the 30° phase error alone, it can be shown that the minimum range distance is approximately

$$S_{min} = 2\frac{D^2}{\lambda} \qquad \text{(Eq 31)}$$

where D is the largest aperture dimension and λ is the free-space wavelength in the same units as D. The phase error over the aperture D for this condition is 1/16 wavelength.

Since aperture size and gain are related by

$$\text{Gain} = \frac{4\pi A_e}{\lambda^2} \qquad \text{(Eq 32)}$$

where A_e is the effective aperture area, the dimension D may be obtained for simple aperture configurations. For a square aperture

$$D^2 = G\frac{\lambda^2}{4\pi} \qquad \text{(Eq 33)}$$

that results in a minimum range distance for a square aperture of

$$S_{min} = G\frac{\lambda}{2\pi} \qquad \text{(Eq 34)}$$

and for a circular aperture of

$$S_{min} = G\frac{2\lambda}{\pi^2} \qquad \text{(Eq 35)}$$

For apertures with a physical area that is not well defined or is much larger in one dimension that in other directions, such as a long thin array for maximum directivity in one plane, it is advisable to use the maximum estimate of D from either the expected gain or physical aperture dimensions.

Up to this point in the range development, only the conditions for minimum range length, S_{min}, have been established, as though the ground surface were not present. This minimum S is therefore a necessary condition even under free-space environment. The presence of the ground further complicates the range selection, not in the determination of S but in the exact location of the source and test antennas above the Earth.

It is always advisable to select a range whose intervening terrain is essentially flat, clear of obstructions, and of uniform surface conditions, such as all grass or all pavement. The extent of the range is determined by the illumination of the source antenna, usually a Yagi, whose gain is no greater than the lowest gain antenna to be measured. For gain measurements the range consists essentially of the region in the beam of the test antenna. For radiation-pattern measurements, the range is considerably larger and consists of all that area illuminated by the source antenna, especially around and behind the test site. Ideally you should choose a site where the test-antenna location is near the center of a large open area and the source antenna is located near the edge where most of the obstacles (trees, poles, fences, etc.) lie.

The primary effect of the range surface is that some of the energy from the source antenna will be reflected into the test antenna, while other energy will arrive on a direct line-of-sight path. This is illustrated in **Figure 27.53**. The use of

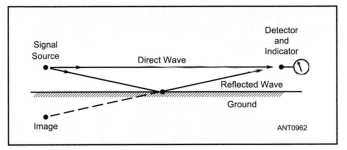

Figure 27.53 — On an antenna test range, energy reaching the receiving equipment may arrive after being reflected from the surface of the ground, as well as by the direct path. The two waves may tend to cancel each other, or may reinforce one another, depending on their phase relationship at the receiving point.

a flat, uniform ground surface assures that there will be essentially a mirror reflection, even though the reflected energy may be slightly weakened (absorbed) by the surface material (ground). In order to perform an analysis you should realize that horizontally polarized waves undergo a 180° phase reversal upon reflection from the Earth. The resulting illumination amplitude at any point in the test aperture is the vector sum of the electric fields arriving from the two directions, the direct path and the reflected path.

If a perfect mirror reflection is assumed from the ground (it is nearly that for practical ground conditions at VHF/UHF) and the source antenna is isotropic, radiating equally in all directions, then a simple geometric analysis of the two path lengths will show that at various points in the vertical plane at the test-antenna site the waves will combine in different phase relationships. At some points the arriving waves will be in phase, and at other points they will be 180° out of phase. Since the field amplitudes are nearly equal, the resulting phase change caused by path length difference will produce an amplitude variation in the vertical test site direction similar to a standing wave, as shown in **Figure 27.54**.

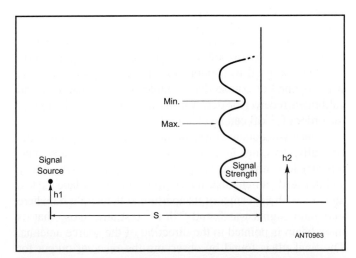

Figure 27.54 — The vertical profile, or plot of signal strength versus test-antenna height, for a fixed height of the signal source above ground and at a fixed distance. See text for definitions of symbols.

The simplified formula relating the location of h2 for maximum and minimum values of the two-path summation in terms of h1 and S is

$$h2 = n\frac{\lambda}{4} \times \frac{S}{h1} \qquad \text{(Eq 36)}$$

with $n = 0, 2, 4, \ldots$ for minimums and $n = 1, 3, 5, \ldots$ for maximums, and S is much larger than either h1 or h2.

The significance of this simple ground reflection formula is that it permits you to determine the approximate location of the source antenna to achieve a nearly plane-wave amplitude distribution *in the vertical direction* over a particular test *aperture size*. It should be clear from examination of the height formula that as h1 is decreased, the vertical distribution pattern of signal at the test site, h2, expands. Also note that the signal level for h2 equal to zero is always zero on the ground regardless of the height of h1.

The objective in using the height formula then is, given an effective antenna aperture to be illuminated from which a minimum S (range length) is determined and a suitable range site chosen, to find a value for h1 (source antenna height). The required value is such that the first maximum of vertical distribution at the test site, h2, is at a practical distance above the ground, and at the same time the signal amplitude over the aperture in the vertical direction does not vary more than about 1 dB. This last condition is not absolutely necessary but is closely related to the particular antenna under test.

In practice these formulas are useful only to initialize the range setup. A final check of the vertical distribution at the test site must be made by direct measurement. This measurement should be conducted with a small low-gain but unidirectional probe antenna such as a corner reflector or 2-element Yagi that you move along a vertical line over the intended aperture site. Care should be exercised to minimize the effects of local environment around the probe antenna and that the beam of the probe be directed at the source antenna at all times for maximum signal. A simple dipole is undesirable as a probe antenna because it is susceptible to local environmental effects.

The most practical way to instrument the vertical distribution measurement is to construct some kind of vertical track, preferably of wood, with a sliding carriage or platform that may be used to support and move the probe antenna. It is assumed of course that a stable source transmitter and calibrated receiver or detector are available so variations of the order of ½ dB can be clearly distinguished.

Once you conduct these initial range measurements successfully, the range is now ready to accommodate any aperture size less in vertical extent than the largest for which S_{min} and the vertical field distribution were selected. Place the test antenna with the center of its aperture at the height h2 where maximum signal was found. Tilt the test antenna so that its main beam is pointed in the direction of the source antenna. The final tilt is found by observing the receiver output for maximum signal. This last process must be done empirically since the apparent location of the source is somewhere between the actual source and its image, below the ground.

An example will illustrate the procedure. Assume that we wish to measure a 7-foot diameter parabolic reflector antenna at 1296 MHz ($\lambda = 0.75$ foot). The minimum range distance, S_{min}, can be readily computed from the formula for a circular aperture.

$$S_{min} = 2\frac{D^2}{\lambda} = 2 \times \frac{49}{0.75} = 131 \text{ feet}$$

Now a suitable site is selected based on the qualitative discussion given before.

Next determine the source height, h1. The procedure is to choose a height h1 such that the first minimum above ground ($n = 2$ in formula) is at least two or three times the aperture size, or about 20 feet.

$$h1 = n\frac{\lambda}{4}\frac{S}{h2} = 2 \times \frac{0.75}{4} \times \frac{131}{20} = 2.5 \text{ feet}$$

Place the source antenna at this height and probe the vertical distribution over the 7-foot aperture location, which will be about 10 feet off the ground.

$$h2 = n\frac{\lambda}{4}\frac{S}{h1} = 1 \times \frac{0.75}{4} \times \frac{131}{2.5} = 9.8 \text{ feet}$$

Plot the measured profile of vertical signal level versus height. From this plot, empirically determine whether the 7-foot aperture can be fitted in this profile such that the 1-dB variation is not exceeded. If the variation exceeds 1 dB over the 7-foot aperture, the source antenna should be lowered and h2 raised. Small changes in h1 can quickly alter the distribution at the test site. **Figure 27.55** illustrates the points of the previous discussion.

The same set-up procedure applies for either horizontal or vertical linear polarization. However, it is advisable to check by direct measurement at the site for each polarization to be sure that the vertical distribution is satisfactory. Distribution probing in the horizontal plane is unnecessary as little or no variation in amplitude should be found, since the reflection geometry is constant. Because of this, antennas

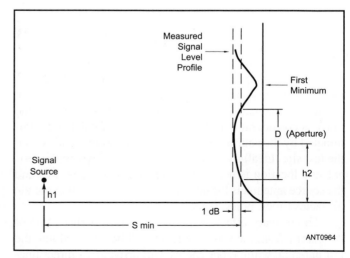

Figure 27.55 — Sample plot of a measured vertical profile.

with apertures that are long and thin, such as a stacked collinear vertical, should be measured with the long dimension parallel to the ground.

A particularly difficult range problem occurs in measurements of antennas that have depth as well as cross-sectional aperture area. Long end-fire antennas such as long Yagis, rhombics, V-beams, or arrays of these antennas, radiate as volumetric arrays and it is therefore even more essential that the illuminating field from the source antenna be reasonably uniform in depth as well as plane wave in cross section. For measuring these types of antennas it is advisable to make several vertical profile measurements that cover the depth of the array. A qualitative check on the integrity of the illumination for long end-fire antennas can be made by moving the array or antenna axially (forward and backward) and noting the change in received signal level. If the signal level varies less than 1 or 2 dB for an axial movement of several wavelengths then the field can be considered satisfactory for most demands on accuracy. Large variations indicate that the illuminating field is badly distorted over the array depth and subsequent measurements are questionable. It is interesting to note in connection with gain measurements that any illuminating field distortion will always result in measurements that are lower than true values.

27.8.3 ABSOLUTE GAIN MEASUREMENT

Having established a suitable range, the measurement of gain relative to an isotropic (point source) radiator is almost always accomplished by direct comparison with a calibrated standard-gain antenna. That is, the signal level with the test antenna in its optimum location is noted. Then you remove the test antenna and place the standard-gain antenna with its aperture at the center of location where the test antenna was located. Measure the difference in signal level between the standard and the test antennas and add to or subtract from the gain of the standard-gain antenna to obtain the absolute gain of the test antenna. Here, *absolute* means with respect to a point source with a gain of unity, by definition. The reason for using this reference rather than a dipole, for instance, is that it is more useful and convenient for system engineering. We assume that both standard and test antennas have been carefully matched to the appropriate impedance and an accurately calibrated and matched detecting device is being used.

A standard-gain antenna may be any type of unidirectional, preferably planar-aperture, antenna, which has been calibrated either by direct measurement or in special cases by accurate construction according to computed dimensions. A standard-gain antenna for VHF and low-UHF bands has been suggested by Richard F. H. Yang (see Bibliography). Shown in **Figure 27.56**, it consists of two in-phase dipoles ½ λ apart and backed up with a ground plane 1 λ square. (It is recommended that the builder cut the dipoles close to their free-space length and trim to resonance.)

In Yang's original design, the stub at the center is a balun formed by cutting two longitudinal slots of ⅛-inch width, diametrically opposite, on a ¼-λ section of ⅞-inch rigid 50-Ω coax. An alternative method of feeding is to feed RG-8 or RG-213 coax through slotted ¾-inch copper tubing with a

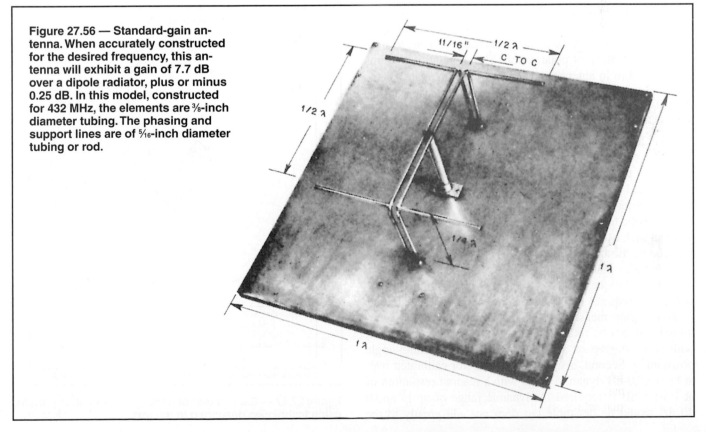

Figure 27.56 — Standard-gain antenna. When accurately constructed for the desired frequency, this antenna will exhibit a gain of 7.7 dB over a dipole radiator, plus or minus 0.25 dB. In this model, constructed for 432 MHz, the elements are ⅜-inch diameter tubing. The phasing and support lines are of ⁵⁄₁₆-inch diameter tubing or rod.

⅞-inch OD. (Due to variations in ID/OD for stock copper tubing, either bring a section of the rigid coax or take careful measurements with a caliper to check for fit between the coax and the balun tubing.)

Be sure to leave the outer jacket on the coax to insulate it from the copper-tubing balun section. When constructed accurately to scale for the frequency of interest, this type of standard will have an absolute gain of 9.85 dBi (7.7 dBd gain over a dipole in free space) with an accuracy of ± 0.25 dB. (The balun is described in detail in the original article.)

At 1296 MHz it may be more practical to build a reference horn out of sheet metal as described by Paul Wade, W1GHZ on his website. (**www.w1ghz.com**) The waveguide section can also be made out of sheet metal.

27.8.4 RADIATION PATTERN MEASUREMENTS

Of all antenna measurements, the radiation pattern is the most demanding in measurement and the most difficult to interpret. Any antenna radiates to some degree in all directions into the space surrounding it. Therefore, the radiation pattern of an antenna is a three-dimensional representation of the magnitude, phase and polarization. In general, and in practical cases for Amateur Radio communications, the polarization is well defined and only the magnitude of radiation is important.

Furthermore, in many of these cases the radiation in one particular plane is of primary interest, usually the plane corresponding to that of the Earth's surface, regardless of polarization. Because of the nature of the range setup, measurement of radiation pattern can be successfully made only in a plane nearly parallel to the Earth's surface. With beam antennas it is advisable and usually sufficient to take two radiation pattern measurements, one in the polarization plane and one at right angles to the plane of polarization. These radiation patterns are referred to in antenna literature as the principal E-plane and H-plane patterns, respectively. *E-plane* means parallel to the electric field that is the polarization plane and *H-plane* means parallel to the magnetic field in free space. The electric field and magnetic field are always perpendicular to each other in a plane wave as it propagates through space.

When the antenna is located over real Earth, the terms *azimuth* and *elevation* planes are commonly used, since the frame of reference is the Earth itself, rather than the electric and magnetic fields in free space. For a horizontally polarized antenna such as a Yagi mounted with its elements parallel to the ground, the azimuth plane is the E-plane and the elevation plane is the H-plane.

The technique to obtain these patterns is simple in procedure but requires more equipment and patience than does making a gain measurement. First, a suitable mount is required that can be rotated in the azimuth plane (horizontal) with some degree of accuracy in terms of azimuth-angle positioning. Second, a signal-level indicator calibrated over at least a 20-dB dynamic range with a readout resolution of at least 2 dB is required. A dynamic range of up to about 40 dB would be desirable but does not add greatly to the

measurement significance.

With this much equipment, the procedure is to locate first the area of maximum radiation from the beam antenna by carefully adjusting the azimuth and elevation positioning. These settings are then arbitrarily assigned an azimuth angle of zero degrees and a signal level of zero decibels. Next, without changing the elevation setting (tilt of the rotating axis), the antenna is carefully rotated in azimuth in small steps that permit signal-level readout of 2 or 3 dB per step. These points of signal level corresponding with an azimuth angle are recorded and plotted on polar coordinate paper. A sample of the results is shown on ARRL coordinate paper in **Figure 27.57**. (See the **Antenna Fundamentals** chapter for more information on coordinate scales.)

On the sample radiation pattern the measured points are marked with an X and a continuous line is drawn in, since the pattern is a continuous curve. Radiation patterns should preferably be plotted on a logarithmic radial scale, rather than a voltage or power scale. The reason is that the log scale approximates the response of the ear to signals in the audio range. Also many receivers have AGC systems that are somewhat logarithmic in response; therefore the log scale is more representative of actual system operation.

Having completed a set of radiation-pattern measurements, one is prompted to ask, "Of what use are they?" The primary answer is as a diagnostic tool to determine if the

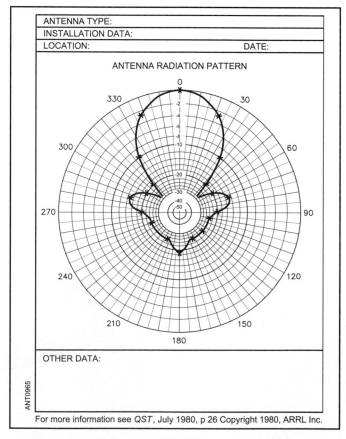

For more information see *QST*, July 1980, p 26 Copyright 1980, ARRL Inc.

Figure 27.57 — Sample plot of a measured radiation pattern, using techniques described in the text.

antenna is functioning as it was intended to. A second answer is to know how the antenna will discriminate against interfering signals from various directions.

Consider now the diagnostic use of the radiation patterns. If the radiation beam is well defined, then there is an approximate formula relating the antenna gain to the measured half-power beamwidth of the E- and H-plane radiation patterns. The half-power beamwidth is indicated on the polar plot where the radiation level falls to 3 dB below the main beam 0-dB reference on either side. The formula is

$$\text{Gain (isotropic)} \cong \frac{41,253}{\theta_E \phi_H} \qquad \text{(Eq 37)}$$

where θ_E and ϕ_H are the half-power beamwidths in degrees of the E- and H-plane patterns, respectively. This equation assumes a lossless antenna system, where any side-lobes are well suppressed. (To obtain gain in dBi, take the log of isotropic gain and multiply by 10.)

To illustrate the use of this equation, assume that we have a Yagi antenna with a boom length of two wavelengths. From known relations (described in the **HF Yagi and Quad Antennas** chapter) the expected free-space gain of a Yagi with a boom length of 2λ is about 13 dBi; its gain, G, equals 20. Using the above relationship, the product of $\theta_E \times \phi_H \approx 2062$ square degrees. Since a Yagi produces a nearly symmetric beam shape in cross section, $\theta_E = \phi_H = 45°$. Now if the measured values of θ_E and ϕ_H are much larger than $45°$, then the gain will be much lower than the expected 13 dBi.

As another example, suppose that the same antenna (a 2-wavelength-boom Yagi) gives a measured gain of 9 dBi but the radiation pattern half power beamwidths are approximately $45°$. This situation indicates that although the radiation patterns seem to be correct, the low gain shows inefficiency somewhere in the antenna, such as lossy materials or poor connections.

Large broadside collinear antennas can be checked for excessive phasing-line losses by comparing the gain computed from the radiation patterns with the direct-measured gain. It seems paradoxical, but it is indeed possible to build a large array with a very narrow beamwidth indicating high gain, but actually having very low gain because of losses in the feed distribution system.

In general, and for most VHF/UHF Amateur Radio communications, gain is the primary attribute of an antenna. However, radiation in directions other than the main beam, called *sidelobe radiation*, should be examined by measurement of radiation patterns for effects such as nonsymmetry on either side of the main beam or excessive magnitude of sidelobes. (Any sidelobe that is less than 10 dB below the main beam reference level of 0 dB should be considered excessive.) These effects are usually attributable to incorrect phasing of the radiating elements or radiation from other parts of the antenna that was not intended, such as the support structure or feed line.

The interpretation of radiation patterns is intimately related to the particular type of antenna under measurement. Reference data should be consulted for the antenna type of interest, to verify that the measured results are in agreement with expected results.

To summarize the use of pattern measurements, if a beam antenna is first checked for gain (the easier measurement to make) and it is as expected, then pattern measurements may be academic. However, if the gain is lower than expected it is advisable to make pattern measurements to help determine the possible causes for low gain.

Regarding radiation pattern measurements, remember that the results measured under proper range facilities will not necessarily be the same as observed for the same antenna at a home-station installation. The reasons may be obvious now in view of the preceding information on the range setup, ground reflections, and the vertical-field distribution profiles. For long paths over rough terrain where many large obstacles may exist, the effects of ground reflection tend to become diffused, although they still can cause unexpected results. For these reasons it is usually unjust to compare VHF/UHF antennas over long paths.

27.9 BIBLIOGRAPHY

Source material and more extended discussion of topics covered in this chapter can be found in the references given below.

Agilent "RF Back to Basics Network Analysis" — enter "Back to Basics" in the search window at **www.agilent.com** and select "Electronic Test and Measurement."

Agilent 5965-7917E, "Network Analyzer Basics."

Agilent 5990-5446EN, "Comparison of Measurement Performance between Vector Network Analyzer and TDR Oscilloscope."

G. Badger, et al, "SWR Analyzer Tips, Tricks and Techniques: SWR Analyzer Hints," *QST*, Sep 1996, p 36-40.

T. Baier, "A Small, Simple USB-Powered Vector Network Analyzer Covering 1 kHz to 1.3 GHz," *QEX*, Jan/Feb 2009, pp 32-36.

T. Baier, "A Simple S-Parameter Test Set for the VNWA2 Vector Network Analyzer," *QEX*, May/Jun 2009, pp 29-32.

A. Bailey, "The Antenna Lab, Parts 1 and 2," *Radio Communication*, Aug and Sep 1983.

J. Belrose, "On Tuning, Matching and Measuring Antenna System Impedance Using a Hand-Held SWR Analyzer," *QST*, Sep 2006, pp 56-68.

L. Blake, *Transmission Lines and Waveguides* (New York: John Wiley & Sons, 1969), pp 244-251.

J. H. Bowen, "A Calorimeter for VHF and UHF Power Measurements," *QST*, Dec 1975, pp 11-13.

D. Bramwell, "An RF Step Attenuator," *QST*, Jun 1995, pp 33-34.

T. Brock-Fisher, "Build a Super-Simple SWR Indicator," *QST*, Jun 1995, pp 40-41.

F. Brown, "A Reflectometer for Twin-Lead," *QST*, Oct 1980, p 15-17.

W. Bruene, "An Inside Picture of Directional Wattmeters," *QST*, Apr 1959, pp 24-28.

CCIR Recommendation 368, Documents of the CCIR XII Plenary assembly, ITU, Geneva, 1967.

J. Carr, "Find Fault with Your Coax," *73*, Oct 1984, pp 10-14.

S. Cooper, "A Compensated, Modular RF Voltmeter," *QEX*, Mar/Apr 2001, pp 26-34.

P. Danzer, "A Simple Transformer to Measure Your Antenna Current," *QST*, Sep 2009, p 35.

D. DeMaw, "In-Line RF Power Metering," *QST*, Dec 1969, pp 11-16.

D. DeMaw, "A QRP Person's VSWR Indicator," *QST*, Aug 1982, p. 45.

D. Fayman, "A Simple Computing SWR Meter," *QST*, Jul 1973, pp 23-33.

J. Gibbons and H. Horn, "A Circuit With Logarithmic Response Over Nine Decades," *IEEE Transactions on Circuit Theory*, Vol CT-11, No. 3, Sep 1964, pp 378-384.

J. Grebenkemper, "Calibrating Diode Detectors," *QEX*, Aug 1990, pp 3-8.

J. Grebenkemper, "The Tandem Match — An Accurate Directional Wattmeter," *QST*, Jan 1987, pp 18-26. Also see corrections in Technical Correspondence, *QST*, Jan 1988, p 49 and "An Updated Tandem Match" in Technical Correspondence, *QST*, Jul 1993, p 50.

J. Grebenkemper, "Improving and Using R-X Noise Bridges," *QST*, Aug 1989, pp 27-32, 52; Feedback, *QST*, Jan 1990, p 27.

E. Hare, "A Current Probe for the RF-Survey Meter," *QST*, Aug 2000, p 43.

F. Hauff, "The Gadget — an SWR Analyzer Add-On," *QST*, Oct 1996, pp 33-35.

W. Kaune, "A Modern Directional Power/SWR Meter," *QST*, Jan 2011, pp 39-43.

T. King, "A Practical Time-Domain Reflectometer," *QST*, May 1989, pp 22-24.

Z. Lau, "A Relative RF Ammeter for Open-Wire Lines," *QST*, Oct 1988, pp 15-17, 20.

Z. Lau and C. Hutchinson, "Improving the HW-9 Transceiver," *QST*, Apr 1988, pp 26-29.

V. G. Leenerts, "Automatic VSWR and Power Meter," *Ham Radio*, May 1980, pp 34-43.

J. Lenk, *Handbook of Oscilloscopes* (Englewood Cliffs, NJ: Prentice-Hall, 1982), pp 288-292.

R. Lewallen, "Notes on Phased Verticals," Technical Correspondence, *QST*, Aug 1979, pp 42-43.

I. Lindell, E. Alanen, K. Mannerslo, "Exact Image Method for Impedance Computation of Antennas Above the Ground," *IEEE Trans. On Antennas and Propagation*, AP-33, Sep 1985.

R. Littlefield, "A Wide-Range RF-Survey Meter," *QST*, Aug 2000, pp 42-44.

L. McCoy, "A Linear Field-Strength Meter," *QST*, Jan 1973, pp 18-20, 35.

T. McDermott and K. Ireland, "A Low-Cost 100 MHz Vector Network Analyzer with USB Interface," *QEX*, Jul/Aug 2004, pp 3-13.

T. McMullen, "The Line Sampler, an RF Power Monitor for VHF and UHF," *QST*, Apr 1972, pp 21-23, 25.

M. W. Maxwell, *Reflections* (Newington: ARRL, 1990), p 20-3. [Out of print.]

C. Michaels, "Determining Line Lengths," Technical Correspondence, *QST*, Sep 1985, pp 43-44.

J. Noakes, "The "No Fibbin" RF Field Strength Meter," *QST*, Aug 2002, pp 28-29.

Orr and Cowan, *Vertical Antennas*, Radio Amateur Call Book, 1986, pp 148-150.

P. Ostapchuk, "A Rugged, Compact Attenuator," *QST*, May 1998, pp 41-43. Also see Technical Correspondence, *QST*, Dec 1998, p 64.

H. Perras, "Broadband Power-Tracking VSWR Bridge," *Ham Radio*, Aug 1979, pp 72-75.

D. Pozar, *Microwave Engineering* (New York: John Wiley & Sons, 2004).

S. Ramo, J. Whinnery and T. Van Duzer, *Fields and Waves in Communication Electronics* (New York: John Wiley & Sons, 1967), Chap 1.

Reference Data for Radio Engineers, 5th edition (Indianapolis: Howard W. Sams, 1968), Chapter 28.

W. Sabin, "The Lumped-Element Directional Coupler," *QEX*, Mar 1995, pp 3-11.

P. Salas, "A Compact 100-W Z-Match Antenna Tuner," *QST*, Jan 2003, p 28-30.

P. N. Saveskie, *Radio Propagation Handbook* (Blue Ridge Summit, PA: TAB Books, 1960).

P. Schuch, "The SWR Analyzer and Transmission Lines," *QST*, Jul 1997, p 68.

J. Sevick, "Short Ground-Radial Systems for Short Verticals," *QST*, Apr 1978, pp 30-33.

J. Sevick, "Measuring Soil Conductivity," *QST*, Mar 1981, pp 38-39.

W. Silver, "Hands-On Radio: Experiment #52 — SWR Meters," *QST*, May 2007, pp 57-58.

R. Skelton, Ron, "Measuring HF Balun Performance," *QEX*, Nov/Dec 2010, pp 39-41.

S. Sparks, "An RF Current Probe for Amateur Use," *QST*, Feb 1999, p 34.

W. Spaulding, "A Broadband Two-Port S-Parameter Test Set," *Hewlett-Packard Journal*, Nov 1984.

F. Sutter, "What, No Meters?," *QST*, Oct 1938, pp 49-50.

D. Turrin, "Antenna Performance Measurements," *QST*, Nov 1974, pp 35-41.

F. Van Zant, "High-Power Operation with the Tandem Match Directional Coupler," Technical Correspondence, *QST*, Jul 1989, pp 42-43.

P. Wade, "Directional Couplers," Microwavelengths, *QST*, Jan 2007, pp 87-88.

P. Wade, "Microwave System Test," Microwavelengths, *QST*, Aug 2010, pp 96-97.

C. Wright, "The Twin-Lamp," *QST*, Oct 1947, pp 22-23, 110, 112.

R. F. H. Yang, "A Proposed Gain Standard for VHF Antennas," *IEEE Transactions on Antennas and Propagation*, Nov 1966.

TABLE OF CONTENTS

Chapter 28

Antenna System Troubleshooting

Even with commercial equipment, there is not a single amateur who, at some time, has not introduced an error into the antenna system either during installation or use. Similarly, of course, nothing remains faultless forever and those are the subjects of this chapter — finding the errors and faults. The first section of the chapter is directed at the beginner, providing a structured process to hunt for and find the problem. It is adapted from the Wireless Institute of Australia *Amateur Radio* magazine's excellent series of "Foundation Corner" articles for new hams. It was originally written by Ted Thrift, VK2ARA, and Ross Pittard, VK3CE. The second section of the chapter is more detailed and assumes more technical background on the part of the reader. It is adapted from material written by Tom Schiller, N6BT, as part of his book *Array of Light*, *3rd Edition* (**www.n6bt.com**).

The goal of this chapter is not to provide an exhaustive procedure that can be followed "cookbook-style" to troubleshoot any antenna or antenna system. There are just too many variables and configurations for that to be possible. Rather, this chapter suggest systematic approaches and general guidelines to apply in order to find problems. Once problems are identified, the solution is usually obvious and even trivial.

Anyone with experience in maintaining or building systems of more than a few parts — whether related to Amateur Radio or not — will recognize the value of a systematic approach to troubleshooting. The underlying lesson in this material is that carefully analyzing a problem with a step-by-step approach pays off in effective troubleshooting, saving time and expense. This is true for antennas, transceivers, computer systems — any sort of technology. Whether the reader is just getting on the air or has a lifetime of experience, there is something for everyone in this chapter.

The final section of this chapter is more about maintenance than troubleshooting but the two are so closely linked that the information will be helpful. It is another adaptation from the WIA *Amateur Radio* "Foundation Corner" columns, this one written by Ross Pittard, VK3CE, and Geoff Emery, VK4ZPP.

28.1 ANTENNA SYSTEM TROUBLESHOOTING FOR BEGINNERS

So you can no longer hear anything and you think your antenna system is faulty. It is very likely that it is, or at least some part of it is faulty. To repair the fault, we first have to find it. To do this we have to treat your antenna system in exactly the same way as fault finding inside a radio. After all, it is an electrical circuit and if not completely correct, will not work in the way that you expect. The process described in the rest of this section can be adapted to most simple antenna systems similar to that shown in **Figure 28.1**.

Start with an inventory of the antenna system. Any of these can be the cause of your problem:
- The support poles and ropes
- The antenna insulators
- The antenna elements
- The feed point or balun
- The feed line
- The entry point to the shack
- The jumper cable to the radio

A *jumper cable* (also called a *patch cable*) is a short piece of coaxial cable with RF connectors on each end. It is used to connect two pieces of equipment together. The discussion below assumes that you have a coaxial feed line to the antenna.

Determine the characteristics of the antenna you are troubleshooting:
- Is it a balanced half-wave dipole?
- Is it an off-center-fed (OCF) dipole?
- Is it a multiband antenna, for example, a G5RV?
- What is the primary band it is designed for?

Consider the characteristics of the radio as well:
- Does it have a built in antenna tuner or do you use an add-on antenna tuner?
- Can you transmit a carrier signal on any band?
- Can you adjust the power level of the carrier?

During the following sequence of testing, be alert for mistaken or loose connections, loose or disconnected power and control cables, wires touching each other that shouldn't be, and so forth. Your main system components may be just fine but not connected properly. This is *very* common!

If you haven't started one yet, this is a great time to start your "shack notebook" in which you record how your station is built. This is where you write down test results, color codes of control cables, modifications to equipment, dates of installation, etc. This information can be a huge time-saver in the future when you are troubleshooting or designing an addition to the station. A spiral-bound or composition book of graph paper is the best option, but a loose-leaf binder works well, too. Remember to put the date on each page as you make an entry.

28.1.1 BEFORE TESTING

If your radio has a built in auto tuner it has by now attempted to match your antenna system, faults and all. You may have also tried other bands to see if you can get "something" to work. To find the fault we must test the system *on the primary band for which it was designed*. Keep this in mind when you start testing.

Test Equipment

In addition to your radio, you will need at least the following items.
- A suitable power/SWR meter.
- A volt-ohm meter to check continuity of cables and wires.
- A suitable 50-Ω dummy load.
- At least two tested and known-good 50-Ω jumper cables.

28.1.2 INITIAL TESTING

This is to ensure that both your radio and your test equipment are working correctly.

1) Remove the antenna coax and connect your test jumper cable.

2) Connect the other end of the jumper cable to your power/SWR meter.

3) Connect your dummy load to the power/SWR meter.

4) Set the power range on the meter to a high scale to prevent overload.

5) Set the radio to the antenna's primary band and engage the auto tuner to tune to the 50-Ω dummy load.

6) Set your radio to CW, AM or FM.

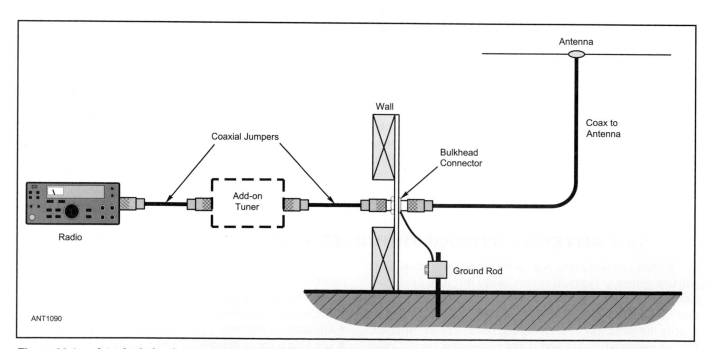

Figure 28.1 — A typical simple antenna system. If the transceiver does not have a built-in auto tuner, an external add-on tuner may be included in the system. It is good practice for the antenna cable to enter the shack through a connector on a grounded wall panel. This bulkhead connector is often a lightning arrestor, as well. Coax jumpers connect the various pieces of equipment together.

7) Adjust output power to minimum.

8) Press (PTT) and adjust output power to (say) 5-10 W.

9) Check that the power indication in the radio and the power/SWR meter are similar.

You have now set a benchmark with known output into a 50-Ω load. *This is an important step.* Do not change any settings on your radio until all tests are completed and the faults fixed.

28.1.3 ANTENNA SYSTEM TESTING

Your Second Test

Here is where we start to eliminate possible causes of your problems. Start by simplifying your antenna system. Remove any extra equipment (switches, filters, etc) between the radio and the antenna, reducing your antenna system to a single connection similar to that in Figure 28.1.

It is likely that you have some kind of receptacle or bulkhead connector (such as a UG-363 adaptor or Amphenol 83-1F) where your antenna coax enters the shack. From there you have a jumper cable to your radio. We test this next.

1) Remove the test jumper cable from the radio to the power/SWR meter.

2) Connect your normal jumper cable from the radio to the power/SWR meter.

3) Press (PTT) and observe the power reading. It should be exactly the same as step 8, above. If not, your jumper cable is faulty or not suitable.

Test and Fix

First, perform a continuity check of the inner and outer conductors of the jumper cable. Then check the cable insulation — there should be no continuity from the inner to outer conductor. Check that the pins on each PL-259 plug are correctly soldered and fit firmly in the SO-239 receptacles. Look for markings on the jacket of the cable to ensure that it is a 50-Ω cable. *If you find a fault and fix it, retest steps 1-3 above.*

Your Third Test

Here is another elimination step. It is very common to have bulkhead connectors that are also lightning arrestors. These are not totally fool-proof and can fail due to a lightning hit or moisture. Even non-arrestor connectors fail from moisture or other reasons. We do need to test this connector. If you do not have any connectors between the antenna and your transceiver, skip this test and proceed to the fourth test below.

1) Disconnect the coax to the antenna from the bulkhead connector.

2) Using your "now tested OK" jumper cable, perform a dc test (continuity test) on the connector using the following steps.

3) Connect the jumper cable to the connector on the inside.

4) Test the insulation from inner to outer conductor using a high resistance scale. If the connector is also a lightning arrestor, test the inner conductor to earth ground (should be an open circuit) then test the outer conductor to earth ground

(should be a short circuit or very low resistance).

5) The easiest way to test continuity of the connector is to connect your 50-Ω dummy load to the outside of the connector. Look for 50 Ω from the inner to outer conductor.

6) Using two jumper cables and the power/SWR meter, apply power from your transmitter to the dummy load on the outside of the connector.

7) Power should be the same as when you tested your jumper lead.

8) SWR must be no higher than 1.1:1 or the connector is faulty at RF.

Before the Fourth Test

When are we going to test the antenna? Very soon but since it does not work we need to perform a visual inspection. Assuming you have some kind of wire antenna, you need to lower it and in the process, inspect and ensure that:

- On the insulators at each end, there is no possibility of contact between the antenna wire and the supporting wire/ropes.
- If there are any splices in the wire elements, they are well crimped or soldered.
- At the center insulator, there is no possibility of contact between the element wires.
- At the balun or coax connection the element connections are soldered or firmly connected.
  - If it is a center-fed dipole it should be a 1:1 choke balun.
  - If it is an OCF dipole, it should be a 4:1 or 6:1 balun.

Cut away the waterproofing around the coax termination and inspect for water damage. If the connector is discolored or corroded it will need to be cleaned if not replaced and the cable checked as well.

Similar steps apply if you have a Yagi or vertical antenna.

Your Fourth Test

Now we are going to carefully test the main antenna coax cable *and* its connectors. First some dc tests, then we can RF test.

1) With the coax disconnected from the antenna *and* bulkhead connector (or radio), test continuity overall of the inner conductor, then the outer conductor. Test the insulation from the inner to outer conductor on the highest scale.

2) Connect the 50-Ω dummy load to the antenna end of the main coax. At the radio end, measure resistance from the inner to outer conductor. You should see close to 50 Ω.

3) Reconnect the bulkhead connector or radio end of the main coax. You should now have connected in sequence; radio, jumper, power/SWR meter, jumper, bulkhead/wall connector, main coax and dummy load as in **Figure 28.2**.

4) Press PTT and note the power reading: It should be very close to your preset 5 or 10 W. Check SWR; it should be no higher than 1.1:1. Be very wary of seeing no reflected power at all. This could mean that the coax is so lossy that reflected power is unreadable. One more test will determine this.

5) Relocate the power/SWR meter from the shack to the

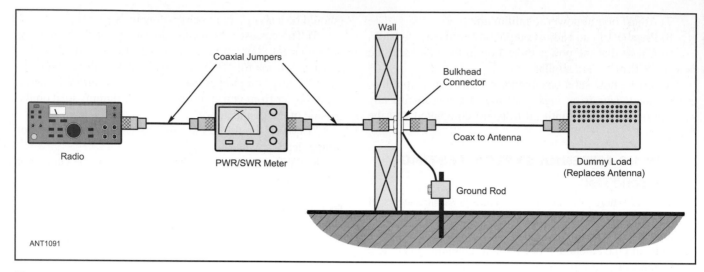

Figure 28.2 — Test setup to check SWR with the antenna replaced by a dummy load.

antenna end of your main coax but put it where it can be seen. The sequence is now: radio, jumper, bulkhead/wall connector, main coax, power/SWR meter, dummy load as in Figure 28.3.

6) Press PTT and note power reading: it should be at least 75% of your preset 5 or 10 W. If much less, the coax is lossy and should be replaced.

7) Check SWR and it should be no higher than 1.1:1.

8) If you do replace the main coax, repeat all of steps 1 to 7 above.

We are nearly done. Reapply the waterproofing to the connection of coax to balun, or at least some temporary tape. (If it now works you will get so busy you may forget to finish it all!) Pull your antenna back up into position, taking care not to put *any* stress on the coax cable. We are going to test the SWR on the primary band *without* the help of the tuner in the radio.

The Final Test

Initially we are going to test without the tuner engaged, so we can see how well the antenna is working on the main band that it was designed for. It is only on this band that we can make any adjustments to the length of the wire elements. Before we start adjusting we need to know which direction to go, so we will test the high end, middle and low end of the band.

Connect the power/SWR meter between the radio and the bulkhead connector or between the radio and the coax to the antenna. *Remember that we are now going to be testing "On Air" so we need to consider others and ask if the frequency is in use.* (You can also use an SWR analyzer as described in the **Antenna and Transmission Line Measurements** chapter.)

Assuming that the main band is 40 meters, tune the radio to, say, 7250 kHz (near the top of the band) and find a quiet spot. Check/ask if the frequency is in use. If it is not,

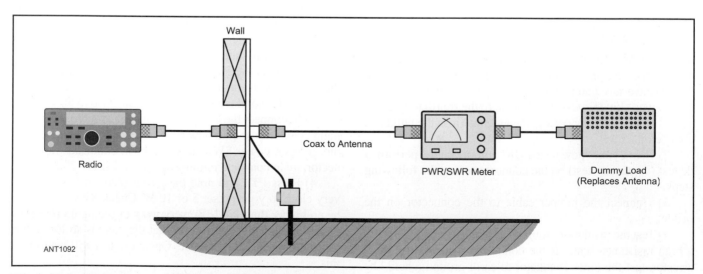

Figure 28.3 — Test setup to check if the main coax is lossy.

announce, "[Your call] testing."

- Set carrier power to a low value such as 10 W.
- Set SWR meter calibrate control to near maximum and increase power just enough to be able to set the calibration reading to full-scale.
- Return the meter to read SWR and write down the reading.

Now tune the radio to the middle of the band and find a quiet spot. Repeat the test procedure using an appropriate mode. Repeat near the bottom of the band.

Compare the three SWR readings and decide if the antenna is long (SWR too high at the high end of the band) or short (SWR too high at the low end of the band), or if no adjustment is required. Note that if all SWR readings are 1.5:1 or lower, very little will be gained by adjusting the length. If SWR is uniformly high everywhere in the band, the antenna itself is at fault.

If the antenna SWR measurements are acceptable, it is now time to let the radio and auto tuner operate. If you use an add-on antenna tuner, you'll need to make sure that the jumper between it and the radio is good as described previously, then reinstall it between the radio and antenna. The following paragraph assumes the auto tuner is internal to the radio.

Remove the power/SWR meter from the antenna feed line so that the antenna is connected directly to the radio through the bulkhead connector and jumper. Engage the auto tuner and let it set up on a convenient frequency. Set the output power control to about 75-80% of maximum, then find a clear frequency as before and initiate the auto tuner operation as instructed for your radio. Since you have confirmed your antenna system presents a reasonable SWR to the radio, your tuner should operate normally and you can resume operating! If the tuner does not operate properly, there may be excessive RF current on the feed line's outer surface. Add a choke balun at the output of the radio or antenna tuner and try again. (See the **Transmission Line Coupling and Impedance Matching** chapter.) If the tuner still doesn't work, you may have a defective tuner.

If the antenna SWR measurements indicate an antenna fault, the exact troubleshooting sequence will depend on the type of antenna. Remember to write everything down in case you need to contact the manufacturer or ask for other help. Start with a visual inspection of the entire antenna looking for loose or corroded elements and joints. Perform a continuity check of all coils, clamps, and capacitors. Wiggle the various pieces while making measurements to look for intermittent connections. If nothing is obviously wrong, try disassembling the antenna, cleaning the various metal-to-metal surfaces using a nonferrous, nonabrasive synthetic cleaning pad such as a Scotch-Brite pad, then reassemble (checking for proper dimensions and orientation of parts) and test. If this fails to restore normal operation, you should contact the manufacturer's customer service department or ask for help from your local club.

28.2 GUIDELINES FOR ANTENNA SYSTEM TROUBLESHOOTING

The antenna is an electrical device implemented via a mechanical construction; therefore, if it is built properly, it should "work" (especially for production units). There are five general categories of problems:

- Test measurements
- Mechanical
- Proximity
- Feed system
- Misunderstandings

Guidelines for dealing with and approaching each type of problem are presented in the following sections. They will be used in subsequent sections in different ways to address different types of problems. Think of them as a kind of toolbox for troubleshooting. Many of them assume you are testing some type of Yagi or other beam antenna but the general guidelines apply to all types of antennas

It is important to remember this simple rule for adjustments and troubleshooting: Do the simplest and easiest adjustment or correction *first*, and only *one* at a time.

When making on-air comparisons, select signals that are at the "margin" and not pushing your receiver well over S9 where it can be difficult to measure differences of a few dB. Terrain has a lot to do with performance as well. If you are comparing with large stations, keep in mind that station location was probably selected carefully and the antennas were placed exactly where they should be for optimum performance on the property.

Remember the Law of Conservation of Energy: Energy can neither be created, nor destroyed. Therefore, the *sum* of all the energies in a system (an antenna system) is a constant. From the perspective of transmitting, we start with so many watts and the energy will go somewhere, either emitted from the antenna and on its way to the destination, or dissipated as heat due to loss.

If you increase your antenna efficiency, you will expand your performance envelope, and thus be able to hear *and* work more stations, providing more enjoyment from radio. If you increase only your transmit power, you will expand your "transmit envelope," but you won't be able to hear any better!

28.2.1 TEST MEASUREMENTS

A. Test the antenna at a minimum height of 15-20 feet. (See **Figure 28.4**) This will move the antenna far enough away from the ground (which acts to add capacitance to the antenna) and enable meaningful measurements. Use sawhorses *only* for construction purposes.

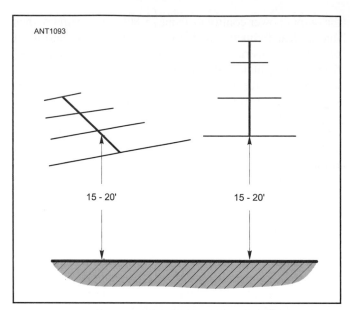

Figure 28.4 — When testing a Yagi or quad antenna, make sure it is at least 15 to 20 feet above ground. If oriented vertically, the reflector should be the closest to ground. Performance will still change as the antenna is raised.

■ A minimum height of 15-20 feet above ground does not mean 5 feet above a 10-15 foot high roof, it means above ground with nothing in between.

■ Antenna resonant frequency will shift upward as it is raised.

■ Feed point impedance will change with a change in height and this applies to both horizontal and vertical antennas.

■ Some antennas are more sensitive to proximity to ground than others.

■ Some antennas are more sensitive to nearby conductive objects (i.e. other antennas) than others.

B. Aiming the antenna upward with the reflector on the ground might coincide with some measurements on rare occasions, but there are no guarantees with this method. The reflector is literally touching a large capacitor (earth) and the driven element is very close, too. Raise the antenna at least 15-20 feet off the ground.

C. When using a hand-held SWR analyzer you are looking for the dip in SWR, not where the impedance or resistance meter indicates 50 Ω. ("Dip" = frequency of lowest SWR value, or lowest swing on the meter.) On the MFJ-259/269 series, the left-hand meter (SWR) is the one you want to watch, not the right-hand meter (IMPEDANCE).

D. Check for nearby broadcast transmitters. The small amount of power used by the hand-held metering devices is no match for several thousand watts. The front-ends of the devices are broadband and will receive this out-of-band broadcast energy and "assume" it is reflected energy. This will manifest itself as the meter never showing a low SWR — sometimes as low as 1.3:1 or higher than 5:1 — all the while the antenna is actually matched properly. The broadcast transmitter will change its power and direction at sunset/sunrise, making daytime and nighttime measurements different. If the signal is from an AM transmitter, you may see the meters move with the programming audio amplitude.

E. Does the SWR and frequency of lowest dip change when the coax length is changed? If so, the balun might be faulty, as in not isolating the load from the coax feed line. Additionally. with an added length of coax and its associated small (hopefully small) amount of loss:

■ The value of SWR is expected to be lower with the additional coax and,

■ The width of the SWR curve is expected to be wider with the additional coax *when measured at the transmitter end of the coax.*

F. Be sure you are watching for the right dip, as some antennas can have a secondary resonance (another "dip"). It is quite possible to see a Yagi reflector's resonant frequency, or some other dip caused by interaction with adjacent antennas.

28.2.2 MECHANICAL

A. Are the dimensions correct? Production units should match the documentation (within reason). When using tubing elements, measure each *exposed* element section during assembly and the element *half-length* (the total length of each half of the element) after assembly. Measuring the entire length is sometimes tricky depending on the center attachment to the boom on Yagis, as the element can bow, or the tape might not lie flat along the tubing sections. Self-designed units might have a taper error.

B. Making the average taper diameter larger will make the equivalent electrical element longer. This makes the antenna act as if the physical element is too long.

C. Making the average taper diameter smaller will make the equivalent electrical element shorter. This makes the antenna act as if the physical element is too short.

D. If the element is a mono-taper (tubing element is the same for the entire length), larger diameter elements will be physically shorter than smaller diameter mono-taper elements to give the same electrical performance at the same frequency.

E. The type of mounting of the element to the boom affects the element length, whether it is attached directly to the boom, or insulated from the boom. Incorrect mounting/mounting plate allocation will upset the antenna tuning:

■ A mounting plate 4 × 8 inches has an equivalent diameter of approximately 2.5 inches and 4 inches in length for each element half.

■ A mounting plate that is 3 × 6 inches has an equivalent diameter of about 1.8 inches and a length of 3 inches for each element half.

■ The mounting plate equivalent will be the first section in a model of the element half.

F. In a Yagi, if the elements are designed to be touching, are the elements touching the boom in the correct locations?

G. In a Yagi, if the elements are designed to be insulated, are the elements insulated from the boom in the correct locations?

H. The center of hairpin matching devices (i.e. on a Yagi) can be grounded to the boom.

I. The boom is "neutral," but it is still a conductor! The center of a dipole element is also "neutral" and can be touched while tuning without affecting the reading. With a hairpin match, the center of the hairpin can also be touched while tuning and touching the whole hairpin might not affect the readings much at all.

J. Tests have shown that in installations with several Yagis on a common mast, insulating the elements from the boom can reduce interaction between the individual antennas.

K. Sufficient spacing between Yagis on a common mast is critical to not lose gain and F/B. Even 10 foot spacing between a 20 meter monoband Yagi and a 15 meter Yagi can significantly reduce the gain on 15 (sometimes by 50%), plus almost completely eliminating the F/B on 15.

L. The higher frequency Yagi in a common stack is the one that will be affected by the lower frequency Yagi(s). If a stack of 20, 15 and 10 meter Yagis (20 being the lowest on the mast — which is the correct stacking sequence), the 15 will be affected by the 20, the 10 will be affected by the 15 and possibly also by the 20.

28.2.3 PROXIMITY

A. What else is nearby (roof, wires, guy lines, gutters)? If it can conduct at all, it can and probably will couple to the antenna!

B. Does the SWR change when the antenna is rotated? If so, this indicates interaction. Note that in some combinations of antennas, there can be destructive interaction even if the SWR does not change. Computer models can be useful here.

C. What is within ¼ wavelength of the antenna? Imagine a sphere (like a big ball) with the antenna in question at the center of the sphere, with the following as a radius, depending on frequency. Think in three dimensions like a sphere — up and down and front and rear as in **Figure 28.5**.

160 meters = 140 foot *radius* for ¼ wavelength
80 meters = 70 foot *radius*
40 meters = 35 foot *radius*
20 meters = 18 foot *radius*
15 meters = 12 foot *radius*
10 meters = 9 foot *radius*

D. Interaction occurs whether or not you are transmitting on the adjacent antennas. When receiving, it simply is not as apparent as when transmitting.

E. Wire antennas under a Yagi can easily affect it. This includes inverted V dipoles for the low bands and multiband dipoles. The wire antennas are typically for lower frequency band(s) and will not be affected by the Yagi(s), as the Yagis are used for the higher bands.

F. Are the higher frequency antennas (Yagis) above the lower frequency ones in the stack? Is there adequate distance between the various antennas? Remember, anything within ¼ wavelength in any direction is a potential problem. Careful modeling might not necessarily indicate the interaction in found in the actual installation. Cross polarization between VHF antennas and HF Yagis on the same mast is OK.

G. An 80 meter rotatable dipole should be parallel to nearby Yagi boom(s) so that it is essentially transparent.

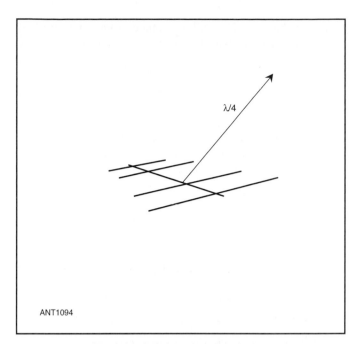

Figure 28.5 — Any conductive material within λ/4 that has a medium to low impedance at the frequency of operation has the potential of interacting with the antenna.

Other antennas that could interfere *might be able* to be positioned at right angles. Orienting the 80 meter dipole parallel to the boom also makes the installation more neutral in the wind. Most Yagis have more wind load from the elements than from the boom which tends to make them "hunt" in the wind. Adding area to the boom can, therefore, help the installation be more manageable in the wind.

28.2.4 FEED SYSTEM

The feed system includes:
- the feed line
- switching mechanisms
- pigtails from the feed point on the antenna to the main feed line or switch
- all feed lines inside the radio room

The feed system is the *entire connection* between the radio and the feed point of the antenna.

A. Is the feed line (coax) known to be good? (Start with the easiest first.) Is there water in the coax? This can give strange readings, even frequency-dependent ones. If there is any question, swap the feed line for a known good one and test again.

B. Are the connectors installed properly? Has a connector been stressed (pulled)? Is the rotation loop done properly to not stress the coax? Is it an old existing loop or a new one? Usually it's alright if new. Type N connectors (especially the older type) are prone to having the center conductor pull out due to the weight of the coax pulling down on the connector. Connectors are easy to do, using the right technique.

C. Is there a "barrel" connector (a PL-258 dual-SO-239 adapter) in the feed line *anywhere*? Has a new or different barrel been inserted? These are a common failure point, even with new barrels. The failures range from micro-bridges across the face of the barrel shorting out the center and shield, to resistance between the two ends of the barrel. Have the new barrels been tested in a known feed system? Always test them before installing. Use only quality RF adapters as these are common system failure points.

D. Is the coax intact and not frayed such that the shield can come into contact with anything? This can cause intermittent problems as the coax shield touches the tower, such as on rotation loops and coax on telescoping towers.

E. Is the tuner OFF on the radio? This is often overlooked when adding a new antenna.

F. Are there any new devices in the line? It might be a good idea to remove everything but the essential items when troubleshooting.

G. Is there a remote antenna switch? Swap to another port.

H. Are there band-pass or low-pass filters in the line? Filters can become defective, causing strange SWR readings.

28.2.5 MISUNDERSTANDINGS

The antenna can be working properly but there may be a misunderstanding of the anticipated readings versus the actual readings. There can also be discrepancies between the observed "performance" (i.e. F/B ratio) and the specification(s). Having an open mind here is a great asset and will aid in understanding and resolving the situation. "Open mind" means no preconceived ideas or bias, which is sometimes difficult. Remember that we are working toward a solution to improve performance. Common misunderstandings:

A. "A low SWR means the antenna has gain." No, it only means it is matched to the feed line. Remember that a dummy load also has low SWR.

B. "A high SWR means the antenna does not have gain." No, it only means it is not matched or is fed improperly.

C. "An SWR that does not go to 1:1 is a serious problem." No, as long as your rig can tune it, use it. Reflected power is not totally lost. As long as the feed line loss is acceptable, SWR does not need to be 1:1. (See the **Transmission Lines** chapter for more information on matched line loss with varying SWR.)

D. "My antenna has a great pattern, so it must have a lot of gain." No, these two antenna aspects are not necessarily related. The Beverage receiving antenna has an excellent pattern, but its gain is about –20 dBd.

E. "Once the antenna is up, it will stay there forever." An antenna is an electrical device implemented via a mechanical structure. Mechanical devices require periodic maintenance, just like your car.

28.3 ANALYZING AN ANTENNA PROBLEM

Having a specific sequence of steps to take for a systematic resolution of installation questions will make the process easier with less frustration. It will also provide a learning environment and future projects will run smoother and be enjoyable, as the prospect of a higher performance envelope is anticipated!

The following typical debugging sequence is divided into five parts. Each one uses the guidelines to address a specific aspect of the resolution process. Not all the steps will be used each time a new antenna is installed; however, reading through them will be beneficial.

The length of this material and the steps noted should not deter anyone from reading — installation difficulties are usually simple to resolve.

28.3.1 PART 1 — SWR

A. The usual reason for debugging is that the SWR is not as expected. This is the only measurement that can be reliably made by the majority of people.
- If the SWR is showing high values (4:1 or higher), do not attempt any adjustment of the antenna before *first* certifying the feed system is correct.
- High values like this are so far away from the expected values that they essentially eliminate the antenna from being the current problem.

B. Remove all devices in the feed system to eliminate possible components with problems, such as low pass filters (especially if 10 meter SWR readings are not as expected); therefore, we want to work as directly as possible with the antenna in a good location.

C. Isolate the feed system as the first step.
- Place a 50-Ω dummy load at the antenna end of the coax feed line.
- Measure the SWR of the coax feed line at the transmitter end (dummy load at the other).
- If you measure anything other than a low SWR (1.2:1 or less), the coax should be changed and/or;
  – If you see a significant drop in power through the coax (use a wattmeter), the coax should be replaced.
  – If the coax is good, proceed to the next steps.

D. Is the antenna at a reasonable height above ground?
- 15-20 feet above ground and roof.
- If not, place it as high as possible and watch for proximity effects.

E. Does the SWR change as it is rotated?
- What else is on the mast?
- Are there any wire antennas nearby?
- What it is rotating above or below to cause a change in measurement?

F. Are the element lengths correct?

G. Are the elements in the proper location?

H. If a hand-held test unit is used, is there a broadcast transmitter within several miles? This is very important on 160, 80/75 or 40 meter antennas.

28.3.2 PART 2 — FEED SYSTEM AND ANTENNA ASSEMBLY

A. Stay calm.

B. Do the easiest thing(s) first.

C. If a simple change was made (i.e. moved an element a few inches), the problem is most often in the feed system.

D. Swap the coax, even if it takes some effort.

E. Try to remove the parts of the antenna feed system one at a time to isolate the culprit.

F. Be sure to track the correct dip in SWR readings.

G. On production antennas, most problems are identified by checking for:

- Element length and tuning (and location on the boom, but extremely rare).
- A local broadcast transmitter affecting the readings — use your transmitter and its SWR meter.
- Antenna mounted properly; clear of proximity issues, including conductive guy wires.
- Correct feed line and matching system adjusted properly.

28.3.3 PART 3 — KEEPING RECORDS

A. Keep sequential notes of each step taken.

- A legal pad or notebook is excellent — number the steps and each page.
- Write down what was done and then write down the observed result.
- Underline the amount of a change and use a + or – sign, or say "longer" or "shorter."

B. If you make a change, do only one item at a time.

- If you change more than one item, you will not know what caused the observed change.
- If nothing appeared to change and more than one item was changed, it is possible that the items changed countered the effect(s) of each other.
- Changing more than one item at a time makes it *impossible* to track.

C. Write on your notepad the initial observation(s) and the conditions, such as height and proximity.

- This increases your situational awareness and it will provide a documented starting point.

28.3.4 PART 4 — HOME-MADE ANTENNAS

A. For noncommercial, home-brew, or "one-off" antennas:

- Follow same procedures for production units.
- Element tapering needs to be verified.
- Element mountings might not be properly accounted for (i.e. insulating boots when using old Hy-Gain mounts for a new design)
- Matching techniques might not be working as expected. Check directly at the feed point without the matching device in place.
  - A hairpin will step up the impedance and might just move it to the high side of 50 Ω, making adjustment

(down) to 50 Ω impossible.
  - If the design is a "forward stagger" type, the forward Yagi needs to be shorted across the feed point (i.e. hairpin); otherwise, the driver will have an open or shorted coaxial stub (the pigtail feeding it) attached across it.

B. Keeping a design notebook, with as much detail as possible using the same note-taking procedure as described earlier is invaluable.

28.3.5 PART 5 — ON-AIR OBSERVATIONS

A. F/B is less than expected.

- Antenna height affects F/B, so does the angle being used. Refer to typical plots to acquaint yourself with these issues.
- F/B specification might be too ambitious. Some specifications are given as peak values, available only across a narrow frequency range (if not tuned properly, might be out of band).
- How much to expect?
  - A 2-element full-size parasitic Yagi will be around 12-16 dB and A 2-element shortened, loaded Yagi can be >20 dB if tuned properly.
  - A 3-element full-size Yagi "naturally" wants to be around 20 dB.
- Stacked Yagis on one mast (for example, 20-15-10 meters) can greatly affect the F/B.
- Rotator clamps not secure, mast slipping.
- Antenna attachment might not be secure, even with the clamps tight, and the antenna is slipping on the mast (typical with hard steel masts).

B. How much gain (redistribution of the constant energy) to expect? **Table 28-1** lists real-life, reasonable, verifiable figures for full-size 20 meter antennas, with gain specified as dB compared to a full size dipole at the same height, same location:

These figures are increased by 2.14 dB when comparing to the isotropic source (4.5 dB + 2.14 = 6.64 dBi); and if ground reflection gain is also included (i.e. at 1 wavelength above ground), add another 5.8 dB. Using both

Table 28-1
Expected Performance Values of Full-Size Antennas

Gain (dBd)	Antenna Type	Full Size Boom Length (20 meter antenna)
0	Dipole	Reference*
4.5	2 element	10' boom
5.5	3 element	20' boom
6.5	4 element	30' boom
7.5	5/6 element	42' boom
8.5	7 element	60' boom
9.5	8 element	80' boom
10.5	9 element	105' boom
12.5	12 element	175' boom
14.5	20 element	330' boom

*The Reference is a dipole is in the exact same location as the Yagi, such as over ground)

of these, the 5.5 dB figure for a 3-element Yagi becomes 13.44 dBi. Whichever the case, the reference must be specified; otherwise, you know nothing about the antenna.

C. Does not seem to be competitive or crack pileups.
- Not aimed in the right direction (being off 30 degrees can be a lot).
- Gain specification in error or loss in the antenna system.
- Coax, switches, antenna tuning, antenna components, radial system.
- Could it be a problem with the operator?

28.3.6 TROUBLESHOOTING HIGH SWR IN YAGI ANTENNAS

This section applies mainly to Yagi antennas; however, it should be useful for other types as well. There are additional sections for other types of antennas.

One thought to keep in mind when tuning a Yagi is that in a Yagi, the primary purpose of the driver (driven element) is to excite the array. The driver tuning has very little to do with the gain and pattern, although the spacing between the driver and adjacent elements is quite important to the Yagi design. In a 2-element Yagi, the driver location does impact the gain and pattern, because it sets the boom length; however, the parasitic element (either a reflector or director) is the primary "controller."

To locate the problem of a high SWR, we need a scope of reasonableness. We need to keep our mind open to locate where the problem is and where the problem is not. Let us say we have just put up a commercially produced Yagi antenna and it has a high SWR at the rig end of the coax. The first thing that comes to mind is that it is the antenna. Perhaps it is, but we need to follow a plan.

Let us say our rig, with the example new antenna, is showing an SWR of 3:1. If the antenna is the culprit, it means the feed line is seeing a load (antenna feed point) that is not close to the characteristic impedance of the coax. In simple form, if the coax is 50 Ω, a 3:1 SWR means the antenna feed point impedance is either 150 Ω or 17 Ω. The feed point impedance of a Yagi can be as low as 17 Ω, but not as high as 150 Ω; therefore, we need to make a choice and we choose that the feed point is 17 Ω. We need to consider there might be an impedance transformation device at the feed point, but this device most likely will never transform the feed point to as high as 150 Ω for an expected 50-Ω feed.

There are times when the feed point will be intentionally transformed high. Band-specific 4:1 coaxial baluns can reduce even harmonics. These baluns require the Yagi feed point to be four times the impedance of the coax, or 200 Ω. This is accomplished using a hairpin across the Yagi feed point. The circuit is: 50-Ω coax up the tower, mast and out to the driver, through the 4:1 coaxial balun and attached to the feed point, which also has the hairpin across the feed point. Back to our example with a 3:1 SWR.

Impedance transformation devices (matching circuits) are used to step up the feed point impedance to match the feed line (some matching circuits step down the impedance, but almost all used in Yagi antennas step up the feed point

impedance). If the Yagi feed point impedance is 17 Ω, a hairpin (inductive reactance across the feed point) can be used to increase the feed point to match the 50-Ω feed line. So, if the Yagi really has 17-Ω feed point impedance and there is a hairpin-matching device, one might want to be sure the hairpin is properly attached and adjusted (if there is an adjustment). An important piece of information is to know the untransformed feed point impedance.

Yagis can be designed with a very low feed point impedance, but most production antennas are not. In our example, let us assume the feed point impedance is in the range of 35 Ω. Now what do we do?

The Yagi, without a hairpin, would have a SWR of about 1.4:1, derived by dividing the characteristic impedance of the coax by the feed point: 50 / 35 = 1.4. Therefore, if we remove the impedance transformation device and measure the driven element directly (at a reasonable test height above ground), we should see an SWR of about 1.4:1. If we do, we can eliminate the Yagi as the cause of the 3:1 SWR we saw at the rig end of the coax feed line. This means the problem is elsewhere, so we can go to the common section below.

28.3.7 TROUBLESHOOTING HIGH SWR IN NON-YAGI ANTENNAS

Full-size dipole antennas will not have a matching device, because their impedance is usually between 45 and 90 Ω, depending on the shape and height above ground. The lower values will be for dipoles that are inverted Vs with the ends not far from the ground. If you have a high SWR on one of these antennas, it is almost sure to be in the feed system.

You should check all the components from the antenna to the rig. This includes the balun (rare to have a problem here), connectors, coax and all equipment in the line, such as SWR meter, antenna switch, etc.

There can be several reasons for a higher than expected SWR. What "a higher than expected SWR" means is that the SWR exceeds the specification by a large margin, such as 2:1, when a 1.3:1 is expected. A difference of a few tenths should not be a serious concern. We are addressing a more major difference. Let us continue the example above for a purchased antenna. If the antenna is one that has been in production, then it is reasonable to expect the antenna to meet the specifications. If the antenna does not meet the specifications, then try the following step first, then move to the longer list below:

Remove the driver element from the array (Yagi), place it on a wooden stepladder. Measure the element to be certain it is built properly, with the correct dimensions. Check the SWR. If the SWR remains at 3:1, the problem is not in the antenna. It must be in the delivery system, because the driver is a dipole and it will not be 3:1 under any circumstances. A dipole's feed point impedance can be between 40 to 90 Ω, depending on its height above ground, which translates into an SWR of not more than 1.8:1. If the SWR is noticeably higher, then the delivery system is suspect and must be checked. This consists of the rig, amplifier, tuner(s), antenna selector(s), all metering equipment (SWR/power meter), all coax lines and connections.

The usual questions to move through the process are:

1) Is the tuner in the line? Many times, a tuner has been left in with settings that cause the rig's SWR indicator to read improperly.

2) Is the SWR/power meter battery powered? A low battery can cause erratic readings.

3) How sure are you that the coax connections are properly made? How good are the solder joints?

4) Is there water in the coax?

5) Is there an RF choke or balun being used to decouple the coax feed line from the antenna?

If the problem is still not solved, here is the longer list:

1) Remember that an antenna is an electrical design implemented in a mechanical structure; therefore, be sure all joints are mechanically secure, making a solid connection.

2) Remember that an antenna is simply an airborne conductor. There is no "magic"!

3) Be sure the new antenna is at a reasonable test height. Having a Yagi antenna a few feet above ground, such as on sawhorses, will not provide much useful information. An antenna covering 20 through 10 meters should be in the clear about 12 feet above ground, preferably higher. A 40 meter dipole or Yagi can be effectively tested down to 15 feet, but will probably shift upward in frequency as the antenna is raised to its final height. The ground contributes a very large amount of capacitance!

4) Aiming a Yagi upward at the sky with the reflector laying on the ground is also not a good idea. The reflector is very closely coupled to the ground and it will not be properly tuned. If the reflector can be raised several feet above the ground (a quarter wave is perfect), the entire antenna can be accurately tuned. Of course, it might be easier to raise the whole antenna horizontally 12-15 feet.

5) Check the dimensions of the assembled antenna to ensure they are reasonably close to the drawings. Unless a particular design is extremely sensitive, a difference of an inch on 20 meter elements should not cause a serious SWR change.

6) Check for other antennas within proximity to the new antenna. Antennas that are related to the new one are of particular interest. A few guidelines are provided in **Table 28-2**. "New Antenna" refers to the one just put up and assumes it is a horizontal design."Watch These" means other antennas that can be influencing the new one. "Coupling Distance" is the distance that the new antenna can effectively couple through the air to another antenna. The coupling distance implies distance to the closest point between the antennas.

7) If the new antenna is a horizontal type, a vertical antenna within near proximity will not usually cause any problems. The anticipated isolation between horizontal and vertical polarization is 20 dB and this is sufficient to isolate the antennas from causing harmful interference, or sufficient influence as to cause a high SWR on either antenna.

8) There are some new SWR meters on the market that make antenna adjustments and testing quite easy. These instruments provide a direct SWR readout, along with the frequency. At least one can display a graph of the SWR curve. If one of the new SWR meters is being utilized, caution should be observed. These instruments send out a low level signal to the antenna under test then sense the reflected power, computing the return loss and the resulting SWR at that point on the feed line. The SWR indicated is the SWR at that point on the line, not necessarily at the actual feed point.

The difficulty using these instruments arises when there is RF energy in the area from sources other than from the antenna under test. Some are so sensitive that a SWR reading of 1:1 on the instrument is not possible. The stray RF energy does not have to be near the frequency being tested, as the front end of the instruments are basically untuned and, therefore, very wide.

During the day, AM broadcast stations can dramatically influence these instruments. At dusk, most AM stations reduce their power and redirect the antenna patterns; however, the redirected energy might just now be in the direction of the antenna under test, whereas during the day the energy was directed somewhere else and was not noticed.

AM broadcast harmonics can be a problem up through 40 meters; maybe higher harmonics are multiples of the operating (fundamental) frequency, such as 1200 kHz (AM band) with harmonics at 2400 kHz and 3600 kHz. Although the harmonics are greatly reduced by the filters at the AM transmitter, reducing a harmonic from a 50 kW transmitter so that it is insignificant compared to the reflected power from a 5 mW signal from one of these SWR devices is a tough order.

Any of these instruments can be used as long as one is aware of this possible problem. Using a transmitter at a few watts will be the most accurate, as the energy from other sources will be substantially less than that of the transmitter.

9) If the antenna is physically correct and the antenna is commercially made, then the problem must be due to other conductors or antennas within close proximity, the match, or feed system. The feed system includes the balun or RF choke and the feed line. The feed line has connectors. Some feed lines purchased pre-made use connectors that are only crimped. Some amateurs believe they should be soldered.

10) A balun should have its leads as short as possible, usually about 2½ inches. An RF choke balun should be wound on a cylinder (solenoidal) to be most effective. (See the **Transmission Line Coupling and Impedance Matching** chapter.)

11) The split portion attached to the feed point needs to be waterproofed so that water will not wick down inside the coax. If there are guy wires, they should be broken up with insulators into nonresonant lengths, or use nonconductive guy cable.

Table 28-2
Potential Interactions

New Antenna	Watch These	Coupling Distance (ft)
40 meters	80, 160 meters	35
20 meters	20, 40, 80 meters	18
15 meters	20, 40 meters	12
10 meters	15, 20, 80 meters	10

12) If the coax feed line is old, it is possibly contaminated. The contamination comes from the jacket of the coax contaminating the interior dielectric.

13) The coax might also have water inside. This can happen when the end is split (i.e. such as for an RF choke or pigtail connection) and the water wicks up the braid and goes inside the coax cable. Water can also find a path on the inner dielectric and flow inside the coax cable. Air-dielectric coax is especially sensitive and vulnerable to water. It has even been suggested that water can condense inside coaxial cable with an air dielectric. An air-dielectric cable is one that uses air, rather than a solid material for the space between the center conductor and the shield.

The above information pertains to antennas you design and build as well, except that the actual SWR specification will probably not be readily known but it will be anticipated. Keep in mind that a vast majority of Yagi designs have an impedance of less than 50 Ω at the feed point. It is rare to find any that are even in the 40+ Ω range. Some go as low as 10 Ω. This means the SWR can be as high as 5:1 without a matching circuit.

28.3.8 YAGI FEED POINT IMPEDANCE NOTES

Most Yagi designs are in the high teens to mid 20-Ω range and the unmatched SWR will be a maximum of 2.5:1 for a 20-Ω feed point (assuming no reactance). The matching systems usually utilized (hairpin, gamma, T) are step-up circuits, which means the matching circuit raises feed point impedance. The feed point can be transformed to values above 50 Ω, even as high at 200 Ω if a 4:1 balun is desired to be used (50-Ω coax × 4 = 200 Ω).

Please note that transformed impedance is not the same as "native" impedance, meaning untransformed. An antenna that has a native impedance of 10 Ω will have the same current flowing in it when the feed point is transformed to 50 Ω to match the coax feed line's characteristic impedance of 50 Ω.

A "dual-driven" 2-element driver design with crossed-over feed straps between the driver elements is a way of transforming the feed point impedance to a higher value, such as 200 Ω. The "native" feed point impedance of that antenna will be much lower, possibly even way below 50 Ω.

28.4 REFURBISHING ALUMINUM ANTENNAS

Whether passed on by another amateur, recovered from the local recycling shop, grabbed as a bargain at a swap meet or just needing to do maintenance, the average amateur often has to bring up to scratch antennas that are the worse for wear.

Two of the most detrimental factors to aluminum are the results of electrolysis caused by poor choice of connectors and the chemistry of the air. Salt near the coast or industrial/automotive particulates can, when mixed with the normal moisture content, eat away at the shiny aluminum. If allowed to progress far enough, the mechanical integrity of the structure is impaired beyond simple repair.

The first procedure is to inspect the antenna. Look for the dreaded white oxide powder around connectors and joints. This points the way to the areas that need particular attention. Next is to try and remove the connector hardware which may be seized beyond recovery. This is particularly the case where steel plated with cadmium or zinc/galvanized hardware has been used. Before struggling with wrenches and screwdrivers, spray the area with penetrating oil such as Kroil or other modern preparations. These are more effective than some of the older preparations such as WD40 and CRC-556.

If the items release, you have had a win. If not then you have to find a suitable method of removal. Sometimes, heating the area with a blowtorch may cause sufficient expansion for the frozen joint to be loosened. Clamps may be cut free using a cutting wheel on a high speed grinding tool — before cutting into the underlying aluminum, try leverage with a small bladed screwdriver and hopefully you will be able to break the metal along the cut without bruising or deformation of the aluminum. Even an old fashioned hacksaw with a fine toothed blade might be suitable in making the cut.

Metal threads that are frozen because of corrosion can be a great frustration. This can be made more difficult if they pass through plastic insulators, as trying to grind the heads off will melt the plastic. A method that has been found helpful is to drill though the head of the metal thread with a sharp drill slightly smaller in diameter than the shank. The hole only needs to be slightly deeper than the depth of the head. Then use a drill slightly smaller than the diameter of the head to remove the head. This method generates less heat from friction than most other methods and is particularly easy to use on PoziDriv or Phillips head hardware as the drill is automatically centered.

Having disassembled the antenna, it is necessary to further inspect its condition and repair and/or treat areas that are damaged. Areas of oxidation need to be removed by abrasion. This can generally be done using a kitchen plastic scouring pad such as Scotch-Brite, if the oxidation is superficial. The advantage of using the plastic pad is that it does not impregnate the surfaces with metal particles of dissimilar metal which will only cause further corrosion later on.

If the pitting is deep, it may be necessary to remove the damaged area and insert a suitable sleeve just to restore mechanical strength. Pitted areas can sometimes be cleaned and an internal sleeve of PVC or similar used but remember to ensure balance if the element or boom section is undamaged on the opposite end. Remember that crystallization occurs in aluminum subjected to constant vibration, a lesson learned from the aircraft industry but obvious in aluminum antennas mounted in windy sites.

If the metal has to be cut, it must be joined to be electrically continuous and particularly at VHF and UHF, the outside diameter must be maintained to keep the tuning characteristics within specification. For this reason, internal sleeves are usually preferable with use of aluminum pop rivets that have aluminum mandrels. Some bargain rivets use steel mandrels and in the right conditions you will have a loose fastening, a nonconductive joint and a noisy antenna.

Once the various components have been cleaned and mended they are ready for reassembly. Replace the hardware with stainless steel and use nylon insert (Nylok) nuts that remain tight without deforming the tubing. Worm drive stainless steel hose clamps are used but not the ones with plain steel worm drives. Boom clamps using U-bolts are expensive items and a wire brush can be used on the threads to remove any rust, followed with a light spray of aluminum-based paint and replacing the washers and nuts with bright steel ones which are then also painted. If possible, after assembly, a further coat of paint is applied to keep the moisture from these components.

Remember that UV light causes many wire jackets to degrade and so any pigtails, whether insulated or not, benefit from having heat shrink tubing applied.

All swaged joints should be cleaned to bright metal on the mating surfaces, remembering the RF skin effect. Use a thin coating of anti-oxidation compound at all metal-to-metal joints as described in the section on Corrosion in the chapter **Building Antenna Systems and Towers**.

On the exterior, if there are concerns of moisture ingress, clean the surface of any contaminants and apply neutral-cure silicone sealant or cover with butyl rubber self-vulcanizing tape. See the section on Waterproofing in the chapter **Building Antenna Systems and Towers**. Do not be tempted to use hot melt glue on external applications as it deteriorates rapidly from UV radiation.

Although there are warnings about painting antennas, particularly where there is evidence of pitting or scratching on the surface a light spray of aluminum-based paint provides added protection against additional damage. The point is that you are not painting a rusty hulk and brushing paint on thickly but lightly coating the surfaces and paint runs will not occur to cause insulation of parts of your antenna.

It is probably wise to have a progressive program of inspection and maintenance of all antenna systems. Birds find our structures good perches, wind can bend things and moisture which is trapped can all cause damage. At least every couple of years is a good program. Look after your antennas and they will serve you well and long.

APPENDIX

This appendix contains a glossary of terms, a list of common abbreviations, length conversion information (feet and inches), metric equivalents and antenna-gain-reference data.

Glossary of Terms

This glossary provides a handy list of terms that are used frequently in Amateur Radio conversation and literature about antennas. With each item is a brief definition of the term. Most terms given here are discussed more thoroughly in the text of this book, and may be located by using the index.

Actual ground — The point within the earth's surface where effective ground conductivity exists. The depth for this point varies with frequency and the condition of the soil.

Antenna — An electrical conductor or array of conductors that radiates signal energy (transmitting) or collects signal energy (receiving).

Antenna tuner — A device containing variable reactances (and perhaps a balun). It is connected between the transmitter and the feed point of an antenna system, and adjusted to "tune" or resonate the system to the operating frequency. It does not "tune" the antenna, only transform impedances.

Aperture, effective — An area enclosing an antenna, on which it is convenient to make calculations of field strength and antenna gain. Sometimes referred to as the "capture area."

Apex — The feed-point region of a V type of antenna.

Apex angle — The included angle between the wires of a V, an inverted-V dipole, and similar antennas, or the included angle between the two imaginary lines touching the element tips of a log periodic array.

Azimuthal pattern — The radiation pattern of an antenna in all horizontal directions around it.

Balanced line — A symmetrical two-conductor feed line for which each conductor has the same impedance to ground.

Balun — A device for feeding a balanced load with an unbalanced line, or vice versa. May be a form of choke, or a transformer that provides a specific impedance transformation (including 1:1). Often used in antenna systems to interface a coaxial transmission line to the feed point of a balanced antenna, such as a dipole.

Base loading — A lumped reactance that is inserted at the base (ground end) of a vertical antenna to resonate the antenna.

Beamwidth — Related to directive antennas. The width, in degrees, of the major lobe between the two directions at which the relative radiated power is equal to one half its value at the peak of the lobe (half power = –3 dB).

Beta match — A form of hairpin match. The two conductors straddle the boom of the antenna being matched, and the closed end of the matching-section conductors is strapped to the boom.

Bridge — A circuit with two or more ports that is used in measurements of impedance, resistance or standing waves in an antenna system. When the bridge is adjusted for a balanced condition, the unknown factor can be determined by reading its value on a calibrated scale or meter.

Capacitance hat — A conductor of large surface area that is connected at the high-impedance end of an antenna to effectively increase the electrical length. It is sometimes mounted directly above a loading coil to reduce the required inductance for establishing resonance. It usually takes the form of a series of wheel spokes or a solid circular disc. Sometimes referred to as a "top hat."

Capture area — See aperture.

Center fed — Transmission-line connection at the electrical center of an antenna radiator.

Center loading — A scheme for inserting inductive reactance (coil) at or near the center of an antenna element for the purpose of lowering its resonant frequency. Used with elements that are less than ¼ wavelength at the operating frequency.

Choke balun — A balun that works by presenting a high impedance to RF current.

Coaxial cable or coax — Any of the coaxial transmission lines that have the outer shield (solid or braided) on the same axis as the inner or center conductor. The insulating material can be air, helium or solid-dielectric compounds.

Collinear array — A linear array of radiating elements (usually dipoles) with their axes arranged in a straight line. Popular at VHF and above.

Common-mode current — Current that flows equally on all conductors of a group or that flows on the outside of the shield of a coaxial feed line.

Conductor — A metal body such as tubing, rod or wire that permits current to travel continuously along its length.

Counterpoise — A wire or group of wires mounted close to ground, but insulated from ground, to form a low-impedance, high-capacitance path to ground. Used at MF and HF to provide an RF ground for an antenna. Also see ground plane.

Current loop — A point of current maxima (antipode) on an antenna.

Current node — A point of current minima on an antenna.

Decade — A factor of ten or frequencies having a 10:1 harmonic relationship

Decibel — A logarithmic power ratio, abbreviated dB. May also represent a voltage or current ratio if the voltages or currents are measured across (or through) identical impedances. Suffixes to the abbreviation indicate references: dBi, isotropic radiator; dBic, isotropic radiator circular; dBm, milliwatt; dBW, watt.

Delta loop — A full-wave loop shaped like a triangle or delta.

Delta match — Center-feed technique used with radiators that are not split at the center. The feed line is fanned near the radiator center and connected to the radiator symmetrically. The fanned area is delta shaped.

Dielectrics — Various insulating materials used in antenna systems, such as found in insulators and transmission lines.

Diffraction — The bending of a wave by the abrupt edge or corner at a change in the medium through which the wave is traveling.

Dipole — An antenna, usually a half wavelength long, with opposing voltages on each half. Also called a "doublet."

Direct ray — Transmitted signal energy that arrives at the receiving antenna directly rather than being reflected by any object or medium.

Directivity — The property of an antenna that concentrates the radiated energy to form one or more major lobes.

Director — A conductor placed in front of a driven element to cause directivity. Frequently used singly or in multiples with Yagi or cubical-quad beam antennas.

Doublet — See dipole.

Driven array — An array of antenna elements which are all driven or excited by means of a transmission line, usually to achieve directivity.

Driven element — A radiator element of an antenna system to which the transmission line is connected.

Dummy load — Synonymous with dummy antenna. A nonradiating substitute for an antenna.

E layer — The ionospheric layer nearest earth from which radio signals can be reflected to a distant point, generally a maximum of 2000 km (1250 miles).

E plane — Related to a linearly polarized antenna, the plane containing the electric field vector of the antenna and its direction of maximum radiation. For terrestrial antenna systems, the direction of the E plane is also taken as the polarization of the antenna. The E plane is at right angles to the H plane.

Efficiency — The ratio of useful output power to input power, determined in antenna systems by losses in the system, including in nearby objects.

EIRP — Effective isotropic radiated power. The power radiated by an antenna in its favored direction, taking the gain of the antenna into account as referenced to isotropic.

Elements — The conductive parts of an antenna system that determine the antenna characteristics. For example, the reflector, driven element and directors of a Yagi antenna.

Elevation pattern — The radiation pattern of antenna at all vertical angles along a fixed direction.

End effect — A condition caused by capacitance at the ends of an antenna element. Insulators and related support wires contribute to this capacitance and lower the resonant frequency of the antenna. The effect increases with conductor diameter and must be considered when cutting an antenna element to length.

End fed — An end-fed antenna is one to which power is applied at one end, rather than at some point between the ends.

F layer — The ionospheric layer that lies above the E layer. Radio waves can be refracted from it to provide communications distances of several thousand miles by means of single- or double-hop skip.

Feed line, feeders — See Transmission Line.

Field strength — The intensity of a radio wave as measured at a point some distance from the antenna. This measurement is usually made in microvolts per meter.

Front to back — The ratio of the radiated power off the front and back of a directive antenna. For example, a dipole would have a ratio of 1, which is equivalent to 0 dB.

Front to rear — Worst-case rearward lobe in the 180°-wide sector behind an antenna's main lobe, in dB.

Front to side — The ratio of radiated power between the major lobe and that 90° off the front of a directive antenna.

Gain — The increase in effective radiated power in the desired direction of the major lobe.

Gamma match — A matching system used with driven antenna elements to effect a match between the transmission line and the feed point of the antenna. It consists of a series capacitor and an arm that is mounted close to the driven element and in parallel with it near the feed point.

Ground plane — A system of conductors placed beneath an elevated antenna to serve as an earth ground. Also see counterpoise.

Ground screen — A wire mesh counterpoise.

Ground wave — Radio waves that travel along the earth's surface.

H plane — Related to a linearly polarized antenna. The plane containing the magnetic field vector of an antenna and its direction of maximum radiation. The H plane is at right angles to the E plane.

HAAT — Height above average terrain. A term used mainly in connection with repeater antennas in determining coverage area.

Hairpin match — A U-shaped conductor that is connected to the two inner ends of a split dipole for the purpose of creating an impedance match to a balanced feeder.

Hardline — A type of low-loss coaxial feed line with a rigid or semi-rigid outer shield.

Harmonic antenna — An antenna that will operate on its fundamental frequency and the harmonics of the fundamental frequency for which it is designed. An end-fed half-wave antenna is one example.

Helical — A helically wound antenna, one that consists of a spiral conductor. If it has a very large winding length to diameter ratio it provides broadside radiation. If the length-to-diameter ratio is small, it will operate in the axial mode and radiate off the end opposite the feed point. The polarization will be circular for the axial mode, with left or right circularity, depending on whether the helix is wound clockwise or counterclockwise.

Image antenna — The imaginary counterpart of an actual antenna. It is assumed for mathematical purposes to be located below the earth's surface beneath the antenna, and is considered symmetrical with the antenna above ground.

Impedance — The ohmic value of an antenna feed point, matching section or transmission line. An impedance may contain a reactance as well as a resistance component.

Impedance Matching Unit — see Antenna Tuner.

Inverted-V (dipole) — A half-wavelength dipole erected in the form of an upside-down V, with the feed point at the apex. Its radiation pattern is similar to that of a horizontal dipole.

Isotropic — An imaginary or hypothetical point-source antenna that radiates equal power in all directions. It is used as a reference for the directive characteristics of actual antennas.

Ladder line — see Open-wire Line.

Lambda — Greek symbol (λ) used to represent a wavelength with reference to electrical dimensions in antenna work.

Line loss — The power lost in a transmission line, usually expressed in decibels.

Line of sight — Transmission path of a wave that travels directly from the transmitting antenna to the receiving antenna.

Litz wire — Stranded wire with individual strands insulated; small wire provides a large surface area for current flow, so losses are reduced for the wire size.

Load — The electrical entity to which power is delivered. The antenna system is a load for the transmitter.

Loading — The process of a transferring power from its source to a load. The effect a load has on a power source.

Lobe — A defined field of energy that radiates from a directive antenna.

Log-periodic antenna — A broadband directive antenna that has a structural format causing its impedance and radiation characteristics to repeat periodically as the logarithm of frequency.

Long wire — A wire antenna that is one wavelength or greater in electrical length. When two or more wavelengths long it provides gain and a multi-lobe

radiation pattern. When terminated at one end it becomes essentially unidirectional off that end.

Marconi antenna — A shunt-fed monopole operated against ground or a radial system. In modern jargon, the term refers loosely to any type of vertical antenna.

Matchbox — see Antenna Tuner

Matching — The process of effecting an impedance match between two electrical circuits of unlike impedance. One example is matching a transmission line to the feed point of an antenna. Maximum power transfer to the load (antenna system) will occur when a matched condition exists.

Monopole — Literally, one pole, an antenna that operates with a single voltage with respect to ground, such as a vertical radiator operated against the Earth or a counterpoise.

Null — A condition during which an electrical unit is at a minimum. A null in an antenna radiation pattern is a point in the 360-degree pattern where a minima in field intensity is observed. An impedance bridge is said to be "pulled" when it has been brought into balance, with a null in the current flowing through the bridge arm.

Octave — A factor of two or frequencies having a 2:1 harmonic relationship.

Open-wire line — Consists of parallel, symmetrical wires with insulating spacers at regular intervals to maintain the line spacing. The dielectric is principally air, making it a low-loss type of line.

Parabolic reflector — An antenna reflector that is a portion of a parabolic revolution or curve. Used mainly at UHF and higher to obtain high gain and a relatively narrow beamwidth when excited by one of a variety of driven elements placed in the plane of and perpendicular to the axis of the parabola.

Parallel-conductor line — see Open-wire Line.

Parasitic array — A directive antenna that has a driven element and at least one independent director or reflector, or a combination of both. The directors and reflectors are not connected to the feed line. Except for VHF and UHF arrays with long booms (electrically), more than one reflector is seldom used. A Yagi antenna is one example of a parasitic array.

Patch antenna — A type of microwave antenna made from flat pieces of conductive material suspended above a ground-plane.

Phase — The relative time relationship of two signals.

Phasing lines — Sections of transmission line that are used to ensure the correct phase relationship between the elements of a driven array, or between bays of an array of antennas. Also used to effect impedance transformations while maintaining the desired phase.

Polarity — The assigned convention of positive and negative for a signal or system.

Polarization — The sense of the wave radiated by an antenna. This can be horizontal, vertical, elliptical or circular (left or right hand circularity), depending on the design and application. (See H plane.)

Q section — Term used in reference to transmission-line

matching transformers and phasing lines.

Quad — A parasitic array using rectangular or diamond shaped full-wave wire loop elements. Often called the "cubical quad." Another version uses delta-shaped elements, and is called a delta loop beam.

Radiation pattern — The radiation characteristics of an antenna as a function of space coordinates. Normally, the pattern is measured in the far-field region and is represented graphically.

Radiation resistance — The ratio of the power radiated by an antenna to the square of the RMS antenna current, referred to a specific point and assuming no losses. The effective resistance at the antenna feed point.

Radiator — A discrete conductor that radiates RF energy in an antenna system.

Random wire — A random length of wire used as an antenna and fed at one end by means of an antenna tuner. Seldom operates as a resonant antenna unless the length happens to be correct.

Reflected ray — A radio wave that is reflected from the earth, ionosphere or a man-made medium, such as a passive reflector.

Reflector — A parasitic antenna element or a metal assembly that is located behind the driven element to enhance forward directivity. Hillsides and large man-made structures such as buildings and towers may act as reflectors.

Refraction — Process by which a radio wave is bent and returned to earth from an ionospheric layer or other medium after striking the medium.

Resonator — In antenna terminology, a loading assembly consisting of a coil and a short radiator section. Used to lower the resonant frequency of an antenna, usually a vertical or a mobile whip.

Rhombic — A rhomboid or diamond-shaped antenna consisting of sides (legs) that are each one or more wavelengths long. The antenna is usually erected parallel to the ground. A rhombic antenna is bidirectional unless terminated by a resistance, which makes it unidirectional. The greater the electrical leg length, the greater the gain, assuming the tilt angle is optimized.

Shunt feed — A method of feeding an antenna driven element with a parallel conductor mounted adjacent to a low- impedance point on the radiator. Frequently used with grounded quarter-wave vertical antennas to provide an impedance match to the feeder. Series feed is used when the base of the vertical is insulated from ground.

Sleeve balun — A type of choke balun consisting of a ¼-wavelength metal tube or sleeve around a coaxial feed line that acts as an open-circuit to RF current.

Stacking — The process of placing similar directive antennas atop or beside one another, forming a "stacked array." Stacking provides more gain or directivity than a single antenna.

Stub — A section of transmission line used to tune an antenna element to resonance or to aid in obtaining an impedance match.

SWR — Standing-wave ratio on a transmission line in an antenna system. More correctly, VSWR, or voltage standing-wave ratio. The ratio of the forward to reflected voltage on the line, and not a power ratio. A VSWR of 1:1

occurs when all parts of the antenna system are matched correctly to one another.

T match — Method for matching a transmission-line to an unbroken driven element. Attached at the electrical center of the driven element in a T-shaped manner. In effect it is a double gamma match.

Tilt angle — Half the angle included between the wires at the sides of a rhombic antenna.

Top hat — See Capacitance hat.

Top loading — Addition of a reactance (usually a capacitance hat) at the end of an antenna element opposite the feed point to increase the electrical length of the radiator.

Transmatch — See Antenna tuner.

Transmission line — A cable that transfers electrical energy between sources and loads.

Trap — Parallel L-C network inserted in an antenna element to provide multiband operation with a single conductor.

Tuner — see Antenna Tuner

Twinlead — A type of open-wire line encased in plastic insulation for its entire length. See also Window line.

Uda — Co-inventor of the Yagi antenna.

Unipole — See monopole.

Unun — Unbalanced-to-unbalanced impedance transformer.

Velocity factor — The ratio of the velocity of radio wave propagation in a dielectric medium to that in free space. When cutting a transmission line to a specific electrical length, the velocity factor of the particular line must be taken into account.

Vivaldi antenna — A type of microwave antenna that uses an exponential cutout as the radiating element, similar to an exponential horn.

VSWR — Voltage standing-wave ratio. See SWR.

Wave — A disturbance or variation that is a function of time or space, or both, transferring energy progressively from point to point. A radio wave, for example.

Wave angle — The angle above the horizon of a radio wave as it is launched from or received by an antenna. Also called elevation angle.

Wave front — A surface that is a locus of all the points having the same phase at a given instant in time.

Window line — A type of twinlead with regular rectangular holes or "windows" in the insulation between conductors.

Yagi — A directive, gain type of antenna that utilizes a number of parasitic directors and a reflector. Named after one of the two Japanese inventors (Yagi and Uda).

Zepp antenna — A half-wave wire antenna that operates on its fundamental and harmonics. It is fed at one end by means of open-wire feeders. The name evolved from its popularity as an antenna on Zeppelins. In modern jargon the term refers loosely to any horizontal antenna.

ABBREVIATIONS

Abbreviations and acronyms that are commonly used throughout this book are defined in the list below. Periods are not part of an abbreviation unless the abbreviation otherwise forms a common English word. When appropriate, abbreviations as shown are used in either singular or plural construction.

A
A — ampere
ac — alternating current
AF — audio frequency
AFSK — audio frequency-shift keying
AGC — automatic gain control
AM — amplitude modulation
ANT — antenna
ARRL — American Radio Relay League
ATV — amateur television
AWG — American wire gauge
az-el — azimuth-elevation

B
balun — balanced to unbalanced
BC — broadcast
BCI — broadcast interference
BW — bandwidth

C
c — centi (prefix)
ccw — counterclockwise
cm — centimeter
coax — coaxial cable
CT — center tap
cw — clockwise
CW — continuous wave

D
D — diode, ionospheric layer
dB — decibel
dBd — decibels referenced to a dipole
dBi — decibels referenced to isotropic
dBic — decibels referenced to isotropic, circular
dBm — decibels referenced to one milliwatt
dBW — decibels referenced to one watt
dc — direct current
DE — driven element
deg — degree
DF — direction finding
dia — diameter
DPDT — double pole, double throw
DPST — double pole, single throw
DVM — digital voltmeter
DX — long distance communication

E
E — ionospheric layer, electric field
ed. — edition
Ed. — editor
EIRP — effective isotropic radiated power
ELF — extremely low frequency
EMC — electromagnetic compatibility
EME — earth-moon-earth
EMF — electromotive force

EMI — electromagnetic interference
ERP — effective radiated power
E_S or Es — sporadic E

F
f — frequency
F — ionospheric layer, farad
F/B — front to back (ratio)
ff — index abbreviation for topic appears on subsequent pages
F/R — worst-case front to rear (ratio)
FM — frequency modulation
FOT — frequency of optimum transmission
ft — foot or feet (unit of length)
F1 — ionospheric layer
F2 — ionospheric layer

G
G — giga (prefix)
GDO — grid- or gate-dip oscillator
GHz — gigahertz
GND — ground

H
H — magnetic field, henry
HAAT — height above average terrain
HF — high frequency (3-30 MHz)
Hz — hertz (unit of frequency)

I
I — current
ID — inside diameter
IEEE — Institute of Electrical and Electronic Engineers
in. — inch
IRE — Institute of Radio Engineers (now IEEE)

J
j — vector notation

K
k — kilo (prefix)
kHz — kilohertz
km — kilometer
kW — kilowatt
kΩ — kilohm

L
L — inductance
lb — pound (unit of mass)
LF — low frequency (30-300 kHz)
LHCP — left-hand circular polarization
ln — natural logarithm
log — common logarithm
LP — log periodic
LPDA — log periodic dipole array

LPVA — log periodic V array
LUF — lowest usable frequency

M
m — meter (unit of length), milli (prefix)
M — mega (prefix)
m/s — meters per second
mA — milliampere
max — maximum
MF — medium frequency (0.3-3 MHz)
mH — millihenry
MHz — megahertz
mi — mile
min — minute
mm — millimeter
MPE — maximum permissible exposure
ms — millisecond
mS — millisiemens
MS — meteor scatter
MUF — maximum usable frequency
mW — milliwatt
MΩ — megohm

N
n — nano (prefix)
NC — no connection, normally closed
NiCd — nickel cadmium
NiMH — nickel metal hydride
NIST — National Institute of Standards and Technology
NO — normally open
no. — number

O
OD — outside diameter

P
p — page (bibliography reference), pico (prefix)
P-P — peak to peak
PC — printed circuit
PDF — Portable Document Format
PEP — peak envelope power
pF — picofarad
pk-to-pk — peak-to-peak
pot — potentiometer
pp — pages (bibliography reference)
Proc — Proceedings

Q
Q — figure of merit

R
R — resistance, resistor
RF — radio frequency
RFC — radio frequency choke
RFI — radio frequency interference
RHCP — right-hand circular polarization
RLC — resistance-inductance-capacitance
r/min — revolutions per minute
RMS — root mean square
r/s — revolutions per second
RSGB — Radio Society of Great Britain
RX — receiver

S
s — second
S — siemen
S/N, SNR — signal-to-noise ratio
SASE — self-addressed stamped envelope
SINAD — signal-to-noise and distortion
SPDT — single pole, double throw
SPST — single pole, single throw
SWR — standing wave ratio
sync — synchronous

T
tpi — turns per inch
TR — transmit-receive
TVI — television interference
TVRO — Television Receive-Only
TX — transmitter

U
UHF — ultra-high frequency (300-3000 MHz)
US — United States
UTC — Universal Time, Coordinated

V
V — volt
VF — velocity factor
VHF — very-high frequency (30-300 MHz)
VLF — very-low frequency (3-30 kHz)
Vol — volume (bibliography reference)
VOM — volt-ohm meter
VSWR — voltage standing-wave ratio
VTVM — vacuum-tube voltmeter

W
W — watt
WPM — words per minute
WRC — World Radio Conference
WVDC — working voltage, direct current

X
X — reactance
XCVR — transceiver
XFMR — transformer
XMTR — transmitter

Z
Z — impedance

Other Symbols and Greek Letters
$°$ — degrees
λ — wavelength
λ/d — wavelength to diameter (ratio)
ε — permittivity
ε_0 — permittivity of free space
ε_r — relative permittivity or dielectric constant
μ — permeability, micro (prefix)
μF — microfarad
μH — microhenry
μV — microvolt
Ω — ohm
ϕ, θ — angles
π — 3.14159
ρ, Γ — reflection coefficient

Advertisers Index

Advertising Department Staff
Debra Jahnke, K1DAJ, *Sales Manager, Business Services*
Janet Rocco, W1JLR, *Account Executive*
Lisa Tardette, KB1MOI, *Account Executive*
Diane Szlachetka, KB1OKV, *Advertising Graphic Design*
Zoe Belliveau, W1ZOE, *Business Services Coordinator*

800-243-7768

Direct Line: 860-594-0207 ■ Fax: 860-594-4285 ■ e-mail: ads@arrl.org ■ Web: www.arrl.org/ads

If your company provides products or services of interest to our readers,
please contact the ARRL Advertising Department today for information on building your business.

MFJ
World Leader in Ham Radio Accessories!
FREE 136 Page Ham Radio Catalog . . . the LARGEST selection in the World!

MFJ Antenna Analyzers

More Hams use MFJ antenna analyzers than all others put together!

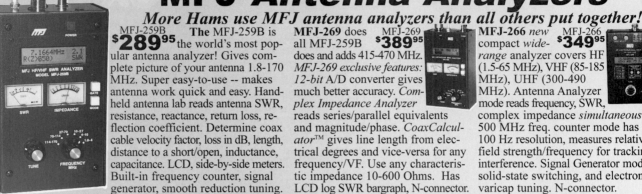

MFJ-259B $289⁹⁵ **The MFJ-259B is** the world's most popular antenna analyzer! Gives complete picture of your antenna 1.8-170 MHz. Super easy-to-use -- makes antenna work quick and easy. Hand-held antenna lab reads antenna SWR, resistance, reactance, return loss, reflection coefficient. Determine coax cable velocity factor, loss in dB, length, distance to a short/open, inductance, capacitance. LCD, side-by-side meters. Built-in frequency counter, signal generator, smooth reduction tuning.

MFJ-269 does **MFJ-269** $389⁹⁵ all MFJ-259B does and adds 415-470 MHz. *MFJ-269 exclusive features:* 12-bit A/D converter gives much better accuracy. *Complex Impedance Analyzer* reads series/parallel equivalents and magnitude/phase. *CoaxCalculator*™ gives line length from electrical degrees and vice-versa for any frequency/VF. Use any characteristic impedance 10-600 Ohms. Has LCD log SWR bargraph, N-connector.

MFJ-266 *new* **MFJ-266** $349⁹⁵ compact *wide-range* analyzer covers HF (1.5-65 MHz), VHF (85-185 MHz), UHF (300-490 MHz). Antenna Analyzer mode reads frequency, SWR, complex impedance *simultaneously*. 500 MHz freq. counter mode has 100 Hz resolution, measures relative field strength/frequency for tracking interference. Signal Generator mode, solid-state switching, and electronic varicap tuning. N-connector.

MFJ *Automatic* Antenna Tuners

| 1.5 kW . . . *Legal Limit* | 600 Watt . . . *for Amps* | 300 Watt - *Wide Range* | 200 Watt . . . *Compact* |

Roam the entire HF spectrum 1.8-30 MHz *hands-free* with full *1500 Watt* legal limit on SSB/CW and near-perfect SWR! Lighted LCD/Cross-Needle Meter. 13Wx4Hx15D inches. **MFJ-998** $699⁹⁵

For 600 Watt amps like Ameritron AL-811/ALS-600/ALS-500M. Matches 12-800 Ohms. 10,000 *Virtual Antenna*™ memories. Cross-Needle SWR/Wattmeter. 10Wx2³/₄Hx9D inches. **MFJ-994B** $359⁹⁵

World's best *selling* automatic antenna tuner is *highly acclaimed the world over* for its ultra high-speed, wide matching range, reliability, ease-of-use! Matches virtually *any* antenna. 10Wx23/4Hx9D". **MFJ-993B** $259⁹⁵

World's fastest compact auto tuner uses MFJ *Adaptive Search*™ and *InstantRecall*™ algorithms. 132,072 tuning solutions instantly match virtually any antenna with near perfect SWR. 6¹/₂Wx2⁷/₈Hx8³/₈D". **MFJ-929** $219⁹⁵

MFJ *Manual* Antenna Tuners

| 1.5 kW . . . *Legal Limit* | 800 Watt . . . *for Amps* | 300 Watt . . . *most used* | 150 Watt . . . *for travel* |

Improved efficiency, lower losses and a *true*-peak reading meter. 1500 Watts SSB/CW, 1.8-30 MHz, including MARS and WARC bands. 6-position antenna switch, dummy load, *500 pF* air variable capacitors, *AirCore*™ Roller Inductor, high voltage current balun, crank knob. 12⁷/₈Wx6Hx11⁵/₈D in. **MFJ-989D** $389⁹⁵

Plan for the *future!* Step up to a KW tuner for an amplifier later. Handles 800 Watts SSB/CW amplifier output (1.5 KW input). Ideal for Ameritron's AL-811/H, ALS-600/500M! *AirCore*™ roller inductor, gear-driven turns counter, peak and average lighted Cross-Needle SWR/Wattmeter, antenna switch, balun, Lexan front, 1.8-30MHz. 10³/₄x4¹/₂x10⁷/₈ inches. **MFJ-962D** $299⁹⁵

More hams use MFJ-949s than any other antenna tuner in the world! Does it all! 1.8-30 MHz, 300 Watts, *full size* peak/average lighted Cross-Needle SWR/Wattmeter, 8 position antenna switch, dummy load. Highly efficient air inductor, 1kV air-variable tuning capacitors. *QRM-Free PreTune*™, scratch proof Lexan front panel. 3¹/₂Hx10⁵/₈Wx7D inches. **MFJ-949E** $179⁹⁵

Tiny 4¹/₂x2¹/₄x3 inch *Travel-Tuner*™. Packs up quickly, takes up little space, full 150 Watts, 80-10 Meters, bypass switch. Tunes coax or random wire. It's no toy -- has gutsy air-variable capacitors 600V, 322 pF and 3 stacked powder iron toroids. Handles *real* power -- not just QRP. **MFJ-904H, $149.95.** Like MFJ-902 with cross-needle SWR/wattmtr, 4:1 balun. 7¹/₄x2¹/₄x2³/₄". **MFJ-902** $99⁹⁵

MFJ Ham Radio *Accessories*

MFJ-1778, $44.95. 160-10 Meter *G5RV* antenna. Use with tuner. 102 feet. 1.5 kW. Use on 160 Meters with tuner/ground. SO-239. **MFJ-1702C, $39.95.** 2-position *antenna switch*, center ground, lightning surge protector. **MFJ-1704, $79.95.** 4-pos.*antenna switch*.

MFJ-4125, $84.95. Tiny switching *power supply*, 13.8 VDC, 22 Amps continuous. 110/220 VAC. **MFJ-260C, $39.95.** 300 Watt dry *dummy load*. SWR 1.1:1 to 30 MHz. With Derating curve. **MFJ-264, $74.95.**1.5kW *dummy load* to 650 MHz.

MFJ-392B, $24.95. High-performance *communication headphones* with super padded headband and ear cushions. 9' cord, works in stereo or mono w/free 1/4" phono adaptor. **MFJ-281, $12.95.** 3 in. *speaker*, 8 Watts, 8 Ohms.

MFJ-1724B, $24.95. Dual Band 144/440 MHz *Mobile Antenna*. Powerful 3-inch magnet mount, 15 ft. coax, PL-259. Free BNC. **MFJ-1729, $39.95.** 5/8 Wave high gain dual band 144/440 MHz magnet mount *mobile antenna*, 12 ft. coax, free BNC.

MFJ-108B, $21.95. Dual 24/12 hour *LCD clock*. 5/8" digits. 4¹/₂Wx1Dx2H".

Free MFJ Catalog
and Nearest Dealer . . . 800-647-1800

http://www.mfjenterprises.com
• 1 Year *No Matter What*™ warranty • 30 day money back guarantee (less s/h) on orders direct from MFJ

MFJ ENTERPRISES, INC. 300 Industrial Pk Rd, Starkville, MS 39759 **PH:** (662) 323-5869 **Tech Help:** (662) 323-0549 **FAX:**(662)323-6551 8-4:30 CST, Mon.-Fri. *Add shipping.* Prices and specifications subject to change. (c) 2012 MFJ Enterprises, Inc.

http://www.mfjenterprises.com

AMERITRON . . . 800 Watts . . . $949!

More hams use Ameritron AL-811/H amplifiers than any other amplifier in the world!

Only the Ameritron AL-811H gives you four *fully neutralized* 811A transmitting

AL-811H
$949
Suggested Retail
4-Tubes, 800 Watts

AL-811
$799
Suggested Retail
3-Tubes, 600 Watts

tubes. You get absolute stability and superb performance on higher bands that can't be matched by un-neutralized tubes.

You get a quiet desktop linear that's so compact it'll slide right into your operating position -- you'll hardly know it's there . . . until QRM sets in. And you can conveniently plug it into your nearest 120 VAC outlet -- no special wiring needed.

You get all HF band coverage (with license) -- including WARC and most MARS

bands at 100% rated output. Ameritron's *Adapt-A-Volt™* hi-silicon core power transformer has a special buck-boost winding that lets you compensate for high/low power line voltages.

You also get efficient full size heavy duty tank coils, slug tuned input coils, operate/standby switch, transmit LED, ALC, dual illuminated meters, QSK with optional QSK-5, pressurized cooling that you can hardly hear, full height computer grade filter capacitors and more. 13³/₄Wx8Hx16D inches.

AL-811, $799. Like AL-811H, but has three 811A tubes and 600 Watts output.

AL-811HD, $1249. Has three 572B tubes.

AMERITRON *no tune* Solid State Amplifiers

ALS-500M 500 Watt Mobile Amp

ALS-500M
$899
Suggested Retail

500 Watts
PEP/400W CW output, 1.5-22 MHz, instant bandswitching, no tuning, no warm-up. SWR, load fault, thermal overload protected. On/Off/Bypass switch. Remote on/off control. DC current meter. Extremely quiet fan. 13.8 VDC. 9Wx3¹/₂Hx15D in., 7 lbs. **ALS-500RC, $49,** Remote Head.

ALS-600 Station 600 Watt FET Amp
No tuning, no fuss, no worries -- just turn on and operate. 600 Watts PEP/500W CW, 1.5-22 MHz, instant bandswitching, SWR protected, extremely quiet, SWR/Wattmeter, ALC control. 120/220 VAC. Inrush protected. 9¹/₂Wx6Hx12D in. **ALS-600S, $1599,** ALS-600 with 10 lb. switching power supply.

ALS-600
$1499
Suggested Retail

Desktop Kilowatt Amplifier

AL-80B
$1449
Suggested Retail

Whisper quiet *desktop* amp plugs into 120 VAC to give *full* kilowatt SSB PEP output. Ameritron's exclusive *DynamicALC™* doubles average SSB power out and *Instantaneous RF Bias™* gives cooler operation. All HF bands. 850 Watts CW out, 500 Watts RTTY out, extra heavy duty power supply, 3-500G tube, 70% efficiency, tuned input, Pi/Pi-L output, inrush current protection, dual Cross-Needle meters, QSK compatible, 48 lbs. 14Wx8¹/₂Hx15¹/₂D in. **Two-year warranty.**

ALS-1300 Solid State 1200 Watt Amp

ALS-1300
$2899
Suggested Retail

Ameritron's *highest power* solid state FET no-tune amplifier gives you instant bandswitching, no tuning, no warm-up, no tubes to baby and no fuss! Outstanding reliability is insured by using eight rugged MRF-150 power FET's mounted on the dual heavy duty heat sink. Run up to 1200 Watts of clean SSB output power (just 100 Watts drive gives full rated power) for continuous coverage between 1.5-22 MHz. Compact 10Wx6¹/₂Hx18D in.

Near Legal Limit ™ Amplifier

AL-572
$1695
Suggested Retail

New class of *Near Legal Limit™* amplifier gives you 1300 Watt PEP SSB power output for *60%* of price of a full legal limit amp! 4 rugged 572B tubes. Instant 3-second warm-up, plugs into 120 VAC. Compact 14¹/₂Wx 8¹/₂Hx15¹/₂D inches fits on desktop. 160-15 Meters. 1000 Watt CW output. Tuned input, instantaneous RF Bias, dynamic ALC, parasitic killer, inrush protection, two lighted cross-needle meters, multi-voltage transformer.

Eimac 3CX800A7 Amplifiers

Suggested Retail
AL-800
$2045
1 Eimac®tube, 1250 W
AL-800H
$3045
2 Eimac® tubes,
1.5 kW Plus
With Imported Tube
AL-800F, $1875
AL-800HF, $2745

These *compact* desktop amplifiers with 3CX800A7 tubes cover 160-15 Meters including WARC bands. Adjustable slug tuned input circuit, grid protection, front panel ALC control, vernier reduction drives, heavy duty 32 lb. silicone steel core transformer, high capacitance computer grade filter capacitors. Multi-voltage operation, dual lighted cross-needle meters. 14¹/₄Wx8¹/₂Hx16¹/₂D in.

AMERITRON *full legal limit* amplifiers

AMERITRON legal limit amps use a *super heavy duty Peter Dahl Hypersil®* power transformer capable of 2.5 kW!

Most powerful -- 3CX1500/8877

AL-1500
$3495
Eimac® Tube
AL-1500F
$3095
Suggested Retail Imported tube

Ameritron's *most powerful* amplifier uses the herculean 3CX1500/8877 ceramic tube. 65 watts drive gives you full legal output -- it's just loafing with a 2500 Watts power supply.

Toughest -- 3CX1200A7

AL-1200
$3459
Suggested Retail

Get ham radio's *toughest* tube with the Ameritron AL-1200 -- the *Eimac®* 3CX1200A7. It has a 50 Watt control grid dissipation. What makes the Ameritron AL-1200 stand out from other legal limit amplifiers? The answer: A super heavy duty power supply that loafs at full legal power -- it can deliver the power of more than 2500 Watts PEP two tone output for a half hour.

Classic -- Dual 3-500Gs

AL-82
$2745
Suggested Retail

This linear gives you full legal output using a *pair* of *genuine* 3-500Gs. Competing linears using 3-500Gs *can't* give you 1500 Watts because their lightweight power supplies *can't* use these tubes to their full potential.

Ameritron brings you the finest high power accessories!

ARB-704 amp-to-rig interface... *$59⁹⁵*
Protects rig from damage by keying line transients and makes hook-up to your rig easy!

RCS-4 Remote Coax Switch... *$159⁹⁵*
Use 1 coax for **4** antennas. No control cable needed. SWR <1.25, 1.5 - 60 MHz. Useable to 100 MHz.

RCS-8V Remote Coax Switch... *$169⁹⁵*
Replace **5** coax with 1! 1.2 SWR at 250 MHz. Useable to 450 MHz. < .1 dB loss, 1kW@150MHz.

RCS-10 Remote Coax Switch... *$179⁹⁵*
Replace **8** coax with 1! SWR<1.3 to 60 MHz. **RCS-10L,$219.95** with lightning arrestors.

Call your dealer for your best price!

Free Catalog: 800-713-3550

AMERITRON®

. . . *the world's high power leader!*
116 Willow Road, Starkville, MS 39759
TECH (662) 323-8211 • **FAX** (662) 323-6551
8 a.m. - 4:30 p.m. CST Monday - Friday
For power amplifier components call (662) 323-8211

http://www.ameritron.com
Prices and specifications subject to change without notice. *©2012 Ameritron.*

Visit http://www.ameritron.com   AMERITRON . . . the world's high power leader!

Cushcraft R8 *8-Band Vertical*

MA-5B *5-Band Beam*
Small Footprint -- Big Signal

Covers 6, 10, 12, 15, 17, 20, 30, and 40 Meters!

R-8
$539⁹⁵

The R-8 provides 360° (omni) coverage on the horizon and a low radiation angle in the vertical plane for a better DX.

The Cushcraft R8 is recognized as the industry gold standard for multi-band verticals, with thousands in use worldwide. Efficient, rugged, and built to withstand the test of time, the R8's unique ground-independent design has a well-earned reputation for delivering top DX results under tough conditions. Best of all, the R8 is easy to assemble, installs just about anywhere, and blends inconspicuously with urban and country settings alike.

Automatic Band Switching: The R8's famous "black box" matching network combines with traps and parallel resonators to cover 8 bands. You QSY instantly, without a tuner!

Rugged Construction: Thick fiberglass insulators, all-stainless hardware, and 6063 aircraft-aluminum tubing that is double or triple walled at key stress points handle anything Mother Nature can dish out.

Compact Footprint: Installs in an area about the size of a child's sandbox -- no ground radials to bury and all RF-energized surfaces safely out of reach.

Legal-Limit Power: Heavy-duty components are contest-proven to handle all the power your amplifier can legally deliver and radiating it as RF rather than heat.

The sunspot count is climbing and long-awaited band openings are finally becoming a reality. Now is the perfect time to discover why Cushcraft's R8 multi-band vertical is the premier choice of DX-wise hams everywhere! **R-8GK, $56.95.** R-8 three-point guy kit for high winds.

MA-5B
$499⁹⁵

The MA-5B is one of Cushcraft's most popular HF antennas, delivering solid *signal-boosting directivity* in a bantam-weight package. Mounts on roof using standard TV hardware. Perfect for exploring exciting DX without the high cost and heavy lifting of installing a large tower and full-sized array. Its 7 foot 3-inch boom has less than 9 feet of turning radius. Contest tough -- handles 1500 Watts.

The unique MA-5B gives you 5-bands, automatic band switching and easy installation in a compact 26-pound package. On 10, 15 and 20 Meters the end elements become a two-element Yagi that delivers solid power-multiplying gain over a dipole on all three bands. On 12 and 17 Meters, the middle element is a highly efficient trap dipole. When working DX, what really matters are the interfering signals and noise you *don't hear*. That's where the MA-5B's impressive side rejection and front-to-back ratio really shines. See *cushcraftamateur.com* for gain figures.

R8 Matching Network

Matching

Broadband matching transformer maintains low VSWR at feed point

Coaxial balun is employed to keep RF off from the exterior of your feedline

All stainless steel hardware

Moisture release vent

RF choke effectively DC grounds the radiator to help prevent static electricity from entering your shack

High strength, high power, low dielectric PC board material

Feedpoint (SO239)

R8's Rugged Design

Generous use of stainless steel machine screws guarantees base integrity

Dual plate rod mount allows for easy assembly of ground components

Plate interfaced mounting system uses aluminum components and stainless steel hardware

Cushcraft 10, 15 & 20 Meter Tribander Beams

Only the best tri-band antennas become DX classics, which is why the Cushcraft World-Ranger A4S, A3S, and A3WS go to the head of the class. For more than 30 years, these pace-setting performers have taken on the world's most demanding operating conditions and proven themselves every time. The key to success comes from attention to basics. For example, element length and spacing has been carefully refined over time, and high-power traps are still hand-made and individually tuned using laboratory-grade instruments. All this

A-3S
$599⁹⁵

A-4S
$699⁹⁵

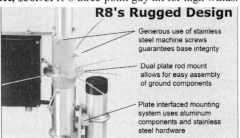

attention to detail means low SWR, wide bandwidth, optimum directivity, and high efficiency -- important performance characteristics you rely on to maintain regular schedules, rack up impressive contest scores, and grow your collection of rare QSLs!

It goes without saying that the World-Ranger lineup is also famous for its rugged construction. In fact, the majority of these antennas sold years ago are still in service today! Conservative mechanical design, rugged over-sized components, stainless-steel hardware, and aircraft-grade 6063 make all the difference.

The 3-element A3S/A3WS and 4-element A4S are world-famous for powerhouse gain and super performance. **A-3WS, $499.95,** 12/17 M. **30/40 Meter** *add-on kits* available.

Cushcraft Dual Band Yagis
One Yagi for Dual-Band FM Radios

A270-10S
$169⁹⁵

A270-6S
$129⁹⁵

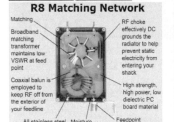

Dual-bander VHF rigs are the norm these days, so why not compliment your FM base station with a dual-band Yagi? Not only will you eliminate a costly feed line, you'll realize extra gain for digital modes like high-speed packet and D-Star! Cushcraft's A270-6S provides three elements per band and the A270-10S provides five for solid point-to-point performance. They're both pre-tuned and assembly is a snap using the fully illustrated manual.

Cushcraft Famous *Ringos* Compact FM Verticals

AR-2
$64⁹⁵

AR-6
$99⁹⁵

AR-10
$109⁹⁵

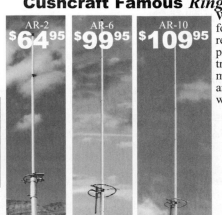

W1BX's famous *Ringo* antenna has been around for a long time and remains unbeaten for solid reliability. The Ringo is broad-banded, lighting protected, extremely rugged, economical, electrically bullet-proof, low-angle, and more -- but mainly, it just plain works! To discover why hams and commercial two-way installers around the world still love this antenna, order yours now!

Free Cushcraft Catalog
and Nearest Dealer . . . 662-323-5803
Call your dealer for your best price!

Cushcraft
Amateur Radio Antennas
308 Industrial Park Road, Starkville, MS 39759 USA
Open: 8-4:30 CST, Mon.-Fri. **Add Shipping.**
• **Sales/Tech:** 662-323-5803 • **FAX:** 662-323-6551
http://www.cushcraftamateur.com
Prices/specifications subject to change without notice/obligation. © Cushcraft®, 2012.

Visit http://www.cushcraftamateur.com

hy-gain. Antennas and Rotators

hy-gain. HF Verticals

Work amazing DX with extremely low radiation angle and omnidirectional pattern. All self supporting, 1500 Watts PEP SSB, low SWR. Heavy duty, slotted, tapered swaged, aircraft quality aluminum tubing. All stainless steel hardware. Recessed SO-239. Two year limited warranty.

AV-640, $399.95. (6,10,12, 15,17,20,30,40 Meters). 25.5 ft., 17.5 lbs. *Hy-Gain's most popular vertical lets you work exciting DX with low 17 degree radiation angle!* Easily mounts on decks, roofs and patios. No ground or radials needed. Extra wide 2:1 SWR bandwidths. Each band individually tunable. Auto bandswitching, handles 1.5 kW, 80 MPH wind survival, low 2.5 sq. ft. wind surface. Aircraft quality aluminum tubing, stainless steel hardware.

AV-620, $299.95. (6,10,12,15,17,20M). 22.5', 10.5 lbs.

AV-14AVQ, $179.95. (10,15,20,40 Meters). 18 ft., 9 lbs. *Classic* AV-14AVQ uses same trap design as famous Hy-Gain Thunderbird beams. 3 air dielectric Hi-Q traps with oversize coils give superb stability and 1/4 wave resonance on all bands. Automatic bandswitching.

AV-12AVQ, $139.95. (10, 15, 20 Meters). 13 ft., 9 lbs. Lowest priced *automatic bandswitching* tri-band vertical! Uses Thunderbird beam design air dielectric traps for extremely hi-Q performance in limited space.

AV-18VS, $119.95 (10,12,15,17,20,30,40,80 M). 18 ft., 4 lbs. Hy-gain's *lowest priced vertical* gives you 8 bands. Easily tuned to any band by adjusting base loading coil.

See our website for even more hy-gain Vertical Antennas!

hy-gain. HF Beams

... are stronger, lighter, have less wind surface and last years longer. **Why?** Hy-gain uses durable tooled components -- massive boom-to-mast bracket, heavy gauge element-to-boom clamps, thick-wall swaged tubing -- no failures!

TH-11DX, $1159.95. 11-element, 4.0 kW PEP, 10,12,15,17,20 Meters. *The choice of top DXers.* With 11-elements, excellent gain and 5-bands, the super rugged TH-11DX is the *"Big Daddy"* of all HF beams! Features low loss log-periodic driven array on all bands with monoband reflectors, BN-4000 high power balun, corrosion resistant wire boom support, hot dipped galvanized and stainless steel parts.

TH-7DX, $869.95. 7-Element, 1.5 kW PEP, 10,15,20 Meters. 7-Elements gives you *the highest average gain* of any Hy-gain tri-bander! Dual driven for broadband operation without compromising gain. SWR less than 2:1 on all bands. Combined monoband and trapped parasitic elements give you an excellent F/B ratio.

TH-3MK4, $469.95. 3-Element, 1.5 kW PEP, 10,15, 20 Meters. Gives most gain for your money in full-power, full-size *hy-gain* tri-bander! Impressive gain and a *whopping* average front-to-back ratio and still fits on an average size lot. 95 MPH wind survival.

TH-3JRS, $359.95. Compact 3-Element, 600 W PEP, 10,15,20 Meters. *Hy-gain's most popular and lowest-priced tri-bander fits smallest lot*, 14.75 ft turning radius, 21 lbs. Excellent gain and front-to-back let *you* compete with the "big guns!" 80 MPH wind survival.

hy-gain. Rotators ... *the first choice of hams around the world!*

HAM-IV ... $649.95

The most popular rotator in the world! For medium communications arrays up to 15 square feet wind load area. *New* 5-second brake delay! *New* Test/Calibrate function. *New* low temperature grease permits normal operation down to -30 degrees F. *New* alloy ring gear gives extra strength up to 100,000 PSI for maximum reliability. *New* indicator potentiometer. *New* ferrite beads reduce RF susceptibility. *New* Cinch plug plus 8-pin plug at control box. Dual 98 ball bearing race for load bearing strength and electric locking steel wedge brake prevents wind induced antenna movement. North or South center of rotation scale on meter, low voltage control, max mast size of 2¹/₁₆ inches.

HAM-V, $1099.95. For medium arrays up to 15 sq. ft. wind load area. Like HAM-IV but has DCU-1 Pathfinder *digital* automatic control unit with gas *plasma* display, 6 preset beam headings.

Tailtwister T-2X ... $799.95

For large medium antenna arrays up to 20 sq. ft. wind load. Choose DCU-1 Pathfinder *digital* (T2XD) or *analog* control box (T2X) with *new* 5-second brake delay and *new* Test/Calibrate function. Low temperature grease, alloy ring gear, indicator potentiometer, ferrite beads on potentiometer wires, *new* weatherproof AMP connectors plus 8-pin plug at control box, triple bearing race with 138 ball bearings for large load bearing strength, electric locking *steel* wedge brake, N or S center of rotation scale on meter, low voltage control, 2¹/₁₆" max. mast.

T-2XD, $1229.95. Tailtwister with DCU-1 *digital* controller.

AR-40, $349.95. For compact antenna arrays and FM/TV up to 3.0 sq. ft. wind load. Dual 12 ball-bearing race. Fully automatic.

CD-45II, $449.95. For antenna arrays up to 8.5 sq. ft. Bell rotator design gives total weather protection. Dual 58 ball bearing race.

hy-gain. VHF/UHF Antennas

V2R, $109.95. 2-Meter *vertical* has two in-phase 5/8 Wave collinear radiators for exceptional high omnidirectional gain. 2 sets of ¹/₄ wave radials decouple radiator from mast. Covers 138-175 MHz. SO-239, handles 500 Watts. 9 ft.

V4R, $109.95. UHF vertical. Like V2R but covers 400-475 MHz. Type N, handles 500 Watts, 4 foot.

V42R, $169.95. Dual band covers 144/440 MHz bands. Two 5/8 Wave collinears.

VB-214FM, $89.95. *14-element* 2-Meter FM *beam* antenna provides exceptional front-to-back ratio and maximum obtainable gains. **VB-23FM, $49.95.** 3-element, **VB-25FM, $59.95.** 5-element, **VB-28FM, $79.95.** 8-element. Threaded stub for feedpoints. Accepts up to 2 inch mast. **DB-2345, $89.95.** Dual band 144(3-el) 440 (5-el) MHz.

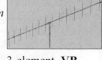

Use hy-gain. for all your DIY antenna parts

Tooled manufacturing is the difference between Hy-Gain antennas and the others -- they just don't have it (it's expensive!).

Die-cast aluminum boom-to-mast bracket and element-to-boom compression clamps are made with specially *tooled* machinery.

Hy-Gain antennas feature *tooled* swaged tubing that is easily and securely clamped in place. All tubing is deburred and cleaned for smooth and easy assembly.

Durable precision injection molded parts.

Hy-Gain antennas are stronger, lighter, have less wind surface area, better wind survival, need no adjustments, look professional and last years longer.

Free Hy-Gain Catalog
and Nearest Dealer ... 800-973-6572
Call your dealer for your best price!

hy-gain.

Antennas, Rotators & Towers
308 Industrial Park Road, Starkville, MS 39759 USA
Toll-free Customer Sales Hotline: 800-973-6572
• TECH: 662-323-9538 • FAX: 662-323-6551
http://www.hy-gain.com
Prices and specifications subject to change without notice or obligation. © Hy-Gain®, 2012.

Visit http://www.hy-gain.com

CABLE X-PERTS, INC.
Connecting You to the World...

1-800-828-3340

FOR PREMIUM ELECTRICAL PERFORMANCE FROM YOUR EQUIPMENT

See these fine loyal dealers for our quality products.

HAM RADIO OUTLET
AES
WORLDWIDE DISTRIBUTION

Private labeling at no charge.

We take great pride in our work!

Custom or Ready-Made Coaxial Assemblies

Visit us on-line for cable selection and great prices.

~ Serving You Since 1989 ~

www.CableXperts.com

The NEW EZ HANG Square Shot Kit
www.ezhang.com

Suggestions from thousands of HAM'S and Cable installers around the world, led to a complete redesign of the **EZ Hang**. Custom designed for YOU, the user in mind. Now safer and easier to use, you will hit your mark every time, with less chance of misfires hitting the yoke.

Over 8,600 Sold Worldwide

THERE'S NONE LIKE IT IN THE WORLD!

$99.95 + $9.05 for shipping when paying by check

MasterCard

540-286-0176
www.ezhang.com
EZ HANG
**32 Princess Gillian Ct.
Fredericksburg, VA 22406**

AMERICAN EXPRESS

VISA

• Tear-resistant • Synthetic paper

Rugged Waterproof All Weather Amateur Radio Log Books

Also Available Custom designed forms in any size.

Sales@waterprooflogbooks.com

WaterProofLogBooks.com

#1 Ham Radio Books and CDs from ARRL!

www.arrl.org/shop

The ARRL Antenna Compendium Vol. 8

The ARRL ANTENNA COMPENDIUM
Proven HF and VHF designs from the pages of QST

The Most Innovative Antenna Projects Yet!

This is the eighth in the very popular *ARRL Antenna Compendium* series. Inside are 60 articles from *QST* magazine featuring practical ideas, tips and some of the best antenna projects.

Volumes 1-7 are also available at www.arrl.org/shop.

**Volume 8
ARRL Order No. 0991
Only $24.95***

*plus shipping and handling

ARRL *The national association for* **AMATEUR RADIO®**

SHOP DIRECT *or call for a dealer near you.*
ONLINE WWW.ARRL.ORG/SHOP
ORDER TOLL-FREE 888/277-5289 (US)

AB 8/2011

Smart Battery Chargers
For Gel-Cell or Lead Acid Batteries

May be left connected indefinitely, will not overcharge your batteries

Small models for QRP and 5A model for Heavy Duty Deep Cycle Batteries
KITs and Assembled units with various cable & solar options, see website

www.a-aengineering.com

VISA MasterCard **A & A Engineering** PayPal

2521 W. LaPalma #K • Anaheim CA 92801
(714) 952-2114 • FAX (714) 952-3280

High Sierra

www.hamcq.com

Our secure online ordering gives you updates via email, notification of shipment, tracking numbers and lower prices.

Now More than 600 Products on the Website!

Since 1993 we have been providing great products and excellent customer service.

Shown here are just some of those products.

Visit us at www.hamcq.com to see ALL that we have to offer.

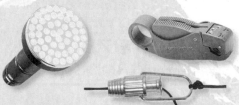

- UHF, BNC, N, TNC & SMA coax connectors and adapters
- RG213, RG8X, RG58 coax cables
- Coax connector crimping tools & sets, coax strippers and dies

- Helping hands, magnifiers, wire srippers, drill bits, soldering stations, solder,
- LED flashlights, emergency lights, work lights, rotating beacons, lasers
- Powerpole connectors, powerpole installation tools, wire for powerpoles, powerpole accessories

- Antenna rope, pulleys, tensioners, insulators
- Antenna mounts, antenna magnet mounts, antenna ball mounts
- Visit our website for many more products and information

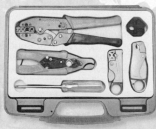

SIGN UP for Our Special Deals Club on the Website

Custom Built Amateur Radio Adjustable Antennas and Accessories

MEET THE NEXT GENERATION OF SCREWDRIVER ANTENNAS

SCORPION
ANTENNAS

Scorpion Antennas and accessories have been designed for the Amateur that demands outstanding performance for their mobile or home installation.

NEW QUICK CONNECTION!

Remove our antenna from your vehicle and install it in the backyard in a snap with the new Scorpion quick connect base!

Three models to choose from:
- **SA-680S – 6-80 meters** (#14 tin plated wire @ 10 turns per inch)
- **SA-680 – 6-80 meters** (#10 tin plated wire @ 6 turns per inch)
- **SA6-160 – 6-160** (#14 tin plated wire @10 turns per inch)

Three styles to choose from:
- **Standard Finish** (rugged 304 stainless tube that's a breeze to maintain). "This is our basic standard order finish"
- **Scorpion Classic** (hand polished 304 stainless tube, "looks like chrome" with black phenolic for coil form) "Up graded finish, can be applied to any model"
- **The Black Widow** (black powder coated stainless tube with black Lexan coil cover) "Up graded finish, can be applied to any model"

■ **Lifetime Warranty** – Everything on Antenna is covered except the Lexan coil cover due to long term sunlight exposure.
■ **30 day Return Policy** – For full refund if not satisfied.

We are The HIGHER Q Antenna Company™

"We use NO Metal Ends Caps on our coil"

WWW.SCORPIONANTENNAS.COM
623-326-8780

At Scorpion Antennas We Exceed Our Customer's Expectations.

BIG BOY ROTATORS
The most powerful antenna rotators available anywhere Amateur, Commercial, Government and Military purposes

CE FC

Model D digital solid state controller, the ultimate in easy to set up controller

- Built in RS232 and Preset
- Programmable soft start-stop
- Programmable North or South stop
- 500° rotation (- 70° + 70° overlap)
- 1° degree accuracy and more……

The ProSisTel rotators were designed to perform under tremendous stress with abnormally large antenna loads.

ProSisTel rotators give you: incredible starting and rotating torque, incredible braking resistence.
The rotators utilizing worm wheel technology far exceeds the specifications on any other amateur rotator made today.

Two years warranty

PRO.SIS.TEL.
Produzione Sistemi Telecomunicazioni

**C.da Conghia 298
I-70043 Monopoli BA Italy
Phone ++39 0808876607
www.prosistel.net
Email: prosistel@prosistel.it**

The ARRL Guide to Antenna Tuners
A Radio Amateur's Guide to Antenna Matching

By Joel R. Hallas, W1ZR

Explore the design, construction and applications of the different types of antenna tuners. Learn what type of tuner is needed in your station and where to install it for maximum improvement. This book will give you a better understanding of your antenna system and the way it can be enhanced through the selection and use of the appropriate antenna tuner.

**ARRL Order No. 0984
Only $22.95***

*plus shipping and handling

 ARRL *The national association for* **AMATEUR RADIO®**
SHOP DIRECT *or call for a dealer near you.*
ONLINE WWW.ARRL.ORG/SHOP
ORDER TOLL-FREE 888/277-5289 (US)

AB 8/2011

RigExpert AA-54
Antenna Analyzer

- 0.1 to 54 MHz
- Graphical display
- Hand-held design
- Connection to a personal computer

Worldwide Distributors

Array Solutions
www.arraysolutions.com

Rig Expert Canada
www.rigexpert.net

KMK UK Limited
www.mixw.co.uk

リグエキスパート ジャパン
www.ja1scw.jp/shop

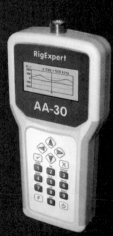

Antenna Analyzers

USB Transceiver Interfaces

www.rigexpert.com

 **BUDDIPOLE**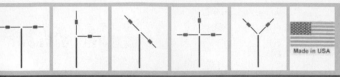

Made in USA

ANTENNAS & MORE

From beaches to mountaintops, condos to RV parks and everywhere in between, the Buddipole line of portable HF antennas and accessories is ideal for both novice and expert operators alike.

We manufacture all of our antennas using custom CNC parts and injection molds with carefully selected materials.

We also manufacture A123 Nanophosphate battery packs for all portable radios. These power packs provide unparalleled performance in the field. See our website for more details.

BUDDIPOLE FEATURES

> Multi-band design works 9 bands (40 meters thru 2 meters) with one set of adjustable coils!

> Rated from QRP to 250 watts PEP

> Modular Design – create dozens of different antennas with interchangeable parts

> Rotatable/Directional

> Lightweight, rugged components

> Rotating Arm Kit allows users to instantly change antenna configurations

> Used by Emergency Services Groups throughout the world

WHAT IS THE BUDDIPOLE?

The Buddipole™ Portable Dipole fits in your travel bag and assembles in minutes. The Buddipole is more than an antenna, it's a versatile system for launching your signal. Optimized for transmit power and proven for DX work, the Buddipole is the secret weapon used by HF portable operators all over the world.

Secure online ordering at:
www.buddipole.com

See our videos
www.youtube.com/buddipole

3028 SE 59th Court, Suite 600
Hillsboro, OR 97123

tel: (503) 591 8001
fax: (503) 214 6802

info@buddipole.com

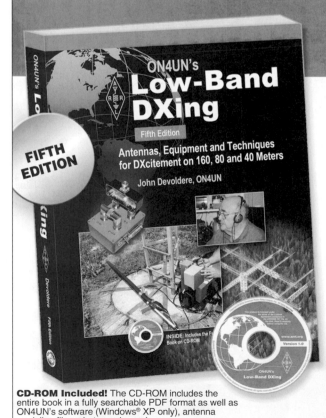

ON4UN's **Low-Band DXing**

Fifth Edition

Antennas, Equipment and Techniques for DXcitement on 160, 80 and 40 Meters

John Devoldere, ON4UN

FIFTH EDITION

INSIDE: Includes the Full Book on CD-ROM

Version 1.0

ON4UN's Low-Band DXing

25 Years of Low Band Success!

ON4UN's Low-Band DXing
Antennas, Equipment and Techniques for DXcitement on 160, 80 and 40 Meters

This fifth edition features new and updated material.

Highlights include...

...a thoroughly revised discussion of **receiving antennas**. You'll discover how to greatly enhance their operational bandwidth. In addition, low-signal transformers for Beverages and other receive-only antennas are analyzed in great detail, along with effective common-mode filters.

...a new examination of **phased arrays**, with new concepts such as the hybrid-fed 4-square array and opposite-voltage feed system. This is a must-read for every serious antenna builder!

...dozens of new propagation maps based on DX Atlas, as well as an in-depth analysis of the influence of sunspot cycles on 160-meter ducting.

...a new discussion of cutting edge technology including **Software Defined Radio** and the revolutionary **LP-500 Digital Station Monitor**.

**Order Online www.arrl.org/shop
or Call Toll-Free 1-888-277-5289 (US)**

ARRL Order No. 8560
Only $44.95*

CD-ROM Included! The CD-ROM includes the entire book in a fully searchable PDF format as well as ON4UN's software (Windows® XP only), antenna modeling files, photographs and more.

System Requirements: Windows® XP, Windows Vista® or Windows® 7, as well as Macintosh® systems, using Adobe® Acrobat® Reader® software. The Acrobat Reader is a free download at www.adobe.com. PDF files are Linux readable.

*Shipping and handling charges apply. Sales Tax is required for all orders shipped to CT, VA, and Canada. Prices and product availability are subject to change without notice.

ARRL The national association for AMATEUR RADIO®
SHOP DIRECT or call for a dealer near you.
ONLINE WWW.ARRL.ORG/SHOP
ORDER TOLL-FREE 888/277-5289 (US)

AB 8/2011

LDG ELECTRONICS

LDG Fiberglass Vertical Antennas and Antenna Tuners!

Purchase an S9V 43', 31' or 18' and fill out the included form. Mail it to LDG Electronics, and we will send you either a 200 watt balun or unun, your choice!

FREE!
RBA-1:1 Balun or RU-4:1 Unun
When You Buy A S9V 43', 31' or 18' Multiband Antenna

S9V 43' $199.99
80-6 meters *Fixed Operation*

The S9V 43' is a high-performance lightweight telescoping fiberglass vertical. The best value in high-performance 'tall' verticals!

S9V 31' $99.99
40-6 meters *Fixed or Portable Operation*

S9V 18' $49.99
20-6 meters *Fixed or Portable Operation*

The S9V 31' and 18' are tapered, ultra-lightweight fiberglass vertical antennas. Friction-locking sections and high-tech polymer tube rings allow the antenna to be quickly and safely deployed in practically any environment without tools!

We have a tuner that will work for you!

Tuners!

We make tuners that will work with any transceiver. Don't know which one is right for you? Give us a call or see the Tuner Comparison Chart on our web site for more selection help!

For more info or to view our full product line visit your favorite dealer or log-on to www.ldgelectronics.com

- • RF Sensing
- • Tunes Automatically
- • No Interface Cables Needed

NEW! AT-200ProII

Handles up to 250 watts SSB or CW on 1.8 – 30 MHz, and 100 watts on 54 MHz (including 6 meters). Rugged and easy-to-read LED bar graphs show power and SWR, and now includes LEDs for the antenna position and if the tuner is in bypass. A function key on the front panel allows you to access data such as mode and status. Includes six foot DC power cable.

Suggested Price $259.99

IT-100
Suggested Price $179.99

AT-600Pro
Suggested Price $359.99

Designed to handle the higher power of the Tokyo Hi Power HL-45B.

NEW! Z-817H
Suggested Price $159.99

Call or visit your favorite dealer today! www.ldgelectronics.com

LDG

LDG Electronics, Inc. 1445 Parran Road, St. Leonard, MD 20685 — Phone 410-586-2177 • Fax 410-586-8475

ALPHA DELTA COMMUNICATIONS, INC. AA

www.alphadeltacom.com

ALPHA DELTA MULTI-BAND DIPOLES
Models DX-CC, DX-DD, DX-EE, DX-LB, DX-LB PLUS

Power ratings: MAX Output (Assuming SWR at the FEED POINT, not tuner, is 2:1 or less). Alpha Delta tests antennas, in the clear (no surrounding objects), at a height of 35 ft., as an inverted-V with the ends at 10 ft. above ground. Approximate SWRs at 1.5:1. or less, and resonances at our test site, depending on antenna model, are: 1810 kHz, 3800 kHz, 7100 kHz, 14,150 kHz, 28,300 kHz, (Use your tuner for 15 meters). With different local site conditions your SWR and resonant frequency will vary, which is normal.

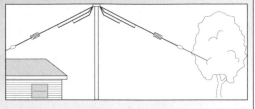

- **Model DX-CC:** 80 thru 10 meters, 1000 watts CW/PEP, ICAS duty cycle.
- **Model DX-DD:** same for 80 and 40 meters as Model DX-CC.
- **Model DX-EE:** 40 thru 10 meters, 1000 watts CW/PEP, ICAS duty cycle.
- **Model DX-LB:** 160, 80 meters, 600 watts CW/PEP; 40 meters, 1000 watts CW/PEP, ICAS duty cycle.
- **Model DX-LB PLUS:** same as above for 160 and 80 meters, and same as Model DX-CC on 40 thru 10 meters.

IMPORTANT NOTE: All models shown above are limited to 250 watts RF output for continuous key down modes like RTTY to prevent overheating of components.

NOTE: With any attic installation, limit power to 100 watts max, any mode. This will minimize coupling to attic wiring, HVAC ducting and outside aluminum gutters and will minimize RFI to home electronics and burglar alarm systems. In your individual site, even lower power may be necessary. Attic installations will require a wide range (10:1) antenna tuner to minimize SWR and broaden out SWR bandwidth. Keep antenna wires as far away as possible (> 3 ft.) from the above metal items, and NEVER touching them. Also offset (> 2 ft.) antenna wires from any wood roof/attic trusses or roof material so they are not in direct contact.

NOTE: Our tests show that the "open coil" design of our ISO-RES™ (Isolator/Resonator) coils are the most efficient designs for multi-band operation, and approach mono-band performance. Typical "trap" designs, where coils are enclosed in a metal or sealed housing, do not show this efficiency and, in fact, can show significant losses depending upon the trap design. The ISO-RES™ coils have a UV protective dip on them and require no further coating. Also, remove any bubble wrap or packing material from the coils before installing. Do not apply any other material over them as this will affect the tuning and efficiency. With the "open coil" design it is NORMAL for the frequency to shift with rain, snow or conditions of high humidity, Just re-adjust your tuner until dry again. This is a small inconvenience to maintain this high efficiency design.

NOTE: Alpha Delta antennas are designed to be used without a balun. Tests show that HF antennas installed less than 1/2 wavelength high (e.g., less than 60 ft. high on 40 meters.) have earth capacity coupling which tends to "even out" the pattern. If you have problems with RF on the coax, just wind about 8 turns of your coax at about an 8" diameter, tape, and install near the feed point of the antenna. Try to make windings as in-line as possible, and not "scrambled" for best results. This is a "choke balun".

Important note on the gas tube **Model SEP** static protector used in Models DX-CC, DD and EE. The **SEP** is rated for 1000 watts PEP/CW assuming the feed point (not tuner) SWR is 2:1 or less. When using a wide range antenna tuner for broad frequency coverage, such as all across 80 meters, or the WARC bands, the feed point SWR becomes high and the **SEP** must be removed to prevent "false triggering".

www.alphadeltacom.com
for product technical details, installation requirements, pricing, dealers and contact information

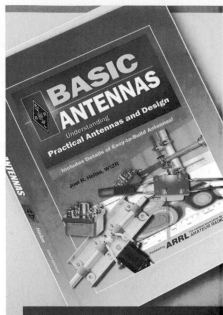

Basic Antennas
Understanding Practical Antennas and Design
By Joel R. Hallas, W1ZR

Basic Antennas is a comprehensive introduction to antennas. It includes basic concepts, practical designs, and details of easy-to-build antennas. You'll learn how to make antennas that really work!

Contents:
- Dipole Antennas
- Antenna Impedance
- Transmission Lines
- Practical Two Element Arrays
- Wideband and Multiband Antennas
- Reflector Antennas
- Yagis for HF and VHF
- Loop Antennas
- Antennas for Microwave Applications
- Vehicle Antennas
- Antenna Measurements

and much more!

Basic Antennas
ARRL Order No. 9994
Only $29.95*

*plus shipping and handling

Also available:
Basic Radio
ARRL Order No. 9558.....**Only $29.95***

Understanding Basic Electronics
ARRL Order No. 0823.....
Limited Offer Only $29.95* (retail $32.95)

ARRL *The national association for* AMATEUR RADIO®

SHOP DIRECT *or call for a dealer near you.*
ONLINE WWW.ARRL.ORG / SHOP
ORDER TOLL-FREE 888/277-5289 (US)

AB 8/2011

TGE
TG Electronics

N8XJK Boosters Regulators

Boost 9 Volts up to 15 Volts DC!
Boost, Filter and Regulate your DC Power!
Custom Boosters and options are available!
See our New Automatic Battery Disconnect.
Check out: www.tgelectronics.org
Call Tim @ 906 370-5031
Email: timig@email.com
Made in the USA

EasyLog5 $89.54
Since 1989!

Get more information, download a trial version, and order at http://www.easylog.com/northamerica/index.html or send an email to w5rya@easylog.com or jbsims_services@att.net
Check the sales page for discount prices.
Congratulations on your new Amateur Radio License!
www.easylog.com

We BUY radios
Contact us for a quote today!

Universal Radio
Call 800 431-3939
Fax 614 866-2339
dx@universal-radio.com
www.universal-radio.com

Array Solutions Your Source for Outstanding Radio Products

Professional Grade Equipment from Array Solutions

NEW!

PowerMaster II

- New Larger, Sharp & Fast LCD Display
- Reduced Energy consumption
- USB and RS-232 interface built-in
- New - Both 3kW and 10kW couplers on one display - switched
- Hi / Lo Power Level Monitoring
- Supports 2 like couplers simultaneously
  (3kW & 3kW, 3kW & V/UHF, 10kW & 10kW)
- SWR Threshold Protection (with amp PTT bypass)

Vector Network Analyzer Model VNA 2180

NEW!

Measures impedance magnitude, phase and transmission parameters for antennas, filters, and discrete components - using one or two ports.

- Frequency range is 5KHz to 180MHz.
- Data plots include: impedance, SWR, return loss, S11 and S21.
- Plots can be saved for before and after comparisons.
- Dual Smith charts with zoom and rotation.
- Time Domain Reflectometer (TDR) Functions.
- New – 6 port VNA multiplexer for measuring directive arrays including Phase/Magnitude vector scope software.

Announcing the NEW Array Solutions...

AIM *uhf* Analyzer

- Frequency range from 5 kHz to 1 GHz.
- Data plots include SWR, RL, R + X, series and parallel, magnitude, phase, and more.

NEW!

- Dual Smith charts with rotation and 20 markers.
- Plots and calibration files can be saved and used anytime in CVS and dynamic formats.
- AIM 4170C is still in production covering 5kHz to 180 MHz.
- Time Domain Reflectometer (TDR) Functions.

Announcing the NEW:

PowerAIM 120
Vector Impedance Analyzer for Broadcast Engineers

- Patented, unique technology offers the broadcast engineer the full capabilities of a single port network analyzer
- Small, lightweight, software-driven instrument
- Easy to carry on airlines and in the field.
- Very simple to set up and use.
- Safe measurements in RF-dense broadcast environments.
- Time Domain Reflectometer (TDR) Functions.

AIM 4170C Antenna Lab RF Analyzer

The AIM 4170C antenna analyzer measures the complex impedance (magnitude and phase) at each frequency of interest in the range of 5KHz to 180 MHz. A PC is used to calculate all RF parameters, including R +/-X, Magnitude and Phase, SWR, Return Loss, line loss, and more and plot the results in an easy to read graph and interactive Smith Chart.

Coming from ACOM...
800S Solid State Amplifier
160 through 6 M
800 W from 1.8 to 54 MHz, no time limit

This Device has NOT been approved by the F.C.C. and my not be offered for sale or lease until approval of the F.C.C. has been obtained.

The information shown is preliminary and may be subject to change without notice or obligation.

Bird Wattmeter Digital Display Conversion Kits

Upgrade for your Bird analog watt meter that will transform your Model 43 into a state of the art digital meter!

AS-43A Average Power Reading Bird Wattmeter Kit Digital meter kit
AS-43P Peak Power Reading Bird Wattmeter Kit Digital meter kit

Other Quality Products from Array Solutions...

| **ACOM**
Sales and Service for
Amplifiers and Accessories | **Phillystran, Inc.**
Official Worldwide
Phillystran Distributor | **RigExpert**
Analyzers and
Interfaces | **Prosistel Rotators**
Strongest Rotators
on the Market | **OptiBeam Antennas**
German Engineering
means High Performance | **Hofi®**
Surge Arrestors &
Antenna Switches | **SSB Electronics**
VHF, UHF, & SHF Preamps
and Switching Systems |

www.arraysolutions.com

Sunnyvale, Texas USA
Phone 214-954-7140
sales@arraysolutions.com
Fax 214-954-7142

Array Solutions' products are in use at top DX and Contest stations worldwide as well as commercial and governmental installations. We provide RF solutions to the DoD, FEMA, Emcomm, UN, WFO, FAA and the State Dept. for products and installation of antennas systems, antenna selection, filtering, switching and grounding. We also offer RF engineering and PE consulting services.

Quality Radio Equipment Since 1942

AMATEUR TRANSCEIVERS

Universal Radio is your authorized dealer for all major amateur radio equipment lines including: Alinco, Icom, Kenwood, TYT, Wouxun and Yaesu.

SHORTWAVE RECEIVERS

Whether your budget is $50, $500 or $5000, Universal can recommend a shortwave receiver to meet your needs. Universal is the *only* North American authorized dealer for *all* major shortwave lines including: Icom, Yaesu, Microtelecom, Ten-Tec, Grundig, etón, Sony, Sangean, Palstar, RFspace and Kaito.

WIDEBAND RECEIVERS

Universal Radio carries a broad selection of wideband and scanner receivers. Alinco, AOR, Icom, Yaesu, GRE and Uniden Bearcat models are offered at competitive prices. Portable and tabletop models are available.

ANTENNAS AND ACCESSORIES

Your antenna is just as important as your radio. Universal carries antennas for every need, space requirement and budget. Please visit our website or request our catalog to learn more about antennas.

BOOKS

Whether your interest is amateur, shortwave or collecting; Universal has the very best selection of radio books and study materials.

■ USED EQUIPMENT

Universal carries an extensive selection of used amateur and shortwave equipment. Buy with confidence. All items have been tested by our service department and carry a 60 day warranty unless stated otherwise. We also buy radios. Request our printed used list or visit:

www.universal-radio.com

◆ VISIT OUR WEBSITE

Guaranteed lowest prices on the web? Not always. But we *do* guarantee that you will find the Universal website to be the **most** informative.

www.universal-radio.com

◆ VISIT OUR SHOWROOM

Showroom Hours
Mon.-Fri. 10:00 - 5:30
Saturday 10:00 - 3:00

FREE 128 PAGE CATALOG

Our informative print catalog covers everything for the amateur, shortwave and scanner enthusiast. All items are also viewable at:

www.universal-radio.com

Universal Radio, Inc.
6830 Americana Pkwy.
Reynoldsburg, OH 43068

➤ 800 431-3939 Orders
➤ 614 866-4267 Information
➤ 614 866-2339 Fax
➤ dx@universal-radio.com

✓ Established in 1942.
✓ We ship worldwide.
✓ Visa, Master and Discover cards.
✓ Used equipment list available.
✓ Returns subject to 15% restocking fee.

universal radio inc.

Antenna Solutions for Every Space!

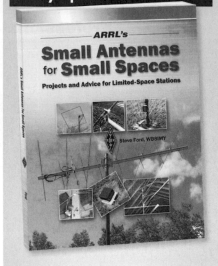

ARRL's
Small Antennas for Small Spaces
Projects and Advice for Limited-Space Stations

Steve Ford, WB8IMY

By Steve Ford, WB8IMY

ARRL's Small Antennas for Small Spaces is a valuable resource for radio amateurs who live in apartments, condominiums, or houses on small lots. Filled with practical advice, it guides you to finding the right antenna design to fit whatever space you have available. You'll find ideas and projects that will get you on the air regardless of where you live!

Includes:

■ **Tips to Get You Started the Right Way**
Learn tips about feed lines, SWR, RF amplifiers, operating modes and RF safety.

■ **Indoor Antennas You Can Install Now**
Design ideas and projects for VHF and HF antennas you can use inside your home.

■ **Outdoor HF Antennas for Any Property**
Dipoles, inverted Ls, end-fed wires, loops, verticals and temporary antennas.

■ **Outdoor Antennas for VHF and Beyond**
Compact omnidirectional and directional antennas you can install anywhere.

■ **Creative Solutions**
A collection of limited-space antenna ideas, including the Folded Skeleton Sleeve 40 and 20 Meter Dipole Antenna.

ARRL's Small Antennas for Small Spaces

ARRL Order No. 8393
Limited Time ARRL Member Price!
Only $22.95* (regular $25.95)

*plus shipping and handling

ARRL *The national association for* **AMATEUR RADIO®**
SHOP DIRECT *or call for a dealer near you.*
ONLINE WWW.ARRL.ORG/SHOP
ORDER TOLL-FREE 888/277-5289 (US)

AB 8/2011

ABR Industries · www.abrind.com · 713-492-2722

To Get the Best Performance from Your Station Use ABR Coax Cable Assemblies

Made In America using state of the art machinery and technology. We guarantee the quality and workmanship of our finished products which are built to the strictest industry standards with integrity and attention to detail.

— Not All Cable Assemblies are Created Equal... See the ABR Difference. —

When is the last time you carefully inspected your coax cable and connectors for damage? Do you realize that coax cable degrades over time? If your coax cable is 5 years old or greater, looks weather-beaten, connectors are corroded or simply want the best from your station, then seriously consider upgrading to our American made, superior grade coax cable assemblies. And it's a smart investment, too!

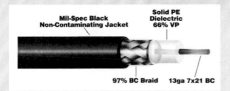

2213A RG213/U MIL-SPEC
Non-contaminating Direct-Burial Ultra-Violet Resistant Jacket. W/SILVER-TEFLON®
PL259 & WEATHERPROOF HST each end.
Attenuation @100ft:
• 0.6dB @ 10MHz.3.43kW.87% E.
• 1.0dB @ 30MHz.1.95kW.79% E.
• 1.4dB @ 50MHz.1.5kW.73% E.

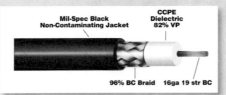

218XA RG8X (240F)
Non-contaminating Direct-Burial Ultra-Violet Resistant Jacket. W/PL259 &
WEATHERPROOF HST each end.
Attenuation @100ft:
• 0.9dB @ 10MHz.2.16kW.80% E.
• 1.4dB @ 30MHz.1.24kW.69% E.
• 2.1dB @ 50MHz 0.96kW .62%E.

25400F 400-FLEX (TYPE)
FLEXIBLE LOW LOSS
Non-contaminating Direct-Burial Ultra-Violet Resistant Jacket. W/SILVER-TEFLON®
PL259 & WEATHERPROOF HST each end.
Attenuation @100ft:
• 0.8dB @ 30MHz.2.77kW.83% E.
• 1.1dB @ 50MHz.2.14kW.78.5% E.
• 1.8dB @ 150MHz.1.22kW.65.4% E.
• 3.3dB @ 450MHz.0.69kW.47.3% E.

- To order go to: www.abrind.com or Call 713-492-2722
- To see our full array of products go to: www.abrind.com
- Sign-up for our email specials go to: www.abrind.com
- Custom work email: info@abrind.com or Call 713-492-2722

Made in America

Ladder Line
100ft 14ga 19/27 BCCS..................... Norm. Impedence: 370 Ω
100ft 18ga Solid BCCS..................... Norm. Impedence: 450 Ω

Rotor Control Cable
100ft 8/Conductor Rotor Control........ (2-16 (19) BC, 6-18 (7) BC
150ft 8/Conductor Rotor Control........ (2-16 (19) BC, 6-18 (7) BC
200ft 8/Conductor Rotor Control........ (2-16 (19) BC, 6-18 (7) BC

Antenna Rope
500ft 3/16" Black Double-Braid........Polyester Rope, Break: 770#
500ft 5/16" Black Double-Braid........Polyester Rope, Break: 1790#
1000ft 3/16" Black Double-Braid......Polyester Rope, Break: 770#

Grounding Braid
Tinned Copper • Ring Terminals Each End.
½" Flat   1" Flat
10ga 53 Amps w/#10RT   7ga 85 Amps w/¼" RT

INDUSTRIES™
American Built & Reliable
8561 Rayson Rd., Ste A, Houston, TX 77080

KØXG Systems

Antenna Rotation Equipment

Orbital Ring Rotor

Unit shown is the 45/55g Orbital Ring rotor with MonstIR Yagi installed.

Models available for any size tower (including cell towers). For any size boom, or tower boom.

1117 Highland Park Dr., Bettendorf, IA 52722
email: k0xg@k0xg.com
(563) 340-5111

Visit our Web Site at:

www.KØXG.com

YAESU

FT-857D

The Yaesu FT-857D is the worlds's smallest HF/VHF/UHF multimode amateur transceiver covering 160 m to 70 cm with 100W on HF. With 60 meters and DSP2 built-in.

FT-897D

The FT-897D is a multi-mode high-power base/mobile transceiver covering 160 m to 70 cm including 60 meters. TCXO built-in. Visit www.universal-radio.com for details!

Universal Radio
6830 Americana Pkwy.
Reynoldsburg, OH 43068
◆ Orders: 800 431-3939
◆ Info: 614 866-4267
www.universal-radio.com

Electronic Products Design, Inc. CUSTOM TRANSFORMERS

Designed to Your Specifications
www.epd-inc.com sales@epd-inc.com
Phone: 919-365-9199 Fax: 919-365-7005
2554 Lake Wendell Road, Wendell, NC 27591
All units manufactured in the USA.
Family owned and operated for over 25 years.

Advanced Specialties Inc.
"New Jersey's Communications Store"
YAESU ■ ALINCO ■ MFJ ■ UNIDEN ■ COMET
...and much, much more!
HUGE ONLINE CATALOG!
www.advancedspecialties.net
800-926-9HAM ■ 201-843-2067
114 Essex Street, Lodi, NJ 07644

RFI Filters
Clean RF transmission

Hi-Q Common-mode Filters (CMF): Trusted by many hams world-wide since 1988. Broad-band (1.5-250MHz) -60dB for 1.8-70MHz operations. 250w: $139.95 5kw: $209.95 **RF Inquiry**

Low pass Filter (LPF): 2 internal Al die-casts for sharp and exceptional attenuation. Double shielding structure. -120dB, 3kw HF(DC-30MHz):$195.95 HF+6m(DC-54MHz): $219.95
SAGAMI ENG MFG

www.RFchoke.com
845-255-0521 Olympix

Second Edition!

Antenna Zoning
for the
Radio Amateur

Fred Hopengarten, K1VR

Don't let the confusing tangle of ordinances and by-laws keep you from installing the antenna you need in order to communicate effectively. This book describes proven techniques and strategies that a ham and his or her attorney can use to obtain an antenna-structure permit. You'll learn to keep peace with the neighbors while enjoying ham radio!

Includes:
• Principles That Will Help You Win
• The Process in a Nutshell
• Your Winning Team
• Basic Preparations
• Getting to Know the Players
• Possible Objections
• Preparing the Permit Application
• Public Hearings—Your Big Moment in the Spotlight
• Deliberations and Decisions
• Now, Get the Permit and Build Your Antenna
• Awkward Post-Permit Situations
• Local and State Law, National Codes
• Drafting or Redrafting a Bylaw or State law
• Federal Law of Ham Radio Structures
• Other Federal Law
• Common Covenants and Restraints
• Canadian Laws

CD-ROM included!

ARRL Order No. 1192
Only $49.95*
*plus shipping and handling

ARRL *The national association for* AMATEUR RADIO®

SHOP DIRECT *or call for a dealer near you.*
ONLINE WWW.ARRL.ORG / SHOP
ORDER TOLL-FREE 888/277-5289 (US)
AB 8/2011

NO ANTENNA, NO HAM RADIO!

Why Choose Anttron® Antennas?

Anttron® Antennas:
- are easy to setup and easy to tune so you spend more time talking
- tune to a lower SWR so you can talk further and stronger
- are designed to give you a wider bandwidth
- every antenna is anaylzed to guarantee performance
- Amercian made and builit to last!

Text "shack" to 46786
or
go to www.anttrondeals.com

for special discounts enter code 993311

*Don't compromise your ability to communicate better,
insist on a genuine Anttron® antenna!*

3540 NW 23rd St. Oklahoma City, OK 73107- Dealer inquires are welcome 405-217-4102

Discount Prices - Great Service - 24 x 7 x 365

Dual-Band

**S9 Antennas
in Stock**

**Comet
CAA-500
Ant. Analyzer**

GRE Scanners

For Discounted Prices and Fast Delivery on These Products and More

www.CheapHam.com

732.716.1600

Amateur Radio - CB - Marine - Parts - Pro Audio - Test Equipment

Index

Editor's Note: Except for commonly used phrases and abbreviations, topics are indexed by their noun names. Many topics are also cross-indexed.

The letters "ff" after a page number indicate coverage of the indexed topic on succeeding pages.

A separate Project index and Author index follow the main index.

Project Index

Author Index

The following authors contributed material new to or referenced by this edition of the *ARRL Antenna Book* or material from previous editions that is included here. Note that in some cases the authors have become Silent Keys and their call signs have been reassigned.

Author	Call Sign	Page Ref
Adler, Dick	K3CXZ	14-20
Angle, Chip	N6CA	15-42
Applegate, Alan	KØBG	16-1ff, 21-1ff
Atchley, Dana	W1CF	9-31
Atkins, Bob	KA1GT	15-62, 15-67
Badger, George	W6TC	27-22
Baker, Allen	KG4JJH	19-11, 20-8
Barrett, Lee	K7NM	18-4
Beazley, Brian	K6STI	9-33, 22-8
Belcher, D	WA4JVE	5-1
Belrose, Jack	VE2CV	9-32
Beverage, Harold	W2BML	22-3ff
Bolljahn, J. T.		10-22
Boyer, Joseph	W6UYH	10-33
Bramwell, Denton	K7OWJ	27-15
Bray, D. W.	K2LMG	4-8
Breakall, Jim	WA3FET	14-20
Breed, Gary	K9AY	10-24, 22-9
Britain, Kent	WA5VJB	15-23, 15-66
Brown, Bruce	W6TWW	21-2
Brown, Fred	W6HPH	20-3
Brown, Gerald	K5OE	17-2ff
Brown, Jim	K9YC	20-3, 24-42
Buchanan, Chester	W3DZZ	10-15, 11-26
Butler, Don	N4UJW	10-10
Buxton, Al	W8NX	10-16
Cadwallader, Joe	K6ZMW	17-12
Cain, Jim	K1TN	12-7
Cake, Brian	KF2YN	9-11, 20-12
Capon, Robert	WA3ULH	20-12
Carcia, Joe	NJ1Q	9-9
Caspar, P	K4HKX	5-1
Cebik, L. B.	W4RNL	5-10, 7-1ff, 8-3, 11-29, 11-33, 15-20ff, 15-49, 16-9
Cerreto, Bob	WA1FXT	16-9
Collings, Cole	WØYNF	11-28
Connelly, Mark	WA1ION	22-13
Cooper, Clarke	K8BP	19-5
Coudé, Roger	VE2DBE	18-2
Cox, Roger	WBØDGF	7-4, 10-22
Cunningham, Earl	K6SE	5-10, 9-18, 22-13
Cutsogeorge, George	W2VJN	24-4
D'Agostino, Philip	W1KSC	15-45
Danzer, Paul	N1II	16-12
Daso, Don	K4ZA	26-1
Demaw, Doug	W1FB	5-10, 9-28, 22-23ff, 27-10
Dietrich, James	WAØRDX	5-1
Dixon, Bob	W8ERD	19-12
Donovan, Frank	W3LPL	23-30
Duffy, Tim	K3LR	9-7
Ehrenfried, Martin	G8JNJ	20-10
Ehrhart, Rod	WN8R	9-14
Elengo, John	W1DQ	25-3
Emery, Geoff	VK4ZPP	28-1ff
Evans, Paul	VP9KF	20-2
Fenwick, Richard	K5RR	11-26
Ford, Steve	WB8IMY	20-1
Geiser, David	WA2ANU	22-27

Author	Call Sign	Page Ref
Gentges, Frank	KØBRA	22-15
Gilbert, Ed	K2SQ	24-43
Gillette, R. F.	W9PE	22-30
Gold, Robert	WBØKIZ	1-18
Gordon, Lew	K4VX	11-28
Grebenkemper, John	KI6WX	27-12
Greene, Clarke	K1JX	14-17
Grover, F. W.		5-14
Guth, Peter		14-26, 18-2
Hagn, George		3-4
Haigwood, Jerry	W5JH	12-4
Haines, Geoff	N1GY	20-9
Hall, Jerry	K1TD	19-2ff
Hallas, Joel	W1ZR	9-7, 21-24, 24-3ff
Halliday, Dave	K2DH	17-1ff
Hansen, Markus	VE7CA	19-9ff
Harbach, Allen	WA4DRU	9-9
Hart, Ted	W5QJM	5-21, 20-10ff
Hauff, Frederick	W3NZ	27-22
Haviland, R. P.	W4MB	3-29, 8-1, 11-30
Healy, Rus	K2UA	22-1ff
Herring, Ron	W7HD	19-4
Heslin, Robert	K7RTY	15-49
Hoch, Gunter	DL6WU	15-27
Hollister, Robert	N7INK	19-4
Hood, Michael	KD8JB	15-8
Hopengarten, Fred	K1VR	14-40, 26-15
Hunkeler, Noel	F5JIO	15-13
Hunt, Dale	WB6BYU	22-27
Hutchinson, Chuck	K8CH	14-2, 19-6
Jansson, Dick	KD1K	17-1ff
Jenkinson, Garth	VK3BBK	23-30
Johnson, Don	W6AAQ	21-14
Johnston, W.	K5ZI	4-26
Jones, Bill	K8CU	10-29
Karl, Ed	KØKL	18-1ff
Kaune, Bill	W7IEQ	27-11
Keller, J. B.		14-21
Kennedy, Hal	N4GG	12-14
King, Tom	KD5HM	27-24
Kirby, Tom	W1EJ	15-29
Knadle, Dick	K2RIW	17-28
Koontz, Floyd	WA2WVL	22-9
Kouyournjian, R. G.		14-22
Kraus, John	W8JK	12-21, 17-10
Krome, Ed	K9EK	15-25, 17-3
Krupp, Daniel	W8NWF	10-33
Lahlum, Robye	W1MK	6-20, 22-1ff
Lambert, Edgar	WA4LVB	10-7
Lattin, William	W4JRW	10-15
Lau, Zack	W1VT	15-22
Lawson, Jim	W2PV	6-6, 11-2ff
Lee, Paul		6-16
Leeson, Dave	W6NL	8-16, 11-10ff, 11-29, 24-29, 25-8
Leggio, Joe	WB2HOL	22-30
Leutzelschwab, Carl	K9LA	4-1ff
Lewallen, Roy	W7EL	6-7, 6-10ff, 11-2
Littlepage, Joseph	WE5Y	19-3

FEEDBACK

Please use this form to give us your comments on this book and what you'd like to see in future editions, or e-mail us at **pubsfdbk@arrl.org** (publications feedback). If you use e-mail, please include your name, call, e-mail address and the book title, edition and printing in the body of your message. Also indicate whether or not you are an ARRL member.

Where did you purchase this book?　□ From ARRL directly　　□ From an ARRL dealer

Is there a dealer who carries ARRL publications within:

　□ 5 miles　　□ 15 miles　　□ 30 miles　of your location?　　□ Not sure.

　License class:

　□ Novice　　□ Technician　　□ Technician with code　　□ General　　□ Advanced　　□ Amateur Extra

Name _____　ARRL member?　□ Yes □ No

_____　Call Sign _____

Address _____

City, State/Province, ZIP/Postal Code _____

Daytime Phone　(　　) _____ Age _____

If licensed, how long? _____

Other hobbies _____　E-mail _____

_____

Occupation _____

For ARRL use only	2012 ANT
Edition	22 23 24 25 26 27 28 29
Printing	1 2 3 4 5 6 7 8 9 10 11 12